MODERN
UNIVERSITY PHYSICS

This book is in the

ADDISON-WESLEY SERIES IN PHYSICS

MODERN
UNIVERSITY PHYSICS

by

JAMES A. RICHARDS
Drexel Institute of Technology

FRANCIS WESTON SEARS
Dartmouth College

M. RUSSELL WEHR
Drexel Institute of Technology

MARK W. ZEMANSKY
College of the City of New York

ADDISON-WESLEY PUBLISHING COMPANY, INC.
READING, MASSACHUSETTS, U.S.A.
LONDON, ENGLAND

PREFACE

This text is both new and old. It is new in that it presents in one volume a course of study which assumes no background in physics but which provides a meaningful introduction to classical, relativistic, and quantum physics. In an ambitious course it can be covered in one year. A background in chemistry is desirable, and a concurrent course in calculus is assumed. Vectors are expressed in boldface type wherever magnitude *and* direction are meant, and both the scalar and vector multiplication operations are introduced. These techniques emphasize vector quantities and permit many physical laws to be presented more concisely.

This text is old in that it is almost entirely taken from two other texts: *University Physics* by Sears and Zemansky and *Physics of the Atom* by Wehr and Richards. Some parts have been rewritten, particularly the discussions of work, energy, and momentum. Considerable material in the source books has been omitted. This shortening has been accomplished for the following reasons. First, there was some material common to both books. Second, most students who use this book will take additional courses which will include topics we have deleted. Third, some topics are applications which will be covered in the laboratory. Fourth, some traditional topics, such as color and musical scales, are of secondary importance to physics, inasmuch as they involve psychology as much as they involve physics. We have retained those topics which provide a foundation in physics and which are essential to a unified development of the subject. Anyone familiar with the source texts will note that those topics we have included here are treated as fully or *more* fully than they were in the sources. Although we have shifted the emphasis, we have retained or increased depth of content.

Both the English and metric systems of units have been introduced and used. The metric mks system is used throughout, and the English engineering system is used for topics where engineers use them. We have introduced special units like the electron volt and the angstrom where these units are essential to the subject matter.

We gratefully reaffirm our thanks to the many students, colleagues, and friends whose comments and suggestions concerning the source books are reflected in *Modern University Physics*.

J.A.R., Jr.
F.W.S.
M.R.W.
M.W.Z.

Philadelphia, Hanover, and New York
May, 1960

CONTENTS

CHAPTER 1

COMPOSITION AND RESOLUTION OF VECTORS

1–1 Introduction. A good mystery story is a kind of game. The author describes a situation—usually violent. The detective inquires into the activities of the principal characters and conducts an investigation, during which various facts are brought out. You, as the reader, try to organize these clues by framing hypotheses which will "explain" the facts. When more information becomes available you may have to revise your hypotheses as they become inconsistent with new facts. A clever author of a good mystery may fool you into several blind alleys before the detective finally resolves the whole matter in an intellectually satisfying way. You remember the clues which set him on the right track and you realize that if you had been as observant as he you would have come to the heart of the matter as quickly as he did.

Scientific investigation is very much like a good mystery story which has no apparent end. Some hypotheses about the universe seem ridiculous today. Ptolemy taught that the earth was the center of the solar system, with the sun and all the planets moving about it in complicated paths. Copernicus, on the other hand, adopted the view that the earth and the other planets revolve about the sun. Only about a hundred years ago there was supposed to be a substance called *caloric* which accounted for an astonishing number of phenomena but which was specifically designed to account for the changed properties of bodies as they are heated and cooled. Heat was considered to *be* caloric, and when a body was heated the caloric entered the body and caused it to expand. Although we now have no need whatsoever for this concept, it still lingers on. We still speak of heat "flow" as though heat were a fluid. We could enumerate similar abandoned hypotheses almost without limit.

Some of the blind alleys into which science has turned have seriously delayed progress. On the other hand, some alleys which seemed to be "dead end" have been far from blind. The alchemists tried to change lead into gold. Their efforts were frustrated, but they discovered many less profound changes which were nevertheless important. They were the first chemists. At the beginning of this century it was thought that light was a wave motion of a substance called the ether. This theory has been abandoned in the sense that we know that we have a better one (which we will discuss later in this book). But the wave theory of light has by no means been abandoned as a means for understanding many phenomena. The wave theory has so much "truth" about it that it is still exceedingly

1

useful. It approximates the truth very, very closely in many situations. It was a fruitful theory because it correlated a tremendous range of observations and suggested possibilities previously unanticipated, and even though it has been replaced, it is still useful and worthy of detailed study.

One might suppose that we could convey the latest ideas about physical reality with a minimum of wasted effort by skipping theories which have been discarded or modified, and instead beginning with the most modern interpretation of physical events. There are several reasons why we must begin with the older classical physics. The familiar languages of words and pictures are sufficient for introducing classical physics but they cannot adequately portray modern theories. The elegant language of modern physics is higher mathematics, since the modern concepts are impossible to visualize. One might begin with modern physics for a group of trained mathematicians, although it would be hard to find such a group which did not include many who had studied classical physics as part of their training. Fortunately, it is possible to convey much of the new physics if, in addition to words and pictures, there are classical concepts to enlarge and modify. A more practical reason for starting with classical physics is that despite its having been replaced theoretically, it is still an extremely useful approximation. It is relatively simple and it is precise enough for the solution of many problems in science and engineering. A third reason is that classical physics came before modern physics. Our treatment is hardly chronological, but we do trace, however loosely, the development of ideas. It spoils a mystery story to read the last page first.

Thus our telling of the "mystery story" of physics will include some ideas which we will later replace with new ideas that are more inclusive or more exact. Since the mystery of physics has no apparent end, the best modern ideas may become old in their turn. One thing, however, is certain. The scientists who devise the theories of tomorrow will be thoroughly familiar with the theories of today.

In order that the "clues" we present may be quantitative, we begin by discussing measurements.

1–2 The fundamental indefinables of mechanics. Physics has been called the science of measurement. To quote from Lord Kelvin (1824–1907), "I often say that when you can measure what you are speaking about, and express it in numbers, you know something about it; but when you cannot express it in numbers, your knowledge is of a meagre and unsatisfactory kind; it may be the beginning of knowledge, but you have scarcely, in your thoughts, advanced to the stage of *Science*, whatever the matter may be."

A definition of a quantity in physics must provide a set of rules for calculating it in terms of other quantities that can be measured. Thus, when momentum is defined as the product of "mass" and "velocity," the rule for calculating momentum is contained within the definition, and all that is necessary is to know how to measure mass and velocity. The definition of velocity is given in terms of length and time, but there are no simpler or more fundamental quantities in terms of which length and time may be expressed. *Length and time are two of the indefinables of mechanics.* It has been found possible to express all the quantities of mechanics in terms of only three indefinables. The third may be taken to be "mass" or "force" with equal justification. *We shall choose mass as the third indefinable of mechanics.*

In geometry, the fundamental indefinable is the "point." The geometer asks his disciple to build any picture of a point in his mind, provided the picture is consistent with what the geometer *says* about the point. In physics, the situation is not so subtle. Physicists from all over the world have international committees at whose meetings the rules of measurement of the indefinables are adopted. The rule for measuring an indefinable takes the place of a definition.

1–3 Standards and units. The measurement of any indefinable of physics involves the application of a simple set of rules. Instead of referring to these rules in the abstract, let us employ them in connection with the quantity "length." The first step is to choose an arbitrary *standard* of length, in the form of an inanimate, solid, durable material. The international standard of length is a bar of platinum-iridium alloy of X-shaped cross section (see Fig. 1–1) called the *standard meter*, which is kept at the International Bureau of Weights and Measures at Sèvres, near Paris. The distance between two lines engraved on gold plugs near the ends of the bar, when the bar is at the temperature of melting ice, is called *one meter*. The meter was originally intended to represent one ten-millionth of the earth's quadrant through Paris, but later, more accurate measurements, have shown that it differs from its intended value by a small amount. This is unimportant. There is no reason why a standard of length should have any connection with the earth's quadrant or with any other length. *A standard is arbitrary, and its virtue lies in the fact that all the scientists of the world accept it.*

The next step is to adopt, also by international agreement, a device or a method by which other lengths may be made equal to the standard, or any multiple or any fraction of the standard. The device for this purpose is a *dividing engine* in which a microscope, mounted on a movable stand, advances along a helical screw when the screw is rotated. With this device two lengths are said to be equal when they both require the same number of rotations of the screw. If one requires one-half the number, it is regarded as half the length, etc. Nowadays, the number of rotations of the

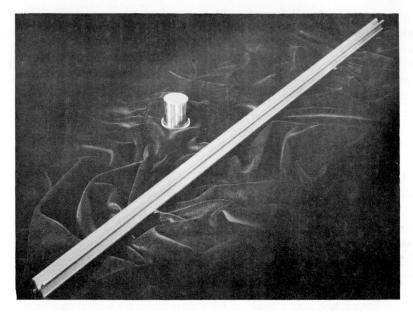

Fig. 1–1. The standard meter and the standard kilogram.

screw is replaced by the number of wavelengths of cadmium red light. This requires the addition of an optical interferometer to the dividing engine.

Any multiple or fraction of the standard, and sometimes the standard itself, may be chosen as a convenient *unit* for some specific purpose. Thus, to measure the dimensions of objects like books or tables, a unit called the *centimeter* is often used, where

$$1 \text{ centimeter } = 10^{-2} \text{ meter.}$$

For atomic dimensions, however, a unit called the *angstrom unit* is found more convenient, where

$$1 \text{ angstrom unit } = 10^{-10} \text{ meter.}$$

In astronomy, a convenient unit of length is the distance light travels in a year, or

$$1 \text{ light-year } = 9.45 \times 10^{15} \text{ meters.}$$

The *yard*, originally embodied by a physical standard like the meter, is now defined as

$$1 \text{ yard } = 0.9144 \text{ meter (exactly),}$$

so that the same physical standard serves for both the yard and the meter. The *foot* is defined as one-third of a yard.

The standard of time is our rotating earth, and the fundamental unit of time is the *mean solar day*, the average time for the earth to make one rotation on its axis with respect to the sun. The length of a solar day increases and decreases gradually in the course of a year because of the orbital motion of the earth. The length of a solar day averaged over a year is the mean solar day. The device for determining whether two time intervals are equal, and also for subdividing the standard time interval into any number of equal subintervals, has been chosen to be the pendulum. The pendulum will be discussed fully in Chapter 11. It is sufficient at this time to know that two time intervals are equal when the same number of pendulum swings occur in each interval. If a pendulum makes 86,400 swings ($60 \times 60 \times 24$) in one mean solar day, the time interval for each swing is said to be one *second*. The second is the most convenient unit of time for most purposes.

The international standard of mass is a cylinder of platinum-iridium (see Fig. 1–1) called the standard *kilogram* (abbreviated kgm). It was originally intended to have a mass equal to that of 1000 cm^3 of pure water at a temperature of 4°C but, as with the standard meter, more precise measurements have shown that this is not exactly true. It is important to emphasize again that the standard kilogram does not have to correspond to a mass of water or of anything else. Whatever it is, it must be accepted by all scientists over the world. The device for determining whether two masses are equal, and also for subdividing the standard kilogram into any number of equal parts or of defining any multiple of the kilogram, is an *equal-arm balance*. The concept of mass as well as the operation of an equal-arm balance will be fully discussed in Chapter 5. It suffices at this time to know that two masses are said to be equal if they balance on an equal-arm balance. If two equal masses that are placed on the left pan balance the standard kilogram on the right pan, then each of the two masses on the left pan is equal to one-half a kilogram. A convenient unit of mass for many purposes is provided by one one-thousandth of a kilogram, or one gram (1 gm).

The pound mass, like the yard, was formerly embodied by a physical standard of its own, but the *standard avoirdupois pound* is now defined in the U.S. as a body of mass 0.4535924277 kgm.

1–4 Symbols for physical quantities. We shall adopt the convention that an algebraic symbol representing a physical quantity, such as F, p, or v, stands for both a *number* and a *unit*. For example, F might represent a force of 10 lb, p a pressure of 15 lb/ft^2, and v a velocity of 15 ft/sec. When we write

$$x = v_0 t + \tfrac{1}{2}at^2,$$

if x is in feet then the terms $v_0 t$ and $\frac{1}{2}at^2$ must be in feet also. Suppose t is in seconds. Then the units of v_0 must be ft/sec and those of a must be ft/sec^2. (The factor $\frac{1}{2}$ is a *pure number*, without units.) As a numerical example, let $v_0 = 10$ ft/sec, $a = 4$ ft/sec^2, $t = 10$ sec. Then the preceding equation would be written

$$x = 10 \frac{\text{ft}}{\text{sec}} \times 10 \text{ sec} + \tfrac{1}{2} \times 4 \frac{\text{ft}}{\text{sec}^2} \times 100 \text{ sec}^2.$$

The units are treated like algebraic symbols. The sec's cancel in the first term and the sec^2's in the second, and

$$x = 100 \text{ ft} + 200 \text{ ft} = 300 \text{ ft}.$$

The beginning student will do well to include the units of all physical quantities, as well as their magnitudes, in all his calculations. This will be done consistently in the numerical examples throughout the book.

1–5 Force. Mechanics is the branch of physics which deals with the motion of material bodies and with the forces that bring about the motion. Since motion is best described by the methods of calculus, and many readers of this book are just beginning their study of this subject, we shall postpone a discussion of motion until Chapter 4, and start with a story of forces.

When we push or pull on a body, we are said to exert a *force* on it. Forces can also be exerted by inanimate objects; a stretched spring exerts forces on the bodies to which its ends are attached, compressed air exerts a force on the walls of its container, a locomotive exerts a force on the train it is drawing. The force of which we are most aware in our daily lives is the force of gravitational attraction exerted on every body by the earth and called the *weight* of the body. Gravitational forces (and electrical and magnetic forces also) can act through empty space without contact. In this respect they differ from the forces mentioned above, where the body doing the pushing or pulling must make contact with the body being pushed or pulled.

We are not yet in a position to show how a unit of force can be defined in terms of the units of mass, length, and time. This will be done in Chapter 5. For the present, a unit of force can be defined as follows. We select as a standard body the standard pound, defined in the preceding section as a certain fraction (approximately 0.454) of a standard kilogram. The force with which the earth attracts this body, at some specified point on the earth's surface, is then a perfectly definite, reproducible force and is called a force of *one pound* (avoirdupois). A particular point on the earth's surface must be specified, since the attraction of the earth for a given body varies slightly from one point to another. If great precision is not required it suffices to take any point at sea level and 45° latitude.

In order that an unknown force can be compared with the force unit, and thereby measured, some measurable effect produced by a force must be used. One such effect is to alter the dimensions or shape of a body on which the force is exerted; another is to alter the state of motion of the body. Both of these effects are used in the measurement of forces. In this chapter we shall consider only the former; the latter will be discussed in Chapter 5.

The instrument most commonly used to measure forces is the spring balance, which consists of a coil spring enclosed in a case for protection and carrying at one end a pointer that moves over a scale. A force exerted on the balance changes the length of the spring. The balance can be calibrated as follows. The standard pound is first suspended from the balance and the position of the pointer is marked 1 lb. Any number of duplicates of the standard can then be prepared by suspending a body from the balance and adding or removing material until the index again stands at 1 lb. Then when two, three, or more of these are suspended simultaneously from the balance the force stretching it is 2 lb, 3 lb, etc., and the corresponding positions of the pointer can be labeled 2 lb, 3 lb, etc. This procedure makes no assumption about the elastic properties of the spring except that the force exerted on it is always the same when the pointer stands at the same position. The calibrated balance can then be used to measure any unknown force.

1–6 Graphical representation of forces. Vectors. Suppose we are to slide a box along the floor by pulling it with a string or pushing it with a stick, as in Fig. 1–2. That is, we are to slide it by exerting a force on it. The point of view which we now adopt is that the motion of the box is caused not by the *objects* which push or pull on it, but by the *forces* which these exert. For concreteness, assume the magnitude of the push or pull to be 10 lb. It is clear that simply to write "10 lb" on the diagram would not completely describe the force, since it would not indicate the direction in which the force was acting. One might write "10 lb, 30° above horizontal to the right," or "10 lb, 45° below horizontal to the right," but all the

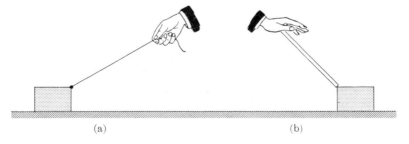

(a)   (b)

FIGURE 1–2

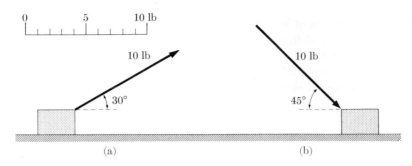

FIGURE 1-3

above information may be conveyed more briefly if we adopt the convention of representing a force by an arrow. The length of the arrow, to some chosen scale, indicates the size or magnitude of the force, and the direction in which the arrow points indicates the direction of the force. Thus Fig. 1–3 is the force diagram corresponding to Fig. 1–2. (There are other forces acting on the box, but these are not shown in the figure.)

Force is not the only physical quantity which requires the specification of direction as well as magnitude. For example, the velocity of an aircraft is not completely specified by stating that it is 300 miles per hour; we need to know the direction also. The concept of volume, on the other hand, has no direction associated with it.

Quantities like volume, which involve a magnitude only, are called *scalars*. Those like force and velocity, which involve both magnitude and direction, are called *vector quantities*. Any vector quantity can be represented by an arrow, and this arrow is called a vector (or if a more specific statement is needed, a force vector or a velocity vector).

Some vector quantities, of which force is one, are not *completely* specified by their magnitude and direction alone. Thus the effect of a force depends also on its *line of action* and its *point of application*. (The line of action is a line of indefinite length, of which the force vector is a segment.) For example, if one is pushing horizontally against a door, the effectiveness of a force of given magnitude and direction depends on the distance of its line of action from the hinges. If a body is deformable, as all bodies are to a greater or lesser extent, the deformation depends on the point of application of the force. However, since many actual objects are deformed only very slightly by the forces acting on them, we shall assume for the present that all objects considered are perfectly rigid. The point of application of a given force acting on a rigid body may be transferred to any other point on the line of action without altering the effect of the force. Thus *a force applied to a rigid body may be regarded as acting anywhere along its line of action.*

1–7 Components of a vector. When a box is pulled or pushed along the floor by an inclined force as in Fig. 1–2, the effectiveness of the force in moving the box along the floor depends upon the direction in which the force acts. Furthermore, each of the forces in Fig. 1–2 is producing another effect in addition to moving the box ahead. That is, the pull of the cord is in part tending to lift the box off the floor, and the push of the stick is in part forcing the box down against the floor. We are thus led to the idea of the *components* of a force, that is, the effective values of a force in directions other than that of the force itself.

The component of a force in any direction can be found by a simple graphical method. Let a given force be represented by the vector **F*** in Fig. 1–4, from O to A. To find the component of **F** in the direction of the line Ob, drop a perpendicular from A to this line, intersecting it at point B. The vector $\mathbf{F}_b$, from O to B, to the same scale as that used for the vector **F**, then represents the component of **F** in the direction Ob, or the effective value of the force in this direction.

Similarly, the vector $\mathbf{F}_c$ from O to C represents the component of **F** in the direction Oc. The component along Od, at right angles to **F**, is zero, and the component along Oa is equal to **F**.

The magnitude of a component of a vector in any direction can be calculated as follows. Referring to Fig. 1–4, we have from the right triangle OAB,

$$\cos \theta_b = \frac{OB}{OA} = \frac{F_b}{F},$$

$$F_b = F \cos \theta_b.$$

If $F = 10$ lb and $\theta_b = 60°$, $\cos \theta_b = 0.500$ and

$$F_b = 10 \text{ lb} \times 0.500 = 5.00 \text{ lb}.$$

In the same way,

$$\cos \theta_c = \frac{OC}{OA} = \frac{F_c}{F},$$

$$F_c = F \cos \theta_c.$$

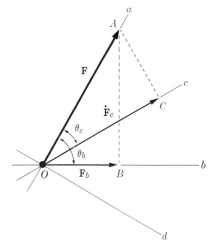

FIG. 1–4. Vectors $\mathbf{F}_b$ and $\mathbf{F}_c$ are the components of **F** in the directions Ob and Oc. The component along Od, perpendicular to **F**, is zero.

---

* A vector quantity is represented by a letter in boldface type. The same letter in italic type represents the magnitude of the quantity. Thus the magnitude of a force **F** is represented by F. In handwritten copy, where boldface type cannot be used, vectors are represented by placing an arrow over the letter symbol, thus: $\vec{F}$.

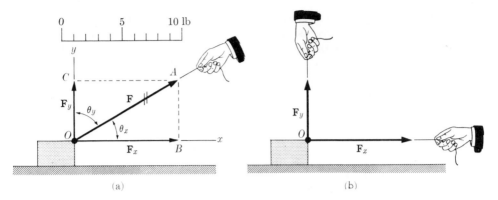

FIG. 1–5. The inclined force **F** may be replaced by its rectangular components **F**$_x$ and **F**$_y$. $F_x = F \cos \theta_x$, $F_y = F \cos \theta_y$.

If $\theta_c = 30°$, $\cos \theta_c = 0.866$ and $F_c = 10$ lb $\times$ 0.866 = 8.66 lb.

In general, then, the magnitude of the component of a vector **F** in any direction making an angle θ with that of the vector is equal to $F \cos \theta$. If $\theta = 90°$, $\cos \theta = 0$ and the component at right angles to the vector is zero. If $\theta = 0$, $\cos \theta = 1$ and the component is equal to **F**.

Figure 1–5 shows the same box as in Figs. 1–2(a) and 1–3(a). The vectors **F**$_x$ and **F**$_y$ are the components of **F** in the mutually perpendicular directions Ox and Oy, and are called the *rectangular components* of **F** in these two directions. But since a vector has no component at right angles to its own direction, **F**$_x$ has no component along Oy and **F**$_y$ has no component along Ox. No further resolution of the force into x- and y-components is therefore possible. Physically, this means that the two forces **F**$_x$ and **F**$_y$, acting simultaneously as in Fig. 1–5(b), are equivalent in all respects to the original force **F**. *Any force may be replaced by its rectangular components.*

As a numerical example, let the force **F** in Fig. 1–5 have a magnitude of 10 lb, and let $\theta_x = 30°$, $\theta_y = 60°$. Then $F_x = 8.66$ lb, $F_y = 5.00$ lb, and these two forces applied simultaneously as in part (b) are found to produce exactly the same effect as the single force of 10 lb in part (a).

It is often convenient to express both the x- and y-components of a vector in terms of the angle between the vector and the x-axis. We see from Fig. 1–5(a) that

$$\sin \theta_x = \frac{BA}{OA} = \frac{OC}{OA} = \frac{F_y}{F}, \qquad F_y = F \sin \theta_x.$$

Hence with the understanding that θ refers to the angle between a vector **F** and the x-axis, we can say, in general, that

$$F_x = F \cos \theta, \qquad F_y = F \sin \theta.$$

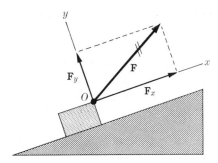

FIG. 1–6. F_x and F_y are the rectangular components of **F**, parallel and perpendicular to the sloping surface of the inclined plane.

The directions in which the rectangular components of a vector may be desired are not necessarily horizontal and vertical. For example, Fig. 1–6 shows a block being dragged up an inclined plane by a force **F**. The vectors F_x and F_y are the components of **F** parallel and perpendicular to the sloping surface of the plane.

1–8 Resultant or vector sum. Ordinarily a body is acted on simultaneously by a number of forces having different magnitudes, directions, and points of application. To begin with, we shall consider only sets of forces which lie in the same plane (*coplanar* forces) and which have the same point of application (*concurrent* forces). It is found by experiment that any set of coplanar, concurrent forces can be replaced by a single force whose effect is the same as that of the given forces and which is called their *resultant*.

In Fig. 1–7, a body is acted on by the two forces F_1 and F_2, both applied at point O. To find their resultant, construct the parallelogram $OACB$, of which the vectors F_1 and F_2 form two adjacent sides. The concurrent

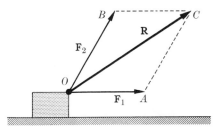

FIG. 1–7. Force **R**, the resultant of F_1 and F_2, is obtained by the parallelogram method.

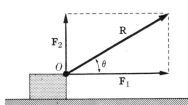

FIG. 1–8. Resultant of two forces at right angles to each other.

diagonal of the parallelogram, that is, the vector $\mathbf{R}$ from O to C, is called the *vector sum* of the vectors $\mathbf{F}_1$ and $\mathbf{F}_2$, and we find by experiment that it represents the resultant force in magnitude and direction.

In the special case in which the forces $\mathbf{F}_1$ and $\mathbf{F}_2$ are at right angles to each other, as in Fig. 1–8, the triangle OAC is a right triangle whose sides are the forces $\mathbf{F}_1$ and $\mathbf{F}_2$. The magnitude and direction of the resultant are then given by

$$R = \sqrt{F_1^2 + F_2^2}, \qquad \tan\theta = \frac{F_2}{F_1}.$$

Another special case is that in which two forces having the same line of action are parallel, as in Fig. 1–9(a), or antiparallel, as in Fig. 1–9(b). If they are parallel, the magnitude of the resultant $\mathbf{R}$ equals the sum of the magnitudes of $\mathbf{F}_1$ and $\mathbf{F}_2$. If they are antiparallel the magnitude of the resultant equals the difference between the magnitudes of $\mathbf{F}_1$ and $\mathbf{F}_2$.

The construction in Fig. 1–7 is called the *parallelogram* method of finding the resultant of two vectors. The *triangle* method, shown in Fig. 1–10, consists of displacing either vector parallel to itself until its tail coincides with the head of the other vector. The resultant $\mathbf{R}$ is then represented by the closing side of the triangle.

When more than two forces are to be combined, one may first find the resultant of any two, then combine this resultant with a third, and so on. The process is illustrated in Fig. 1–11, which shows the four forces $\mathbf{F}_1$, $\mathbf{F}_2$, $\mathbf{F}_3$, and $\mathbf{F}_4$ acting simultaneously at the point O. In Fig. 1–11(b), forces $\mathbf{F}_1$ and $\mathbf{F}_2$ are first combined by the triangle method, giving a re-

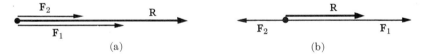

FIG. 1–9. Resultant of (a) two parallel forces, (b) two antiparallel forces.

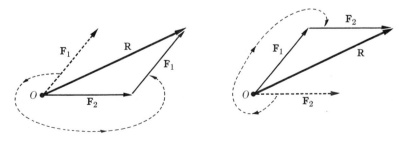

FIG. 1–10. The triangle method for finding the resultant of two forces.

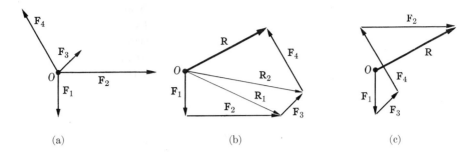

Fig. 1-11. Polygon method.

sultant R_1; force R_1 is then combined by the same process with F_3, giving a resultant R_2; finally R_2 and F_4 are combined to obtain the resultant R. Evidently the vectors R_1 and R_2 need not have been drawn—one need only draw the given vectors in succession, with the tail of each at the head of the one preceding it, and complete the polygon by a vector R from the tail of the first to the head of the last vector. The order in which the vectors are drawn makes no difference, as shown in Fig. 1-11(c).

1-9 Resultant by rectangular resolution. While the polygon method is a satisfactory graphical one for finding the resultant of a number of forces, it is awkward for computation because one must, in general, solve a number of oblique triangles. Therefore the usual analytical method of finding the resultant is first to resolve all forces into rectangular components along any convenient pair of axes and then combine these into a single resultant. This makes it possible to work with right triangles only.

Figure 1-12(a) shows three concurrent forces F_1, F_2, and F_3, whose resultant we wish to find. Let a pair of rectangular axes be constructed in an arbitrary direction. Simplification results if one axis coincides with one of the forces, which is always possible. In Fig. 1-12(b), the x-axis coincides with F_1. Let us first resolve each of the given forces into x- and y-components. According to the usual conventions of analytic geometry, x-components toward the right are considered positive and those toward the left, negative. Upward y-components are positive and downward y-components are negative.

Force F_1 lies along the x-axis and need not be resolved. The magnitudes of the components of F_2 are $F_{2x} = F_2 \cos \theta$, $F_{2y} = F_2 \sin \theta$. Both of these are positive, and F_{2x} has been slightly displaced upward to show it more clearly. The components of F_3 are $F_{3x} = F_3 \cos \phi$, $F_{3y} = F_3 \sin \phi$. Both of these are negative.

We now imagine F_2 and F_3 to be removed and replaced by their rectangular components. To indicate this, the vectors F_2 and F_3 are crossed

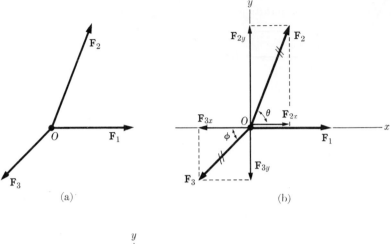

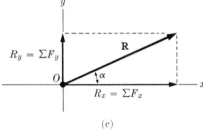

Fɪɢ. 1–12.   Vector **R**, the resultant of **F**₁, **F**₂, and **F**₃, is obtained by the method of rectangular resolution. The rectangular components of **R** have the magnitudes $R_x = \Sigma F_x$, $R_y = \Sigma F_y$.

out lightly.   All the x-components can now be combined into a single force **R**$_x$ whose magnitude equals the algebraic sum of the x-components, or ΣF_x, and all the y-components can be combined into a single force **R**$_y$ of magnitude ΣF_y.

$$R_x = \Sigma F_x, \qquad R_y = \Sigma F_y.$$

Finally, these can be combined as in part (c) of the figure to form the resultant **R** whose magnitude, since R_x and R_y are perpendicular to each other, is

$$R = \sqrt{R_x^2 + R_y^2}.$$

The angle α between **R** and the x-axis can now be found from any one of its trigonometric functions. For example,

$$\tan \alpha = \frac{R_y}{R_x}.$$

EXAMPLE. In Fig. 1–12, let $F_1 = 120$ lb, $F_2 = 200$ lb, $F_3 = 150$ lb, $\theta = 60°$, $\phi = 45°$. The computations can be arranged systematically as follows:

Force	Angle	x-component	y-component
$F_1 = 120$ lb	0	$+120$ lb	0
$F_2 = 200$ lb	60°	$+100$ lb	$+173$ lb
$F_3 = 150$ lb	45°	-106 lb	-106 lb
		$\sum F_x = +114$ lb	$\sum F_y = +67$ lb

$$R = \sqrt{(114 \text{ lb})^2 + (67 \text{ lb})^2} = 132 \text{ lb},$$

$$\alpha = \tan^{-1}\frac{67 \text{ lb}}{114 \text{ lb}} = \tan^{-1} 0.588 = 30.4°.$$

1–10 Vector difference. It is sometimes necessary to subtract one vector from another. The process of subtracting one *algebraic* quantity from another is equivalent to adding the negative of the quantity to be subtracted. That is,

$$a - b = a + (-b).$$

Similarly, the process of subtracting one *vector* quantity from another is equivalent to adding (vectorially) the negative of the vector to be subtracted, where the negative of a given vector is defined as a vector of the same magnitude but in the opposite direction. That is, if **A** and **B** are two vectors,

$$\mathbf{A} - \mathbf{B} = \mathbf{A} + (-\mathbf{B}).$$

Vector subtraction is illustrated in Fig. 1–13. The given vectors are shown in part (a). In part (b), the vector sum of **A** and $-\mathbf{B}$, or the

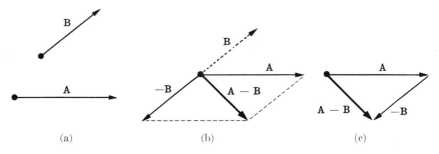

FIG. 1–13. The vector difference **A** — **B** is found in part (b) by the parallelogram method and in part (c) by the triangle method.

vector difference **A** — **B**, is found by the parallelogram method. In part (c), the triangle method has been used.

Vector differences may also be found by the method of rectangular resolution. Both vectors are resolved into x- and y-components. The difference between the x-components is the x-component of the desired vector difference, and the difference between the y-components is the y-component of the vector difference.

Vector subtraction is not often used when dealing with forces, but we shall use it frequently in connection with velocities and accelerations.

1-1. (a) Find graphically the horizontal and vertical components of a 40-lb force the direction of which is 50° above the horizontal to the right. Let 1/16 in. = 1 lb. (b) Check your results by calculating the components.

1-2. A box is pushed along the floor as in Fig. 1-2 by a force of 40 lb making an angle of 30° with the horizontal. Using a scale of 1 in. = 10 lb, find the horizontal and vertical components of the force by the graphical method. Check your results by calculating the components.

1-3. A block is dragged up an inclined plane of slope angle 20° by a force **F** making an angle of 30° with the plane, as in Fig. 1-6. (a) How large a force **F** is necessary in order that the component F_x parallel to the plane shall be 16 lb? (b) How large will the component F_y then be? Solve graphically, letting 1 in. = 8 lb.

1-4. The three forces shown in Fig. 1-14 act on a body located at the origin. (a) Find the x- and y-components of each of the three forces. (b) Use the method of rectangular resolution to find the resultant of the forces. (c) Find the magnitude and direction of a fourth force which must be added to make the resultant force zero. Indicate the fourth force by a diagram.

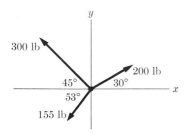

FIGURE 1-14

1-5. Find graphically the magnitude and direction of the resultant of the three forces in Fig. 1-14. Use the polygon method.

1-6. Two men and a boy want to push a crate in the direction marked x in Fig. 1-15. The two men push with forces **F₁** and **F₂** whose magnitudes and directions are indicated in the figure. Find the magnitude and direction of the smallest force which the boy should exert.

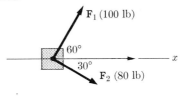

FIGURE 1-15

1-7. Find graphically the resultant of two 10-lb forces applied at the same point: (a) when the angle between the forces is 30°; (b) when the angle between them is 130°. Use any convenient scale.

1-8. Two men pull horizontally on ropes attached to a post, the angle between the ropes being 45°. If man A exerts a force of 150 lb and man B a force of 100 lb, find the magnitude of the resultant force and the angle it makes with A's pull. Solve: (a) graphically, by the parallelogram method; (b) graphically, by the triangle method; (c) analytically, by the method of rectangular resolution. Let 1 in. = 50 lb in (a) and (b).

1-9. Use the method of rectangular resolution to find the resultant of the following set of forces and the angle it makes with the horizontal: 200 lb, along the x-axis toward the right; 300 lb, 60° above the x-axis to the right;

100 lb, 45° above the x-axis to the left; 200 lb, vertically down.

1–10. (a) Find graphically the vector sum $\mathbf{A} + \mathbf{B}$ and the vector difference $\mathbf{A} - \mathbf{B}$ in Fig. 1–16. (b) Use the method of rectangular resolution to find the magnitude and direction of the vector sum and the vector difference.

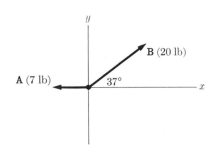

FIGURE 1–16

1–11. Vector $\mathbf{A}$ is 2 in. long and is 60° above the x-axis in the first quadrant. Vector $\mathbf{B}$ is 2 in. long and is 60° below the x-axis in the fourth quadrant. Find graphically (a) the vector sum $\mathbf{A} + \mathbf{B}$, and (b) the vector differences $\mathbf{A} - \mathbf{B}$ and $\mathbf{B} - \mathbf{A}$.

1–12. A vector $\mathbf{A}$ of length 10 units makes an angle of 30° with a vector $\mathbf{B}$ of length 6 units. Find the magnitude of the vector difference $\mathbf{A} - \mathbf{B}$ and the angle it makes with vector $\mathbf{A}$: (a) by the parallelogram method; (b) by the triangle method; (c) by the method of rectangular resolution.

1–13. Two forces, $\mathbf{F}_1$ and $\mathbf{F}_2$, act at a point. The magnitude of $\mathbf{F}_1$ is 8 lb and its direction is 60° above the x-axis in the first quadrant. The magnitude of $\mathbf{F}_2$ is 5 lb and its direction is 53° below the x-axis in the fourth quadrant. (a) What are the horizontal and vertical components of the resultant force? (b) What is the magnitude of the resultant? (c) What is the magnitude of the vector difference $\mathbf{F}_1 - \mathbf{F}_2$?

1–14. Two forces, $\mathbf{F}_1$ and $\mathbf{F}_2$, act upon a body in such a manner that the resultant force $\mathbf{R}$ has a magnitude equal to that of $\mathbf{F}_1$ and makes an angle of 90° with $\mathbf{F}_1$. Let $F_1 = R = 10$ lb. Find the magnitude of the second force, and its direction (relative to $\mathbf{F}_1$).

1–15. The resultant of four forces is 1000 lb in the direction 30° west of north. Three of the forces are 400 lb, 60° north of east; 300 lb, south; and 400 lb, 53° west of south. Find the rectangular components of the fourth force.

CHAPTER 2

EQUILIBRIUM

2–1 Introduction. The science of mechanics is based on three natural laws which were clearly stated for the first time by Sir Isaac Newton (1643–1727) and were published in 1686 in his *Philosophiae Naturalis Principia Mathematica* ("The Mathematical Principles of Natural Science"). It should not be inferred, however, that the science of mechanics began with Newton. Many men had preceded him in this field, the most outstanding being Galileo Galilei (1564–1642), who in his studies of accelerated motion had laid much of the groundwork of Newton's three laws.

In this chapter we shall make use of only two of Newton's laws, the first and the third. Newton's second law will be discussed in Chapter 5.

2–2 Equilibrium. Newton's first law. One effect of a force is to alter the dimensions or shape of a body on which the force acts; another is to alter the state of motion of the body.

The motion of a body can be considered as made up of its motion as a whole, or its *translational* motion, together with any *rotational* motion the body may have. In the most general case, a single force acting on a body produces a change in both its translational and rotational motion. However, when several forces act on a body simultaneously, their effects can compensate one another, with the result that there is no *change* in either the translational or rotational motion. When this is the case, the body is said to be in *equilibrium*. This means that (1) the body as a whole either remains at rest or moves in a straight line with constant speed, and (2) that the body is either not rotating at all or is rotating at a constant rate.

Let us consider some (idealized) experiments from which the laws of equilibrium can be deduced. Figure 2–1 represents a flat, rigid object of arbitrary shape on a level surface having negligible friction. If a single force F_1 acts on the body, as in Fig. 2–1(a), and if the body is originally at rest, it at once starts to move and to rotate clockwise. If originally in motion, the effect of the force is to change the translational motion of the body in magnitude or direction (or both) and to increase or decrease its rate of rotation. In either case, the body does not remain in equilibrium.

Equilibrium can be maintained, however, by the application of a second force F_2 as in Fig. 2–1(b), provided that F_2 is equal in magnitude to F_1,

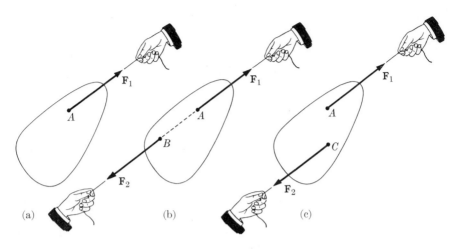

FIG. 2–1. A rigid body acted on by two forces is in equilibrium if the forces are equal in magnitude, opposite in direction, and have the same line of action, as in part (b).

is opposite in direction to $\mathbf{F}_1$, and has the same line of action as $\mathbf{F}_1$. The resultant of $\mathbf{F}_1$ and $\mathbf{F}_2$ is then zero. If the lines of action of the two forces are not the same, as in Fig. 2–1(c), the body will be in translational but not in rotational equilibrium.

In Fig. 2–2(a), a body is acted on by three nonparallel coplanar forces $\mathbf{F}_1$, $\mathbf{F}_2$, and $\mathbf{F}_3$. Any force applied to a rigid body may be regarded as acting anywhere along its line of action. Therefore, let any two of the force vectors, say $\mathbf{F}_1$ and $\mathbf{F}_2$, be transferred to the point of intersection of their lines of action and their resultant $\mathbf{R}$ obtained, as in Fig. 2–2(b). The forces are now reduced to two, $\mathbf{R}$ and $\mathbf{F}_3$, and for equilibrium these must (1) be equal in magnitude, (2) be opposite in direction, and (3) have the same line of action. It follows from the first two conditions that the resultant of the three forces is zero. The third condition can be fulfilled only if the line of action of $\mathbf{F}_3$ passes through the point of intersection of the lines of action of $\mathbf{F}_1$ and $\mathbf{F}_2$. In other words, the three forces must be *concurrent*.

Problems involving more than three forces are usually best treated with the help of the concept of the *moment* of a force, which we shall postpone until the next chapter. This concept will also enable us to find the resultant of parallel forces, a problem we have not yet considered.

The construction in Fig. 2–2 provides a satisfactory graphical method for the solution of problems in equilibrium. For an analytical solution, it is usually simpler to deal with the rectangular components of the forces. We have shown that the magnitudes of the rectangular components of the

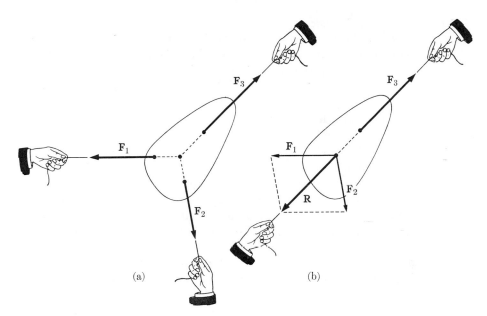

(a)   (b)

Fɪɢ. 2–2. When a body acted on by three nonparallel coplanar forces is in equilibrium, the forces are concurrent and the resultant of any two is equal and opposite to the third.

resultant **R** of any set of coplanar forces are

$$R_x = \Sigma F_x, \qquad R_y = \Sigma F_y.$$

When a body is in equilibrium, the resultant of all of the forces acting on it is zero. Both rectangular components are then zero and hence, for a body in equilibrium,

$$\boxed{\Sigma F_x = 0, \qquad \Sigma F_y = 0.}$$

These equations are called the *first condition of equilibrium.*

The *second condition of equilibrium* is that two forces in equilibrium must have the same line of action, or that three forces in equilibrium must be concurrent.

The first condition of equilibrium ensures that a body shall be in translational equilibrium; the second, that it be in rotational equilibrium. The statement that a body is in complete equilibrium when both conditions are satisfied is the essence of *Newton's first law of motion.* Newton did not state his first law in exactly these words. His original statement (translated from the Latin in which the *Principia* was written) reads: *"Every body continues in its state of rest, or of uniform motion in a straight line, unless it is compelled to change that state by forces impressed on it."*

Although rotational motion was not explicitly mentioned by Newton, it is clear from his work that he fully understood the conditions that the forces must satisfy when the rotation is zero or is constant.

2–3 Newton's third law of motion. Any given force is but one aspect of a mutual interaction between *two* bodies. It is found that *whenever one body exerts a force on another, the second always exerts on the first a force which is equal in magnitude, opposite in direction, and has the same line of action.* A single, isolated force is therefore an impossibility.

The two forces involved in every interaction between two bodies are often called an "action" and a "reaction," but this does not imply any difference in their nature, or that one force is the "cause" and the other its "effect." *Either* force may be considered the "action," and the other the "reaction" to it.

This property of forces was stated by Newton in his *third law of motion.* In his own words, *"To every action there is always opposed an equal reaction: or, the mutual actions of two bodies upon each other are always equal, and directed to contrary parts."*

As an example, suppose that a man pulls on one end of a rope attached to a block as in Fig. 2–3. The weight of the block, and the force exerted on it by the surface, are not shown. The block may or may not be in

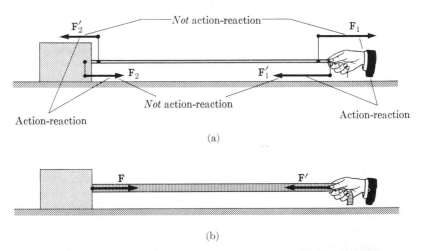

FIG. 2–3. (a) Forces $\mathbf{F}_1$ and $\mathbf{F}'_1$ form one action-reaction pair, and forces $\mathbf{F}_2$ and $\mathbf{F}'_2$ another. $\mathbf{F}_1$ is *always* equal to $\mathbf{F}'_1$, $\mathbf{F}_2$ is *always* equal to $\mathbf{F}'_2$. $\mathbf{F}_1$ and $\mathbf{F}'_2$ are equal only if the rope is in equilibrium, and force $\mathbf{F}'_2$ is *not* the reaction to $\mathbf{F}_1$. (Actually, all forces lie along the rope.) (b) If the rope is in equilibrium it can be considered to transmit a force from the man to the block, and vice versa.

equilibrium. The resulting action-reaction pairs of forces are indicated in the figure. (Actually, the lines of action of all the forces lie along the rope. The force vectors have been offset from this line to show them more clearly.) Vector $\mathbf{F}_1$ represents the force exerted on the rope by the man. Its reaction is the equal and opposite force $\mathbf{F}_1'$ exerted on the man by the rope. Vector $\mathbf{F}_2$ represents the force exerted on the block by the rope. The reaction to it is the equal and opposite force $\mathbf{F}_2'$ exerted on the rope by the block.

It is very important to realize that the forces $\mathbf{F}_1$ and $\mathbf{F}_2'$, although they are opposite in direction and have the same line of action, do *not* constitute an action-reaction pair. For one thing, both of these forces act on the *same* body (the rope), while an action and its reaction necessarily act on *different* bodies. Furthermore, the forces $\mathbf{F}_1$ and $\mathbf{F}_2'$ are not *necessarily* equal in magnitude. If the block and rope are moving to the right with increasing speed, the rope is not in equilibrium and F_1 is greater than F_2'. Only in the special case when the rope remains at rest or moves with constant speed are the forces $\mathbf{F}_1$ and $\mathbf{F}_2'$ equal in magnitude, but this is an example of Newton's *first* law, not his *third*. Even when the speed of the rope is changing, however, the action-reaction forces $\mathbf{F}_1$ and $\mathbf{F}_1'$ are equal to *each other*, and the action-reaction forces F_2 and F_2' are equal to *each other*, although then F_1 is not equal to F_2'.

In the special case when the rope is in equilibrium, and when no forces act on it except those at its ends, F_2' equals F_1 by Newton's *first* law. Since F_2 *always* equals F_2', by Newton's *third* law, then in this special case F_2 also equals F_1 and the force exerted on the block by the rope is equal to the force exerted on the rope by the man. The rope can therefore be considered to "transmit" to the block, without change, the force exerted on it by the man. This point of view is often useful, but it is important to remember that it applies only under the restricted conditions above.

If we adopt this point of view, the rope itself need not be considered and we have the simpler force diagram of Fig. 2–3(b), where the man is considered to exert a force $\mathbf{F}$ directly on the block. The reaction is the force $\mathbf{F}'$ exerted by the block on the man. The only effect of the rope is to transmit these forces from one body to the other.

A body like the rope in Fig. 2–3, which is subjected to pulls at its ends, is said to be in *tension*. The tension at any point equals the force exerted at that point. Thus in Fig. 2–3(a) the tension at the right-hand end of the rope equals the magnitude of $\mathbf{F}_1$ (or of $\mathbf{F}_1'$) and the tension at the left-hand end equals the magnitude of $\mathbf{F}_2$ (or of $\mathbf{F}_2'$). If the rope is in equilibrium and if no forces act except at its ends, as in Fig. 2–3(b), the tension is the same at both ends. If, for example, in Fig. 2–3(b) the magnitudes of $\mathbf{F}$ and $\mathbf{F}'$ are each 50 lb, the tension in the rope is 50 lb (*not* 100 lb).

2–4 Examples of equilibrium. The conditions of equilibrium express certain relations among the forces acting *on* a body in equilibrium. A carefully drawn diagram, in which each force exerted on a body is represented by a vector, is essential in the solution of problems of this sort. The standard procedure is as follows: First, make a neat sketch of the apparatus or structure. Second, choose some one body which is in equilibrium and show *all* the forces exerted *on* it. This is called "isolating" the chosen body, and the diagram is called a *force diagram* or a *free-body* diagram. On the diagram, which should be sufficiently large to avoid crowding, write the numerical values of all given forces, angles, and dimensions, and assign letters to all unknown quantities. When a structure is composed of several members, a separate force diagram must be constructed for each. Third, construct a set of rectangular axes and indicate on each force diagram the rectangular components of any inclined forces. Cross out lightly those forces which have been resolved. Fourth, obtain the necessary algebraic or trigonometric equations from the condition of equilibrium,

$$\sum F_x = 0, \qquad \sum F_y = 0.$$

A force which will be encountered in many problems is the *weight* of a body, that is, the force of gravitational attraction exerted on the body by the earth. We shall show in the next chapter that the line of action of this force always passes through a point called the *center of gravity* of the body.

EXAMPLE 1. To begin with a simple example, consider the body in Fig. 2–4, hanging at rest from the ceiling by a vertical cord. Part (b) of the figure is the free-body diagram for the body. The forces on it are its weight $\mathbf{w}_1$ and the upward force $\mathbf{T}_1$ exerted on it by the cord. If we take the x-axis horizontal and the y-axis vertical, there are no x-components of force, and the y-components are the forces $\mathbf{w}_1$ and $\mathbf{T}_1$. Then from the condition that $\sum F_y = 0$, we have

$$\sum F_y = T_1 - w_1 = 0, \qquad T_1 = w_1. \quad \text{(1st law)}$$

In order that both forces have the same line of action, the center of gravity of the body must lie vertically below the point of attachment of the cord.

Let us emphasize again that the forces $\mathbf{w}_1$ and $\mathbf{T}_1$ are *not* an action-reaction pair, although they are equal in magnitude, opposite in direction, and have the same line of action. The weight $\mathbf{w}_1$ is a force of attraction exerted on the body by the earth. Its reaction is an equal and opposite force of attraction exerted on the earth by the body. This reaction is one of the set of forces acting *on the earth,* and therefore it does not appear in the free-body diagram of the suspended block.

The reaction to the force $\mathbf{T}_1$ is an equal downward force, $\mathbf{T}'_1$, exerted *on the cord* by the suspended body.

$$T_1 = T'_1. \quad \text{(3rd law)}$$

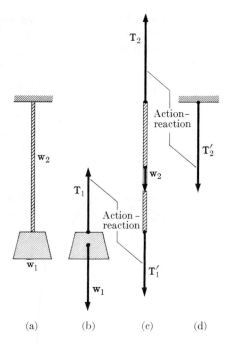

FIG. 2–4. (a) Block hanging at rest from vertical cord. (b) The block is isolated and *all* forces acting *on* it are shown. (c) Forces on the cord. (d) Downward force on the ceiling. Lines connect action-reaction pairs.

The force $\mathbf{T}_1'$ is shown in part (c), which is the free-body diagram of the cord. The other forces on the cord are its own weight $\mathbf{w}_2$ and the upward force $\mathbf{T}_2$ exerted on its upper end by the ceiling. Since the cord is also in equilibrium,

$$\sum F_y = T_2 - w_2 - T_1' = 0,$$

$$T_2 = w_2 + T_1'. \quad \text{(1st law)}$$

The reaction to $\mathbf{T}_2$ is the downward force $\mathbf{T}_2'$ in part (d), exerted on the ceiling by the cord.

$$T_2 = T_2'. \quad \text{(3rd law)}$$

As a numerical example, let the body weigh 20 lb and the cord weigh 1 lb. Then

$$T_1 = w_1 = 20 \text{ lb},$$

$$T_1' = T_1 = 20 \text{ lb},$$

$$T_2 = w_2 + T_1' = 1 \text{ lb} + 20 \text{ lb} = 21 \text{ lb},$$

$$T_2' = T_2 = 21 \text{ lb}.$$

If the weight of the cord were so small as to be negligible, then in effect no forces would act on it except at its ends. The forces T_2 and T_2' would then each equal 20 lb and, as explained earlier, the cord could be considered to transmit a 20-lb force from one end to the other without change. We could then consider the upward pull of the cord on the block as an "action" and the downward pull on the ceiling as its "reaction." The tension in the cord would then be 20 lb.

EXAMPLE 2. In Fig. 2–5(a), a block of weight w hangs from a cord which is knotted at O to two other cords fastened to the ceiling. We wish to find the tensions in these three cords. The weights of the cords are negligible.

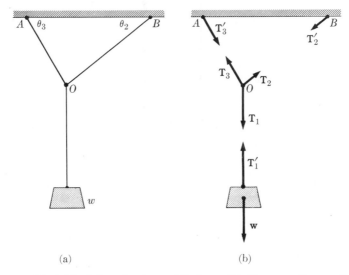

(a)   (b)

FIG. 2–5. (a) A block hanging in equilibrium. (b) Forces acting on the block, on the knot, and on the ceiling.

In order to use the conditions of equilibrium to compute an unknown force, we must consider some body which is in equilibrium and on which the desired force acts. The hanging block is one such body and, as shown in the preceding example, the tension in the vertical cord supporting the block is equal to the weight of the block. The inclined cords do not exert forces on the block, but they do act on the knot at O. Hence we consider the *knot* as a small body in equilibrium whose own weight is negligible.

The free-body diagrams for the block and the knot are shown in Fig. 2–5(b), where T_1, T_2, and T_3 represent the forces exerted *on the knot* by the three cords and T_1', T_2', and T_3' are the reactions to these forces.

Consider first the hanging block. Since it is in equilibrium,

$$T_1' = w. \qquad \text{(1st law)}$$

Since $\mathbf{T}_1$ and $\mathbf{T}'_1$ form an action-reaction pair,

$$T'_1 = T_1. \qquad \text{(3rd law)}$$

Hence

$$T_1 = w.$$

To find the forces $\mathbf{T}_2$ and $\mathbf{T}_3$, we resolve these forces (see Fig. 2–6) into rectangular components. Then, from Newton's *first* law,

$$\sum F_x = T_2 \cos \theta_2 - T_3 \cos \theta_3 = 0,$$

$$\sum F_y = T_2 \sin \theta_2 + T_3 \sin \theta_3 - T_1 = 0.$$

As a numerical example, let $w = 50$ lb, $\theta_2 = 30°$, $\theta_3 = 60°$. Then $T_1 = 50$ lb, and from the two preceding equations,

$$T_2 = 25 \text{ lb}, \qquad T_3 = 43.3 \text{ lb}.$$

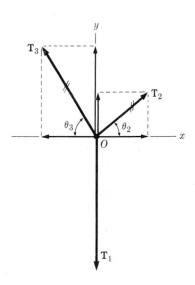

Fig. 2–6. Forces on the knot O in Fig. 2–5, resolved into x- and y-components.

Finally, we know from Newton's *third* law that the inclined cords exert on the ceiling the forces $\mathbf{T}'_2$ and $\mathbf{T}'_3$, equal and opposite to $\mathbf{T}_2$ and $\mathbf{T}_3$ respectively.

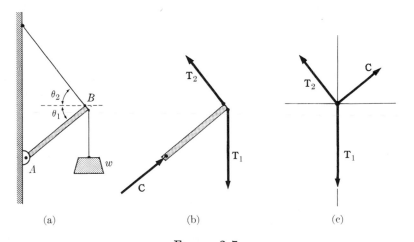

(a)　　　　　　　(b)　　　　　　　(c)

FIGURE 2–7

EXAMPLE 3. Figure 2–7(a) shows a strut AB, pivoted at end A, attached to a wall by a cable, and carrying a load w at end B. The weights of the strut and of the cable are negligible. Suppose the weight w, and the angles θ_1 and θ_2 are known.

Figure 2–7(b) shows the forces acting on the strut. $\mathbf{T}_1$ is the force exerted by the vertical cable, $\mathbf{T}_2$ is the force exerted by the inclined cable, and $\mathbf{C}$ is the force exerted by the pivot. Force $\mathbf{T}_1$ is known both in magnitude and in direction; force $\mathbf{T}_2$ is known in direction only, and neither the magnitude nor the direction of $\mathbf{C}$ is known. However, the forces $\mathbf{T}_1$ and $\mathbf{T}_2$ must intersect at the outer end of the strut, and since the strut is in equilibrium under three forces, the line of action of force $\mathbf{C}$ must also pass through the outer end of the strut. In other words, the direction of force $\mathbf{C}$ is along the line of the strut.

Hence the resultant of $\mathbf{T}_1$ and $\mathbf{T}_2$ is also along this line and the strut, in effect, is acted on by forces at its ends, directed toward each other along the line of the strut. The effect of these forces is to compress the strut, and it is said to be in *compression*.

If the forces acting on a strut are *not* all applied at its ends, the direction of the resultant force at the ends is *not* along the line of the strut. This is illustrated in the next example.

In Fig. 2–7(c), the force $\mathbf{C}$ has been transferred along its line of action to the point of intersection of the three forces. The force diagram is exactly like that of Fig. 2–6, and the problem is solved in the same way.

EXAMPLE 4. In Fig. 2–8, block A of weight w_1 rests on a frictionless inclined plane of slope angle θ. The center of gravity of the block is at its center. A flexible cord is attached to the center of the right face of the block, passes over a frictionless pulley, and is attached to a second block B of weight w_2. The weight of the cord and friction in the pulley are negligible. If w_1 and θ are given, find the weight w_2 for which the system is in equilibrium, that is, for which it remains at rest or moves in either direction at constant speed.

The free-body diagrams for the two blocks are shown at the left and right. The forces on block B are its weight $\mathbf{w}_2$ and the force $\mathbf{T}$ exerted on it by the cord. Since it is in equilibrium,

$$T - w_2 = 0. \quad \text{(1st law)} \tag{2-1}$$

Block A is acted on by its weight $\mathbf{w}_1$, the force $\mathbf{T}$ exerted on it by the cord, and the force $\mathbf{N}$ exerted on it by the plane. We can use the same symbol $\mathbf{T}$ for the force

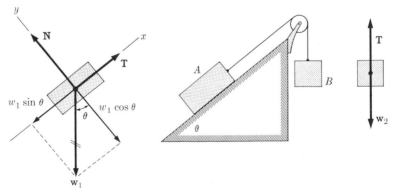

FIG. 2–8. Forces on a block in equilibrium on a frictionless inclined plane.

exerted on each block by the cord, because, as explained in Section 2–3, these forces are equivalent to an action-reaction pair and have the same magnitude. The force $\mathbf{N}$, if there is no friction, is perpendicular or *normal* to the surface of the plane. Since the lines of action of $\mathbf{w}_1$ and $\mathbf{T}$ intersect at the center of gravity of the block, the line of action of $\mathbf{N}$ passes through this point also. It is simplest to choose x- and y-axes parallel and perpendicular to the surface of the plane, because then only the weight $\mathbf{w}_1$ needs to be resolved into components. The conditions of equilibrium give

$$\left. \begin{array}{l} \sum F_x = T - w_1 \sin\theta = 0, \\ \sum F_y = N - w_1 \cos\theta = 0. \end{array} \right\} \quad \text{(1st law)} \qquad \begin{array}{l} (2\text{–}2) \\ (2\text{–}3) \end{array}$$

Thus if $w_1 = 100$ lb and $\theta = 30°$, we have from Eqs. (2–1) and (2–2),

$$w_2 = T = w_1 \sin\theta = 100 \text{ lb} \times 0.500 = 50 \text{ lb},$$

and from Eq. (2–3),

$$N = w_1 \cos\theta = 100 \text{ lb} \times 0.866 = 86.6 \text{ lb}.$$

Note carefully that *in the absence of friction* the same weight w_2 of 50 lb is required whether the system remains at rest or moves with constant speed in *either* direction. This is not the case when friction is present.

2–5 Friction. Whenever the surface of one body slides over that of another, each body exerts a frictional force on the other, parallel to the surfaces. The force *on* each body is opposite to the direction of its motion relative to the other. Thus when a block slides from left to right along the surface of a table, a frictional force to the left acts on the block and an equal force toward the right acts on the table. Frictional forces may also act when there is no relative motion. A horizontal force on a heavy packing case resting on the floor may not be enough to set the case in motion, the applied force being balanced by an equal frictional force exerted on the case by the floor.

The origin of these frictional forces is not fully understood, and the study of them is an important field of research. When one unlubricated metal slides over another, there appears to be an actual momentary welding of the metals together at the "high spots" where they make contact. The observed friction force is the force required to break these tiny welds. The mechanism of the friction force between two blocks of wood, or between two bricks, must be quite different.

Friction forces also act on a body moving through a fluid (liquid or gas). The fluid is said to exhibit *viscosity*. The motion of one body rolling on another is opposed by a force called *rolling friction* and which results from the deformation of the two bodies where they make contact.

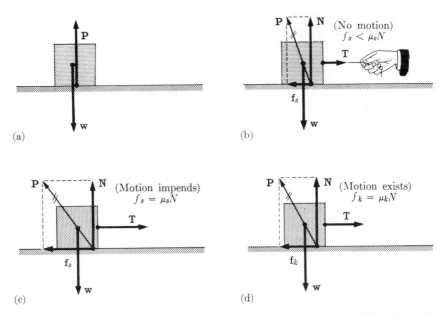

Fig. 2–9. The friction force f is less than or equal to $\mu_s N$ when there is no relative motion, and is equal to $\mu_k N$ when motion exists.

In this chapter we shall consider only so-called "dry friction," the force observed when the surface of one unlubricated solid slides over that of another.

In Fig. 2–9(a) a block is at rest on a horizontal surface, in equilibrium under the action of its weight $\mathbf{w}$ and the upward force $\mathbf{P}$ exerted on it by the surface.

Suppose now that a cord is attached to the block as in Fig. 2–9(b) and the tension $\mathbf{T}$ in the cord is gradually increased. Provided the tension is not too great, the block remains at rest. The force $\mathbf{P}$ exerted on the block by the surface is inclined toward the left as shown, since the three forces $\mathbf{P}$, $\mathbf{w}$, and $\mathbf{T}$ must be concurrent. The component of $\mathbf{P}$ parallel to the surface is called the *force of static friction*, $\mathbf{f}_s$. The other component, $\mathbf{N}$, is the *normal* force exerted on the block by the surface. From the conditions of equilibrium, the force of static friction $\mathbf{f}_s$ equals the force $\mathbf{T}$, and the normal force $\mathbf{N}$ equals the weight $\mathbf{w}$.

As the force $\mathbf{T}$ is increased further, a limiting value is reached at which the block breaks away from the surface and starts to move. In other words, there is a certain maximum value which the force of static friction $\mathbf{f}_s$ can have. Figure 2–9(c) is the force diagram when $\mathbf{T}$ is just below its limiting value and motion impends. If the force $\mathbf{T}$ exceeds this limiting value the block is no longer in equilibrium.

For a given pair of surfaces, the maximum value of f_s is nearly proportional to the normal force N. The actual force of static friction can therefore have any value between zero (when there is no applied force parallel to the surface) and a maximum value proportional to N or equal to $\mu_s N$. The factor μ_s is called the *coefficient of static friction*. Thus,

$$\boxed{f_s \leqq \mu_s N.}$$

(2–4)

The equality sign holds only when the applied force **T**, parallel to the surface, has such a magnitude that motion is about to start [Fig. 2–9(c)]. When T is less than this, [Fig. 2–9(b)], the inequality sign holds and the magnitude of the friction force must be computed from the conditions of equilibrium.

As soon as sliding begins, it is found that the friction force decreases. This new friction force, for a given pair of surfaces, is also nearly proportional to the normal force. The proportionality factor, μ_k, is called the *coefficient of sliding friction* or *kinetic* friction. Thus, when the block is in motion, the force of sliding or kinetic friction is given by

$$\boxed{f_k = \mu_k N.}$$

(2–5)

This is illustrated in Fig. 2–9(d).

The coefficients of static and sliding friction depend primarily on the nature of both of the surfaces in contact, being relatively large if the surfaces are rough and small if they are smooth. The coefficient of sliding friction varies somewhat with the relative velocity, but for simplicity we shall assume it to be independent of velocity. It is also nearly independent of the contact area. However, since two real surfaces actually touch each other only at a relatively small number of high spots, the true contact area is very different from the over-all area. Equations (2–4) and (2–5) are useful empirical relations, but do not represent fundamental physical laws like Newton's laws.

EXAMPLE 1. In Fig. 2–9, suppose that the block weighs 20 lb, that the tension T can be increased to 8 lb before the block starts to slide, and that a force of 4 lb will keep the block moving at constant speed once it has been set in motion. Find the coefficients of static and kinetic friction.

From Fig. 2–11(c) and the data above, we have

$$\left. \begin{array}{l} \sum F_y = N - w = N - 20 \text{ lb} = 0, \\ \sum F_x = T - f_s = 8 \text{ lb} - f_s = 0, \end{array} \right\} \quad \text{(1st law)}$$

$$f_s = \mu_s N \text{ (motion impends).}$$

Hence

$$\mu_s = \frac{f_s}{N} = \frac{8 \text{ lb}}{20 \text{ lb}} = 0.40.$$

From Fig. 2–9(d), we have

$$\left.\begin{array}{l} \sum F_y = N - w = N - 20 \text{ lb} = 0, \\ \sum F_x = T - f_k = 4 \text{ lb} - f_k = 0, \end{array}\right\} \quad \text{(1st law)}$$

$$f_k = \mu_k N \text{ (motion exists)}.$$

Hence

$$\mu_k = \frac{f_k}{N} = \frac{4 \text{ lb}}{20 \text{ lb}} = 0.20.$$

EXAMPLE 2. What is the friction force if the block in Fig. 2–9(b) is at rest on the surface and a horizontal force of 5 lb is exerted on it?

We have

$$\sum F_x = T - f_s = 5 \text{ lb} - f_s = 0, \quad \text{(1st law)}$$

$$f_s = 5 \text{ lb}.$$

Note that in this case

$$f_s < \mu_s N.$$

EXAMPLE 3. What force T, at an angle of 30° above the horizontal, is required to drag a 20-lb block to the right at constant speed as in Fig. 2–10, if the coefficient of kinetic friction between block and surface is 0.20?

The forces on the block are shown in the diagram. From the first condition of equilibrium,

$$\sum F_x = T \cos 30° - 0.2N = 0,$$

$$\sum F_y = T \sin 30° + N - 20 \text{ lb} = 0.$$

Simultaneous solution gives

$$T = 4.15 \text{ lb},$$

$$N = 17.9 \text{ lb}.$$

Notice that in this example the normal force N is not equal to the weight of the block, but is less than the weight by the vertical component of the force T.

EXAMPLE 4. In Fig. 2–11, a block has been placed on an inclined plane and the slope angle θ of the plane has been adjusted until the block slides down the plane at constant speed, once it has been set in motion. Find the angle θ.

The forces on the block are its weight **w** and the normal and frictional components of the force exerted by the plane. Since motion exists, the friction force $f_k = \mu_k N$. Take axes perpendicular and parallel to the surface of the plane. Then

$$\left.\begin{array}{l} \sum F_x = \mu_k N - w \sin \theta = 0, \\ \sum F_y = N - w \cos \theta = 0. \end{array}\right\} \quad \text{(1st law)}$$

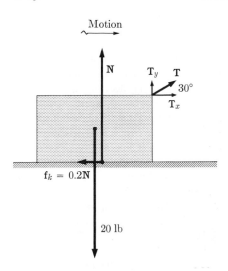

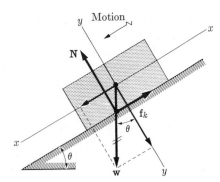

FIG. 2–10. Forces on a block being dragged to the right on a level surface at constant speed.

FIG. 2–11. Forces on a block sliding down an inclined plane (with friction) at constant speed.

Hence

$$\mu_k N = w \sin \theta,$$
$$N = w \cos \theta.$$

Dividing the former by the latter, we get

$$\mu_k = \tan \theta.$$

It follows that a block, regardless of its weight, slides down an inclined plane with constant speed if the tangent of the slope angle of the plane equals the coefficient of kinetic friction. Measurement of this angle then provides a simple experimental method of determining the coefficient of kinetic friction.

It is left as a problem for the reader to show that if a block is placed on an inclined plane and the slope angle of the plane is slowly increased, the block breaks away from the plane and starts to slide when the tangent of the slope angle becomes equal to the coefficient of static friction, μ_s.

PROBLEMS

2–1. A block rests on a horizontal surface. (a) What two forces act on it? (b) By what bodies are each of the forces exerted? (c) What are the reactions to these forces? (d) On what body is each reaction exerted, and by what body is each exerted?

2–2. A block is given a push along a table top, and slides off the edge of the table. (a) What force or forces are exerted on it while it is falling from the table to the floor? (b) What is the reaction to each force, that is, on what body and by what body is the reaction exerted? Neglect air resistance.

2–3. Two 10-lb weights are suspended at opposite ends of a rope which passes over a light frictionless pulley. The pulley is attached to a chain which goes to the ceiling. (a) What is the tension in the rope? (b) What is the tension in the chain?

2–4. In Fig. 2–5, let the weight of the hanging block be 50 lb. Find the tensions T_2 and T_3, (a) if $\theta_2 = \theta_3 = 60°$, (b) if $\theta_2 = \theta_3 = 10°$, (c) if $\theta_2 = 60°$, $\theta_3 = 0$, and (d) if $AB = 10$ ft, $AO = 6$ ft, $OB = 8$ ft.

2–5. Find the tension in each cord in Fig. 2–12 if the weight of the suspended body is 200 lb.

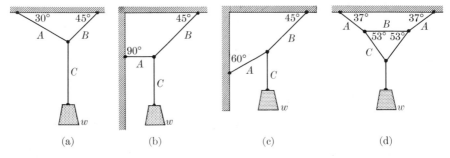

FIGURE 2–12

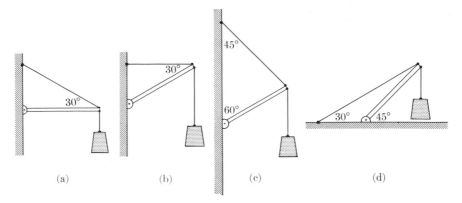

FIGURE 2–13

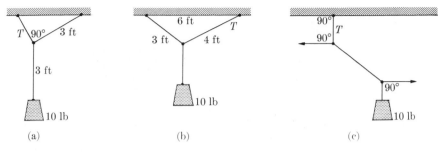

FIGURE 2-14

2-6. Find the tension T in the cable, and the magnitude and direction of the force C exerted on the strut by the pivot in the arrangements in Fig. 2-13. Let the weight of the suspended object in each case be 1000 lb. Neglect the weight of the strut.

2-7. (a) In which of the arrangements in Fig. 2-14 can the tension T be computed, if the only quantities known are those explicitly given? (b) For each case in which insufficient information is given, state one additional quantity, a knowledge of which would permit solution.

2-8. A horizontal boom 8 ft long is hinged to a vertical wall at one end, and a 500-lb body hangs from its outer end. The boom is supported by a guy wire from its outer end to a point on the wall directly above the boom. (a) If the tension in this wire is not to exceed 1000 lb, what is the minimum height above the boom at which it may be fastened to the wall? (b) By how

many pounds would the tension be increased if the wire were fastened 1 ft below this point, the boom remaining horizontal? Neglect the weight of the boom.

2-9. One end of a rope 50 ft long is attached to an automobile. The other end is fastened to a tree. A man exerts a force of 100 lb at the mid-point of the rope, pulling it 2 ft to the side. What is the force exerted on the automobile?

2-10. Find the largest weight w which can be supported by the structure in Fig. 2-15 if the maximum tension the upper rope can withstand is 1000 lb and the maximum compression the strut can withstand is 2000 lb. The vertical rope is strong enough to carry any load required. Neglect the weight of the strut.

2-11. (a) Block A in Fig. 2-16 weighs 100 lb. The coefficient of static friction between the block and the sur-

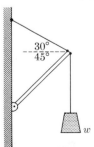

FIGURE 2-15

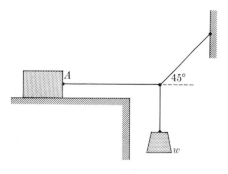

FIGURE 2-16

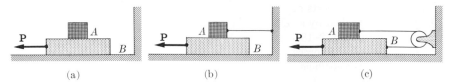

FIGURE 2–17

face on which it rests is 0.30. The weight w is 20 lb and the system is in equilibrium. Find the friction force exerted on block A. (b) Find the maximum weight w for which the system will remain in equilibrium.

2–12. A block is pulled to the right at constant velocity by a 10-lb force acting 30° above the horizontal. The coefficient of sliding friction between block and surface is 0.5. What is the weight of the block? Assume all of the forces on the block to act at its center.

2–13. A block weighing 14 lb is placed on an inclined plane and connected to a 10-lb block by a cord passing over a small frictionless pulley, as in Fig. 2–8. The coefficient of sliding friction between the block and the plane is 1/7. For what two values of θ will the system move with constant velocity? Assume that all the forces on the 14-lb block act at its center. [*Hint:* $\cos \theta = \sqrt{1 - \sin^2 \theta}$.]

2–14. A block weighing 100 lb is placed on an inclined plane of slope angle 30° and is connected to a second hanging block of weight w by a cord passing over a small frictionless pulley, as in Fig. 2–8. The coefficient of static friction is 0.40 and the coefficient of sliding friction is 0.30. (a) Find the weight w for which the 100-lb block moves up the plane at constant speed. (b) Find the weight w for which it moves down the plane at constant speed. (c) For what range of values of w will the block remain at rest?

2–15. What force P at an angle ϕ above the horizontal is needed to drag a box of weight w at constant speed along a level floor if the coefficient of sliding friction between box and floor is μ?

2–16. A safe weighing 600 lb is to be lowered at constant speed down skids 8 ft long, from a truck 4 ft high. If the coefficient of sliding friction between safe and skids is 0.30, (a) will the safe need to be pulled down or held back? (b) How great a force parallel to the plane is needed?

2–17. Block A in Fig. 2–17 weighs 4 lb and block B weighs 8 lb. The coefficient of sliding friction between all surfaces is 0.25. Find the force P necessary to drag block B to the left at constant speed (a) if A rests on B and moves with it, (b) if A is held at rest, and (c) if A and B are connected by a light flexible cord passing around a fixed frictionless pulley.

2–18. Block A, of weight w, slides down an inclined plane S of slope angle 37° at constant velocity while the plank

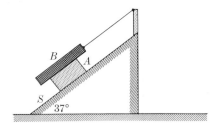

FIGURE 2–18

B, also of weight w, rests on top of A. The plank is attached by a cord to the top of the plane (Fig. 2–18). (a) Draw a diagram of all the forces acting on block A. (b) If the coefficient of kinetic friction is the same between the surfaces A and B and between S and A, determine its value.

2–19. If a force of 86 lb parallel to the surface of a 20° inclined plane will push a 120-lb block up the plane at constant speed, (a) what force parallel to the plane will push it down at constant speed? (b) What is the coefficient of sliding friction?

2–20. Two blocks, A and B, are placed as in Fig. 2–19 and connected by ropes to block C. Both A and B weigh 20 lb and the coefficient of sliding friction between each block and the surface is 0.5. Block C descends with constant velocity. (a) Draw two separate force diagrams showing the forces acting on A and B. (b) Find the tension in the rope connecting blocks A and B. (c) What is the weight of block C?

2–21. A flexible chain of weight w hangs between two hooks at the same height, as shown in Fig. 2–20. At each end the chain makes an angle θ with the horizontal. (a) What is the magnitude and direction of the force F exerted by the chain on the hook at the left? (b) What is the tension T in the chain at its lowest point?

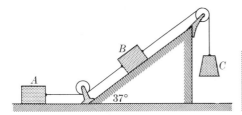

FIGURE 2–19

FIGURE 2–20

CHAPTER 3

EQUILIBRIUM. MOMENT OF A FORCE

3–1 Moment of a force. The effect produced on a body by a force of given magnitude and direction depends on the position of the *line of action* of the force. Thus in Fig. 3–1 the force $\mathbf{F}_1$ would produce a counter-clockwise rotation (together with a translation toward the right), while $\mathbf{F}_2$ would produce a clockwise rotation.

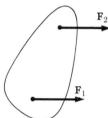

FIGURE 3–1

The line of action of a force can be specified by giving the perpendicular distance from some reference point to the line of action. In many instances, we shall be studying the motion of a body which is free to rotate about some axis, and which is acted on by a number of coplanar forces all lying in a plane perpendicular to the axis. It is then most convenient to select as the reference point the point at which the axis intersects the plane of the forces. The perpendicular distance from this point to the line of action of a force is called the *force arm* or the *moment arm* of the force about the axis. The product of the magnitude of a force and its force arm is called the *moment* of the force about the axis, or the *torque*.

Thus Fig. 3–2 is a top view of a flat object, pivoted about an axis perpendicular to the plane of the diagram and passing through point O. The body is acted on by the forces $\mathbf{F}_1$ and $\mathbf{F}_2$, lying in the plane of the diagram. The moment arm of $\mathbf{F}_1$ is the perpendicular distance OA, of length l_1, and the moment arm of $\mathbf{F}_2$ is the perpendicular distance OB of length l_2.

The effect of the force $\mathbf{F}_1$ is to produce counterclockwise rotation about the axis, while that of $\mathbf{F}_2$ is to produce clockwise rotation. To distinguish between these directions of rotation, we shall adopt the convention that counterclockwise moments are positive, and that clockwise moments are negative. Hence the moment Γ_1 (Greek "Gamma") of the force $\mathbf{F}_1$ about the axis through O is

$$\Gamma_1 = +F_1 l_1,$$

and the moment Γ_2 of $\mathbf{F}_2$ is

$$\Gamma_2 = -F_2 l_2.$$

If forces are expressed in pounds and lengths in feet, torques are expressed in pound·feet.

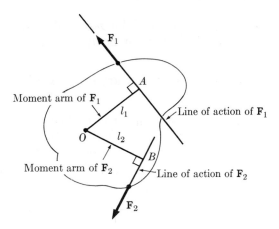

FIG. 3–2. The moment of a force about an axis is the product of the force and its moment arm.

3–2 The second condition of equilibrium. We saw in Section 2–2 that when a body is acted on by any number of coplanar forces, the forces can always be reduced to two, as in Fig. 2–2. If the body is in equilibrium, these forces must (a) be equal in magnitude and opposite in direction, and (b) must have the same line of action.

Requirement (a) is satisfied by the *first condition of equilibrium,*

$$\Sigma F_x = 0, \qquad \Sigma F_y = 0.$$

Requirement (b), which is the second condition of equilibrium, can be simply expressed in terms of the moments of the forces. Figure 3–3 again shows a flat object acted on by two forces $\mathbf{F}_1$ and $\mathbf{F}_2$. If the object is in equilibrium, the magnitudes of $\mathbf{F}_1$ and $\mathbf{F}_2$ are equal and both forces have the same line of action. Hence they have the same moment arm OA, of length l, about an axis perpendicular to the plane of the body and passing through any arbitrary point O. Their moments about the axis are therefore equal in magnitude and opposite in sign, and the algebraic sum of their moments is zero. The necessary and sufficient condition, therefore, that two equal and opposite forces have the same line of action is that the algebraic sum of

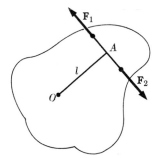

FIG. 3–3. When two forces are in equilibrium, their resultant moment about any axis is zero.

their moments, about any axis, shall be zero. The *second condition of equilibrium* may therefore be expressed analytically as

$$\sum \Gamma = 0 \text{ (about any arbitrary axis)}.$$

It is not necessary to first reduce a set of coplanar forces to two forces in order to calculate the sum of their moments. One need only calculate the moment of each force separately, and then add these moments algebraically. Thus if a body is in equilibrium under the action of any number of coplanar forces, the algebraic sum of the torques about any arbitrary axis is zero.

EXAMPLE 1. A rigid rod whose own weight is negligible (Fig. 3–4) is pivoted at point O and carries a body of weight w_1 at end A. Find the weight w_2 of a second body which must be attached at end B if the rod is to be in equilibrium, and find the force exerted on the rod by the pivot at O.

Figure 3–4(b) is the free-body diagram of the rod. The forces T_1 and T_2 are equal respectively to w_1 and w_2. The conditions of equilibrium, taking moments about an axis through O, perpendicular to the diagram, give

$$\sum F_y = P - T_1 - T_2 = 0, \quad \text{(1st condition)}$$
$$\Gamma_O = T_1 l_1 - T_2 l_2 = 0. \quad \text{(2nd condition)}$$

Let $l_1 = 3$ ft, $l_2 = 4$ ft, $w_1 = 4$ lb. Then, from the equations above,

$$P = 7 \text{ lb}, \qquad T_2 = w_2 = 3 \text{ lb}.$$

To illustrate that the resultant moment about *any* axis is zero, let us compute moments about an axis through point A.

$$\sum \Gamma_A = P l_1 - T_2(l_1 + l_2) = 7 \text{ lb} \times 3 \text{ ft} - 4 \text{ lb} \times 7 \text{ ft} = 0.$$

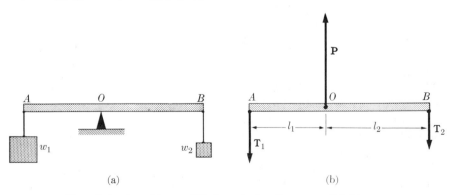

(a)   (b)

FIG. 3–4. A rod in equilibrium under three parallel forces.

The point about which moments are computed need not lie on the rod.   To verify this, let the reader calculate the resultant moment about a point 1 ft to the left of A and 1 ft above it.

EXAMPLE 2.   In Fig. 3–5 a ladder 20 ft long, of weight 80 lb, with its center of gravity at its center, in equilibrium, leans against a vertical frictionless wall and makes an angle of 53° with the horizontal.   We wish to find the magnitudes and directions of the forces $\mathbf{F}_1$ and $\mathbf{F}_2$.

If the wall is frictionless, $\mathbf{F}_1$ is horizontal.   The direction of $\mathbf{F}_2$ is unknown (except in special cases, its direction does *not* lie along the ladder).   Instead of considering its magnitude and direction as unknowns, it is simpler to resolve the force $\mathbf{F}_2$ into x- and y-components and solve for these.   The magnitude and direction of $\mathbf{F}_2$ may then be computed.   The first condition of equilibrium therefore provides the equations

$$\left. \begin{array}{l} \Sigma F_x = F_2 \cos \theta - F_1 = 0, \\ \Sigma F_y = F_2 \sin \theta - 80 \text{ lb} = 0. \end{array} \right\} \quad \text{(1st condition)}$$

In writing the second condition, moments may be computed about an axis through any point.   The resulting equation is simplest if one selects a point through which two or more forces pass, since these forces then do not appear in

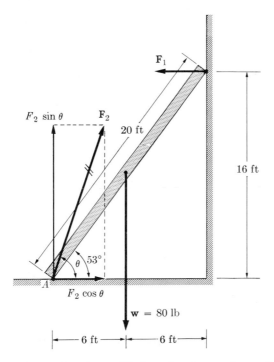

FIG. 3–5.   Forces on a ladder in equilibrium, leaning against a frictionless wall.

the equation. Let us therefore take moments about an axis through point A.

$$\Sigma\Gamma_A = F_1 \times 16 \text{ ft} - 80 \text{ lb} \times 6 \text{ ft} = 0. \qquad \text{(2nd condition)}$$

From the second equation, $F_2 \sin\theta = 80$ lb, and from the third,

$$F_1 = \frac{480 \text{ lb·ft}}{16 \text{ ft}} = 30 \text{ lb.}$$

Then from the first equation,

$$F_2 \cos\theta = 30 \text{ lb.}$$

Hence

$$F_2 = \sqrt{(80 \text{ lb})^2 + (30 \text{ lb})^2} = 85.5 \text{ lb,}$$

$$\theta = \tan^{-1}\frac{80 \text{ lb}}{30 \text{ lb}} = 69.5°.$$

EXAMPLE 3. Figure 3–6 illustrates a problem that has already been solved, in part, in Example 3 at the end of Section 2–5. (a) What force T, at an angle of 30° above the horizontal, is required to drag a block of weight $w = 20$ lb to the right at constant speed along a level surface if the coefficient of sliding friction between block and surface is 0.20?　(b) Determine the line of action of the normal force **N** exerted on the block by the surface. The block is 1 ft high, 2 ft long, and its center of gravity is at its center.

From the first condition of equilibrium,

$$\left.\begin{aligned}\Sigma F_x &= T\cos 30° - f_k = 0,\\ \Sigma F_y &= T\sin 30° + N - 20 \text{ lb} = 0.\end{aligned}\right\} \qquad \text{(1st condition)}$$

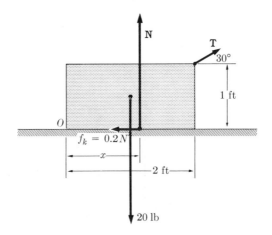

FIGURE 3–6

Let x represent the distance from point O to the line of action of $\mathbf{N}$, and take moments about an axis through O. Then, from the second condition of equilibrium,

$$\Sigma\Gamma_O = T \sin 30° \times 2 \text{ ft} - T \cos 30° \times 1 \text{ ft} + N \times x - 20 \text{ lb} \times 1 \text{ ft} = 0.$$
(2nd condition)

From the first two equations, we get

$$T = 4.15 \text{ lb}, \qquad N = 17.9 \text{ lb},$$

and from the third equation,

$$x = 1.08 \text{ ft.}$$

The line of action of $\mathbf{N}$ therefore lies 0.08 ft to the right of the center of gravity.

3–3 Resultant of parallel forces. The direction of the resultant of a set of parallel forces is the same as that of the forces, and its magnitude equals the sum of their magnitudes. The line of action of the resultant can be found from the requirement that the moment of the resultant, about any axis, shall equal the sum of the moments of the given forces.

Consider the parallel forces $\mathbf{F}_1$ and $\mathbf{F}_2$ in Fig. 3–7. Point O is any arbitrary point and the x-axis has been taken at right angles to the directions of the forces. The forces have no x-components, so the magnitude of the resultant is

$$R = \Sigma F_y = F_1 + F_2.$$

If x_1 and x_2 are the perpendicular distances from O to the lines of action of the forces, their resultant moment about an axis through O is

$$\Sigma\Gamma_O = x_1 F_1 + x_2 F_2.$$

Let $\bar{x}$ represent the distance from O to the line of action of the resultant.

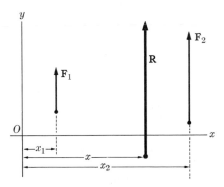

FIG. 3–7. Vector $\mathbf{R}$ represents the resultant of the parallel forces $\mathbf{F}_1$ and $\mathbf{F}_2$, in magnitude, direction, and line of action.

The moment of the resultant about O is then

$$R\bar{x} = (F_1 + F_2)\bar{x},$$

and since this equals the resultant moment, we have

$$(F_1 + F_2)\bar{x} = F_1 x_1 + F_2 x_2.$$

Therefore

$$\bar{x} = \frac{F_1 x_1 + F_2 x_2}{F_1 + F_2},$$

and the magnitude, direction, and line of action of the resultant are determined.

The resultant of any number of parallel forces is found in the same way. The magnitude of the resultant is

$$R = \Sigma F,$$

and, if the forces are parallel to the y-axis, the x-coordinate of its line of action is

$$\bar{x} = \frac{\Sigma F x}{\Sigma F} = \frac{\Sigma F x}{R}.$$

EXAMPLE. When a body is in equilibrium under the action of three forces, the resultant of any two is equal and opposite to the third and has the same line of action. Show that these conditions are satisfied by the three parallel forces in Fig. 3–4(b).

It was shown in Example 1 at the end of Section 3–2 that if $l_1 = 3$ ft, $l_2 = 4$ ft, and $T_1 = 4$ lb, then $T_2 = 3$ lb and $P = 7$ lb.

Let us first find the resultant of $\mathbf{T}_1$ and $\mathbf{T}_2$. Take the x-axis along the rod with origin at point A. The magnitude of the resultant is

$$R = \Sigma F = -4\,\text{lb} - 3\,\text{lb} = -7\,\text{lb}.$$

The coordinate of its line of action is

$$\bar{x} = \frac{\Sigma F x}{\Sigma F} = \frac{4\,\text{lb} \times 0 - 3\,\text{lb} \times 7\,\text{ft}}{-7\,\text{lb}} = 3\,\text{ft}.$$

Hence the resultant of $\mathbf{T}_1$ and $\mathbf{T}_2$ is equal and opposite to $\mathbf{P}$ and has the same line of action.

The resultant of $\mathbf{P}$ and $\mathbf{T}_2$ has a magnitude

$$R = \Sigma F = 7\,\text{lb} - 3\,\text{lb} = 4\,\text{lb}.$$

The coordinate of its line of action is

$$\bar{x} = \frac{\sum Fx}{\sum F} = \frac{7\ \text{lb} \times 3\ \text{ft} - 3\ \text{lb} \times 7\ \text{ft}}{4\ \text{lb}} = 0,$$

so the resultant of $\mathbf{P}$ and $\mathbf{T}_2$ is equal and opposite to $\mathbf{T}_1$ and has the same line of action.

3–4 Center of gravity. Every particle of matter in a body is attracted by the earth, and the single force which we call the *weight* of the body is the resultant of all these forces of attraction. The direction of the force on each particle is toward the center of the earth, but the distance to the earth's center is so great that for all practical purposes the forces can be considered parallel to one another. Hence the weight of a body is the resultant of a large number of parallel forces.

Figure 3–8(a) shows a flat object of arbitrary shape in the xy-plane, the y-axis being vertical. Let the body be subdivided into a large number of small particles of weights $\mathbf{w}_1$, $\mathbf{w}_2$, etc., and let the coordinates of these particles be x_1 and y_1, x_2 and y_2, etc. The total weight W of the object is

$$W = w_1 + w_2 + \cdots = \sum w. \tag{3–1}$$

The x-coordinate of the line of action of $\mathbf{W}$ is

$$\bar{x} = \frac{w_1 x_1 + w_2 x_2 + \cdots}{w_1 + w_2 + \cdots} = \frac{\sum wx}{\sum w} = \frac{\sum wx}{W}. \tag{3–2}$$

Now let the object and the reference axes be rotated 90° clockwise or, which amounts to the same thing, let us consider the gravitational forces

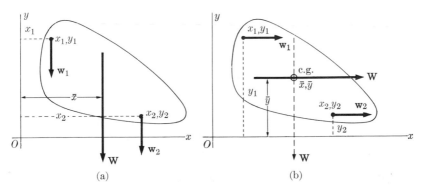

(a) (b)

Fɪɢ. 3–8. The body's weight $\mathbf{W}$ is the resultant of a large number of parallel forces. The line of action of $\mathbf{W}$ always passes through the center of gravity.

to be rotated 90° counterclockwise as in Fig. 3–8(b). The total weight W is unaltered and the y-coordinate of its line of action is

$$\bar{y} = \frac{w_1 y_1 + w_2 y_2 + \cdots}{w_1 + w_2 + \cdots} = \frac{\sum wy}{\sum w} = \frac{\sum wy}{W}. \tag{3-3}$$

The point of intersection of the lines of action of **W** in the two parts of Fig. 3–8 has the coordinates $\bar{x}$ and $\bar{y}$ and is called the *center of gravity* of the object. By considering some arbitrary orientation of the object, one can show that the line of action of **W** *always* passes through the center of gravity.

If the centers of gravity of each of a number of bodies have been determined, the coordinates of the center of gravity of the combination can be computed from Eqs. (3–1) and (3–2), letting w_1, w_2, etc., be the weights of the bodies and x_1 and y_1, and y_2, etc., be the coordinates of the center of gravity of each.

Symmetry considerations are often useful in finding the position of the center of gravity. Thus the center of gravity of a homogeneous sphere, cube, circular disk, or rectangular plate is at its center. That of a cylinder or right circular cone is on the axis of symmetry, and so on.

EXAMPLE. Locate the center of gravity of the machine part in Fig. 3–9, consisting of a disk 2 in. in diameter and 1 in. long, and a rod 1 in. in diameter and 6 in. long, constructed of a homogeneous material.

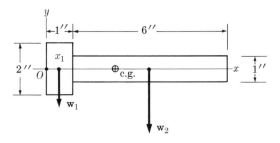

FIGURE 3–9

By symmetry, the center of gravity lies on the axis and the center of gravity of each part is midway between its ends. The volume of the disk is π in^3 and that of the rod is $3\pi/2$ in^3. Since the weights of the two parts are proportional to their volumes,

$$\frac{w \text{ (disk)}}{w \text{ (rod)}} = \frac{w_1}{w_2} = \frac{\pi}{3\pi/2} = \frac{2}{3}.$$

Take the origin O at the left face of the disk, on the axis. Then $x_1 = 0.5$ in., $x_2 = 4.0$ in., and

$$\bar{x} = \frac{w_1 \times 0.5 \text{ in.} + \frac{3}{2}w_1 \times 4.0 \text{ in.}}{w_1 + \frac{3}{2}w_1} = 2.6 \text{ in.}$$

The center of gravity is on the axis, 2.6 in. to the right of O.

The center of gravity of a flat object can be located experimentally as shown in Fig. 3–10. In part (a) the body is suspended from some arbitrary point A. When allowed to come to equilibrium, the center of gravity must lie on a vertical line through A. When the object is suspended from a second point B, as in part (b), the center of gravity lies on a vertical line through B and hence lies at the point of intersection of this line and the first. If the object is now suspended from a third point C, as in part (c), a vertical line through C will be found to pass through the point of intersection of the first two lines.

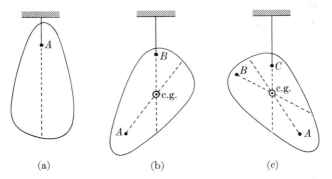

FIG. 3–10. Locating the center of gravity of a flat object.

The center of gravity of a body has another important property. A force **F** whose line of action lies at one side or the other of the center of gravity, as in Fig. 3–11(a), will change both the translational and rotational motion of the body on which it acts. However, if the line of action passes through the center of gravity, as in part (b), only the translational motion is affected and the body remains in rotational equilibrium. Thus when a body is tossed in the air with a whirling motion it continues to rotate at a constant rate, since the line of action of its weight passes through the center of gravity.

It may also be pointed out that when one object rests on or slides over another, the normal and frictional forces are sets of parallel forces distributed over the area in contact. The single vectors which have been used to represent these forces are therefore actually the resultants of sets of parallel forces.

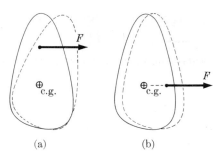

Fɪɢ. 3–11. A body is in rotational but not translational equilibrium when acted on by a force whose line of action passes through the center of gravity, as in (b).

3–5 Couples. It often happens that the forces on a body reduce to two forces of equal magnitude and opposite direction, having lines of action which are parallel but do not coincide. Such a pair of forces is called a *couple*. A common example is afforded by the forces on a compass needle in the earth's magnetic field. The north and south poles of the needle are acted on by equal forces, one toward the north and the other toward the south as shown in Fig. 3–12. Except when the needle points in the N-S direction, the two forces do not have the same line of action.

Figure 3–13 shows a couple consisting of two forces, each of magnitude F, separated by a perpendicular distance l. The resultant R of the forces is

$$R = F - F = 0.$$

The fact that the resultant force is zero means that a couple has no effect in producing translation as a whole of the body on which it acts. The only effect of a couple is to produce rotation.

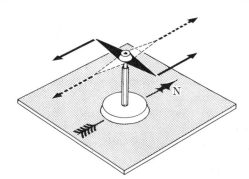

Fɪɢ. 3–12. Forces on the poles of a compass needle.

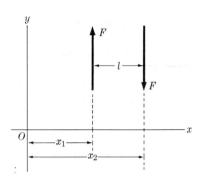

Fig. 3–13. Two equal and opposite forces having different lines of action are called a couple. The moment of the couple is the same about all points, and is equal to lF.

The resultant torque of the couple in Fig. 3–13, about an arbitrary point O, is

$$\Gamma_O = x_1 F - x_2 F$$
$$= x_1 F - (x_1 + l)F$$
$$= -lF.$$

Since the distances x_1 and x_2 do not appear in the result, we conclude that the torque of the couple is the same about *all* points in the plane of the forces forming the couple and is equal to the product of the magnitude of either force and the perpendicular distance between their lines of action.

A body acted on by a couple can be kept in equilibrium only by another couple of the same moment and in the opposite direction. As an example, the ladder in Fig. 3–5 can be considered as acted on by two couples, one formed by the forces $F_2 \sin \theta$ and w, the other by the forces $F_2 \cos \theta$ and F_1. The moment of the first is

$$\Gamma_1 = 6 \text{ ft} \times 80 \text{ lb} = 480 \text{ lb·ft}.$$

The moment of the second is

$$\Gamma_2 = 16 \text{ ft} \times 30 \text{ lb} = 480 \text{ lb·ft}.$$

The first moment is clockwise and the second is counterclockwise.

Problems

3–1. Give an example to show that the following statement is false: Any two forces acting on a body can be combined into a single resultant force that would have the same effect.

3–2. The center of gravity of a log 10 ft long and weighing 100 lb is 4 ft from one end of the log. It is to be carried by two men, one at the heavy end. Where should the other man hold the log if each is to carry half the load?

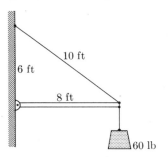

FIGURE 3–14

3–3. The strut in Fig. 3–14 weighs 40 lb and its center of gravity is at its center. Find (a) the tension in the cable and (b) the horizontal and vertical components of the force exerted on the strut at the wall.

3–4. A single force is to be applied to the bar in Fig. 3–15 to maintain it in equilibrium in the position shown. The weight of the bar can be neglected. (a) What are the x- and y-components

of the required force? (b) What is the tangent of the angle which the force must make with the bar? (c) What is the magnitude of the required force? (d) Where should the force be applied?

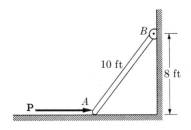

FIGURE 3–16

3–5. End A of the bar AB in Fig. 3–16 rests on a frictionless horizontal surface, while end B is hinged. A horizontal force $\mathbf{P}$ of 12 lb is exerted on end A. Neglect the weight of the bar. What are the horizontal and vertical components of the force exerted by the bar on the hinge at B?

3–6. A circular disk 1 ft in diameter, pivoted about a horizontal axis through its center, has a cord wrapped around its rim. The cord passes over a frictionless pulley P and is attached to a body of weight 48 lb. A uniform rod 4 ft long is fastened to the disk with one end at the center of the disk. The apparatus is in equilibrium, with the rod horizontal, as shown in Fig. 3–17. (a) What is the weight of the rod?

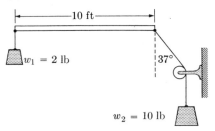

FIGURE 3–15

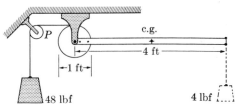

FIGURE 3–17

(b) What is the new equilibrium direction of the rod when a second body weighing 4 lb is suspended from the outer end of the rod, as shown by the dotted line?

3-7. A roller whose diameter is 20 in. weighs 72 lb. What horizontal force is necessary to pull the roller over a brick 2 in. high when (a) the force is applied at the center, (b) at the top?

3-8. Find the tension in the cable and the components of the force exerted on the strut by the wall in Fig. 3-18. Neglect the weight of the strut.

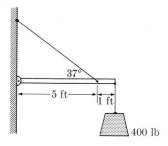

FIGURE 3-18

3-9. The boom in Fig. 3-19 is uniform and weighs 500 lb. Find the tension in the guy wire, and the horizontal and vertical components of the force exerted on the boom at its lower end.

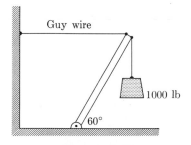

FIGURE 3-19

3-10. Find the tension in cord A in Fig. 3-20. The boom is uniform and weighs 400 lb.

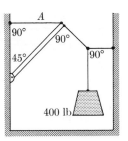

FIGURE 3-20

3-11. A door 7 ft high and 3 ft wide is hung from hinges 6 ft apart and 6 in. from the top and bottom of the door. The door weighs 60 lb, its center of gravity is at its center, and each hinge carries half the weight of the door. Find the horizontal component of the force exerted on the door at each hinge.

3-12. A gate 8 ft long and 4 ft high weighs 80 lb. Its center of gravity is at its center, and it is hinged at A and B. To relieve the strain on the top hinge a wire CD is connected as shown in Fig. 3-21. The tension in CD is increased until the horizontal force at hinge A is zero. (a) What is the tension in the wire CD? (b) What is the magnitude of the horizontal component of force at hinge B? (c) What is the combined vertical force exerted by hinges A and B?

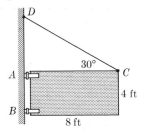

FIGURE 3-21

3-13. A garage door is mounted on an overhead rail as in Fig. 3-22. The wheels at A and B have rusted so that

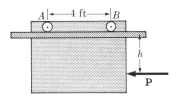

FIGURE 3–22

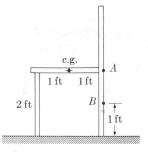

FIGURE 3–24

they do not roll, but slide along the track. The coefficient of sliding friction is 0.5. The distance between the wheels is 4 ft, and each is 1 ft in from the vertical sides of the door. The door is symmetrical and weighs 160 lb. It is pushed to the left at constant velocity by a horizontal force **P**. (a) If the distance h is 3 ft, what is the vertical component of the force exerted on each wheel by the track? (b) Find the maximum value h can have without causing one wheel to leave the track.

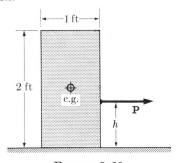

FIGURE 3–23

3–14. A rectangular block 1 ft wide and 2 ft high is dragged to the right along a level surface at constant speed by a horizontal force **P**, as shown in Fig. 3–23. The coefficient of sliding friction is 0.40, the block weighs 50 lb, and its center of gravity is at its center. (a) Find the force P required. (b) Find the line of action of the normal force **N** exerted on the block by the surface, if the height h is 6 in. (c) Find the value of h at which the block just starts to tip.

3–15. The chair in Fig. 3–24 is to be dragged to the right at constant speed along a horizontal surface, the coefficient of sliding friction being 0.30. The chair weighs 50 lb. (a) What horizontal force is needed? (b) What is the upward force at each leg if the force dragging the chair is applied at point A? (c) What is the upward force at each leg if the force is applied at point B? (d) What is the maximum height at which the dragging force can be applied without causing the chair to tip?

3–16. A freight elevator weighing 2000 lb and having dimensions of $8 \times 8 \times 12$ ft hangs from a cable with a small clearance between vertical frictionless guides, G and G', as shown in Fig. 3–25. A load of 1200 lb is placed in the elevator with its center of gravity 2 ft to the left of the center of the floor. The elevator is then moved upward at constant velocity.

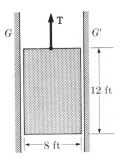

FIGURE 3–25

(a) Show in a diagram the location and direction of the forces exerted by the guides on the elevator. (b) Compute the magnitude of these forces.

3–17. A ladder 13 ft long leans against a vertical frictionless wall with its lower end 5 ft from the wall. The ladder weighs 80 lb and its center of gravity is at its center. Find the magnitude and direction of the force exerted on the lower end of the ladder.

3–18. A uniform ladder 35 ft long rests against a frictionless vertical wall with its lower end 21 ft from the wall. The ladder weighs 80 lb. The coefficient of static friction between the foot of the ladder and the ground is 0.4. A man weighing 150 lb starts up the ladder. How far up the ladder can he climb before the ladder starts to slip?

3–19. A table 8 ft long and 3 ft high, weighing 100 lb, has its center of gravity 6 in. below the center of the table top. The table is pushed at constant speed along a horizontal surface by a horizontal force applied at one end of the table top. The coefficient of sliding friction is 0.40. Compute the upward force and the friction force at each table leg.

3–20. A uniform box weighing 200 lb is 5 ft long and 3 ft high. It rests on a floor with its long side horizontal and with its lower right-hand edge pushed tightly against a cleat. (a) What must be the magnitude of the force applied at the edge diagonally opposite the cleat in the direction of 37° above the horizontal (first quadrant) so that the box will just begin to turn about the edge

at the cleat? (b) If the cleat is removed, what is the value of the coefficient of friction between the box and the floor so that the box will be about to slide when the force in part (a) is applied?

3–21. Find the magnitude and line of action of the resultant of the four forces in Fig. 3–26.

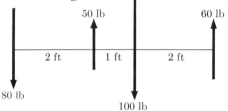

FIGURE 3–26

3–22. Weights of 3, 6, 9, and 12 lb are fastened to the corners of a light wire frame 2 ft square. Find the position of the center of gravity of the weights.

3–23. Find the position of the center of gravity of the T-shaped plate in Fig. 3–27

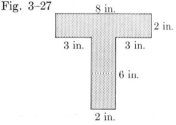

FIGURE 3–27

3–24. A machine part, shown in cross section in Fig. 3–28, consists of two homogeneous, solid, coaxial cylinders. Where is its center of gravity?

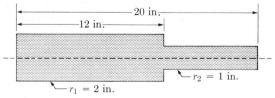

FIGURE 3–28

CHAPTER 4

RECTILINEAR MOTION

4–1 Motion. At the beginning of Chapter 1 it was stated that mechanics deals with the relations of force, matter, and motion. The preceding chapters have been concerned with forces, and we are now ready to discuss the mathematical methods of describing motion. This branch of mechanics is called *kinematics*.

Motion may be defined as a continuous change of position. In most actual motions, different points in a body move along different paths. The complete motion is known if we know how each point in the body moves, so to begin with we consider only a moving point, or a very small body called a *particle*.

The position of a particle is conveniently specified by its projections onto the three axes of a rectangular coordinate system. As the particle moves along any path in space, its projections move in straight lines along the three axes. The actual motion can be reconstructed from the motions of these three projections, so we shall begin by discussing the motion of a single particle along a straight line, or *rectilinear motion*.

4–2 Average velocity. Consider a particle moving along the x-axis, as in Fig. 4–1(a). The curve in Fig. 4–1(b) is a graph of its coordinate x plotted as a function of time t. At a time t_1 the particle is at point P in Fig. 4–1(a), where its coordinate is x_1, and at a later time t_2 it is at point Q, whose coordinate is x_2. The corresponding points on the coordinate-time graph in part (b) are lettered p and q.

The *displacement* of a particle as it moves from one point of its path to another is defined as the vector $\Delta \mathbf{x}$ drawn from the first point to the second. Thus in Fig. 4–1(a) the vector PQ, of magnitude $x_2 - x_1 = \Delta x$, is the displacement. The *average velocity* of the particle is defined as the ratio of the displacement to the time interval $t_2 - t_1 = \Delta t$. We shall represent average velocity by the symbol $\bar{\mathbf{v}}$ (the bar signifying an average value).

$$\bar{\mathbf{v}} = \frac{\Delta \mathbf{x}}{\Delta t}.$$

Average velocity is a vector, since the ratio of a vector to a scalar is itself a vector. Its direction is the same as that of the displacement vector. The magnitude of the average velocity is therefore

$$\bar{v} = \frac{x_2 - x_1}{t_2 - t_1} = \frac{\Delta x}{\Delta t}. \tag{4–1}$$

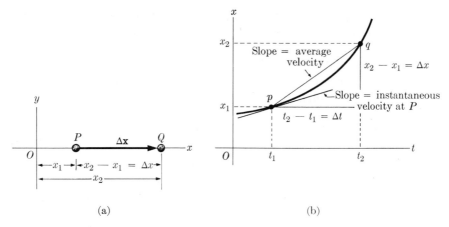

FIG. 4–1. (a) Particle moving on the x-axis. (b) Coordinate-time graph of the motion. The average velocity between t_1 and t_2 equals the slope of the chord pq. The instantaneous velocity at p equals the slope of the tangent at p.

In Fig. 4–1(b), the average velocity is represented by the slope of the chord pq (due allowance being made for the scales to which x and t are plotted), since the slope is the ratio of the "rise," $x_2 - x_1$ or Δx, to the "run," $t_2 - t_1$ or Δt.

Equation (4–1) can be cleared of fractions and written

$$x_2 - x_1 = \bar{v}\,(t_2 - t_1). \tag{4–2}$$

Since our time-measuring device can be started at any instant, we can let $t_1 = 0$ and let t_2 be any arbitrary time t. Then if x_0 is the coordinate when $t = 0$ (x_0 is called the *initial position*), and x is the coordinate at time t, Eq. (4–2) becomes

$$x - x_0 = \bar{v}t. \tag{4–3}$$

If the particle is at the origin when $t = 0$, then $x_0 = 0$ and Eq. (4–3) simplifies further to

$$x = \bar{v}t. \tag{4–4}$$

4–3 Instantaneous velocity. The velocity of a particle at some one instant of time, or at some one point of its path, is called its *instantaneous velocity*. This concept requires careful definition.

Suppose we wish to find the instantaneous velocity of the particle in Fig. 4–1 at the point P. The average velocity between points P and Q is associated with the entire displacement Δx, and with the entire time interval Δt. Imagine the second point Q to be taken closer and closer to the first point P, and let the average velocity be computed over these shorter and shorter displacements and time intervals. The instantaneous velocity at the first point can then be defined as the *limiting value* of the average velocity when the second point is taken closer and closer to the first. Although the displacement then becomes extremely small, the time interval by which it must be divided becomes small also and the quotient is not necessarily a small quantity.

In the notation of calculus, the limiting value of $\Delta x/\Delta t$, as Δt approaches zero, is written dx/dt and is called the *derivative* of x with respect to t.

Then if **v** represents the instantaneous velocity, its magnitude is

$$v = \lim_{\Delta t \to 0} \frac{\Delta x}{\Delta t} = \frac{dx}{dt}. \qquad (4\text{--}5)$$

Instantaneous velocity is also a vector, whose direction is the limiting direction of the displacement vector Δ**x**. Since Δt is necessarily positive, it follows that v has the same algebraic sign as Δx. Hence a positive velocity indicates motion toward the right along the x-axis, if we use the usual convention of signs.

As point Q approaches point P in Fig. 4–1(a), point q approaches point p in Fig. 4–1(b). In the limit, the slope of the chord pq equals the slope of the *tangent* to the curve at point p, due allowance being made for the scales to which x and t are plotted. *The instantaneous velocity at any point of a coordinate-time graph therefore equals the slope of the tangent to the graph at that point.* If the tangent slopes upward to the right, its slope is positive, the velocity is positive, and the motion is toward the right. If the tangent slopes downward to the right, the velocity is negative. At a point where the tangent is horizontal, its slope is zero and the velocity is zero.

If we express distance in feet and time in seconds, velocity is expressed in *feet per second* (ft/sec). Other common units of velocity are meters per second (m/sec), centimeters per second (cm/sec), miles per hour (mi/hr), and knots (1 knot = 1 nautical mile per hour).

EXAMPLE. Suppose the motion of the particle in Fig. 4–1 is described by the equation

$$x = a + bt^2,$$

where $a = 20$ cm and $b = 4$ cm/sec^2. (a) Find the displacement of the particle in the time interval between $t_1 = 2$ sec and $t_2 = 5$ sec.

At time $t_1 = 2$ sec,

$$x_1 = 20 \text{ cm} + 4 \frac{\text{cm}}{\text{sec}^2} \times (2 \text{ sec})^2 = 36 \text{ cm}.$$

At time $t_2 = 5$ sec,

$$x_2 = 20 \text{ cm} + 4 \frac{\text{cm}}{\text{sec}^2} \times (5 \text{ sec})^2 = 120 \text{ cm}.$$

The displacement is therefore

$$x_2 - x_1 = 120 \text{ cm} - 36 \text{ cm} = 84 \text{ cm}.$$

(b) Find the average velocity in this time interval.

$$\bar{v} = \frac{x_2 - x_1}{t_2 - t_1} = \frac{84 \text{ cm}}{3 \text{ sec}} = 28 \frac{\text{cm}}{\text{sec}}.$$

This corresponds to the slope of the chord pq in Fig. 4–1(b).

(c) Find the instantaneous velocity at time $t_1 = 2$ sec. The instantaneous velocity is given by

$$v = \frac{dx}{dt} = \frac{d}{dt}(a + bt^2) = 2bt.$$

Hence at time $t_1 = 2$ sec,

$$v = 2 \times 4 \frac{\text{cm}}{\text{sec}^2} \times 2 \text{ sec} = 16 \frac{\text{cm}}{\text{sec}}.$$

This corresponds to the slope of the tangent at point p in Fig. 4–1(b).

The term *speed* has two different meanings. It is sometimes used to mean the *magnitude* of the instantaneous velocity. In this sense, two automobiles traveling at 50 mi/hr, one north and the other south, are both said to have a speed of 50 mi/hr. In another sense, the *average speed* of a body means the total length of path covered, divided by the elapsed time. Thus if an automobile travels a total distance of 90 miles in 3 hours, its average speed is said to be 30 mi/hr even if the trip starts and ends at the same point. The average *velocity*, in the latter case, would be zero, since the displacement is zero.

4–4 Average and instantaneous acceleration. Except in certain special cases, the velocity of a moving body changes continuously as the motion proceeds. When this is the case the body is said to move with *accelerated motion*, or to have an *acceleration*.

Figure 4–2(a) shows a particle moving along the x-axis. The vector $\mathbf{v}_1$ represents its instantaneous velocity at point P, and the vector $\mathbf{v}_2$ represents its instantaneous velocity at point Q. Figure 4–2(b) is a graph of

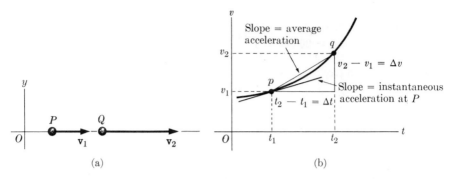

FIG. 4–2. (a) Particle moving on the x-axis. (b) Velocity-time graph of the motion. The average acceleration between t_1 and t_2 equals the slope of the chord pq. The instantaneous acceleration at p equals the slope of the tangent at p.

the instantaneous velocity v plotted as a function of time, points p and q corresponding to P and Q in part (a).

The *average acceleration* of the particle as it moves from P to Q is defined as the ratio of the change in velocity to the elapsed time.

$$\bar{\mathbf{a}} = \frac{\mathbf{v}_2 - \mathbf{v}_1}{t_2 - t_1} = \frac{\Delta \mathbf{v}}{\Delta t}, \tag{4–6}$$

where t_1 and t_2 are the times corresponding to the velocities $\mathbf{v}_1$ and $\mathbf{v}_2$. Since $\mathbf{v}_1$ and $\mathbf{v}_2$ are vectors, the quantity $\mathbf{v}_2 - \mathbf{v}_1$ is a *vector difference* and must be found by the methods explained in Section 1–7. However, since in rectilinear motion both vectors lie in the same straight line, the magnitude of the vector difference in this special case equals the difference between the magnitudes of the vectors. The more general case, in which $\mathbf{v}_1$ and $\mathbf{v}_2$ are not in the same direction, will be considered in Chapter 6.

In Fig. 4–2(b), the magnitude of the average acceleration is represented by the slope of the chord pq.

The *instantaneous acceleration* of a body, that is, its acceleration at some one instant of time or at some one point of its path, is defined in the same way as instantaneous velocity. Let the second point Q in Fig. 4–2(a) be taken closer and closer to the first point P, and let the average acceleration be computed over shorter and shorter intervals of time. The instantaneous acceleration at the first point is defined as the limiting value of the average acceleration when the second point is taken closer and closer to the first.

$$a = \lim_{\Delta t \to 0} \frac{\Delta v}{\Delta t} = \frac{dv}{dt}. \tag{4–7}$$

The direction of the instantaneous acceleration is the limiting direction of the vector change in velocity, $\Delta\mathbf{v}$.

Instantaneous acceleration plays an important part in the laws of mechanics. Average acceleration is less frequently used. Hence from now on when the term "acceleration" is used we shall understand it to mean instantaneous acceleration.

The definition of acceleration just given applies to motion along any path, straight or curved. When a particle moves in a curved path the *direction* of its velocity changes and this change in direction also gives rise to an acceleration, as will be explained in Chapter 6.

As point Q approaches point P in Fig. 4–2(a), point q approaches point p in Fig. 4–2(b) and the slope of the chord pq approaches the slope of the tangent to the velocity-time graph at point p. *The instantaneous acceleration at any point of the graph therefore equals the slope of the tangent to the graph at that point.*

The acceleration $a = dv/dt$ can be expressed in various ways. Since $v = dx/dt$, it follows that

$$a = \frac{dv}{dt} = \frac{d}{dt}\left(\frac{dx}{dt}\right) = \frac{d^2x}{dt^2}.$$

The acceleration is therefore the *second* derivative of the coordinate with respect to time.

We can also use the chain rule and write

$$a = \frac{dv}{dt} = \frac{dv}{dx}\frac{dx}{dt} = v\frac{dv}{dx}, \qquad (4\text{–}8)$$

which expresses the acceleration in terms of the *space* rate of change of velocity, dv/dx.

If we express velocity in feet per second and time in seconds, acceleration is expressed in feet per second, per second (ft/sec/sec). This is usually written as ft/sec^2, and is read "feet per second squared." Other common units of acceleration are meters per second squared (m/sec^2) and centimeters per second squared (cm/sec^2).

When the absolute value of the magnitude of the velocity of a body is decreasing (in other words, when the body is slowing down), the body is said to be *decelerated* or to have a *deceleration*.

EXAMPLE. Suppose the velocity of the particle in Fig. 4–2 is given by the equation

$$v = m + nt^2,$$

where $m = 10$ cm/sec and $n = 2$ cm/sec^3. (a) Find the change in velocity of the particle in the time interval between $t_1 = 2$ sec and $t_2 = 5$ sec.

At time $t_1 = 2$ sec,

$$v_1 = 10 \frac{\text{cm}}{\text{sec}} + 2 \frac{\text{cm}}{\text{sec}^3} \times (2 \text{ sec})^2$$

$$= 18 \frac{\text{cm}}{\text{sec}}.$$

At time $t_2 = 5$ sec,

$$v_2 = 10 \frac{\text{cm}}{\text{sec}} + 2 \frac{\text{cm}}{\text{sec}^3} \times (5 \text{ sec})^2$$

$$= 60 \frac{\text{cm}}{\text{sec}}.$$

The change in velocity is therefore

$$v_2 - v_1 = 60 \frac{\text{cm}}{\text{sec}} - 18 \frac{\text{cm}}{\text{sec}}$$

$$= 42 \frac{\text{cm}}{\text{sec}}.$$

(b) Find the average acceleration in this time interval.

$$\bar{a} = \frac{v_2 - v_1}{t_2 - t_1} = \frac{42 \text{ cm/sec}}{3 \text{ sec}}$$

$$= 14 \frac{\text{cm}}{\text{sec}^2}.$$

This corresponds to the slope of the chord pq in Fig. 4–2(b).

(c) Find the instantaneous acceleration at time $t_1 = 2$ sec. The instantaneous acceleration is given by

$$a = \frac{dv}{dt} = \frac{d}{dt}(m + nt^2)$$

$$= 2nt.$$

Hence when $t = 2$ sec,

$$a = 2 \times 2 \frac{\text{cm}}{\text{sec}^3} \times 2 \text{ sec}$$

$$= 8 \frac{\text{cm}}{\text{sec}^2}.$$

This corresponds to the slope of the tangent at point p in Fig. 4–2(b).

4–5 Rectilinear motion with constant acceleration. The simplest kind of accelerated motion is rectilinear motion in which the acceleration is constant, that is, in which the velocity changes at the same rate throughout the motion. The velocity-time graph is then a straight line as in Fig. 4–3, the velocity increasing by equal amounts in equal intervals of time. The slope of a chord between any two points on the line is the same as the slope of a tangent at any point, and the average and instantaneous accelerations are equal. Hence in Eq. (4–6) the average acceleration $\bar{a}$ can be replaced by the constant acceleration a, and we have

$$a = \frac{v_2 - v_1}{t_2 - t_1}.$$

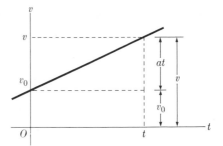

FIG. 4–3. Velocity-time graph for rectilinear motion with constant acceleration.

Now let $t_1 = 0$ and let t_2 be any arbitrary time t. Let v_0 represent the velocity when $t = 0$ (v_0 is called the *initial* velocity), and let v be the velocity at time t. Then the preceding equation becomes

$$a = \frac{v - v_0}{t - 0},$$

or

$$\boxed{v = v_0 + at.} \tag{4–9}$$

This equation can be interpreted as follows. The acceleration a is the constant rate of change of velocity, or the change per unit time. The term at is the product of the change in velocity per unit time, a, and the duration of the time interval, t. Therefore it equals the total change in velocity. The velocity v at the time t then equals the velocity v_0 at the time $t = 0$, plus the change in velocity at. Graphically, the ordinate v at time t, in Fig. 4–3, can be considered as the sum of two segments: one of length v_0, equal to the initial velocity, the other of length at equal to the change in velocity in time t.

To find the displacement of a particle moving with constant acceleration, we make use of the fact that when the acceleration is constant and the velocity-time graph is a straight line, as in Fig. 4–3, the average velocity in any time interval equals one-half the sum of the velocities at the beginning and the end of the interval. Hence the average velocity between zero and t is

$$\bar{v} = \frac{v_0 + v}{2}. \tag{4–10}$$

This is *not* true, in general, when the acceleration is not constant and the velocity-time graph is curved as in Fig. 4–2.

We have shown that for a particle which is at the origin when $t = 0$, the coordinate x at any time t is

$$x = \bar{v}t, \tag{4–11}$$

where $\bar{v}$ is the average velocity. Hence from the two preceding equations,

$$x = \frac{v_0 + v}{2} \times t. \tag{4-12}$$

Two more very useful equations can be obtained from Eqs. (4–9) and (4–12), first by eliminating v and then by eliminating t. When we substitute in Eq. (4–12) the expression for v in Eq. (4–9), we get

$$x = \frac{v_0 + v_0 + at}{2} \times t,$$

or

$$x = v_0 t + \tfrac{1}{2}at^2. \tag{4-13}$$

When Eq. (4–9) is solved for t and the result substituted in Eq. (4–12), we have

$$x = \frac{v_0 + v}{2} \times \frac{v - v_0}{a}$$

$$= \frac{v^2 - v_0^2}{2a}$$

or, finally,

$$v^2 = v_0^2 + 2ax. \tag{4-14}$$

Equations (4–9), (4–12), (4–13), and (4–14) are the *equations of motion with constant acceleration*, for the special case where the particle is at the origin when $t = 0$.

The curve in Fig. 4–4 is the coordinate-time graph for motion with constant acceleration. That is, it is a graph of Eq. (4–13). The curve is

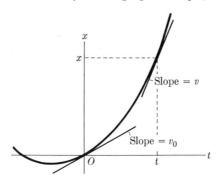

FIGURE 4–4

a *parabola*. The slope of the tangent at $t = 0$ equals the initial velocity v_0, and the slope of the tangent at time t equals the velocity v at that time. It is evident that the slope continually increases, and measurements would show that the *rate* of increase is constant, that is, that the acceleration is constant.

A special case of motion with constant acceleration is that in which the acceleration is zero. The *velocity* is then constant and the equations of motion become simply

$$v = \text{constant,}$$

$$x = vt.$$

4–6 Velocity and coordinate by integration. If the coordinate x of a particle moving on the x-axis is given as a function of time, the velocity can be found by differentiation, from the definition $v = dx/dt$. A second differentiation gives the acceleration, since $a = dv/dt$. We now consider the converse process: given the acceleration, to find the velocity and the coordinate. This can be done by the methods of *integral* calculus. We shall discuss first the indefinite and then the definite integral.

Suppose we are given the acceleration $a(t)$ as a function of time. Then, since

$$\frac{dv}{dt} = a(t),$$

we have

$$dv = a(t)\, dt,$$

$$\int dv = \int a(t)\, dt,$$

and

$$v = \int a(t)\, dt + C_1, \qquad (4\text{–}15)$$

where C_1 is an integration constant whose value can be determined if the velocity is known at any time. It is customary to express C_1 in terms of the velocity v_0 when $t = 0$.

When the integral above has been evaluated, we have the velocity $v(t)$ as a function of time. Then, since

$$\frac{dx}{dt} = v(t),$$

we have

$$dx = v(t)\, dt,$$

$$\int dx = \int v(t)\, dt,$$

$$x = \int v(t)\, dt + C_2, \qquad (4\text{–}16)$$

where C_2 is a second integration constant whose value can be determined if the coordinate is known at any time. It is customary to express C_2 in terms of the coordinate x_0 when $t = 0$.

If the acceleration is given as a function of x, we can use Eq. (4–8):

$$v \frac{dv}{dx} = a(x),$$

$$\int v \, dv = \int a(x) \, dx,$$

$$\frac{v^2}{2} = \int a(x) \, dx + C_3. \tag{4-17}$$

EXAMPLE. Derive the equations of motion with constant acceleration, using the indefinite integral.

If a is constant, then from Eq. (4–15)

$$v = at + C_1.$$

But $v = v_0$ when $t = 0$, so

$$v_0 = 0 + C_1$$

and

$$v = v_0 + at,$$

which is Eq. (4–9).

From Eq. (4–16), when a is constant,

$$x = \int (v_0 + at) \, dt = v_0 t + \tfrac{1}{2} a t^2 + C_2.$$

If $x = 0$ when $t = 0$, then $C_2 = 0$ and

$$x = v_0 t + \tfrac{1}{2} a t^2,$$

which is Eq. (4–13).

From Eq. (4–17), when a is constant,

$$\frac{v^2}{2} = ax + C_3.$$

If $v = v_0$ when $x = 0$, then $C_3 = v_0^2/2$ and

$$v^2 = v_0^2 + 2ax,$$

which is Eq. (4–14).

Consider next the definite integral. Let the area under the velocity-time graph in Fig. 4–5, between the vertical lines at t_1 and t_2, be subdivided into narrow rectangular strips of width Δt. The ordinate of the

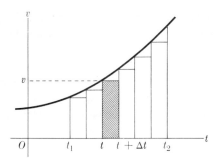

FIG. 4–5. The area under a velocity-time graph equals the displacement.

graph at any time t equals the instantaneous velocity v at that time. If the velocity remained constant at this value, the displacement Δx in the time interval between t and $t + \Delta t$ would equal $v\,\Delta t$. But this is the *area* of the shaded strip, since its height is v and its width is Δt. The *sum* of the areas of all such rectangles, between t_1 and t_2, is approximately equal to the *total* displacement $x_2 - x_1$ in this time interval.

$$x_2 - x_1 \approx \sum v\,\Delta t.$$

The smaller the time intervals Δt, the more closely does $v\,\Delta t$ approach the actual displacement. In the limit, as Δt approaches zero, the sum of the areas becomes exactly equal to the total area under the curve, and to the total displacement $x_2 - x_1$. The limit of the sum of the areas is the definite integral from t_1 to t_2, so

$$x_2 - x_1 = \int_{t_1}^{t_2} v\,dt. \tag{4–18}$$

The displacement in any time interval is therefore equal to the area between a velocity-time graph and the time axis, bounded by vertical lines at the beginning and end of the interval.

In the same way, the area under an acceleration-time graph can be subdivided into vertical strips of height a and width Δt. If the acceleration remained constant, the change in velocity Δv in time Δt would equal $a\,\Delta t$, the area of a rectangular strip. The total change in velocity, $v_2 - v_1$, in the time interval from t_1 to t_2, is approximately equal to the sum of all such areas.

$$v_2 - v_1 \approx \sum a\,\Delta t.$$

In the limit, as Δt approaches zero,

$$v_2 - v_1 = \int_{t_1}^{t_2} a\,dt. \tag{4–19}$$

The change in velocity in any time interval is therefore equal to the area between an acceleration-time graph and the time axis, bounded by vertical lines at the beginning and end of the interval.

EXAMPLE. Use the definite integral to find the velocity and coordinate, at any time t of a body moving on the x-axis with constant acceleration. The initial velocity is v_0 and the initial coordinate is zero.

As the limits of integration, we take $t_1 = 0$ and $t_2 = t$. Then, from Eq. (4–19),

$$v - v_0 = \int_0^t a \, dt = at,$$

which is Eq. (4–9).

From Eq. (4–18),

$$x - 0 = \int_0^t (v_0 + at) \, dt = v_0 t + \tfrac{1}{2} a t^2,$$

which is Eq. (4–13).

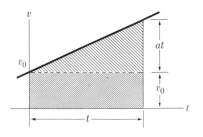

FIG. 4–6. The area under a velocity-time graph equals the displacement, $x - x_0$.

It is not always necessary to use the methods of integral calculus to find the area under a graph. Figure 4–6 is the velocity-time graph for motion with constant acceleration. The area under the graph, between $t = 0$ and $t = t$, can be subdivided into a rectangle and a triangle. The area of the rectangle is $v_0 t$ and that of the triangle is $\tfrac{1}{2} \times a \times at = \tfrac{1}{2} a t^2$. Since the displacement equals the total area,

$$x - x_0 = v_0 t + \tfrac{1}{2} a t^2,$$

which reduces to Eq. (4–13) if $x_0 = 0$.

4–7 Freely falling bodies. The most common example of motion with (nearly) constant acceleration is that of a body falling toward the earth. In the absence of air resistance it is found that all bodies, regardless of their size or weight, fall with the same acceleration at the same point on the earth's surface, and if the distance covered is not too great the acceleration remains constant throughout the fall. The effect of air resistance and the decrease in acceleration with altitude will be neglected. This idealized motion is spoken of as "free fall," although the term includes rising as well as falling.

The acceleration of a freely falling body is called the acceleration due to gravity, or the acceleration of gravity, and is denoted by the letter g. At or near the earth's surface its magnitude is approximately 32 ft/sec^2, 9.8 m/sec^2, or 980 cm/sec^2. More precise values, and small variations with latitude and elevation, will be considered later.

NOTE. The quantity "g" is sometimes referred to simply as "gravity," or as "the force of gravity," both of which are incorrect. "Gravity" is a phenomenon, and the "force of gravity" means the force with which the earth attracts a body, otherwise known as the weight of the body. The letter "g" represents the *acceleration* caused by the force resulting from the phenomenon of gravity.

EXAMPLE 1. A body is released from rest and falls freely. Compute its position and velocity after 1, 2, 3, and 4 seconds. Take the origin O at the elevation of the starting point, the y-axis vertical, and the upward direction as positive.

The initial coordinate y_0 and the initial velocity v_0 are both zero. The acceleration is downward, in the negative y-direction, so $a = -g = -32$ ft/sec^2.

From Eqs. (4–13) and (4–9),

$$y = v_0 t + \tfrac{1}{2}at^2 = 0 - \tfrac{1}{2}gt^2 = -16\,\frac{\text{ft}}{\text{sec}^2} \times t^2,$$

$$v = v_0 + at = 0 - gt = -32\,\frac{\text{ft}}{\text{sec}^2} \times t.$$

When $t = 1$ sec,

$$y = -16\,\frac{\text{ft}}{\text{sec}^2} \times 1\,\text{sec}^2 = -16\,\text{ft},$$

$$v = -32\,\frac{\text{ft}}{\text{sec}^2} \times 1\,\text{sec} = -32\,\frac{\text{ft}}{\text{sec}}.$$

The body is therefore 16 ft below the origin (y is negative) and has a downward velocity (v is negative) of magnitude 32 ft/sec.

The position and velocity at 2, 3, and 4 sec are found in the same way. The results are illustrated in Fig. 4–7.

EXAMPLE 2. A ball is thrown (nearly) vertically upward from the cornice of a tall building, leaving the thrower's hand with a speed of 48 ft/sec and just missing the cornice on the way down. (See Fig. 4–8. The dotted line does not represent the actual path of the body.) Find (a) the position and velocity of the ball, 1 sec and 4 sec after leaving the thrower's hand; (b) the velocity when the ball is 20 ft above its starting point; (c) the maximum height reached and the time at which it is reached. Take the origin at the elevation at which the ball leaves the thrower's hand, the y-axis vertical and positive upward.

The initial position y_0 is zero. The initial velocity v_0 is $+48$ ft/sec, and the acceleration is -32 ft/sec^2.

The velocity at any time is

$$v = v_0 + at = 48\,\frac{\text{ft}}{\text{sec}} - 32\,\frac{\text{ft}}{\text{sec}^2} \times t. \qquad (4\text{--}20)$$

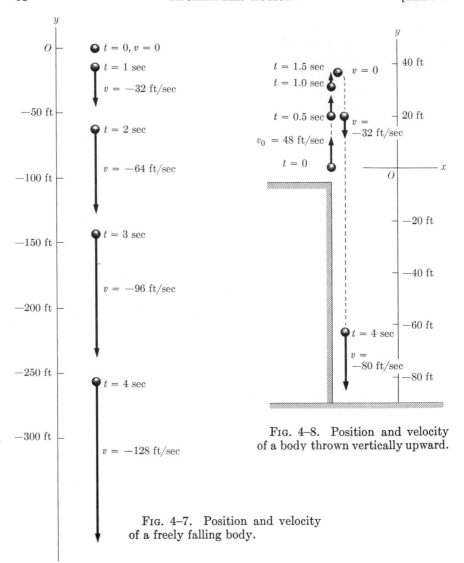

FIG. 4-8. Position and velocity
of a body thrown vertically upward.

FIG. 4-7. Position and velocity
of a freely falling body.

The coordinate at any time is

$$y \;=\; v_0 t + \tfrac{1}{2}at^2 \;=\; 48\,\frac{\text{ft}}{\text{sec}} \times t - 16\,\frac{\text{ft}}{\text{sec}^2} \times t^2.$$

The velocity at any coordinate is

$$v^2 \;=\; v_0^2 + 2ay \;=\; \left(48\,\frac{\text{ft}}{\text{sec}}\right)^2 - 64\,\frac{\text{ft}}{\text{sec}^2} \times y. \qquad (4\text{-}21)$$

(a) When $t = 1$ sec,

$$y = +32 \text{ ft}, \qquad v = +16 \frac{\text{ft}}{\text{sec}}.$$

The ball is 32 ft above the origin (y is positive) and it has an upward velocity (v is positive) of 16 ft/sec.

When $t = 4$ sec,

$$y = -64 \text{ ft}, \qquad v = -80 \frac{\text{ft}}{\text{sec}}.$$

The ball has passed its highest point and is 64 ft *below* the origin (y is negative). It has a *downward* velocity (v is negative) of magnitude 80 ft/sec. Note that it is not necessary to find the highest point reached, or the time at which it was reached. The equations of motion give the position and velocity at *any* time, whether the ball is on the way up or the way down.

(b) When the ball is 20 ft above the origin,

$$y = +20 \text{ ft}$$

and

$$v^2 = 1024 \frac{\text{ft}^2}{\text{sec}^2}, \qquad v = \pm 32 \frac{\text{ft}}{\text{sec}}.$$

The ball passes this point twice, once on the way up and again on the way down. The velocity on the way up is $+32$ ft/sec, and on the way down it is -32 ft/sec.

(c) At the highest point, $v = 0$. Hence

$$y = +36 \text{ ft}.$$

The time can now be found either from Eq. (4–20), setting $v = 0$, or from Eq. (4–21), setting $y = 36$ ft. From either equation, we get

$$t = 1.5 \text{ sec}.$$

Figure 4–9 is a "multiflash" photograph of a freely falling golf ball. This photograph was taken with the aid of the ultra-high-speed stroboscopic light source developed by Dr. Harold E. Edgerton of the Massachusetts Institute of Technology. By means of this source a series of intense flashes of light can be produced. The interval between successive flashes is controllable at will, and the duration of each flash is so short (a few millionths of a second) that there is no blur in the image of even a rapidly moving body. The camera shutter is left open during the entire motion, and as each flash occurs the position of the ball at that instant is recorded on the photographic film.

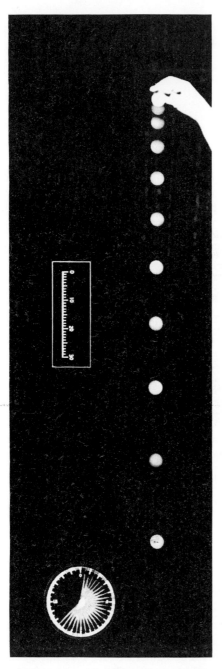

The equally spaced light flashes subdivide the motion into equal time intervals Δt. Since the time intervals are all equal, the velocity of the ball between any two flashes is directly proportional to the separation of its corresponding images in the photograph. If the velocity were constant, the images would be equally spaced. The increasing separation of the images during the fall shows that the velocity is continually increasing or the motion is accelerated. By comparing two successive displacements of the ball, the *change* in velocity in the corresponding time interval can be found. Careful measurements, preferably on an enlarged print, show that this change in velocity is the same in each time interval. In other words, the motion is one of *constant* acceleration.

4–8 Velocity components. Relative velocity. Velocity is a vector quantity involving both magnitude and direction. A velocity may therefore be resolved into components, or a number of velocity components combined into a resultant. As an example of the former process, suppose that a ship is steaming 30° E of N at 20 mi/hr in still water. Its velocity may be represented by the arrow in Fig. 4–10, and one finds by the usual method that its velocity component toward the east is 10 mi/hr, while toward the north it is 17.3 mi/hr.

The velocity of a body, like its position, can only be specified relative to some other body. The

Fig. 4–9. Multiflash photograph (retouched) of freely falling golf ball.

second body may be in motion
relative to a third, and so on. Thus
when we speak of "the velocity of
an automobile," we usually mean
its velocity relative to the earth.
But the earth is in motion relative
to the sun, the sun is in motion
relative to some other star, and
so on.

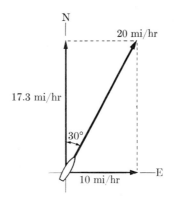

Suppose a long train of flatcars is
moving to the right along a straight
level track as in Fig. 4–11, and that
a daring automobile driver is driving to the right along the flatcars.
The vector $\mathbf{v}_{FE}$ in Fig. 4–11 repre-

FIG. 4–10. Resolution of a velocity
vector into components.

sents the velocity of the flatcars F relative to the earth E, and the vector
$\mathbf{v}_{AF}$ the velocity of the automobile A relative to the flatcars F. The
velocity of the automobile relative to the earth, v_{AE}, is evidently equal
to the sum of the relative velocities v_{AF} and v_{FE}.

$$v_{AE} = v_{AF} + v_{FE}. \tag{4–22}$$

Thus if the flatcars are traveling relative to the earth at 30 mi/hr $(=v_{FE})$
and the automobile is traveling relative to the flatcars at 40 mi/hr $(=v_{AF})$,
the velocity of the automobile relative to the earth (v_{AE}) is 70 mi/hr.

Imagine now that the flatcars are wide enough so that the automobile
can drive on them in any direction. The velocity of the automobile relative to the earth is then the *vector* sum of its velocity relative to the
flatcars and the velocity of the flatcars relative to the earth. The preceding equation is therefore a special case of the more general *vector* equation,

$$\mathbf{v}_{AE} = \mathbf{v}_{AF} + \mathbf{v}_{FE}. \tag{4–23}$$

Thus if the automobile were driving transversely across the flatcars
at 40 mi/hr, its velocity relative to the earth would be 50 mi/hr at an
angle of 37° with the railway track.

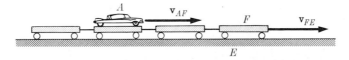

FIG. 4–11. Vector $\mathbf{v}_{FE}$ is the velocity of the flatcars F relative to the earth E,
and $\mathbf{v}_{AF}$ is the velocity of automobile A relative to the flatcars.

In the special case in which $\mathbf{v}_{AF}$ and $\mathbf{v}_{FE}$ are along the same line, as in Fig. 4–11, the velocity v_{AE} is the *algebraic* sum of v_{AF} and v_{FE}. Thus if the automobile were traveling to the left with a velocity of 40 mi/hr relative to the flatcars, $v_{AF} = -40$ mi/hr and the velocity of the automobile relative to the earth would be -10 mi/hr. That is, it would be traveling to the left, relative to the earth.

Equation (4–23) can be extended to include any number of relative velocities. For example, if a bug B crawls along the floor of the automobile with a velocity relative to the automobile of $\mathbf{v}_{BA}$, his velocity relative to the earth is the vector sum of his velocity relative to the automobile and that of the velocity of the automobile relative to the earth:

$$\mathbf{v}_{BE} = \mathbf{v}_{BA} + \mathbf{v}_{AE}.$$

When this is combined with Eq. (4–23), we get

$$\mathbf{v}_{BE} = \mathbf{v}_{BA} + \mathbf{v}_{AF} + \mathbf{v}_{FE}. \tag{4–24}$$

This equation illustrates the general rule for combining relative velocities. (1) Write each velocity with a double subscript in the *proper order*, meaning "velocity of (first subscript) relative to (second subscript)." (2) When adding relative velocities, the first letter of any subscript is to be the same as the last letter of the preceding subscript. (3) The first letter of the subscript of the first velocity in the sum, and the second letter of the subscript of the last velocity, are the subscripts, in that order, of the relative velocity represented by the sum. This somewhat lengthy statement should be clear when it is compared with Eq. (4–24).

Any of the relative velocities in an equation like Eq. (4–24) can be transferred from one side of the equation to the other, with sign reversed. Thus Eq. (4–23) can be written

$$\mathbf{v}_{AF} = \mathbf{v}_{AE} - \mathbf{v}_{FE}.$$

The velocity of the automobile relative to the flatcar equals the *vector difference* between the velocities of automobile and flatcar, both relative to the earth.

One more point should be noted. The velocity of body A relative to body B, $\mathbf{v}_{AB}$, is the negative of the velocity of B relative to A, $\mathbf{v}_{BA}$:

$$\mathbf{v}_{AB} = -\mathbf{v}_{BA}.$$

That is, $\mathbf{v}_{AB}$ is equal in magnitude and opposite in direction to $\mathbf{v}_{BA}$. If the automobile in Fig. 4–11 is traveling to the right at 40 mi/hr relative to the flatcars, the flatcars are traveling to the left at 40 mi/hr, relative to the automobile.

EXAMPLE 1. An automobile driver A, traveling relative to the earth at 65 mi/hr on a straight level road, is ahead of motorcycle officer B traveling in the same direction at 80 mi/hr. What is the velocity of B relative to A?

We have given
$$v_{AE} = 65 \text{ mi/hr}, \qquad v_{BE} = 80 \text{ mi/hr},$$

and we wish to find v_{BA}.

From the rule for combining velocities (along the same line)
$$v_{BA} = v_{BE} + v_{EA}.$$
But
$$v_{EA} = -v_{AE},$$
so
$$v_{BA} = v_{BE} - v_{AE}$$
$$= 80 \text{ mi/hr} - 65 \text{ mi/hr} = 15 \text{ mi/hr},$$

and the officer is overtaking the driver at 15 mi/hr.

EXAMPLE 2. How would the relative velocity be altered if B were ahead of A?

Not at all. The relative *positions* of the bodies does not matter. The velocity of B relative to A is still $+15$ mi/hr, but he is now pulling ahead of A at this rate.

EXAMPLE 3. The compass of an aircraft indicates that it is headed due north, and its airspeed indicator shows that it is moving through the air at 120 mi/hr. If there is a wind of 50 mi/hr from west to east, what is the velocity of the aircraft relative to the earth?

Let subscript A refer to the aircraft, and subscript F to the moving air (which now corresponds to the flatcar in Fig. 4–11). Subscript E refers to the earth. We have given

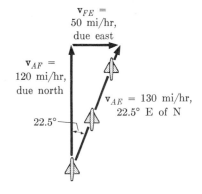

$$\mathbf{v}_{AF} = 120 \text{ mi/hr, due north}$$
$$\mathbf{v}_{FE} - 50 \text{ mi/hr, due east,}$$

and we wish to find the magnitude and direction of $\mathbf{v}_{AE}$.

$$\mathbf{v}_{AE} = \mathbf{v}_{AF} + \mathbf{v}_{FE}.$$

The three relative velocities are shown in Fig. 4–12. It follows from this diagram that

FIGURE 4–12

$$\mathbf{v}_{AE} = 130 \text{ mi/hr, } 22.5° \text{ E of N.}$$

EXAMPLE 4. In what direction should the pilot head in order to travel due north? What will then be his velocity relative to the earth? The magnitude of his airspeed, and the wind velocity, are the same as in the preceding example.

We now have given:

$$\mathbf{v}_{AF} = 120 \text{ mi/hr, direction unknown,}$$

$$\mathbf{v}_{FE} = 50 \text{ mi/hr, due east,}$$

and we wish to find $\mathbf{v}_{AE}$, whose magnitude is unknown but whose direction is due north. (Note that both this and the preceding example require us to determine two unknown quantities. In the former example, these were the *magnitude and direction* of $\mathbf{v}_{AE}$. In this example, the unknowns are the *direction* of v_{AF} and the *magnitude* of v_{AE}.)

The three relative velocities must still satisfy the *vector equation*

$$\mathbf{v}_{AE} = \mathbf{v}_{AF} + \mathbf{v}_{FE}.$$

The problem can be solved graphically as follows. First construct the vector $\mathbf{v}_{FE}$ (see Fig. 4–13), known in magnitude and direction. At the head of this vector draw a construction line of indefinite length due north, in the known direction of $\mathbf{v}_{AE}$. With the tail of $\mathbf{v}_{FE}$ as a center, construct a circular arc of radius equal to the known magnitude of $\mathbf{v}_{AF}$. Vectors $\mathbf{v}_{AF}$ and $\mathbf{v}_{AE}$ may then be drawn from the point of intersection of this arc and the construction line, to the ends of the vector $\mathbf{v}_{FE}$. We find on solving the right triangle that the magnitude of $\mathbf{v}_{AE}$ is 109 mi/hr and the direction of $\mathbf{v}_{AF}$ is 24.5° W of N. That is, the pilot should head 24.5° W of N, and his ground speed will be 109 mi/hr.

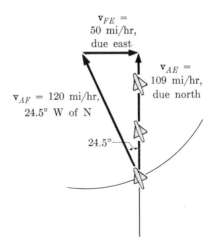

FIGURE 4–13

Problems

4–1. Suppose that a runner on a straight track covers a distance of 1 mile in exactly 4 minutes. What was his average velocity in (a) mi/hr, (b) ft/sec, (c) cm/sec?

4–2. A body moves along a straight line, its distance from the origin at any instant being given by the equation $x = 8t - 3t^2$, where x is in centimeters and t is in seconds. Find the average velocity of the body in the interval from $t = 0$ to $t = 1$ sec, and in the interval from $t = 0$ to $t = 4$ sec.

4–3. Refer to the example at the end of Section 4–3, in which the motion of a body along the x-axis was described by the equation $x = (10 \text{ cm/sec}^2)t^2$. Compute the instantaneous velocity of the body at time $t = 3$ sec. Let Δt first equal 0.1 sec, then 0.01 sec, and finally 0.001 sec. What limiting value do the results seem to be approaching?

4–4. An automobile is provided with a speedometer calibrated to read ft/sec rather than mi/hr. The following series of speedometer readings was obtained during a start.

Time (sec) 0 2 4 6 8 10 12 14 16
Velocity
(ft/sec) 0 0 2 5 10 15 20 22 22

(a) Compute the average acceleration during each 2-sec interval. Is the acceleration constant? Is it constant during any part of the time? (b) Make a velocity-time graph of the data above, using scales of 1 in. = 2 sec horizontally, and 1 in. = 5 ft/sec vertically. Draw a smooth curve through the plotted points. What distance is represented by 1 sq in.? What is the displacement in the first 8 sec? What is the acceleration when $t = 8$ sec? When $t = 13$ sec? When $t = 15$ sec?

4–5. The graph in Fig. 4–14 shows the velocity of a body plotted as a function of time.

(a) What is the instantaneous acceleration at $t = 3$ sec?

(b) What is the instantaneous acceleration at $t = 7$ sec?

(c) What is the instantaneous acceleration at $t = 11$ sec?

(d) How far does the body go in the first 5 sec?

(e) How far does the body go in the first 9 sec?

(f) How far does the body go in the first 13 sec?

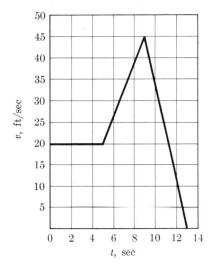

FIGURE 4–14

4–6. Each of the following changes in velocity takes place in a 10-sec interval. What is the magnitude, the algebraic sign, and the direction of the average acceleration in each interval?

(a) At the beginning of the interval a body is moving toward the right along the x-axis at 5 ft/sec, and at the end of the interval it is moving toward the right at 20 ft/sec.

(b) At the beginning it is moving toward the right at 20 ft/sec, and at the end it is moving toward the right at 5 ft/sec.

(c) At the beginning it is moving toward the left at 5 ft/sec, and at the end it is moving toward the left at 20 ft/sec.

(d) At the beginning it is moving toward the left at 20 ft/sec, and at the end it is moving toward the left at 5 ft/sec.

(e) At the beginning it is moving toward the right at 20 ft/sec, and at the end it is moving toward the left at 20 ft/sec.

(f) At the beginning it is moving toward the left at 20 ft/sec, and at the end it is moving toward the right at 20 ft/sec.

(g) In which of the above instances is the body decelerated?

4–7. The makers of a certain automobile advertise that it will accelerate from 15 to 50 mi/hr in high in 13 sec. Compute (a) the acceleration in ft/sec^2, and (b) the distance the car travels in this time, assuming the acceleration to be constant.

4–8. An airplane taking off from a landing field has a run of 1200 ft. If it starts from rest, moves with constant acceleration, and makes the run in 30 sec, with what velocity in ft/sec did it take off?

4–9. An automobile starts from rest and acquires a velocity of 40 mi/hr in 15 sec. (a) Compute the acceleration in miles per hour per second, and in feet per second per second, assuming it to be constant. (b) If the automobile continues to gain velocity at the same rate, how many more seconds are needed for it to acquire a velocity of 60 mi/hr? (c) Find the distances covered by the automobile in parts (a) and (b).

4–10. A body moving with constant acceleration covers the distance between two points 180 ft apart in 6 sec. Its velocity as it passes the second point is 45 ft/sec. (a) What is its acceleration? (b) What is its velocity at the first point?

4–11. A ball is released from rest and rolls down an inclined plane, requiring 4 sec to cover a distance of 100 cm. (a) What was its acceleration in cm/sec^2? (b) How many centimeters would it have fallen vertically in the same time?

4–12. The "reaction time" of the average automobile driver is about 0.7 sec. (The reaction time is the interval between the perception of a signal to stop and the application of the brakes.) If an automobile can decelerate at 16 ft/sec^2, compute the total distance covered in coming to a stop after a signal is observed: (a) from an initial velocity of 30 mi/hr, (b) from an initial velocity of 60 mi/hr.

4–13. At the instant the traffic lights turn green, an automobile that has been waiting at an intersection starts ahead with a constant acceleration of 6 ft/sec^2. At the same instant a truck, traveling with a constant velocity of 30 ft/sec, overtakes and passes the automobile. (a) How far beyond its starting point will the automobile overtake the truck? (b) How fast will it be traveling?

4–14. The engineer of a passenger train traveling at 100 ft/sec sights a freight train whose caboose is 600 ft ahead on the same track. The freight train is traveling in the same direction as the passenger train with a velocity of 30 ft/sec. The engineer of the passenger train immediately applies the brakes, causing a constant deceleration of 4 ft/sec^2, while the freight train continues with constant speed.

(a) Will there be a collision? (b) If so, where will it take place?

4–15. A sled starts from rest at the top of a hill and slides down with a constant acceleration. The sled is 140 ft from the top of the hill 2 sec after passing a point which is 92 ft from the top. Four sec after passing the 92-ft point it is 198 ft from the top, and 6 sec after passing the point it is 266 ft from the top.

(a) What is the average velocity of the sled during each of the 2-sec intervals after passing the 92-ft point?

(b) What is the acceleration of the sled?

(c) What was the velocity of the sled when it passed the 92-ft point?

(d) How long did it take to go from the top to the 92-ft point?

(e) How far did the sled go during the first sec after passing the 92-ft point?

(f) How long does it take the sled to go from the 92-ft point to the midpoint between the 92-ft and the 140-ft mark?

(g) What is the velocity of the sled as it passes the midpoint in part (f)?

4–16. A subway train starts from rest at a station and accelerates at a rate of 4 ft/sec^2 for 10 sec. It then runs at constant speed for 30 sec, and decelerates at 8 ft/sec^2 until it stops at the next station. Find the *total* distance covered.

4–17. A body starts from rest, moves in a straight line with constant acceleration, and covers a distance of 64 ft in 4 sec. (a) What was the final velocity? (b) How long a time was required to cover half the total distance? (c) What was the distance covered in one-half the total time? (d) What was the velocity when half the total distance had been covered? (e) What was the velocity after one-half the total time?

4–18. The speed of an automobile going north is reduced from 45 to 30 mi/hr in a distance of 264 ft. Find (a) the magnitude and direction of the acceleration, assuming it to be constant, (b) the elapsed time, (c) the distance in which the car can be brought to rest from 30 mi/hr, assuming the acceleration of part (a).

4–19. An automobile and a truck start from rest at the same instant, with the automobile initially at some distance behind the truck. The truck has a constant acceleration of 4 ft/sec^2 and the automobile an acceleration of 6 ft/sec^2. The automobile overtakes the truck after the truck has moved 150 ft. (a) How long does it take the auto to overtake the truck? (b) How far was the auto behind the truck initially? (c) What is the velocity of each when they are abreast?

4–20. (a) With what velocity must a ball be thrown vertically upward in order to rise to a height of 50 ft? (b) How long will it be in the air?

4–21. A ball is thrown vertically downward from the top of a building, leaving the thrower's hand with a velocity of 30 ft/sec.

(a) What will be its velocity after falling for 2 sec?

(b) How far will it fall in 2 sec?

(c) What will be its velocity after falling 30 ft?

(d) If it moved a distance of 3 ft while in the thrower's hand, find its acceleration while in his hand.

(e) If the ball was released at a point 120 ft above the ground, in how many seconds will it strike the ground?

(f) What will be its velocity when it strikes?

4–22. A balloon, rising vertically with a velocity of 16 ft/sec, releases a sandbag at an instant when the balloon is 64 ft above the ground. (a) Compute the position and velocity of the sandbag at the following times after its release: $\frac{1}{4}$ sec, $\frac{1}{2}$ sec, 1 sec, 2 sec. (b) How many seconds after its release will the bag strike the ground? (c) With what velocity will it strike?

4–23. A stone is dropped from the top of a tall cliff, and 1 sec later a second stone is thrown vertically down with a velocity of 60 ft/sec. How far below the top of the cliff will the second stone overtake the first?

4–24. A ball dropped from the cornice of a building takes 0.25 sec to pass a window 9 ft high. How far is the top of the window below the cornice?

4–25. A ball is thrown nearly vertically upward from a point near the cornice of a tall building. It just misses the cornice on the way down, and passes a point 160 ft below its starting point 5 sec after it leaves the thrower's hand. (a) What was the initial velocity of the ball? (b) How high did it rise above its starting point? (c) What were the magnitude and direction of its velocity at the highest point? (d) What were the magnitude and direction of its acceleration at the highest point? (e) What was the magnitude of its velocity as it passed a point 64 ft below the starting point?

4–26. A juggler performs in a room whose ceiling is 9 ft above the level of his hands. He throws a ball vertically upward so that it just reaches the ceiling. (a) With what initial velocity does he throw the ball? (b) What time is required for the ball to reach the ceiling?

He throws a second ball upward with the same initial velocity, at the instant that the first ball is at the ceiling. (c) How long after the second ball is thrown do the two balls pass each other?

(d) When the balls pass each other, how far are they above the juggler's hands?

4–27. An object is thrown vertically upward. It has a speed of 32 ft/sec when it has reached one-half its maximum height. (a) How high does it rise? (b) What is its velocity and acceleration 1 sec after it is thrown? (c) 3 sec after? (d) What is the average velocity during the first half-sec?

4–28. A student determined to test the law of gravity for himself walks off a skyscraper 900 ft high, stopwatch in hand, and starts his free fall (zero initial velocity). Five seconds later, Superman arrives at the scene and dives off the roof to save the student. (a) What must Superman's initial velocity be in order that he catch the student just before the ground is reached? (b) What must be the height of the skyscraper so that even Superman can't save him? (Assume that Superman's acceleration is that of any freely falling body.)

4–29. A ball is thrown vertically upward from the ground and a student gazing out of the window sees it moving upward past him at 16 ft/sec. The window is 32 ft above the ground. (a) How high does the ball go above the ground? (b) How long does it take to go from a height of 32 ft to its highest point? (c) Find its velocity and acceleration $\frac{1}{2}$ sec after it left the ground, and 2 sec after it left the ground.

4–30. A ball is thrown vertically upward from the ground with a velocity of 80 ft/sec. (a) How long will it take to rise to its highest point? (b) How high does the ball rise? (c) How long after projection will the ball have a velocity of 16 ft/sec upward? (d) of 16 ft/sec downward?   (e) When is the displacement of the ball zero? (f) When is the magnitude of the ball's velocity equal to half its velocity of projection? (g) When is the magnitude of the ball's displacement equal to half the greatest height to which it rises? (h) What are the magnitude and direction of the acceleration while the ball is moving upward? (i) While moving downward? (j) When at the highest point?

4–31. A ball rolling on an inclined plane moves with a constant acceleration. One ball is released from rest at the top of an inclined plane 18 m long and reaches the bottom 3 sec later. At the same instant that the first ball is released, a second ball is projected upward along the plane from its bottom with a certain initial velocity. The second ball is to travel part way up the plane, stop, and return to the bottom so that it arrives simultaneously with the first ball. (a) Find the acceleration. (b) What must be the initial velocity of the second ball? (c) How far up the plane will it travel?

4–32. Two piers A and B are located on a river, one mile apart. Two men must make round trips from pier A to pier B and return. One man is to row a boat at a velocity of 4 mi/hr relative to the water, and the other man is to walk on the shore at a velocity of 4 mi/hr. The velocity of the river is 2 mi/hr in the direction from A to B. How long does it take each man to make the round trip?

4–33. A passenger on a ship traveling due east with a speed of 18 knots observes that the stream of smoke from the ship's funnels makes an angle of 20° with the ship's wake. The wind is blowing from south to north. Assume that the smoke acquires a velocity (with respect to the earth) equal to the velocity of the wind, as soon as it leaves the funnels. Find the velocity of the wind.

4–34. An airplane pilot wishes to fly due north. A wind of 60 mi/hr is blowing toward the west. If the flying speed of the plane (its speed in still air) is 180 mi/hr, in what direction should the pilot head? What is the speed of the plane over the ground? Illustrate with a vector diagram.

4–35. An airplane pilot sets a compass course due west and maintains an air speed of 120 mi/hr. After flying for one-half hour he finds himself over a town which is 75 mi west and 20 mi south of his starting point. (a) Find the wind velocity, in magnitude and direction. (b) If the wind velocity were 60 mi/hr due south, in what direction should the pilot set his course in order to travel due west? Take the same air speed of 120 mi/hr.

4–36. When a train has a speed of 10 mi/hr eastward, raindrops which are falling vertically with respect to the earth make traces on the windows of the train, which are inclined 30° to the vertical. (a) What is the horizontal component of a drop's velocity with respect to the earth? with respect to the train? (b) What is the velocity of the raindrop with respect to the earth? with respect to the train?

4–37. A river flows due north with a velocity of 3 mi/hr. A man rows a boat across the river, his velocity relative to the water being 4 mi/hr due east. (a) What is his velocity relative to the earth? (b) If the river is 1 mi wide, how far north of his starting point will he reach the opposite bank? (c) How long a time is required to cross the river?

4–38. (a) In what direction should the rowboat in Problem 4–37 be headed in order to reach a point on the opposite bank directly east from the start? (b) What will be the velocity of the boat relative to the earth? (c) How long a time is required to cross the river?

4–39. A motor boat is observed to travel 10 mi/hr relative to the earth in the direction 37° north of east. If the velocity of the boat due to the wind is 2 mi/hr eastward and that due to the current is 4 mi/hr southward, what is the magnitude and direction of the velocity of the boat due to its own power?

4–40. After the engine of a moving motorboat is cut off, the boat has an acceleration in the opposite direction to its velocity and directly proportional to the square of the velocity. That is,

$$\frac{dv}{dt} = -kv^2,$$

where k is a constant. Suppose the engine is cut off when the velocity $v_0 = 20$ ft/sec, and that the velocity decreases to 10 ft/sec in a time of 15 sec. (a) Show that the velocity v at a time t after the engine is cut off is given by

$$\frac{1}{v} = \frac{1}{v_0} + kt.$$

(b) Find the value of k. (c) Find the acceleration at the instant the engine is cut off. (d) Show that the distance traveled in a time t is

$$x = \frac{1}{k} \ln (v_0 kt + 1).$$

(e) Show that the velocity after traveling a distance x is

$$v = v_0 e^{-kx}.$$

4–41. A ball is suspended from a coil spring, pulled down, and released. The y-coordinate of the ball, measured from its equilibrium position, is given by

$$y = A \cos 2\pi ft,$$

where A and f are constants. Find the expressions for (a) the velocity of the ball at any time, (b) the acceleration of the ball at any time, and (c) the acceleration of the ball at any coordinate.

4–42. The motion of a body falling from rest in a resisting medium is described by the equation

$$\frac{dv}{dt} = A - Bv,$$

where A and B are constants. In terms of A and B, find (a) the initial acceleration, and (b) the velocity at which the acceleration becomes zero (the terminal velocity). (c) Show that the velocity at any time t is given by

$$v = \frac{A}{B} (1 - e^{-Bt}).$$

CHAPTER 5

NEWTON'S SECOND LAW. GRAVITATION

5–1 Introduction. In the preceding chapters we have discussed separately the concepts of force and acceleration. We have made use, in problems in equilibrium, of Newton's first law, which states that when the resultant force on a body is zero, the acceleration of the body is also zero. The next logical step is to ask how a body behaves when the resultant force on it is *not* zero. The answer to this question is contained in Newton's second law, which states that when the resultant force is not zero the body moves with accelerated motion, and that the acceleration, with a given force, depends on a property of the body known as its *mass*.

This part of mechanics, which includes both the study of motion and the forces that bring about the motion, is called *dynamics*. In its broadest sense, dynamics includes nearly the whole of mechanics. Statics treats of special cases in which the acceleration is zero, and kinematics deals with motion only.

5–2 Newton's second law. Mass. We know from experience that an object at rest will never start to move of itself; a push or pull must be exerted on it by some other body. It is also a familiar fact that a force is required to slow down or to stop a body which is already in motion, and that a sidewise force must be exerted on a moving body to deviate

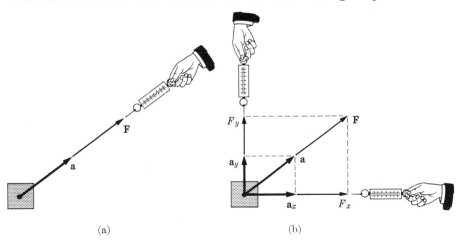

(a)   (b)

FIG. 5–1. (a) The acceleration **a** is in the same direction as the resultant force **F**. (b) Each component of a force can be considered to produce its own component of acceleration.

it from a straight line. All the processes above (i.e., speeding up, slowing down, or changing direction) involve a change in either the magnitude or the direction of the velocity of the body. In other words, in every case the body is accelerated, and an external force must act on it to produce this acceleration.

Let us consider the following experiments. As shown in Fig. 5–1(a), which is a top view, an arbitrary body is placed on a level frictionless surface and a horizontal force **F** is exerted on it. We shall assume that the body is not rotating and that the line of action of the force passes through the center of gravity of the body. The body acquires no rotational motion and only its translational motion is affected. For concreteness, suppose that the force is measured by a spring balance calibrated in pounds, as described in Section 1–2. With a stopwatch and scale we determine the resulting acceleration a. Let a large number of similar pairs of measurements of force and acceleration be made, first on the same body, using forces that differ in magnitude and direction, and then using different bodies. The results of these experiments show the following:

(a) In every case, the *direction* of the acceleration is the same as that of the force. This is true whether the body is initially at rest or is moving in any direction and with any speed.

(b) For a given body, the ratio of the magnitude of the force to that of the acceleration is always the same, or is a constant.

$$\frac{F}{a} = \text{constant (for a given body)}.$$

The ratio is, in general, different for different bodies.

This constant ratio of force to acceleration can be considered a property of the body called its *mass m*, where

$$m = \frac{F}{a},$$

or

$$\mathbf{F} = m\mathbf{a}. \tag{5–1}$$

Mass is a scalar quantity.

The mass of a body therefore represents *the force per unit of acceleration.* Since experiment shows that the ratio of force to acceleration is always the same, for a given body, it suffices to make one pair of measurements of force and acceleration to determine the mass. For example, if the acceleration of a certain body is found to be 5 ft/sec^2 when the force is 20 lb, the mass of the body is

$$m = \frac{F}{a} = \frac{20\ \text{lb}}{5\ \text{ft/sec}^2} = 4\ \frac{\text{lb}}{\text{ft/sec}^2}.$$

When a large force is needed to speed up a body, slow it down, or deviate it sidewise if it is moving, the mass of the body is large. In everyday language, we would say that the body has a large *inertia*. If only a small force is needed per unit of acceleration, the mass is small and the inertia is small. The mass of a body can therefore be considered to represent in a quantitative way that property of matter which is described qualitatively by the word *inertia*.

The equation

$$\mathbf{F} = m\mathbf{a}$$

is a *vector* equation. That is, the vector $\mathbf{F}$ has the same magnitude and direction as a vector which is m times as great as the vector $\mathbf{a}$. If two vectors are equal their rectangular components are equal also and the vector equation above (for forces and accelerations in the xy-plane) is equivalent to the pair of scalar equations

$$F_x = ma_x, \qquad F_y = ma_y. \tag{5–2}$$

For example, suppose that instead of applying the force $\mathbf{F}$ directly, as in Fig. 5–1(a), we apply instead the force components F_x and F_y as in Fig. 5–1(b). We find that the acceleration $\mathbf{a}$ has the same magnitude and direction as in part (a), and that the components a_x and a_y are those given by Eq. (5–2). This means that each component of the force can be considered to produce its own component of acceleration.

It follows that if any number of forces act on a body simultaneously, the forces may be resolved into x- and y-components, the algebraic sums $\sum F_x$ and $\sum F_y$ may be computed, and the components of acceleration are given by

$$\sum F_x = ma_x, \qquad \sum F_y = ma_y. \tag{5–3}$$

This pair of equations is equivalent to the single vector equation

$$\sum \mathbf{F} = m\mathbf{a}, \tag{5–4}$$

where $\sum \mathbf{F}$ is the vector sum or *resultant* of *all* the *external* forces acting *on* the body.

Equation (5–4) is the mathematical statement of Newton's *second law of motion*. Newton phrased the law as follows: "*The change of motion is proportional to the motive force impressed; and is made in the direction of the straight line in which that force is impressed.*" If for "change of motion" we read "rate of change of velocity," or acceleration, the second law states that *the acceleration is proportional to the resultant force and is in the same direction as this force.*

We can see from Eq. (5–4) the physical conditions that must be fulfilled for motion with *constant* acceleration; namely, if **a** is constant, then the resultant force $\sum$**F** must be constant also. In other words, motion with constant acceleration is motion under the action of a constant force. If the force varies, the acceleration varies in direct proportion, since the mass m is constant.

It is also evident from Eq. (5–4) that if the resultant force on a body is zero, the acceleration of the body is zero and its velocity is constant. Hence, if the body is in motion, it continues to move with no change in the magnitude or direction of its velocity; if at rest, it remains at rest (its velocity is then constant and equal to zero). But these are evidently the conditions to which Newton's *first* law applies, and we see that the first law is merely a special case of the second when the resultant force and the acceleration are both zero. There are thus only two independent laws of Newton, the second and the third.

Since Newton must have realized that the first law is a special case of the second, one may question why he stated the first law at all. The answer is undoubtedly that the first law was discovered by Galileo and it enabled Newton to propose the more general second law.

Galileo was studying accelerated motion. Rather than study a freely falling body, he studied a ball rolling down an incline, in order to reduce the acceleration and make it more observable. Having observed the ball rolling down, Galileo tried letting the ball roll up a second inclined plane, as in Fig. 5–2. When he did this he made a striking observation. He noted that regardless of the inclination of the second incline the ball rolled to the same height it started from. Galileo realized that if he made the second plane horizontal the ball could never achieve its original

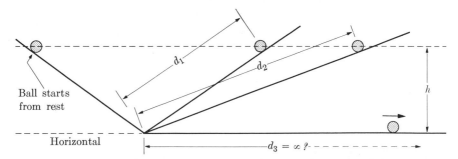

Fig. 5–2. Galileo's inclined plane apparatus. Ball rolls down incline at left and then up a second incline at the right. The latter can be set at any inclination including the limiting position—horizontal. Three positions are shown. The ball rolls up the second plane until it has reached the height h from which it started.

height and would presumably roll on forever. Thus Galileo was the first person to realize that *when there is no resultant force acting on a moving body, the body will continue in that motion indefinitely.* This observation was completely counter to all previous thought, which was that a force was necessary to keep a body moving. The brilliance of Galileo's observation is brought home to us by the fact that people still ask questions like "What keeps an earth satellite going?" Galileo's observation undergirds all dynamics, and Newton made this observation his first law because, conceptually, it paves the way for his second law.

Newton's second law and its corollary, the first law, do not hold for an observer who is accelerated. If Galileo, while swinging on a child's swing, had observed the motion of a body subject to no force parallel to the direction of its motion, it would not have appeared to him that the motion of the body was uniform. A set of coordinates fixed relative to an observer is called the observer's reference frame, and since Newton's laws hold only for a nonaccelerated reference frame, such a frame is called a galilean-newtonian or inertial reference frame. A reference frame tied to the earth is not strictly newtonian because of the rotation of the earth. Defining a newtonian reference frame as one for which Newton's laws hold is perhaps as far as we should go at the moment. We will assume that the earth is an inertial reference frame until we return to this question in the chapter on relativity.

5–3 Systems of units. The mass of a body is the ratio of the resultant force on the body to its acceleration. Consider first the *British engineering system* of units, in which forces are expressed in pounds and accelerations in ft/sec². In this system, the mass of a body is expressed in $\text{lb}/(\text{ft/sec}^2)$. It is often convenient to introduce a single term for the combination of units in which a physical quantity is expressed, and the unit above, $1 \text{ lb}/(\text{ft/sec}^2)$, is called one *slug*. (This term arose from the concept of mass as inertia or sluggishness.) Thus

$$\sum F \text{ (lb)} = m \text{ (slugs)} \times a \text{ (ft/sec}^2).$$

For example, if the acceleration of a body is 5 ft/sec² when the resultant force on it is 20 lb, its mass is

$$m = \frac{\sum F}{a} = \frac{20 \text{ lb}}{5 \text{ ft/sec}^2} = 4 \frac{\text{lb}}{\text{ft/sec}^2} = 4 \text{ slugs}.$$

In setting up the *meter-kilogram-second* (mks) system of units, the mass of the *standard kilogram* is chosen to be the unit of mass. The unit of force in this system is then that force which gives a standard kilogram an acceleration of 1 m/sec². This force is called *one newton*, and is

TABLE 5–1

SYSTEMS OF UNITS

System of units	Force	Mass	Acceleration
Engineering	pound (lb)	slug	ft/sec^2
mks	newton (n)	kilogram (kgm)	m/sec^2
cgs	dyne	gram (gm)	cm/sec^2

approximately equal to one-quarter of a pound of force (more precisely, 1 newton = 0.22481 lb).

Thus, in the mks system,

$$F \text{ (newtons)} = m \text{ (kgm)} \times a \text{ (m/sec}^2\text{)}.$$

The mass unit in the *centimeter-gram-second* (cgs) system is *one gram*, equal to 1/1000 kilogram. The force unit in this system is the force which gives a body of mass 1 gm an acceleration of 1 cm/sec^2, and is called *one dyne*. In the cgs system, then,

$$\sum F \text{ (dynes)} = m \text{ (gm)} \times a \text{ (cm/sec}^2\text{)}.$$

Since 1 kgm = 10^3 gm and 1 m/sec^2 = 10^2 cm/sec^2, it follows that 1 newton = 10^5 dynes.

The units of force, mass, and acceleration in the three systems are summarized in Table 5–1.

It is unnecessary for the National Bureau of Standards to maintain a physical object embodying the engineering mass unit, the slug, or the engineering unit of length, the foot, since both of these are defined in terms of the standard kilogram and the standard meter. One foot, by definition, is exactly 1200/3937 meter. One standard pound, by definition, is a body of mass 0.4535924277 kgm. The pound of force is the force which gives a standard pound an acceleration equal to the standard acceleration of gravity, 32.1740 ft/sec^2. Finally, the slug is the mass of a body whose acceleration is 1 ft/sec^2 when the force on it is one pound.

5–4 Mass and weight. The *weight* of a body means the gravitational force exerted on it by the earth. When a body is released and allowed to fall freely, the only force acting on it is its weight **w**, and its acceleration is that of any freely falling body, the acceleration of gravity **g**. Its mass is then

$$m = \frac{\sum F}{a} = \frac{w}{g}.$$

Since the weight of a body is a force, it must be expressed in units of force. Thus in the engineering system weight is expressed in *pounds;* in the mks system, in *newtons;* and in the cgs system, in *dynes.* The preceding equation gives the relation between the mass and weight of a body in any consistent system of units. In the engineering system a body is usually described by stating its weight w in pounds, and computing its mass m in slugs, if this is desired. Thus the mass of a man whose weight is 160 lb at a point where $g = 32.0$ ft/sec^2 is

$$m = \frac{w}{g} = \frac{160 \text{ lb}}{32.0 \text{ ft/sec}^2} = 5.00 \text{ slugs.}$$

His weight at a second point where $g = 32.2$ ft/sec^2 is

$$w = mg = 5.00 \text{ slugs} \times 32.2 \frac{\text{ft}}{\text{sec}^2} = 161 \text{ lb.}$$

Thus, unlike his mass, which is a constant, his weight varies from one point to another on the earth's surface.

If the mass of a body is 1 slug, its weight at a point where $g = 32.0$ ft/sec^2 is

$$w = mg = 1 \text{ slug} \times 32.0 \frac{\text{ft}}{\text{sec}^2} = 32.0 \text{ lb.}$$

In the mks and cgs systems, a body is usually described by stating its mass m in kilograms or grams, and computing its weight w if this is desired. Thus, at a point where $g = 9.80$ m/sec^2, the weight of a body whose mass is 10 kgm is

$$w = mg = 10 \text{ kgm} \times 9.80 \frac{\text{m}}{\text{sec}^2} = 98.0 \text{ newtons.}$$

Since 10 kgm $= 10^4$ gm, and 9.80 m/sec$^2 = 980$ cm/sec^2, the weight of the same body in cgs units is

$$w = mg = 10^4 \text{ gm} \times 980 \frac{\text{cm}}{\text{sec}^2} = 9.80 \times 10^6 \text{ dynes.}$$

The mass of a body whose weight at a point where $g = 9.80$ m/sec^2 is 1 newton, is

$$m = \frac{w}{g} = \frac{1 \text{ n}}{9.80 \text{ m/sec}^2} = 0.102 \text{ kgm,}$$

and the mass of a body whose weight at the same point is 1 dyne, is

$$m = \frac{w}{g} = \frac{1 \text{ dyne}}{980 \text{ cm/sec}^2} = 1.02 \times 10^{-3} \text{ gm,}$$

or about a milligram.

There are also two other systems of units in which, as in the engineering system, the unit of force rather than of mass is arbitrarily defined. These systems take as their units of force the weight of the standard kilogram and the weight of a gram. The former force is called "one kilogram of force" and the latter "one gram of force." One "kilogram of force" is about 2.2 lb of force or about 9.8 newtons; one "gram of force" is about 0.0022 lb or 980 dynes. The "gram of force" is commonly used as a force unit in elementary physics texts, where the reader has probably met it. The "kilogram force" is used as a force unit in engineering work in those countries which use the metric system exclusively. We shall use neither of these units in this book, and "gram" and "kilogram" will refer to mass only.

5–5 Newton's law of universal gravitation. Throughout our study of mechanics we have been continually encountering forces due to gravitational attraction between the earth and bodies on its surface, forces which are called the weights of the bodies. We now wish to study this phenomenon of gravitation in somewhat more detail.

The law of universal gravitation was discovered by Sir Isaac Newton, and was first announced by him in the year 1686. It may be stated:

Every particle of matter in the universe attracts every other particle with a force which is directly proportional to the product of the masses of the particles and inversely proportional to the square of the distance between them.

$$F \propto \frac{mm'}{r^2}.$$

The proportion above may be converted to an equation on multiplication by a constant G, which is called the *gravitational constant.*

$$F = G\frac{mm'}{r^2}. \tag{5–5}$$

There seems to be some evidence that Newton was led to deduce this law from speculations concerning the fall of an apple to the earth. However, his first published calculations to justify its correctness had to do with the motion of the moon around the earth.

The numerical value of the constant G depends on the units in which force, mass, and distance are expressed. Its magnitude can be found experimentally by measuring the force of gravitational attraction between two bodies of known masses m and m', at a known separation. For bodies of moderate size the force is extremely small, but it can be measured with an instrument which was invented by the Rev. John Michell, although it was first used for this purpose by Sir Henry Cavendish in 1798. The same type of instrument was also used by Coulomb for studying forces of electrical and magnetic attraction and repulsion.

The Cavendish balance consists of two small spheres of mass m (Fig. 5–3) mounted at opposite ends of a light horizontal rod which is supported at its center by a fine vertical fiber such as a quartz thread. A small mirror fastened to the fiber reflects a beam of light onto a scale. To use the balance, two large spheres of mass m' are brought up to the positions shown. The forces of gravitational attraction between the large and small spheres result in a couple which twists the fiber and mirror through a small angle, thereby moving the light beam along the scale.

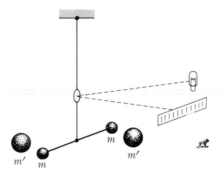

FIG. 5–3. Principle of the Cavendish balance.

By using an extremely fine fiber, the deflection of the light beam may be made sufficiently large so that the gravitational forces can be measured quite accurately. The gravitational constant, measured in this way, is found to be

$$G = 6.670 \times 10^{-8} \text{ dyne} \cdot \text{cm}^2/\text{gm}^2$$

$$= 6.670 \times 10^{-11} \text{ newton} \cdot \text{m}^2/\text{kgm}^2.$$

EXAMPLE: Compute the force of gravitational attraction between the large and small spheres of a Cavendish balance, if $m = 1$ gm, $m' = 500$ gm, $r = 5$ cm. (Two uniform spheres attract each other as if the mass of each were concentrated at its center.)

$$F = \frac{(6.67 \times 10^{-8} \text{ dyne} \cdot \text{cm}^2/\text{gm}^2) \times (1 \text{ gm}) \times (500 \text{ gm})}{(5 \text{ cm})^2} = 1.33 \times 10^{-6} \text{ dyne},$$

or about one-millionth of a dyne!

5–6 The mass of the earth. Since the constant G in Eq. (5–5) can be found from measurements in the laboratory, the mass of the earth may be computed. From measurements on freely falling bodies, we know that the earth attracts a one-gram mass at its surface with a force of (about)

980 dynes. The distance between the centers of the masses is the radius of the earth, 6380 km or 6.38×10^8 cm. Therefore,

$$980 \text{ dynes} = \frac{(6.67 \times 10^{-8} \text{ dyne} \cdot \text{cm}^2/\text{gm}^2) \times (1 \text{ gm}) \times m_E}{(6.38 \times 10^8 \text{ cm})^2},$$

where m_E is the mass of the earth. Hence

$$m_E = 5.98 \times 10^{27} \text{ gm}.$$

The volume of the earth is

$$V = \tfrac{4}{3}\pi R^3 = 1.09 \times 10^{27} \text{ cm}^3.$$

The mass divided by the volume is known as the *density*, the value for water being 1 gm/cm^3. The average density of the earth is therefore

$$\frac{m_E}{V} = \frac{5.98 \times 10^{27} \text{ gm}}{1.09 \times 10^{27} \text{ cm}^3} = 5.5 \frac{\text{gm}}{\text{cm}^3}.$$

This is considerably larger than the average density of the material near the earth's surface, so that the interior of the earth must be of much higher density.

5–7 Variations in "g." The acceleration of gravity, g, is the acceleration imparted to a body by its own weight. Its weight, however, can be written

$$w = G\frac{mm_E}{r^2},$$

where m is the mass of the body, m_E is the mass of the earth, and R is the distance to the earth's center. Then, since $w = mg$,

$$mg = G\frac{mm_E}{r^2},$$

$$g = \frac{Gm_E}{r^2}. \tag{5–6}$$

Since G and m_E are constants, the acceleration of gravity decreases with increasing distance from the center of the earth, and it is only approximately correct to state that a body falls toward the earth with constant acceleration. Actually, the acceleration continually increases as the body approaches the earth, air resistance being neglected. For most purposes, however, this variation is negligible. The acceleration of gravity varies somewhat from point to point on the earth's surface, partly because of variations in the distance to the earth's center and partly because of local deposits of ore, oil, or other substances whose density is greater

TABLE 5–2

VARIATIONS OF g WITH LATITUDE AND ELEVATION

Station	North latitude	Elevation, m	g, cm/sec^2	g, ft/sec^2
Canal Zone	9°	0	978.243	32.0944
Jamaica	18°	0	978.591	32.1059
Bermuda	32°	0	979.806	32.1548
Denver	40°	1638	979.609	32.1393
Cambridge	42°	0	980.398	32.1652
Standard station			980.665	32.1740
Greenland	70°	0	982.534	32.2353

or less than the average density of the earth. The greatest variation, however, arises from the rotation of the earth, and will be discussed in Chapter 6.

From a survey of variations in the value of g, conclusions can be drawn as to the presence of deposits of ore or oil beneath the earth's surface. Hence the precise measurement of g is one of the methods of geophysical prospecting. Some representative values of g are given in Table 5–2.

5–8 Applications of Newton's second law. We now give a number of examples of the application of Newton's second law to specific problems. In all these examples, and in the problems at the end of the chapter, it will be assumed that the acceleration of gravity is 32.0 ft/sec^2 or 9.8 m/sec^2, unless otherwise specified.

EXAMPLE 1. What is the resultant force on a body weighing 48 lb when its acceleration is 6 ft/sec^2?

We must first find the mass of the body. From the relation $m = w/g$,

$$m = \frac{48 \text{ lb}}{32 \text{ ft/sec}^2} = 1.5 \frac{\text{lb}}{\text{ft/sec}^2} = 1.5 \text{ slugs.}$$

Hence

$$\sum F = ma = 1.5 \text{ slugs} \times 6 \frac{\text{ft}}{\text{sec}^2} = 9 \text{ lb.}$$

EXAMPLE 2. What is the resultant force on a body of mass 48 kgm when its acceleration is 6 m/sec^2?

The mass of the body is given, and hence

$$\sum F = ma = 48 \text{ kgm} \times 6 \frac{\text{m}}{\text{sec}^2} = 288 \text{ newtons.}$$

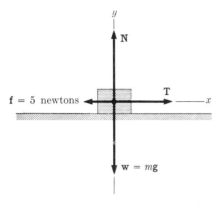

$f = 5$ newtons

$w = mg$

FIGURE 5–4

EXAMPLE 3. A block whose mass is 10 kgm rests on a horizontal surface. What constant horizontal force **T** is required to give it a velocity of 4 m/sec in 2 sec, starting from rest, if the friction force between the block and the surface is constant and is equal to 5 newtons? Assume that all forces act at the center of the block. (See Fig. 5–4.)

The mass of the block is given. Its y-acceleration is zero. Its x-acceleration can be found from the data on the velocity acquired in a given time. Since the forces are constant, the x-acceleration is constant and from the equations of motion with constant acceleration,

$$a_x = \frac{v - v_0}{t} = \frac{4 \text{ m/sec} - 0}{2 \text{ sec}} = 2 \frac{\text{m}}{\text{sec}^2}.$$

Hence from Newton's second law in component form,

$$\sum F_y = ma_y, \qquad N - w = 0,$$

$$N = w = mg = 10 \text{ kgm} \times 9.80 \frac{\text{m}}{\text{sec}^2} = 98 \text{ newtons},$$

$$\sum F_x = ma_x, \qquad T - 5 \text{ n} = 10 \text{ kgm} \times 2 \frac{\text{m}}{\text{sec}^2},$$

$$T = 25 \text{ newtons}.$$

EXAMPLE 4. An elevator and its load weigh a total of 1600 lb. Find the tension **T** in the supporting cable when the elevator, originally moving downward at 20 ft/sec, is brought to rest with constant acceleration in a distance of 50 ft. (See Fig. 5–5.)

The mass of the elevator is

$$m = \frac{w}{g} = \frac{1600 \text{ lb}}{32 \text{ ft/sec}^2} = 50 \text{ slugs}.$$

From the equations of motion with constant acceleration,

$$v^2 = v_0^2 + 2ay, \qquad a = \frac{v^2 - v_0^2}{2y}.$$

The initial velocity v_0 is -20 ft/sec; the velocity v is zero. If we take the origin at the point where the deceleration begins, then $y = -50$ ft. Hence

$$a = \frac{0 - (-20 \text{ ft/sec})^2}{-2 \times 50 \text{ ft}} = 4 \frac{\text{ft}}{\text{sec}^2}.$$

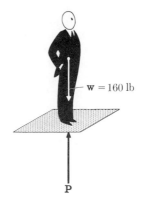

$$\text{w} = 160 \text{ lb}$$

FIG. 5–5. The resultant force has the magnitude $T - w$.

FIG. 5–6. The resultant force has the magnitude $P - w$.

The acceleration is therefore positive (upward).
From the free-body diagram (Fig. 5–5) the resultant force is

$$\sum F = T - w = T - 1600 \text{ lb}.$$

Hence

$$\sum F = ma,$$

$$T - 1600 \text{ lb} = 50 \text{ slugs} \times 4 \, \frac{\text{ft}}{\text{sec}^2} = 200 \text{ lb},$$

$$T = 1800 \text{ lb}.$$

EXAMPLE 5. With what force will the feet of a passenger press downward on the elevator floor when the elevator has the acceleration above, if the passenger weighs 160 lb?

This example illustrates a problem that is frequently encountered, in which it is necessary to find a desired force by first computing the force that is the *reaction* to the one desired, and then using Newton's third law. That is, we first calculate the force with which the elevator floor pushes upward on the passenger; the force desired is the reaction to this.

Figure 5–6 shows the forces acting on the passenger. The resultant force is $P - w$, and since the mass of the passenger is 5 slugs and his acceleration is the same as that of the elevator,

$$\sum F = ma,$$

$$P - 160 \text{ lb} = 5 \text{ slugs} \times 4 \, \frac{\text{ft}}{\text{sec}^2} = 20 \text{ lb},$$

$$P = 180 \text{ lb}.$$

The passenger exerts an equal and opposite force downward on the elevator floor.

EXAMPLE 6. What is the acceleration of a block on a frictionless plane inclined at an angle θ with the horizontal?

The only forces acting on the block
are its weight **w** and the normal force **N**
exerted by the plane (Fig. 5–7). Since
neither the weight nor the mass of the
block is given, a letter must be used to
represent one or the other. Let us call
the mass m; the weight is then mg.
Take axes parallel and perpendicular to
the surface of the plane and resolve the
weight into x- and y-components. Then

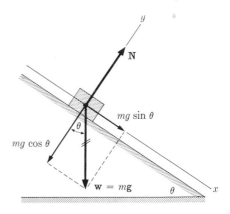

FIG. 5–7. A block on a frictionless
inclined plane.

$$\sum F_y = N - mg \cos \theta,$$

$$\sum F_x = mg \sin \theta.$$

But we know that $a_y = 0$, so from the equation $\sum F_y = ma_y$ we find that $N = mg \cos \theta$. From the equation $\sum F_x = ma_x$, we have

$$mg \sin \theta = ma_x,$$

$$a_x = g \sin \theta.$$

The mass does not appear in the final result, which means that any block, regardless of its mass, will slide on a frictionless inclined plane with an acceleration
down the plane of $g \sin \theta$. (Note that the *velocity* is not necessarily down the
plane.)

EXAMPLE 7. Refer to Fig. 2–3 (Chapter 2). Let the mass of the block be 4
kgm and that of the rope be 0.5 kgm. If the force F_1 is 9 newtons, what are the
forces $\mathbf{F}_1'$, $\mathbf{F}_2$, and $\mathbf{F}_2'$? The surface on which the block moves is level and frictionless.

We know from Newton's third law that $F_1 = F_1'$ and that $F_2 = F_2'$. Hence
$F_2' = 9$ newtons. The force F_2 could be computed by applying Newton's second
law to the block, if its acceleration were known, or the force F_2' could be computed
by applying this law to the rope if its acceleration were known. The acceleration
is not given, but it can be found by considering the block and rope together as a
single system. The vertical forces on this system need not be considered. Since
there is no friction, the resultant *external* force acting *on* the system is the force
F_1. (The forces F_2 and F_2' are *internal* forces when we consider block and rope
as a single system, and the force F_1' does not act on the system, but *on the man*.)
Then, from Newton's second law,

$$\sum F = ma,$$

$$9 \text{ n} = (4 \text{ kgm} + 0.5 \text{ kgm}) \times a,$$

$$a = 2 \frac{\text{m}}{\text{sec}^2}.$$

We can now apply Newton's second law to the block.

$$\sum F = ma,$$

$$F_2 = 4 \text{ kgm} \times 2 \frac{m}{\sec^2} = 8 \text{ newtons.}$$

Considering the rope alone, the resultant force on it is

$$\sum F = F_1 - F_2' = 9 \text{ n} - F_2',$$

and from the second law,

$$9 \text{ n} - F_2' = 0.5 \text{ kgm} \times 2 \frac{m}{\sec^2} = 1 \text{ n,}$$

$$F_2' = 8 \text{ newtons.}$$

In agreement with Newton's third law, which was tacitly used when the forces F_2 and F_2' were omitted in considering the system as a whole, we find that F_2 and F_2' are equal in magnitude. Notice, however, that the forces F_1 and F_2 are *not* equal and opposite (the rope is not in equilibrium) and that these forces are *not* an action-reaction pair.

EXAMPLE 8. In Fig. 5–8, a block of weight $w_1 = 16$ lb moves on a level frictionless surface, connected by a light flexible cord passing over a small frictionless pulley to a second hanging block of weight $w_2 = 8$ lb. What is the acceleration of the system, and what is the tension in the cord connecting the two blocks?

The diagram shows the forces acting on each block. The forces exerted on the blocks by the cord can be considered an action-reaction pair, so we have used the same symbol **T** for each. For the block on the surface,

$$\sum F_x = T = 0.5 \text{ slug} \times a,$$
$$\sum F_y = N - w_1 = N - 16 \text{ lb} = 0.$$

For the hanging block,

$$\sum F_y = w_2 - T = 8 \text{ lb} - T$$
$$= 0.25 \text{ slug} \times a.$$

Since a is the same for both blocks, on solving the first and third equations simultaneously, we obtain

$$a = 10.7 \frac{\text{ft}}{\sec^2}, \qquad T = 5.3 \text{ lb.}$$

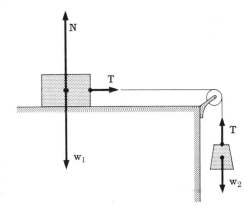

FIGURE 5–8

Note carefully that although the earth pulls on the hanging block with a force of 8 lb, the force exerted on the 16-lb block is only 5.3 lb. It is the connecting cord which pulls on the 16-lb block, and the tension in this cord must be less than 8 lb or the hanging block would not accelerate downward.

EXAMPLE 9. Up to this point, applications of Newton's second law have been limited to cases where the resultant force acting on a body was constant, thereby imparting to the body a constant acceleration. Such cases are very important, but make only slight demands on one's mathematical knowledge. When the resultant force is variable, however, the acceleration is not constant and the simple equations of motion with constant acceleration do not apply. We conclude this section with three examples of motion under the action of a variable force.

An automobile of mass 50 slugs is traveling at 30 ft/sec. The driver applies the brakes in such a way that the velocity decreases to zero according to the relation

$$v = v_0 - kt^2,$$

where $v_0 = 30$ ft/sec, $k = 0.30$ ft/sec^3, and t is the time in seconds after the brakes are applied. Find the resultant force decelerating the automobile, 5 sec after the brakes are applied.

The mass of the automobile is given. To find the resultant force on it from Newton's second law we must first compute its acceleration. This is given by

$$a = \frac{dv}{dt} = \frac{d}{dt}(v_0 - kt^2) = -2kt.$$

Hence when $t = 5$ sec,

$$a = -2 \times 0.30 \frac{\text{ft}}{\text{sec}^3} \times 5 \text{ sec} = -3 \frac{\text{ft}}{\text{sec}^2}.$$

Therefore at this instant

$$\sum F = ma = 50 \text{ slugs} \times \left(-3 \frac{\text{ft}}{\text{sec}^2}\right) = -150 \text{ lb.}$$

(What is the significance of the negative sign?)

EXAMPLE 10. An automobile of mass 50 slugs accelerates from rest. During the first 10 sec, the resultant force acting on it is given by $\sum F = F_0 - kt$, where $F_0 = 200$ lb, $k = 10$ lb/sec, and t is the time in seconds after the start. Find the velocity at the end of 10 sec, and the distance covered in this time.

The mass of the automobile and the resultant force acting on it are both given. The acceleration can be found from Newton's second law and the principles of kinematics can then be used to find the velocity and the position. From the second law,

$$a = \frac{dv}{dt} = \frac{\sum F}{m} = \frac{F_0}{m} - \frac{k}{m}t.$$

Therefore

$$dv = \frac{F_0}{m}dt - \frac{k}{m}t\,dt,$$

$$\int dv = \frac{F_0}{m}\int dt - \frac{k}{m}\int t\,dt,$$

$$v = \frac{F_0}{m}t - \frac{k}{2m}t^2 + C_1, \qquad (5\text{--}7)$$

where C_1 is a constant of integration. Since $v = 0$ when $t = 0$, C_1 is zero also. Hence when $t = 10$ sec,

$$v = \frac{200 \text{ lb}}{50 \text{ slugs}} \times 10 \text{ sec} - \frac{10 \text{ lb/sec}}{100 \text{ slugs}} \times (10 \text{ sec})^2$$

$$= 40 \frac{\text{ft}}{\text{sec}} - 10 \frac{\text{ft}}{\text{sec}} = 30 \frac{\text{ft}}{\text{sec}}.$$

To find the position, return to Eq. (5–7).

$$v = \frac{dx}{dt} = \frac{F_0}{m} t - \frac{k}{2m} t^2,$$

$$\int dx = \frac{F_0}{m} \int t \, dt - \frac{k}{2m} \int t^2 \, dt + C_2,$$

$$x = \frac{F_0}{2m} t^2 - \frac{k}{6m} t^3 + C_2.$$

If the origin is at the starting point, $x = 0$ when $t = 0$ and hence $C_2 = 0$. When $t = 10$ sec,

$$x = \frac{200 \text{ lb}}{100 \text{ slugs}} \times (10 \text{ sec})^2 - \frac{10 \text{ lb/sec}}{300 \text{ slugs}} \times (10 \text{ sec})^3$$

$$= 200 \text{ ft} - 33 \text{ ft} = 167 \text{ ft}.$$

EXAMPLE 11. Discuss the motion of a freely falling body (or a body projected vertically upward), taking into account the variation of the gravitational force on the body with its distance from the earth's center. Neglect air resistance.

The gravitational force on the body at a distance r from the earth's center is Gmm_E/r^2, and from Newton's second law its acceleration is

$$a = \frac{F}{m} = -\frac{Gm_E}{r^2},$$

where the positive direction is upward (or better, radially outward).

It was shown in Eq. (4–8) that the acceleration can be expressed as

$$a = v \frac{dv}{dr}.$$

Then

$$v \frac{dv}{dr} = -\frac{Gm_E}{r^2},$$

$$\int_{v_1}^{v_2} v \, dv = -Gm_E \int_{r_1}^{r_2} \frac{dr}{r^2},$$

where v_1 and v_2 are the velocities at the radial distances r_1 and r_2. It follows that

$$v_2^2 - v_1^2 = 2Gm_E \left(\frac{1}{r_2} - \frac{1}{r_1} \right). \tag{5–8}$$

As an illustration, let us find the initial velocity v_1 required to project a body vertically upward so that it rises to a height above the earth's surface equal to the earth's radius R. Then $v_2 = 0$, $r_1 = R$, $r_2 = 2R$, and

$$v_1^2 = \frac{Gm_E}{R}. \tag{5-9}$$

Let g_0 represent the acceleration of gravity at the earth's surface, where $r = R$. Then from Eq. (5–6),

$$Gm_E = g_0 R^2$$

and Eq. (5–9) can be written

$$v_1^2 = g_0 R. \tag{5-10}$$

How does this compare with the velocity that would be required if the acceleration had the *constant* value g_0?

5–9 The equal-arm analytical balance. As with many other physical quantities, the mass of a body can be measured in several different ways. One is to use the relation by which the quantity is defined, which in this case is the ratio of the force on the body to its acceleration. A measured force is applied to the body, its acceleration is measured, and the unknown mass is obtained by dividing the force by the acceleration. This method is used exclusively to measure masses of atomic particles.

The second method consists of finding by trial some other body whose mass (a) is equal to that of the given body, and (b) is already known. Consider first a method of determining when two masses are equal. It will be recalled that at the same point on the earth's surface all bodies fall freely with the same acceleration g. Since the weight w of a body equals the product of its mass m and the acceleration g, it follows that if, at the same point, the weights of two bodies are equal, their masses are equal also. The *equal-arm balance* is an instrument by means of which one can determine very precisely when the weights of two bodies are equal, and hence when their masses are equal.

The essential feature of the balance, shown schematically in Fig. 5–9, is a light, rigid beam on which are firmly mounted three equally spaced agate knife-edges, parallel to one another and perpendicular to the length of the beam. The central knife-edge at O rests on a polished plane agate plate supported from the floor of the balance case. The scale pans are hung from two similar plates at A and B. A pointer fastened to the beam swings in front of the scale S. The knife-edges and plates act as practically frictionless pivots. Since the scale pans can swing freely about their supporting knife-edges, the centers of gravity of the pans and of any bodies placed on them will always be directly below the knife-edges.

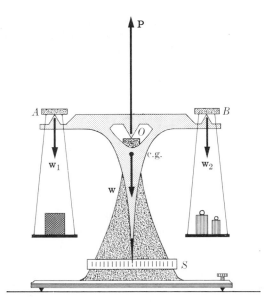

FIG. 5–9. The equal-arm analytical balance.

The weight of the beam is **w**, and its center of gravity is directly below the central knife-edge when the beam is horizontal. The weights of the scale pans are equal.

In using the balance, the body whose mass m_1 is desired is placed in the left scale pan, and a combination of known masses m_2 is placed in the right pan. If the combined weights of bodies and scale pans, w_1 and w_2, are exactly equal, the beam remains in stable equilibrium in a horizontal position as in Fig. 5–8, under the action of the four parallel forces w_1, w_2, **w**, and the upward force **P** exerted at the central knife-edge. Then the weight of the unknown body equals that of the bodies in the right scale pan, and hence their masses m_1 and m_2 are equal also.

There remains the question as to how a set of bodies of known mass (usually referred to as a set of "weights") is obtained in the first place. This is also done with the equal-arm balance. Let us start with a standard kilogram and make two bodies (a) whose masses are *equal*, as determined by the balance, and (b) which when combined will just balance the standard kilogram. Each of these then has a mass of one-half kilogram, or 500 grams. Other submultiples, or multiples, of the standard can be prepared by a similar procedure.

PROBLEMS

(For problem work, use the approximate values of $g = 32 \text{ ft/sec}^2 = 9.80 \text{ m/sec}^2 = 980 \text{ cm/sec}^2$. A force diagram should be constructed for each problem.)

5–1. (a) What resultant force is required to give an automobile weighing 1600 lb an acceleration of 8 ft/sec²? (b) What resultant force is required to give a block whose mass is 1600 gm an acceleration of 8 cm/sec²? (c) What resultant force is required to give a block of mass 1600 kgm an acceleration of 8 m/sec²?

5–2. The Springfield rifle bullet weighs 150 grains (7000 grains = 1 lb), its muzzle velocity is 2700 ft/sec, and the length of the rifle barrel is 30 in. Compute the resultant force accelerating the bullet, assuming it to be constant.

5–3. A body of mass 15 kgm rests on a frictionless horizontal plane and is acted on by a horizontal force of 30 newtons. (a) What acceleration is produced? (b) How far will the body travel in 10 sec? (c) What will be its velocity at the end of 10 sec?

5–4. A body of mass 50 gm is at rest at the origin, $x = 0$, on a horizontal frictionless surface. At time $t = 0$ a force of 10 dynes is applied to the body parallel to the x-axis, and 5 sec later this force is removed. (a) What are the position and velocity of the body at $t = 5$ sec? (b) If the same force (10 dynes) is again applied at $t = 15$ sec, what are the position and velocity of the body at $t = 20$ sec?

5–5. If action and reaction are always equal in magnitude and opposite in direction, why don't they always cancel one another and leave no net force for accelerating a body?

5–6. The mass of a certain object is 10 gm. (a) What would its mass be if taken to the planet Mars? (b) Is the expression $F = ma$ valid on Mars? (c) Newton's second law is sometimes written in the form $F = wa/g$ instead of $F = ma$. Would this expression be valid on Mars? (d) If a Martian scientist hangs a standard pound body on a spring balance calibrated correctly on the earth, would the spring balance read 1 lb? Explain.

5–7. A constant horizontal force of 10 lb acts on a body on a smooth horizontal plane. The body starts from rest and is observed to move 250 ft in 5 sec. (a) What is the mass of the body? (b) If the force ceases to act at the end of 5 sec, how far will the body move in the next 5 sec?

5–8. A .22 rifle bullet, traveling at 36,000 cm/sec, strikes a block of soft wood, which it penetrates to a depth of 10 cm. The mass of the bullet is 1.8 gm. Assume a constant retarding force. (a) How long a time was required for the bullet to stop? (b) What was the decelerating force, in dynes? in lb?

5–9. An electron (mass = 9×10^{-28} gm) leaves the cathode of a radio tube with zero initial velocity and travels in a straight line to the anode, which is 1 cm away. It reaches the anode with a velocity of 6×10^8 cm/sec. If the accelerating force was constant, compute (a) the accelerating force, in dynes, (b) the time to reach the anode, (c) the acceleration. The gravitational force on the electron may be neglected.

5–10. A 5-kgm block is supported by a cord and pulled upward with an acceleration of 2 m/sec². (a) What is the tension in the cord? (b) After the block has been set in motion the tension in the cord is reduced to 49 newtons. What sort of motion will the block perform? (c) If the cord is now slackened completely, the block is observed to move up 2 meters farther before coming to rest. With what velocity was it traveling?

5–11. A body of mass 10 kgm is moving with a constant velocity of 5 m/sec on a horizontal surface. The coefficient of sliding friction between body and surface is 0.20. (a) What horizontal force is required to maintain the motion? (b) If the force is removed, how soon will the body come to rest?

5–12. A hockey puck leaves a player's stick with a velocity of 30 ft/sec and slides 120 ft before coming to rest. Find the coefficient of friction between the puck and the ice.

5–13. A 16-lb block rests on a horizontal surface. The coefficient of sliding friction between block and surface is 0.25, and the coefficient of static friction is 0.30. (a) What is the resultant force on the block when an external horizontal force of 8 lb is exerted on it? (b) If the 8-lb force acts for 4 sec and is then removed, find the total distance moved by the block before coming to rest.

5–14. An elevator weighing 3200 lb rises with an acceleration of 4 ft/sec². What is the tension in the supporting cable?

5–15. An 8-lb block is accelerated upward by a cord whose breaking strength is 20 lb. Find the maximum acceleration which can be given the block without breaking the cord.

5–16. A block weighing 10 lb is held up by a string which can be moved up or down. What conclusions can you draw regarding magnitude and direction of the acceleration and velocity of

the upper end of the string when the tension in the string is (a) 5 lb, (b) 10 lb, (c) 15 lb?

5–17. A body hangs from a spring balance supported from the roof of an elevator. (a) If the elevator has an upward acceleration of 4 ft/sec² and the balance reads 45 lb, what is the true weight of the body? (b) Under what circumstances will the balance read 35 lb? (c) What will the balance read if the elevator cable breaks?

5–18. A transport plane is to takeoff from a level landing field with two gliders in tow, one behind the other. Each glider weighs 2400 lb, and the friction force or drag on each may be assumed constant and equal to 400 lb. The tension in the towrope between the transport plane and the first glider is not to exceed 2000 lb. (a) If a velocity of 100 ft/sec is required for the take-off, how long a runway is needed? (b) What is the tension in the towrope between the two gliders while the planes are accelerating for the take-off?

5–19. If the coefficient of friction between tires and road is 0.5, what is the shortest distance in which an automobile can be stopped when traveling at 60 mi/hr?

5–20. An 80-lb packing case is on the floor of a truck. The coefficient of static friction between the case and the truck floor is 0.30, and the coefficient of sliding friction is 0.20. Find the magnitude and direction of the friction force acting on the case (a) when the truck is accelerating at 6 ft/sec², (b) when it is decelerating at 10 ft/sec².

5–21. A block of mass 2.5 slugs rests on a horizontal surface. The coefficient of static friction between the block and the surface is 0.30, and the coefficient of sliding friction is 0.25. The block is acted upon by a variable horizontal force P. This force is initially zero and increases with time at the constant rate of 2 lb/sec. (a) When will the block start to move? (b) What is its acceleration 8 sec after it starts to move?

5–22. A 200-gm body starts from rest and slides down a smooth inclined plane. If it travels 120 cm during the third second, what is the angle of inclination of the plane?

5–23. A balloon is descending with a constant acceleration a, less than the acceleration of gravity g. The weight of the balloon, with its basket and contents, is w. What weight, W, of ballast should be released so that the balloon will begin to be accelerated upward with constant acceleration a? Neglect air resistance.

5–24. A 64-lb block is pushed up a 37° inclined plane by a horizontal force of 100 lb. The coefficient of sliding friction is 0.25. Find (a) the acceleration, (b) the velocity of the block after it has moved a distance of 20 ft along the plane, (c) the normal force exerted by the plane. Assume that all forces act at the center of the block.

5–25. A block rests on an inclined plane which makes an angle θ with the horizontal. The coefficient of sliding friction is 0.50, and the coefficient of static friction is 0.75. (a) As the angle θ is increased, find the minimum angle at which the block starts to slip. (b) At this angle, find the acceleration once the block has begun to move. (c) How long a time is required for the block to slip 20 ft along the inclined plane?

5–26. (a) What constant horizontal force is required to drag a 16-lb block along a horizontal surface with an acceleration of 4 ft/sec² if the coefficient of sliding friction between block and surface is 0.5? (b) What weight, hanging from a cord attached to the 16-lb block and passing over a small frictionless pulley, will produce this acceleration?

5–27. A block weighing 8 lb resting on a horizontal surface is connected by a cord passing over a light frictionless pulley to a hanging block weighing 8 lb. The coefficient of friction between the block and the horizontal surface is 0.5. Find (a) the tension in the cord, and (b) the acceleration of each block.

5–28. A block having a mass of 2 kgm is projected up a long 30° incline with an initial velocity of 22 m/sec. The coefficient of friction between the block and the plane is 0.3. (a) Find the friction force acting on the block as it moves up the plane. (b) How long does the block move up the plane? (c) How far does the block move up the plane? (d) How long does it take the block to slide down from its position in part (c) to its starting point? (e) With what velocity does it arrive at this point? (f) If the mass of the block had been 5 kgm instead of 2 kgm, would the answers in the preceding parts be changed?

5–29. A 30-lb block on a level frictionless surface is attached by a cord passing over a small frictionless pulley to a hanging block originally at rest 4 ft above the floor. The hanging block strikes the floor in 2 sec. (a) Find the weight of the hanging block. (b) Find the tension in the string while both blocks were in motion.

5–30. Two blocks, each having mass 20 kgm, rest on frictionless surfaces as

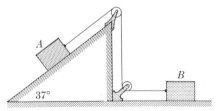

FIGURE 5–10

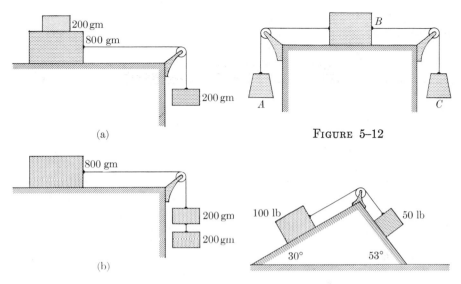

(a)

FIGURE 5–12

(b)

FIGURE 5–11

FIGURE 5–13

shown in Fig. 5–10. Assuming the pulleys to be light and frictionless, compute: (a) the time required for block A to move 1 m down the plane, starting from rest, (b) the tension in the cord connecting the blocks.

5–31. A block of mass 200 gm rests on the top of a block of mass 800 gm. The combination is dragged along a level surface at constant velocity by a hanging block of mass 200 gm as in Fig. 5–11(a). (a) The first 200-gm block is removed from the 800-gm block and attached to the hanging block, as in Fig. 5–11(b). What is now the acceleration of the system? (b) What is the tension in the cord attached to the 800-gm block in part (b) of the figure?

5–32. Block A in Fig. 5–12 weighs 3 lb and block B weighs 30 lb. The coefficient of friction between B and the horizontal surface is 0.1. (a) What is the weight of block C if the acceleration of B is 6 ft/sec^2 toward the right? (b) What is the tension in each cord

when B has the acceleration stated above?

5–33. Two blocks connected by a cord passing over a small frictionless pulley rest on frictionless planes as shown in Fig. 5–13. (a) Which way will the system move? (b) What is the acceleration of the blocks? (c) What is the tension in the cord?

5–34. Two 100-gm blocks hang at the ends of a light flexible cord passing

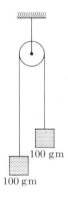

FIGURE 5–14

over a small frictionless pulley as in Fig. 5–14. A 40-gm block is placed on the block on the right, and removed after 2 sec. (a) How far will each block move in the first second after the 40-gm block is removed? (b) What was the tension in the cord before the 40-gm block was removed? after it was removed? (c) What was the tension in the cord supporting the pulley before the 40-gm block was removed? Neglect the weight of the pulley.

5–35. Two 10-lb blocks hang at the ends of a cord as in Fig. 5–14. What weight must be added to one of the blocks to cause it to move down a distance of 4 ft in 2 sec?

5–36. An 8-kgm and a 16-kgm block are suspended at opposite ends of a cord passing over a pulley. Compute (a) the acceleration of the system, (b) the tension in the cord connecting the blocks, and (c) the tension in the cord supporting the pulley. The weight of the pulley may be neglected.

5–37. A force of 10 lb is exerted horizontally against a 60-lb block, which in turn pushes a 40-lb block as in Fig. 5–15. What force does one block exert on the other (a) if the blocks are on a frictionless surface? (b) if the coefficient of friction between each block and the surface is 0.06? (c) Is it a coincidence that the answers to parts (a) and (b) are the same? [*Hint:* Solve the problem in general terms.]

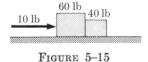

FIGURE 5–15

5–38. In terms of m_1, m_2, and g, find the accelerations of both blocks in Fig. 5–16. Neglect all friction and the masses of the pulleys.

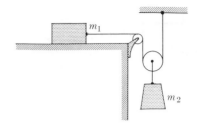

FIGURE 5–16

5–39. The bodies A and B in Fig. 5–17 weigh 40 lb and 24 lb respectively. They are initially at rest on the floor and are connected by a weightless string passing over a weightless and frictionless pulley. An upward force **F** is applied to the pulley. Find the accelerations a_1 of body A and a_2 of body B when F is (a) 24 lb, (b) 40 lb, (c) 72 lb, (d) 90 lb, (e) 120 lb.

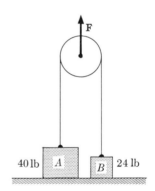

FIGURE 5–17

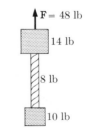

FIGURE 5–18

5–40. The two blocks in Fig. 5–18 are connected by a heavy uniform rope which weighs 8 lb. An upward force of 48 lb is applied as shown. (a) What is the acceleration of the system? (b) What is the tension at the top of the 8-lb rope? (c) What is the tension at the midpoint of the rope?

5–41. A body moves horizontally through a resisting medium. The vertical forces cancel and the only horizontal force is a resisting force which varies directly as the velocity. (a) Draw a diagram showing the direction of motion and indicating with the aid of vectors all of the forces acting on the body. (b) Apply Newton's second law and infer from the resulting equation the general properties of the motion.

5–42. A body falls through a resisting medium which exerts a resisting force that varies directly as the square of the velocity. (a) Draw a diagram showing the direction of motion and indicating with the aid of vectors all of the forces acting on the body. (b) Apply Newton's second law and infer from the resulting equation the general properties of the motion. (c) Show that the body achieves a terminal velocity and calculate it.

5–43. A motorboat of mass m is acted on by a resisting force R which varies directly with the square of the velocity.

$$R = kv^2.$$

Suppose the power is cut off when the motorboat has a velocity v_0. (a) Find the expression for the acceleration of the motorboat, dv/dt, in terms of m, k, and v. (b) Is the acceleration constant? (c) What is the initial acceleration? (d) Find by integration the velocity at any time t. (e) If the initial velocity v_0 is 30 ft/sec, and if the velocity decreases to 20 ft/sec in 10 sec,

find the resisting force R at a velocity of 30 ft/sec. The mass m of the motorboat is 100 slugs.

5–44. Two blocks, weighing 8 and 16 lb respectively, are connected by a string and slide down a 30° inclined plane, as in Fig. 5–19. The coefficient of sliding friction between the 8-lb block and the plane is 0.25, and between the 16-lb block and the plane it is 0.50. (a) Calculate the acceleration of each block. (b) Calculate the tension in the string.

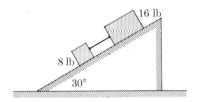

FIGURE 5–19

5–45. Two bodies weighing 10 lb and 6 lb respectively hang 4 ft above the floor from the ends of a cord 12 ft long passing over a frictionless pulley. Both bodies start from rest. Find the maximum height reached by the 6-lb body.

5–46. A man who weighs 160 lb stands on a platform which weighs 80 lb. He pulls a rope which is fastened to the platform and runs over a pulley on the ceiling. With what force does he have to pull in order to give himself and the platform an upward acceleration of 2 ft/sec²?

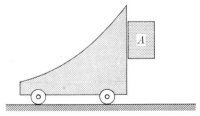

FIGURE 5–20

5–47. What acceleration must the cart in Fig. 5–20 have in order that the block A will not fall? The coefficient of friction between the block and the cart is μ.

5–48. Give arguments either for or against the statement that "the only reason an apple falls downward to meet the earth instead of the earth falling upward to meet the apple is that the earth, being so much more massive, exerts the greater pull."

5–49. In an experiment using the Cavendish balance to measure the gravitational constant G, it is found that a sphere of mass 800 gm attracts another sphere of mass 4 gm with a force of 13×10^{-6} dyne when the distance between the centers of the spheres is 4 cm. The acceleration of gravity at the earth's surface is 980 cm/sec^2, and the radius of the earth is 6400 km. Compute the mass of the earth from these data.

5–50. Two spheres, each of mass 6400 gm, are fixed at points A and

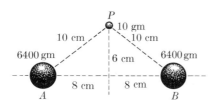

P
10 gm
10 cm   10 cm
6400 gm   6400 gm
6 cm
8 cm   8 cm
A B

FIGURE 5–21

B (Fig. 5–21). Find the magnitude and direction of the initial acceleration of a sphere of mass 10 gm if released from rest at point P and acted on only by forces of gravitational attraction of the spheres at A and B.

5–51. The mass of the moon is one eighty-first, and its radius one-fourth, that of the earth. What is the acceleration of gravity on the surface of the moon?

5–52. In round numbers, the distance from the earth to the moon is 250,000 mi, the distance from the earth to the sun is 93 million miles, the mass of the earth is 6×10^{27} gm, and the mass of the sun is 2×10^{33} gm. Approximately, what is the ratio of the gravitational pull of the sun on moon to that of the earth on the moon?

5–53. (a) In terms of the acceleration of gravity at the earth's surface, g_0, and the earth's radius R, find the velocity with which a body must be projected vertically upward, in the absence of air resistance, to rise to an infinite distance above the earth's surface. This is called the *escape velocity*. (b) In terms of the same quantities, find the velocity with which a body will strike the earth's surface if it falls from rest toward the earth from an infinitely distant point. (c) Compute both of these velocities in mi/hr. (d) Explain why the velocities are not infinitely large.

CHAPTER 6

MOTION IN A PLANE

6–1 Motion of a projectile. Thus far we have considered only motion along a straight line, or *rectilinear motion*. In this chapter we shall discuss two common types of motion along a curved path, namely, the motion of a projectile and of a particle moving in a circle.

The term "projectile" is applied to a baseball or golf ball, a bomb released from an airplane, or a rifle bullet. The path followed by a projectile is called its *trajectory*. The trajectory is affected to a large extent by air resistance, which makes an exact analysis of the motion extremely complex. We shall, however, neglect the important effect of air resistance and assume that the motion takes place in empty space. The only force on the projectile is then its weight $m\mathbf{g}$. Since the force is known, we can use Newton's second law to find the acceleration and then use the principles of kinematics to determine the velocity and position.

Newton's second law, in rectangular component form, is

$$\Sigma F_x = ma_x, \qquad \Sigma F_y = ma_y.$$

In our present problem, if the x-axis is horizontal and the y-axis vertical,

$$\Sigma F_x = 0, \qquad \Sigma F_y = -mg.$$

Therefore

$$a_x = \frac{\Sigma F_x}{m} = 0, \qquad a_y = \frac{\Sigma F_y}{m} = \frac{-mg}{m} = -g.$$

That is, the horizontal component of acceleration is zero, and the vertical component is downward and equal to that of a freely falling body. Since zero acceleration means constant velocity, the motion can be described as a combination of *horizontal motion with constant velocity* and *vertical motion with constant acceleration*.

Consider next the velocity of the projectile. In Fig. 6–1, x- and y-axes have been constructed with the origin at the point where the projectile begins its flight, i.e., just outside the muzzle of the gun or just after leaving the thrower's hand. We shall set $t = 0$ at this point. The velocity at the origin is represented by the vector $\mathbf{v}_0$, called the *initial velocity* or the *muzzle velocity* if the projectile is shot from a gun or rifle. The angle θ_0 is the *angle of departure*. The initial velocity has been resolved into horizontal and vertical components $\mathbf{v}_{0x}$ and $\mathbf{v}_{0y}$, of magnitudes

$$v_{0x} = v_0 \cos \theta, \qquad v_{0y} = v_0 \sin \theta.$$

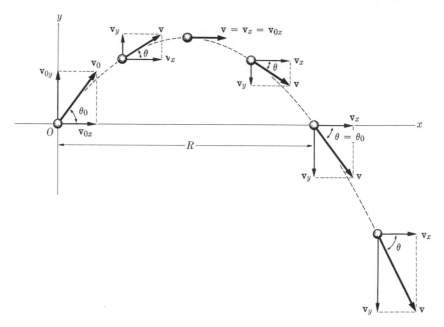

FIG. 6–1. Trajectory of a body projected with an initial velocity v_0 at an angle of departure θ_0. The distance R is the *horizontal range*.

Since the horizontal acceleration a_x is zero, the horizontal component of velocity v_x remains constant throughout the motion, and at any later time t we have

$$v_x = v_{0x} = v_0 \cos \theta_0.$$

The vertical velocity v_y at any time, since the vertical acceleration $a_y = -g$, is

$$v_y = v_{0y} - gt = v_0 \sin \theta_0 - gt.$$

The magnitude of the resultant velocity v at any instant is

$$v = \sqrt{v_x^2 + v_y^2},$$

and the angle θ it makes with the horizontal can be found from

$$\tan \theta = \frac{v_y}{v_x}.$$

The velocity vector $\mathbf{v}$, at every point, is tangent to the trajectory. The x-coordinate at any time, since the x-velocity is constant, is

$$x = (v_0 \cos \theta_0)t. \qquad (6\text{--}1)$$

The y-coordinate is

$$y = (v_0 \sin \theta_0)t - \tfrac{1}{2}gt^2. \tag{6–2}$$

The two preceding expressions give the equation of the trajectory in terms of the parameter t. The equation in terms of x and y can be obtained by eliminating t. From Eq. (6–1),

$$t = \frac{x}{v_0 \cos \theta_0},$$

and substitution in Eq. (6–2) gives

$$y = \frac{v_0 \sin \theta_0}{v_0 \cos \theta_0} x - \frac{g}{2v_0^2 \cos^2 \theta_0} x^2.$$

The quantities v_0, $\sin \theta_0$, $\cos \theta_0$, and g are constants, so the equation has the form

$$y = ax - bx^2,$$

which will be recognized as the equation of a *parabola*.

EXAMPLE 1. A ball is projected horizontally with a velocity v_0 of 8 ft/sec. Find its position and velocity after $\tfrac{1}{4}$ sec (see Fig. 6–2).

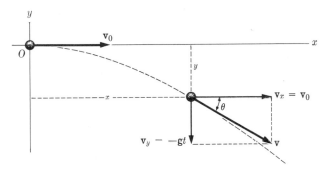

FIGURE 6–2

In this case, the departure angle is zero. The initial vertical velocity component is therefore zero. The horizontal velocity component equals the initial velocity and is constant.

The x- and y-coordinates, when $t = \tfrac{1}{4}$ sec, are

$$x = v_x t = 8\,\frac{\text{ft}}{\text{sec}} \times \frac{1}{4}\,\text{sec} = 2\,\text{ft},$$

$$y = -\frac{1}{2}gt^2 = -\frac{1}{2} \times 32\,\frac{\text{ft}}{\text{sec}^2} \times \left(\frac{1}{4}\,\text{sec}\right)^2 = -1\,\text{ft}.$$

The components of velocity are

$$v_x = v_0 = 8 \frac{\text{ft}}{\text{sec}},$$

$$v_y = -gt = -32 \frac{\text{ft}}{\text{sec}^2} \times \frac{1}{4} \text{ sec} = -8 \frac{\text{ft}}{\text{sec}}.$$

The resultant velocity is

$$v = \sqrt{v_x^2 + v_y^2} = \sqrt{(8 \text{ ft/sec})^2 + (-8 \text{ ft/sec})^2} = 8\sqrt{2} \frac{\text{ft}}{\text{sec}}.$$

The angle θ is

$$\theta = \tan^{-1} \frac{v_y}{v_x} = \tan^{-1} \frac{-8 \text{ ft/sec}}{8 \text{ ft/sec}} = -45°.$$

That is, the velocity is 45° *below* the horizontal.

EXAMPLE 2. In Fig. 6–1, let $v_0 = 160$ ft/sec, $\theta_0 = 53°$. Then

$$v_0 \cos \theta_0 = 160 \frac{\text{ft}}{\text{sec}} \times 0.60 = 96 \frac{\text{ft}}{\text{sec}},$$

$$v_0 \sin \theta_0 = 160 \frac{\text{ft}}{\text{sec}} \times 0.80 = 128 \frac{\text{ft}}{\text{sec}}.$$

(a) Find the position of the projectile, and the magnitude and direction of its velocity, when $t = 2.0$ sec. We have

$$x = 96 \frac{\text{ft}}{\text{sec}} \times 2.0 \text{ sec} = 192 \text{ ft},$$

$$y = 128 \frac{\text{ft}}{\text{sec}} \times 2.0 \text{ sec} - \frac{1}{2} \times 32 \frac{\text{ft}}{\text{sec}^2} \times (2.0 \text{ sec})^2 = 192 \text{ ft},$$

$$v_x = 96 \frac{\text{ft}}{\text{sec}},$$

$$v_y = 128 \frac{\text{ft}}{\text{sec}} - 32 \frac{\text{ft}}{\text{sec}^2} \times 2.0 \text{ sec} = 64 \frac{\text{ft}}{\text{sec}},$$

$$\theta = \tan^{-1} \frac{64 \text{ ft/sec}}{96 \text{ ft/sec}} = \tan^{-1} 0.667 = 33.5°.$$

(b) Find the time at which the projectile reaches the highest point of its flight, and find the elevation of this point.

At the highest point, the vertical velocity v_y is zero. If t_1 is the time at which this point is reached,

$$v_y = 0 = 128 \frac{\text{ft}}{\text{sec}} - 32 \frac{\text{ft}}{\text{sec}^2} \times t_1, \qquad t_1 = 4 \text{ sec}.$$

The elevation of the point is then

$$y = 128 \frac{\text{ft}}{\text{sec}} \times 4 \text{ sec} - \frac{1}{2} \times 32 \frac{\text{ft}}{\text{sec}^2} \times (4 \text{ sec})^2 = 256 \text{ ft}.$$

(c) Find the *horizontal range R*, that is, the horizontal distance from the starting point to the point at which the projectile returns to its original elevation and at which, therefore, $y = 0$. Let t_2 be the time at which this point is reached. Then

$$y = 0 = 128 \frac{\text{ft}}{\text{sec}} \times t_2 - \frac{1}{2} \times 32 \frac{\text{ft}}{\text{sec}^2} \times t_2^2.$$

This quadratic equation has two roots,

$$t_2 = 0 \quad \text{and} \quad t_2 = 8 \text{ sec},$$

corresponding to the two points at which $y = 0$. Evidently the time desired is the second root, $t_2 = 8$ sec, which is just twice the time to reach the highest point. The time of descent therefore equals the time of rise.

The horizontal range is

$$R = v_x t_2 = 96 \frac{\text{ft}}{\text{sec}} \times 8 \text{ sec} = 768 \text{ ft}.$$

The vertical velocity at this point is

$$v_y = 96 \frac{\text{ft}}{\text{sec}} - 32 \frac{\text{ft}}{\text{sec}^2} \times 8 \text{ sec} = -96 \frac{\text{ft}}{\text{sec}}.$$

That is, the vertical velocity has the same magnitude as the initial vertical velocity, but the opposite direction. Since v_x is constant, the angle below the horizontal at this point equals the angle of departure.

(d) If unimpeded, the projectile continues to travel beyond its horizontal range. It is left as an exercise to compute the position and velocity at a time 10 sec after the start, corresponding to the last position shown in Fig. 6–1. The results are:

$$x = 960 \text{ ft}, \quad y = -320 \text{ ft}, \quad v_x = 96 \frac{\text{ft}}{\text{sec}}, \quad v_y = -192 \frac{\text{ft}}{\text{sec}}.$$

For a given initial velocity, there is one particular angle of departure for which the horizontal range is a maximum. To find this angle, write the general algebraic expression for R (see the example above) as

$$R = v_x t_2 = v_0 \cos \theta_0 \times \frac{2v_0 \sin \theta_0}{g}$$

$$= \frac{2v_0^2 \sin \theta_0 \cos \theta_0}{g} = \frac{v_0^2 \sin 2\theta_0}{g}.$$

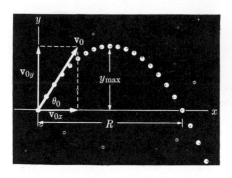

FIG. 6–3. Trajectory of a body pro-   FIG. 6–4. An angle of elevation of 45°
jected at an angle with the horizontal.   gives the maximum horizontal range.

The quantities v_0 and g are constants, so the maximum range results when $\sin 2\theta_0$ is a maximum. This occurs when $2\theta_0 = 90°$, or when $\theta_0 = 45°$.

Figure 6–3 is a multiflash photograph of the trajectory of a ball, to which have been added x- and y-axes and the initial velocity vector. The horizontal distances between consecutive positions are all equal, showing that the horizontal velocity component is constant. The vertical distances first decrease and then increase, showing that the vertical motion is accelerated.

Figure 6–4 is a composite photograph of three trajectories with departure angles of 30°, 45°, and 60°. Note that the horizontal range is the same for the angles of 30° and 60°, and is less than that for the angle of 45°.

6–2 Circular motion. Let us consider next a small body (a particle) revolving in a circle of radius R. Points Q and P in Fig. 6–5(a) represent two successive positions of the particle. Its displacement as it moves from Q to P is the vector Δs. The *average velocity* $\bar{v}$ is defined, just as in the case of rectilinear motion, as the vector Δs divided by the elapsed time Δt:

$$\bar{v} = \frac{\Delta s}{\Delta t}. \tag{6–3}$$

The direction of $\bar{v}$ is the same as that of Δs.

The *instantaneous velocity* v, at the point P, is defined as the limit of the average velocity when Q is taken closer and closer to P and when Δs and Δt approach zero.

$$v = \lim_{\Delta t \to 0} \frac{\Delta s}{\Delta t}. \tag{6–4}$$

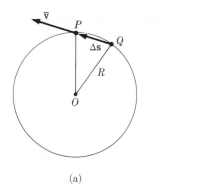 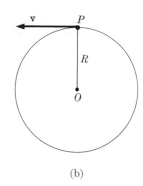

(a)   (b)

FIG. 6–5. (a) The average velocity $\bar{v}$, as the particle moves from Q to P, is in the same direction as Δs and equals the ratio of Δs to Δt. (b) The instantaneous velocity v, at point P, is tangent to the circle and is defined as the limiting ratio of Δs to Δt when Q approaches P.

As point Q approaches point P, the direction of the vector Δs approaches that of the *tangent* to the circle at P, so that *the direction of the instantaneous velocity vector is tangent to the circle*, as shown in Fig. 6–5(b).

At this point we shall discuss only the special case in which the *magnitude* of the velocity is constant. If T is the time of a complete revolution, the magnitude of the velocity is equal to the circumference of the circle, $2\pi R$, divided by T.

$$v = \frac{2\pi R}{T}.\tag{6–5}$$

Although the magnitude of the velocity is constant, its *direction* is not. In Fig. 6–6, the vectors v_1 and v_2 represent the instantaneous velocities at Q and P. The vectors have the same length, but different directions. Again, just as in rectilinear motion, we define the *average acceleration* $\bar{a}$ as the *vector change in velocity* between Q and P, divided by the elapsed

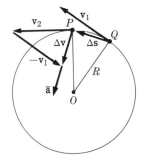

FIG. 6–6. Vector Δv is the *vector change* in velocity between points P and Q.

time. The vector change in velocity means the *vector difference* $\mathbf{v}_2 - \mathbf{v}_1$, which we write as $\Delta\mathbf{v}$.

$$\bar{\mathbf{a}} = \frac{(\mathbf{v}_2 - \mathbf{v}_1)}{\Delta t} = \frac{\Delta\mathbf{v}}{\Delta t}. \qquad (6\text{--}6)$$

It was shown in Section 1–10 that the vector difference $\mathbf{v}_2 - \mathbf{v}_1$ can be considered as the vector *sum* of $\mathbf{v}_2$ and $-\mathbf{v}_1$, where $-\mathbf{v}_1$ is a vector of the same length as $\mathbf{v}_1$ but in the opposite direction. We therefore construct the vector $-\mathbf{v}_1$, as shown in Fig. 6–6, with its tail at the head of the vector $\mathbf{v}_2$, and find the vector difference $\mathbf{v}_2 - \mathbf{v}_1 = \Delta\mathbf{v}$ by the triangle method. Thus, although the *magnitude* of the velocity does not change, there is nevertheless a *vector change* in velocity because of the change in the *direction* of motion.

The average acceleration vector $\bar{\mathbf{a}}$, equal to $\Delta\mathbf{v}/\Delta t$, points inward in the same direction as $\Delta\mathbf{v}$. The magnitude of the average acceleration can be expressed as follows. The *velocity* triangle whose sides are $\mathbf{v}_2$, $-\mathbf{v}_1$, and $\Delta\mathbf{v}$ is similar to the *space* triangle OPQ. (Why?) Hence if v represents the magnitude of either $\mathbf{v}_1$ or $\mathbf{v}_2$, we have

$$\frac{\Delta v}{v} = \frac{\Delta s}{R},$$

or

$$\Delta v = \frac{v}{R}\,\Delta s.$$

The average acceleration $\bar{a}$ is therefore

$$\bar{a} = \frac{\Delta v}{\Delta t} = \frac{v}{R}\frac{\Delta s}{\Delta t}.$$

The *instantaneous acceleration* $\mathbf{a}$ at the point P is defined in magnitude and direction as the limit of the average acceleration when a approaches P and $\Delta\mathbf{v}$ and Δt approach zero. As this occurs, the vector $\Delta\mathbf{v}$ becomes shorter and its direction approaches that of the radius PO. In the limit, $\Delta\mathbf{v}$ points radially inward and hence the instantaneous acceleration $\mathbf{a}$ is inward also, toward the center of the circle.

The magnitude of the instantaneous acceleration is

$$a = \lim_{\Delta t\to 0} \frac{v}{R}\frac{\Delta s}{\Delta t} = \frac{v}{R}\lim_{\Delta t\to 0}\frac{\Delta s}{\Delta t}.$$

But

$$\lim_{\Delta t\to 0}\frac{\Delta s}{\Delta t} = v,$$

so

$$\boxed{a = \frac{v^2}{R}.} \qquad (6\text{--}8)$$

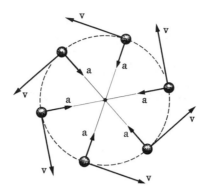

Fig. 6–7. Velocity and acceleration vectors of a particle in uniform circular motion.

The magnitude of the instantaneous acceleration is therefore equal to the square of the velocity divided by the radius, and its direction is toward the center of the circle. Because of this it is called a *central*, a *centripetal*, or a *radial* acceleration. (The term "centripetal" means "seeking a center.") The units of radial acceleration are the same as those of an acceleration resulting from a change in the *magnitude* of a velocity. Thus in the engineering system the units or v^2/R are

$$\frac{(\text{ft/sec})^2}{\text{ft}} = \frac{\text{ft}}{\text{sec}^2}.$$

Figure 6–7 shows the directions of the velocity and acceleration vectors at a number of points for a particle revolving in a circle with a velocity of constant magnitude.

EXAMPLE. The moon revolves about the earth in a circle (very nearly) of radius $R = 239{,}000$ mi or 12.6×10^8 ft, and requires 27.3 days or 23.4×10^5 sec to make a complete revolution. (a) What is the acceleration of the moon toward the earth?

The velocity of the moon is

$$v = \frac{2\pi R}{T} = \frac{2\pi \times 12.6 \times 10^8 \text{ ft}}{23.4 \times 10^5 \text{ sec}} = 3360 \frac{\text{ft}}{\text{sec}}.$$

Its radial acceleration is therefore

$$a = \frac{v^2}{R} = \frac{(3360 \text{ ft/sec})^2}{12.6 \times 10^8 \text{ ft}} = 0.00896 \frac{\text{ft}}{\text{sec}^2}.$$

(b) If the gravitational force exerted on a body by the earth is inversely proportional to the square of the distance from the earth's center, the acceleration produced by this force should vary in the same way. Therefore, if the acceleration of the moon is caused by the gravitational attraction of the earth, the ratio of the moon's acceleration to that of a falling body at the earth's surface should equal the ratio of the square of the earth's radius (3950 mi or 2.09×10^6 ft) to the square of the radius of the moon's orbit. Is this true?

The ratio of the two accelerations is

$$\frac{8.96 \times 10^{-3} \text{ ft/sec}^2}{32.2 \text{ ft/sec}^2} = 2.78 \times 10^{-4}.$$

The ratio of the squares of the distances is

$$\frac{(2.09 \times 10^6 \text{ ft})^2}{(12.6 \times 10^8 \text{ ft})^2} = 2.75 \times 10^{-4}.$$

The agreement is very close, although not exact because we have used average values.

It was the calculation above which Newton made to first justify his hypothesis that gravitation was truly *universal* and that the earth's pull extended out indefinitely into space. The numerical values available in Newton's time were not highly precise. While he did not obtain as close an agreement as that above, he states that he found his results to "answer pretty nearly," and he concluded that his hypothesis was verified.

6–3 Centripetal force. Having obtained an expression for the acceleration of a particle revolving in a circle, we can now use Newton's second law to find the resultant force on the particle. Since the magnitude of the acceleration equals v^2/R, and its direction is toward the center, the magnitude of the resultant force on a particle of mass m is

$$\Sigma F = m \frac{v^2}{R}. \tag{6–9}$$

The direction of the resultant force is toward the center also, and it is called a *centripetal force*. (It is unfortunate that it has become common practice to characterize the force by the adjective "centripetal," since this seems to imply that there is some difference in nature between centripetal forces and other forces. This is not the case. Centripetal forces, like other forces, are pushes and pulls exerted by sticks and strings, or arise from the action of gravitational or other causes. The term "centripetal" refers to the *effect* of the force, that is, to the fact that it results in a change in the *direction* of the velocity of the body on which it acts, rather than a change in the *magnitude* of this velocity.)

Anyone who has ever tied an object to a cord and whirled it in a circle will realize the necessity of exerting this inward, centripetal force. If the cord breaks, the direction of the velocity ceases to change (unless other forces are acting) and the object flies off along a tangent to the circle.

Some readers may wish to add to the forces on a rotating body an outward, "centrifugal" force, to "keep the body out there" or to "keep it in equilibrium." ("Centrifugal" means "fleeing a center.") Let us examine this point of view. In Chapter 5 we pointed out that Newton's laws hold only for an observer in a newtonian inertial frame of reference, and we agreed to consider the earth such a frame. Such an observer should not look for a force to "keep the body out there" because the body doesn't stay there. A moment later it will be at a different position on its circular path. If there were an outward centrifugal force equal to the inward centripetal force, the body would be in equilibrium and it would travel in a straight line.

If an observer rotates with the body as though he were on a merry-go-round he is *not* in a newtonian inertial frame and Newton's laws *do not apply* for him. To him the rotating body *appears* to be in equilibrium and at rest. If he *invents* a system of mechanics which includes the concept that bodies at rest experience no resultant force, then he must invent a *fictitious outward force* that is sometimes called the centrifugal force. Observations from these two frames of reference are problems in classical relativity which we shall discuss again in Chapter 39.

EXAMPLE 1. A small body of mass 200 gm revolves in a circle on a horizontal frictionless surface, attached by a cord 20 cm long to a pin set in the surface. If the body makes two complete revolutions per second, find the force P exerted on it by the cord. (See Fig. 6–8.)

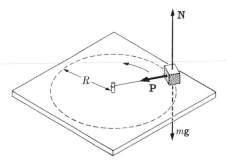

FIGURE 6–8

The circumference of the circle is $2\pi \times 20$ cm $= 40\pi$ cm, so the velocity is 80π cm/sec. The magnitude of the centripetal acceleration is

$$a = \frac{v^2}{R} = \frac{(80\pi \text{ cm/sec})^2}{20 \text{ cm}} = 3150 \frac{\text{cm}}{\text{sec}^2}.$$

Since the body has no vertical acceleration, the forces $\mathbf{N}$ and $m\mathbf{g}$ are equal and opposite and the force $\mathbf{P}$ is the resultant force. Therefore

$$\sum F = P = ma = 200 \text{ gm} \times 3150 \frac{\text{cm}}{\text{sec}^2} = 6.3 \times 10^5 \text{ dynes.}$$

EXAMPLE 2. Figure 6–9 is a view of the earth looking down on the north pole and showing a (greatly enlarged) view of a body of mass m at the equator, hanging from a spring balance. The forces on the hanging body are the force of gravitational attraction $\mathbf{F}$ and the upward pull $\mathbf{w}$ of the spring balance. Since the body is carried along by the earth's rotation, it is not in equilibrium but has a radial acceleration a_R toward the earth's center. The force F must therefore be slightly larger than the force w in order to provide the necessary centripetal force. That is, the balance reading w is somewhat less than the true force of gravitational attraction.

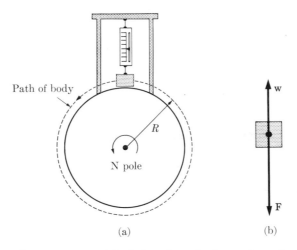

Path of body

R

N pole

w

F

(a)   (b)

FIG. 6–9. The apparent weight is less than the force of gravitational attraction.

From Newton's law of gravitation,

$$F = G \frac{m m_E}{R^2},$$

where m_E is the mass of the earth.

From Newton's second law,

$$F - w = m a_R.$$

Replacing F by $G(m m_E / R^2)$ and w by mg, where g is the acceleration of gravity at the equator, we get, after canceling m,

$$g \text{ (equator)} = \frac{G m_E}{R^2} - a_R.$$

At the poles, where v and a_R are zero,

$$g \text{ (poles)} = \frac{G m_E}{R^2}.$$

This is the expression we previously derived for g in Eq. (5–6), where the rotation of the earth was neglected. We can now see that the effect of the rotation is to reduce the value of g at the equator, relative to that at the poles, by an amount equal to a_R, where for the equator

$$a_R = \frac{v^2}{R} = \frac{(2\pi R/T)^2}{R} = \frac{4\pi^2 R}{T^2}.$$

Approximate numerical values are

$$R = 6.4 \times 10^8 \text{ cm},$$

$$T = 8.64 \times 10^4 \text{ sec}.$$

Hence

$$a_R = 3.37 \frac{\text{cm}}{\text{sec}^2}.$$

Reference to Table 5–2 will show that this effect is sufficient to account for most of the difference between the observed values of g at low and high latitudes.

EXAMPLE 3. Figure 6–10 represents a small body of mass m revolving in a horizontal circle with velocity v of constant magnitude at the end of a cord of length L. As the body swings around its path, the cord sweeps over the surface of a cone. The cord makes an angle θ with the vertical, so the radius of the circle in which the body moves is $R = L \sin \theta$ and the magnitude of the velocity v equals $2\pi L \sin \theta/T$, where T is the time for one complete revolution.

The forces exerted on the body when in the position shown are its weight mg and the tension $\mathbf{P}$ in the cord. Let $\mathbf{P}$ be resolved into a horizontal component $P \sin \theta$ and a vertical component $P \cos \theta$. The body has no vertical acceleration, so the forces $P \cos \theta$ and mg are equal, and the resultant inward, radial, or centripetal force is the component $P \sin \theta$. Then

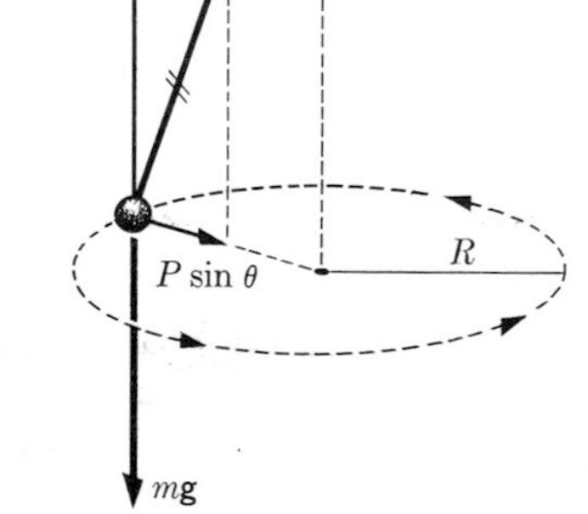

$$P \sin \theta = m \frac{v^2}{R}, \qquad P \cos \theta = mg.$$

When the first of these equations is divided by the second, we get

$$\tan \theta = \frac{v^2}{Rg}. \tag{6–10}$$

This equation indicates how the angle θ depends on the velocity v. As v increases, $\tan \theta$ increases and θ increases. The angle never becomes 90°, however, since this requires that $v = \infty$.

FIG. 6–10. The conical pendulum.

Making use of the relations $R = L \sin \theta$ and $v = 2\pi L \sin \theta / T$, we can also write

$$\cos \theta = \frac{gT^2}{4\pi^2 L}, \tag{6-11}$$

or

$$T = 2\pi \sqrt{L \cos \theta / g}. \tag{6-12}$$

Equation (6–12) is similar in form to the expression for the time of swing of a simple pendulum, which will be derived in Chapter 11. Because of this similarity, the present device is called a *conical pendulum*.

EXAMPLE 4. Figure 6–11(a) represents an automobile or a railway car rounding a curve of radius R on a level road or track. The forces acting on it are its weight mg, the normal force $\mathbf{N}$, and the centripetal force $\mathbf{T}$. The force $\mathbf{T}$ must be provided by friction, in the case of an automobile, or by a force exerted by the rails against the flanges on the wheels of a railway car.

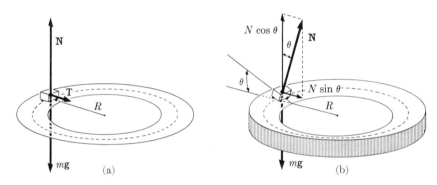

FIG. 6–11. (a) Forces on a vehicle rounding a curve on a level track. (b) Forces when the track is banked.

In order not to have to rely on friction, or to reduce wear on the rails and flanges, the road or the track may be banked as shown in Fig. 6–11(b). The normal force $\mathbf{N}$ then has a vertical component $N \cos \theta$, and a horizontal component $N \sin \theta$ toward the center, which provides the centripetal force. The banking angle θ can be computed as follows. If v is the velocity and R the radius, then

$$N \sin \theta = \frac{mv^2}{R}.$$

Since there is no vertical acceleration,

$$N \cos \theta = mg.$$

Dividing the first equation by the second, we get

$$\tan \theta = \frac{v^2}{Rg}.$$

The tangent of the angle of banking is proportional to the square of the velocity and inversely proportional to the radius. For a given radius no one angle is correct for all velocities. Hence in the design of highways and railroads, curves are banked for the average velocity of the traffic over them.

The same considerations apply to the correct banking angle of a plane when it makes a turn in level flight.

Note that the banking angle is given by the same expression as that for the angle with the vertical made by the cord of a conical pendulum. In fact, the force diagrams in Fig. 6–10 and Fig. 6–11 are identical.

6–4 Motion of a satellite. A satellite of the earth travels in an elliptical orbit with the earth's center at one of the foci of the ellipse, provided the only force on the satellite is that of the earth's gravitational attraction. A circular orbit is a special case of an elliptical orbit in which both foci coincide at the earth's center.

The moon is, of course, an earth satellite, and its orbit is very nearly circular. The planets are satellites of the sun and their orbits are also very nearly circular.

Let us consider for simplicity an earth satellite traveling in a circular orbit. The gravitational force exerted on the satellite by the earth then provides the centripetal force that retains the satellite in its orbit. (Were it not for this force, the satellite would fly off in the direction of its tangential velocity.)

Let r represent the radius of the orbit, m the mass of the satellite, and m_E the mass of the earth. The centripetal force is then

$$F = G \frac{m m_E}{r^2},$$

and if v is the velocity of the satellite,

$$G \frac{m m_E}{r^2} = \frac{m v^2}{r},$$

$$v^2 = \frac{G m_E}{r}. \qquad (6\text{–}13)$$

The velocity does not depend on the mass m of the satellite, but only on the radius of its orbit. The larger the radius, the smaller the velocity.

It was shown in Eq. (5–6) that if the rotation of the earth is neglected, the acceleration of gravity at the earth's surface, g_0, is given by

$$g_0 = \frac{G m_E}{R^2},$$

where R is the radius of the earth. Hence Eq. (6–13) can be written as

$$v^2 = \frac{g_0 R^2}{r}.$$

EXAMPLE. What is the velocity of an earth satellite traveling in a circular orbit at a height above the earth's surface equal to the earth's radius?

For this orbit, $r = 2R$ and

$$v^2 = \frac{Gm_E}{2R} = \tfrac{1}{2}g_0 R.$$

Compare this tangential velocity with the radial velocity discussed in Example 11, Chapter 5.

PROBLEMS

(In all the problems in projectile motion, let $g = 32.0$ ft/sec^2 or 980 cm/sec^2, and neglect air resistance.)

6–1. A ball rolls off the edge of a horizontal tabletop 4 ft high and strikes the floor at a distance of 5 ft horizontally from the edge of the table. What was the velocity of the ball at the instant of leaving the table?

6–2. A block slides off a horizontal tabletop 4 ft high with a velocity of 12 ft/sec. Find (a) the horizontal distance from the table at which the block strikes the floor, and (b) the horizontal and vertical components of its velocity when it reaches the floor.

6–3. A level-flight bomber, flying at 300 ft/sec, releases a bomb at an elevation of 6400 ft. (a) How long before the bomb strikes the earth? (b) How far does it travel horizontally? (c) Find the horizontal and vertical components of its velocity when it strikes.

6–4. A block passes a point 10 ft from the edge of a table with a velocity of 12 ft/sec. It slides off the edge of the table, which is 4 ft high, and strikes the floor 4 ft from the edge of the table. What was the coefficient of sliding friction between block and table?

6–5. A golf ball is driven horizontally from an elevated tee with a velocity of 80 ft/sec. It strikes the fairway 2.5 sec later. (a) How far has it fallen vertically? (b) How far has it traveled horizontally? (c) Find the horizontal and vertical components of its velocity, and the magnitude and direction of its resultant velocity, just before it strikes.

6–6. A .22 rifle bullet is fired in a horizontal direction with a muzzle velocity of 900 ft/sec. In the absence of air resistance, how far will it have dropped in traveling a horizontal dis-

tance of (a) 50 yd? (b) 100 yd? (c) 150 yd? (d) How far will it drop in one second?

6–7. A bomb is released from an airplane flying horizontally at an elevation of 1600 ft, with a velocity of 200 mi/hr. (a) How far does the bomb travel horizontally before striking the earth? (b) What will be the magnitude and direction of its velocity just before striking? (c) How long is it in the air?

6–8. A level-flight bombing plane, flying at an altitude of 1024 ft with a velocity of 240 ft/sec, is overtaking a motor torpedo boat traveling at 80 ft/sec in the same direction as the plane. At what distance astern of the boat should a bomb be released in order to hit the boat?

6–9. A bomber is making a horizontal bombing run on a destroyer from an altitude of 25,600 ft. The magnitude of the velocity of the bomber is 300 mi/hr. (a) How much time is available for the destroyer to change its course after the bombs are released? (b) If the bomber is to be shot down before its bombs can reach the ship, what is the maximum angle that the line of sight from ship to bomber can make with the horizontal? Draw a diagram, showing distances approximately to scale.

6–10. A ball is projected with an initial upward velocity component of 80 ft/sec and a horizontal velocity component of 100 ft/sec. (a) Find the position and velocity of the ball after 2 sec; 3 sec; 6 sec. (b) How long a time is required to reach the highest point of the trajectory? (c) How high is this point? (d) How long a time is required for the ball to return to its original level? (e) How far has it traveled horizontally during this time? Show your results in a neat sketch, large enough to show all features clearly.

6–11. A batted baseball leaves the bat at an angle of 30° above the horizontal, and is caught by an outfielder 400 ft from the plate. (a) What was the initial velocity of the ball? (b) How high did it rise? (c) How long was it in the air?

6–12. A golf ball is driven with a velocity of 200 ft/sec at an angle of 37° above the horizontal. It strikes a green at a horizontal distance of 800 ft from the tee. (a) What was the elevation of the green above the tee? (b) What was the velocity of the ball when it struck the green?

6–13. If a baseball player can throw a ball a maximum distance of 200 ft over the ground, what is the maximum vertical height to which he can throw it? Assume the ball to have the same initial speed in each case.

6–14. A player kicks a football at an angle of 37° with the horizontal and with an initial velocity of 48 ft/sec. A second player standing at a distance of 100 ft from the first in the direction of the kick starts running to meet the ball at the instant it is kicked. How fast must he run in order to catch the ball before it hits the ground?

6–15. A baseball leaves the bat at a height of 4 ft above the ground, traveling at an angle of 45° with the horizontal, and with a velocity such that the horizontal range would be 400 ft. At a distance of 360 ft from home plate is a fence 30 ft high. Will the ball be a home run?

6–16. A ball A is projected from O with an initial velocity $v_0 = 700$ cm/sec in a direction 37° above the horizontal. A ball B 300 cm from O on a line 37°

above the horizontal is released from rest at the instant A starts. (a) How far will B have fallen when it is hit by A? (b) In what direction is A moving when it hits B? (See Fig. 6–12.)

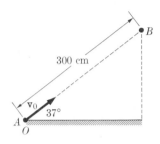

FIGURE 6–12

6–17. A projectile shot at an angle of 60° above the horizontal strikes a building 80 ft away at a point 48 ft above the point of projection. (a) Find the velocity of projection. (b) Find the magnitude and direction of the velocity of the projectile when it strikes the building.

6–18. (a) What must be the velocity of a projectile fired vertically upward to reach an altitude of 20,000 ft? (b) What velocity is required to reach the same height if the gun makes an angle of 45° with the vertical? (c) Compute the time required to reach the highest point in both trajectories. (d) How many feet would a plane traveling at 300 mi/hr move in this time?

6–19. The angle of elevation of an anti-aircraft gun is 70° and the muzzle velocity is 2700 ft/sec. For what time after firing should the fuse be set if the shell is to explode at an altitude of 5000 ft?

6–20. A projectile has an initial velocity of 80 ft/sec at an angle of 53° above the horizontal. Calculate (a) the horizontal distance from the starting point three seconds after it is fired, (b) the vertical distance above the starting point at the same time, and (c) the horizontal and vertical components of its velocity at this time.

6–21. A trench mortar fires a projectile at an angle of 53° above the horizontal with a muzzle velocity of 200 ft/sec. A tank is advancing directly toward the mortar on level ground at a speed of 10 ft/sec. What should be the distance from mortar to tank at the instant the mortar is fired in order to score a hit?

6–22. The projectile of a trench mortar has a muzzle velocity of 300 ft/sec. (a) Find the two angles of elevation to hit a target at the same level as the mortar and 300 yd distant. (b) Compute the maximum height of each trajectory, and (c) the time of flight of each. Make a neat sketch of the trajectories, approximately to scale.

6–23. A gun fires a projectile with a muzzle velocity of 1200 ft/sec. It is desired to hit a target 1000 yd distant horizontally from the gun, and at an elevation of 980 ft above it. What is the minimum angle of elevation of the gun?

6–24. A bomber, diving at an angle of 53° with the vertical, releases a bomb at an altitude of 2400 ft. The bomb is observed to strike the ground 5 sec after its release. (a) What was the velocity of the bomber, in ft/sec? (b) How far did the bomb travel horizontally during its flight? (c) What were the horizontal and vertical components of its velocity just before striking?

6–25. A 15-lb stone is dropped from a cliff in a high wind. The wind exerts a steady horizontal 10-lb force on the stone as it falls. Is the path of the stone a straight line, a parabola, or some more complicated path? Explain.

6–26. A ball is thrown, as shown in Fig. 6–13, with an initial velocity v_0 at

an angle of 37° above the horizontal, from a point 192 ft from the edge of a vertical cliff 160 ft high. The ball just misses the edge of the cliff. (a) Find the initial velocity v_0. (b) Find the distance x beyond the foot of the cliff where the ball strikes the ground.

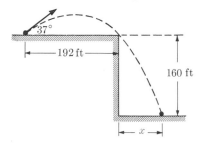

FIGURE 6–13

6–27. An arrow is shot with a velocity of 150 ft/sec at 53° above the horizontal from the edge of a cliff 96 ft high. (a) Is the motion of the arrow directed above or below the horizontal 3 sec after release? (b) What is the magnitude and direction of the arrow's velocity when it strikes the plain at the bottom of the cliff?

6–28. A man is riding on a flatcar traveling with a constant velocity of 30 ft/sec (Fig. 6–14). He wishes to throw a ball through a stationary hoop 16 ft above the height of his hands in such a manner that the ball will move horizontally as it passes through the hoop. He throws the ball with a

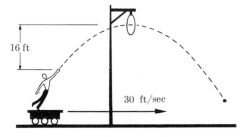

FIGURE 6–14

velocity of 40 ft/sec with respect to himself. (a) What must be the vertical component of the initial velocity of the ball? (b) How many seconds after he releases the ball will it pass through the hoop? (c) At what horizontal distance in front of the hoop must he release the ball?

6–29. At time $t = 0$ a body is moving east at 10 cm/sec. At time $t = 2$ sec it is moving 25° north of east at 14 cm/sec. Find graphically the magnitude and direction of its change in velocity and the magnitude and direction of its average acceleration.

6–30. The radius of the earth's orbit around the sun (assumed circular) is 93×10^6 miles, and the earth travels around this orbit in 365 days. (a) What is the magnitude of the orbital velocity of the earth, in mi/hr? (b) What is the radial acceleration of the earth toward the sun, in ft/sec^2?

6–31. A stone of mass 1 kgm is attached to one end of a string 1 m long, of breaking strength 500 newtons, and is whirled in a horizontal circle on a frictionless tabletop. The other end of the string is kept fixed. Find the maximum velocity the stone can attain without breaking the string.

6–32. A phonograph turntable rotates at a constant rate of 78 rev/min. It is found that a small object placed on a record will remain at rest relative to the record if its distance from the center is less than 3 in., but will slip if the distance is any greater. What is the coefficient of static friction between the object and the record?

6–33. (a) At how many revolutions per second must the apparatus of Fig. 6–15 rotate about a vertical axis in order that the cord shall make an angle of 45° with the vertical? (b) What is then the tension in the cord? (Given: $L = 20$ cm, $a = 10$ cm, $m = 200$ gm.)

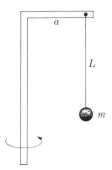

FIGURE 6–15

6–34. The 8-lb block in Fig. 6–16 is attached to a vertical rod by means of two strings. When the system rotates about the axis of the rod the strings are extended as shown in the diagram. (a) How many revolutions per minute must the system make in order that the tension in the upper cord shall be 15 lb? (b) What is then the tension in the lower cord?

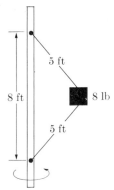

FIGURE 6–16

6–35. A curve of 600 ft radius on a level road is banked at the correct angle for a velocity of 30 mi/hr. If an automobile rounds this curve at 60 mi/hr, what is the minimum coefficient of friction between tires and road so that the automobile will not skid? Assume all forces to act at the center of gravity.

6–36. A 2400-lb automobile rounds a level curve of radius 400 ft, on an unbanked road, with a velocity of 40 mi/hr. (a) What is the minimum coefficient of friction between tires and road in order that the automobile shall not skid? (b) At what angle should the roadbed be banked for this velocity?

6–37. An aircraft in level flight is said to make a standard turn when it makes a complete circular turn in two minutes. (a) What is the banking angle in a standard turn if the velocity of the plane is 400 ft/sec? (b) What is the radius of the circle in which it turns?

6–38. The pilot of a dive bomber who has been diving at a velocity of 400 mi/hr pulls out of the dive by changing his course to a circle in a vertical plane. (a) What is the minimum radius of the circle in order that the acceleration at the lowest point shall not exceed "$7g$"? (b) How much does a 180-lb pilot apparently weigh at the lowest point of the pull-out?

6–39. A ball is held at rest in position A in Fig. 6–17 by two light cords. The

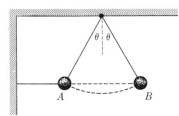

FIGURE 6–17

horizontal cord is cut, and the ball swings to position B. What is the ratio of the tension in the cord, in position B, to that in position A?

6–40. What would be the length of a day if the rate of rotation of the earth were such that $g = 0$ at the equator?

6–41. The weight of a man as determined by a spring balance at the equator is 180 lb. By how many ounces does this differ from the true force of gravitational attraction at the same point?

6–42. The questions are often asked: "What keeps an earth satellite moving in its orbit?" and "What keeps the satellite up?" (a) What are your answers to these questions? (b) Are your answers applicable to the moon?

6–43. What is the period of revolution of a man-made satellite of mass m which is orbiting the earth in a circular path of radius 8000 km? (Mass of earth $= 5.98 \times 10^{24}$ kgm.)

6–44. Suppose one wishes to establish a space platform or satellite moving in a circle in the earth's equatorial plane and at such a height above the earth's surface that it remains always above the same point. Find the height of the space platform.

6–45. It is desired to launch a satellite 400 miles above the earth in a circular orbit. If suitable rockets are used to reach this elevation, what horizontal orbital velocity must be imparted to the satellite? The radius of the earth is 3950 miles.

CHAPTER 7

WORK AND ENERGY

7–1 Introduction. The dashed line in Fig. 7–1 represents the trajectory or path of a small body of mass m moving in the xy-plane and acted on by a resultant external force **F** which may vary from point to point of the path in magnitude and direction. Let us resolve the force into a component $\mathbf{F}_s$ along the path and a component $\mathbf{F}_n$ at right angles to (or normal to) the path.

The component $\mathbf{F}_n$, at right angles to the velocity **v**, is a *centripetal* force, and its only effect is to change the *direction* of the velocity. The effect of the component $\mathbf{F}_s$ is to change the *magnitude* of the velocity, and from Newton's second law,

$$F_s = m \frac{dv}{dt}.$$

Let s be the distance of the body from some fixed point O, measured along the path. Then, as shown in Eq. (4–8), we can express the *time* rate of change of velocity, dv/dt, in terms of its *space* rate of change, dv/ds, as follows:

$$\frac{dv}{dt} = v \frac{dv}{ds}.$$

Hence

$$F_s = mv \frac{dv}{ds}, \qquad F_s\, ds = mv\, dv.$$

But

$$mv\, dv = d(\tfrac{1}{2}mv^2),$$

so

$$F_s\, ds = d(\tfrac{1}{2}mv^2). \tag{7–1}$$

The quantity $F_s\, ds$, the product of the displacement ds and the force component F_s in the direction of the displacement, is called the *work dW*

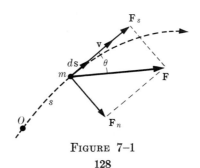

FIGURE 7–1

of the force **F** in this displacement. Since the displacement is infinitesimal, the work is infinitesimal also.

$$dW = F_s \, ds.$$

One-half the product of the mass of a body and the square of the magnitude of its velocity is called the *kinetic energy* of the body, E_k:

$$E_k = \tfrac{1}{2}mv^2.$$

The term on the right of Eq. (7–1) is therefore the change in kinetic energy of the body, and this equation may be stated: *The work of the resultant force on a body is equal to the change in kinetic energy of the body.*

Work and kinetic energy are both *scalar* quantities.

Now consider a finite displacement of the body in Fig. 7–1, in which s changes from s_1 to s_2 and v changes from v_1 to v_2. The total work W is the *algebraic* sum (or integral) of the infinitesimal works dW, and the total change in kinetic energy is the integral of the infinitesimal changes. That is,

$$W = \int dW = \int_{s_1}^{s_2} F_s \, ds,$$

$$E_{k2} - E_{k1} = \int d(E_k) = \int_{v_1}^{v_2} d(\tfrac{1}{2}mv^2) = \tfrac{1}{2}mv_2^2 - \tfrac{1}{2}mv_1^2.$$

Hence,

$$W = E_{k2} - E_{k1},$$

or

$$\int F_s \, ds = \tfrac{1}{2}mv_2^2 - \tfrac{1}{2}mv_1^2. \tag{7–2}$$

Thus in any finite motion, *the work of the resultant force on a body equals the change in its kinetic energy.* This statement is known as the *work-energy principle.*

We now discuss these concepts of work and kinetic energy in more detail.

7–2 Work. In everyday life, the word *work* is applied to any form of activity that requires the exertion of muscular or mental effort. In physics, the term is used in a very restricted sense. Work is done only when a force is exerted on a body while the body at the same time moves in such a way that the force has a component along the line of motion of its point of application. If the component of the force is in the *same direction* as the displacement the work is *positive.* If it is *opposite* to the displacement, the work is negative. If the force is at *right angles* to the displacement it has no component in the direction of the displacement and the work is *zero.*

Thus when a body is lifted, the work of the lifting force is positive; when a spring is stretched, the work of the stretching force is positive; when a gas is compressed in a cylinder, again the work of the compressing force is positive. On the other hand, the work of the gravitational force on a body being lifted is negative, since the (downward) gravitational force is opposite to the (upward) displacement. When a body slides on a fixed surface, the work of the frictional force exerted *on the body* is negative since this force is always opposite to the displacement of the body. No work is done by the frictional force acting *on the fixed surface* because there is no motion of this surface. Also, although it would be considered "hard work" to hold a heavy object stationary at arm's length, no work would be done in the technical sense because there is no motion. Even if one were to walk along a level floor while carrying the object, no work would be done since the (vertical) supporting force has no component in the direction of the (horizontal) motion. Similarly, the work of the normal force exerted on a body by a surface on which it moves is zero, as is the work of the centripetal force on a body moving in a circle.

In the engineering system, the unit of force is the pound and the unit of distance is the foot. The unit of work in this system is therefore *one foot-pound* (ft·lb). (The order of terms is interchanged to distinguish this unit from the unit of torque, the pound·foot.) *One foot-pound* may be defined as *the work done when a constant force of one pound is exerted on a body which moves a distance of one foot in the same direction as the force.*

In the mks system, where forces are expressed in newtons and distances in meters, the unit of work is the *newton·meter* (n·m). The reader can supply the definition of a newton·meter from the definition above of a foot·pound. In the cgs system the unit of work is the *dyne·centimeter* (dyne·cm). One dyne·centimeter is called *one erg;* one newton·meter is called *one joule.* There is no corresponding single term for one foot·pound.

Since 1 meter = 100 cm and 1 newton = 10^5 dynes, it follows that 1 newton·meter = 10^7 dynes·centimeters, or

$$1 \text{ joule} = 10^7 \text{ ergs.}$$

Also, from the relations between the newton and pound, and the meter and foot,

$$1 \text{ joule} = 0.7376 \text{ foot·pound,}$$

$$1 \text{ foot·pound} = 1.356 \text{ joules.}$$

The expression for the work of a force can be written in several ways. If θ is the angle between the force vector $\mathbf{F}$ and the infinitesimal displacement vector $d\mathbf{s}$, the component F_s is equal to $F \cos \theta$, so

$$W = \int dW = \int_{s_1}^{s_2} F_s \, ds = \int_{s_1}^{s_2} F \cos \theta \, ds.$$

The definition of work suggests that we introduce a new vector operation. In Chapter 1 we discussed the *addition* and *subtraction* of vectors. In computing the work of a force, we multiply the magnitude of the vector $d\mathbf{s}$ by the magnitude of the component of another vector $\mathbf{F}$ in the direction of $d\mathbf{s}$. The product is called the *scalar product* or the *dot product* of the vectors. Thus if $\mathbf{A}$ and $\mathbf{B}$ are any two vectors, their scalar or dot product is defined as the product of the magnitudes of the vectors and the cosine of the angle θ between their positive directions:

$$\mathbf{A} \cdot \mathbf{B} = AB \cos \theta.$$

Evidently, $\mathbf{A} \cdot \mathbf{B} = \mathbf{B} \cdot \mathbf{A}$. In this new notation, the work of a force can be written as

$$W = \int dW = \int_{s_1}^{s_2} \mathbf{F} \cdot d\mathbf{s}.$$

In the special case in which the force $\mathbf{F}$ is constant in magnitude and makes a constant angle with the direction of motion of its point of application, $F \cos \theta$ is constant and may be taken outside the integral sign. If in addition we measure displacements from the starting point of the motion and let $s_1 = 0$ and $s_2 = s$, the work of the force is

$$W = \int_0^s F \cos \theta \, ds = F \cos \theta \int_0^s ds = (F \cos \theta)s.$$

If the force is constant and in the same direction as the motion or opposite to the motion, the angle θ equals zero or $180°$, $\cos \theta = \pm 1$, and

$$W = \pm Fs.$$

That is, in this *very special case only*, we can say, "Work equals force times distance." It is important to remember, however, that the *general* definition of the work of a force is

$$\boxed{W = \int_{s_1}^{s_2} \mathbf{F} \cdot d\mathbf{s} = \int_{s_1}^{s_2} F \cos \theta \, ds.} \qquad (7\text{–}3)$$

In the preceding discussion, the force $\mathbf{F}$ has represented the *resultant* of *all* external forces on a body. We often wish to consider the works of the separate forces that may act on a body. Each of these may be computed from the general definition of work in Eq. (7–3). Then, since work is a scalar quantity, the total work is the algebraic sum of the individual works. Note, however, that only the *total* work is equal to the change in kinetic energy of the body.

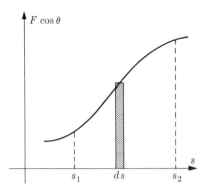

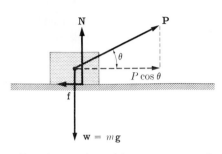

Fig. 7–2. Work is equal to the area under the $F \cos \theta$ vs. s curve.

Fig. 7–3. An object on a rough horizontal surface moving to the right under the action of a force **P** inclined at an angle θ.

The work of a force can be represented graphically by plotting the component $F \cos \theta$ as a function of s, as in Fig. 7–2. The work in a displacement from s_1 to s_2 is then equal to the *area* under the curve between vertical lines drawn at s_1 and s_2.

EXAMPLE 1. Figure 7–3 shows a box being dragged along a horizontal surface by a constant force **P** making a constant angle θ with the direction of motion. The other forces on the box are its weight $\mathbf{w} = m\mathbf{g}$, the normal upward force **N** exerted by the surface, and the friction force **f**. What is the work of each force when the box moves a distance s along the surface to the right?

The component of **P** in the direction of motion is $P \cos \theta$. The work of the force **P** is therefore

$$W_P = (P \cos \theta) \cdot s.$$

The forces **w** and **N** are both at right angles to the displacement. Hence

$$W_w = 0, \qquad W_N = 0.$$

The friction force **f** is opposite to the displacement, so the work of the friction force is

$$W_f = -fs.$$

Since work is a scalar quantity, the total work W of all forces on the body is the algebraic (not the vector) sum of the individual works.

$$
\begin{aligned}
W &= W_P + W_w + W_N + W_f \\
  &= (P \cos \theta) \cdot s + 0 + 0 - f \cdot s \\
  &= (P \cos \theta - f)s.
\end{aligned}
$$

But $(P \cos \theta - f)$ is the *resultant* force on the body. Hence *the total work of all forces is equal to the work of the resultant force.*

Suppose that $w = 100$ lb, $P = 50$ lb, $f = 15$ lb, $\theta = 37°$, and $s = 20$ ft. Then

$$W_P = (P \cos \theta) \cdot s = 50 \times 0.8 \times 20 = 800 \text{ ft·lb},$$

$$W_f = -fs = -15 \times 20 = -300 \text{ ft·lb},$$

$$W = W_P + W_w + W_N + W_f$$

$$= 800 \text{ ft·lb} + 0 + 0 - 300 \text{ ft·lb}$$

$$= 500 \text{ ft·lb}.$$

As a check, the total work may be expressed as

$$W = (P \cos \theta - f) \cdot s$$

$$= (40 \text{ lb} - 15 \text{ lb}) \times 20 \text{ ft}$$

$$= 500 \text{ ft·lb}.$$

EXAMPLE 2. A small object of weight **w** hangs from a string of length l, as shown in Fig. 7–4. A *variable* horizontal force **P**, which starts at zero and gradually increases, is used to pull the object very slowly (so that equilibrium exists at all times) until the string makes an angle θ with the vertical. Calculate the work of the force **P**.

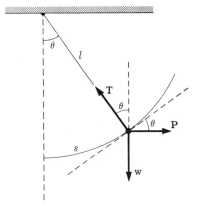

FIG. 7–4. A variable horizontal force **P** acts on a small object while the displacement varies from zero to s.

Since the object is in equilibrium, the sum of the horizontal forces equals zero, whence

$$P = T \sin \theta.$$

Equating the sum of the vertical forces to zero, we find

$$w = T \cos \theta.$$

Dividing these two equations, we get

$$P = w \tan \theta.$$

The point of application of **P** swings through the arc s. Since $s = l\theta$, $ds = l\,d\theta$ and

$$W = \int \mathbf{P} \cdot d\mathbf{s} = \int P \cos\theta\,ds$$

$$= \int_0^\theta w \tan\theta \cos\theta\, l\,d\theta$$

$$= wl \int_0^\theta \sin\theta\,d\theta$$

$$= wl(1 - \cos\theta). \tag{7-4}$$

A graph of $P \cos\theta$ ($=w \sin\theta$) plotted against s ($=l\theta$) is shown in Fig. 7–5. The work during any displacement is represented by the area under this curve. The shaded area is the work when the point of application of **P** moves from a position where $s_1 = 0.3l$ to a place where $s_2 = 0.9l$.

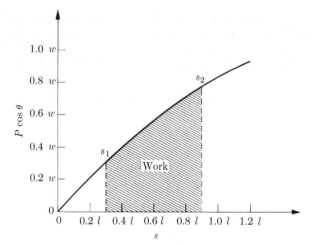

FIG. 7–5. The work of a force **P** when its point of application moves from $s_1 = 0.3l$ to $s_2 = 0.9l$ is the shaded area under the curve of $P \cos\theta$, plotted against s.

7–3 Kinetic energy. Kinetic energy, like work, is a scalar quantity. The kinetic energy of a moving body depends only on the *magnitude* of its velocity (or its speed) and not on the direction in which it is moving or on the particular process by which it was set in motion.

It follows from the work-energy principle that the *change* in kinetic energy of a body depends only on the work $W = \int \mathbf{F} \cdot d\mathbf{s}$ and not on the individual values of F and s. That is, the force could have been large and the displacement small, or the reverse might have been true. If the mass m and the speeds v_1 and v_2 are known, the *work* of the resultant force can be found without any knowledge of the force and the displacement.

If the work W is *positive*, the final kinetic energy is greater than the initial kinetic energy and the kinetic energy *increases*. If the work is *negative*, the kinetic energy *decreases*. In the special case in which the work is *zero*, the kinetic energy remains *constant*.

In computing the kinetic energy of a body, consistent units must be used for m and v. In the cgs system, m must be expressed in grams and v in cm/sec. In the mks system, m must be in kilograms and v in m/sec. In the engineering system, m must be in slugs and v in ft/sec. The corresponding units of kinetic energy are $1\ \text{gm·cm}^2/\text{sec}^2$, $1\ \text{kgm·m}^2/\text{sec}^2$, and $1\ \text{slug·ft}^2/\text{sec}^2$. However, the unit of kinetic energy in any system is equal to the unit of work in that system, and kinetic energy is customarily expressed in ergs, joules, or foot·pounds. That is,

$$ 1\ \text{gm}\ \frac{\text{cm}^2}{\text{sec}^2} = 1\ \frac{\text{dyne}}{\text{cm/sec}^2}\ \frac{\text{cm}^2}{\text{sec}^2} = 1\ \text{dyne·cm} = 1\ \text{erg}. $$

In the same way,

$$ 1\ \text{kgm}\ \frac{\text{m}^2}{\text{sec}^2} = 1\ \text{joule}, \qquad 1\ \text{slug}\ \frac{\text{ft}^2}{\text{sec}^2} = 1\ \text{ft·lb}. $$

EXAMPLE. Refer again to the body in Fig. 7–3 and the numerical values given at the end of Example 1. The total work of the external forces was shown to be 500 ft·lb. Hence the kinetic energy of the body increases by 500 ft·lb. To verify this, suppose the initial speed v_1 is 4 ft/sec. The initial kinetic energy is

$$ E_{k1} = \frac{1}{2}\ mv_1^2 = \frac{1}{2}\ \frac{100}{32}\ \text{slugs} \times 16\ \frac{\text{ft}^2}{\text{sec}^2} = 25\ \text{ft·lb}. $$

To find the final kinetic energy we must first find the acceleration:

$$ a = \frac{F}{m} = \frac{40\ \text{lb} - 15\ \text{lb}}{(100/32)\ \text{slugs}} = 8\ \frac{\text{ft}}{\text{sec}^2}. $$

Then

$$ v_2^2 = v_1^2 + 2as = 16\ \frac{\text{ft}^2}{\text{sec}^2} + 2 \times 8\ \frac{\text{ft}}{\text{sec}^2} \times 20\ \text{ft} = 336\ \frac{\text{ft}^2}{\text{sec}^2}, $$

and

$$ E_{k2} = \frac{1}{2}\ \frac{100}{32}\ \text{slugs} \times 336\ \frac{\text{ft}^2}{\text{sec}^2} = 525\ \text{ft·lb}. $$

The increase in kinetic energy is therefore 500 ft·lb.

7–4 Gravitational potential energy. Suppose a body of mass m (and of weight $\mathbf{w} = m\mathbf{g}$) moves vertically, as in Fig. 7–6(a), from a point where its center of gravity is at a height y_1 above an arbitrarily chosen plane (the *reference level*) to a point at a height y_2. For the present, we shall consider only displacements near the earth's surface, so that variations of gravitational force with distance from the earth's center can be neglected. The downward gravitational force on the body is then constant and equal to $m\mathbf{g}$. Let $\mathbf{P}$ represent the resultant of all other forces acting on the body, and let W' be the work of these forces. The direction of the gravitational force $m\mathbf{g}$ is opposite to the upward displacement, and the work of this force is

$$W_{\text{grav}} = -mg(y_2 - y_1) = -(mgy_2 - mgy_1). \qquad (7\text{–}5)$$

(The reader should convince himself that the work of the gravitational force is given by $-mg(y_2 - y_1)$ whether the body moves up or down.)

Now suppose that the body starts at the same elevation y_1 but is moved up to the elevation y_2 along some arbitrary path, as in Fig. 7–6(b). Part (c) of the figure is an enlarged view of a small portion of the path.

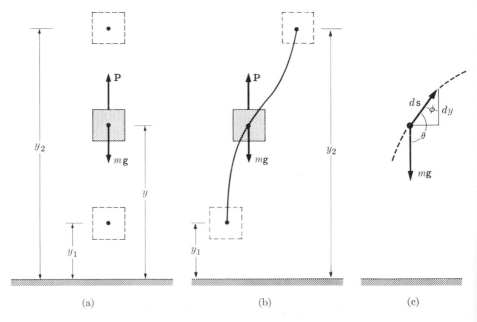

(a)   (b)   (c)

FIG. 7–6. Work of the gravitational force $m\mathbf{g}$ during the motion of an object from one point in a gravitational field to another.

The work of the gravitational force in the displacement ds along the path is

$$dW = mg \cos \theta \, ds.$$

Let ϕ represent the angle between ds and its vertical component dy. Then $dy = ds \cos \phi$, and since $\phi = 180° - \theta$,

$$\cos \phi = -\cos \theta.$$

Hence

$$dW = -mg \cos \phi \, ds = -mg \, dy,$$

and the work of the gravitational force, when y increases from y_1 to y_2, is

$$W_{\text{grav}} = -mg(y_2 - y_1). \tag{7–6}$$

The work of the gravitational force therefore depends only on the initial and final elevations and not on the path. If these points are at the *same* elevation the work is zero.

Since the *total* work equals the change in kinetic energy,

$$W' + W_{\text{grav}} = \Delta E_k,$$

$$W' - (mgy_2 - mgy_1) = (\tfrac{1}{2}mv_2^2 - \tfrac{1}{2}mv_1^2).$$

The quantities $\tfrac{1}{2}mv_2^2$ and $\tfrac{1}{2}mv_1^2$ depend only on the final and initial *speeds;* the quantities mgy_2 and mgy_1 depend only on the final and initial *elevations.* Let us therefore rearrange this equation, transferring the quantities mgy_2 and mgy_1 from the "work" side of the equation to the "energy" side.

$$W' = (\tfrac{1}{2}mv_2^2 - \tfrac{1}{2}mv_1^2) + (mgy_2 - mgy_1). \tag{7–7}$$

The left side of Eq. (7–7) contains only the work of the force **P**. The terms on the right depend only on the final and initial states of the body (its speed and elevation) and not specifically on the way in which it moved. The quantity mgy, the product of the weight mg of the body and the height y of its center of gravity above the reference level, is called its *gravitational potential energy,* E_p.

$$E_p \text{ (gravitational)} = mgy. \tag{7–8}$$

The first expression in parentheses on the right of Eq. (7–7) is the change in kinetic energy of the body, and the second is the change in its gravitational potential energy.

Equation (7-7) can also be written

$$W' = (\tfrac{1}{2}mv_2^2 + mgy_2) - (\tfrac{1}{2}mv_1^2 + mgy_1). \qquad (7\text{-}9)$$

The sum of the kinetic and potential energy of the body is called its *total mechanical energy*. The first expression in parentheses on the right of Eq. (7-9) is the final value of the total mechanical energy, and the second is the initial value. Hence, *the work of all forces acting on the body,* **with the exception of the gravitational force,** *equals the change in the total mechanical energy of the body.* If the work W' is positive, the mechanical energy increases. If W' is negative, the energy decreases.

In the special case in which the *only* force on the body is the gravitational force, the work W' is zero. Equation (7-9) can then be written

$$\tfrac{1}{2}mv_2^2 + mgy_2 = \tfrac{1}{2}mv_1^2 + mgy_1.$$

Under these conditions, then, the *total mechanical energy remains constant,* or is *conserved.* This is a special case of the *principle of the conservation of mechanical energy.*

EXAMPLE 1. A man holds a ball of weight $w = \tfrac{1}{4}$ lb at rest in his hand. He then throws the ball vertically upward. In this process, his hand moves up 2 ft and the ball leaves his hand with an upward velocity of 48 ft/sec. Discuss the motion of the ball from the work-energy standpoint.

First consider the throwing process. Take the reference level at the initial position of the ball. Then $E_{k1} = 0$, $E_{p1} = 0$. Take point 2 at the point where the ball leaves the thrower's hand. Then

$$E_{p2} = mgy_2 = \tfrac{1}{4}\text{ lb} \times 2\text{ ft} = 0.5\text{ ft·lb},$$

$$E_{k2} = \tfrac{1}{2}mv_2^2 = \tfrac{1}{2} \times (\tfrac{1}{4}/32)\text{ slug} \times (48\text{ ft/sec})^2 = 9\text{ ft·lb}.$$

Let P represent the upward force exerted on the ball by the man in the throwing process. The work W' is then the work of this force, and is equal to the sum of the changes in kinetic and potential energy of the ball.

The kinetic energy of the ball increases by 9 ft·lb and its potential energy by 0.5 ft·lb. The work W' of the upward force P is therefore 9.5 ft·lb. *If the force P is constant,* the work of this force is given by

$$W' = P(y_2 - y_1),$$

and the force P is then

$$P = \frac{W'}{y_2 - y_1} = \frac{9.5\text{ ft·lb}}{2\text{ ft}} = 4.75\text{ lb}.$$

However, the *work* of the force P is 9.5 ft·lb whether or not the force is constant.

Now consider the flight of the ball after it leaves the thrower's hand. In the absence of air resistance, the only force on the ball is then its weight mg. Hence the total mechanical energy of the ball remains constant. The calculations will be simplified if we take a new reference level at the point where the ball leaves the thrower's hand. Calling this point 1, we have

$$E_{k1} = 9 \text{ ft·lb}, \qquad E_{p1} = 0,$$

$$E_k + E_p = 9 \text{ ft·lb},$$

and the total mechanical energy at any point of the path equals 9 ft·lb.

Suppose we wish to find the speed of the ball at a height of 20 ft above the reference level. Its potential energy at this elevation is 5 ft·lb. (Why?) Its kinetic energy is therefore 4 ft·lb. To find its speed, we have

$$\tfrac{1}{2}mv^2 = E_k, \qquad v = \pm\sqrt{2E_k/m} = \pm \, 32 \, \frac{\text{ft}}{\text{sec}}.$$

The significance of the $\pm$ sign is that the ball passes this point *twice*, once on the way up and again on the way down. Its *potential* energy at this point is the same whether it is moving up or down. Hence its kinetic energy is the same and its *speed* is the same. The algebraic sign of the speed is $+$ when the ball is moving up and $-$ when it is moving down.

Next, let us find the height of the highest point reached. At this point, $v = 0$ and $E_k = 0$. Therefore $E_p = 9$ ft·lb, and the ball rises to a height of 36 ft above the point where it leaves the thrower's hand.

Finally, suppose we were asked to find the speed at a point 40 ft above the reference level. The potential energy at this point would be 10 ft·lb. But the total energy is only 9 ft·lb, so the ball never reaches a height of 40 ft.

EXAMPLE 2. A body slides down a curved track which is one quadrant of a circle of radius R, as in Fig. 7–7. If it starts from rest and there is no friction, find its speed at the bottom of the track.

The equations of motion with constant acceleration cannot be used, since the acceleration decreases during the motion. (The slope angle of the track becomes

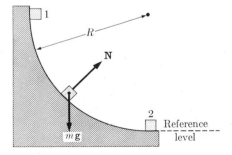

FIG. 7–7. An object sliding down a frictionless curved track.

smaller and smaller as the body descends.) However, if there is no friction, the only force on the body in addition to its weight is the normal force $\mathbf{N}$ exerted on it by the track. The work of this force is zero, so $W' = 0$ and mechanical energy is conserved. Take point 1 at the starting point and point 2 at the bottom of the track. Take the reference level at point 2. Then $y_1 = R$, $y_2 = 0$, and

$$E_{k2} + E_{p2} = E_{k1} + E_{p1},$$

$$\tfrac{1}{2}mv_2^2 + 0 = 0 + mgR,$$

$$v_2 = \pm\sqrt{2gR}.$$

The speed is therefore the same as if the body had fallen *vertically* through a height R. (What is now the significance of the $\pm$ sign?)

As a numerical example, let $R = 1$ m. Then

$$v = \pm\sqrt{2 \times 9.8(\text{m/sec}^2) \times 1\text{ m}} = \pm 4.43\ \frac{\text{m}}{\text{sec}}.$$

EXAMPLE 3. Suppose a body of mass 0.5 kgm slides down a track of radius $R = 1$ m, like that in Fig. 7–7, but its speed at the bottom is only 3 m/sec. What was the work of the frictional force acting on the body?

In this case, $W' = W_f$, and

$$W_f = (\tfrac{1}{2}mv_2^2 - \tfrac{1}{2}mv_1^2) + (mgy_2 - mgy_1)$$

$$= \left(\frac{1}{2} \times 0.5\text{ kgm} \times 9\ \frac{\text{m}^2}{\text{sec}^2} - 0\right) + \left(0 - 0.5\text{ kgm} \times 9.8\ \frac{\text{m}}{\text{sec}^2} \times 1\text{ m}\right)$$

$$= 2.25\text{ j} - 4.9\text{ j} = -2.65\text{ j}.$$

The frictional work was therefore -2.65 j, and the total mechanical energy *decreased* by 2.65 joules. The mechanical energy of a body is *not* conserved when friction forces act on it.

EXAMPLE 4. In the absence of air resistance, the only force on a projectile is its weight, and the mechanical energy of the projectile remains constant. Figure 7–8 shows two trajectories of a projectile with the same initial velocity (and hence the same total energy) but with different angles of departure. At all points at the same elevation the potential energy is the same; hence the kinetic energy is the same and the speed is the same.

EXAMPLE 5. A small object of weight $\mathbf{w}$ hangs from a string of length l, as shown in Fig. 7–9. A *variable* horizontal force $\mathbf{P}$, which starts at zero and gradually increases, is used to pull the object very slowly until the string makes an angle θ with the vertical. Calculate the work of the force $\mathbf{P}$.

The sum of the works W' of all the forces other than the gravitational force must equal the change of kinetic energy plus the change of gravitational potential energy. Hence

$$W' = W_P + W_T = \Delta E_k + \Delta E_p.$$

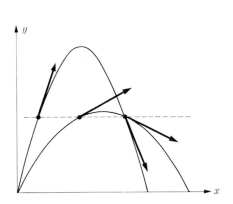

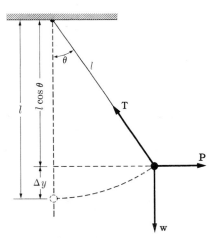

FIG. 7–8. For the same initial velocity, the speed is the same at all points
at the same elevation.

FIG. 7–9. $\Delta y = l(1 - \cos \theta)$.

Since $\mathbf{T}$ is perpendicular to the path of its point of application, $W_T = 0$; and since the body was pulled very slowly at all times, the change of kinetic energy is also zero. Hence

$$W_P = \Delta E_p = w \, \Delta y,$$

where Δy is the distance that the object has been raised. From Fig. 7–9, Δy is seen to be $l(1 - \cos \theta)$. Therefore

$$W_P = wl(1 - \cos \theta).$$

———————

The reader is referred to the example at the end of Section 7–2 where this same problem was solved by performing the integration in the equation $W_P = \int P \cos \theta \, ds$. The two answers, of course, are identical, but how much more simply the energy principle leads to the final result!

It has been assumed thus far in this section that the changes in elevation were small enough so that the gravitational force on a body could be considered constant. We now consider the more general case. The force mg in Fig. 7–6 is the force of gravitational attraction exerted on the body by the earth, and the general expression for the magnitude of this force is

$$G \frac{m m_E}{r^2},$$

where m_E is the mass of the earth and r is the distance from the earth's center. When r increases from r_1 to r_2, the work of the gravitational force is

$$W_{\text{grav}} = -Gmm_E \int_{r_1}^{r_2} \frac{dr}{r^2}$$
$$= \left(\frac{Gmm_E}{r_2} - \frac{Gmm_E}{r_1} \right).$$

Setting the total work equal to the change in kinetic energy and re-arranging terms, we get, instead of Eq. (7–9),

$$W' = \left(\tfrac{1}{2}mv_2^2 - \frac{Gmm_E}{r_2} \right) - \left(\tfrac{1}{2}mv_1^2 - \frac{Gmm_E}{r_1} \right).$$

The quantity $[-G(mm_E/r)]$ is therefore the general expression for the gravitational potential energy of a body attracted by the earth.

$$E_p \text{ (gravitational)} = -G\,\frac{mm_E}{r}. \qquad\qquad (7\text{–}10)$$

The total mechanical energy of the body, the sum of its kinetic energy and potential energy, is

$$E = E_k + E_p = \tfrac{1}{2}mv^2 - G\,\frac{mm_E}{r}.$$

If the only force on the body is the gravitational force, then $W' = 0$ and the total mechanical energy remains constant, or is conserved.

EXAMPLE. Use the principle of conservation of mechanical energy to find the velocity with which a body must be projected vertically upward, in the absence of air resistance, to rise to a height above the earth's surface equal to the earth's radius, R.

Let v_1 be the initial velocity. Then $r_1 = R$, $r_2 = 2R$, $v_2 = 0$, and

$$\tfrac{1}{2}mv_1^2 - G\,\frac{mm_E}{R} = 0 - G\,\frac{mm_E}{2R},$$

or

$$v_1^2 = \frac{Gm_E}{R}.$$

This agrees with the result obtained in Example 11 at the end of Section 5–8.

It may be puzzling at first sight that the general expression for gravitational potential energy should contain a minus sign. The reason for this lies in the choice of a reference state or reference level in which the potential energy is considered zero. If we set $E_p = 0$ in Eq. (7–10) and solve for r, we get

$$r = \infty.$$

That is, *the gravitational potential energy of a body is now considered to be zero when the body is at an infinite distance from the earth.* Since the potential energy *decreases* as the body approaches the earth, it must be *negative* at any finite distance from the earth. The *change* in potential energy of a body as it moves from one point to another is the same, whatever the choice of reference level, and it is only changes in potential energy that are significant.

Finally, we show that the general expression for the change in potential energy reduces to Eq. (7–6) for small changes in elevation near the earth's surface. Thus the increase in potential energy of a body of mass m, when its distance from the earth's center increases from r_1 to r_2, is

$$E_{p2} - E_{p1} = -G\frac{mm_E}{r_2} - \left(-G\frac{mm_E}{r_1}\right)$$

$$= Gmm_E\left(\frac{1}{r_1} - \frac{1}{r_2}\right)$$

$$= Gmm_E\left(\frac{r_2 - r_1}{r_1 r_2}\right).$$

If points 1 and 2 are at elevations y_1 and y_2 above the earth's surface, then

$$r_2 - r_1 = y_2 - y_1.$$

Furthermore, if y_1 and y_2 are both small compared with the earth's radius R, the product $r_1 r_2$ is very nearly equal to R^2. The preceding equation then reduces to

$$E_{p2} - E_{p1} = \frac{Gmm_E}{R^2}(y_2 - y_1).$$

But

$$\frac{Gm_E}{R^2} = g,$$

where g is the acceleration of gravity at the earth's surface, so

$$E_{p2} - E_{p1} = mg(y_2 - y_1),$$

which is the same as the expression derived earlier when variations in g were neglected.

7–5 Elastic potential energy. Figure 7–10 shows a body of mass m on a level surface. One end of a spring is attached to the body and the other end of the spring is fixed. Take the origin of coordinates at the position of the body when the spring is unstretched (Fig. 7–10a). An outside agent exerts a force $\mathbf{P}$ of sufficient magnitude to cause the spring to stretch. As soon as the slightest extension takes place, a force $\mathbf{F}$ is created within the spring which acts in a direction opposite that of increasing x, and therefore opposite that of $\mathbf{P}$. The force $\mathbf{F}$ is called an *elastic force*. If the force $\mathbf{P}$ is reduced or made zero, the elastic force will restore the spring to its original unstretched condition. It may therefore be referred to as a *restoring force*. The subject of elastic restoring forces was first studied by Robert Hooke, in 1678, who observed that, if the extension x of a spring was not so great as to permanently distort the spring, *the elastic force is directly proportional to the extension*, or

$$F = kx, \tag{7-11}$$

a relation known as *Hooke's law*. The constant of proportionality k is called the *spring constant* or the *stiffness coefficient*.

The work of the elastic force W_{el}, during any process in which the spring is extended from a value x_1 to x_2, is

$$W_{\mathrm{el}} = \int \mathbf{F} \cdot d\mathbf{s} = \int_{x_1}^{x_2} F \cos \theta \, dx.$$

Since the direction of F is opposite the direction of dx, $\cos \theta = -1$, whence

$$W_{\mathrm{el}} = -\int_{x_1}^{x_2} kx \, dx,$$

or

$$W_{\mathrm{el}} = -(\tfrac{1}{2}kx_2^2 - \tfrac{1}{2}kx_1^2).$$

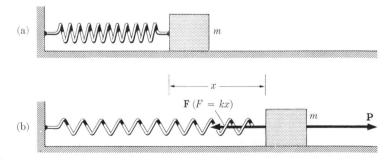

Fig. 7–10. When an applied force $\mathbf{P}$ produces an extension x of a spring, an elastic restoring force $\mathbf{F}$ is created within the spring, where $F = kx$.

Let W' stand for the work of the applied force **P**. Setting the total work equal to the change in kinetic energy of the body, we have

$$W' + W_{el} = \Delta E_k,$$

$$W' - (\tfrac{1}{2}kx_2^2 - \tfrac{1}{2}kx_1^2) = (\tfrac{1}{2}mv_2^2 - \tfrac{1}{2}mv_1^2).$$

The quantities $\tfrac{1}{2}kx_2^2$ and $\tfrac{1}{2}kx_1^2$ depend only on the initial and final positions of the body and not specifically on the way in which it moved. Let us therefore transfer them from the "work" side of the equation to the "energy" side. Then

$$W' = (\tfrac{1}{2}mv_2^2 - \tfrac{1}{2}mv_1^2) + (\tfrac{1}{2}kx_2^2 - \tfrac{1}{2}kx_1^2). \qquad (7\text{–}12)$$

The quantity $\tfrac{1}{2}kx^2$, one-half the product of the force constant and the square of the coordinate of the body, is called the *elastic potential energy* of the body, E_p. (The symbol E_p is used for any form of potential energy.)

$$E_p \text{ (elastic)} = \tfrac{1}{2}kx^2. \qquad (7\text{–}13)$$

Hence the work W' of the force **P** equals the sum of the change in the kinetic energy of the body and the change in its elastic potential energy. Equation (7–12) can also be written

$$W' = (\tfrac{1}{2}mv_2^2 + \tfrac{1}{2}kx_2^2) - (\tfrac{1}{2}mv_1^2 + \tfrac{1}{2}kx_1^2).$$

The sum of the kinetic and potential energies of the body is its total mechanical energy and *the work of all forces acting on the body*, **with the exception of the elastic force**, *equals the change in the total mechanical energy of the body.*

If the work W' is positive, the mechanical energy increases. If W' is negative, it decreases. In the special case in which W' is zero, the mechanical energy remains constant or is *conserved.*

EXAMPLE 1. Let the force constant k of the spring in Fig. 7–10 be 24 newtons/meter, and let the mass of the body be 4 kgm. The body is initially at rest, and the spring is initially unstretched. Suppose that a constant force **P** of 10 newtons is exerted on the body, and that there is no friction. What will be the speed of the body when it has moved 0.50 meters?

The equations of motion with constant acceleration cannot be used, since the resultant force on the body varies as the spring is stretched. However, the speed can be found from energy considerations.

$$W' = \Delta E_k + \Delta E_p,$$

$$10 \text{ n} \times 0.5 \text{ m} = (\tfrac{1}{2} \times 4 \text{ kgm} \times v_2^2 - 0) + \left(\frac{1}{2} \times 24 \, \frac{\text{n}}{\text{m}} \times 0.25 \text{ m}^2 - 0\right),$$

$$v_2 = 1 \, \frac{\text{m}}{\text{sec}} \cdot$$

EXAMPLE 2. Suppose the force **P** ceases to act when the body has moved 0.50 m. How much farther will the body move before coming to rest?

The elastic force is now the only force, and mechanical energy is conserved. The kinetic energy is $\tfrac{1}{2}mv^2 = 2$ joules, and the potential energy is $\tfrac{1}{2}kx^2 = 3$ joules. The total energy is therefore 5 joules (equal to the work of the force **P**). When the body comes to rest, its kinetic energy is zero and its potential energy is therefore 5 joules. Hence

$$\tfrac{1}{2}kx_{\text{max}}^2 = 5 \text{ j}, \qquad x_{\text{max}} = 0.707 \text{ m}.$$

7–6 Conservative and dissipative forces. When an object is moved from any position above a zero reference level to any other position, the work of the gravitational force is found to be independent of the path and equal to the difference between the final and the initial values of a function called the gravitational potential energy. If the gravitational force alone acts on the object, the total mechanical energy (the sum of the kinetic and gravitational potential energies) is constant or conserved, and therefore the gravitational force is called a *conservative force*. Thus, if the object is ascending, the work of the gravitational force is accomplished at the expense of the kinetic energy. If, however, the object is descending, the work of the gravitational force serves to increase the kinetic energy, or, in other words, this work is *completely recovered*. Complete recoverability is an important aspect of the work of a conservative force.

When an object attached to a spring is moved from one value of the spring extension to any other value, the work of the elastic force is also independent of the path and equal to the difference between the final and initial values of a function called the elastic potential energy. If the elastic force alone acts on the object, the sum of the kinetic and elastic potential energies is conserved, and therefore the elastic force is also a conservative force. If the object moves so as to increase the extension of the spring, the work of the elastic force is accomplished at the expense of the kinetic energy. If, however, the extension is decreasing, the work of the elastic force serves to increase the kinetic energy so that this work is completely recovered also.

To summarize, the work of a conservative force has the following properties:

(1) It is independent of the path.

(2) It is equal to the difference between the final and initial values of an energy function.

(3) It is completely recoverable.

Contrast a conservative force with a friction force exerted on a moving object by a fixed surface. The work of the friction force *depends* on the path; the longer the path, the greater the work. There is *no* function the difference in two values of which equals the work of the friction force. When we slide an object on a rough fixed surface back to its original position, the friction force reverses, and instead of recovering the work done in the first displacement we must again do work on the return trip. In other words, frictional work is *not* completely recoverable. When the friction force acts alone, the total mechanical energy is *not* conserved. The friction force is therefore called a *nonconservative* or a *dissipative* force. *The mechanical energy of a body is conserved only when no dissipative forces act on it.*

We find that when friction forces act on a moving body, *heat* is always developed. The more general principle of conservation of energy includes this heat as another form of energy, along with kinetic and potential energy, and when it is included the *total* energy of any system remains constant. We shall study this general conservation principle more fully in a later chapter.

EXAMPLE. Example 3 in Section 7–4 illustrates the motion of a body acted on by a dissipative, friction force. The initial mechanical energy of the body is its initial potential energy of 4.9 j. Its final mechanical energy is its final kinetic energy of 2.25 j. The frictional work W_f is —2.65 j. A quantity of heat equivalent to 2.65 j is developed as the body slides down the track. The sum of this heat and the final mechanical energy equals the initial mechanical energy, and the total energy of the system is conserved.

7–7 Internal work and internal potential energy. Thus far in this chapter we have considered only the work of the *external* forces on a *single* body. The work of these forces is called *external work*, W^e. When two (or more) bodies exert forces on each other and we wish to consider them as a single system, the forces between the bodies become *internal* forces. The work of these forces is called *internal work*, W^i.

Suppose that both external and internal forces act on the bodies of a system. The total work W of all forces, external and internal, is the sum of the works W^e and W^i and is equal to the change in the total kinetic energy of the system.

$$W = W^e + W^i = \Delta E_k.$$

EXAMPLE 1. A man stands at rest on frictionless roller skates on a level surface, facing a brick wall. He sets himself in motion (backward) by pushing against the wall. Discuss the problem from the work-energy standpoint.

The *external* forces on the man are his weight, the upward force exerted by the surface, and the horizontal force exerted by the wall. (The latter is the reaction to the force with which the man pushes against the wall.) No work is done by the first two forces because they are at right angles to the motion. No work is done by the third force because there is no motion of its point of application. The external work is therefore zero and the internal work (of the man's muscular forces) equals the change in his kinetic energy.

If any of the *external* forces on the bodies of a system are conservative (gravitational or elastic), the work of these forces can be transferred to the energy side of the work-energy equation and called the change in *external potential energy.* In many instances, the *internal* forces depend only on the distances between pairs of bodies. The internal work then depends only on the initial and final distances between the bodies, and not on the particular way in which they moved. The work of these internal forces can then also be transferred to the energy side of the work-energy equation and called the change in *internal potential energy of the system.* Internal potential energy is a property of the system as a whole and cannot be assigned to any specific body.

Let W' represent the works of all external and internal forces that have *not* been transferred to the energy side of the work-energy equation and called changes in external and internal potential energy. Let E_p^e and E_p^i represent the external and internal potential energies. The work-energy equation then takes the form

$$W' = \Delta E_k + \Delta E_p^e + \Delta E_p^i, \qquad (7\text{--}14)$$

where the total mechanical energy now includes the kinetic energy of the system and both its external and internal potential energy. If the work W' is zero, the total mechanical energy is conserved.

EXAMPLE 2. Consider a system consisting of two bodies in "outer space," very far from all other matter. No external forces act on the system, no external work is done when the bodies move, and the system has no external potential energy. A gravitational force of attraction acts between the bodies, which depends only on the distance between them. We can therefore say that the system has an internal potential energy. Suppose the bodies start from rest and accelerate toward each other. The total kinetic energy of the system increases and its internal potential energy decreases. The sum of its kinetic energy and internal potential energy remains constant.

Energy considerations *alone* do not suffice to tell us how much kinetic energy is gained by each body separately. This can be determined, however, from *momentum* considerations, as will be explained in the next chapter.

EXAMPLE 3. In Section 7–5 we computed the elastic potential energy of a body acted on by a force exerted by a spring. This force was an *external* force acting on the body, and the elastic potential energy $\frac{1}{2}kx^2$ should properly be called the *external* elastic potential energy *of the body*.

Let us now consider the spring itself. The spring is a *system*, composed of an enormous number of molecules which exert internal forces on one another. When the spring is stretched, the distances between its molecules change. The intermolecular forces depend only on the distances between pairs of molecules, so that a stretched spring has an internal elastic potential energy. To calculate this, suppose the spring is slowly stretched from its no-load length by equal and opposite forces applied at its ends. The work of these forces was shown to equal $\frac{1}{2}kx^2$, where x is the elongation of the spring above its no-load length. Let us retain this work on the left side of the work-energy equation so that it becomes the work W' in Eq. (7–14). There is no change in the kinetic energy of the spring and no change in its external potential energy. If we call the internal potential energy zero when $x = 0$, the *change* in internal potential energy in the stretching process equals the final potential energy E_p^i. Then

$$W' = \Delta E_p^i = E_p^i, \qquad E_p^i = \tfrac{1}{2}kx^2.$$

Hence the *internal elastic potential energy of a stretched spring* is equal to $\frac{1}{2}kx^2$. Note that the internal potential energy can be calculated without any detailed information regarding the intermolecular forces.

EXAMPLE 4. A block of mass m, initially at rest, is dropped from a height h onto a spring whose force constant is k. Find the maximum distance y that the spring will be compressed. See Fig. 7–11.

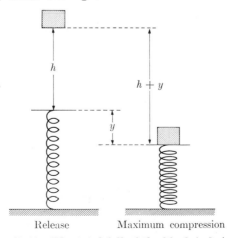

FIG. 7–11. The total fall of the block is $h + y$.

This is a process for which the principle of the conservation of mechanical energy holds. At the moment of release, the kinetic energy is zero. At the moment when maximum compression occurs, there is also no kinetic energy. Hence, the loss of gravitational potential energy of the block equals the gain of elastic potential energy of the spring. As shown in Fig. 7–11, the total fall of the block is $h + y$, whence

$$mg(h + y) = \tfrac{1}{2}ky^2,$$

or

$$y^2 - \frac{2mg}{k} y - \frac{2mgh}{k} = 0.$$

Therefore

$$y = \frac{1}{2}\left[\frac{2mg}{k} \pm \sqrt{(2mg/k)^2 + (8mgh/k)}\,\right].$$

7–8 Power. The time element is not involved in the definition of work. The same amount of work is done in raising a given weight through a given height whether the work is done in one second, or one hour, or one year. In many instances, however, it is necessary to consider the *rate* at which work is done as well as the total amount of work accomplished. The rate at which work is done by a working agent is called the *power* developed by that agent.

If a quantity of work W is done in a time interval t, the average power $\overline{P}$ is defined as

$$\text{Average power} = \frac{\text{work done}}{\text{time interval}}, \qquad \overline{P} = \frac{W}{t}.$$

If the rate of doing work is not uniform, the power at any instant is the ratio of the work done to the time interval, when both are extremely small.

$$\boxed{\text{Instantaneous power } P = \frac{dW}{dt}.} \qquad (7\text{–}15)$$

In the engineering system, where work is expressed in foot·pounds and time in seconds, the unit of power is 1 foot·pound per second. Since this unit is inconveniently small, a larger unit called the *horsepower* (hp) is in common use. 1 hp = 550 ft·lb/sec = 33,000 ft·lb/min. That is, a 1-hp motor running at full load is doing 33,000 ft·lb of work every minute it runs.

The mks unit of power is 1 joule per second, which is called one *watt*. This is also an inconveniently small unit, and power is more commonly expressed in *kilowatts* (1 kw = 1000 watts = 1000 joules/sec) or *megawatts* (1 megawatt = 1000 kw = 1,000,000 watts).

The cgs power unit is 1 erg per second. No single term is assigned to this unit.

A common misconception is that there is something inherently *electrical* about a watt or a kilowatt. This is not the case. It is true that electrical power is usually expressed in watts or kilowatts, but the power consumption of an incandescent lamp could equally well be expressed in horse-power, or an automobile engine rated in kilowatts.

From the relations between the newton, pound, meter, and foot, it is easy to show that 1 hp = 746 watts = 0.746 kw, or about $\frac{3}{4}$ of a kilowatt. This is a useful figure to remember.

Having defined two units of power, the horsepower and the kilowatt, we may use these in turn to define two new units of work, the *horsepower·hour* and the *kilowatt·hour* (kwh).

One horsepower·hour is the work done in one hour by an agent working at the constant rate of one horsepower.

Since such an agent does 33,000 ft·lb of work each minute, the work done in one hour is 60 × 33,000 = 1,980,000 ft·lb.

$$1 \text{ horsepower·hour} = 1.98 \times 10^6 \text{ foot·pounds.}$$

One kilowatt·hour is the work done in one hour by an agent working at the constant rate of one kilowatt.

Since such an agent does 1000 joules of work each second, the work done in one hour is 3600 × 1000 = 3,600,000 joules.

$$1 \text{ kilowatt·hour} = 3.6 \times 10^6 \text{ joules.}$$

Note carefully that the horsepower hour and the kilowatt·hour are units of *work*, not power.

One aspect of work or energy which may be pointed out here is that although it is an abstract physical quantity, it nevertheless has a monetary value. A pound of force or a foot per second of velocity are not things which are bought and sold as such, but a foot·pound or a kilowatt·hour of energy are quantities offered for sale at a definite market rate. In the form of electrical energy, a kilowatt·hour can be purchased at a price varying from a few tenths of a cent to a few cents, depending on the locality and the quantity purchased. In the form of heat, 778 ft·lb (one Btu) costs about a thousandth of a cent.

7–9 Power and velocity. Suppose a force **F** is exerted on a body while the body undergoes a displacement $d\mathbf{x}$ in the direction of the force. The work is

$$dW = F \, dx,$$

and the power developed is

$$P = \frac{dW}{dt} = F\frac{dx}{dt}.$$

But dx/dt is the velocity v. Hence

$$\boxed{P = Fv,} \tag{7–16}$$

where P and v are instantaneous values. If **F** is not in the direction of **v**, we have

$$\boxed{P = \mathbf{F} \cdot \mathbf{v}.} \tag{7–17}$$

EXAMPLE. The engine of a jet aircraft develops a thrust of 3000 lb. What horsepower does it develop at a velocity of 600 mi/hr = 880 ft/sec?

$$P = Fv = 3000 \text{ lb} \times 880\,\frac{\text{ft}}{\text{sec}} = 2{,}640{,}000\,\frac{\text{ft·lb}}{\text{sec}}$$

$$= \frac{2.64 \times 10^6 \text{ ft·lb/sec}}{550 \text{ (ft·lb/sec)/hp}} = 4800 \text{ hp.}$$

PROBLEMS

7–1. The locomotive of a freight train exerts a constant force of 6 tons on the train while drawing it at 50 mi/hr on a level track. How many foot·pounds of work are done in a distance of 1 mi?

7–2. An 80-lb block is pushed a distance of 20 ft along a level floor at constant speed by a force at an angle of 30° below the horizontal. The coefficient of friction between block and floor is 0.25. How many foot·pounds of work are done?

7–3. A horse is towing a canal boat, the towrope making an angle of 10° with the towpath. If the tension in the rope is 100 lb, how many foot·pounds of work are done while moving 100 ft along the towpath?

7–4. A block is pushed 4 ft along a fixed horizontal surface by a horizontal force of 10 lb. The opposing force of friction is 2 lb. (a) How much work is done by the 10-lb force? (b) What is the work of the friction force?

7–5. (a) Compute the kinetic energy of an 1800-lb automobile traveling at 30 mi/hr. (b) How many times as great is the kinetic energy if the velocity is doubled?

7–6. Compute the kinetic energy, in ergs and in joules, of a 2-gm rifle bullet traveling at 500 m/sec.

7–7. An electron strikes the screen of a cathode-ray tube with a velocity of 10^9 cm/sec. Compute its kinetic energy in ergs. The mass of an electron is 9×10^{-28} gm.

7–8. What is the potential energy of a 1600-lb elevator at the top of the Empire State building, 1248 ft above street level? Assume the potential energy at street level to be zero.

7–9. What is the increase in potential energy of a 1-kgm body when lifted from the floor to a table 1 meter high?

7–10. A meter stick whose mass is 300 gm is pivoted at one end as in Fig. 7–12 and displaced through an angle of 60°. What is the increase in its potential energy?

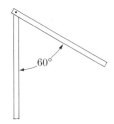

FIGURE 7–12

7–11. The force in pounds required to stretch a certain spring a distance of x ft beyond its unstretched length is given by $F = 10x$. (a) What force will stretch the spring 6 in.? 1 ft? 2 ft? (b) How much work is required to stretch the spring 6 in.? 1 ft? 2 ft?

7–12. The scale of a certain spring balance reads from zero to 400 lb and is 8 in. long. (a) What is the potential energy of the spring when it is stretched 8 in.? 4 in.? (b) When a 50-lb weight hangs from the spring?

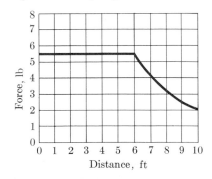

FIGURE 7–13

7–13. A body moves a distance of 10 ft under the action of a force which has the constant value of 5.5 lb for the first 6 ft and then decreases to a value of 2 lb, as shown by the graph in Fig. 7–13. (a) How much work is done in the first 6 ft of the motion? (b) How much work is done in the last 4 ft?

7–14. A block weighing 16 lb is pushed 20 ft along a horizontal frictionless surface by a horizontal force of 8 lb. The block starts from rest. (a) How much work is done? What becomes of this work? (b) Check your answer by computing the acceleration of the block, its final velocity, and its kinetic energy.

7–15. In the preceding problem, suppose the block had an initial velocity of 10 ft/sec, other quantities remaining the same. (a) How much work is done? (b) Check by computing the final velocity and the increase in kinetic energy.

7–16. A 16-lb block is lifted vertically at a constant velocity of 10 ft/sec through a height of 20 ft. (a) How great a force is required? (b) How much work is done? What becomes of this work?

7–17. A 25-lb block is pushed 100 ft up the sloping surface of a plane inclined at an angle of 37° to the horizontal by a constant force F of 32.5 lb acting parallel to the plane. The coefficient of friction between the block and plane is 0.25. (a) What is the work of the force F? (b) Compute the increase in kinetic energy of the block. (c) Compute the increase in potential energy of the block. (d) Compute the work done against friction. What becomes of this work? (e) What can you say about the sum of (b), (c), and (d)?

7–18. A man weighing 150 lb sits on a platform suspended from a movable

FIGURE 7–14

pulley and raises himself by a rope passing over a fixed pulley (Fig. 7–14). Assuming no friction losses, find (a) the force he must exert, (b) the increase in his energy when he raises himself 2 ft. Answer part (b) by calculating his increase in potential energy, and also by computing the product of the force on the rope and the length of rope passing through his hands.

7–19. A barrel weighing 250 lb is suspended by a rope 30 ft long. (a) What horizontal force is necessary to hold the barrel sideways 5 ft from the vertical? (b) How much work is done in moving it to this position?

7–20. The system in Fig. 7–15 is released from rest with the 24-lb block 8 ft above the floor. Use the principle of conservation of energy to find the

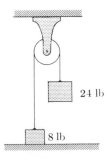

FIGURE 7–15

velocity with which the block strikes the floor. Neglect friction and inertia of the pulley.

7-21. The spring of a spring gun has a force constant of 3 lb per inch. It is compressed 2 inches and a ball weighing 0.02 lb is placed in the barrel against the compressed spring. (a) Compute the maximum velocity with which the ball leaves the gun when released. (b) Determine the maximum velocity if a resisting force of 2.25 lb acts on the ball.

7-22. A block weighing 2 lb is forced against a horizontal spring of negligible mass, compressing the spring an amount $x_1 = 6$ inches. When released, the block moves on a horizontal table top a distance $x_2 = 2$ ft before coming to rest. The spring constant k is 8 lb/ft (Fig. 7-16). What is the coefficient of friction, μ, between the block and the table?

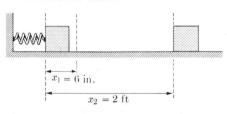

$$x_1 = 6 \text{ in.}$$

$$x_2 = 2 \text{ ft}$$

FIGURE 7-16

7-23. A 2-kgm block is dropped from a height of 40 cm onto a spring whose force constant k is 1960 newtons/meter. Find the maximum distance the spring will be compressed.

7-24. A 16-lb projectile is fired from a gun with a muzzle velocity of 800 ft/sec at an angle of departure of 45°. The angle is then increased to 90° and a similar projectile is fired with the same muzzle velocity. (a) Find the maximum heights attained by the projectiles. (b) Show that the total energy at the top of the trajectory

is the same in the two cases. (c) Using the energy principle, find the height attained by a similar projectile if fired at an angle of 30°.

7-25. A block weighing 2 lb is released from rest at point A on a track which is one quadrant of a circle of radius 4 ft (Fig. 7-17). It slides down the track and reaches point B with a velocity of 12 ft/sec. From point B it slides on a level surface a distance of 9 ft to point C, where it comes to rest. (a) What was the coefficient of sliding friction on the horizontal surface? (b) How much work was done against friction as the body slid down the circular arc from A to B?

FIGURE 7-17

7-26. A small sphere of mass m is fastened to a weightless string of length 2 ft to form a pendulum. The pendulum is swinging so as to make a maximum angle of 60° with the vertical. (a) What is the velocity of the sphere when it passes through the vertical position? (b) What is the instantaneous acceleration when the pendulum is at its maximum deflection?

7-27. A ball is tied to a cord and set in rotation in a vertical circle. Prove that the tension in the cord at the lowest point exceeds that at the highest point by six times the weight of the ball.

7-28. A small body of mass m slides without friction around the loop-the-loop apparatus shown in Fig. 7-18. It starts from rest at point A at a height $3R$ above the bottom of the loop.

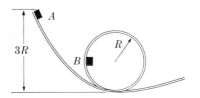

FIGURE 7–18

When it reaches point B at the end of a horizontal diameter of the loop, compute (a) its radial acceleration, and (b) its tangential acceleration.

7–29. A meter stick, pivoted about a horizontal axis through its center, has a body of mass 2 kgm attached to one end and a body of mass 1 kgm attached to the other. The mass of the meter stick can be neglected. The system is released from rest with the stick horizontal. What is the velocity of each body as the stick swings through a vertical position?

7–30. A variable force **P** is maintained tangent to a frictionless cylindrical surface of radius a, as shown in Fig. 7–19. By slowly varying this force, a block of weight w is moved and the spring to which it is attached is stretched from position 1 to position 2. The spring, of force constant k, is unstretched in position 1. Calculate the work of the force **P**, (a) by integration, (b) by use of the energy principle.

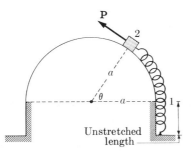

FIGURE 7–19

7–31. What average horsepower is developed by a 180-lb man when climbing in 10 sec a flight of stairs which rises 20 ft vertically? Express this power in watts and kilowatts.

7–32. The hammer of a pile driver weighs 1000 lb and must be lifted a vertical distance of 6 ft in 3 sec. What horsepower engine is required?

7–33. A ski tow is to be operated on a 37° slope 800 ft long. The rope is to move at 8 mi/hr and power must be provided for 80 riders at one time, each weighing, on an average, 150 lb. Estimate the horsepower required to operate the tow.

7–34. (a) If energy costs 5 cents per kwh, how much is one horsepower·hour worth? (b) How many ft·lb can be purchased for one cent?

7–35. Compute the monetary value of the kinetic energy of the projectile of a 14-in. naval gun, at the rate of 2 cents per kwh. The projectile weighs 1400 lb and its muzzle velocity is 2800 ft/sec.

7–36. At 5 cents per kwh, what does it cost to operate a 10-hp motor for 8 hr?

7–37. The engine of an automobile develops 20 hp when the automobile is traveling at 30 mi/hr. (a) What is the resisting force in pounds? (b) If the resisting force is proportional to the velocity, what horsepower will drive the car at 15 mi/hr? At 60 mi/hr?

7–38. The engine of a motorboat delivers 40 hp to the propeller while the boat is making 20 mi/hr. What would be the tension in the towline if the boat were being towed at the same speed?

7–39. A man whose mass is 70 kgm walks up to the third floor of a building. This is a vertical height of 12 meters above the street level. (a) How many joules of work has he done? (b) By how much has he increased his potential energy? (c) If he climbs the stairs in 20 sec, what was his rate of working in horsepower?

7-40. A pump is required to lift 200 gallons of water per minute from a well 20 ft deep and eject it with a speed of 30 ft/sec. (a) How much work is done per minute in lifting the water? (b) How much in giving it kinetic energy? (c) What horsepower engine is needed?

7-41. A 4800-lb elevator starts from rest and is pulled upward with a constant acceleration of 10 ft/sec². (a) Find the tension in the supporting cable. (b) What is the velocity of the elevator after it has risen 45 ft? (c) Find the kinetic energy of the elevator 3 sec after it starts. (d) How much is its potential energy increased in the first 3 sec? (e) What horsepower is required when the elevator is traveling 22 ft/sec?

7-42. An automobile weighing 2000 lb has a speed of 100 ft/sec on a horizontal road when the engine is developing 50 hp. What is its speed, with the same horsepower, if the road rises 1 ft in 20 ft? Assume all friction forces to be constant.

7-43. (a) If 20 hp are required to drive a 2400-lb automobile at 30 mi/hr on a level road, what is the retarding force of friction, windage, etc.? (b) What power is necessary to drive the car at 30 mi/hr up a 10% grade, i.e., one rising 10 ft vertically in 100 ft horizontally? (c) What power is necessary to drive the car at 30 mi/hr *down* a 2% grade? (d) Down what grade would the car coast at 30 mi/hr?

7-44. A string is attached to the upper side of a 350-gm block of wood placed on an inclined plane. When the string is parallel to the plane, a tension of 260,000 dynes in the string will pull the block up the plane at a constant speed. When the tension in the string is 150,000 dynes, the block moves down the plane with constant speed. What is the force of friction between the block and the plane?

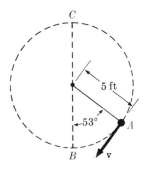

FIGURE 7-20

7-45. A small 4-lb mass is fastened to a weightless string 5 ft long to form a pendulum, as shown in Fig. 7-20. The mass is pulled aside until the string makes an angle of 53° with the vertical. (a) With what tangential speed v must the body be started from point A so that it will reach C, the highest point, with a tangential speed of 10 ft/sec? (b) With what speed does it pass through the lowest point B when started from A with the speed v? (c) What is the tension in the cord as the body passes through B? (d) If the body is started from A with the tangential speed v of part (a) in the direction opposite to that shown, with what speed will it then arrive at C?

7-46. An earth satellite of mass m revolves in a circle at a height above the earth equal to twice the earth's radius, $2R$. In terms of m, R, the gravitational constant G, and the mass of the earth m_E, what are the values of (a) the kinetic energy of the satellite, (b) its gravitational potential energy, and (c) its total mechanical energy?

7–47. A body is attracted toward the origin with a force given by

$$F = -6x^3,$$

where F is in lb and x in ft. (a) What force is required to hold the body at point a, 1 ft from the origin? (b) At point b, 2 ft from the origin? (c) How much work must be done to move the body from point a to point b?

7–48. The force exerted by a gas in a cylinder on a piston whose area is A is given by

$$F = pA,$$

where p is the force per unit area, or *pressure*. During an infinitesimal displacement dx of the piston the work dW is

$$f\,dx = pA\,dx = p\,dV,$$

where dV is the accompanying infinitesimal change of volume of the gas. If the gas expands a finite amount from volume V_1 to volume V_2, the total work done is equal to

$$W = \int_{V_1}^{V_2} p\,dV.$$

(a) During an expansion of a gas at constant temperature (isothermal) the pressure depends on the volume according to the relation

$$p = \frac{nRT}{V},$$

where n and R are constants and T is the constant temperature. Calculate the work done by the gas in expanding isothermally from volume V_1 to volume V_2.

(b) During an expansion of a gas at constant entropy (adiabatic) the pressure depends on the volume according to the relation

$$p = \frac{K}{V^\gamma},$$

where K and γ are constants. Calculate the work done by the gas in expanding adiabatically from V_1 to V_2.

CHAPTER 8

IMPULSE AND MOMENTUM

8–1 Impulse and momentum. In the preceding chapter it was shown how the concepts of work and energy are developed from Newton's laws of motion. We shall next see how two similar concepts, those of *impulse* and *momentum*, also arise from these laws.

Let us again consider a small body of mass m moving in the xy-plane, as in Fig. 8–1, and acted on by a resultant force $\mathbf{F}$ that may vary in magnitude and direction. Newton's second law states that at every instant

$$\mathbf{F} = m\,\frac{d\mathbf{v}}{dt}, \quad \text{or} \quad \mathbf{F}\,dt = m\,d\mathbf{v}.$$

Since $m\,d\mathbf{v} = d(m\mathbf{v})$, we can write the preceding equation as

$$\mathbf{F}\,dt = d(m\mathbf{v}), \tag{8–1}$$

in which form it is analogous to Eq. (7–1).

The quantity $\mathbf{F}\,dt$, the product of the force $\mathbf{F}$ and the infinitesimal time interval dt, is called the *impulse* of the force in this time interval.

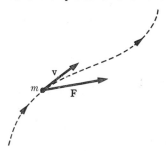

FIGURE 8–1

The unit of impulse, in any system, equals the product of the units of force and time in that system. Thus in the cgs system the unit is 1 dyne·sec, in the mks system it is 1 n·sec, and in the engineering system it is 1 lb·sec.

The concept of impulse finds its chief application in connection with forces of short duration, such as those arising in collisions or explosions. Such forces are called *impulsive forces*.

The product of the mass of a body and its velocity is called its *linear momentum*. (We refer to this product as *linear* momentum to distinguish

159

it from a similar quantity called angular momentum which will be discussed later. When there is no opportunity for confusion, we shall speak of the linear momentum simply as the momentum.)

The unit of momentum is the product of the unit of mass and the unit of velocity. Thus in the cgs system it is 1 gm·cm/sec, in the mks system it is 1 kgm·m/sec, and in the engineering system it is 1 slug·ft/sec. Since 1 slug = 1 lb·sec^2/ft, etc., it follows that the unit of momentum in any system equals the unit of impulse in that system.

Note that in contrast to work and energy, which are scalars, *impulse* and *momentum* are *vector quantities*.

In terms of impulse and momentum, Eq. (8–1) can be stated:

The impulse of the resultant force on a body is equal in magnitude and direction to the change in momentum of the body.

Like every vector equation, Eq. (8–1) is equivalent (for forces and velocities in the xy-plane) to *two* scalar equations:

$$F_x \, dt = d(mv_x), \qquad F_y \, dt = d(mv_y). \tag{8–2}$$

Now consider a finite time interval from t_1 to t_2, during which the vector velocity of the body changes from $\mathbf{v}_1$ to $\mathbf{v}_2$. Then

$$\int_{t_1}^{t_2} F_x \, dt = \int_{mv_{x1}}^{mv_{x2}} d(mv_x) = mv_{x2} - mv_{x1},$$

with a similar equation for the y-component. Both of these equations can be combined in the single vector equation

$$\int_{t_1}^{t_2} \mathbf{F} \, dt = m\mathbf{v}_2 - m\mathbf{v}_1, \tag{8–3}$$

which implies a corresponding scalar equation for each component. Hence we can say: *The vector impulse of the resultant force on a body, in any time interval, is equal in magnitude and direction to the **vector change** in momentum of the body.* This is known as the *impulse-momentum* principle, and it is analogous to the work-energy principle.

For the special case of a force that is constant in magnitude and direction, we can take $\mathbf{F}$ outside the integral sign in Eq. (8–4), and if we let $t_1 = 0$ and $t_2 = t$, we have

$$\mathbf{F}t = m\mathbf{v}_2 - m\mathbf{v}_1. \tag{8–4}$$

That is, the impulse of a *constant* force equals the product of the force and the time interval during which it acts. The *vector change* in momentum produced by such a force, $(m\mathbf{v}_2 - m\mathbf{v}_1)$, is in the same direction as the force.

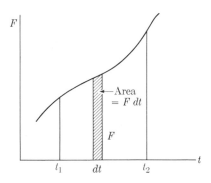

FIGURE 8–2

If the force and the velocities $\mathbf{v}_1$ and $\mathbf{v}_2$ are in the same direction, Eq. (8–4) reduces to the scalar equation

$$Ft = mv_2 - mv_1.$$

The impulse of any force component, or any force whose direction is constant, can be represented graphically by plotting the force vertically and the time horizontally, as in Fig. 8–2. The *area* under the curve, between vertical lines at t_1 and t_2, is equal to the impulse of the force in this time interval.

If the impulse of a force is *positive*, the momentum of the body on which it acts *increases* algebraically. If the impulse is *negative*, the momentum *decreases*. If the impulse is *zero*, there is no change in momentum.

EXAMPLE 1. Consider the changes in momentum produced by the following forces: (a) A body moving on the x-axis is acted on for 2 sec by a constant force of 10 n toward the right. (b) The body is acted on for 2 sec by a constant force of 10 n toward the right and then for 2 sec by a constant force of 20 n toward the left. (c) The body is acted on for 2 sec by a constant force of 10 n toward the right and then for 1 sec by a constant force of 20 n toward the left.

The three forces are shown graphically in Fig. 8–3.

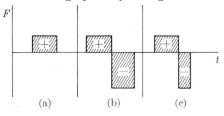

(a)   (b)   (c)

FIGURE 8–3

(a) The impulse of the force is $+20$ n $\times$ 2 sec $= +20$ n·sec. Hence the momentum of *any* body on which the force acts increases by 20 kgm·m/sec. This change is the same whatever the mass of the body and whatever the magnitude and direction of its initial velocity.

Suppose the mass of the body is 2 kgm and that it is initially at rest. Its *final* momentum then equals its *change* in momentum and its final *velocity* is 10 m/sec toward the right. (The reader should verify by computing the acceleration.)

Had the body been initially moving toward the right at 5 m/sec, its initial momentum would have been 10 kgm·m/sec, its final momentum 30 kgm·m/sec, and its final velocity 15 m/sec toward the right.

Had the body been moving initially toward the *left* at 5 m/sec, its initial momentum would have been -10 kgm·m/sec, its final momentum $+10$ kgm·m/sec, and its final velocity 5 m/sec toward the right. That is, the constant force of 10 n toward the right would first have brought the body to rest and then given it a velocity in the direction opposite to its initial velocity.

(b) The impulse of this force is $(+10$ n $\times$ 2 sec $-$ 20 n $\times$ 2 sec$) = -20$ n·sec. The momentum of *any* body on which it acts is decreased by 20 kgm·m/sec. The reader should examine various possibilities, as in the preceding example.

(c) The impulse of this force is $(+10$ n $\times$ 2 sec -20 n $\times$ 1 sec$) = 0$. Hence the momentum of any body on which it acts is not changed. Of course, the momentum of the body is *increased* during the first two seconds but it is *decreased* by an equal amount in the next second. As an exercise, describe the motion of a body of mass 2 kgm, moving initially to the left at 5 m/sec, and acted on by this force. It will help to construct a graph of velocity *vs.* time.

EXAMPLE 2. A ball of mass 100 gm is thrown against a brick wall. When it strikes the wall it is moving horizontally to the left at 3000 cm/sec, and it rebounds horizontally to the right at 2000 cm/sec. Find the impulse of the force exerted on the ball by the wall.

The initial momentum of the ball is 100 gm $\times$ -3000 cm/sec $= -30 \times 10^4$ gm·cm/sec. The final momentum is $+20 \times 10^4$ gm·cm/sec. The *change* in momentum is

$$mv_2 - mv_1 = 20 \times 10^4 \text{ gm·cm/sec} - (-30 \times 10^4 \text{ gm·cm/sec})$$

$$= 50 \times 10^4 \text{ gm·cm/sec}.$$

Hence the impulse of the force exerted on the ball was 50×10^4 dyne·sec. Since the impulse is *positive*, the force is toward the right.

Note that the *force* exerted on the ball cannot be found without further information regarding the collision. The general nature of the force-time graph is shown by one of the curves in Fig. 8–4. The force is zero before impact, rises to a maximum, and decreases to zero when the ball leaves the wall. If the ball is relatively rigid, like a baseball, the time of collision is small and the maximum force is large, as in curve (a). If the ball is more yielding, like a tennis ball, the collision time is larger and the maximum force is less, as in curve (b). In any event, the *area* under the force-time graph must equal 50×10^4 dyne·sec.

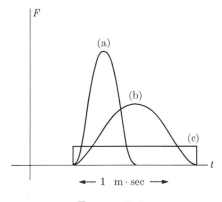

FIGURE 8–4

For an idealized case in which the force is constant and the collision time is 1 msec (10^{-3} sec), as represented by the horizontal straight line, the force is 50×10^7 dynes.

Explain why one "eases off" when catching a fast ball.

8–2 Conservation of linear momentum. Whenever there is a force of interaction between two bodies, the momentum of each body is changed as a result of the force exerted on it by the other. (The force may be gravitational, electric, magnetic, or of any other origin.) Furthermore, since by Newton's *third* law the force on one body is always equal in magnitude and opposite in direction to that on the other, the impulses of the forces are equal in magnitude and opposite in direction. It follows that *the vector change in momentum of either body,* in any time interval, *is equal in magnitude and opposite in direction to the vector change in momentum of the other.* The *net change in momentum of the* **system** (the two bodies together) *is therefore zero.*

The pair of action-reaction forces are *internal* forces of the system and we conclude that *the total momentum of a system of bodies cannot be changed by internal forces between the bodies.* Hence if the *only* forces acting on the bodies of a system are *internal* forces (that is, if there are no *external* forces), the total momentum of the system remains constant in magnitude and direction. This is the *principle of conservation of linear momentum: When no resultant* **external** *force acts on a system, the total momentum of the system remains constant in magnitude and direction.*

The principle of conservation of momentum is one of the most fundamental and important principles of mechanics. Note that it is more general than the principle of conservation of mechanical energy; mechanical energy is conserved only when the internal forces are conservative. The principle of conservation of momentum holds whatever the nature of the internal forces.

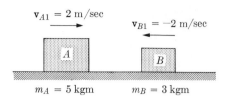

FIGURE 8–5

EXAMPLE 1. Figure 8–5 shows a body A of mass m_A moving toward the right on a level frictionless surface with a velocity $\mathbf{v}_{A1}$. It collides with a second body B of mass m_B, moving toward the left with a velocity $\mathbf{v}_{B1}$. Since there is no friction and the resultant vertical force on the system is zero, the only forces on the bodies are the internal action-reaction forces which they exert on each other in the collision process, and the momentum of the system remains constant in magnitude and direction.

Let $\mathbf{v}_{A2}$ and $\mathbf{v}_{B2}$ represent the velocities of A and B after the collision. Then

$$m_A\mathbf{v}_{A1} + m_B\mathbf{v}_{B1} = m_A\mathbf{v}_{A2} + m_B\mathbf{v}_{B2}. \qquad (8\text{–}5)$$

EXAMPLE 2. In Fig. 8–6, body A of mass m_A is initially moving toward the right with a velocity $\mathbf{v}_{A1}$. It collides with body B, initially at rest, after which the bodies separate and move with velocities $\mathbf{v}_{A2}$ and $\mathbf{v}_{B2}$. No forces act on the system except those in the collision process.

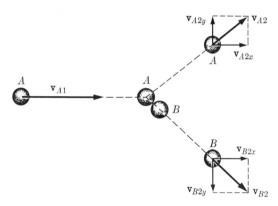

FIGURE 8–6

This example illustrates the *vector* nature of momentum, that is, the x- and y-components of momentum are *both* conserved. Let us take the x-axis in the direction of $\mathbf{v}_{A1}$. The initial x-momentum is $m_A v_{A1}$ and the initial y-momentum is zero.

The final x-momentum of the system is

$$m_A v_{A2x} + m_B v_{B2x}$$

and the final y-momentum is

$$m_A v_{A2y} - m_B v_{B2y}.$$

Therefore

$$m_A v_{A2x} + m_B v_{B2x} = m_A v_{A1}, \qquad (8\text{--}6)$$

$$m_A v_{A2y} - m_B v_{B2y} = 0. \qquad (8\text{--}7)$$

8-3 Elastic and inelastic collisions. Suppose we are given the masses and initial velocities of two colliding bodies, and we wish to compute their velocities after the collision. If the collision is "head-on," as in Fig. 8-5, Eq. (8-5) provides one equation for the velocities $\mathbf{v}_{A2}$ and $\mathbf{v}_{B2}$. If it is of the type shown in Fig. 8-6, Eqs. (8-6) and (8-7) provide two equations for the four velocity components v_{A2x}, v_{A2y}, v_{B2x}, and v_{B2y}. Hence momentum considerations *alone* do not suffice to completely determine the final velocities; we must have more information about the collision process.

If the forces of interaction between the bodies are *conservative*, the total kinetic energy is the same before and after the collision and the collision is said to be *completely elastic*. Such a collision is closely approximated if one end of an inverted U-shaped steel spring is attached to one of the bodies, as in Fig. 8-7. When the bodies collide the spring is momentarily compressed and some of the original kinetic energy is momentarily converted to elastic potential energy. The spring then expands and when the bodies separate this potential energy is reconverted to kinetic energy.

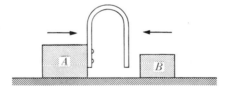

FIGURE 8-7

At the opposite extreme from a completely elastic collision is one in which the colliding bodies stick together and move as a unit after the collision. Such a collision is called a *completely inelastic* collision, and will result if the bodies in Fig. 8-5 are provided with a coupling mechanism like that between two freight cars, or if the bodies in Fig. 8-7 are locked together at the instant when their velocities become equal and the spring is fully compressed.

For the special case of a completely inelastic collision between two bodies A and B, we have, from the definition of such a collision,

$$\mathbf{v}_{A2} = \mathbf{v}_{B2} = \mathbf{v}_2.$$

When this is combined with the principle of conservation of momentum, we obtain

$$m_A \mathbf{v}_{A1} + m_B \mathbf{v}_{B1} = (m_A + m_B)\mathbf{v}_2, \qquad (8\text{–}8)$$

and the final velocity can be computed if the initial velocities, and the masses, are known.

The kinetic energy of the system before collision is

$$E_{k1} = \tfrac{1}{2} m_A v_{A1}^2 + \tfrac{1}{2} m_B v_{B1}^2.$$

The final kinetic energy is

$$E_{k2} = \tfrac{1}{2}(m_A + m_B)v_2^2.$$

For the special case in which body B is initially at rest, $v_{B1} = 0$ and the ratio of the final to the initial kinetic energy is

$$\frac{E_{k2}}{E_{k1}} = \frac{(m_A + m_B)v_2^2}{m_A v_{A1}^2}.$$

Inserting the expression for v_2 from Eq. (8–8), we find that this reduces to

$$\frac{E_{k2}}{E_{k1}} = \frac{m_A}{m_A + m_B}.$$

The right side is necessarily less than unity, so *the total kinetic energy decreases* in the collision.

EXAMPLE 1. Suppose the collision in Fig. 8–5 is completely inelastic and that the masses and velocities have the values shown. The velocity after the collision is then

$$v_2 = \frac{m_A v_{A1} + m_B v_{B1}}{m_A + m_B} = 0.5 \text{ m/sec.}$$

Since v_2 is positive, the system moves to the right after the collision.

The kinetic energy of body A before the collision is

$$\tfrac{1}{2} m_A v_{A1}^2 = 10 \text{ joules,}$$

and that of body B is

$$\tfrac{1}{2} m_B v_{B1}^2 = 6 \text{ joules.}$$

The total kinetic energy before collision is therefore 16 joules.

Note that the kinetic energy of body B is positive, although its velocity v_{B1} and its momentum $m v_{B1}$ are both negative.

The kinetic energy after the collision is

$$\tfrac{1}{2}(m_A + m_B)v_2^2 = 1 \text{ joule.}$$

Hence, far from remaining constant, the final kinetic energy is only 1/16 of the original, and 15/16 is "lost" in the collision. If the bodies couple together like two freight cars, most of this energy is converted to heat through the production of elastic waves which are eventually absorbed.

If there is a spring between the bodies, as in Fig. 8–7, and the bodies are locked together when their velocities become equal, the energy is trapped as potential energy in the compressed spring. If all these forms of energy are taken into account, the *total* energy of the system is conserved although its *kinetic* energy is not. However, *momentum is always conserved* in a collision, whether or not the collision is elastic.

Example 2. The *ballistic pendulum* is a device for measuring the velocity of a bullet. The bullet is allowed to make a completely inelastic collision with a body of much greater mass. The momentum of the system immediately after the collision equals the original momentum of the bullet, but since the velocity is very much smaller it can be determined more easily. Although the ballistic pendulum has now been superseded by other devices, it is still an important laboratory experiment for illustrating the concepts of momentum and energy.

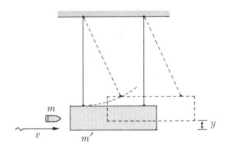

Fig. 8–8. The ballistic pendulum.

In Fig. 8–8, the pendulum, consisting perhaps of a large wooden block of mass m', hangs vertically by two cords. A bullet of mass m, traveling with a velocity v, strikes the pendulum and remains embedded in it. If the collision time is very small compared with the time of swing of the pendulum, the supporting cords remain practically vertical during this time. Hence no external horizontal forces act on the system during the collision, and the horizontal momentum is conserved. Then if V represents the velocity of bullet and block immediately after the collision,

$$mv = (m + m')V.$$

The kinetic energy of the system, immediately after the collision, is

$$E_k = \tfrac{1}{2}(m + m')V^2.$$

The pendulum now swings to the right and upward until its kinetic energy is converted to gravitational potential energy. (Small frictional effects can be neglected.)

$K.E. = P.E.$

Hence

$$\tfrac{1}{2}(m + m')V^2 = (m + m')gy,$$ $\tfrac{1}{2}m\omega^2 = m\alpha \cdot x.$

and

$(mgh).$

$$v = \frac{m + m'}{m}\sqrt{2gy}.$$

By measuring m, m', and y, the original velocity v of the bullet can be computed.

It is important to remember that kinetic energy is not conserved *in the collision*. The ratio of the kinetic energy of bullet and pendulum, after the collision, to the original kinetic energy of the bullet, is

$$\frac{\tfrac{1}{2}(m + m')V^2}{\tfrac{1}{2}mv^2} = \frac{m}{m + m'}.$$

Thus if $m' = 1000$ gm and $m = 1$ gm, only about one-tenth of one percent of the original energy remains as kinetic energy; 99.9% is converted to heat.

———————

Consider next a perfectly elastic "head-on" or *central* collision between two bodies A and B. The bodies separate after the collision and have different velocities, $\mathbf{v}_{A2}$ and $\mathbf{v}_{B2}$. Since kinetic energy and momentum are *both* conserved, we have:

Conservation of kinetic energy:

$$\tfrac{1}{2}m_A v_{A1}^2 + \tfrac{1}{2}m_B v_{B1}^2 = \tfrac{1}{2}m_A v_{A2}^2 + \tfrac{1}{2}m_B v_{B2}^2.$$

Conservation of momentum:

$$m_A v_{A1} + m_B v_{B1} = m_A v_{A2} + m_B v_{B2}.$$

Hence if the masses and initial velocities are known, we have two independent equations from which the final velocities can be found. Simultaneous solution of these two equations gives

$$(v_{B2} - v_{A2}) = -(v_{B1} - v_{A1}). \tag{8-9}$$

All these velocities are measured relative to the earth. The difference $(v_{B2} - v_{A2})$ is therefore the velocity of B relative to A after the collision, while $(v_{B1} - v_{A1})$ is the relative velocity before the collision. Thus, from Eq. (8-9), *the relative velocity of two bodies in a central, completely elastic collision, is unchanged in magnitude but reversed in direction.*

———————

EXAMPLE. Suppose the collision in Fig. 8–5 is completely elastic. What are the velocities of A and B after the collision?

From the principle of conservation of momentum,

$$5 \text{ kgm} \times 2 \frac{m}{\text{sec}} + 3 \text{ kgm} \times \left(-2 \frac{m}{\text{sec}}\right) = 5 \text{ kgm} \times v_{A2} + 3 \text{ kgm} \times v_{B2},$$

$$5v_{A2} + 3v_{B2} = 4 \frac{m}{\text{sec}}.$$

Since the collision is completely elastic,

$$(v_{B2} - v_{A2}) = -(v_{B1} - v_{A1}) = 4 \frac{m}{\text{sec}}.$$

When these equations are solved simultaneously, we get

$$v_{A2} = -1 \frac{m}{\text{sec}}, \qquad v_{B2} = 3 \frac{m}{\text{sec}}.$$

Both bodies therefore reverse their directions of motion, A traveling to the left at 1 m/sec and B to the right at 3 m/sec.

The total kinetic energy after the collision is

$$\tfrac{1}{2} \cdot 5 \text{ kgm} \cdot \left(-1 \frac{m}{\text{sec}}\right)^2 + \tfrac{1}{2} \cdot 3 \text{ kgm} \cdot \left(3 \frac{m}{\text{sec}}\right)^2 = 16 \text{ joules},$$

which equals the total kinetic energy before the collision.

8–4 Recoil. Figure 8–9 shows two blocks A and B, between which there is a compressed spring. When the system is released from rest, the spring exerts equal and opposite forces on the blocks until it has expanded to its natural unstressed length. It then drops to the surface, while the blocks continue to move. The original momentum of the system is zero, and if frictional forces can be neglected, the resultant external force on the system is zero. The momentum of the system therefore remains constant and equal to zero. Then if $\mathbf{v}_A$ and $\mathbf{v}_B$ are the velocities acquired by A and B, we have

$$m_A v_A + m_B v_B = 0, \qquad \frac{v_A}{v_B} = -\frac{m_B}{m_A}.$$

The velocities are of opposite sign and their magnitudes are inversely proportional to the corresponding masses.

The original kinetic energy of the system is also zero. The final kinetic energy is

$$E_k = \tfrac{1}{2} m_A v_A^2 + \tfrac{1}{2} m_B v_B^2.$$

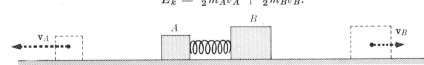

FIG. 8–9. Conservation of momentum in recoil.

The source of this energy is the original elastic potential energy of the system. The ratio of kinetic energies is

$$\frac{\frac{1}{2}m_A v_A^2}{\frac{1}{2}m_B v_B^2} = \frac{m_A}{m_B}\left(\frac{v_A}{v_B}\right)^2 = \frac{m_B}{m_A}.$$

Thus, although the momenta are equal in magnitude, the kinetic energies are inversely proportional to the corresponding masses, the body of smaller mass receiving the larger share of the original potential energy. The reason is that the change in *momentum* of a body equals the *impulse* of the force acting on it ($\int \mathbf{F}\,dt$), while the change in *kinetic energy* equals the *work* of the force ($\int \mathbf{F}\cdot d\mathbf{s}$). The forces on the two bodies are equal in magnitude and act for equal times, so they produce equal and opposite changes in momentum. The points of application of the forces, however, do not move through equal distances (except when $m_A = m_B$), since the acceleration, velocity, and displacement of the smaller body are greater than those of the larger. Hence more work is done on the body of smaller mass.

Considerations like those above also apply to the firing of a rifle. The initial momentum of the system is zero. When the rifle is fired, the bullet and the powder gases acquire a forward momentum, and the rifle (together with any system to which it is attached) acquires a rearward momentum of the same magnitude. The ratio of velocities cannot be expressed as simply as in the case discussed above. The bullet travels with a definite velocity, but different portions of the powder gases have different velocities. Because of the relatively large mass of the rifle compared with that of the bullet and powder charge, the velocity and kinetic energy of the rifle are much smaller than those of the bullet and powder gases.

In the processes of radioactive decay and nuclear fission, a nucleus splits into two or more parts which fly off in different directions. Although we do not yet understand the nature of the forces which act in these processes, it has been verified by many experiments that the principle of conservation of momentum applies to them also. The total (vector) momentum of the products equals the original momentum of the system. The source of the kinetic energy of the products is the so-called *binding energy* of the original nucleus, analogous to the chemical energy of the powder charge in a rifle.

8–5 Newton's second law. Newton himself did not state his second law in the form in which we have used it. A free translation (Newton's *Principia* was written in Latin) is as follows:

> *Change of motion is proportional to the applied force, and takes place in the direction of the force.... Quantity of motion is proportional to mass and velocity conjointly.*

From Newton's definition of "motion," or "quantity of motion," it is evident that he used this term for the concept we now call linear momentum. It is also clear from his writings that the term "change" meant "rate of change" and that the "applied force" referred to the resultant force. Hence in current terminology Newton's statement is:

Rate of change of linear momentum is proportional to the resultant force and is in the direction of this force.

In mathematical language this becomes

$$\frac{d(m\mathbf{v})}{dt} \propto \mathbf{F},$$

or

$$\mathbf{F} = k\,\frac{d(m\mathbf{v})}{dt}. \tag{8–10}$$

If the mass m is constant, this reduces to

$$\mathbf{F} = km\,\frac{d\mathbf{v}}{dt} = km\mathbf{a},$$

which is the form we have used, with k made equal to unity by proper choice of units.

8–6 The rocket. A rocket motor is merely a combustion chamber in which liquid or solid fuel is burned and which has an opening to direct the gaseous products of combustion in the desired direction. An ascending rocket can be compared to a machine gun pointed vertically downward and firing a steady stream of blank cartridges. The gases expelled from the rocket acquire a downward momentum and the rocket, like a recoiling machine gun, acquires an equal upward momentum.

Let us consider the flight of a rocket directed vertically upward from the earth's surface. Figure 8–10(a) shows the rocket at an instant when the mass of rocket and unburned fuel is m, the upward velocity is v, and the momentum is mv. In a short time interval Δt, a mass Δm of gas is ejected from the rocket. Let v_r represent the downward velocity of this gas *relative to the rocket*. The velocity v' of the gas relative to the earth, the inertial reference frame, is then

$$v' = v - v_r,$$

and its momentum is

$$\Delta m \cdot v' = \Delta m(v - v_r).$$

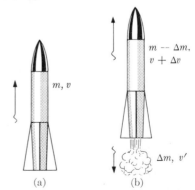

FIGURE 8–10

172   IMPULSE AND MOMENTUM   [CHAP. 8

At the end of the time interval, the mass of rocket and unburned fuel has decreased to $m - \Delta m$, and its velocity has increased to $v + \Delta v$. Its momentum is therefore

$$(m - \Delta m)(v + \Delta v).$$

Figure 8–10(b) represents rocket and ejected gas at this time.

We now make use of Eq. (8–10), with $k = 1$, writing it as

$$F\,\Delta t = \Delta(mv).$$

That is, the product of the resultant external force F on a system, and the time interval Δt during which it acts, is equal to the change in momentum of the system. If air resistance is neglected, the external force F on the rocket is its weight, $-mg$. (We take the upward direction as positive.) The change in momentum, in time Δt, is the difference between the momentum of the system at the end and at the beginning of the time interval. Hence

$$-mg\,\Delta t = [(m - \Delta m)(v + \Delta v) + \Delta m(v - v_r)] - mv.$$

Now expand the right side of this equation and neglect the term $\Delta m\,\Delta v$ (the product of two small quantities). After canceling and rearranging terms, we get

$$m\,\frac{\Delta v}{\Delta t} = v_r\,\frac{\Delta m}{\Delta t} - mg.$$

The ratio $\Delta v/\Delta t$ is the acceleration of the rocket, so the left side of this equation (mass times acceleration) equals the resultant force on the rocket. The first term on the right equals the upward thrust on the rocket, and the resultant force equals the difference between this thrust and the weight of the rocket, mg. It will be seen that the upward thrust is proportional both to the relative velocity v_r of the ejected gas and to the mass of gas ejected per unit time, $\Delta m/\Delta t$.

The acceleration is

$$a = \frac{\Delta v}{\Delta t} = \frac{v_r}{m}\,\frac{\Delta m}{\Delta t} - g. \tag{8–11}$$

As the rocket rises, the value of g decreases according to Newton's law of gravitation. (In "outer space," far from all other bodies, g becomes negligibly small.) The values of v_r and $\Delta m/\Delta t$ remain approximately constant while the fuel is being consumed, but the remaining mass m continually decreases. Hence the acceleration *increases* until all the fuel is burned.

EXAMPLE. In the first second of its flight, a rocket ejects 1/60 of its mass with a relative velocity of 6800 ft/sec. What is the acceleration of the rocket?

We have: $\Delta m = m/60$, $\Delta t = 1$ sec.

$$\frac{\Delta v}{\Delta t} = 6800 \frac{\text{ft}}{\text{sec}} \times \frac{1}{60} \times \frac{1}{1 \text{ sec}} - 32 \frac{\text{ft}}{\text{sec}^2}$$

$$= 113 \frac{\text{ft}}{\text{sec}^2} - 32 \frac{\text{ft}}{\text{sec}^2} = 81 \frac{\text{ft}}{\text{sec}^2}.$$

In order to find the value of the velocity at any moment, Eq. (8–11) must be written in differential form and then integrated. It may be seen from Fig. 8–10 that Δm was taken to be the *decrease* of mass, a positive quantity. When differential notation is used, dm must represent the *change* of mass, which has a negative value when the mass decreases. Equation (8–11) therefore becomes

$$\frac{dv}{dt} = -\frac{v_r}{m}\frac{dm}{dt} - g$$

or

$$dv = -v_r \frac{dm}{m} - g\,dt.$$

Assuming that v_r and g remain constant, and starting at rest when $m = m_0$, we write

$$\int_0^v dv = -v_r \int_{m_0}^m \frac{dm}{m} - g \int_0^t dt,$$

which yields the relation

$$v = v_r \ln \frac{m_0}{m} - gt.$$

EXAMPLE. Suppose the ratio of initial mass to final mass for the rocket above is 4 and that the fuel is consumed in a time $t = 60$ sec. The velocity at the end of this time is then

$$v = 6800 \frac{\text{ft}}{\text{sec}} \times \ln 4 - 32 \frac{\text{ft}}{\text{sec}^2} \times 60 \text{ sec}$$

$$= 9420 \frac{\text{ft}}{\text{sec}} - 1920 \frac{\text{ft}}{\text{sec}} = 7500 \frac{\text{ft}}{\text{sec}}.$$

At the start of the flight, when the velocity of the rocket is zero, the ejected gases are moving downward, relative to the earth, with a velocity equal to the relative velocity v_r. When the velocity of the rocket has increased to v_r, the ejected gases have a velocity zero relative to the earth.

When the rocket velocity becomes greater than v_r, the velocity of the ejected gases is in the same direction as that of the rocket. Thus the velocity acquired by the rocket can be greater (and is often much greater) than the relative velocity v_r. In the example above, where the final velocity of the rocket was 7500 ft/sec and the relative velocity was 6800 ft/sec, the last portion of the ejected fuel had an upward velocity of (7500 − 6800) ft/sec = 700 ft/sec.

Problems

8–1. (a) What is the momentum of a 10-ton truck whose velocity is 30 mi/hr? At what velocity will a 5-ton truck have (b) the same momentum, (c) the same kinetic energy?

8–2. A baseball weighs $5\frac{1}{2}$ oz. (a) If the velocity of a pitched ball is 80 ft/sec, and after being batted it is 120 ft/sec in the opposite direction, find the change in momentum of the ball and the impulse of the blow. (b) If the ball remains in contact with the bat for 0.002 sec, find the average force of the blow.

8–3. A bullet having a mass of 0.05 kgm, moving with a velocity of 400 m/sec, penetrates a distance of 0.1 m in a wooden block firmly attached to the earth. Assume the decelerating force constant. Compute (a) the deceleration of the bullet, (b) the decelerating force, (c) the time of deceleration, (d) the impulse of the collision. Compare the answer to part (d) with the initial momentum of the bullet.

8–4. An empty freight car weighing 10 tons rolls at 3 ft/sec along a level track and collides with a loaded car weighing 20 tons, standing at rest with brakes released. If the two cars couple together, find (a) their velocity after the collision, and (b) the decrease in kinetic energy as a result of the collision.

8–5. With what velocity should the loaded car in Problem 8–4 be rolling toward the empty one in order that both shall be brought to rest by the collision?

8–6. A bullet weighing 0.02 lb is fired with a muzzle velocity of 2700 ft/sec from a rifle weighing 7.5 lb. (a) Compute the recoil velocity of the rifle, assuming it free to recoil. (b) Find the ratio of the kinetic energy of the bullet to that of the rifle.

8–7. A 75-mm gun fires a projectile weighing 16 lb with a muzzle velocity of 1900 ft/sec. By how many mi/hr is the velocity of a plane mounting such a gun decreased when a projectile is fired directly ahead? The plane weighs 32,000 lb.

8–8. The projectile of a 16-in. sea-coast gun weighs 2400 lb, travels a distance of 38 ft in the bore of the gun, and has a muzzle velocity of 2250 ft/sec. The gun weighs 300,000 lb. (a) Compute the initial recoil velocity of the gun, assuming it free to recoil. (b) Find the ratio of the kinetic energy of the projectile to that of the recoiling gun.

8–9. A 4000-lb automobile going eastward on Chestnut Street at 40 mi/hr collides with a truck weighing 4 tons which is going southward across Chestnut Street at 15 mi/hr. If they become coupled on collision, what is the magnitude and direction of their velocity immediately after colliding?

8–10. A body of mass 600 gm is initially at rest. It is struck by a second body of mass 400 gm initially moving with a velocity of 125 cm/sec toward the right along the x-axis. After the collision the 400-gm body has a velocity of 100 cm/sec at an angle of 37° above the x-axis in the first quadrant. Both bodies move on a horizontal frictionless plane. (a) What is the magnitude and direction of the velocity of the 600-gm body after the collision? (b) What is the loss of kinetic energy during the collision?

8–11. (a) Prove that when a moving body makes a perfectly inelastic collision with a second body of equal mass, initially at rest, one-half of the original kinetic energy is "lost." (b) Prove that when a very heavy particle makes a perfectly elastic collision with a very light particle that is at rest, the light one goes off with twice the velocity of the heavy one.

8–12. On a frictionless table, a 3-kgm block moving 4 m/sec to the right collides with an 8-kgm block moving 1.5 m/sec to the left. (a) If the two blocks stick together, what is the final velocity? (b) If the two blocks make a completely elastic head-on collision, what are their final velocities? (c) How much mechanical energy is converted into heat in the collision of part (a)?

8–13. Two blocks of mass 300 gm and 200 gm are moving toward each other along a horizontal frictionless surface with velocities of 50 cm/sec and 100 cm/sec, respectively. (a) If the blocks collide and stick together, find their final velocity. (b) Find the loss of kinetic energy during the collision. (c) Find the final velocity of each block if the collision is completely elastic.

8–14. A 10-gm block slides with a velocity of 20 cm/sec on a smooth level surface and makes a head-on collision with a 30-gm block moving in the opposite direction with a velocity of 10 cm/sec. If the collision is perfectly elastic, find the velocity of each block after the collision.

8–15. A block of mass 200 gm, sliding with a velocity of 12 cm/sec on a smooth level surface, makes a perfectly elastic head-on collision with a block of mass m gm, initially at rest. After the collision the velocity of the 200-gm block is 4 cm/sec in the same direction as its initial velocity. Find (a) the mass m, and (b) its velocity after the collision.

8–16. A rifle bullet of mass 10 gm strikes and embeds itself in a block of mass 990 gm which rests on a horizontal frictionless surface and is attached to a coil spring, as shown in Fig. 8–11. The impact compresses the spring 10 cm. Calibration of the spring shows that a force of 100,000 dynes is required to compress the spring 1 cm. (a) Find the maximum potential energy of the spring. (b) Find the velocity of the block just after the impact. (c) What was the initial velocity of the bullet?

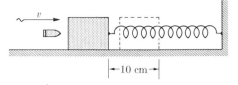

FIGURE 8–11

8–17. A projectile is fired at an angle of departure of 60° and with a muzzle velocity of 1200 ft/sec. At the highest point of its trajectory the projectile explodes into two fragments of equal mass, one of which falls vertically. How far from the point of firing does the other fragment strike if the terrain is level?

8–18. A railroad handcar is moving along straight frictionless tracks. In each of the following cases the car initially has a total weight (car and contents) of 500 lb and is traveling with a velocity of 10 ft/sec. Find the final velocity of the car in each of the three cases. (a) A 50-lb weight is thrown sideways out of the car with a velocity of 8 ft/sec relative to the car. (b) A 50-lb weight is thrown backwards out of the car with a velocity of 10 ft/sec relative to the car. (c) A 50-lb weight is thrown into the car with a velocity of 12 ft/sec relative to the ground and opposite in direction to the velocity of the car.

8–19. An open-topped freight car weighing 10 tons is coasting without friction along a level track. It is raining very hard, with the rain falling vertically down. The car is originally empty and moving with a velocity of 2 ft/sec. What is the velocity of the car after it has traveled long enough to collect one ton of rain water?

8–20. A neutron of mass 1.67×10^{-24} gm, moving with a velocity of 2×10^6 cm/sec, makes a head-on collision with a boron nucleus of mass 17.0×10^{-24} gm, originally at rest. (a) If the collision is completely inelastic, what is the final kinetic energy of the system, expressed as a fraction of the original kinetic energy? (b) If the collision is perfectly elastic, what fraction of its original kinetic energy does the neutron transfer to the boron nucleus?

8–21. A nucleus, originally at rest, decays radioactively by emitting an electron of momentum 9.22×10^{-16} gm·cm/sec, and at right angles to the direction of the electron a neutrino with momentum 5.33×10^{-16} gm·cm/sec. (a) In what direction does the residual nucleus recoil? (b) What is its momentum? (c) If the mass of the residual nucleus is 3.90×10^{-22} gm, what is its kinetic energy?

8–22. When a bullet of mass 10 gm strikes a ballistic pendulum of mass 2 kgm, the center of gravity of the pendulum is observed to rise a vertical distance of 10 cm. The bullet remains embedded in the pendulum. Calculate the velocity of the bullet.

8–23. A bullet weighing 0.01 lb is shot through a 2-lb wooden block suspended on a string 5 ft long. The center of gravity of the block is observed to rise a distance of 0.0192 ft. Find the speed of the bullet as it emerges from the block if the initial speed is 1000 ft/sec.

8–24. A bullet of mass 2 gm, traveling in a horizontal direction with a velocity of 500 m/sec, is fired into a wooden block of mass 1 kgm, initially at rest on a level surface. The bullet passes through the block and emerges with its velocity reduced to 100 m/sec. The block slides a distance of 20 cm along the surface from its initial position. (a) What was the coefficient of sliding friction between block and surface? (b) What was the decrease in kinetic energy of the bullet? (c) What was the kinetic energy of the block at the instant after the bullet passed through it?

8–25. A rifle bullet weighing 0.02 lb is fired with a velocity of 2500 ft/sec into a ballistic pendulum. The pendulum weighs 10 lb and is suspended from a cord 3 ft long. Compute (a) the vertical height through which the pendulum rises, (b) the initial kinetic energy of the bullet, (c) the kinetic energy of bullet and pendulum after the bullet is embedded in the pendulum.

8–26. A 5-gm bullet is fired horizontally into a 3-kgm wooden block resting on a horizontal surface. The coefficient of sliding friction between block and surface is 0.20. The bullet remains embedded in the block, which is observed to slide 25 cm along the surface. What was the velocity of the bullet?

8–27. A bullet of mass 2 gm, traveling at 500 m/sec, is fired into a ballistic pendulum of mass 1 kgm suspended from a cord 1 m long. The bullet penetrates the pendulum and emerges with a velocity of 100 m/sec. Through what vertical height will the pendulum rise?

8–28. A 160-lb man standing on ice throws a 6-oz ball horizontally with a speed of 80 ft/sec. (a) With what speed and in what direction will the man begin to move? (b) If the man throws 4 such balls every 3 sec, what is the average force acting on him? [*Hint:* average force equals average rate of change of momentum.]

8–29. Find the average recoil force on a machine gun firing 120 shots per minute. The weight of each bullet is 0.025 lb, and the muzzle velocity is 2700 ft/sec.

8–30. A rifleman, who together with his rifle weighs 160 lb, stands on roller skates and fires 10 shots horizontally from an automatic rifle. Each bullet weighs 0.0257 lb (180 grains) and has a muzzle velocity of 2500 ft/sec. (a) If the rifleman moves back without friction, what is his velocity at the end of the ten shots? (b) If the shots were fired in 10 sec, what was the average force exerted on him? (c) Compare his kinetic energy with that of the 10 bullets.

8–31. A rocket burns 50 gm of fuel per second, ejecting it as a gas with a velocity of 500,000 cm/sec. (a) What force does this gas exert on the rocket? Give the result in dynes and newtons. (b) Would the rocket operate in free space? (c) If it would operate in free space, how would you steer it? Could you brake it?

8–32 A bullet of mass 2 gm emerges from the muzzle of a gun with a velocity of 300 m/sec. The resultant force on the bullet, while it is in the gun barrel, is given by

$$F = 400 - \frac{4 \times 10^5}{3} t,$$

where F is in newtons and t in seconds. Compute the time required for the bullet to travel the length of the barrel.

CHAPTER 9

ROTATION

9–1 Introduction. The most general type of motion which a body can undergo is a combination of *translation* and *rotation*. Thus far we have considered only the special case of translational motion, along a straight line or along a curve. We next discuss motion of rotation about a fixed axis, that is, motion of rotation without translation. We shall see that many of the equations describing rotation about a fixed axis are exactly analogous to those encountered in rectilinear motion as shown in Table 9–1. If the axis is *not* fixed, the problem becomes much more complicated, and we shall not attempt to give a complete discussion of the general case of translation plus rotation.

9–2 Angular velocity. Figure 9–1 represents a rigid body of arbitrary shape rotating about a fixed axis through point O and perpendicular to the plane of the diagram. Line OP is a line fixed with respect to the body and rotating with it. The position of the entire body is evidently completely specified by the angle θ which the line OP makes with some reference line fixed in space, such as Ox. The motion of the body is therefore analogous to the rectilinear motion of a particle, whose position is completely specified by a single coordinate such as x or y. The equations of motion are greatly simplified if the angle θ is expressed in *radians*.

One radian is the angle subtended at the center of a circle by an arc of length equal to the radius of the circle [Fig. 9–2(a)]. Since the radius is contained 2π times ($2\pi = 6.28 \ldots$) in the circumference, there are 2π or $6.28 \ldots$ radians in

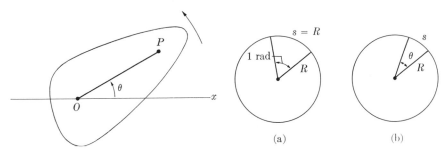

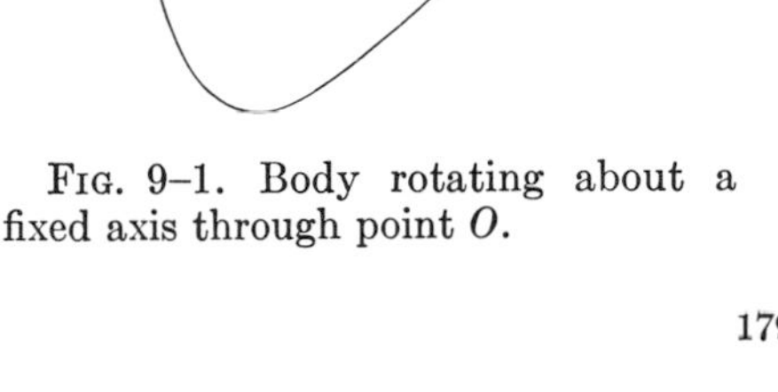

FIG. 9–1. Body rotating about a fixed axis through point O.

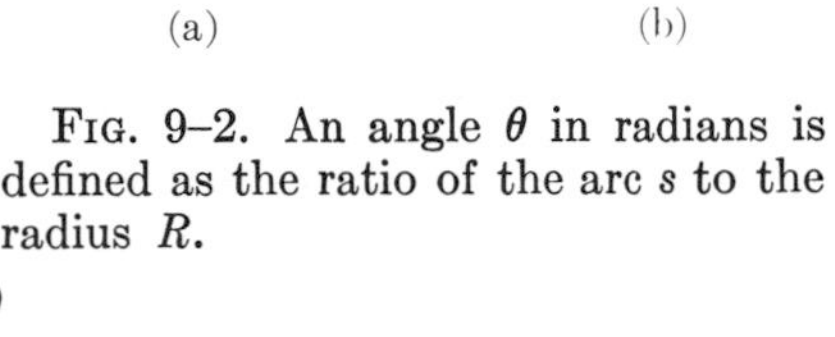

FIG. 9–2. An angle θ in radians is defined as the ratio of the arc s to the radius R.

179

TABLE 9-1

ANALOGY BETWEEN TRANSLATIONAL AND ROTATIONAL QUANTITIES

Concept	Translation	Rotation	Comments
Displacement	s	θ	$s = r\theta$
Velocity	$v = ds/dt$	$\omega = d\theta/dt$	$v = r\omega$
Acceleration	$a = dv/dt$	$\alpha = d\omega/dt$	$a_T = r\alpha$
Force, moment	F	Γ	$\Gamma = Fr$
Equilibrium	$\sum F\text{'s} = 0$	$\sum \Gamma\text{'s} = 0$	
Acceleration constant	$v = v_0 + at$ $s = s_0 + v_0 t + \frac{1}{2}at^2$ $v^2 = v_0^2 + 2as$	$\omega = \omega_0 + \alpha t$ $\theta = \theta_0 + \omega_0 t + \frac{1}{2}\alpha t^2$ $\omega^2 = \omega_0^2 + 2\alpha\theta$	
Mass, moment of inertia	m	I	$I = \sum mr^2$
Newton's 2nd Law	$F = ma$	$\Gamma = I\alpha$	
Work	$dW = F\,ds$	$dW = \Gamma\,d\theta$	
Power	$P = Fv$	$P = \Gamma\omega$	
Potential energy	$E_p = mgy$		
Kinetic energy	$E_k = \frac{1}{2}mv^2$	$E_k = \frac{1}{2}I\omega^2$	
Impulse	$\int F\,dt$	$\int \Gamma\,dt$	
Momentum	mv	$L = I\omega$	

one complete revolution or 360°. Hence

$$1 \text{ radian} = \frac{360}{2\pi} = 57.3 \ldots \text{degrees}$$

$$360° = 2\pi \text{ radians} = 6.28 \ldots \text{radians}$$
$$180° = \pi \qquad \text{``} \qquad = 3.14 \ldots \qquad \text{``}$$
$$90° = \pi/2 \qquad \text{``} \qquad = 1.57 \ldots \qquad \text{``}$$
$$60° = \pi/3 \qquad \text{``} \qquad = 1.05 \ldots \qquad \text{``}$$

and so on.

In general [Fig. 9–2(b)], if θ represents any arbitrary angle subtended by an arc of length s on the circumference of a circle of radius R, then θ (in radians) is equal to the length of the arc s divided by the radius R.

$$\theta = \frac{s}{R}, \qquad s = R\theta. \qquad (9\text{--}1)$$

An angle in radians, being defined as the ratio of a length to a length, is a pure number.

In Fig. 9–3, a reference line OP in a rotating body makes an angle θ_1 with the reference line Ox, at a time t_1. At a later time t_2 the angle has increased to θ_2. The *average angular velocity* of the body, $\bar{\omega}$, in the time interval between t_1 and t_2, is defined as the ratio of the *angular displacement* $\theta_2 - \theta_1$, or $\Delta\theta$, to the elapsed time $t_2 - t_1$ or Δt.

$$\bar{\omega} = \frac{\theta_2 - \theta_1}{t_2 - t_1} = \frac{\Delta\theta}{\Delta t}.$$

The *instantaneous angular velocity* ω is defined as the limit approached by this ratio as Δt approaches zero.

$$\omega = \lim_{\Delta t \to 0} \frac{\Delta\theta}{\Delta t} = \frac{d\theta}{dt}. \qquad (9\text{--}2)$$

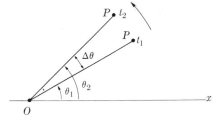

FIG. 9–3. Angular displacement $\Delta\theta$ of a rotating body.

Since the body is rigid, *all* lines in it rotate through the same angle in the same time, and the angular velocity is characteristic of the body as a whole. If the angle θ is in radians, the angular velocity is in *radians per second*. Other units, such as the revolution per minute, are in common use.

9–3 Angular acceleration. When the angular velocity of a body changes, it is said to have an angular acceleration. If ω_1 and ω_2 are the instantaneous angular velocities at times t_1 and t_2, the *average angular acceleration* $\bar{\alpha}$ is defined as

$$\bar{\alpha} = \frac{\omega_2 - \omega_1}{t_2 - t_1} = \frac{\Delta\omega}{\Delta t},$$

and the *instantaneous angular acceleration* α is defined as the limit of this ratio when Δt approaches zero:

$$\alpha = \lim_{\Delta t \to 0} \frac{\Delta\omega}{\Delta t} = \frac{d\omega}{dt}. \qquad (9\text{--}3)$$

Angular acceleration is expressed in rad/sec^2.

Just as for rectilinear motion, another useful expression for the angular acceleration can be obtained by multiplying and dividing Eq. (9–3) by $d\theta$ and rearranging terms.

$$\alpha = \frac{d\omega}{dt}\frac{d\theta}{d\theta} = \frac{d\theta}{dt}\frac{d\omega}{d\theta} = \omega\frac{d\omega}{d\theta}. \qquad (9\text{–}4)$$

Angular velocity and angular acceleration are exactly analogous to linear velocity and acceleration.

9–4 Rotation with constant angular acceleration. The simplest type of accelerated rotational motion is that in which the angular acceleration is constant. When this is the case, the expressions for the angular velocity and angular coordinate can readily be found by integration. (They can also be derived algebraically from the average angular velocity, as was done for the corresponding linear case in Chapter 4.) We have

$$\alpha = \frac{d\omega}{dt} = \text{constant,}$$

$$\int d\omega = \int \alpha\, dt,$$

$$\omega = \alpha t + C_1.$$

If ω_0 is the angular velocity when $t = 0$, the integration constant $C_1 = \omega_0$ and

$$\boxed{\omega = \omega_0 + \alpha t.} \qquad (9\text{–}5)$$

Then, since $\omega = d\theta/dt$,

$$\int d\theta = \int \omega_0\, dt + \int \alpha t\, dt,$$

$$\theta = \omega_0 t + \tfrac{1}{2}\alpha t^2 + C_2.$$

In general, the integration constant C_2 is the value of θ when $t = 0$, say θ_0; then

$$\boxed{\theta = \theta_0 + \omega_0 t + \tfrac{1}{2}\alpha t^2.} \qquad (9\text{–}6)$$

If we write the angular acceleration as

$$\alpha = \omega\frac{d\omega}{d\theta},$$

then

$$\int \alpha\, d\theta = \int \omega\, d\omega + C_3,$$

$$\alpha\theta = \tfrac{1}{2}\omega^2 + C_3.$$

If the angle θ is zero when $t = 0$, and if the initial angular velocity is ω_0, then $C_3 = -\frac{1}{2}\omega_0^2$ and

$$\omega^2 = \omega_0^2 + 2\alpha\theta. \qquad (9\text{–}7)$$

Equations (9–5), (9–6), and (9–7) are exactly analogous to the corresponding equations for linear motion with constant acceleration as shown in Table 9–1.

EXAMPLE. The angular velocity of a body is 4 rad/sec at time $t = 0$, and its angular acceleration is constant and equal to 2 rad/sec^2. A line OP in the body is horizontal ($\theta_0 = 0$) at time $t = 0$. (a) What angle does this line make with the horizontal at time $t = 3$ sec? (b) What is the angular velocity at this time?

(a) $\qquad \theta = \omega_0 t + \frac{1}{2}\alpha t^2$

$\qquad\qquad = 4\,\dfrac{\text{rad}}{\text{sec}} \times 3\text{ sec} + \frac{1}{2} \times 2\,\dfrac{\text{rad}}{\text{sec}^2} \times (3\text{ sec})^2$

$\qquad\qquad = 21$ radians

$\qquad\qquad = 3.34$ revolutions.

(b) $\qquad \omega = \omega_0 + \alpha t$

$\qquad\qquad = 4\,\dfrac{\text{rad}}{\text{sec}} + 2\,\dfrac{\text{rad}}{\text{sec}} \times 3\text{ sec} = 10\,\dfrac{\text{rad}}{\text{sec}}.$

Alternatively, from Eq. (9–7),

$$\omega^2 = \omega_0^2 + 2\alpha\theta$$

$$= \left(4\,\frac{\text{rad}}{\text{sec}}\right)^2 + 2 \times 2\,\frac{\text{rad}}{\text{sec}^2} \times 21\text{ rad}$$

$$= 100\,\frac{\text{rad}^2}{\text{sec}^2},$$

$$\omega = 10\,\frac{\text{rad}}{\text{sec}}.$$

9–5 Relation between angular and linear velocity and acceleration. In Section 6–2 we discussed the linear velocity and acceleration of a *particle* revolving in a circle. When a *rigid body* rotates about a fixed axis, every point in the body moves in a circle whose center is on the axis and which lies in a plane perpendicular to the axis. There are some useful and simple relations between the angular velocity and acceleration of the rotating body and the linear velocity and acceleration of points within it.

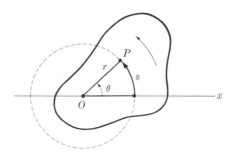

FIG. 9–4. The distance s moved through by point P equals $r\theta$.

Let r be the distance from the axis to some point P in the body, so that the point moves in a circle of radius r, as in Fig. 9–4. When the radius makes an angle θ with the reference axis, the distance s to the point P, measured along the circular path, is

$$s = r\theta, \qquad (9\text{--}8)$$

if θ is in radians. Differentiating both sides of this equation with respect to t, we have, since r is constant,

$$\frac{ds}{dt} = r\,\frac{d\theta}{dt}.$$

But ds/dt is the magnitude of the linear velocity v of point P, and from Eq. (9–2) $d\theta/dt$ is the angular velocity ω of the rotating body. Hence

$$v = r\omega \qquad (9\text{--}9)$$

and the linear velocity v equals the product of the angular velocity ω and the distance r of the point from the axis.

Differentiating Eq. (9–9) with respect to t gives

$$\frac{dv}{dt} = r\,\frac{d\omega}{dt}.$$

But dv/dt is the magnitude of the tangential component of acceleration a_T of point P, and $d\omega/dt$ is the angular acceleration α of the rotating body, so

$$a_T = r\alpha \qquad (9\text{--}10)$$

and the tangential component of acceleration equals the product of the angular acceleration and the distance from the axis.

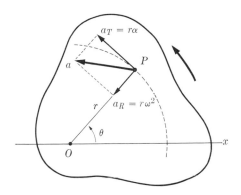

Fɪɢ. 9–5. Nonuniform rotation about a fixed axis through point O. The tangential component of acceleration of point P equals $r\alpha$; the radial component equals $r\omega^2$.

The *radial* component of acceleration v^2/r of the point P can also be expressed in terms of the angular velocity.

$$a_R = \frac{v^2}{r} = r\omega^2. \tag{9–11}$$

The tangential and radial components of acceleration of any arbitrary point P in a rotating body are shown in Fig. 9–5.

9–6 Kinetic energy of rotation. Moment of inertia. We have shown that the magnitude of the velocity of a particle in a rigid body rotating about a fixed axis is

$$v = r\omega,$$

where r is the distance of the particle from the axis and ω is the angular velocity of the body. The kinetic energy of a particle of mass m is therefore

$$\tfrac{1}{2}mv^2 = \tfrac{1}{2}mr^2\omega^2.$$

The total kinetic energy of the body is the sum of the kinetic energy of all particles in the body.

$$E_k = \textstyle\sum \tfrac{1}{2}mr^2\omega^2.$$

Since ω is the same for all particles in a rigid body,

$$E_k = \tfrac{1}{2}[\textstyle\sum mr^2]\omega^2. \tag{9–12}$$

To obtain the sum $\sum mr^2$ the body is subdivided (in imagination) into a large number of particles, the mass of each particle is multiplied by the square of its distance from the axis, and these products are summed over all particles. The result is called the *moment of inertia* of the body, about the axis of rotation, and is represented by I.

$$I = \sum mr^2. \tag{9-13}$$

Moment of inertia is expressed in *slug·feet*^{2}, *kilogram·meters*^{2}, or *gram·centimeters*^{2}.

The rotational kinetic energy can now be written as

$$E_k = \tfrac{1}{2}I\omega^2, \tag{9-14}$$

in which form it is exactly analogous to the translational kinetic energy,

$$E_k = \tfrac{1}{2}mv^2.$$

That is, for rotation about a fixed axis, moment of inertia I is analogous to mass m (or inertia), and angular velocity ω is analogous to linear velocity v.

EXAMPLE. Three small bodies, which can be considered as particles, are connected by light rigid rods as in Fig. 9–6. What is the moment of inertia of the system (a) about an axis through point A, perpendicular to the plane of the diagram, and (b) about an axis coinciding with the rod BC?

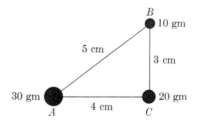

FIGURE 9–6

(a) The particle at point A lies on the axis. Its distance *from* the axis is zero and it contributes nothing to the moment of inertia. Therefore

$$I = \sum mr^2 = 10 \text{ gm} \times (5 \text{ cm})^2 + 20 \text{ gm} \times (4 \text{ cm})^2$$

$$= 570 \text{ gm·cm}^2.$$

(b) The particles at B and C both lie on the axis. The moment of inertia is

$$I = \sum mr^2 = 30 \text{ gm} \times (4 \text{ cm})^2 = 480 \text{ gm·cm}^2.$$

This illustrates the important fact that the moment of inertia of a body, unlike its mass, is not a unique property of the body but depends on the axis about which it is computed.

(c) If the body rotates about an axis through A and perpendicular to the plane of the diagram, with an angular velocity $\omega = 4$ rad/sec, what is the rotational kinetic energy?

$$E_k = \tfrac{1}{2}I\omega^2 = \tfrac{1}{2} \times 570 \text{ gm·cm}^2 \times \left(4\,\frac{\text{rad}}{\text{sec}}\right)^2$$

$$= 4560 \text{ ergs.}$$

For a body which is not composed of discrete point masses but is a continuous distribution of matter, the summation expressed in the definition of moment of inertia, $I = \Sigma mr^2$, must be evaluated by the methods of calculus. The body is imagined to be subdivided into infinitesimal elements, each of mass dm. Let r be the distance from any element to the axis of rotation. If each mass dm is multiplied by the square of its distance from the axis and all the products $r^2\, dm$ summed over the whole body, the moment of inertia is obtained. Thus

$$\boxed{I = \int r^2\, dm.}$$

(9–15)

The evaluation of integrals of this type may present considerable difficulty if the body is irregular, but for bodies of simple shape the integration can be carried out relatively easily. As an example, let us calculate the moment of inertia of a uniform solid cylinder about its axis of symmetry.

In Fig. 9–7 we choose as the most convenient mass element the infinitesimally thin cylindrical shell of radius r, thickness dr, and length L. If we represent by the Greek letter ρ (rho) the density of the material, i.e., the mass per unit volume, then

$$dm = \rho\, dV,$$

where dV, the volume of the cylindrical shell, is

$$dV = (2\pi r\, dr) \times L.$$

Hence,

$$dm = 2\pi L\rho r\, dr.$$

The moment of inertia is given by

$$I = \int r^2\, dm = 2\pi L \int_0^R \rho r^3\, dr.$$

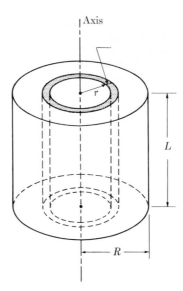

Fig. 9–7. Computing the moment of inertia of a hollow cylinder.

If the body were of nonuniform density, one would have to know ρ as a function of r before the integration could be carried out. For a uniform solid, however, ρ is constant, and

$$I = 2\pi L\rho \int_0^R r^3 \, dr = 2\pi L\rho \, \frac{R^4}{4} = \rho\pi R^2 L \, \frac{R^2}{2}.$$

The mass m of the entire cylinder is the product of its density ρ and its volume $\pi R^2 L$, or

$$m = \rho\pi R^2 L.$$

Therefore we may write the expression for the moment of inertia in the simple form

$$I = \tfrac{1}{2}mR^2.$$

The moments of inertia of a few simple but important bodies are listed in Fig. 9–8 for convenience.

Whatever the shape of a body, it is always possible to find a radial distance from any given axis at which the mass of the body could be concentrated without altering the moment of inertia of the body about that axis. This distance is called the *radius of gyration* of the body about the given axis, and is represented by k.

If the mass m of the body actually were concentrated at this distance, the moment of inertia would be that of a particle of mass m at a distance k

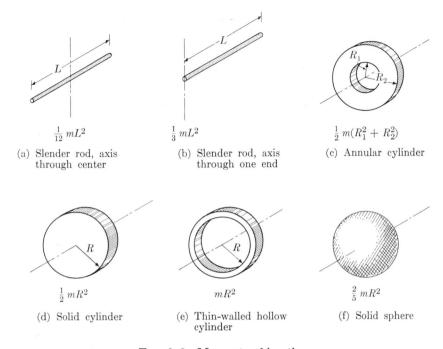

$\frac{1}{12} mL^2$

(a) Slender rod, axis through center

$\frac{1}{3} mL^2$

(b) Slender rod, axis through one end

$\frac{1}{2} m(R_1^2 + R_2^2)$

(c) Annular cylinder

$\frac{1}{2} mR^2$

(d) Solid cylinder

mR^2

(e) Thin-walled hollow cylinder

$\frac{2}{5} mR^2$

(f) Solid sphere

FIG. 9–8. Moments of inertia.

from an axis, or mk^2. Since this equals the actual moment of inertia, I, then

$$mk^2 = I,$$

$$k = \sqrt{\frac{I}{m}}. \tag{9–16}$$

Equation (9–16) may be considered the definition of radius of gyration.

EXAMPLE.   What is the radius of gyration of a slender rod of mass m and length L about an axis perpendicular to its length and passing through the center?

The moment of inertia about an axis through the center is $I_0 = \frac{1}{12}mL^2$. Hence

$$k_0 = \sqrt{\frac{\frac{1}{12}mL^2}{m}} = \frac{L}{2\sqrt{3}} = 0.289L.$$

The radius of gyration, like the moment of inertia, depends on the location of the axis.

Note carefully that, in general, the mass of a body can *not* be considered as concentrated at its center of gravity for the purpose of computing its moment of inertia. For example, when a rod is pivoted about its center, the distance from the axis to the center of gravity is zero, although the radius of gyration is $L/2\sqrt{3}$.

9–7 Work and power in rotational motion. In Fig. 9–9, a body is pivoted about an axis through point O, perpendicular to the plane of the diagram. An external force F is exerted on the body at point P. As the body rotates through a small angle $d\theta$, point P moves a distance ds along its circular path, where

$$ds = r\, d\theta.$$

The component of **F** in the direction of ds is $F\cos\phi$, and the work dW done by the force is

$$dW = F\cos\phi\, ds = F\cos\phi \cdot r\, d\theta.$$

The product $F\cos\phi \cdot r$, however, is the moment Γ of the force F about the axis, so

$$dW = \Gamma\, d\theta, \qquad (9\text{–}17)$$

which is the rotational analogue of the expression $F\, ds$ for the work done by a force F in a displacement ds. That is, "torque times angle" (in radians) corresponds to "force times distance."

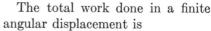

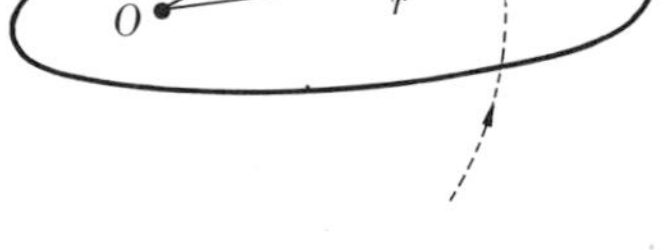

The total work done in a finite angular displacement is

$$W = \int dW = \int_{\theta_1}^{\theta_2} \Gamma\, d\theta.$$

If the torque is constant,

$$W = \Gamma(\theta_2 - \theta_1).$$

When both sides of Eq. (9–17) are divided by the short time interval dt, we have

$$\frac{dW}{dt} = \Gamma\frac{d\theta}{dt}.$$

Fig. 9–9.

Work $= (F\cos\phi) \cdot ds = \Gamma\, d\theta.$

But dW/dt is the rate of doing work, or the power P, and $d\theta/dt$ is the angular velocity ω. Hence

$$P = \Gamma\omega,$$

which is the analogue of $P = Fv$ for linear motion.

EXAMPLE The drive shaft of an automobile rotates at 3600 rev/min and transmits 80 hp from the engine to the rear wheels. Compute the torque developed by the engine.

$$\omega = 3600 \times \frac{2\pi}{60} = 120\pi \text{ rad/sec},$$

$$80 \text{ hp} = 44,000 \text{ ft·lb/sec},$$

$$\Gamma = \frac{P}{\omega} = \frac{44,000 \text{ ft·lb/sec}}{120\pi \text{ rad/sec}} = 117 \text{ lb·ft}.$$

9–8 Torque and angular acceleration. If a number of forces act on a body pivoted about a fixed axis, the torque Γ in Eq. (9–17) must be replaced by the resultant torque $\Sigma\Gamma$, so in general the work dW done in an infinitesimal angular displacement $d\theta$ is

$$dW = (\Sigma\Gamma) \cdot d\theta.$$

The forces on the body can be classified as (a) external forces whose lines of action pass through the axis, (b) external forces whose lines of action do not pass through the axis, and (c) internal forces exerted by the particles on each other. The forces in (a) have no moment about the axis, and do no work if the axis is fixed. By Newton's third law, for every internal force in (c) there is an equal and opposite internal force having the same line of action. Hence the resultant moment of the internal forces is zero. Also, if the body is rigid, the internal forces do no work. Thus the resultant moment about the axis, and the work done on the body, both arise wholly from those external forces in (b) whose lines of action do not pass through the axis. The expression above therefore gives the net work done on the body, and this is equal to the increase in kinetic energy of the body.

Net work = change in kinetic energy,

$$(\Sigma\Gamma) \cdot d\theta = d(\tfrac{1}{2}I\omega^2) = I\omega \, d\omega,$$

$$\Sigma\Gamma = I\omega \frac{d\omega}{d\theta}.$$

But from Eq. (9–4) $\omega(d\omega/d\theta)$ is the angular acceleration α, so

$$\boxed{\Sigma\Gamma = I\alpha.} \qquad (9\text{–}18)$$

This is the rotational analogue of Newton's second law, $\Sigma F = ma$, for rotation of a rigid body about a fixed axis.

EXAMPLE. A wheel of radius R and moment of inertia I is mounted on an axle supported in fixed bearings as in Fig. 9-10. A light flexible cord is wrapped around the rim of the wheel and carries a body of mass m_1. Friction in the bearings can be neglected. Discuss the motion of the system, from the standpoint of Newton's second law and from that of work and energy.

To apply Newton's second law, we must consider the resultant *force* on the suspended body and the resultant *torque* on the wheel. Let T represent the tension in the cord and P the upward force exerted on the shaft of the wheel by the bearings.

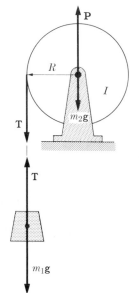

The resultant torque on the wheel, about the axis, is TR, and from Newton's second law for rotation

$$\sum \Gamma = TR = I\alpha.$$

The resultant force on the suspended body is $m_1 g - T$, and from Newton's second law for linear motion,

$$\sum F = m_1 g - T = m_1 a.$$

[We have taken the downward direction as positive in order that a positive (counterclockwise) angular displacement of the wheel shall correspond to a positive linear displacement of the suspended body.]

Since the linear acceleration of the suspended body equals the tangential acceleration of the rim of the wheel, we have

$$a = R\alpha.$$

Simultaneous solution of these equations gives

$$a = g \, \frac{m_1}{m_1 + (I/R^2)}.$$

FIGURE 9-10

If the system starts from rest, the linear velocity v of the suspended body, after descending a distance y (the acceleration is constant) is given by

$$v^2 = 2ay = 2 \left(g \, \frac{m_1}{m_1 + (I/R^2)} \right) y.$$

Now consider the problem from the energy standpoint. Looking at the system as a whole, the external forces are the forces P and $m_2 g$, which do no work, and the force $m_1 g$, which is conservative. We can therefore apply the principle of conservation of energy, setting the decrease in potential energy of the body, as it descends a distance y, equal to the *sum* of the increase in translational kinetic energy of the body and the increase in rotational kinetic energy of the wheel.

$$m_1 g y = \tfrac{1}{2} m_1 v^2 + \tfrac{1}{2} I \omega^2.$$

But
$$v = \omega R,$$
and again we find that
$$v^2 = 2 \left(g \, \frac{m_1}{m_1 + (I/R^2)} \right) y.$$

9–9 Angular momentum. The equation
$$\Gamma = I\alpha$$
can be written as
$$\Gamma = I \frac{d\omega}{dt} = \frac{d}{dt} (I\omega). \tag{9–19}$$

(For brevity, we shall let Γ represent the *resultant* external torque on the body.)

The product of moment of inertia I and angular velocity ω is the rotational analogue of the product of mass m and linear velocity v. The latter product is the linear momentum, and by analogy we call the product $I\omega$ the *angular momentum L.*

$$\boxed{L = I\omega.} \tag{9–20}$$

(Although in this special case of a rigid body rotating about a fixed axis the angular momentum is equal to $I\omega$, this is not the general definition of this quantity.)

Equation (9–19) can now be written
$$\Gamma = \frac{dL}{dt}, \tag{9–21}$$

or, *the resultant external torque is equal to the rate of change of angular momentum,* just as the resultant external force equals the rate of change of linear momentum.

When cleared of fractions, this equation becomes
$$\Gamma \, dt = dL. \tag{9–22}$$

The product $\Gamma \, dt$ is called the *angular impulse* of the torque and is analogous to the impulse of a force, $F \, dt$. The preceding equation is therefore the analogue of the impulse-momentum principle in linear motion. That is, *the resultant angular impulse of the torque on a body is equal to the change in angular momentum of the body.*

Thus far we have considered only problems of rotation about a fixed axis, in which all of the forces were in a plane perpendicular to the axis. When the motion of a body does not take place about a fixed axis it is useful to generalize our definition of the moment of a force.

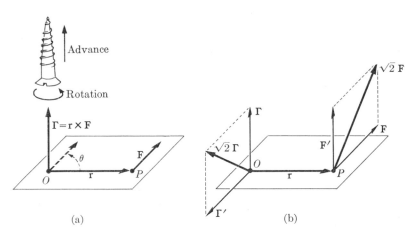

Fig. 9–11. (a) Vector **Γ** is the vector moment of the force **F** about the point O: **Γ** = **r** × **F**. (b) The resultant vector moment of two forces equals the vector sum of their moments.

In Fig. 9–11(a), a force **F**, lying in the horizontal plane, is applied at the point P. Point O is at a perpendicular distance r from point P, and **r** is the vector from O to P. There may or may not be an axis through point O. If there *were* an axis through O, perpendicular to the plane of **r** and **F**, the moment **Γ** of the force **F** about this axis would be

$$\Gamma = rF.$$

We define the *vector moment* of the force **F**, *about the* **point** O, as a vector **Γ** whose magnitude equals the moment rF and whose direction is perpendicular to the plane of **r** and **F**, as shown. The sense of **Γ** along the axis is specified by the *right-hand screw rule:* Rotate the first vector (**r**) through the smaller angle (θ) that will bring it into parallelism with the second vector (**F**), as shown by the broken line in the diagram. The vector **Γ** then points in the direction of *advance* of a right-hand screw when it is *rotated* through the same angle θ.

The vector moment of **F** about point O has the same magnitude and direction whatever the direction of an actual axis through O, or even if there is no actual axis through this point.

Since **r** and **F** are vectors, the definition above suggests that we define a new product of two vectors called the *vector product* or *cross product*. The vector product of any two vectors **A** and **B** is written **A** × **B** and is defined as a *vector* of magnitude $AB \sin \theta$, where θ is the angle between **A** and **B**. Then if **C** represents this product,

$$\mathbf{C} = \mathbf{A} \times \mathbf{B}, \qquad C = AB \sin \theta.$$

The direction and sense of the vector product is specified by the right-hand screw rule given above.

The vector moment of the force **F** about the point O can therefore be written in general as

$$\mathbf{\Gamma} = \mathbf{r} \times \mathbf{F},$$

where

$$\Gamma = rF \sin \theta.$$

For the special case in Fig. 9–11, $\theta = 90°$ and $\sin \theta = 1$.

The justification for representing the moment of a force by a vector becomes evident when we ask: How do the moments of two forces add; that is, do they add like numbers or like vectors? Suppose that a second force **F′**, which for simplicity we take equal in magnitude to the first, is also applied at the point P but in a vertically upward direction, as in Fig. 9–11(b). The magnitude of its moment about O also equals rF, and from the right-hand screw rule its direction is perpendicular to that of the first moment vector, as shown.

If the moments of the two forces added *algebraically*, the net moment about O would be $2rF$. But the two forces at P can be combined into a resultant of magnitude $F\sqrt{2}$, and the moment of the resultant about O is $\sqrt{2}\,rF$, which is the result obtained if the moment vectors are added *vectorially*.

Figure 9–12 shows a horizontal flat plate rotating about a fixed vertical axis through point O with an angular velocity ω. A particle of the plate of mass m, at a distance r from the axis, has a linear velocity $v = r\omega$ and a linear momentum mv. The angular momentum L of the particle is defined as the product of the distance r and the linear momentum:

$$L = rmv.$$

Since angular momentum is defined in the same way as the moment of a force, it is also called the *moment of momentum*.

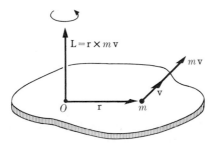

FIG. 9–12. Vector **L** represents the *moment of momentum*, or *angular momentum*, of a particle of mass m about point O: $\mathbf{L} = \mathbf{r} \times m\mathbf{v}$.

The *vector angular momentum* of the particle is defined as the *vector product* of **r** and m**v**.

$$\mathbf{L} = \mathbf{r} \times m\mathbf{v}.$$

By the right-hand screw rule, the vector **L** points along the axis of rotation, as shown.

The vector angular momentum of any body is the *vector sum* of the angular momenta of the particles composing it. However, since in this case the angular momentum vectors of all particles are in the same direction, the *vector* sum becomes an *arithmetic* sum and the magnitude of the angular momentum of the plate is

$$L = \sum rmv.$$

But $v = r\omega$, and ω has the same value for all particles. Hence

$$L = (\sum mr^2)\omega = I\omega,$$

and this definition of angular momentum leads to the same expression for L as that previously derived.

Now suppose that an external torque Γ is exerted on the plate. The angular momentum of the plate changes by dL, where, as shown above,

$$dL = \Gamma \, dt.$$

Since the *vectors* $d\mathbf{L}$ and $\boldsymbol{\Gamma}$ are both along the axis of rotation, this can be written as a *vector* equation:

$$d\mathbf{L} = \boldsymbol{\Gamma} \, dt. \tag{9–23}$$

An analysis of the general case, where **L** and $\boldsymbol{\Gamma}$ may not be in the same direction, shows that the result above is always true. That is, *the* **vector change** *in angular momentum of a body*, $d\mathbf{L}$, *is equal in magnitude and direction to the vector impulse* $\boldsymbol{\Gamma} \, dt$ *of the resultant external torque on the body.*

Let us now apply these vector concepts of torque and angular momentum to a specific example. In Fig. 9–13, a disk is mounted on a shaft through its center, the shaft being supported by fixed bearings. If the disk is rotating as indicated, its angular momentum vector **L** points toward the right, along the axis.

Suppose a cord is wrapped around the rim of the disk and a force **F** is exerted on the cord. The magnitude of the resultant torque on the disk is $\Gamma = FR$, and the torque vector $\boldsymbol{\Gamma}$ also points along the axis. In a time dt, the torque produces a vector change $d\mathbf{L}$ in the angular momentum, equal to $\boldsymbol{\Gamma} \, dt$ and having the same direction as $\boldsymbol{\Gamma}$. When this change is added vectorially to the original angular momentum **L**, the

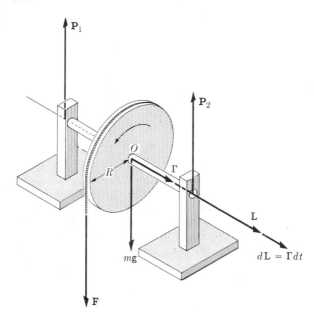

FIG. 9–13. Vector $d\mathbf{L}$ is the change in angular momentum produced in time dt by the moment $\boldsymbol{\Gamma}$ of the force $\mathbf{F}$. Vectors $d\mathbf{L}$ and $\boldsymbol{\Gamma}$ are in the same direction.

resultant is a vector of length $\mathbf{L} + d\mathbf{L}$, in the same direction as $\mathbf{L}$. In other words, the *magnitude* of the angular momentum is increased, its *direction* remaining the same. An increase in the magnitude of the angular momentum simply means that the body rotates more rapidly.

The lengthy argument above appears at first to be nothing more than a difficult way of solving an easy problem in rotation about a fixed axis. However, the vector nature of torque and angular momentum are essential to an understanding of the gyroscope, to be discussed in the next section.

If the resultant external torque on a body is zero, then from Eq. (9–23) $d\mathbf{L}$ is zero and *the angular momentum vector remains constant in magnitude and direction* (rotational analogue of Newton's first law). This is the principle of *conservation of angular momentum,* and it ranks with the principles of conservation of linear momentum and conservation of energy as one of the most fundamental relations of mechanics.

A circus acrobat, a diver, or a skater performing a pirouette on the toe of one skate, all take advantage of the principle. Suppose an acrobat has just left a swing, as in Fig. 9–14, with arms and legs extended and with a small clockwise angular momentum. When he pulls his arms and legs in, his moment of inertia I becomes much smaller. Since his angular momentum $I\omega$ remains constant and I decreases, his angular velocity ω increases.

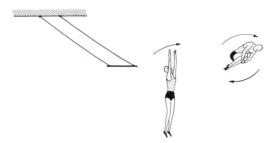

FIG. 9–14. Conservation of angular momentum.

EXAMPLE. A man stands at the center of a turntable, holding his arms extended horizontally with a 10-lb weight in each hand. He is set rotating about a vertical axis with an angular velocity of one revolution in 2 sec. Find his new angular velocity if he drops his hands to his sides. The moment of inertia of the man may be assumed constant and equal to 4 slug·ft². The original distance of the weights from the axis is 3 ft, and their final distance is 6 in.

If friction in the turntable is neglected, no external torques act about a vertical axis and the angular momentum about this axis is constant. That is,

$$I\omega = (I\omega)_0 = I_0\omega_0,$$

where I and ω are the final moment of inertia and angular velocity, and I_0 and ω_0 are the initial values of these quantities.

$$I = I_{\text{man}} + I_{\text{weights}},$$

$$I = 4 + 2\left(\frac{10}{32}\right)\left(\frac{1}{2}\right)^2 = 4.16 \text{ slug·ft}^2,$$

$$I_0 = 4 + 2\left(\frac{10}{32}\right)(3)^2 = 9.63 \text{ slug·ft}^2,$$

$$\omega_0 = \pi \text{ rad/sec},$$

$$\omega = \omega_0 \frac{I_0}{I} = 2.31\pi \text{ rad/sec}.$$

That is, the angular velocity is more than doubled.

9–10 Rotation about a moving axis. The top and the gyroscope. A symmetrical object rotating about an axis, one point of which is fixed, is called a *top*. If the fixed point is at the center of gravity, the object is called a *gyroscope*. The axis of rotation of a top or gyroscope can itself rotate about the fixed point. When this is the case, the angular momentum vector no longer lies on the axis. However, if the angular velocity *of* the axis is small compared with the angular velocity *about* the axis, the

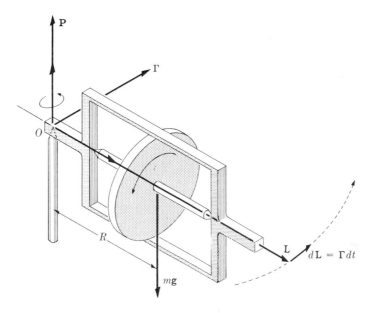

FIG. 9–15. Vector $d\mathbf{L}$ is the change in angular momentum produced in time dt by the moment $\boldsymbol{\Gamma}$ of the force $m\mathbf{g}$. Vectors $d\mathbf{L}$ and $\boldsymbol{\Gamma}$ are in the same direction. (Compare with Fig. 9–13.)

component of angular momentum arising from the former effect is small and we shall neglect it.

Figure 9–15 illustrates the usual mounting of a toy gyroscope, more properly called a top, since the fixed point O is not at the center of gravity. Vector $\mathbf{L}$ is the angular momentum. The upward force $\mathbf{P}$ at the pivot has no moment about this point; the resultant moment is that due to the weight $m\mathbf{g}$ and the magnitude is given by

$$\Gamma = mgR.$$

Its direction is perpendicular to the axis of rotation as shown. In a time dt (compare with the analysis of Fig. 9–13) this torque produces a change $d\mathbf{L}$ in the angular momentum, having the same direction as $\boldsymbol{\Gamma}$ and given by

$$d\mathbf{L} = \boldsymbol{\Gamma} \, dt.$$

The angular momentum $\mathbf{L} + d\mathbf{L}$, after a time dt, is the vector sum of $\mathbf{L}$ and $d\mathbf{L}$. Since $d\mathbf{L}$ is perpendicular to $\mathbf{L}$ and is infinitesimal, the new angular momentum vector has the same *magnitude* as the old but a different *direction*. The tip of the angular momentum vector moves as shown, and as time goes on it swings around a horizontal circle. But since the angular momentum vector lies along the gyroscope axis, the axis turns also, rotating in a horizontal plane about the point O. This motion of the axis of rotation is called *precession*.

The angle $d\phi$ turned through by the vector $\mathbf{L}$ in time dt is

$$d\phi = \frac{dL}{L}.$$

The *angular velocity of precession*, Ω, is

$$\Omega = \frac{d\phi}{dt} = \frac{1}{L}\frac{dL}{dt}.$$

But

$$\frac{dL}{dt} = \Gamma,$$

so

$$\Omega = \frac{\Gamma}{L}.$$

The angular velocity of precession is therefore inversely proportional to the angular momentum. If this is large, the precessional angular velocity will be small.

A gyroscope does not necessarily retain a fixed direction in space. We can make the gyroscope turn in any direction we please by applying the appropriate torque.

Why doesn't the gyroscope in Fig. 9–15 fall? The answer is that the upward force $\mathbf{P}$ exerted on it by the pivot is just equal to its weight $m\mathbf{g}$, so that the resultant vertical *force* is zero and the vertical acceleration of the center of gravity is zero. In other words, the vertical component of its linear momentum remains zero, since there is no resultant vertical force. The two forces $\mathbf{P}$ and $m\mathbf{g}$ constitute a *couple* of moment $\Gamma = mgR$, so the resultant moment is *not* zero and the angular momentum changes. If the gyroscope were not rotating, it would have no angular momentum $\mathbf{L}$ to start with. Its angular momentum after a time Δt would be that acquired from the couple acting on it and would be in the same direction as the moment of this couple. In other words, the gyroscope would rotate about an axis through O in the direction of the vector $\boldsymbol{\Gamma}$. But if the gyroscope is originally rotating, the change in its angular momentum produced by the couple adds vectorially to the large angular momentum it already has, and since $d\mathbf{L}$ is horizontal and perpendicular to $\mathbf{L}$, the result is a motion of precession with both the angular momentum vector and the axis remaining horizontal.

To understand why the vertical force $\mathbf{P}$ should equal $m\mathbf{g}$, we must look further into the way in which the precessional motion in Fig. 9–15 originated. If the frame of the gyroscope is initially held at rest, say by supporting the projecting portion of the frame opposite O with one's finger, the upward forces exerted by the finger and by the pivot are each equal to $mg/2$. If the finger is suddenly removed, the upward force at O, at the first instant, is still $mg/2$. The resultant vertical *force* is not zero, and the center of gravity has an initial downward acceleration. At the same time, precessional motion begins, although with a smaller angular velocity than that in the final steady state. The result of this motion is to cause the end of the frame at O to press down on the pivot with a greater force, so that the upward force at O increases and eventually becomes greater than mg. When this happens, the center of gravity starts to accelerate upward. The process repeats itself and the motion consists of a precession together with an up-and-down oscillation of the axis called *nutation*.

To start the gyroscope off with pure precession, it is necessary to give the outer end of the axis a push in the direction in which it would normally precess. This causes the end of the frame at O to bear down on the pivot so that the upward force at O increases. When this force equals mg, the vertical forces are in equilibrium, the outer end can be released, and the precession continues as in Fig. 9–15.

PROBLEMS

9–1. (a) What angle in radians is subtended by an arc 6 ft in length, on the circumference of a circle whose radius is 4 ft?   (b) What angle in radians is subtended by an arc of length 78.54 cm on the circumference of a circle of diameter 100 cm? What is this angle in degrees? (c) The angle between two radii of a circle is 0.60 radian.   What length of arc is intercepted on the circumference of a circle of radius 200 cm? of radius 200 ft?

9–2. Compute the angular velocity, in rad/sec, of the crankshaft of an automobile engine rotating at 4800 rev/min.

9–3. (a) A cylinder 6 in. in diameter rotates in a lathe at 750 rev/min. What is the tangential velocity of the surface of the cylinder? (b) The proper tangential velocity for machining cast iron is about 2 ft/sec.   At how many rev/min should a piece of stock 2 in. in diameter be rotated in a lathe?

9–4. An electric motor running at 1800 rev/min has on its shaft three pulleys, of diameters 2, 4, and 6 in. respectively. Find the linear velocity of the surface of each pulley in ft/sec. The pulleys may be connected by a belt to a similar set on a countershaft, the 2 in. to the 6 in., the 4 in. to the 4 in., and the 6 in. to the 2 in. Find the three possible angular velocities of the countershaft in rev/min.

9–5. A wheel 2.4 ft in diameter starts from rest and accelerates uniformly to an angular velocity of 100 rad/sec in 20 sec. Find the angular acceleration and the angle turned through.

9–6. The angular velocity of a flywheel decreases uniformly from 1000 rev/min to 400 rev/min in 5 sec. Find the angular acceleration and the number of revolutions made by the wheel

in the 5-sec interval. How many more seconds are required for the wheel to come to rest?

9–7. A flywheel requires 3 sec to rotate through 234 radians. Its angular velocity at the end of this time is 108 rad/sec. Find its constant angular acceleration.

9–8. A flywheel whose angular acceleration is constant and equal to 2 rad/sec^2, rotates through an angle of 100 radians in 5 sec. How long had it been in motion at the beginning of the 5-sec interval if it started from rest?

9–9. (a) Distinguish clearly between tangential and radial acceleration. (b) A flywheel rotates with constant angular velocity. Does a point on its rim have a tangential acceleration? a radial acceleration? (c) A flywheel is rotating with constant angular acceleration. Does a point on its rim have a tangential acceleration? a radial acceleration? Are these accelerations constant in magnitude?

9–10. A wheel 30 in. in diameter is rotating about a fixed axis with an initial angular velocity of 2 rev/sec. The acceleration is 3 rev/sec^2.   (a) Compute the angular velocity after 6 sec. (b) Through what angle has the wheel turned in this time interval? (c) What is the tangential velocity of a point on the rim of the wheel at $t = 6$ sec? (d) What is the resultant acceleration of a point on the rim of the wheel at $t = 6$ sec?

9–11. A wheel having a diameter of 1 ft starts from rest and accelerates uniformly to an angular velocity of 900 rev/min in 5 sec. (a) Find the position at the end of 1 sec of a point originally at the top of the wheel. (b) Compute and show in a diagram the magnitude and direction of the acceleration at the end of 1 sec.

9–12. A flywheel of radius 30 cm starts from rest and accelerates with a constant angular acceleration of 0.50 rad/sec². Compute the tangential acceleration, the radial acceleration, and the resultant acceleration, of a point on its rim (a) at the start, (b) after it has turned through 120°, (c) after it has turned through 240°.

9–13. A wheel starts from rest and accelerates uniformly to an angular velocity of 900 rev/min in 20 sec. At the end of 1 sec, (a) find the angle through which the wheel has rotated, and (b) compute and show in a diagram the magnitude and direction of the tangential and radial components of acceleration of a point 6 in. from the axis.

9–14. A wheel rotates with a constant angular velocity of 10 rad/sec. (a) Compute the radial acceleration of a point 2 ft from the axis, from the relation $a_R = \omega^2 R$. (b) Find the tangential velocity of the point, and compute its radial acceleration from the relation $a_R = v^2/R$.

9–15. Find the required angular velocity of an ultracentrifuge, in rev/min, in order that the radial acceleration of a point 1 cm from the axis shall equal 300,000 g (i.e., 300,000 times the acceleration due to gravity).

9–16. (a) Prove that when a body starts from rest and rotates about a fixed axis with constant angular acceleration, the radial acceleration of a point in the body is directly proportional to its angular displacement. (b) Through what angle will the body have turned when the resultant acceleration makes an angle of 60° with the radial acceleration?

9–17. Find the moment of inertia of a rod 4 cm in diameter and 2 m long, of mass 8 kgm, (a) about an axis perpen-

dicular to the rod and passing through its center, (b) about an axis perpendicular to the rod and passing through one end, (c) about a longitudinal axis through the center of the rod.

9–18. The inner radius of a hollow cylinder is 3 in., the outer radius is 4 in., and the length is 6 in. What is the radius of gyration of the cylinder about its axis?

9–19. The four bodies shown in Fig. 9–16 have equal masses m. Body A is a solid cylinder of radius R. Body B is a hollow thin cylinder of radius R. Body C is a solid square with length of side $= 2R$. Body D is the same size as C, but hollow (i.e., made up of four thin walls). The bodies have axes of rotation perpendicular to the page and through the center of gravity of each body. (a) Which body has the smallest moment of inertia? (b) Which body has the largest moment of inertia?

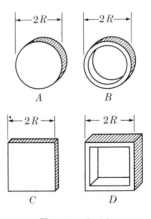

FIGURE 9–16

9–20. Small blocks, each of mass m, are clamped at the ends and at the center of a light rigid rod of length L. Compute the moment of inertia and the radius of gyration of the system about an axis perpendicular to the rod and passing through a point one-quarter of the length from one end. Neglect the moment of inertia of the rod.

9–21. The radius of the earth is 4000 mi and its mass is 4×10^{21} slugs (approximately). Find (a) its moment of inertia about an axis through its center, and (b) its radius of gyration in miles. Assume the density to be uniform.

9–22. A flywheel consists of a solid disk 1 ft in diameter and 1 in. thick, and two projecting hubs 4 in. in diameter and 3 in. long. If the material of which it is constructed weighs 480 lb/ft^3, find (a) its moment of inertia, and (b) its radius of gyration about the axis of rotation.

9–23. A grinding wheel 6 in. in diameter, weighing 4 lb, is rotating at 3600 rev/min. (a) What is its kinetic energy? (b) How far would it have to fall to acquire the same kinetic energy?

9–24. A disk of mass m and radius R is pivoted about a horizontal axis through its center, and a small body of mass m is attached to the rim of the disk. If the disk is released from rest with the small body at the end of a horizontal radius, find the angular velocity when the small body is at the bottom.

9–25. The flywheel of a gasoline engine is required to give up 380 ft·lb of kinetic energy while its angular velocity decreases from 600 rev/min to 540 rev/min. What moment of inertia is required?

9–26. The flywheel of a punch press has a moment of inertia of 15 slug·ft^2 and it runs at 300 rev/min. The flywheel supplies all the energy needed in a quick punching operation. (a) Find the speed in rev/min to which the flywheel will be reduced by a sudden punching operation requiring 4500 ft·lb of work. (b) What must be the con-

stant power supply to the flywheel in horsepower to bring it back to its initial speed in 5 sec?

9–27. A magazine article described a passenger bus in Zurich, Switzerland, which derived its motive power from the energy stored in a large flywheel. The wheel was brought up to speed periodically, when the bus stopped at a station, by an electric motor which could then be attached to the electric power lines. The flywheel was a solid cylinder of mass 1000 kgm, diameter 180 cm, and its top speed was 3000 rev/min. (a) At this speed, what is the kinetic energy of the flywheel? (b) If the average power required to operate the bus is 25 hp, how long can it operate between stops?

9–28. A grindstone in the form of a solid cylinder has a radius of 2 ft and weighs 96 lb. (a) What torque will bring it from rest to an angular velocity of 300 rev/min in 10 sec? (b) What is its kinetic energy when rotating at 300 rev/min?

9–29. The flywheel of a motor weighs 640 lb and has a radius of gyration of 4 ft. The motor develops a constant torque of 1280 lb·ft, and the flywheel starts from rest. (a) What is the angular acceleration of the flywheel? (b) What will be its angular velocity after making 4 revolutions? (c) How much work is done by the motor during the first 4 revolutions?

9–30. The flywheel of a stationary engine has a moment of inertia of 20 slugs·ft^2. (a) What constant torque is required to bring it up to an angular velocity of 900 rev/min in 10 sec, starting from rest? (b) What is its final kinetic energy?

9–31. A grindstone 3 ft in diameter, weighing 96 lb, is rotating at 900 rev/min. A tool is pressed normally against the rim with a force of 45 lb, and the grindstone comes to rest in 10 sec. Find the coefficient of friction between the tool and the grindstone. Neglect friction in the bearings.

9–32. A 128-lb grindstone is 3 ft in diameter and has a radius of gyration of $\frac{3}{4}$ ft. A tool is pressed down on the rim with a normal force of 10 lb. The coefficient of sliding friction between the tool and stone is 0.6 and there is a constant friction torque of 3 lb·ft between the axle of the stone and its bearings. (a) How much force must be applied normally at the end of a crank handle 15 in. long to bring the stone from rest to 120 rev/min in 9 sec? (b) After attaining a speed of 120 rev/min, what must the normal force at the end of the handle become to maintain a constant speed of 120 rev/min? (c) How long will it take the grindstone to come from 120 rev/min to rest if it is acted on by the axle friction alone?

9–33. A constant torque of 20 newton·meters is exerted on a pivoted wheel for 10 sec, during which time the angular velocity of the wheel increases from zero to 100 rev/min. The external torque is then removed and the wheel is brought to rest by friction in its bearings in 100 sec. Compute (a) the moment of inertia of the wheel, (b) the friction torque, (c) the total number of revolutions made by the wheel.

9–34. A cord is wrapped around the rim of a flywheel 2 ft in radius, and a steady pull of 10 lb is exerted on the cord, as in Fig. 9–17(a). The wheel is mounted in frictionless bearings on a horizontal shaft through its center. The moment of inertia of the wheel is 2 slugs·ft^2. (a) Compute the angular acceleration of the wheel. (b) Show that the work done in unwinding 20 ft of cord equals the gain in kinetic energy of the wheel. (c) If a 10-lb

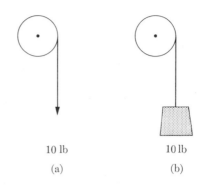

10 lb   10 lb

(a)   (b)

FIGURE 9–17

weight hangs from the cord as in Fig. 9–17(b), compute the angular acceleration of the wheel. Why is this not the same as in part (a)?

9–35. A solid cylinder of mass 15 kgm, 30 cm in diameter, is pivoted about a horizontal axis through its center, and a rope wrapped around the surface of the cylinder carries at its end a block of mass 8 kgm. (a) How far does the block descend in 5 sec, starting from rest? (b) What is the tension in the rope? (c) What is the force exerted on the cylinder by its bearings?

9–36. A bucket of water weighing 64 lb is suspended by a rope wrapped around a windlass in the form of a solid cylinder 1 ft in diameter, also weighing 64 lb. The bucket is released from rest at the top of a well and falls 64 ft to the water. (a) What is the tension in the rope while the bucket is falling? (b) With what velocity does the bucket strike the water? (c) What was the time of fall? Neglect the weight of the rope.

9–37. A 16-lb block rests on a horizontal frictionless surface. A cord attached to the block passes over a pulley, whose diameter is 6 in., to a hanging block which also weighs 16 lb.

The system is released from rest, and the blocks are observed to move 16 ft in 2 sec. (a) What was the moment of inertia of the pulley? (b) What was the tension in each part of the cord?

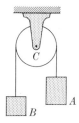

FIGURE 9–18

9–38. Figure 9–18 represents an Atwood's machine. Find the linear accelerations of blocks A and B, the angular acceleration of the wheel C, and the tension in each side of the cord (a) if the surface of the wheel is frictionless, (b) if there is no slipping between the cord and the surface of the wheel. Let the weights of blocks A and B be 8 lb and 4 lb respectively, the moment of inertia of the wheel about its axis be 0.125 slug·ft², and the radius of the wheel be 0.5 ft.

9–39. A flywheel 3 ft in diameter is pivoted on a horizontal axis. A rope is wrapped around the outside of the flywheel and a steady pull of 10 lb is exerted on the rope. It is found that 24 ft of rope are unwound in 4 sec. (a) What was the angular acceleration of the flywheel? (b) What was its final angular velocity? (c) What was its final kinetic energy? (d) What is its moment of inertia?

9–40. A light rigid rod 100 cm long has a small block of mass 50 gm attached at one end. The other end is pivoted, and the rod rotates in a vertical circle. At a certain instant the rod makes an angle of 53° with the vertical,

and the tangential speed of the block is 400 cm/sec. (a) What are the horizontal and vertical components of the velocity of the block? (b) What is the moment of inertia of the system? (c) What is the radial acceleration of the block? (d) What is the tangential acceleration of the block? (e) What is the tension or compression in the rod?

9–41. (a) Compute the torque developed by an airplane engine whose output is 2000 hp at an angular velocity of 2400 rev/min. (b) If a drum 18 in. in diameter were attached to the motor shaft, and the power output of the motor were used to raise a weight hanging from a rope wrapped around the shaft, how large a weight could be lifted? (c) With what velocity would it rise?

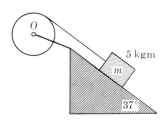

FIGURE 9–19

9–42. A block of mass $m = 5$ kgm slides down a surface inclined 37° to the horizontal, as shown in Fig. 9–19. The coefficient of sliding friction is 0.25. A string attached to the block is wrapped around a flywheel on a fixed axis at O. The flywheel has a mass $M = 20$ kgm, an outer radius $R = 0.2$ m, and a radius of gyration with respect to the axis $k_0 = 0.1$ m. (a) What is the acceleration of the block down the plane? (b) What is the tension in the string?

9–43. A man sits on a piano stool holding a pair of dumbbells at a distance of 3 ft from the axis of rotation of the stool. He is given an angular velocity of 2 rad/sec, after which he pulls the dumbbells in until they are but 1 ft distant from the axis. The moment of inertia of the man about the axis of rotation is 3 slugs·ft^2 and may be considered constant. The dumbbells weigh 16 lb each and may be considered point masses. Neglect friction. (a) What is the initial angular momentum of the system? (b) What is the angular velocity of the system after the dumbbells are pulled in toward the axis? (c) Compute the kinetic energy of the system before and after the dumbbells are pulled in. Account for the difference, if any.

9–44. A block of mass 50 gm is attached to a cord passing through a hole in a horizontal frictionless surface as in Fig. 9–20. The block is originally revolving at a distance of 20 cm from the hole with an angular velocity of 3 rad/sec. The cord is then pulled from below, shortening the radius of the circle in which the block revolves to 10 cm. The block may be considered a point mass. (a) What is the new angular velocity? (b) Find the change in kinetic energy of the block.

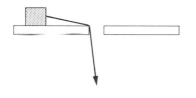

FIGURE 9–20

9–45. A small block weighing 8 lb is attached to a cord passing through a hole in a horizontal frictionless surface. The block is originally revolving in a circle of radius 2 ft about the hole with a tangential velocity of 12 ft/sec. The cord is then pulled slowly from below, shortening the radius of the circle in which the block revolves. The breaking strength of the cord is 144 lb. What will be the radius of the circle when the cord breaks?

9–46. A block of mass M rests on a turntable which is rotating at constant angular velocity ω. A smooth cord runs from the block through a hole in the center of the table down to a hanging block of mass m. The coefficient of friction between the first block and the turntable is μ. (See Fig. 9–21.) Find the largest and smallest values of the radius r for which the first block will remain at rest relative to the turntable.

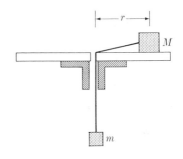

FIGURE 9–21

9–47. A uniform rod of mass 30 gm and 20 cm long rotates in a horizontal plane about a fixed vertical axis through its center. Two small bodies, each of mass 20 gm, are mounted so that they can slide along the rod. They are initially held by catches at positions 5 cm on each side of the center of the rod, and the system is rotating at 15 rev/min. Without otherwise changing the system, the catches are released and the masses slide outward along the rod and fly off at the ends. (a) What is the angular velocity of the system at the instant when the small masses reach the ends of the rod? (b) What is the angular velocity of the rod after the small masses leave it?

9–48. A turntable rotates about a fixed vertical axis, making one revolution in 10 sec. The moment of inertia of the turntable about this axis is 720 slugs·ft^2. A man weighing 160 lb, initially standing at the center of the turntable, runs out along a radius. What is the angular velocity of the turntable when the man is 6 ft from the center?

9–49. Disks A and B are mounted on a shaft SS and may be connected or disconnected by a clutch C, as in Fig. 9–22. The moment of inertia of disk A is one-half that of disk B. With the clutch disconnected, A is brought up to an angular velocity ω_0. The accelerating torque is then removed from A and it is coupled to disk B by the clutch. Bearing friction may be neglected. It is found that 3000 ft·lb of heat are developed in the clutch when the connection is made. What was the original kinetic energy of disk A?

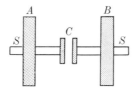

FIGURE 9–22

9–50. A man weighing 160 lb stands at the rim of a turntable of radius 10 ft and moment of inertia 2500 slugs·ft^2, mounted on a vertical frictionless shaft at its center. The whole system is initially at rest. The man now walks along the outer edge of the turntable with a velocity of 2 ft/sec, relative to the earth. (a) With what angular velocity and in what direction does the turntable rotate? (b) Through what angle will it have rotated when the man reaches his initial position on the turntable? (c) Through what angle will it have rotated when he reaches his initial position relative to the earth?

9–51. A man weighing 160 lb runs around the edge of a horizontal turntable mounted on a vertical frictionless axis through its center. The velocity of the man, relative to the earth, is 4 ft/sec. The turntable is rotating in the opposite direction with an angular velocity of 0.2 rad/sec. The radius of the turntable is 8 ft and its moment of inertia about the axis of rotation is 320 slugs·ft^2. Find the final angular velocity of the system if the man comes to rest, relative to the turntable.

9–52. Two flywheels, A and B, are mounted on shafts which can be connected or disengaged by a friction clutch C. (Fig. 9–22.) The moment of inertia of wheel A is 4 slugs·ft^2. With the clutch disengaged, wheel A is brought up to an angular velocity of 600 rev/min. Wheel B is initially at rest. The clutch is now engaged, accelerating B and decelerating A until both wheels have the same angular velocity. The final angular velocity of the system is 400 rev/min. (a) What was the moment of inertia of wheel B? (b) How much energy was lost in the process? Neglect all bearing friction.

9–53. The stabilizing gyroscope of a ship weighs 50 tons, its radius of gyration is 5 ft, and it rotates about a vertical axis with an angular velocity of 900 rev/min. (a) How long a time is required to bring it up to speed, starting from rest, with a constant power input of 100 hp? (b) Find the torque needed to cause the axis to precess in a vertical fore-and-aft plane at the rate of 1 degree/sec.

9–54. The mass of the rotor of a toy gyroscope is 150 gm and its moment of inertia about its axis is 1500 gm·cm². The mass of the frame is 30 gm. The gyroscope is supported on a single pivot as in Fig. 9–23, with its center of gravity distant 4 cm horizontally from the pivot, and is precessing in a horizontal plane at the rate of one revolution in 6 sec. (a) Find the upward

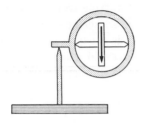

FIGURE 9–23

force exerted by the pivot. (b) Find the angular velocity with which the rotor is spinning about its axis, expressed in rev/min. (c) Copy the diagram, and show by vectors the angular momentum of the rotor and the torque acting on it.

9–55. The moment of inertia of the front wheel of a bicycle is 0.25 slug·ft², its radius is 15 in., and the forward speed of the bicycle is 20 ft/sec. With what angular velocity must the front wheel be turned about a vertical axis to counteract the capsizing torque due to a weight of 120 lb, one inch horizontally to the right or left of the line of contact of wheels and ground? (Bicycle riders: compare with experience and see if your answer seems reasonable.)

CHAPTER 10

ELASTICITY

10–1 Stress. The preceding chapter dealt with the motion of a "rigid" body, a convenient mathematical abstraction since every real substance yields to some extent under the influence of applied forces. Ultimately, the change in shape or volume of a body when outside forces act on it is determined by the forces between its molecules. Although molecular theory is at present not sufficiently advanced to enable one to calculate the elastic properties of, say, a block of copper starting from the properties of a copper atom, the study of the solid state is an active subject in many research laboratories and our knowledge of it is steadily increasing. In this chapter we shall, however, confine ourselves to quantities that are directly measurable, and not attempt any molecular explanation of the observed behavior.

Figure 10–1(a) shows a bar of uniform cross-sectional area A subjected to equal and opposite pulls **F** at its ends. The bar is said to be in *tension.* Consider a section through the bar at right angles to its length, as indicated by the dotted line. Since every portion of the bar is in equilibrium, that portion at the right of the section must be pulling on the portion at the left with a force **F**, and vice versa. If the section is not too near the ends of the bar, these pulls are uniformly distributed over the cross-sectional area A, as indicated by the short arrows in Fig. 10–1(b). We define the *stress* S at the section as the ratio of the force F to the area A.

$$\text{Stress} = \frac{F}{A}. \tag{10–1}$$

The stress is called a *tensile* stress, meaning that each portion *pulls* on the other, and it is also a *normal* stress because the distributed force is

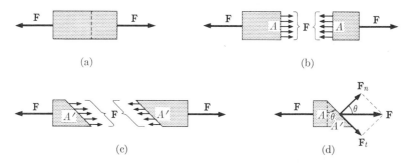

Fɪɢ. 10–1. (a) A bar in tension. (b) The stress at a perpendicular section equals F/A. (c) and (d) The stress at an inclined section can be resolved into a *normal stress,* F_n/A', and a *tangential* or *shearing* stress, F_t/A'.

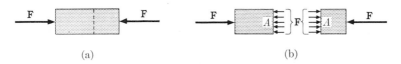

Fig. 10–2. A bar in compression.

perpendicular to the area. Stress is expressed in newtons/m^2, dynes/cm^2, and lb/ft^2. (The lb/in^2 is also commonly used, but it is not a unit of the engineering system.)

Consider next a section through the bar in some arbitrary direction, as in Fig. 10–1(c). The resultant force exerted on the portion at either side of this section, by the portion at the other, is equal and opposite to the force F at the end of the section. Now, however, the force is distributed over a larger area A' and is not at right angles to the area. If we represent the resultant of the distributed forces by a single vector of magnitude F, as in Fig. 10–1(d), this vector can be resolved into a component F_n normal to the area A', and a component F_t tangent to the area. The *normal* stress is defined, as before, as the ratio of the component F_n to the area A'. The ratio of the component F_t to the area A' is called the *tangential* stress or, more commonly, the *shearing* stress at the section.

$$\left. \begin{array}{c} \text{Normal stress} = \dfrac{F_n}{A'} \\[1.5em] \text{Tangential (shearing) stress} = \dfrac{F_t}{A'} \end{array} \right\} \qquad (10\text{–}2)$$

Stress is not a vector quantity since, unlike a force, we cannot assign to it a specific direction. The *force* acting on the portion of the body on a specified side of a section has, of course, a definite direction. Stress is one of a class of physical quantities called *tensors*.

A bar subjected to pushes at its ends, as in Fig. 10–2, is said to be in *compression*. The stress on the dotted section, illustrated in part (b), is also a normal stress but is now a *compressive* stress, since each portion pushes on the other. It should be evident that if we take a section in some arbitrary direction it will be subject to both a tangential (shearing) and a normal stress, the latter now being a compression.

As another example of a body under stress, consider the block of square cross section in Fig. 10–3(a), acted on by two equal and opposite couples produced by the pairs of forces $\mathbf{F}_x$ and $\mathbf{F}_y$ distributed over its surfaces. The block is in equilibrium, and any portion of it is in equilibrium also. Thus the distributed forces over the diagonal face in part (b) must have a

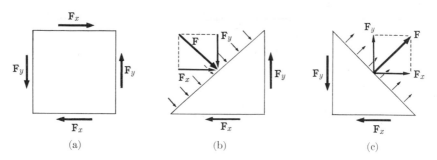

FIG. 10–3. (a) A body in shear. The stress on one diagonal, part (b), is a pure compression; that on the other, part (c), is a pure tension.

resultant **F** whose components are equal to $\mathbf{F}_x$ and $\mathbf{F}_y$. The stress at this section is therefore a pure compression, although the stresses at the right face and the bottom are both shearing stresses. Similarly, we see from Fig. 10–3(c) that the other diagonal is in pure tension.

Consider next a fluid under pressure. The term "fluid" means a substance that can flow, hence the term applies to both liquids and gases. If there is a shearing stress at any point in a fluid, the fluid slips sidewise so long as the stress is maintained. Hence in a fluid at rest, the shearing stress is everywhere zero. Figure 10–4 represents a fluid in a cylinder provided with a piston, on which is exerted a downward force. The triangle is a side view of a wedge-shaped portion of the fluid. If for the moment we neglect the weight of the fluid, the only forces on this portion are those exerted by the rest of the fluid, and since these forces can have no shearing (or tangential) component, they must be normal to the surfaces of the wedge. Let $\mathbf{F}_x$, $\mathbf{F}_y$, and **F** represent the forces against the three faces. Since the fluid is in equilibrium, it follows that

$$F \sin \theta = F_x, \quad F \cos \theta = F_y.$$

Also,

$$A \sin \theta = A_x, \quad A \cos \theta = A_y.$$

Dividing the upper equations by the lower, we find

$$\frac{F}{A} = \frac{F_x}{A_x} = \frac{F_y}{A_y}.$$

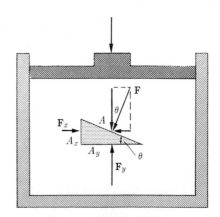

FIG. 10–4. A fluid under hydrostatic pressure. The force on a surface in any direction is normal to the surface.

Hence the force per unit area is the *same*, regardless of the direction of the section, and is always a compression. Any one of the preceding ratios defines the *hydrostatic pressure p* in the fluid.

$$p = \frac{F}{A}, \qquad F = pA. \tag{10–3}$$

Pressure is expressed in newtons/m^2, dynes/cm^2, or lb/ft^2. Like other types of stress, pressure is not a vector quantity and no direction can be assigned to it. The *force* against any area within (or bounding) a fluid at rest and under pressure is normal to the area, regardless of the orientation of the area. This is what is meant by the common statement that "the pressure in a fluid is the same in all directions."

The stress within a solid can also be a hydrostatic pressure, provided the stress at all points of the surface of the solid is of this nature. That is, the force per unit area must be the same at *all* points of the surface, and the force must be normal to the surface and directed inward. This is not the case in Fig. 10–2, where forces are applied at the ends of the bar only, but it is automatically the case if a solid is immersed in a fluid under pressure.

10–2 Strain. The term *strain* refers to the relative change in dimensions or shape of a body which is subjected to stress. Associated with each type of stress described in the preceding section is a corresponding type of strain.

Figure 10–5 shows a bar whose natural length is l_0 and which elongates to a length l when equal and opposite pulls are exerted at its ends. The elongation, of course, does not occur at the ends only; every element of the bar stretches in the same proportion as does the bar as a whole. The *tensile strain* in the bar is defined as the ratio of the increase in length to the original length.

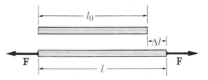

$$\text{Tensile strain} = \frac{l - l_0}{l_0} = \frac{\Delta l}{l_0}. \tag{10–4}$$

FIG. 10–5. The longitudinal strain is defined as $\Delta l/l_0$.

The *compressive strain* of a bar in compression is defined in the same way, as the ratio of the decrease in length to the original length.

Figure 10–6(a) illustrates the nature of the deformation when shearing stresses act on the faces of a block, as in Fig. 10–3. The dotted outline *abcd* represents the unstressed block, and the full lines *a'b'c'd'* represent the block under stress. In part (a), the centers of the stressed and unstressed block coincide. In part (b), the edges *ad* and *a'd'* coincide. The

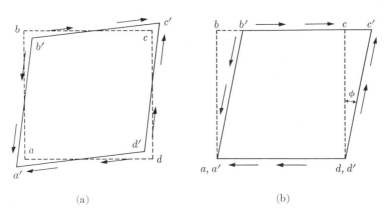

(a)   (b)

Fig. 10–6. Change in shape of a block in shear. The shearing strain is defined as $\tan \phi \approx \phi$.

lengths of the faces under shear remain very nearly constant, while all dimensions parallel to the diagonal ac increase in length, and those parallel to the diagonal bd decrease in length. Note that this is to be expected in view of the nature of the corresponding internal stresses (see Fig. 10–3). This type of strain is called a *shearing strain*, and is defined as the tangent of the angle ϕ. Since ϕ is always small, $\tan \phi$ is very nearly equal to ϕ (in radians).

$$\text{Shearing strain} = \tan \phi \approx \phi \text{ (radians)}. \qquad (10\text{–}5)$$

Like other types of strain, shearing strain is a pure number.

The strain produced by a hydrostatic pressure, called a *volume strain*, is defined as the ratio of the change in volume, ΔV, to the original volume V_0. It also is a pure number.

$$\text{Volume strain} = \frac{\Delta V}{V_0}. \qquad (10\text{–}6)$$

10–3 Elastic modulus. The ratio of a stress to the corresponding strain is called an *elastic modulus* and, provided the elastic limit is not exceeded, this ratio is found experimentally to be constant, characteristic of a given material. In other words, the stress is directly proportional to the strain, or is a linear function of the strain (within the elastic limit). This linear relationship between stress and strain is called *Hooke's law*.

Let us first consider longitudinal (i.e., tensile or compressive) stresses and strains. Experiment shows that with a given material, a given longitudinal stress produces a strain of the same magnitude whether the stress is a compression or a tension. Hence the ratio of tensile stress to tensile strain, for a given material, equals the ratio of compressive stress to com-

Table 10–1

Approximate Elastic Moduli

Material	Young's modulus, Y		Shear modulus, S		Bulk modulus, B	
	10^{12} dynes $\overline{\text{cm}^2}$	10^6 lb $\overline{\text{in}^2}$	10^{12} dynes $\overline{\text{cm}^2}$	10^6 lb $\overline{\text{in}^2}$	10^{12} dynes $\overline{\text{cm}^2}$	10^6 lb $\overline{\text{in}^2}$
Aluminum	0.70	10	0.24	3.4	0.70	10
Brass	0.91	13	0.36	5.1	0.61	8.5
Copper	1.1	16	0.42	6.0	1.4	20
Glass	0.55	7.8	0.23	3.3	0.37	5.2
Iron	0.91	13	0.70	10	1.0	14
Lead	0.16	2.3	0.056	0.8	0.077	1.1
Nickel	2.1	30	0.77	11	2.6	34
Steel	2.0	29	0.84	12	1.6	23
Tungsten	3.6	51	1.5	21	2.0	29

pressive strain. This ratio is called the *stretch modulus* or *Young's modulus* of the material and will be denoted by Y.

$$Y = \frac{\text{tensile stress}}{\text{tensile strain}} = \frac{\text{compressive stress}}{\text{compressive strain}}$$

or

$$Y = \frac{F_n/A}{\Delta l/l_0}. \tag{10–7}$$

Since a strain is a pure number, the units of Young's modulus are the same as those of stress, namely, force per unit area. Tabulated values are usually in lb/in^2 or dynes/cm^2. Some typical values are listed in Table 10–1.

The ratio of a shearing stress to the corresponding shearing strain is called the *shear modulus* of a material and will be represented by S. It is also called the *modulus of rigidity* or the *torsion modulus*.

$$S = \frac{\text{shearing stress}}{\text{shearing strain}} = \frac{F_t/A}{\phi}. \tag{10–8}$$

(Refer to Fig. 10–6 for the meaning of ϕ.) The shear modulus of a material is also expressed as force per unit area. For most materials it is one-half to one-third as great as Young's modulus.

The modulus relating an increase in hydrostatic pressure to the corresponding fractional decrease in volume is called the *bulk modulus*, and we shall represent it by B.

$$B = -\frac{p}{\Delta V/V_0}. \tag{10-9}$$

The minus sign is included in the definition of B since an increase of pressure always causes a decrease in volume. That is, if p is positive, ΔV is negative. By including a minus sign in its definition, the bulk modulus itself is a positive quantity.

The reciprocal of the bulk modulus is called the *compressibility*, k. Tables of physical constants often list the compressibility rather than the bulk modulus. From its definition,

$$k = \frac{1}{B} = -\frac{1}{p}\frac{\Delta V}{V_0}. \tag{10-10}$$

The ratio $\Delta V/V_0$ is the fractional change in volume. Hence the compressibility of a substance may be defined as its fractional change in volume per unit increase in pressure.

The units of a bulk modulus, from Eq. (10–9), are the same as those of pressure, and the units of compressibility, from Eq. (10–10), are those of a reciprocal pressure. In tabulating compressibilities, the pressure is often expressed in atmospheres (1 atmosphere = 14.7 lb/in^2). The corresponding units of compressibility are therefore "reciprocal atmospheres," or atm^{-1}. For example, the statement that the compressibility of water (see Table 10–2) is 50×10^{-6} atm^{-1}, or 50×10^{-6} per atmosphere, means that the volume decreases by 50 one-millionths of the original volume for each atmosphere increase in pressure.

Table 10–3 shows the relation between the various types of stress, strain, and elastic moduli.

When a metal rod is subjected to an increasing tensile stress, the strain is found to change as in Fig. 10–7. The first part of the curve, from O to

TABLE 10–2

COMPRESSIBILITY OF LIQUIDS

Liquid	Compressibility, 10^{-6} atm^{-1}
Carbon disulphide	66
Ethyl alcohol	112
Glycerine	22
Mercury	3.8
Water	50

TABLE 10–3

STRESSES AND STRAINS

Type of stress	Stress	Strain	Elastic modulus	Name of modulus
Tension	$\dfrac{F_n}{A}$	$\dfrac{\Delta l}{l_0}$	$Y = \dfrac{F_n/A}{\Delta l/l_0}$	Young's modulus
Compression	$\dfrac{F_n}{A}$	$\dfrac{\Delta l}{l_0}$	$Y = \dfrac{F_n/A}{\Delta l/l_0}$	
Shear	$\dfrac{F_t}{A}$	$\tan \phi \approx \phi$	$S = \dfrac{F_t/A}{\phi}$	Shear modulus
Hydrostatic pressure	$p\left(= \dfrac{F_n}{A}\right)$	$\dfrac{\Delta V}{V_0}$	$B = -\dfrac{p}{\Delta V/V_0}$	Bulk modulus

A, is a straight line. That is, in this region there is a linear relationship between stress and strain and the material obeys Hooke's law. If the stress is not carried beyond that corresponding to point A, the specimen returns to its original length when the stress is removed. In other words, the portion of the curve from O to A is the region of perfect elasticity.

If the stress is increased to a value corresponding to point B and then removed, the specimen does not return to its original length but retains a *permanent strain* or a *set*. Point A is called the *elastic limit* or the *proportional limit* of the material. Finally, when the stress is increased sufficiently, the specimen breaks at point C.

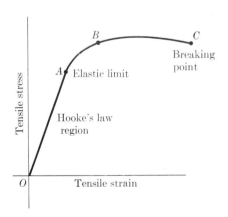

FIG. 10–7. Stress-strain diagram for a metal in tension.

EXAMPLE 1. In an experiment to measure Young's modulus, a load of 1000 lb hanging from a steel wire 8 ft long, of cross section 0.025 in², was found to stretch the wire 0.12 in. above its no-load length. What were the stress, the strain, and the value of

Young's modulus for the steel of which the wire was composed?

$$\text{Stress} = \frac{F_n}{A} = \frac{1000}{0.025} = 40,000 \; \frac{\text{lb}}{\text{in}^2} \cdot$$

$$\text{Strain} = \frac{\Delta l}{l_0} = \frac{0.010}{8} = 0.00125.$$

$$Y = \frac{\text{stress}}{\text{strain}} = \frac{40,000}{0.00125} = 32 \times 10^6 \; \frac{\text{lb}}{\text{in}^2} \cdot$$

EXAMPLE 2. Suppose the object in Fig. 10–6 is a brass plate 2 ft square and $\frac{1}{4}$ in. thick. How large a force F must be exerted on each of its edges if the displacement cc' in Fig. 10–6(b) is 0.01 in.? The shear modulus of brass is 5×10^6 lb/in².

The shearing stress on each edge is

$$\text{Shearing stress} = \frac{F_t}{A} = \frac{F}{24 \times \frac{1}{4}} = \frac{F}{6} \frac{\text{lb}}{\text{in}^2} \cdot$$

The shearing strain is

$$\text{Shearing strain} = \tan \phi = \frac{0.01}{24} = 4.17 \times 10^{-4}.$$

$$\text{Shear modulus } S = \frac{\text{stress}}{\text{strain}},$$

$$5 \times 10^6 = \frac{F/6}{4.17 \times 10^{-4}},$$

$$F = 12,500 \text{ lb.}$$

EXAMPLE 3. The volume of oil contained in a certain hydraulic press is 5 ft³. Find the decrease in volume of the oil when subjected to a pressure of 2000 lb/in². The compressibility of the oil is 20×10^{-6} per atm.

The volume decreases by 20 parts per million for a pressure increase of one atm. Since 2000 lb/in² = 136 atm, the volume decrease is $136 \times 20 = 2720$ parts per million. Since the original volume is 5 ft³, the actual decrease is

$$\frac{2720}{1,000,000} \times 5 \text{ ft}^3 = 0.0136 \text{ ft}^3 = 23.5 \text{ in}^3.$$

Or, from Eq. (10–10),

$$\Delta V = -kV_0 p = -20 \times 10^{-6} \text{ atm}^{-1} \times 5 \text{ ft}^3 \times 136 \text{ atm}$$

$$= -0.0136 \text{ ft}^3.$$

10–4 The force constant. The various elastic moduli are quantities which describe the elastic properties of a particular *material* and do not directly indicate how much a given rod, cable, or spring constructed of the material will distort under load. If Eq. (10–7) is solved, for F, one obtains

$$F = \frac{YA}{l_0} \Delta l$$

or, if YA/l_0 is replaced by a single constant k, and the elongation Δl is represented by x,

$$F = kx. \tag{10–11}$$

In other words, the elongation of a body in tension above its no-load length is directly proportional to the stretching force. Hooke's law was originally stated in this form, rather than in terms of stress and strain.

When a helical wire spring is stretched, the stress in the wire is practically a pure shear. The elongation of the spring as a whole is directly proportional to the stretching force. That is, an equation of the form $F = kx$ still applies, the constant k depending on the shear modulus of the wire, its radius, the radius of the coils, and the number of coils.

The constant k, or the ratio of the force to the elongation, is called the *force constant* or the *stiffness* of the spring, and is expressed in pounds per foot, newtons per meter, or dynes per centimeter. It is equal numerically to the force required to produce unit elongation.

Problems

10–1. A steel wire 10 ft long and 0.1 square inch in cross section is found to stretch 0.01 ft under a tension of 2500 lb. What is Young's modulus for this steel?

10–2. The elastic limit of a steel elevator cable is 40,000 lb/in². Find the maximum upward acceleration which can be given a 2-ton elevator when supported by a cable whose cross section is $\frac{1}{2}$ in² if the stress is not to exceed $\frac{1}{4}$ of the elastic limit.

10–3. A copper wire 12 ft long and 0.036 in. in diameter was given the test below. A load of 4.5 lb was originally hung from the wire to keep it taut. The position of the lower end of the wire was read on a scale.

Added load (lb)	Scale reading (in.)
0	3.02
2	3.04
4	3.06
6	3.08
8	3.10
10	3.12
12	3.14
14	3.65

(a) Make a graph of these values, plotting the increase in length horizontally and the added load vertically. (b) Calculate the value of Young's modulus. (c) What was the stress at the elastic limit?

10–4. A steel wire has the following properties:

Length = 10 ft
Cross section = 0.01 in²
Young's modulus = 30,000,000 lb/in²
Shear modulus = 10,000,000 lb/in²
Elastic limit = 60,000 lb/in²
Breaking stress = 120,000 lb/in²

The wire is fastened at its upper end and hangs vertically. (a) How great a load can be supported without exceeding the elastic limit? (b) How much will the wire stretch under this load? (c) What is the maximum load that can be supported?

10–5. (a) What is the maximum load that can be supported by an aluminum wire 0.05 in. in diameter without exceeding the elastic limit of 14,000 lb/in²? (b) If the wire was originally 20 ft long, how much will it elongate under this load?

10–6. A 10-lb weight hangs on a vertical steel wire 2 ft long and 0.001 in² in cross section. Hanging from the bottom of this weight is a similar steel wire which supports a 5-lb weight. Compute (a) the longitudinal strain, and (b) the elongation of each wire.

10–7. A 32-lb weight, fastened to the end of a steel wire of unstretched length 2 ft, is whirled in a vertical circle with an angular velocity at the bottom of the circle of 2 rev/sec. The cross section of the wire is 0.01 in². Calculate the elongation of the wire when the weight is at the lowest point of its path.

10–8. A copper wire 320 inches long and a steel wire 160 in. long, each of cross section 0.1 in², are fastened end-to-end and stretched with a tension of 100 lb. (a) What is the change in length of each wire? (b) What is the elastic potential energy of the system?

10–9. A copper rod of length 3 ft and cross-sectional area 0.5 in² is fastened end-to-end to a steel rod of length L and cross-sectional area 0.2 in². The compound rod is subjected to equal and opposite pulls of magnitude 6000 lb at its ends. (a) Find the length L of the steel rod if the elongations of the two rods are equal. (b) What is the stress in each rod? (c) What is the strain in each rod?

10–10. A rod 105 cm long, whose weight is negligible, is supported at its ends by wires A and B of equal length. The cross section of A is 1 mm^2, that of B is 2 mm^2. Young's modulus for wire A is 30×10^6 lb/in^2 and for B it is 20×10^6 lb/in^2. At what point along the bar should a weight w be suspended in order to produce (a) equal stresses in A and B, (b) equal strains in A and B? (Fig. 10–8.)

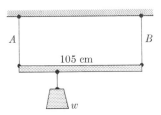

105 cm

w

FIGURE 10–8

10–11. A bar of length L, cross-sectional area A, Young's modulus Y, is subjected to a tension F. Represent the stress in the bar by S and the strain by P. Derive the expression for the elastic potential energy, per unit volume, of the bar in terms of S and P.

10–12. The compressibility of sodium is to be measured by observing the displacement of the piston in Fig. 10–4 when a force is applied. The sodium is immersed in an oil which fills the cylinder below the piston. Assume that the piston and walls of the cylinder are perfectly rigid, that there is no friction, and no oil leak. Compute the compressibility of the sodium in terms of the applied force F, the piston displacement x, the piston area A, the initial volume of the oil V_0, the initial volume of the sodium v_0, and the compressibility of the oil k_0.

10–13. Two strips of metal are riveted together at their ends by four rivets, each of diameter 0.25 in. What is the maximum tension that can be exerted by the riveted strip if the shearing stress on the rivets is not to exceed 10,000 lb/in^2? Assume each rivet to carry one-quarter of the load.

10–14. Find the weight per cubic foot of ocean water at a depth where the pressure is 4700 lb/ft^2. The weight at the surface is 64 lb/ft^3.

10–15. Compute the compressibility of steel, in reciprocal atmospheres, and compare with that of water. Which material is the more readily compressed?

10–16. A steel post 6 in. in diameter and 10 ft long is placed vertically and is required to support a load of 20,000 lb. (a) What is the stress in the post? (b) What is the strain in the post? (c) What is the change in length of the post?

10–17. A hollow cylindrical steel column 10 ft high shortens 0.01 in. under a compression load of 72,000 lb. If the inner radius of the cylinder is 0.80 of the outer one, what is the outer radius?

10–18. A bar of cross section A is subjected to equal and opposite tensile forces $\mathbf{F}$ at its ends. Consider a plane through the bar making an angle θ with a plane at right angles to the bar (Fig. 10–9). (a) What is the tensile (normal) stress at this plane, in terms of F, A, and θ? (b) What is the shearing (tangential) stress at the

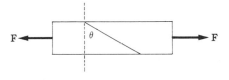

F ← θ → F

FIGURE 10–9

plane, in terms of F, A, and θ? (c) For what value of θ is the tensile stress a maximum? (d) For what value of θ is the shearing stress a maximum?

10–19. Suppose the block in Fig. 10–3 is rectangular instead of square, but is in equilibrium under the action of shearing stresses on those outside faces perpendicular to the plane of the diagram. (Note that then $F_x \neq F_y$.) (a) Show that the shearing stress is the same on all outside faces perpendicular to the plane of the diagram. (b) Show that on all sections perpendicular to the plane of the diagram and making an angle of 45° with an end face, the stress is still a pure tension or compression.

CHAPTER 11

HARMONIC MOTION

11–1 Introduction. When a body executes a to-and-fro motion about some fixed point, its motion is said to be *oscillatory*. In this chapter we consider a special type of oscillatory motion called *harmonic motion*. Motion of this sort is closely approximated by that of a body suspended from a spring, by a pendulum swinging with a small amplitude, and by the balance wheel of a watch. The vibrations of the strings and air columns of musical instruments either are harmonic or are a superposition of harmonic motions. Modern atomic theory leads us to believe that the molecules of a solid body oscillate with nearly harmonic motion about their fixed lattice positions, although of course their motion cannot be directly observed.

In every form of wave motion, the particles of the medium in which the wave is traveling oscillate with harmonic motion or with a superposition of such motions. This is true even for light waves and radiowaves in empty space, except that instead of material particles the quantities that oscillate are the electric and magnetic intensities associated with the wave. As a final example, the equations describing the behavior of an electrical circuit in which there is an alternating current have the same form as those for the harmonic motion of a material body. It can be seen that a study of harmonic motion will lay the foundation for future work in many different fields of physics.

11–2 Elastic restoring forces. It has been shown in Chapter 10 that when a body is caused to change its shape, the distorting force is proportional to the amount of the change, provided the proportional limit of elasticity is not exceeded. The change may be in the nature of an increase in length, as of a rubber band or a coil spring, or a decrease in length, or a bending as of a flat spring, or a twisting of a rod about its axis, or of many other forms. The term "force" is to be interpreted liberally as the force, or torque, or pressure, or whatever may be producing the distortion. If we restrict the discussion to the case of a push or a pull, where the distortion is simply the displacement of the point of application of the force, the force and displacement are related by Hooke's law,

$$F = kx,$$

where k is a proportionality constant called the *force constant* and x is the displacement from the equilibrium position.

In this equation, F stands for the force which must be exerted *on* an elastic body to produce the displacement x. The force with which the elastic body pulls back on an object to which it is attached is called the *restoring force* and is equal to $-kx$.

11–3 Definitions. To fix our ideas, suppose that a flat strip of steel such as a hacksaw blade is clamped vertically in a vise and a small body is attached to its upper end, as in Fig. 11–1. Assume that the strip is sufficiently long and the displacement sufficiently small so that the motion is essentially along a straight line. The mass of the strip itself is negligible.

Let the top of the strip be pulled to the right a distance A, as in Fig. 11–1, and released. The attached body is then acted on by a restoring force exerted by the steel strip and directed toward the equilibrium position O. It therefore accelerates in the direction of this force, and moves in toward the center with increasing speed. The *rate* of increase (i.e., the acceleration) is not constant, however, since the accelerating force becomes smaller as the body approaches the center.

When the body reaches the center the restoring force has decreased to zero, but because of the velocity which has been acquired, the body "overshoots" the equilibrium position and continues to move toward the left. As soon as the equilibrium position is passed the restoring force again comes into play, directed now toward the right. The body therefore decelerates, and at a rate which increases with increasing distance from O. It will therefore be brought to rest at some point to the left of O, and repeat its motion in the opposite direction.

Both experiment and theory show that the motion will be confined to a range $\pm A$ on either side of the equilibrium position, each to-and-fro movement taking place in the same length of time. If there were no loss of energy by friction the motion would continue indefinitely once it had been started. This type of motion, under the influence of an elastic restoring force and in the absence of all friction, is called *simple harmonic motion*, often abbreviated SHM.

Any sort of motion which repeats itself in equal intervals of time is called *periodic*, and if the motion is back and forth over the same path it is also called *oscillatory*.

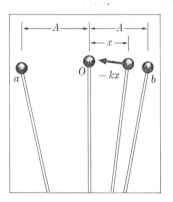

FIG. 11–1. Motion under an elastic restoring force.

A *complete vibration* or *oscillation* means one round trip, say from a to b and back to a, or from O to b to O to a and back to O.

The *periodic time*, or simply the *period* of the motion, represented by T, is the time required for one complete vibration.

The *frequency*, f, is the number of complete vibrations per unit time. Evidently the frequency is the reciprocal of the period, or

$$T = \frac{1}{f}.$$

The *coordinate*, x, at any instant, is the distance away from the equilibrium position or center of the path at that instant.

The *amplitude*, A, is the maximum coordinate. The total range of the motion is therefore $2A$.

11–4 Equations of simple harmonic motion. We now wish to find expressions for the coordinate, velocity, and acceleration of a body moving with simple harmonic motion, just as we found those for a body moving with constant acceleration. It must be emphasized that the equations of motion with *constant* acceleration cannot be applied, since the acceleration is continually changing.

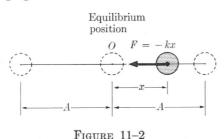

Equilibrium position

$O \quad F = -kx$

FIGURE 11–2

Figure 11–2 represents the vibrating body of Fig. 11–1 at some instant when its coordinate is x. The resultant force on it is simply the elastic restoring force, $-kx$, and from Newton's second law,

$$F = -kx = ma = mv\,\frac{dv}{dx}.$$

From the second and fourth terms, we have

$$mv\,\frac{dv}{dx} + kx = 0. \qquad (11\text{–}1)$$

Therefore

$$\int mv\,dv + \int kx\,dx = 0,$$

which integrates to

$$\tfrac{1}{2}mv^2 + \tfrac{1}{2}kx^2 = C_1. \qquad (11\text{–}2)$$

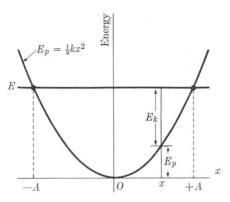

FIG. 11-3. Relation between total energy E, potential energy E_p, and kinetic energy E_k, for a body oscillating with SHM.

The first term on the left is the kinetic energy E_k of the body and the second is its elastic potential energy E_p. Equation (11-2) therefore states that the total energy of the system is constant, and the integration constant C_1 equals the total energy E. (This result is only to be expected, since the system is conservative.)

$$E_k + E_p = E.$$

The significance of this relation can be brought out by the graph shown in Fig. 11-3, in which energy is plotted vertically and the coordinate x horizontally. First, the curve representing the potential energy, $E_p = \frac{1}{2}kx^2$, is constructed. (This curve is a parabola.) Next, a horizontal line is drawn at a height equal to the total energy E. We see at once that the motion is restricted to values of x lying between the points at which the horizontal line intersects the parabola, since if x were outside this range the potential energy would exceed the total energy, which is impossible. The motion of the vibrating body is analogous to that of a particle released at a height E on a frictionless track shaped like the potential energy curve, and the motion is said to take place in a "potential energy well."

If a vertical line is constructed at any value of x within the permitted range, the length of the segment between the x-axis and the parabola represents the potential energy E_p at that value of x, and the length of the segment between the parabola and the horizontal line at height E represents the corresponding kinetic energy E_k. At the endpoints, therefore, the energy is all potential and at the midpoint it is all kinetic. The velocity at the midpoint has its maximum (absolute) value v_{max}:

$$\frac{1}{2}mv_{max}^2 = E,$$

$$v_{max} = \pm\sqrt{2E/m}, \qquad\qquad (11\text{-}3)$$

the sign of v being positive or negative depending on the direction of motion.

At the ends of the path the coordinate has its maximum (absolute) value x_{max}, equal to the amplitude A:

$$\tfrac{1}{2}kx_{max}^2 = E, \qquad x_{max} = \pm\sqrt{2E/k},$$

$$A = |x_{max}| = \sqrt{2E/k}. \tag{11-4}$$

The velocity v at any coordinate x, from Eq. (11–2), is

$$v = \sqrt{\frac{2E - kx^2}{m}}. \tag{11-5}$$

Making use of Eq. (11–4), this can be written

$$v = \sqrt{k/m}\,\sqrt{A^2 - x^2}. \tag{11-6}$$

The expression for the coordinate x as a function of time can now be obtained by replacing v with dx/dt, in Eq. (11–6), and integrating. This gives

$$\int \frac{dx}{\sqrt{A^2 - x^2}} = \sqrt{\frac{k}{m}} \int dt,$$

$$\sin^{-1}\frac{x}{A} = \sqrt{\frac{k}{m}}\,t + C_2. \tag{11-7}$$

Let x_0 be the value of x when $t = 0$. The integration constant C_2 is then

$$C_2 = \sin^{-1}\frac{x_0}{A}.$$

That is, C_2 is the *angle* (in radians) whose sine equals x_0/A. Let us represent this angle by θ_0:

$$\sin\theta_0 = \frac{x_0}{A}, \qquad \theta_0 = \sin^{-1}\frac{x_0}{A}. \tag{11-8}$$

Equation (11–7) can now be written

$$\sin^{-1}\frac{x}{A} = \sqrt{\frac{k}{m}}\,t + \theta_0,$$

$$x = A\sin\left(\sqrt{\frac{k}{m}}\,t + \theta_0\right). \tag{11-9}$$

The coordinate x is therefore a *sinusoidal* function of the time t. The term in parentheses is an *angle*, in radians. It is called the *phase angle*, or simply the *phase* of the motion. The angle θ_0 is the *initial phase angle*, and is also referred to as the *epoch angle*.

The period T is the time required for one complete oscillation. That is, the coordinate x has the same value at the times t and $t + T$. In other words, the phase angle $(\sqrt{k/m}\,t + \theta_0)$ increases by 2π radians in the time T:

$$\sqrt{k/m}\,(t + T) + \theta_0 = (\sqrt{k/m}\,t + \theta_0) + 2\pi,$$

$$T = 2\pi\,\sqrt{\frac{m}{k}}. \tag{11–10}$$

The period T therefore depends only on the mass m and the force constant k. It does not depend on the amplitude (or on the total energy). For given values of m and k, the time of one complete oscillation is the same whether the amplitude is large or small. A motion that has this property is said to be *isochronous* (equal time).

The frequency f, or the number of complete oscillations per unit time, is the reciprocal of the period T:

$$f = \frac{1}{T} = \frac{1}{2\pi}\,\sqrt{\frac{k}{m}}.$$

The *angular frequency* ω is defined as

$$\omega = 2\pi f$$

and is expressed in radians/sec. It follows from the two preceding equations that

$$\omega = \sqrt{k/m},$$

and Eqs. (11–9) and (11–6) can be written more compactly as

$$x = A\,\sin\,(\omega t + \theta_0), \tag{11–11}$$

$$v = \omega\sqrt{A^2 - x^2}. \tag{11–12}$$

Expressions for the velocity and acceleration as functions of time can now be obtained by differentiation:

$$v = \frac{dx}{dt} = \omega A\,\cos\,(\omega t + \theta_0), \tag{11–13}$$

$$a = \frac{dv}{dt} = -\omega^2 A\,\sin\,(\omega t + \theta_0). \tag{11–14}$$

Since $A\,\sin\,(\omega t + \theta_0) = x$, the expression for the acceleration as a function of x is

$$a = -\omega^2 x. \tag{11–15}$$

TABLE 11–1

Rectilinear motion with constant acceleration	Simple harmonic motion (in terms of ω and θ_0)
$a = $ constant	$a = -\omega^2 x$ $a = -\omega^2 A \sin(\omega t + \theta_0)$
$v^2 = v_0^2 + 2a(x - x_0)$ $v = v_0 + at$	$v = \pm\omega\sqrt{A^2 - x^2}$ $v = \omega A \cos(\omega t + \theta_0)$
$x = x_0 + v_0 t + \frac{1}{2}at^2$	$x = A \sin(\omega t + \theta_0)$
$\omega = 2\pi/T = 2\pi f = \sqrt{k/m}, \qquad \sin\theta_0 = x_0/A$	

The equations of simple harmonic motion may be summarized by comparing them with similar equations for rectilinear motion with constant acceleration. This is done in Table 11–1.

Figure 11–4 shows corresponding graphs of the coordinate x, velocity v, and acceleration a of a body oscillating with simple harmonic motion, plotted as functions of the time t (or of the angle ωt). The initial coordinate is x_0 and the initial velocity is v_0. The angle θ_0 has been taken as $\pi/4$ rad. Each curve repeats itself in a time interval equal to the period T, during which the angle ωt increases by 2π rad. Note that when the body is at either end of its path, i.e., when the coordinate x has its maximum positive or negative value ($\pm A$), the velocity is zero and the acceleration has its maximum negative or positive value ($\mp a_{\max}$). Note also that when the body passes through its equilibrium position ($x = 0$) the velocity has its maximum positive or negative value ($\pm v_{\max}$) and the acceleration is zero.

The equations of motion take a simpler form if we set $t = 0$ when the body is at the midpoint, or is at one end of its path. For example, suppose we let $t = 0$ when the body has its maximum positive displacement. Then $x_0 = +A$, $\sin\theta_0 = 1$, $\theta_0 = \pi/2$, and

$$\left.\begin{aligned} x &= A \sin(\omega t + \pi/2) = A \cos\omega t, \\ v &= -\omega A \sin\omega t, \\ a &= -\omega^2 A \cos\omega t. \end{aligned}\right\} \qquad (11\text{–}16)$$

This corresponds to moving the origin from the point O, in Fig. 11–4, to the point O'. The graph of x vs. t becomes a cosine curve, that of v vs. t a negative sine curve, and that of a a negative cosine curve.

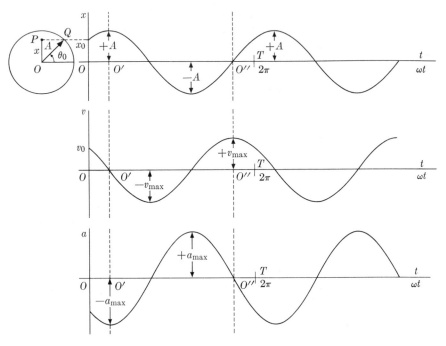

FIG. 11–4. Graphs of coordinate x, velocity v, and acceleration a of a body oscillating with simple harmonic motion.

If we set $t = 0$ when the body is at the midpoint and moving toward the right, then $x_0 = 0$, $\sin \theta_0 = 0$, $\theta_0 = 0$ and

$$\left.\begin{aligned} x &= A \sin \omega t, \\ v &= \omega A \cos \omega t, \\ a &= -\omega^2 A \sin \omega t. \end{aligned}\right\} \tag{11–17}$$

This corresponds to displacing the origin to the point O'' in Fig. 11–4.

EXAMPLE. Let the mass of the body in Fig. 11–2 be 25 gm, the force constant k be 400 dynes/cm, and let the motion be started by displacing the body 10 cm to the right of its equilibrium position and imparting to it a velocity toward the right of 40 cm/sec. Compute (a) the period T, (b) the frequency f, (c) the angular frequency ω, (d) the total energy E, (e) the amplitude A, (f) the angle θ_0, (g) the maximum velocity $v_{\max}$, (h) the maximum acceleration $a_{\max}$, (j) the coordinate, velocity, and acceleration at a time $\pi/8$ sec after the start of the motion.

(a) $T = 2\pi \sqrt{\dfrac{m}{k}} = 2\pi \sqrt{\dfrac{25 \text{ gm}}{400 \text{ dynes/cm}}} = \dfrac{\pi}{2} \text{ sec} = 1.57 \text{ sec.}$

(b) $f = \dfrac{1}{T} = \dfrac{2}{\pi} \dfrac{\text{vib}}{\text{sec}} = 0.638 \dfrac{\text{vib}}{\text{sec}}.$

(c) $\omega = 2\pi f = 4 \text{ rad/sec.}$

(d) $E = \frac{1}{2}mv_0^2 + \frac{1}{2}kx_0^2 = 40{,}000 \text{ ergs.}$

(e) $A = \sqrt{2E/k} = 10\sqrt{2} \text{ cm.}$

(f) $\sin \theta_0 = x_0/A = 1/\sqrt{2}, \qquad \theta_0 = \pi/4 \text{ rad.}$

(g) $|v_{max}| = \sqrt{2E/m} = 40\sqrt{2} \text{ cm/sec} = 56.6 \text{ cm/sec.}$

The maximum velocity occurs at the midpoint, where $x = 0$. Hence, from Eq. (11–12),

$$|v_{max}| = \omega A = 40\sqrt{2} \text{ cm/sec.}$$

(h) The maximum acceleration occurs at the ends of the path where the force is a maximum. From Eq. (11–15),

$$|a_{max}| = \omega^2 x_{max} = 160\sqrt{2} \text{ cm/sec}^2.$$

(j) The equations of motion are:

$$x = 10\sqrt{2} \sin\left(4t + \frac{\pi}{4}\right),$$

$$v = 40\sqrt{2} \cos\left(4t + \frac{\pi}{4}\right),$$

$$a = -160\sqrt{2} \sin\left(4t + \frac{\pi}{4}\right).$$

When $t = (\pi/8)$ sec, the phase angle is

$$\left(4t + \frac{\pi}{4}\right) = \frac{3\pi}{4} \text{ rad,}$$

$$x = 10\sqrt{2} \sin(3\pi/4) = 10 \text{ cm,}$$

$$v = 40\sqrt{2} \cos(3\pi/4) = -40 \text{ cm/sec,}$$

$$a = -160\sqrt{2} \sin(3\pi/4) = -160 \text{ cm/sec}^2.$$

The curves of Fig. 11–4 represent the motion of the body in this example, if the scales of x, v, a, and t are such that $A = 10\sqrt{2}$ cm, $v_{max} = 40\sqrt{2}$ cm/sec, $a_{max} = 160\sqrt{2}$ cm/sec^2, and $T = \pi/2$ sec.

The equations of simple harmonic motion can be given a geometrical interpretation as follows. Let the line segment OQ in Fig. 11–5(a), of length equal to the amplitude A, rotate with an angular velocity ω about the fixed point O. The rotating line segment is often referred to as a *rotating vector*, but strictly speaking it is not a vector quantity. That is, while it has a specified direction *in a diagram*, it has no specified direction *in space*. It is better described as a *rotor*. (The German term is "Zeiger," meaning a pointer in the sense of a clock hand or the pointer on a pressure gauge.) Let the rotor OQ make an angle with the horizontal axis, at time $t = 0$, equal to the initial phase angle θ_0. Point P is the projection of point Q onto the vertical axis, and as OQ rotates, point P oscillates along this axis.

We now show that the equations of motion of P are the same as those of a body oscillating with simple harmonic motion of amplitude A, angular frequency ω, and initial phase angle θ_0. Let x represent the length of OP. At any time t, the angle between the radius OQ and the horizontal axis equals the phase angle $\omega t + \theta_0$ and

$$x = A \sin (\omega t + \theta_0).$$

The velocity of point Q [see Fig. 11–5(b)] is ωA, and its vertical component, equal to the velocity of P, is

$$v = \omega A \cos (\omega t + \theta_0).$$

The acceleration of Q is its radial acceleration $\omega^2 A$ [see Fig. 11–5(c)] and its vertical component, equal to the acceleration of P, is

$$a = -\omega^2 A \sin (\omega t + \theta_0).$$

The negative sign must be included because the acceleration is negative whenever the sine of the phase angle is positive, and vice versa.

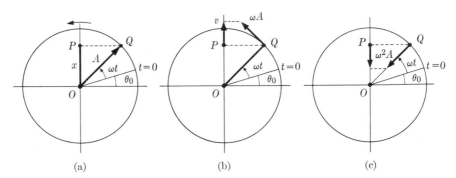

FIG. 11–5. Representation of simple harmonic motion by the projection onto the vertical axis of the tip of the rotor OQ.

These equations are, of course, just the general equations of harmonic motion. In the special case corresponding to Eqs. (11–16), the initial phase angle is 90° and the reference point Q is at the top of the circle when $t = 0$. If the reference point is at the right-hand end of the horizontal diameter when $t = 0$, then $\theta_0 = 0$ and the motion is described by Eqs. (11–17).

11–5 Motion of a body suspended from a coil spring. Figure 11–6(a) shows a coil spring of force constant k and no-load length l. When a body of mass m is attached to the spring as in part (b), it hangs in equilibrium with the spring extended by an amount Δl such that the upward force P exerted by the spring is equal to the weight of the body, mg. But $P = k\,\Delta l$, so

$$k\,\Delta l = mg.$$

Now suppose the body is at a distance x above its equilibrium position, as in part (c). The extension of the spring is now $\Delta l - x$, the upward force it exerts on the body is $k(\Delta l - x)$, and the resultant force F on the body is

$$F = k(\Delta l - x) - mg = -kx.$$

The resultant force is therefore proportional to the displacement of the body *from its equilibrium position*, and if set in vertical motion the body oscillates with an angular frequency $\omega = \sqrt{k/m}$.

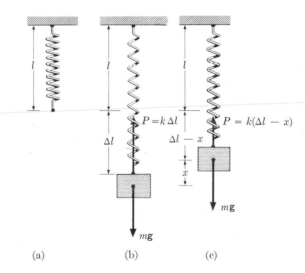

FIG. 11–6. The restoring force on a body suspended by a spring is proportional to the coordinate measured from the equilibrium position.

EXAMPLE. A body of mass 500 gm is suspended from a coil spring of negligible mass, and stretches the spring 7 cm. Find the frequency and amplitude of the ensuing motion if the body is displaced 3 cm below its equilibrium position and given a downward velocity of 40 cm/sec.

The force constant of the spring is

$$k = \frac{mg}{\Delta l} = 70,000 \text{ dynes/cm.}$$

The angular frequency is

$$\omega = \sqrt{k/m} = 11.8 \text{ rad/sec.}$$

The initial potential energy (taking the equilibrium position as the reference level of potential energy) is

$$\tfrac{1}{2}kx_0^2 = 315,000 \text{ ergs.}$$

The initial kinetic energy is

$$\tfrac{1}{2}mv_0^2 = 400,000 \text{ ergs.}$$

The total energy is 715,000 ergs and this equals the elastic potential energy when the displacement is equal to the amplitude. Hence

$$\tfrac{1}{2}kA^2 = 715,000 \text{ ergs,}$$

$$A = 4.5 \text{ cm.}$$

11–6 The simple pendulum. A *simple pendulum* (also called a *mathematical pendulum*) is defined as a particle suspended from a fixed point by a weightless, inextensible string. When the pendulum is displaced from the vertical by an angle θ, as in Fig. 11–7, the restoring force is $mg \sin \theta$, and the displacement s from the equilibrium position equals $L\theta$, where L is the length of the string and θ is in radians. The motion is therefore *not* harmonic, since the restoring force is proportional to $\sin \theta$ while the displacement is proportional to θ. However, if the angle θ is small we can approximate $\sin \theta$ by θ, and the restoring force is then

$$F \approx -mg\theta \approx -\left(\frac{mg}{L}\right)s.$$

The effective force constant of the pendulum is therefore $k = mg/L$, and the period is

$$T \approx 2\pi\sqrt{m/k} \approx 2\pi\sqrt{L/g}. \tag{11–18}$$

It can be shown that the exact equation for the period, when the maximum angular displacement is ϕ, is given by the infinite series

$$T = 2\pi\sqrt{\frac{L}{g}}\left(1 + \frac{1^2}{2^2}\sin^2\frac{\phi}{2} + \frac{1^2 \cdot 3^2}{2^2 \cdot 4^2}\sin^4\frac{\phi}{2} + \cdots\right). \tag{11–19}$$

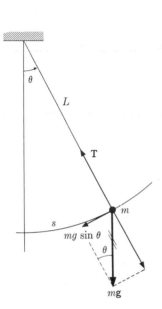

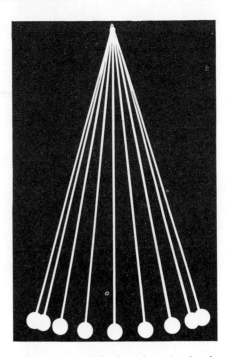

Fig. 11–7. Forces on the bob of a simple pendulum.

Fig. 11–8. A single swing of a simple pendulum.

The period can be computed to any desired degree of precision by taking enough terms in the series. When $\phi = 15°$, the true period differs from that given by the approximate equation (11–18) by less than one-half of one percent.

The utility of the pendulum as a timekeeper is based on the fact that the period is practically independent of the amplitude. Thus, as a pendulum clock runs down and the amplitude of the swings becomes slightly smaller, the clock will still keep very nearly correct time.

The simple pendulum is also a precise and convenient method of measuring the acceleration of gravity, g, without actually resorting to free fall, since L and T may readily be measured. More complicated pendulums find considerable application in the field of geophysics. Local deposits of ore or oil, if their density differs from that of their surroundings, affect the local value of g, and precise measurements of this quantity over an area which is being prospected often furnish valuable information regarding the nature of underlying deposits.

Figure 11–8 is a multiflash photograph of a single swing of a simple pendulum.

PROBLEMS

11–1. A body is vibrating with simple harmonic motion of amplitude 15 cm and frequency 4 vib/sec. Compute (a) the maximum values of the acceleration and velocity, (b) the acceleration and velocity when the coordinate is 9 cm, (c) the time required to move from the equilibrium position to a point 12 cm distant from it.

11–2. A body of mass 10 gm moves with simple harmonic motion of amplitude 24 cm and period 4 sec. The coordinate is $+24$ cm when $t = 0$. Compute (a) the position of the body when $t = 0.5$ sec, (b) the magnitude and direction of the force acting on the body when $t = 0.5$ sec, (c) the minimum time required for the body to move from its initial position to the point where $x = -12$ cm, (d) the velocity of the body when $x = -12$ cm.

11–3. The motion of the piston of an automobile engine is approximately simple harmonic. (a) If the stroke of an engine (twice the amplitude) is 4 in. and the angular velocity is 3600 rev/min, compute the acceleration of the piston at the end of its stroke. (b) If the piston weighs 1 lb, what resultant force must be exerted on it at this point? (c) What is the velocity of the piston, in mi/hr, at the midpoint of its stroke?

11–4. A 4-lb weight hung from a spring is found to stretch the spring 8 in. (a) What is the force constant of the spring? (b) What would be the period of vibration of the 4-lb weight, if suspended from this spring? (c) What would be the period of an 8-lb weight hanging from the same spring?

11–5. The scale of a spring balance reading from zero to 32 lb is 6 in. long. A body suspended from the balance is observed to oscillate vertically at 1.5 vib/sec. What is the weight of the body?

11–6. A body of mass 100 gm hangs from a long spiral spring. When pulled down 10 cm below its equilibrium position and released, it vibrates with a period of 2 sec. (a) What is its velocity as it passes through the equilibrium position? (b) What is its acceleration when it is 5 cm above the equilibrium position? (c) When it is moving upward, how long a time is required for it to move from a point 5 cm below its equilibrium position to a point 5 cm above it? (d) How much will the spring shorten if the body is removed?

11–7. A body whose mass is 4.9 kgm hangs from a spring and oscillates with a period of 0.5 sec. How much will the spring shorten when the body is removed?

11–8. Four passengers whose combined weight is 600 lb are observed to compress the springs of an automobile by 2 in. when they enter the automobile. If the total load supported by the springs is 1800 lb, find the period of vibration of the loaded automobile.

11–9. Two springs, each of unstretched length 20 cm but having different force constants k_1 and k_2, are attached to opposite ends of a block of mass m on a level frictionless surface. The outer ends of the springs are now attached to the two pins P_1 and P_2, 10 cm from the original positions of the springs. Let $k_1 = 1000$ dynes/cm, $k_2 = 3000$ dynes/cm, $m = 100$ gm. (See Fig. 11–9.) (a) Find the length of each spring when the block is in its new equilibrium position, after the springs have been attached to the pins. (b) Show that the effective force constant of the combination is 4000

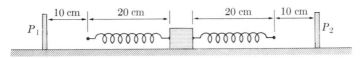

FIGURE 11–9

dynes/cm. (c) Find the period of vibration of the block if it is slightly displaced from its new equilibrium position and released.

11–10. A block suspended from a spring vibrates with simple harmonic motion. At an instant when the displacement of the block is equal to one-half the amplitude, what fraction of the total energy of the system is kinetic and what fraction is potential?

11–11. The block in Problem 11–9 and Fig. 11–9 is oscillating with an amplitude of 5 cm. At the instant it passes through its equilibrium position, a lump of putty of mass 100 gm is dropped vertically onto the block and sticks to it. (a) Find the new period and amplitude. (b) Would the answers be the same if the putty had been dropped on the block when it was at one end of its path?

11–12. A body weighing 8 lb is attached to a coil spring and oscillates vertically in simple harmonic motion. The amplitude is 2 ft, and at the highest point of the motion the spring has its natural unstretched length. Calculate the elastic potential energy of the spring, the kinetic energy of the body, its gravitational potential energy relative to the lowest point of the motion, and the sum of these three energies, when the body is (a) at its lowest point, (b) at its equilibrium position, and (c) at its highest point.

11–13. A load of 320 lb suspended from a wire whose unstretched length l_0 is 10 ft is found to stretch the wire by 0.12 in. The cross-sectional area of the wire, which can be assumed con-

stant, is 0.016 in^2. (a) If the load is pulled down a small additional distance and released, find the frequency at which it will vibrate. (b) Compute Young's modulus for the wire.

11–14. (a) With what additional force must a vertical spring carrying an 8-lb body in equilibrium be stretched so that, when released, it will perform 48 complete oscillations in 32 sec with an amplitude of 3 in.? (b) What force is exerted by the spring on the body when it is at the lowest point, the middle, and the highest point of the path? (c) What is the kinetic energy of the system when the body is 1 in. below the middle of the path? its potential energy?

11–15. A force of 12 lb stretches a certain spring 9 in. A body weighing 8 lb is hung from this spring and allowed to come to rest. It is then pulled down 4 in. and released. (a) What is the period of the motion? (b) What is the magnitude and direction of the acceleration of the body when it is 2 in. above the equilibrium position, moving upward? (c) What is the tension in the spring when the body is 2 in. above the equilibrium position? (d) What is the shortest time required to go from the equilibrium position to the point 2 in. above? (e) If a small object were placed on the oscillating body would it remain or leave? (f) If a small object were placed on the oscillating body and its amplitude doubled, where would the object and the oscillating body begin to separate?

11–16. A small block is executing simple harmonic motion in a horizontal plane with an amplitude of 10 cm. At a point 6 cm away from equilibrium the velocity is ± 24 cm/sec. (a) What is the period? (b) What is the displacement when the velocity is ± 12 cm/sec? (c) If a small object placed on the oscillating block is just on the verge of slipping at the endpoint of the path, what is the coefficient of friction?

11–17. A force of 6 lb stretches a vertical spring 9 in. (a) What weight must be suspended from the spring so that the system will oscillate with a period of $\pi/4$ sec? (b) If the amplitude of the motion is 3 in., where is the body and in what direction is it moving $\pi/12$ sec after it has passed the equilibrium position, moving downward? (c) What force does the spring exert on the body when it is 1.8 in. below the equilibrium position, moving upward?

11–18. A simple pendulum 8 ft long swings with an amplitude of 1 ft. (a) Compute the velocity of the pendulum at its lowest point. (b) Compute its acceleration at the ends of its path.

11–19. Find the length of a simple pendulum whose period is exactly 1 sec at a point where $g = 32.2$ ft/sec^2.

11–20. A pendulum clock which keeps correct time at a point where $g = 980.0$ cm/sec^2 is found to lose 10 sec per day at a higher altitude. Find the value of g at the new location.

11–21. A simple pendulum with a supporting steel wire of cross-sectional area 0.01 cm^2 is observed to have a period of 2 sec when a 10-kgm lead bob is used. The lead bob is replaced by an aluminum bob of the same dimensions having a mass of 2 kgm, and the period is remeasured. (a) What was the length of the pendulum with the lead bob? (b) By what fraction is the period changed when the aluminum bob is used? Is it an increase or decrease? [*Hint.* Use differentials.]

CHAPTER 12

WAVE MOTION

12–1 Propagation of a disturbance in a medium. Imagine a medium consisting of a large number of particles, each connected or coupled to its neighbors by *elastic* material. If one end of the medium is disturbed or displaced in any way, the displacement will not occur immediately at all other parts of the medium. The original displacement will give rise to an elastic force in the material adjacent to it, then the next particle will be displaced, and then the next, and so on. In other words, *the displacement will be propagated along the medium with a definite speed.*

In Fig. 12–1(a) the medium is a spring, or just a wire under tension. If the left end is given a small displacement in a direction perpendicular to the medium, this transverse displacement will occur at successive

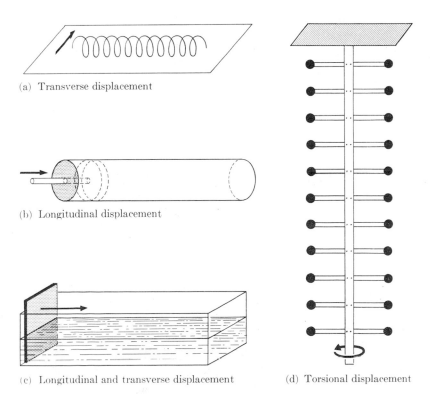

(a) Transverse displacement

(b) Longitudinal displacement

(c) Longitudinal and transverse displacement

(d) Torsional displacement

Fig. 12–1. Propagation of disturbances.

intervals of time at each coil of the spring and there will result the propagation of a *transverse pulse* along the spring.

In Fig. 12–1(b) the medium is to be regarded as either a liquid or a gas contained in a tube closed at the right end with a rigid wall and at the left end with a movable piston. If the piston is moved slightly toward the right, a *longitudinal pulse* will be propagated through the medium in the tube.

In Fig. 12–1(c) the medium is a liquid contained in a trough. The horizontal motion of a flat piece of wood at the left end will provide a displacement of the liquid which is both longitudinal and slightly transverse, and this disturbance will travel along the medium.

In Fig. 12–1(d) the medium is a set of "dumbbells" connected to a steel strip. A slight rotation of the lowest dumbbell constitutes a *torsional displacement* which will be propagated up the medium with a finite speed.

It will be shown in the next section that the speed of a pulse produced by a *small* displacement depends only on certain physical properties *of the medium itself* and not on the rapidity of the original displacement.

12–2 Calculation of the speed of a transverse pulse. Consider the string depicted in Fig. 12–2, under a tension T and with linear density (mass per unit length) μ. In Fig. 12–2(a) the string is at rest. At time $t = 0$, a constant transverse force F is applied at the left end of the string. As a result, this end moves up with a constant transverse speed v. Figure 12–2(b) shows the shape of the string after a time t has elapsed. All points of the string at the left of the point P are moving with speed v, whereas all points at the right of P are still at rest. The boundary between the moving and the stationary portions is traveling to the right with the *speed of propagation u*. The left end of the string has moved up a distance vt and the boundary point P has advanced a distance ut.

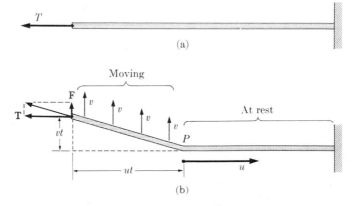

FIG. 12–2. Propagation of a transverse disturbance in a string.

The speed of propagation u can be calculated by setting the transverse impulse (transverse force $\times$ time) equal to the change of transverse momentum of the moving portion (mass $\times$ transverse velocity). The impulse of the transverse force F in time t is Ft. By similar triangles,

$$\frac{F}{T} = \frac{vt}{ut}, \qquad F = T\,\frac{v}{u}.$$

Hence

$$\text{Transverse impulse} = T\,\frac{v}{u}\,t.$$

The mass of the moving portion is the product of the mass per unit length μ and the length ut. Hence

$$\text{Transverse momentum} = \mu u t v.$$

Applying the impulse-momentum theorem, we get

$$T\,\frac{v}{u}\,t = \mu u t v,$$

and therefore

$$\boxed{u = \sqrt{T/\mu}.} \qquad \text{(Transverse)} \qquad\qquad (12\text{--}1)$$

Thus it is seen that the velocity of propagation of a transverse pulse in a string depends only on the tension and the mass per unit length.

In numerical applications of Eq. (12–1), attention must be paid to the units employed. With cgs units, T must be expressed in dynes and μ in grams per centimeter. With mks units, T must be in newtons and μ in kilograms per meter. Finally, in engineering units, T must be in pounds and μ in slugs per foot. The corresponding units of velocity will then be, respectively, centimeters per second, meters per second, and feet per second.

EXAMPLE. Calculate the velocity of a transverse pulse in a string under a tension of 20 lb if the string weighs 0.003 lb/ft.

$$T = 20 \text{ lb},$$

$$\mu = \frac{0.003}{32}\,\frac{\text{lb/ft}}{\text{ft/sec}^2},$$

$$u = \sqrt{\frac{20 \text{ lb} \times 32 \text{ ft/sec}^2}{0.003 \text{ lb/ft}}} = 461\,\frac{\text{ft}}{\text{sec}}.$$

12–3 Calculation of the speed of a longitudinal pulse. Figure 12–3 shows a fluid (liquid or gas) of density ρ in a tube of cross-sectional area A and under a pressure p. In Fig. 12–3(a) the fluid is at rest. At time $t = 0$, the piston at the left end of the tube is set in motion toward the right with a speed v. Figure 12–3(b) shows the fluid after a time t has elapsed. All portions of the fluid at the left of point P are moving with speed v, whereas all portions at the right of P are still at rest. The boundary between the moving and the stationary portions travels to the right with the speed of propagation u. The piston has moved a distance vt and the boundary has advanced a distance ut. As for a transverse disturbance in a string, the speed of propagation can be computed from the impulse-momentum theorem.

The quantity of fluid set in motion in time t is that originally occupying a volume of length ut and of cross-sectional area A. The mass of this fluid is therefore ρutA and the longitudinal momentum it has acquired is

$$\text{Longitudinal momentum} = \rho utAv.$$

We next compute the increase of pressure, Δp, in the moving fluid. The original volume of the moving fluid, Aut, has been decreased by an amount Avt. From the definition of bulk modulus B (see Chapter 10),

$$B = \frac{\text{change in pressure}}{\text{fractional change in volume}} = \frac{\Delta p}{Avt/Aut}.$$

Therefore

$$\Delta p = B\,\frac{v}{u}.$$

The pressure in the moving fluid is therefore $p + \Delta p$, and the force exerted on it by the piston is $(p + \Delta p)A$. The *net* force on the moving

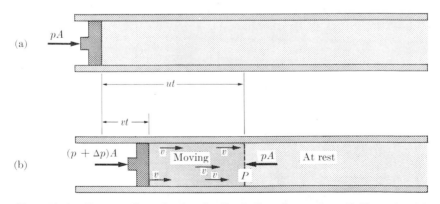

FIG. 12–3. Propagation of a longitudinal disturbance in a fluid confined in a tube.

fluid [see Fig. 12–3(b)] is $\Delta p A$, and the longitudinal impulse is

$$\text{Longitudinal impulse} = \Delta p A t = B \frac{v}{u} A t.$$

Applying the impulse-momentum theorem, we get

$$B \frac{v}{u} A t = \rho u t A v,$$

and therefore

$$\boxed{u = \sqrt{B/\rho}. \quad \text{(Longitudinal)}} \tag{12–2}$$

The speed of propagation of a longitudinal pulse in a fluid therefore depends only on the bulk modulus and density of the medium.

When a solid bar is struck a blow at one end, the situation is somewhat different from that of a fluid confined in a tube of constant cross section, since the bar will expand slightly sidewise when it is compressed longitudinally. It can be shown by the same type of reasoning as that just given that the velocity of a longitudinal pulse in the bar is given by

$$\boxed{u = \sqrt{Y/\rho}, \quad \text{(Longitudinal)}} \tag{12–3}$$

where Y is Young's modulus, defined in Chapter 10.

12–4 The motion of a wave. Up to this point we have considered the simplest type of disturbance that could be imparted to a medium, namely, a single transverse or longitudinal displacement. Suppose now that one end of a medium is forced to vibrate periodically, the displacement y (either transverse or longitudinal) varying with the time according to the equation of simple harmonic motion:

$$y = A \cos 2\pi f t.$$

During half a cycle, a displacement in one direction is propagated through the medium, and during the other half, a displacement in the opposite direction is caused to proceed. The resulting continuous train of disturbances traveling with a speed depending on the properties of the medium is called a *wave*.

To fix our ideas, suppose that one end of a stretched string is forced to vibrate periodically in a transverse direction with simple harmonic motion of amplitude A, frequency f, and period $T = 1/f$. For the present we shall assume the string to be long enough so that any effects at the

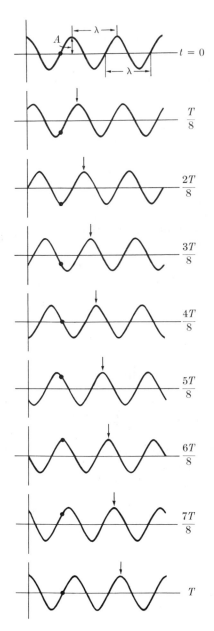

far end need not be considered. A *continuous train* of transverse sinusoidal waves then advances along the string. The shape of a portion of the string near the end, at intervals of $\frac{1}{8}$ of a period, is shown in Fig. 12–4 for a total time of one period. The string is assumed to have been vibrating for a sufficiently long time so that the shape of the string is sinusoidal for an indefinite distance from the driven end. It will be seen from the figure that the wave form advances steadily toward the right, as indicated by the short arrow pointing to one particular wave crest, while any one point on the string (see the black dot) oscillates about its equilibrium position with simple harmonic motion. It is important to distinguish between the motion of the *wave form*, which moves with constant velocity u along the string, and the motion of *a particle of the string*, which is simple harmonic and transverse to the string.

The distance between two successive maxima (or between any two successive points in the same phase) is the *wavelength* of the wave and is denoted by λ. Since the wave form, traveling with constant velocity u, advances a distance of one wavelength in a time interval of one period, it follows that $u = \lambda T$, or

$$u = f\lambda. \qquad (12\text{–}4)$$

That is, *the velocity of propagation equals the product of frequency and wavelength.*

Fig. 12–4. A sinusoidal transverse wave traveling toward the right, shown at intervals of $\frac{1}{8}$ of a period.

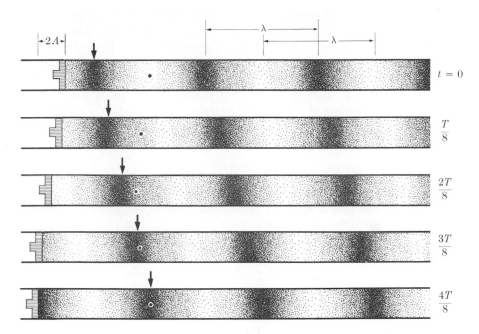

FIG. 12–5. A sinusoidal longitudinal wave traveling toward the right, shown at intervals of ⅛ of a period.

To understand the mechanics of a longitudinal wave, consider the long tube filled with a fluid and provided with a plunger at the left end, as shown in Fig. 12–5. The dots represent particles of the fluid. Suppose the plunger is forced to undergo a simple harmonic vibration parallel to the direction of the tube. During a part of each oscillation, a region whose pressure is above the equilibrium pressure is formed. Such a region is called a *condensation* and is represented by closely spaced dots. Following the production of a condensation, a region is formed in which the pressure is lower than the equilibrium value. This is called a *rarefaction* and is represented by widely spaced dots. The condensations and rarefactions move to the right with constant velocity u, as indicated by successive positions of the small vertical arrow. The velocity of longitudinal waves in air (sound) at 20°C is 344 m/sec or 1130 ft/sec. The motion of a single particle of the medium, shown by a heavy black dot, is simple harmonic, parallel to the direction of propagation.

The wavelength is the distance between two successive condensations or two successive rarefactions, and the same fundamental equation. $u = f\lambda$, holds in this, as in all types of waves.

12–5 Mathematical representation of a traveling wave. Suppose that a wave of any sort travels from left to right in a medium. Let us compare the motion of any one particle of the medium with that of a second particle to the right of the first. We find that the second particle moves in the same manner as the first, but after a lapse of time that is greater, the greater the distance of the second particle from the first. Thus in Fig. 12–2, the particle at the left end of the string started to move up with a transverse velocity v at time $t = 0$; the particle at P is just starting to move up with the same transverse velocity but its motion begins at a later time t.

Hence if one end of a stretched string oscillates with simple harmonic motion, all other points oscillate with simple harmonic motion of the same amplitude and frequency. The *phase angle* of the motion, however, is different for different points.

Let the displacement of a particle at the origin ($x = 0$) be given by

$$y = A \sin \omega t.$$

The displacement of a particle at the right of the origin lags this by some angle ϕ. That is,

$$y = A \sin (\omega t - \phi).$$

The lag angle ϕ is proportional to the distance of the particle from the origin, or to its coordinate x.

$$\phi = kx, \tag{12-5}$$

where k is a constant. Hence for such a particle

$$\boxed{y = A \sin (\omega t - kx).} \tag{12-6}$$

This equation represents a sine wave traveling to the *right*. If the wave travels to the *left*, particles at the right of the origin *lead* the particle at the origin in phase and the equation of the wave is

$$y = A \sin (\omega t + kx).$$

A particle at a distance of one wavelength from the origin vibrates in step with that at the origin. Hence it lags (or leads) by an angle $\phi = 2\pi$. By setting $x = \lambda$ and $\phi = 2\pi$ in Eq. (12–5), we get

$$2\pi = k\lambda, \qquad k = \frac{2\pi}{\lambda}.$$

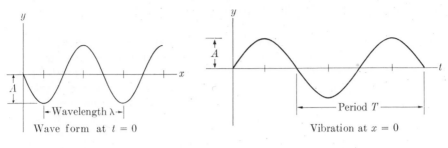

FIGURE 12–6   FIGURE 12–7

The proportionality constant k is therefore 2π times the reciprocal of the wavelength. Since $\omega = 2\pi f = 2\pi/T$, the equation of a traveling wave can also be written as

$$y = A \sin 2\pi \left(\frac{t}{T} \pm \frac{x}{\lambda} \right).$$

At any given *time* t, Eq. (12–6) gives the displacement y of a particle, from its equilibrium position, as a function of the *coordinate* x of the particle. If the wave is a transverse wave in a string, the equation represents the *shape* of the string at that instant, as if we had taken a snapshot of the string. Thus at time $t = 0$,

$$y = A \sin (-kx) = -A \sin kx = -A \sin 2\pi \frac{x}{\lambda}.$$

This curve is plotted in Fig. 12–6.

At any given *coordinate* x, Eq. (12–6) gives the displacement y of the particle at that coordinate, as a function of *time*. Thus at the coordinate $x = 0$,

$$y = A \sin \omega t = A \sin 2\pi \frac{t}{T}.$$

This curve is plotted in Fig. 12–7.

We see, therefore, that the displacement y of a particle depends both on the coordinate of the particle and on the time. In other words, y *is a function of two* **independent** *variables*, x and t. A graph of Eq. (12–6) would be a *surface* if we plotted x and t along rectangular axes in a horizontal plane, and plotted y vertically above this plane.

PROBLEMS

12–1. A steel wire 2 m long has a mass of 20 gm and is stretched with a tension of 1000 newtons. What is the velocity of propagation of a transverse wave in the wire?

12–2. One end of a horizontal string is attached to a prong of an electrically driven tuning fork whose frequency of vibration is 240 vib/sec. The other end passes over a pulley and supports a weight of 6 lb. The linear weight density of the string is 0.0133 lb/ft. (a) What is the speed of a transverse wave in the string? (b) What is the wavelength?

12–3. A steel pipe 200 ft long is struck at one end. A person at the other end hears two sounds as a result of two longitudinal waves, one in the pipe and the other in the air. What is the time interval between the two sounds? Take Young's modulus of steel to be 30×10^6 lb/in^2.

12–4. What must be the stress (F/A) in a stretched wire of a material whose Young's modulus is Y in order that the velocity of longitudinal waves shall equal 10 times the velocity of transverse waves?

12–5. Provided the amplitude is sufficiently great, the human ear can respond to longitudinal waves over a range of frequencies from about 20 vib/sec to about 20,000 vib/sec. Compute the wavelengths corresponding to these frequencies (a) for waves in air, (b) for waves in water.

12–6. The sound waves from a loudspeaker spread out nearly uniformly in all directions when their wavelength is large compared with the diameter of the speaker. When the wavelength is small compared with the diameter of the speaker, much of the sound energy is concentrated in the forward direction. For a speaker of diameter 10 in., compute the frequency for which the wavelength of the sound waves, in air, is (a) 10 times the diameter of the speaker, (b) equal to the diameter of the speaker, (c) 1/10 the diameter of the speaker.

12–7. Show that Eq. (12–6) may be written

$$y = -A \sin \frac{2\pi}{\lambda} (x - ut).$$

12–8. A traveling transverse wave on a string is represented by the equation in Problem 12–7. Let $A = 1$ in., $\lambda = 2$ in., and $u = \frac{1}{4}$ in/sec. (a) At time $t = 0$, compute the transverse displacement y at $\frac{1}{4}$-in. intervals of x (i.e., at $x = 0$, $x = \frac{1}{4}$ in., $x = \frac{1}{2}$ in., etc.) from $x = 0$ to $x = 4$ in. Show the results in a graph. This is the shape of the string at time $t = 0$. (b) Repeat the calculations, for the same values of x, at times $t = 1$ sec, $t = 2$ sec, $t = 3$ sec, and $t = 4$ sec. Show on the same graph the shape of the string at these instants. In what direction is the wave traveling?

12–9. The equation of a transverse traveling wave on a string is

$$y = -2 \sin [\pi(0.5x - 200t)],$$

where x and y are in cm and t is in sec. (a) Find the amplitude, wavelength, frequency, period, and velocity of propagation. (b) Sketch the shape of the string at the following values of t: 0, 0.0025, and 0.005 sec. (c) If the mass per unit length of the string is 5 gm/cm, find the tension.

FIGURES 12–8 and 12–9

To use these diagrams, cut a slit about $4\frac{1}{4}''$ long and about $\frac{1}{16}''$ wide in a card. Place the card over the diagram and move it vertically with constant velocity. The portions of the curves that appear in the slit will correspond to the oscillations of the particles in a longitudinal traveling wave in Fig. 12–8, and to a longitudinal stationary wave in Fig. 12–9.

FIGURE 12–8

FIGURE 12–9

CHAPTER 13

VIBRATING BODIES—SOUND

13–1 Boundary conditions for a string. Let us now consider what will happen when a wave pulse or wave train, advancing along a stretched string, arrives at the end of the string. If fastened to a rigid support, the end must evidently remain at rest. The arriving pulse exerts a force on the support, and the reaction to this force "kicks back" on the string and sets up a *reflected* pulse traveling in the reverse direction. At the opposite extreme from a rigidly fixed end would be one which was perfectly free—a case of no great importance here (it may be realized by a string hanging vertically) but which is of interest since its analogue does occur in other types of waves. At a free end the arriving pulse causes the string to "overshoot" and a reflected wave is also set up. The conditions which must be satisfied at the ends of the string are called *boundary conditions*.

The multiflash photograph of Fig. 13–1 shows the reflection of a pulse at a fixed end of a string. (The camera was tipped vertically while the photographs were taken so that successive images lie one under the other. The "string" is a rubber tube and it sags somewhat.) It will be seen that the pulse is reflected with its displacement and its velocity both reversed. When reflection takes place at a free end, the direction of the velocity is reversed but the direction of the displacement is unchanged.

Fig. 13–1. A pulse starts in the upper left corner and is reflected from the fixed end of the string at the right.

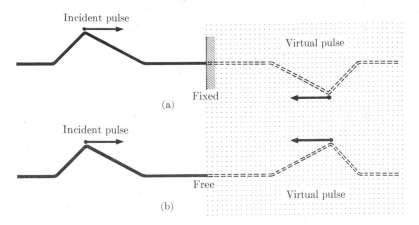

Fig. 13–2. Description of reflection of a pulse (a) at a fixed end of a string, and (b) at a free end, in terms of an imaginary "virtual" pulse.

It is helpful to think of the process of reflection in the following way. Imagine the string to be extended indefinitely beyond its actual terminus. The actual pulse can be considered to continue on into the imaginary portion as though the support were not there, while at the same time a "virtual" pulse, which has been traveling in the imaginary portion, moves out into the real string and forms the reflected pulse. The nature of the reflected pulse depends on whether the end is fixed or free. The two cases are shown in Fig. 13–2.

The displacement at a point where the actual and virtual pulses cross each other is the algebraic sum of the displacements in the individual pulses. Figures 13–3 and 13–4 show the shape of the end of the string for both types of reflected pulses. It will be seen that Fig. 13–3 corresponds to a free end and Fig. 13–4 to a fixed end. In the latter case, the incident and reflected pulses combine in such a way that the displacement of the end of the string is always zero.

13–2 Stationary waves in a string. When a continuous train of waves arrives at a fixed end of a string, a continuous train of reflected waves appears to originate at the end and travel in the opposite direction. Provided the elastic limit of the string is not exceeded and the displacements are sufficiently small, the actual displacement of any point of the string is the algebraic sum of the displacements of the individual waves, a fact which is called the *principle of superposition*. This principle is extremely important in all types of wave motion and applies not only to waves in a string but to sound waves in air, to light waves, and, in fact, to wave motion of any sort. The general term *interference* is applied to

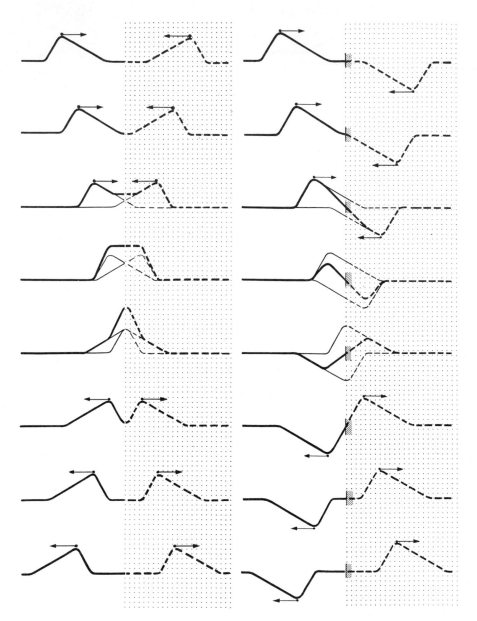

FIG. 13–3. Reflection at a free end.   FIG. 13–4. Reflection at a fixed end.

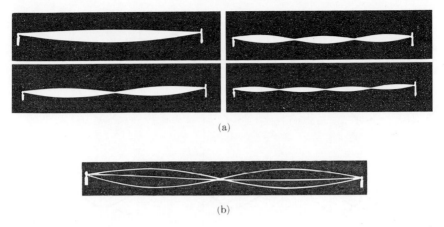

(a)

(b)

Fig. 13–5. (a) Standing waves in a stretched string (time exposure). (b) Multiflash photograph of a standing wave, with nodes at the center and at the ends.

the effect produced by two (or more) sets of wave trains which are simultaneously passing through a given region.

The appearance of the string in these circumstances gives no evidence that two waves are traversing it in opposite directions. If the frequency is sufficiently great so that the eye cannot follow the motion, the string appears subdivided into a number of segments, as in the time exposure photograph of Fig. 13–5(a). A multiflash photograph of the same string, in Fig. 13–5(b), indicates a few of the instantaneous shapes of the string. At any instant (except those when the string is straight) its shape is a sine curve, but whereas in a traveling wave the amplitude remains constant while the wave progresses, here the wave form remains fixed in position (longitudinally) while the amplitude fluctuates. Certain points known as the *nodes* remain always at rest. Midway between these points, at the *loops* or *antinodes*, the fluctuations are a maximum. The vibration as a whole is called a *stationary* wave.

To understand the formation of a stationary wave, consider the four separate graphs of wave form at four instants $\frac{1}{8}$ of a period apart, shown in Fig. 13–6. The system of short dashed curves represents a wave traveling to the right. The system of long dashed curves represents a wave of the same velocity, same wavelength, and same amplitude traveling to the left. The heavy curve represents the resultant wave form, obtained by applying the principle of superposition, that is, by adding displacements. At those places on the string marked N, the resultant displacements are always zero. These are the nodes. Midway between the nodes, the vibrations have the largest amplitude. These are the antinodes.

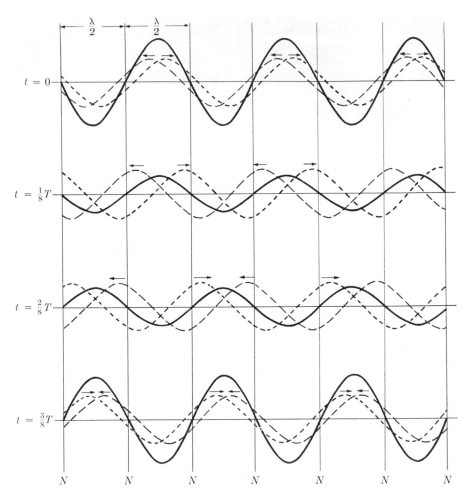

Fig. 13–6. The formation of a stationary wave.

It is evident from the figure that

$$\left\{ \begin{array}{c} \text{Distance between adjacent nodes} \\ \text{or} \\ \text{Distance between adjacent antinodes} \end{array} \right\} = \frac{\lambda}{2}.$$

The equation of a standing wave may be obtained by adding the displacements of two waves of equal amplitude, period, and wavelength, but traveling in opposite directions.

Thus if

$$y_1 = A \sin (\omega t - kx) \qquad \text{(positive x-direction)},$$

$$y_2 = A \sin (\omega t + kx) \qquad \text{(negative x-direction)},$$

then

$$y_1 + y_2 = A \left[\sin (\omega t - kx) + \sin (\omega t + kx)\right].$$

Introducing the expressions for the sine of the sum and difference of two angles and combining terms, we obtain

$$y_1 + y_2 = [2A \sin \omega t] \cos kx$$

$$= [2A \sin 2\pi ft] \cos \frac{2\pi x}{\lambda}. \tag{13-1}$$

The shape of the string at each instant is, therefore, a cosine curve whose amplitude (the expression in brackets) varies with time.

13-3 Vibration of a string fixed at both ends. Thus far we have been discussing a long string fixed at one end and have considered the stationary waves set up near that end by interference between the incident and reflected waves. Let us next consider the more usual case, that of a string fixed at both ends. A continuous train of sine or cosine waves is reflected and re-reflected, and since the string is fixed at both ends, both ends must be nodes. Since the nodes are one-half a wavelength apart, the length of the string may be $\lambda/2$, $2(\lambda/2)$, $3(\lambda/2)$, or, in general, any integral number of half-wavelengths. Or, to put it differently, if one considers a particular string of length L, stationary waves may be set up in the string by vibrations of a number of different frequencies, namely, those which give rise to waves of wavelengths $2L/1$, $2L/2$, $2L/3$, etc.

From the relation $f = u/\lambda$, and since u is the same for all frequencies, the possible frequencies are

$$\frac{u}{2L}, \qquad 2\,\frac{u}{2L}, \qquad 3\,\frac{u}{2L}, \cdots$$

The lowest frequency, $u/2L$, is called the *fundamental* frequency f_1 and the others are the *overtones*. The frequencies of the latter are, there-fore, $2f_1$, $3f_1$, $4f_1$, and so on. Overtones whose frequencies are integral multiples of the fundamental are said to form a *harmonic series*. The fundamental is the *first harmonic*. The frequency $2f_1$ is the *first overtone* or the *second harmonic*, the frequency $3f_1$ is the *second overtone* or the *third harmonic*, and so on.

We can now see an important difference between a spring-mass system and a vibrating string. The former has but one natural frequency, while the vibrating string has an infinite number of natural frequencies, the fundamental and all the overtones. If a body suspended from a spring is pulled down and released, only one frequency of vibration will ensue. If a string is initially distorted so that its shape is the same as *any one* of the possible harmonics, it will vibrate, when released, at the frequency of that particular harmonic. But when a piano string is struck, not only the fundamental, but many of the overtones are present in the resulting vibration. The fundamental frequency of the vibrating string is $f_1 = u/2L$, where $u = \sqrt{T/\mu}$. It follows that

$$f_1 = \frac{1}{2L} \sqrt{T/\mu}. \tag{13-2}$$

Stringed instruments afford many examples of the implications of this equation. For example, all such instruments are "tuned" by varying the tension T, an increase of tension increasing the frequency or pitch, and vice versa. The inverse dependence of frequency on length L is illustrated by the long strings of the bass section of the piano or the bass viol compared with the shorter strings of the piano treble or the violin. One reason for winding the bass strings of a piano with wire is to increase the mass per unit length μ, so as to obtain the desired low frequency without resorting to a string which is inconveniently long.

13–4 Resonance. In general, whenever a body capable of oscillating is acted on by a periodic series of impulses having a frequency equal to one of the natural frequencies of oscillation of the body, the body is set into vibration with a relatively large amplitude. This phenomenon is called *resonance*, and the body is said to *resonate* with the applied impulses.

A common example of mechanical resonance is provided by pushing a swing. The swing is a pendulum with a single natural frequency depending on its length. If a series of regularly spaced pushes is given to the swing, with a frequency equal to that of the swing, the motion may be made quite large. If the frequency of the pushes differs from the natural frequency of the swing, or if the pushes occur at irregular intervals, the swing will hardly execute a vibration at all.

Unlike a simple pendulum, which has only one natural frequency, a stretched string (and other systems to be discussed later in this chapter) has a large number of natural frequencies. Suppose that one end of a stretched string is fixed while the other is moved back and forth in a transverse direction. The amplitude at the driven end is fixed by the driving mechanism. Stationary waves will be set up in the string, whatever the value of the frequency f. If the frequency is not equal to one of the natural frequencies of the string, the amplitude at the antinodes will be fairly small. However, if the frequency is equal to *any one* of the natural frequencies, the string is in resonance and the amplitude at the antinodes will be very much larger than that at the driven end. In other words, although the driven end is not a node, it lies much closer to a node than to an antinode when the string is in resonance. In Fig. 13–5(a), the right end of the string was fixed and the left end was forced to oscillate vertically with small amplitude. Stationary waves of relatively large amplitude resulted when the frequency of oscillation of the left end was equal to the fundamental frequency or to any of the first three overtones.

A bridge or, for that matter, any structure, is capable of vibrating with certain natural frequencies. If the regular footsteps of a column of soldiers were to have a frequency equal to one of the natural frequencies of a bridge which the soldiers are crossing, a vibration of dangerously large amplitude might result. Therefore, in crossing a bridge, a column of soldiers is ordered to break step.

Tuning a radio is an example of electrical resonance. By turning a dial, the natural frequency of an alternating current in the receiving circuit is made equal to the frequency of the waves broadcast by the desired station. Optical resonance may also take place between atoms in a gas at low pressure and light waves from a lamp containing the same atoms. Thus light from a sodium lamp may cause the sodium atoms in a glass bulb to glow with characteristic yellow sodium light.

The phenomenon of resonance may be demonstrated with the aid of the longitudinal waves set up in air by a vibrating plate or tuning fork. If two identical tuning forks are placed some distance apart and one is struck, the other will be heard when the first is suddenly damped. Should a small piece of wax or modeling clay be put on one of the forks, the frequency of that fork will be altered enough to destroy the resonance.

13–5 Interference of longitudinal waves. The phenomenon of interference between two longitudinal waves in air may be demonstrated with the aid of the apparatus depicted in Fig. 13–7. A wave emitted by an electrically driven diaphragm S is sent into a metal tube, where it divides into two waves, one following the constant path SAR, the other the path SBR, which may be varied by sliding the tube B to the right. Suppose the frequency of the source is 1100 vibrations per second. Then, since the velocity of sound in air at room temperature is about 1100 ft/sec, the wavelength $\lambda = u/f = 1$ ft. If both paths are of equal length, the two waves will arrive at R at the same time and the vibrations set up by both waves will be in phase. The resulting vibration will have an amplitude equal to the sum of the two individual amplitudes and the phenomenon of *reinforcement* may be detected either with the ear at R or with the aid of a microphone, amplifier, and loudspeaker.

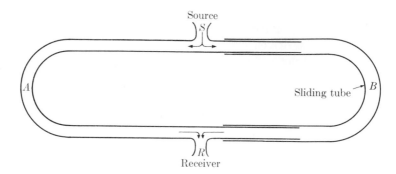

FIG. 13–7. Apparatus for demonstrating interference of longitudinal waves.

Now suppose the tube B is moved out a distance of 3 inches, thereby making the path SBR 6 inches longer than the path SAR. The right-hand wave will have traveled a distance $\lambda/2$ greater than the left-hand wave, and the vibration set up at R by the right-hand wave will therefore be in opposite phase to that set up by the left-hand wave. The consequent interference is shown by the marked reduction in sound at R.

If the tube B is now pulled out another 3 inches, so that the *path difference*, SBR minus SAR, is one foot (one wavelength), the two vibrations at R will again reinforce each other. Thus

$$\left\{ \begin{matrix} \text{Reinforcement takes place} \\ \text{when the path difference} \end{matrix} \right\} = 0,\ \lambda,\ 2\lambda,\ \text{etc.}$$

$$\left\{ \begin{matrix} \text{Interference takes place} \\ \text{when the path difference} \end{matrix} \right\} = \frac{\lambda}{2},\ \frac{3\lambda}{2},\ \frac{5\lambda}{2},\ \text{etc.}$$

An acoustical interferometer of this sort is of value only in demonstrating the phenomenon of interference. Optical interferometers, however, whose principles of operation are the same, have many practical uses in physical optics.

13–6 Stationary longitudinal waves. Longitudinal waves traveling along a tube of finite length are reflected at the ends of the tube in much the same way that transverse waves in a string are reflected at its ends. Interference between the waves traveling in opposite directions gives rise to stationary waves.

If reflection takes place at a closed end, the displacement of the particles at that end must necessarily be always zero. Hence a closed end is a *node*. If the end of the tube is open, the nature of the reflection is more complex and depends on whether the tube is wide or narrow com-

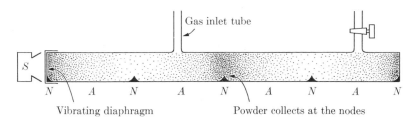

Gas inlet tube

S

N   A   N   A   N   A   N   A   N

Vibrating diaphragm   Powder collects at the nodes

Fig. 13–8. Kundt's tube for determining the velocity of sound in a gas. The dots represent the density of the gas molecules at an instant when the pressure at the displacement nodes is a maximum or a minimum.

pared with the wavelength. If the tube is narrow compared with the wavelength, which is the case in most musical instruments, the reflection is such as to make the open end an *antinode*. Therefore the longitudinal waves in a column of fluid are reflected at the closed and open ends of a tube in the same way that transverse waves in a string are reflected at fixed and free ends respectively.

The reflections at the openings where the instrument is blown are found to be such that an antinode is located at or near the opening. The effective length of the air column of a wind instrument is thus less definite than the length of a string fixed at its ends.

Stationary longitudinal waves in a column of gas may be demonstrated conveniently with the aid of the apparatus shown in Fig. 13–8, known as Kundt's tube. A glass tube a few feet long is closed at one end with glass and at the other with a flexible diaphragm. The gas to be studied is admitted to the tube at a known temperature and at atmospheric pressure. A powerful source of longitudinal waves S, whose frequency may be varied, causes vibration of the flexible diaphragm. A small amount of light powder or cork dust is sprinkled uniformly along the tube.

When a frequency is found at which the air column is in resonance, the amplitude of the stationary waves becomes large enough for the gas particles to sweep the cork dust along the tube, at all points where the gas is in motion. The powder therefore collects at the displacement nodes, where the gas remains at rest. Sometimes a wire running along the axis of the tube is maintained at a dull red heat by an electric current, and the nodes show themselves as hot points compared with the antinodes.

With careful manipulation and with a good variable frequency source, a fair determination of the velocity of the wave may be obtained with Kundt's tube. Since, in a stationary wave, the distance between two adjacent nodes is one-half a wavelength, the wavelength λ is obtained by measuring the distance between alternate clumps of powder. Knowing the frequency f, the velocity u is then

$$u = f\lambda.$$

Gas flames

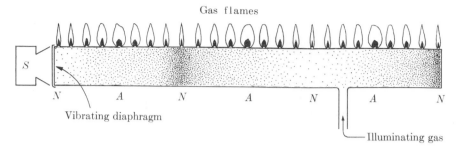

Vibrating diaphragm

Illuminating gas

FIG. 13–9. The variations in gas pressure are greatest at the displacement nodes. The dots represent the density of the gas molecules at an instant when the pressure at the displacement nodes is a maximum or a minimum.

A constant frequency source may be used if the vibrating element is a piston which may be moved along the tube until resonance is obtained.

At a displacement node, the pressure variations above and below the average are a maximum, whereas at an antinode, there are no pressure variations. This may be understood easily when it is realized that two small masses of gas on opposite sides of a node are vibrating in *opposite phase*. Thus, when they approach each other, the pressure at the node is a maximum, and when they recede from each other, the pressure at the node is a minimum. Two small masses of gas, however, on opposite sides of an antinode vibrate *in phase*, and hence give rise to no pressure variations at the antinode. This may be demonstrated in the case of illuminating gas with the aid of the apparatus shown in Fig. 13–9, where the amplitude of the harmonic variations of gas pressure determines the shape and color of the gas flames.

13–7 Vibrations in organ pipes. If one end of a pipe is open and a stream of air is directed against an edge, vibrations are set up and the tube resonates at its natural frequencies. As in the case of a plucked string, the fundamental and overtones exist at the same time. In the case of an open pipe, the fundamental frequency f_1 corresponds to an antinode at each end and a node in the middle, as shown at the top of Fig. 13–10. Succeeding diagrams of Fig. 13–10 show two of the overtones, which are seen to be the second and third harmonics. *In an open pipe the fundamental frequency is u/2L and all harmonics are present.*

The properties of a closed pipe are shown in the diagrams of Fig. 13–11. The fundamental frequency is seen to be $u/4L$, which is one-half that of an open pipe of the same length. In the language of music, the pitch of a closed pipe is one octave lower than that of an open pipe of equal length. From the remaining diagrams of Fig. 13–11, it may be seen that the second, fourth, etc., harmonics are missing. Hence, *in a closed pipe, the fundamental frequency is u/4L and only the odd harmonics are present.*

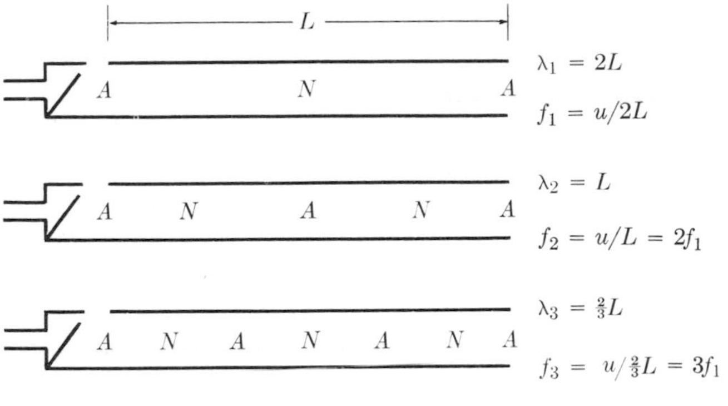

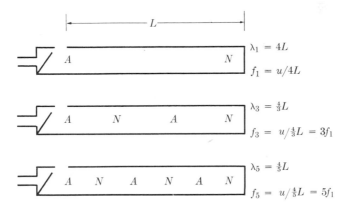

FIG. 13–10. Modes of vibration of an open organ pipe.

FIG. 13–11. Modes of vibration of a closed organ pipe.

13–8 Vibrations of rods and plates. A rod may be set in longitudinal vibration by clamping it at some point and stroking it with a chamois skin that has been sprinkled with rosin. In Fig. 13–12(a) the rod is clamped in the middle, and consequently when it is stroked near the end, a stationary wave is set up with a node in the middle and antinodes at each end, exactly the same as the fundamental mode of an open organ pipe. The fundamental frequency of the rod is then $u/2L$, where u is the velocity of a longitudinal wave in the rod. Since the velocity of a longitudinal wave in a solid is much greater than that in air, a rod has a higher fundamental frequency than an open organ pipe of the same length.

By clamping the rod at a point $\frac{1}{4}$ of its length from one end, as shown in Fig. 13–12(b), the second harmonic may be produced.

If a stretched flexible membrane, such as a drumhead, is struck a blow, a two-dimensional pulse travels outward from the struck point and is

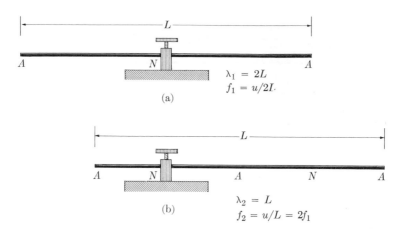

$\lambda_1 = 2L$

$f_1 = u/2l.$

(a)

$\lambda_2 = L$

$f_2 = u/L = 2f_1$

(b)

FIG. 13–12. Modes of vibration of a rod.

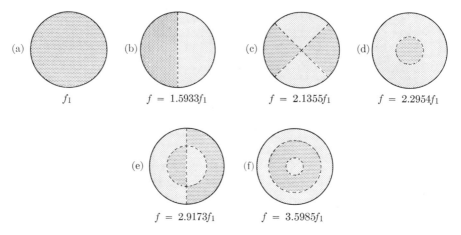

(a) f_1

(b) $f = 1.5933f_1$

(c) $f = 2.1355f_1$

(d) $f = 2.2954f_1$

(e) $f = 2.9173f_1$

(f) $f = 3.5985f_1$

FIG. 13–13. Possible modes of vibration of a membrane, showing nodal lines. The frequency of each is given in terms of the fundamental frequency, f_1.

reflected and re-reflected at the boundary of the membrane. If some point of the membrane is forced to vibrate periodically, continuous trains of waves travel along the membrane. Just as with the stretched string, stationary waves can be set up in the membrane and each of these waves has a certain natural frequency. The lowest frequency is the fundamental and the others are overtones. In general, when the membrane is vibrating, a number of overtones are present.

The nodes of a vibrating membrane are lines (nodal lines) rather than points. The boundary of the membrane is evidently one such line. Some of the other possible nodal lines of a circular membrane are shown in Fig. 13–13, with the modes of vibration arranged in order of increasing frequency. The natural frequency of each mode is given in terms of the fundamental f_1. It will be noted that the frequencies of the overtones are *not* integral multiples of f_1. That is, they are not harmonics.

The restoring force in a vibrating flexible membrane arises from the tension with which it is stretched. A metal plate, if sufficiently thick, will vibrate in a similar way, the restoring force being produced by bending stresses in the plate. The study of vibrations of membranes and plates is of importance in connection with the design of loudspeaker diaphragms and the diaphragms of telephone receivers and microphones.

13–9 Pressure variations in a sound wave. We shall limit ourselves here to the consideration of longitudinal waves only, and in particular to those which, when striking the ear, give rise to the sensation of sound. Such waves, within the frequency range from 20 to 20,000 vibrations per second, are called, for simplicity, *sound waves.*

The reception of a sound wave by the ear gives rise to a vibration of the air particles at the eardrum with a definite frequency and a definite amplitude. This vibration may also be described in terms of the variation of air pressure at the same point. The air pressure rises above atmospheric pressure and then sinks below atmospheric pressure with simple harmonic motion of the same frequency as that of an air particle. The maximum amount by which the pressure differs from atmospheric pressure is called the *pressure amplitude*. It can be proved that the pressure amplitude is proportional to the displacement amplitude.

Measurements of sound waves show that the maximum pressure variations in the loudest sounds which the ear can tolerate are of the order of magnitude of 280 dynes/cm^2 (above and below atmospheric pressure of about 1,000,000 dynes/cm^2). The corresponding maximum displacement for a frequency of 1000 vibrations per second is about a thousandth of a centimeter. The displacement amplitudes, even in the loudest sounds, are therefore extremely small.

The maximum pressure variations in the *faintest* sound of frequency 1000 vibrations per second are only about 2×10^{-4} dyne/cm^2. The corresponding displacement amplitude is about 10^{-9} cm. By way of comparison, the wavelength of yellow light is 6×10^{-5} cm, and the diameter of a molecule about 10^{-8} cm. It will be appreciated that the ear is an extremely sensitive organ.

13–10 Quality and pitch. A string that has been plucked or a plate that has been struck, if allowed to vibrate freely, will vibrate with many frequencies at the same time. It is a rare occurrence for a body to vibrate with only one frequency. A carefully made tuning fork struck lightly on a rubber block may vibrate with only one frequency, but in the case of musical instruments, the fundamental and many harmonics are usually present at the same time. The impulses that are sent from the ear to the brain give rise to one net effect which is characteristic of the instrument. Suppose, for example, the sound spectrum of a tone consisted of a fundamental of 200 vibrations per second and harmonics 2, 3, 4, and 5, all of different intensity, whereas the sound spectrum of another tone consisted of exactly the same frequencies but with a different intensity distribution. The two tones would sound different; they are said to differ in *quality*.

Adjectives used to describe the quality of musical tones are purely subjective in character, such as reedy, golden, round, mellow, tinny, etc. *The quality of a sound is determined by the number of overtones present and their respective intensities.* The sound spectra of various musical instruments are shown in Fig. 13–14.

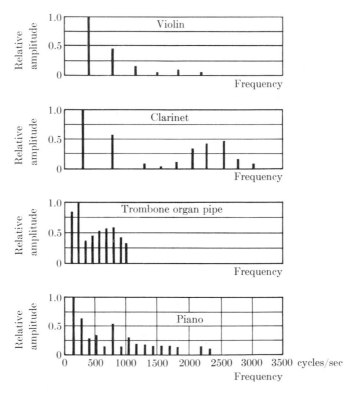

FIG. 13–14. Sound spectra of some musical instruments. (Courtesy of Dr. Harvey Fletcher.)

Another subjective attribute of a musical sound that is described with the aid of the adjectives high, medium, low, etc., is called the *pitch*. It is a simple matter to explain the pitch of a sound produced by a wave of only one frequency. If we take a set of tuning forks differing in size and cause each one to sound its fundamental only, then it becomes apparent that the greater the frequency, the higher the pitch. The situation, however, is very much more complicated when the sound is produced by a wave of many frequencies. If the fundamental is considerably more intense than any of the overtones, then the pitch is determined by the frequency of the fundamental. But this is not always the case. It is possible to construct a tone consisting of many frequencies whose pitch corresponds to a frequency that actually does not exist in the tone itself.

13-11 Beats. Stationary waves in an air column have been cited as one example of interference. They arise when two wave trains of the same amplitude and frequency are traveling through the same region in opposite directions. We now wish to consider another type of interference which results when two wave trains of equal amplitude but slightly different frequency travel through the same region. Such a condition exists when two tuning forks of slightly different frequency are sounded simultaneously or when two piano wires struck by the same key are slightly "out of tune."

Let us consider some one point of space through which the waves are simultaneously passing. The displacements due to the two waves separately are plotted as a function of the time on graph (a) in Fig. 13–15. If the total extent of the time axis represents one second, the graphs correspond to frequencies of 16 vibrations per second and of 18 vibrations per second. Applying the principle of superposition to find the resultant vibration, we get graph (b), where it is seen that the amplitude varies with the time. These variations of amplitude give rise to variations of

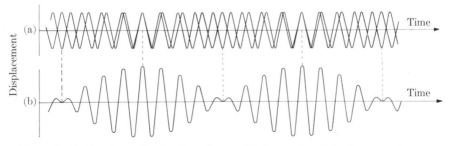

FIG. 13–15. Beats are fluctuations in amplitude produced by two sound waves of slightly different frequency.

loudness which are called *beats*. Two strings may be tuned to the same frequency by tightening one of them while sounding both until the beats disappear.

The production of beats may be treated mathematically as follows. The displacements due to the two waves passing simultaneously through some one point of space may be written

$$y_1 = A \sin \omega_1 t, \qquad y_2 = A \sin \omega_2 t.$$

(The amplitudes are assumed equal.)

By the principle of superposition, the resultant displacement is

$$y = y_1 + y_2 = A [\sin \omega_1 t + \sin \omega_2 t],$$

and, since

$$\sin a + \sin b = 2 \sin \frac{a + b}{2} \cos \frac{a - b}{2},$$

this may be written

$$y = \left[2A \cos \left(\frac{\omega_1 - \omega_2}{2} \right) t \right] \sin \frac{\omega_1 + \omega_2}{2} t$$

$$= \left[2A \cos 2\pi \left(\frac{f_1 - f_2}{2} \right) t \right] \sin 2\pi \frac{f_1 + f_2}{2} t.$$

The resulting vibration can then be considered to be of frequency $(f_1 + f_2)/2$, or the average frequency of the two tones, and of amplitude given by the expression in brackets. The amplitude therefore varies with time at a frequency $(f_1 - f_2)/2$. If f_1 and f_2 are nearly equal, this term is small and the amplitude fluctuates very slowly. When the amplitude is large, the sound is loud, and vice versa. A beat, or a maximum of amplitude, will occur when $\cos 2\pi t (f_1 - f_2)/2$ equals 1 or -1. Since each of these values occurs once in each cycle, the number of beats per second is twice the frequency $(f_1 - f_2)/2$, or *the number of beats per second equals the difference of the frequencies.*

13–12 The Doppler effect. When a source of sound, or a listener, or both, are in motion relative to the air, the pitch of the sound, as heard by the listener, is in general not the same as when source and listener are at rest. The most common example is the sudden drop in pitch of the sound from an automobile horn as one meets and passes a car proceeding in the opposite direction. This phenomenon is called the *Doppler effect.*

We shall consider only the special case in which the velocities of listener and source, v_L and v_S, lie along the line joining them. Since these ve-

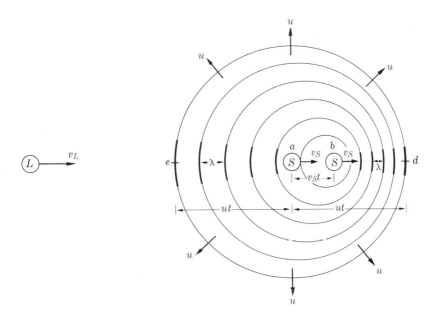

FIG. 13–16. Wave surfaces emitted by a moving source.

locities may be in the same or opposite directions, and the listener may be either ahead of or behind the source, a convention of signs is required. We shall take the positive directions of v_L and v_S as that *from* the position of the listener *to* the position of the source. The velocity of propagation of sound waves, u, will always be considered positive.

In Fig. 13–16, a listener L is at the left of a source S. The positive direction is then from left to right, and both v_L and v_S are positive in the diagram. The sound source is at point a at time $t = 0$ and at point b at time t. The outer circle represents the wave surface emitted at time $t = 0$. This surface (in free space) is a sphere with center at a, and is traveling radially outward at all points with velocity u. (The fact that the wave originated at a *moving* source does not affect its velocity after leaving the source. The wave velocity u is a property of the *medium* only; the waves forget about the source as soon as they leave it.) The radius of this sphere (the distance ea or ad) is therefore ut. The distance ab equals $v_S t$, so

$$eb = (u + v_S)t, \qquad bd = (u - v_S)t.$$

In the time interval between $t = 0$ and $t = t$, the number of waves emitted by the source is $f_S t$, where f_S is the frequency of the source. In front of the source these waves are crowded into the distance bd, while behind the source they are spread out over the distance eb. The wavelength in front of the source is therefore

$$\lambda = \frac{(u - v_S)t}{f_S t} = \frac{u - v_S}{f_S},$$

while the wavelength behind the source is

$$\lambda = \frac{(u + v_S)t}{f_S t} = \frac{u + v_S}{f_S}.$$

The waves approaching the moving listener L have a velocity of propagation relative to him, given by $u + v_L$. The frequency at which he encounters these waves is

$$f = \frac{u + v_L}{\lambda} = \frac{u + v_L}{(u + v_S)/f_S},$$

or

$$\frac{f}{u + v_L} = \frac{f_S}{u + v_S}, \tag{13–3}$$

which expresses the frequency f as heard by the listener in terms of the frequency f_S of the source. It is unnecessary to derive equations for other special cases if consistent use is made of the sign convention given above. See the following examples.

If the medium in which the waves are traveling has a velocity v_M parallel to the line joining listener and source, then

$$\frac{f}{u + v_L - v_M} = \frac{f_S}{u + v_S - v_M}.$$

EXAMPLE. Let $f_S = 1000$ cycles/sec, $u = 1000$ ft/sec. The wavelength of the waves emitted by a stationary source is then $u/f_S = 1.00$ ft.

(a) What are the wavelengths ahead of and behind the moving source in Fig. 13–16 if its velocity is 100 ft/sec?

In front of the source,

$$\lambda = \frac{u - v_S}{f_S} = \frac{1000 - 100}{1000} = 0.90 \text{ ft.}$$

Behind the source,

$$\lambda = \frac{u + v_S}{f_S} = \frac{1000 + 100}{1000} = 1.10 \text{ ft.}$$

(b) If the listener L in Fig. 13–16 is at rest and the source is moving away from him at 100 ft/sec, what is the frequency as heard by the listener?

Since $v_L = 0$ and $v_S = 100$ ft/sec,

$$f = f_S \frac{u}{u + v_S} = 1000 \frac{1000}{1000 + 100} = 909 \frac{\text{cycles}}{\text{sec}}.$$

(c) If the source in Fig. 13–16 is at rest and the listener is moving toward the left at 100 ft/sec, what is the frequency as heard by the listener?

The positive direction (from listener to source) is still from left to right, so

$$v_L = -100 \frac{\text{ft}}{\text{sec}}, \qquad v_S = 0,$$

$$f = f_S \frac{u + v_L}{u} = 1000 \frac{1000 - 100}{1000} = 900 \frac{\text{cycles}}{\text{sec}}.$$

Thus while the frequency as heard by the listener is less than the frequency f_S both when the source moves away from the listener and when the listener moves away from the source, the decrease in frequency is not the same for the same velocity of recession.

The Doppler effect is not, of course, confined to sound waves. Light waves are emitted as a result of electronic rearrangements in atoms, and presumably the frequency of these light sources is the same whether a given atom is on the earth or in a star. The wavelength of the light from certain stars is found to be slightly longer, and from other stars slightly shorter, than that from the same atoms in a source on the earth. The inference is that the stars are moving toward or away from the earth, and their velocities can be computed from the observed wavelength difference. Even in a gas discharge tube in the laboratory, the atoms are not at rest, but are flying about with relatively large velocities. Hence the light from such a source, resulting from a given atomic process, is a mixture of waves with a slight "spread" of wavelengths. Another interesting example is the reflection of radar waves from a moving object such as a plane or an automobile. The wavelength of the reflected waves is increased if the object is moving toward the source, decreased if it is moving away from the source. The same phenomenon occurs when underwater sound waves (sonar) are reflected by a moving submarine. The velocities of earth satellites are determined from the Doppler shift in frequency of the radio waves they transmit.

Problems

[Use 348 m/sec or 1140 ft/sec for the velocity of sound in air (27°C).]

13–1. Two transverse cosine waves, each of amplitude 1 in. and wavelength 2 in., travel in opposite directions in a string with a speed of $\frac{1}{4}$ in/sec. Construct graphs of the shape of the string at the following times: $t = 0$, $t = 2$ sec, $t = 4$ sec.

13–2. The equation of a transverse wave in a stretched string is

$$ y = -4 \sin 2\pi \left(\frac{t}{0.02} - \frac{x}{400} \right), $$

where y and x are in centimeters and t is in seconds. (a) Is the wave a traveling wave or a standing wave? (b) What is the amplitude of the wave? (c) What is its wavelength? (d) What is its velocity of propagation? (e) What is its frequency?

13–3. A steel piano wire 50 cm long. of mass 5 gm, is stretched with a tension of 400 newtons. (a) What is the frequency of its fundamental mode of vibration? (b) What is the number of the highest overtone that could be heard by a person who can hear frequencies up to 10,000 cycles/sec?

13–4. A steel wire of length $L = $ 100 cm and density $\rho = 8$ gm/cm^3 is stretched tightly between two rigid supports. Vibrating in its fundamental mode, the frequency is $f = 200$ cycles/sec. (a) What is the velocity of transverse waves on this wire? (b) What is the longitudinal stress in the wire (in dynes/cm^2)? (c) If the maximum acceleration at the midpoint of the wire is 80,000 cm/sec^2, what is the amplitude of vibration at the midpoint?

13–5. A stretched string is observed to vibrate with a frequency of 30 cycles/sec in its fundamental mode when the supports are 60 cm apart. The amplitude at the antinode is 3 cm. The string has a mass of 30 gm. (a) What is the velocity of propagation of a transverse wave in the string? (b) Compute the tension in the string.

13–6. Suppose the piano wire in Problem 13–3 is set vibrating at twice its fundamental frequency. (a) What is the wavelength of transverse waves in the wire? (b) What is the wavelength, in air, of the sound waves emitted by the wire?

13–7. Stationary waves are set up in a Kundt's tube by the longitudinal vibration of an iron rod 1 m long, clamped at the center. If the frequency of the iron rod is 2480 vib/sec and the powder heaps within the tube are 6.9 cm apart, (a) what is the velocity of the waves in the iron rod, and (b) in the gas?

13–8. A copper rod 1 m long, clamped at the $\frac{1}{4}$ point, is set in longitudinal vibration and is used to produce stationary waves in a Kundt's tube containing air. Heaps of cork dust within the tube are found to be 4.95 cm apart. What is the velocity of longitudinal waves in copper?

13–9. Find the fundamental frequency and the first four overtones in air of a 6-in. pipe (a) if the pipe is open at both ends, (b) if the pipe is closed at one end.

13–10. A long tube contains air at a pressure of 1 atm and temperature 77°C. The tube is open at one end and closed at the other by a movable piston. A tuning fork near the open end is vibrating with a frequency of 500 cycles/sec. Resonance is produced when the piston is at distances 18.0, 55.5, and 93.0 cm from the open end. From these measurements, what is the velocity of sound in air at 77°C?

13–11. An organ pipe A of length 2 ft, closed at one end, is vibrating in the first overtone. Another organ pipe B of length 1.35 ft, open at both ends, is vibrating in its fundamental mode. Neglect end corrections. (a) What is the frequency of the tone from A? (b) What is the frequency of the tone from B?

13–12. A plate cut from a quartz crystal is often used to control the frequency of an oscillating electrical circuit. Longitudinal standing waves are set up in the plate, with displacement antinodes at opposite faces. The fundamental frequency of vibration is given by the equation

$$f_1 = \frac{2.87 \times 10^5}{s},$$

where f_1 is in cycles/sec and s is the thickness of the plate in cm. (a) Compute Young's modulus for the quartz plate. (b) Compute the thickness of plate required for a frequency of 1200 kilocycles/sec. (1 kilocycle = 1000 cycles.) The density of quartz is 2.66 gm/cm^3.

13–13. Two identical piano wires when stretched with the same tension have a fundamental frequency of 400 vib/sec. By what fractional amount must the tension in one wire be increased in order that 4 beats/sec shall occur when both wires vibrate simultaneously? (Approximate finite changes by differentials.)

13–14. Two whistles, A and B, each have a frequency of 500 cycles/sec. A is stationary and B is moving toward the right (away from A) at a velocity of 200 ft/sec. An observer is between

the two whistles, moving toward the right with a velocity of 100 ft/sec. (a) What is the frequency from A as heard by the observer? (b) What is the frequency from B as heard by the observer? (c) What is the beat frequency heard by the observer?

13–15. A railroad train is traveling at 100 ft/sec in still air. The frequency of the note emitted by the locomotive whistle is 500 cycles/sec. What is the wavelength of the sound waves (a) in front of the locomotive, and (b) behind it? What would be the frequency of the sound heard by a stationary listener (c) in front of, (d) behind the locomotive? What frequency would be heard by a passenger on a second train traveling at 50 ft/sec and (e) approaching the first, (f) receding from the first? (g) How is each of the preceding answers altered if a wind of velocity 30 ft/sec is blowing in the same direction as that in which the first locomotive is traveling?

13–16. Compare the frequencies heard by a listener under the following circumstances: (a) A listener in still air moves with a velocity of 100 ft/sec directly toward a stationary source emitting sound waves of frequency 1000 cycles/sec. (b) The listener remains at rest while the source moves directly toward him at 100 ft/sec.

13–17. A man stands at rest in front of a large smooth wall. Directly in front of him, between him and the wall, he holds a vibrating tuning fork of frequency f_0 cycles/sec. He now moves the fork toward the wall with a velocity v. How many beats per second will he hear between the sound waves reaching him directly from the fork, and those reaching him after being reflected from the wall? Represent the velocity of sound in air by V. For a numerical example, let $f_0 = 400$ cycles/sec and $v = 4$ ft/sec.

13–18. A source of sound waves S, emitting waves of frequency 1000 cycles/sec, is traveling toward the right in still air with a velocity of 100 ft/sec. At the right of the source is a large smooth reflecting surface moving toward the left with a velocity of 400 ft/sec. (a) How far does an emitted wave travel in 0.01 sec? (b) What is the wavelength of the emitted waves in front of (i.e., at the right of) the source? (c) How many waves strike the reflecting surface in 0.01 sec? (d) What is the velocity of the reflected waves? (e) What is the wavelength of the reflected waves?

13–19. A stationary source emits waves of frequency f_0 and speed c. These waves fall normally on a reflector that is moving away from the source with a speed v, and the reflected waves of frequency f are received by a sta-tionary "listener" located at the source. (a) Show that $f/f_0 = (c - v)/(c + v)$ and, assuming that $c \gg v$, show that $(f_0 - f)/f_0 = 2v/c$. (b) In the radar determination of automobile speeds, a stationary transmitter sends a beam of radio waves along the highway and the waves reflected from a moving car are received by a stationary receiver near the source. Find the value of $(f_0 - f)$ when the reflecting automobile is mov-ing away from the source at a speed of 35 mi/hr (15.6 m/sec). The value of c is 3×10^8 m/sec, and $f_0 = 2460 \times 10^6$ cycles/sec. (c) If the automobile is approaching the source at 35 mi/hr, will the magnitude of $(f_0 - f)$ differ from that in part (b)? (d) Would the results of any of the preceding parts be different if the directions of the trans-mitted and reflected beams were not along the direction of motion of the car?

CHAPTER 14

HYDROSTATICS

14–1 Introduction. The term "hydrostatics" is applied to the study of fluids at rest, and "hydrodynamics" to fluids in motion. The special branch of hydrodynamics relating to the flow of gases and of air in particular is called "aerodynamics."

A fluid is a substance which can flow. Hence the term includes both liquids and gases. Liquids and gases differ markedly in their compressibilities; a gas is easily compressed, while a liquid is practically incompressible. The small volume changes of a liquid under pressure can usually be neglected in this part of the subject.

The density of a homogeneous material is defined as its mass per unit volume. Densities are therefore expressed in grams per cubic centimeter, kilograms per cubic meter, or slugs per cubic foot. We shall represent density by the Greek letter ρ (rho).

$$\rho = \frac{m}{V}, \qquad m = \rho V. \tag{14–1}$$

For example, the weight of 1 cubic foot of water is 62.5 lb; its density is $62.5/32.2 = 1.94$ slugs per cubic foot.

TABLE 14–1

DENSITIES

Material	Density, gm/cm^3	Material	Density, gm/cm^3
Aluminum	2.7	Silver	10.5
Brass	8.6	Steel	7.8
Copper	8.9	Mercury	13.6
Gold	19.3	Ethyl alcohol	0.81
Ice	0.92	Benzene	0.90
Iron	7.8	Glycerin	1.26
Lead	11.3	Water	1.00
Platinum	21.4		

The *specific gravity* of a material is the ratio of its density to that of water and is therefore a pure number. "Specific gravity" is an exceedingly poor term, since it has nothing to do with gravity. "Relative density" would describe the concept more precisely.

14–2 Pressure in a fluid. When the concept of hydrostatic pressure was introduced in Section 10–1, the weight of the fluid was neglected and the pressure was assumed the same at all points. It is a familiar fact, however, that atmospheric pressure decreases with increasing altitude and that the pressure in a lake or in the ocean decreases with increasing distance from the bottom. We therefore generalize the definition of pressure and define the pressure *at any point* as the ratio of the normal force ΔF exerted on a small area ΔA including the point, to the area ΔA.

$$p = \frac{\Delta F}{\Delta A}, \qquad \Delta F = p\,\Delta A. \qquad (14\text{--}2)$$

If the pressure is the same at all points of a finite plane surface of area A, these equations reduce to Eqs. (10–3),

$$p = \frac{F}{A}, \qquad F = pA.$$

Let us find the general relation between the pressure p at any point in a fluid and the elevation of the point, y. If the fluid is in equilibrium, every volume element is in equilibrium. Consider an element in the form of a thin slab, shown in Fig. 14–1, whose thickness is Δy and whose faces have an area A. If ρ is the density of the fluid, the mass of the element is $\rho A\,\Delta y$ and its weight Δw is $\rho g A\,\Delta y$. The force exerted on the element by the surrounding fluid is everywhere normal to its surface. By symmetry, the resultant horizontal force on its rim is zero. The upward force on

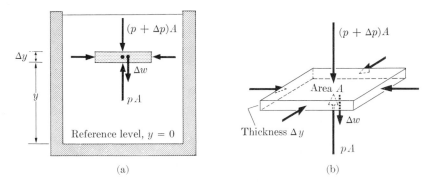

(a)   (b)

FIG. 14–1. Forces on an element of fluid in equilibrium.

its lower face is pA, and the downward force on its upper face is $(p + \Delta p)A$. Since it is in equilibrium,

$$\Sigma F_y = 0,$$

$$pA - (p + \Delta p)A - \rho gA\,\Delta y = 0,$$

or

$$dp = -\rho g\,dy. \qquad (14\text{–}3)$$

Since ρ and g are both positive quantities it follows that a positive dy (an increase of elevation) is accompanied by a negative dp (decrease of pressure). If p_1 and p_2 are the pressures at elevations y_1 and y_2 above some reference level, then integration of Eq. (14–3), when ρ and g are constant, gives

$$p_2 - p_1 = -\rho g(y_2 - y_1).$$

Let us apply this equation to a liquid in an open vessel, such as that shown in Fig. 14–2. Take point 1 at any level and let p represent the pressure at this point. Take point 2 at the top where the pressure is atmospheric pressure, p_a. Then

$$p_a - p = -\rho g(y_2 - y_1),$$

$$p = p_a + \rho gh. \qquad (14\text{–}4)$$

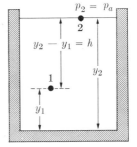

FIGURE 14–2

Note that the shape of the containing vessel does not affect the pressure, and that the pressure is the same at all points at the same depth. It also follows from Eq. (14–4) that if the pressure p_a is increased in any way, say by inserting a piston on the top surface and pressing down on it, the pressure p at any depth must increase by exactly the same amount. This fact was stated by the French scientist Blaise Pascal (1623–1662) in 1653 and is called "Pascal's law." It is often stated: "Pressure applied to an enclosed fluid at rest is transmitted undiminished to every portion of the fluid and the walls of the containing vessel." We can see now that it is not an independent principle but a necessary consequence of the laws of mechanics.

Pascal's law is illustrated by the operation of a hydraulic press, shown in Fig. 14–3. A piston of small cross-sectional area a is used to exert a small force f directly on a liquid such as oil. The pressure $p = f/a$ is transmitted through the connecting pipe to a larger cylinder equipped with a larger piston of area A. Since the pressure is the same in both cylinders,

$$p = \frac{f}{a} = \frac{F}{A}$$

and

$$F = \frac{A}{a} \times f.$$

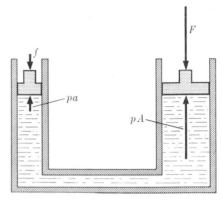

It follows that the hydraulic press is a force-multiplying device with an ideal mechanical advantage equal to the ratio of the areas of the two pistons. Barber chairs, dentist chairs, car lifts, and hydraulic brakes are all devices that make use of the principle of the hydraulic press.

FIG. 14–3. Principle of the hydraulic press.

14–3 The hydrostatic paradox. If a number of vessels of different shapes are interconnected as in Fig. 14–4(a), it will be found that a liquid poured into them will stand at the same level in each. Before the principles of hydrostatics were completely understood, this seemed a very puzzling phenomenon and was called the "hydrostatic paradox." It would appear at first sight, for example, that vessel C should develop a greater pressure at its base than should B, and hence that liquid would be forced from C into B.

Equation (14–4), however, states that the pressure depends only on the depth below the liquid surface and not at all on the shape of the containing vessel. Since the depth of the liquid is the same in each vessel, the pressure at the base of each is the same and hence the system is in equilibrium.

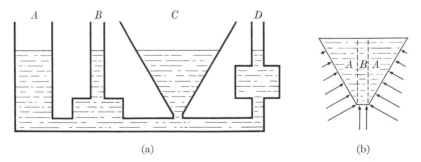

(a)   (b)

FIG. 14–4. (a) The hydrostatic paradox. The top of the liquid stands at the same level in each vessel. (b) Forces on the liquid in vessel C.

A more detailed explanation may be helpful in understanding the situation. Consider vessel C in Fig. 14–4(b). The forces exerted against the liquid by the walls are shown by arrows, the force being everywhere perpendicular to the walls of the vessel. The inclined forces at the sloping walls may be resolved into horizontal and vertical components. The weight of the liquid in the sections lettered A is supported by the vertical components of these forces. Hence the pressure at the base of the vessel is due only to the weight of the liquid in the cylindrical column B. Any vessel, regardless of its shape, may be treated the same way.

14–4 Pressure gauges. The simplest type of pressure gauge is the open-tube manometer, illustrated in Fig. 14–5(a). It consists of a U-shaped tube containing a liquid, one end of the tube being at the pressure p which it is desired to measure, while the other end is open to the atmosphere.

The pressure at the bottom of the left column is

$$p + \rho g y_1,$$

while that at the bottom of the right column is

$$p_a + \rho g y_2,$$

where ρ is the density of the manometric liquid. Since these pressures

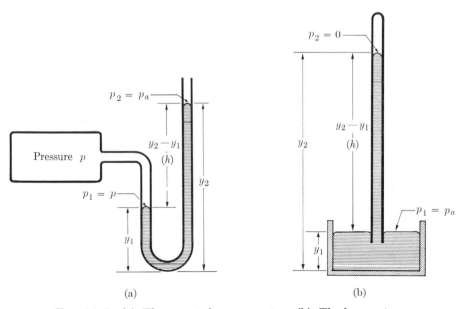

(a)   (b)

Fig. 14–5. (a) The open-tube manometer. (b) The barometer.

both refer to the same point, it follows that

$$p + \rho g y_1 = p_a + \rho g y_2,$$

and

$$p - p_a = \rho g(y_2 - y_1) = \rho g h.$$

The pressure p is called the *absolute pressure*, whereas the difference $p - p_a$ between this and the atmospheric pressure is called the *gauge pressure*. It is seen that the gauge pressure is proportional to the difference in height of the liquid columns.

The mercury barometer is a long glass tube that has been filled with mercury and then inverted in a dish of mercury, as shown in Fig. 14–5(b). The space above the mercury column contains only mercury vapor whose pressure, at room temperature, is so small that it may be neglected. It is easily seen that

$$p_a = \rho g(y_2 - y_1) = \rho g h.$$

Because mercury manometers and barometers are used so frequently in laboratories, it is customary to express atmospheric pressure and other pressures as so many "inches of mercury" or "centimeters of mercury." An "inch of mercury," however, is *not* a real unit of pressure, since pressure is the ratio of force to area.

EXAMPLE. Compute the atmospheric pressure on a day when the height of the barometer is 76.0 cm.

The height of the mercury column depends on ρ and g as well as on the atmospheric pressure. Hence both the density of mercury and the local acceleration of gravity must be known. The density varies with the temperature, and g with the latitude and elevation above sea level. All accurate barometers are provided with a thermometer and with a table or chart from which corrections for temperature and elevation can be found. If we assume $g = 980$ cm/sec² and $\rho = 13.6$ gm/cm³,

$$p_a = \rho g h = 13.6 \frac{\text{gm}}{\text{cm}^3} \times 980 \frac{\text{cm}}{\text{sec}^2} \times 76 \text{ cm}$$

$$= 1{,}013{,}000 \frac{\text{dynes}}{\text{cm}^2}$$

(about a million dynes per square centimeter). In British engineering units,

$$76 \text{ cm} = 30 \text{ in.} = 2.5 \text{ ft,}$$

$$\rho g = 850 \frac{\text{lb}}{\text{ft}^3},$$

$$p_a = 2120 \frac{\text{lb}}{\text{ft}^2} = 14.7 \frac{\text{lb}}{\text{in}^2}.$$

A pressure of 1.013×10^6 dynes/cm^2 = 1.013×10^5 newtons/m^2 = 14.7 lb/in^2, is called *one atmosphere*. A pressure of exactly one million dynes per square centimeter is called one *bar*, and a pressure one one-thousandth as great is one *millibar*. Atmospheric pressures are of the order of 1000 millibars, and are now stated in terms of this unit by the United States Weather Bureau.

The Bourdon-type pressure gauge is more convenient for most purposes than a liquid manometer. It consists of a flattened brass tube closed at one end and bent into a circular form. The closed end of the tube is connected by a gear and pinion to a pointer which moves over a scale. The open end of the tube is connected to the apparatus, the pressure within which is to be measured. When pressure is exerted within the flattened tube, it straightens slightly just as a bent rubber hose straightens when water is admitted. The resulting motion of the closed end of the tube is transmitted to the pointer.

14–5 Archimedes' principle. The irregular outline in Fig. 14–6 represents an imaginary surface bounding an arbitrary portion of a fluid at rest. The short arrows represent the forces exerted by the surrounding fluid against small elements of the boundary surface of equal area ΔA. The force $\Delta \mathbf{F}$ against each element is normal to that element and equal to $p\, \Delta A$, where p depends only on the vertical depth below the free surface and not on the shape or orientation of the boundary surface.

Since the entire fluid is at rest, the x-component of the resultant of these surface forces is zero. The y-component of the resultant, $\mathbf{F}_y$, must equal the weight of the fluid inside the arbitrary surface, mg, and its line of action must pass through the center of gravity of this fluid.

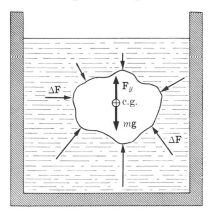

Now suppose the fluid inside the surface to be removed and replaced by a solid body having exactly the same shape. The pressure at every point will be exactly the same as before, so the force exerted on the body by the surrounding fluid will be unaltered. That is, *the fluid exerts on the body an upward force* $\mathbf{F}_y$, *which is equal to the weight* $m\mathbf{g}$ *of the fluid originally occupying the boundary surface and whose line of action passes through the original center of gravity.*

The submerged body, in general, will *not* be in equilibrium. Its weight may be greater or less than $\mathbf{F}_y$, and

FIG. 14–6.   Archimedes' principle. The buoyant force $\mathbf{F}_y$ equals the weight of the displaced fluid.

if it is not homogeneous, its center of gravity may not lie on the line of $\mathbf{F}_y$. Therefore, in general, it will be acted on by a resultant force through its own center of gravity and by a couple, and will rise or fall and also rotate.

The fact that a body immersed in a fluid should be "buoyed up" with a force equal to the weight of the displaced fluid was deduced by Archimedes (287–212 B.C.) from reasoning along the same lines as above. It is called *Archimedes' principle* and is, of course, a consequence of Newton's laws and the properties of a fluid. The position of the line of action of the upward force, usually omitted from a statement of the principle, is equal in importance to the magnitude of the force.

The weight of a dirigible floating in air, or of a submarine floating at some depth below the surface of the water, is just equal to the weight of a volume of air, or water, that is equal to the volume of the dirigible or submarine. That is, the average density of the dirigible equals that of air, and the average density of the submarine equals the density of water.

A body whose average density is less than that of a liquid can float *partially* submerged at the free upper surface of the liquid. However, we not only want a ship to float, but to float upright in stable equilibrium without capsizing. This requires that normally the line of action of the buoyant force should pass through the center of gravity of the ship and also, when the ship heels, the couple set up by its weight and the buoyant force should be in such a direction as to right it.

Figure 14–7 represents a section of the hull of a yacht, when on an even keel and when heeled over. In (a), the weight $\mathbf{w}$ of the yacht and the buoyant force $\mathbf{B}$ are equal and opposite, and the lines of action of both pass through the center of gravity of the yacht (c.g.). In (b), the center of gravity of the displaced water has shifted to point b and the line of

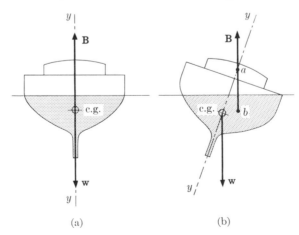

(a)   (b)

FIG. 14–7. Forces on the hull of a yacht.

action of the buoyant force **B** passes through this point.   The line of
action of **w** still passes through the center of gravity of the yacht. (Actually, a simple diagram like Fig. 14–7 would apply only if the shape of the
hull were the same at all cross sections.) The weight **w** and the buoyant
force **B** give rise to a couple in such a direction as to right the yacht.
If the line of action of **B** should intersect yy at a point below the center
of gravity, the yacht would be unstable and would capsize.

When making "weighings" with a sensitive analytical balance, correction must be made for the buoyant force of the air if the density of the
body being "weighed" is very different from that of the standard "weights,"
which are usually of brass.   For example, suppose a block of wood of
density 0.4 gm/cm^3 is balanced on an equal-arm balance by brass "weights"
of 20 gm, density 8.0 gm/cm^3. The apparent weight of each body is the
difference between its true weight and the buoyant force of the air.   If
ρ_w, ρ_b, and ρ_a are the densities of the wood, brass, and air, and V_w and V_b
are the volumes of the wood and brass, the apparent weights, which are
equal, are

$$\rho_w V_w g - \rho_a V_w g = \rho_b V_b g - \rho_a V_b g.$$

The true mass of the wood is $\rho_w V_w$, and the true mass of the standard
is $\rho_b V_b$. Hence,

$$\text{True mass} = \rho_w V_w = \rho_b V_b + \rho_a(V_w - V_b)$$
$$= \text{mass of standard} + \rho_a(V_w - V_b).$$

In the specific example cited

$$V_w = \frac{20}{0.4} = 50 \text{ cm}^3 \text{ (very nearly)},$$

$$V_b = \frac{20}{8} = 2.5 \text{ cm}^3, \qquad \rho_a = 0.0013 \; \frac{\text{gm}}{\text{cm}^3}.$$

Hence

$$\rho_a(V_w - V_b) = 0.0013 \times 47.5 = 0.062 \text{ gm}.$$

$$\text{True mass} = 20.062 \text{ gm}.$$

If measurements are being made to one one-thousandth of a gram, it is
obvious that the correction of 62 thousandths is of the greatest importance.

EXAMPLE. A tank containing water is placed on a spring scale, which registers
a total weight **W**. A stone of weight **w** is hung from a string and lowered into the
water without touching the sides or bottom of the tank [Fig. 14–8(a)]. What will
be the reading on the spring scale?

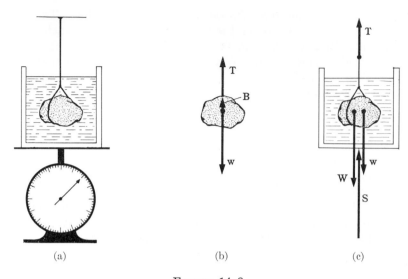

FIGURE 14–8

First, for the stone alone, the forces are as shown in Fig. 14–8(b), where **B** is the buoyant force and **T** is the tension in the string. Since $\sum F_y = 0$,

$$T + B = w.$$

Next, for the tank with the water and stone in it, the forces are as shown in Fig. 14–8(c), where **S** is the force exerted by the spring scale on the isolated system and, by Newton's third law, is equal in magnitude and opposite in direction to the force exerted on the scale. The condition for equilibrium yields the equation

$$T + S = w + W.$$

Subtracting the first equation from the second, we get

$$S = W + B.$$

That is, the reading of the spring scale has been increased by an amount equal to the buoyant force.

PROBLEMS

14–1. The piston of a hydraulic automobile lift is 12 in. in diameter. What pressure, in lb/in^2, is required to lift a car weighing 2400 lb?

14–2. The expansion tank of a household hot-water heating system is open to the atmosphere and is 30 ft above a pressure gauge attached to the furnace. What is the gauge pressure at the furnace, in lb/in^2?

14–3. The submarine Squalus sank at a depth of 240 ft. Compute the absolute pressure at this depth, in lb/in^2 and lb/ft^2. The specific gravity of sea water is 1.025.

14–4. A piece of gold-aluminum alloy weighs 10 lb. When suspended from a spring balance and submerged in water, the balance reads 8 lb. What is the weight of gold in the alloy if the specific gravity of gold is 19.3 and the specific gravity of aluminum is 2.5?

14–5. What is the area of the smallest block of ice 1 ft thick that will just support a man weighing 180 lb? The specific gravity of the ice is 0.917, and it is floating in fresh water.

14–6. A cubical block of wood 10 cm on a side floats at the interface between oil and water as in Fig. 14–9, with its lower surface 2 cm below the interface. The density of the oil is 0.6 gm/cm^3. (a) What is the mass of the block? (b) What is the gauge pressure at the lower face of the block?

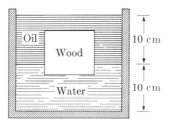

FIGURE 14–9

14–7. The densities of air, helium, and hydrogen (at standard conditions) are, respectively, 0.00129 gm/cm^3, 0.000178 gm/cm^3, and 0.0000899 gm/cm^3. What is the volume in cubic feet displaced by a hydrogen-filled dirigible which has a total "lift" of 10 tons? What would be the "lift" if helium were used instead of hydrogen?

14–8. A piece of wood is 2 ft long, 1 ft wide, and 2 in. thick. Its specific gravity is 0.6. What volume of lead must be fastened underneath to sink the wood in calm water so that its top is just even with the water level?

14–9. A cubical block of wood 10 cm on a side and of density 0.5 gm/cm^3 floats in a jar of water. Oil of density 0.8 gm/cm^3 is poured on the water until the top of the oil layer is 4 cm below the top of the block. (a) How deep is the oil layer? (b) What is the gauge pressure at the lower face of the block?

14–10. A cubical block of steel (density = 7.8 gm/cm^3) floats on mercury (density = 13.6 gm/cm^3). (a) What fraction of the block is above the mercury surface? (b) If water is poured on the mercury surface, how deep must the water layer be so that the water surface just rises to the top of the steel block?

14–11. Block A in Fig. 14–10 hangs by a cord from spring balance D and is submerged in a liquid C contained in beaker B. The weight of the beaker is 2 lb, the weight of the liquid is 3 lb. Balance D reads 5 lb and balance E reads 15 lb. The volume of block A is 0.1 ft^3. (a) What is the weight per unit volume of the liquid? (b) What will each balance read if block A is pulled up out of the liquid?

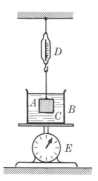

FIGURE 14–10

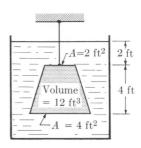

FIGURE 14–11

14–12. A hollow sphere of inner radius 9 cm and outer radius 10 cm floats half submerged in a liquid of specific gravity 0.8. (a) Calculate the density of the material of which the sphere is made. (b) What would be the density of a liquid in which the hollow sphere would just float completely submerged?

14–13. Two spherical bodies having the same diameter are released simultaneously from the same height. If the mass of one is ten times that of the other and if the air resistance on each is the *same*, show that the heavier body will arrive at the ground first.

14–14. When a life preserver having a volume of 0.75 ft^3 is immersed in sea water (specific gravity 1.1) it will just support a 160-lb man (specific gravity 1.2) with 2/10 of his volume above water. What is the weight per unit volume of the material composing the life preserver?

14–15. An object in the shape of a truncated cone weighs 1000 lb in vacuum and is suspended by a rope in an open tank of liquid density 2 slugs/ft^3, as in Fig. 14–11. (a) Find the total downward force exerted by the liquid on the top of the object, of area 2 ft^2. (b) Find the total upward force exerted

by the liquid on the bottom of the object, of area 4 ft^2. (c) Find the tension in the cord supporting the object.

14–16. A hollow cylindrical can 20 cm in diameter floats in water with 10 cm of its height above the water line when a 10-kgm iron block hangs from its bottom. If the block is now placed inside the can, how much of the cylinder's height will be above the water line? The density of iron is 7.8 gm/cm^3.

14–17. A block of balsa wood placed in one scale pan of an equal-arm balance is found to be exactly balanced by a 100-gm brass "weight" in the other scale pan. Find the true mass of the balsa wood, if its specific gravity is 0.15.

14–18. A 3200-lb cylindrical can buoy floats vertically in salt water (specific gravity = 1.03). The diameter of the buoy is 3 ft. Calculate (a) the additional distance the buoy will sink when a 150-lb man stands on top, (b) the period of the resulting vertical simple harmonic motion when the man dives off.

14–19. A uniform rod AB, 12 ft long, weighing 24 lb, is supported at end B by a flexible cord and weighted at end A with a 12-lb lead weight. The rod

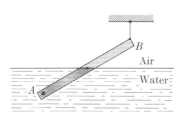

FIGURE 14–12

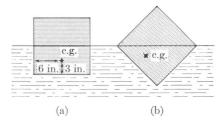

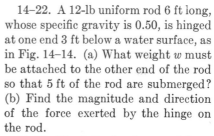

FIGURE 14–13

floats as shown in Fig. 14–12, with one-half its length submerged. The buoyant force on the lead weight can be neglected. (a) Show in a diagram all the forces acting on the rod. (b) Find the tension in the cord. (c) Find the total volume of the rod.

14–20. A cubical block of wood 1 ft on a side is weighted so that its center of gravity is at the point shown in Fig. 14–13(a), and it floats in water with one-half its volume submerged. Compute the righting moment when the block is "heeled" at an angle of 45°, as in Fig. 14–13(b).

14–21. A hydrometer consists of a spherical bulb and a cylindrical stem of cross section 0.4 cm². The total volume of bulb and stem is 13.2 cm³. When immersed in water the hydrometer floats with 8 cm of the stem above the water surface. In alcohol, 1 cm of the stem is above the surface. Find the density of the alcohol.

14–22. A 12-lb uniform rod 6 ft long, whose specific gravity is 0.50, is hinged at one end 3 ft below a water surface, as in Fig. 14–14. (a) What weight w must be attached to the other end of the rod so that 5 ft of the rod are submerged? (b) Find the magnitude and direction of the force exerted by the hinge on the rod.

14–23. The following is quoted from a letter. How would you reply?

"It is the practice of carpenters hereabouts, when laying out and leveling up the foundations of relatively long buildings, to use a garden hose filled with water, into the ends of the hose being thrust glass tubes 10–12 inches long.

"The theory is that the water, seeking a common level, will be of the same height in both the tubes and thus effect a level. Now the question rises as to what happens if a bubble of air is left in the hose. Our greybeards contend the air will not

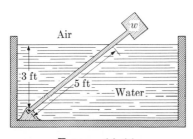

FIGURE 14–14

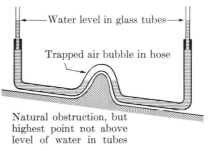

Natural obstruction, but highest point not above level of water in tubes

FIGURE 14–15

affect *the reading from one end to the* *other. Others say that it will cause im-* *portant inaccuracies.*

"Can you give a relatively simple *answer to this question, together with an* *explanation? I include a rough sketch* (Fig. 14–15) *of the situation that caused* *the dispute."*

14–24. A glass tube is bent into a rectangular U, as in Fig. 14–16, and partially filled with a liquid. The length of the horizontal portion of the U is L. Find the expression for the difference in height h between the tops of the liquid columns in the vertical arms (a) when the tube has a linear acceleration a in the direction of the x-axis, (b) when the tube has a uniform angular velocity ω about the y-axis.

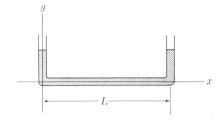

FIGURE 14–16

CHAPTER 15

TEMPERATURE—EXPANSION

15–1 Concept of temperature. To describe the equilibrium states of mechanical systems, as well as to study and predict the motions of rigid bodies and fluids, only three fundamental indefinables were needed: length, mass, and time. All other physical quantities of importance in mechanics could be expressed in terms of these three indefinables. We come now, however, to a series of phenomena, called *thermal effects* or *heat phenomena*, which involve aspects that are essentially nonmechanical and which require for their description a fourth fundamental indefinable, the *temperature*.

Consider a cake of ice with a volume of about 1 cubic foot at atmospheric pressure. It is in mechanical equilibrium because the vector sum of the forces acting on it is zero. Suppose, in the neighborhood of the ice, there is a small spherical rubber balloon inflated with air. It is also in mechanical equilibrium because the difference between the inside and outside pressure is balanced by the tension in the curved rubber. Even though the ice and the air balloon are separately in mechanical equilibrium, it will be found that both systems undergo changes when they are placed together: the volume of the ice decreases (because some of it melts) and both the pressure and volume of the air in the balloon change. After a while these changes cease. The final state of the two systems is called *thermal equilibrium*.

The tendency of systems originally in mechanical equilibrium to change their states when placed in contact cannot be explained in terms of length, mass, and time alone. The results of many experiments on systems which change their mechanical states when placed together and finally reach thermal equilibrium lead us to infer that all ordinary objects have a new physical property that determines whether they will be in thermal equilibrium when placed in contact with other objects. This property is called *temperature. The temperatures associated with two objects are said to be equal only when the two objects are in thermal equilibrium.* The temperature of all objects in thermal equilibrium may be represented by a number. The establishment of a temperature scale is merely the adoption of a set of rules for assigning different numbers to different temperatures. Once this is done the necessary and sufficient condition for thermal equilibrium between two systems is that they have the same temperature. Also, when the temperatures are different, we may be sure that the systems are not in thermal equilibrium.

Human beings are endowed with a temperature sense which enables them to tell at least roughly whether two objects will be in thermal equilibrium when placed together. We have learned to describe our sensations when touching other objects by using adjectives such as "cold," "warm," "hot," etc. These words mean roughly the same thing to most people, just as the words "low pitch" and "high pitch" or "red" and "blue" mean about the same thing when used to describe our sensations on hearing sounds or seeing colors. When two objects of the same material have been left together for some time and are then touched, their "hotness" or "coldness" feel about the same and the two objects are described as having the same temperature. Temperature is therefore related to our sensation of hotness or coldness when we touch a body.

Our temperature sense is much too unreliable to serve as a means of measurement. An object with at least one easily measurable property that changes appreciably while the object is coming to thermal equilibrium may be used as a temperature-measuring device, or *thermometer*. With the aid of an arbitrarily chosen thermometer it is possible to formulate a set of rules for representing temperatures with numbers, that is, for setting up a *temperature scale*.

15–2 Thermometers. Of all the properties of systems that have been studied with an eye toward possible use in the measurement of temperature, *the pressure of a gas* whose volume is maintained constant has been found to excel in *sensitivity, accuracy* of measurement, and *reproducibility*. The constant-volume gas thermometer is illustrated schematically in Fig. 15–1. The materials, construction, and dimensions differ in various laboratories throughout the world and depend on the nature of the gas and the temperature range to be covered.

The gas, usually hydrogen or helium, is contained in bulb C, and the pressure exerted by it can be measured by the open-tube mercury ma-

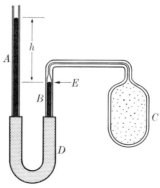

FIG. 15–1. Constant-volume gas thermometer.

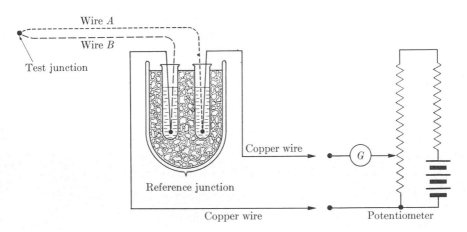

FIG. 15–2. Thermocouple of wires A and B with a reference junction consisting of two junctions with copper, connected to a potentiometer.

nometer. As the temperature of the gas is increased, it expands, forcing the mercury down in tube B and up in tube A. Tubes A and B are connected by the flexible rubber tube D, and by raising A, the mercury level in B may be brought back to the reference mark E. The gas is thus kept at constant volume.

Gas thermometers are absolute instruments and are used mainly in bureaus of standards and in some university research laboratories. They are usually large, bulky, and slow in coming to thermal equilibrium.

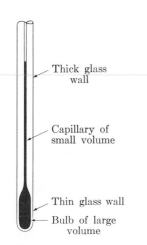

FIG. 15–3. Construction of liquid-in-glass-thermometer.

In most research and engineering laboratories, secondary thermometers that are small and fast must be used. The most commonly used is the *thermocouple*, which consists of a junction of two different metals or alloys. Since the junction is small and has a small mass, it can follow temperature changes rapidly and come to equilibrium quickly. The junction forms part of an electric circuit, as shown in Fig. 15–2. When it is in contact with an object or immersed in a fluid, the temperature measurement is accomplished by measuring a quantity called an emf (ee-em-eff, electromotive force) with an instrument known as a potentiometer.

The best known but not the most accurate thermometer is a liquid such as mercury or alcohol contained in a bulb which communicates with a very narrow tube or capillary, as shown in Fig. 15–3. The height of the liquid in the capillary is an indication of the temperature. The main fault of the liquid-in-glass thermometer is that its reading changes over the years because of aging of the glass.

In each of the three thermometers mentioned above there is one physical quantity called a *thermometric property* whose change is used to indicate a change of temperature. In the case of a gas at constant volume it is the pressure p; with the thermocouple it is the emf $\mathcal{E}$; and with the liquid-in-glass thermometer it is the height h of the liquid in the capillary.

15–3 The establishment of a temperature scale. Let p stand for the absolute pressure in a constant-volume gas thermometer. Let us define the temperature T common to the thermometer and to all systems in thermal equilibrium with it as a linear function of p. That is,

$$T = ap,$$

where a is an arbitrary constant. It follows that two temperatures on this "linear p scale" are to each other as the ratio of the corresponding p's, or

$$\frac{T_1}{T_2} = \frac{p_1}{p_2}. \tag{15–1}$$

Note that the linear function of p was an *arbitrary choice*. A different algebraic function, or even a logarithmic function, could have been chosen, and the resulting temperature scale would be equally legitimate.

To determine the temperature T of any system, the thermometer must first be brought to thermal equilibrium with *an arbitrarily chosen standard system in an easily reproducible state*. The temperature of the standard system in the chosen state is called a *fixed point*. Before 1954 there were two fixed points: (1) the temperature of pure ice in equilibrium with air-saturated water at one atmosphere pressure (the ice point), and (2) the equilibrium temperature of pure water and pure steam at one atmosphere pressure (the steam point). The temperature interval between these two fixed points was chosen to be 100 so-called "centigrade" degrees.

The use of two fixed points was found unsatisfactory, partly because of the difficulty of achieving equilibrium between pure ice and air-saturated water. When ice melts, it surrounds itself with pure water and thus prevents intimate contact of ice and air-saturated water. Also, the steam point is extremely sensitive to a change in pressure. The temperature scale in use since 1954 is based on one fixed point only. This is the temperature at which ice, liquid water, and water vapor coexist in equilibrium, a state known as the *triple point* of water. To obtain the best agreement between the old and new scales, the temperature of the triple point is assigned the value 273.16 degrees kelvin, abbreviated 273.16°K. (The reason for the use of Kelvin's name will be made clear later.) Thus, designating the triple point of water by the subscript 3, we have from Eq. (15–1),

$$\frac{T}{T_3} = \frac{p}{p_3},$$

with

$$T_3 = 273.16°K.$$

Hence,

$$T = 273.16° \frac{p}{p_3}. \tag{15–2}$$

The temperature of the triple point of water is the *standard fixed point* of thermometry. To achieve the triple point, water of the highest purity is distilled into a vessel like that shown schematically in Fig. 15–4. When all air has been removed, the vessel is sealed off. With the aid of a freezing mixture in the inner well, a layer of ice is formed around the well, as shown in Fig. 15–4(a). When the freezing mixture is replaced by a thermometer bulb, a thin layer of ice is melted nearby, as shown in Fig. 15–4(b). So long as the solid, liquid, and vapor phases coexist in equilibrium, the

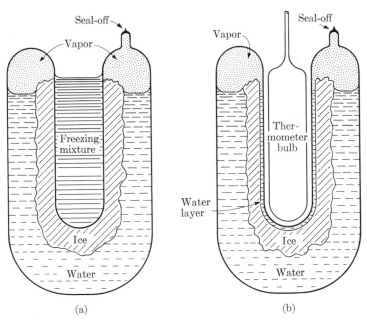

FIG. 15–4. Triple-point cell, (a) with freezing mixture in the central well to freeze a layer of ice; (b) with a thermometer in the well, which melts a thin layer of ice nearby.

system is at the triple point. The actual shape of the apparatus used by the U.S. National Bureau of Standards is shown in Fig. 15–5.

To determine an unknown temperature T using a gas thermometer, two measurements of p have to be made: one at the unknown temperature and the other at the triple point of water. The temperature is then found from Eq. (15–2).

If a series of tests is carried out in which the temperature of a given system is measured with a number of different thermometers, each making use of a different thermometric property, the thermometers will be found to give slightly different results. The smallest variation, however, is found among different gas thermometers operated at low pressure. For this reason, and also because of its accuracy and reproducibility, a particular gas-thermometer technique has been chosen as a world standard. The principles of operation are as follows. Suppose that an amount of gas is introduced into the bulb of a constant-volume gas thermometer so that the pressure p_3, when the bulb is surrounded

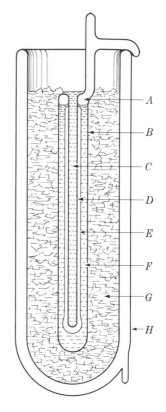

Fig. 15–5. Diagram of the NBS triple-point cell (B, D) in use in an ice bath (G) within a Dewar flask (H). A, water vapor; C, thermometer well; E, ice mantle; F, liquid water.

by water at its triple point, is equal to 1000 mm Hg. Keeping the volume constant, measure the pressure p when the bulb is at some unknown temperature, such as that of steam condensing at atmospheric pressure, and calculate the quantity

$$273.16° \; \frac{p}{1000} \, .$$

Now remove some of the gas so that the pressure p_3 has a smaller value, say 500 mm Hg. Measure the new pressure p when the bulb is at the temperature of condensing steam, and calculate the quantity

$$273.16° \; \frac{p}{500} \, .$$

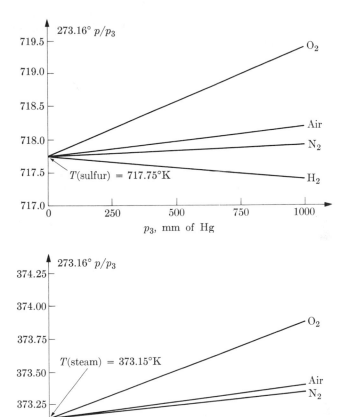

Fig. 15–6. Readings of a constant-volume gas thermometer for the temperature of condensing steam and for that of condensing sulfur, when different gases are used at various values of p_3.

The value of this quantity will be found to be slightly different from that obtained with $p_3 = 1000$ mm Hg.

Continue reducing the amount of gas in the bulb and calculate the quantity $273.16° \, p/p_3$ at each value of p_3. Construct a graph of this quantity against the pressure p_3 and extrapolate the resulting curve to the axis where $p_3 = 0$.

The results of a series of measurements of this sort are plotted in Fig. 15–6, for the temperatures of condensing steam and of condensing sulfur. The graphs show that although the readings of a constant-volume gas thermometer depend both on the kind of gas used and on the pressure p_3, *all gases indicate the same temperature as p_3 is lowered and approaches zero.* We therefore define the gas temperature T by the equation

$$T = [273.16°K] \lim_{p_3 \to 0} \left(\frac{p}{p_3}\right)_{\text{const. vol.}} . \qquad (15\text{-}3)$$

It should be emphasized that this equation, or the set of rules for measuring temperature which it embodies, does not rest on the assumption that "the pressure of a gas at constant volume is directly proportional to the temperature." Such a statement, before a temperature scale is set up, is meaningless.

Although the temperature scale of Eq. (15-3) is independent of the properties of any one particular gas, it still depends on the properties of gases in general. To measure a low temperature, a gas that does not liquefy at the low temperature must be used. The lowest temperature that can be measured with a gas thermometer is about 1°K, provided low-pressure helium is used. *The temperature $T = 0$ remains as yet undefined.*

The kelvin temperature scale, which is independent of the properties of any particular substance, will be described in Chapter 17. It can be shown that in the temperature region in which a gas thermometer can be used, the gas scale and the kelvin scale are identical. In anticipation of this result, we write °K after a gas temperature. It will also be shown in Chapter 17 how the absolute zero of temperature is defined on the kelvin scale. Until then, the term "absolute zero" will have no meaning. The statement made so often that all molecular activity ceases at the temperature $T = 0$ is entirely erroneous. When it is necessary in statistical mechanics to correlate temperature with molecular activity, it is found that classical statistical mechanics must be modified with the aid of quantum mechanics. When this modification is carried out, the molecules of a substance at absolute zero have a *finite* amount of kinetic energy known as the *zero-point* energy.

15–4 The celsius, rankine, and fahrenheit scales. The celsius temperature scale (formerly called the centigrade scale in the United States and Great Britain) employs a degree of the same magnitude as that of the kelvin scale, but its zero point is shifted so that *the celsius temperature of the triple point of water is 0.01 degree celsius,* abbreviated 0.01°C. Thus, if t denotes the celsius temperature,

$$t = T - 273.15°K. \qquad (15\text{-}4)$$

The celsius temperature t_S at which steam condenses at 1 atm pressure is

$$t_S = T_S - 273.15°K,$$

and reading T_S from Fig. 15–6,

$$t_S = 373.15° - 273.15°$$

or

$$t_S = 100.00°C.$$

There are two other scales in common use in engineering and in everyday life in the United States and in Great Britain. The *rankine* temperature T_R (written °R) is proportional to the kelvin temperature according to the relation

$$T_R = \tfrac{9}{5}T. \tag{15–5}$$

A degree of the same size is used in the *fahrenheit* scale t_F (written °F), but with the zero point shifted according to the relation

$$t_F = T_R - 459.67°R. \tag{15–6}$$

Substituting Eqs. (15–4) and (15–5) into Eq. (15–6), we get

$$t_F = \tfrac{9}{5}t + 32°F, \tag{15–7}$$

from which it follows that the fahrenheit temperature of the ice point ($t = 0°C$) is 32°F and of the steam point ($t = 100°C$) is 212°F. The 100 celsius or kelvin degrees between the ice point and the steam point correspond to 180 fahrenheit or rankine degrees, as shown in Fig. 15–7, where the four scales are compared.

The accurate measurement of a boiling point or melting point with the aid of a gas thermometer requires months of painstaking laboratory work and mathematical computation. Fortunately, this has been done for a large number of substances which are obtainable with high purity. Some of these results are shown in Table 15–1. With the aid of these basic fixed points other thermometers may be calibrated. The calibration of the liquid-in-glass thermometer is accomplished by immersing it first in a mixture of ice and water and later in a steam bath and marking the liquid level in both cases. Subdividing the space between these two marks into 100 equal divisions provides a rough celsius scale, and the subdivision into 180 equal divisions, a rough fahrenheit scale.

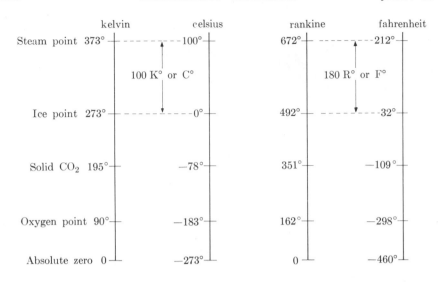

FIG. 15–7. Relations among kelvin, celsius, rankine, and fahrenheit temperature scales. Temperatures have been rounded off to the nearest degree.

TABLE 15–1

TEMPERATURES OF FIXED POINTS

Basic fixed points	T, °K	t, °C	T_R, °R	t_F, °F
Standard: Triple point of water	**273.16**	**0.01**	**491.688**	**32.018**
Boiling point of oxygen	90.18	−182.97	162.32	−297.35
Equil. of ice and air-saturated water (ice point)	273.15	0.00	491.67	32.00
Boiling point of water (steam point)	373.15	100.00	671.67	212.00
Boiling point of sulfur	717.75	444.60	1291.95	832.28
Melting point of antimony	903.65	630.50	1626.57	1166.90
Melting point of silver	1233.95	960.80	2221.11	1761.44
Melting point of gold	1336.15	1063.00	2405.07	1945.40

Suppose the temperature of a beaker of water is raised from 20°C to 30°C, through a temperature interval of 10 celsius degrees. It is desirable to distinguish between such a temperature interval and the actual temperature of 10 degrees above the celsius zero. Hence we shall use the phrase "10 degrees celsius," or "10°C," when referring to an *actual temperature*, and "10 celsius degrees," or "10 C°" to mean a temperature *interval*. Thus there is an interval of 10 celsius degrees between 20 degrees celsius and 30 degrees celsius.

15–5 Linear expansion. With a few exceptions, the dimensions of all substances increase as the temperature of the substance is increased. If a given specimen is in the form of a rod or cable, one is usually interested in its change of *length* with changes in temperature. Figure 15–8 represents a rod whose length is L_0 at some reference temperature t_0, and whose length is L at some higher temperature t. The difference $L - L_0 = \Delta L$ is the amount the rod has expanded on heating. It is found experimentally that the increase in length, ΔL, is proportional to the original length L_0, and very nearly proportional to the increase in temperature, $t - t_0$ or Δt. That is,

$$\Delta L \propto L_0\,\Delta t, \qquad \text{or} \qquad \Delta L = \alpha L_0\,\Delta t, \tag{15–8}$$

where α is a proportionality constant, different for different materials, and is called the *coefficient of linear expansion.*

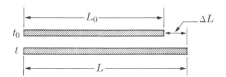

FIG. 15–8. Linear expansion.

Equation (15–8) may be solved for α and written

$$\boxed{\alpha = \frac{\Delta L}{L_0}\frac{1}{\Delta t}.} \tag{15–9}$$

The coefficient of linear expansion of a substance may therefore be described as the fractional change in length per degree rise in temperature. Another useful relation is obtained by replacing ΔL by $L - L_0$ and solving for L.

$$\boxed{L = L_0(1 + \alpha\,\Delta t).} \tag{15–10}$$

Since L_0, L, and ΔL are all expressed in the same unit, the units of α are "reciprocal degrees" (celsius or fahrenheit). Thus the coefficient of linear expansion of copper is written

$$\alpha = 14 \times 10^{-6} \text{ per celsius degree}$$

or

$$\alpha = 14 \times 10^{-6}\ (C°)^{-1}.$$

TABLE 15–2

COEFFICIENTS OF LINEAR EXPANSION

Substance	$\alpha, (C°)^{-1}$
Aluminum	24×10^{-6}
Brass	20×10^{-6}
Copper	14×10^{-6}
Glass	$4\text{–}9 \times 10^{-6}$
Steel	12×10^{-6}
Invar	0.9×10^{-6}
Quartz (fused)	0.4×10^{-6}
Zinc	26×10^{-6}

This means that a copper rod one centimeter long at 0°C increases in length by 0.000014 cm when heated to 1°C. A rod one foot long at 0°C increases by 0.000014 ft, and so on.

Since the fahrenheit degree is only $\frac{5}{9}$ as large as the celsius degree, coefficients of expansion per fahrenheit degree are $\frac{5}{9}$ as large as their values on the celsius scale.

EXAMPLE. An iron steam pipe is 200 ft long at 0°C. What will be its increase in length when heated to 100°C? $\alpha = 10 \times 10^{-6}$ per celsius degree.

$$L_0 = 200 \text{ ft}, \qquad \alpha = 10 \times 10^{-6} \text{ per C°}, \qquad t = 100°C, \qquad t_0 = 0°C.$$

$$\begin{aligned}
\text{Increase in length} = \Delta L &= \alpha L_0 \, \Delta t \\
&= (10 \times 10^{-6})\,(200)\,(100) \\
&= 0.20 \text{ ft.}
\end{aligned}$$

The coefficient of expansion of a substance in the form of a rod is measured by making two fine lines on the rod near its ends, and measuring the displacement of each line with a measuring microscope while the temperature of the rod is changed by a measured amount.

The *bimetallic* element is a device which has come into wide use in recent years, both as a thermometer and as a part of many thermostatic controls. It consists of two thin flat strips of different metals, welded or riveted together as in Fig. 15–9(a). If metal A has a larger coefficient of expansion than metal B, the compound strip, if originally straight, bends into a curve when heated, as shown in Fig. 15–9(b). The transverse motion of the end of the strip is very much larger than the increase in length of either metal.

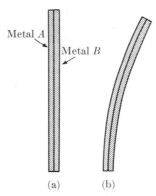

FIG. 15–9 The bimetallic element.

When used as a thermostat, one end of the strip is fixed and the motion of the other end is made to open or close an electrical control circuit. The common oven thermometer consists of a bimetallic strip coiled in a helix. With changes in temperature the helix winds or unwinds, and this motion is transmitted to a pivoted pointer which moves over a calibrated scale. Because of lost motion and friction, such thermometers are not precision instruments.

15–6 Surface and volume expansion. When a plate or sheet of material is heated, both the length and breadth of the plate increase. Consider a rectangular plate whose length and breadth at temperature t_0 are L_0 and b_0 respectively. When heated to a temperature t, these dimensions become

$$L = L_0(1 + \alpha \, \Delta t),$$

and

$$b = b_0(1 + \alpha \, \Delta t).$$

The original area of the plate was

$$A_0 = L_0 b_0,$$

and the area after heating is

$$A = Lb = L_0 b_0 (1 + \alpha \, \Delta t)\,(1 + \alpha \, \Delta t).$$
$$= A_0[1 + 2\alpha \, \Delta t + (\alpha \, \Delta t)^2].$$

But since α is a small quantity, α^2 will be extremely small and the term $(\alpha \, \Delta t)^2$ may be neglected. Hence

$$A = A_0(1 + 2\alpha \, \Delta t).$$

TABLE 15-3

COEFFICIENTS OF CUBICAL EXPANSION

Substance	$\beta,(C°)^{-1}$
Alcohol, ethyl	0.745×10^{-3}
Carbon disulphide	1.140×10^{-3}
Glycerin	0.485×10^{-3}
Mercury	0.182×10^{-3}
Petroleum	0.899×10^{-3}

If we now define a *surface* coefficient of expansion γ so that

$$A = A_0(1 + \gamma \, \Delta t), \qquad (15\text{--}11)$$

it follows that

$$\boxed{\gamma = 2\alpha,}$$

and the coefficient of surface expansion is twice the coefficient of linear expansion. Although derived for the special case of a rectangular plate, the result holds for a plate of any shape whatever.

If the plate contains a hole, the area *of the hole* expands at the same rate as does the surrounding material. This remains true even if the hole becomes so large that the "plate" is reduced to nothing but a rim around the hole. Thus the area of the "hole" enclosed by a steel wagon tire expands at the same rate as would a disk of this size, if constructed of the same kind of steel as is the rim.

By considering a solid block of material in the form of a rectangular parallelepiped whose dimensions at t_0 are L_0, b_0, and c_0, it is easy to show by the same type of reasoning that

$$V = V_0(1 + 3\alpha \, \Delta t) = V_0(1 + \beta \, \Delta t), \qquad (15\text{--}12)$$

where V is the volume at the temperature t, V_0 is the volume at t_0, and

$$\boxed{\beta = 3\alpha}$$

is the *volume* coefficient or coefficient of *cubical* expansion. This equation holds regardless of the shape of the body.

It is also true that the volume enclosed by a solid, such as the volume of a tank, a flask, or a thermometer bulb, expands at the same rate as would a solid body of the same material as that of which the walls are composed.

Equation (15–12) may also be used to compute the expansion of a liquid. The linear and surface coefficients of expansion of a liquid are of little significance.

EXAMPLE. The volume of the bulb of a mercury thermometer at 0°C is V_0, and the cross section of the capillary is A_0. The coefficient of linear expansion of the glass is α_G per C°, and the coefficient of cubical expansion of mercury is β_M per C°. If the mercury just fills the bulb at 0°C, what is the length of the mercury column in the capillary at a temperature of t°C?

The volume of the bulb at a temperature t is

$$V = V_0(1 + \beta_G t),$$

where $\beta_G = 3\alpha_G$ is the coefficient of cubical expansion of the glass.

The volume of the mercury at a temperature t is

$$V_M = V_0(1 + \beta_M t).$$

The volume of mercury that has been expelled from the bulb is the difference between these, or

$$V_0(1 + \beta_M t) - V_0(1 + \beta_G t) = V_0 t(\beta_M - \beta_G).$$

This volume is also equal to the length l of the mercury column multiplied by the cross section A of the capillary, where

$$A = A_0(1 + 2\alpha_G t).$$

Table 15–2 shows that the coefficient of linear expansion of glass is of the order of 5×10^{-6} per C°. Hence even if t is as great as 300°C, the term $2\alpha_G t$ is only 0.003. It may therefore be neglected in comparison with unity, which is equivalent to considering the cross section of the capillary constant. Then

$$lA_0 = V_0 t(\beta_M - \beta_G)$$

and

$$l = \frac{V_0}{A_0}(\beta_M - \beta_G)t.$$

The length of the mercury column is therefore proportional to the temperature and to the difference between the coefficients of cubical expansion of mercury and the glass of which the thermometer is constructed.

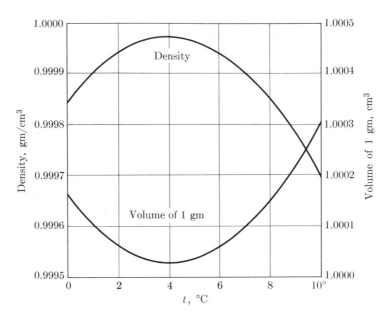

FIG. 15–10. Density of water, and volume of 1 gm, in the temperature range from 0°C to 10°C.

Water, in the temperature range from 0°C to 4°C, *decreases* in volume with increasing temperature, contrary to the behavior of most substances. That is, between 0°C and 4°C, the coefficient of expansion of water is *negative*. Above 4°C, water expands when heated. Since the volume of a given mass of water is smaller at 4°C than at any other temperature, the density of water is a maximum at 4°C. This behavior of water is the reason why lakes and ponds freeze first at their upper surfaces. Figure 15–10 illustrates the anomalous expansion of water in the temperature range from 0°C to 10°C.

PROBLEMS

15-1. (a) What is the melting point of silver in degrees fahrenheit? (See Table 15-1.) (b) What is the coefficient of linear expansion of copper in $(F°)^{-1}$? (c) What is the coefficient of volume expansion of copper in $(C°)^{-1}$? (d) At what temperature do the fahrenheit and celsius scales coincide?

15-2. The pendulum shaft of a clock is of aluminum. What is the fractional change in length of the shaft when it is cooled from 75°F to 45°F?

15-3. The length of Technology Bridge is about 2000 ft. Find the difference between its length on a winter day when the temperature is −20°F, and a summer day when the temperature is 100°F. Use the coefficient of expansion of steel.

15-4. A surveyor's 100-ft steel tape is correct at a temperature of 65°F. The distance between two points, as measured by this tape on a day when the temperature is 95°F, is 86.57 ft. What is the true distance between the points?

15-5. One steel meter bar is correct at 0°C, and another at 25°C. What is the difference between their lengths at 20°C?

15-6. To ensure a tight fit, the aluminum rivets used in airplane construction are made slightly larger than the rivet holes and cooled by "dry ice" (solid CO_2) before being driven. If the diameter of a hole is 0.2500 in., what should be the diameter of a rivet at 20°C if its diameter is to equal that of the hole when the rivet is cooled to −78°C, the temperature of dry ice?

15-7. A glass flask whose volume is exactly 1000 cm^3 at 0°C is filled level full of mercury at this temperature.

When flask and mercury are heated to 100°C, 15.2 cm^3 of mercury overflow. If the cubical coefficient of expansion of mercury is 0.000182 per celsius degree, compute the linear coefficient of expansion of the glass.

15-8. Steel rails 120 ft long are laid with their ends in contact on a day when the temperature is 110°F. What length gap will there be between rails on a day when the temperature is −20°F?

15-9. A steel wire which is 10 ft long at 20°C is found to increase in length by $\frac{3}{4}$ in. when heated to 520°C. (a) Compute its coefficient of linear expansion. (b) Find the stress in the wire if it is stretched taut at 520° and cooled to 20° without being allowed to contract.

15-10. A wire 60 cm long is bent into a circular ring, having a gap of 1.0 cm. The temperature of the wire is increased uniformly by 100C°. At the new temperature the gap is found to be 1.002 cm. What is the temperature coefficient of linear expansion of the wire? Assume no stresses within the wire before or after heating.

15-11. A steel ring of 3.000 in. inside diameter at 20°C is to be heated and slipped over a brass shaft measuring 3.002 in. in diameter at 20°C. (a) To what temperature should the ring be heated? (b) If the ring and shaft together are cooled by some means such as liquid air, at what temperature will the ring just slip off the shaft?

15-12. At a temperature of 20°C, the volume of a certain glass flask, up to a reference mark on the stem of the flask, is exactly 100 cm^3. The flask is filled to this point with a liquid whose coefficient of cubical expansion is

120×10^{-5} per C°, with both flask and liquid at 20°C. The coefficient of linear expansion of the glass is 8×10^{-6} per C°. The cross section of the stem is 1 mm² and can be considered constant. How far will the liquid rise or fall in the stem when the temperature is raised to 40°C?

15–13. A clock whose pendulum makes one vibration in 2 sec is correct at 25°C. The pendulum shaft is of steel and its mass may be neglected compared with that of the bob. (a) What is the fractional change in length of the shaft when it is cooled to 15°C? (b) How many seconds per day will the clock gain or lose at 15°C? [*Hint.* Use differentials.]

CHAPTER 16

WORK AND HEAT

16–1 External work. When the temperature of a body is raised, many different effects may take place: gases expand, solids and liquids usually expand but in rare instances they may contract, thermocouples develop an electromotive force, wires undergo a change of resistance, and many other phenomena occur. Such processes are often attended by the application of a force which undergoes a displacement, thereby bringing about the performance of work.

If a system as a whole exerts a force on its surroundings and a displacement takes place, the work that is done either by or on the system is called *external work*. Thus, a gas confined in a cylinder and at uniform pressure, while expanding and imparting motion to a piston, does external work on its surroundings.

Work done by one part of a system on another part of the same system is called *internal work*. The interactions of the molecules or electrons of a system on one another constitute internal work. We shall be concerned with external work only.

16–2 Work in changing the volume. Imagine any solid or fluid contained in a cylinder equipped with a movable piston on which the system and the surroundings may act. Suppose that the cylinder has a cross-sectional area A and that the pressure exerted by the system at the piston face is p. The force on the piston is therefore pA. If the piston moves out an infinitesimal distance dx, the work dW of this force is equal to

$$dW = pA\, dx.$$

But

$$A\, dx = dV,$$

where dV is the change of volume. Therefore

$$\boxed{dW = p\, dV.} \tag{16-1}$$

If the pressure remains constant while the volume changes a finite amount, say from V_1 to V_2, then the work W is

$$W = p(V_2 - V_1) \text{ (constant pressure only).} \tag{16-2}$$

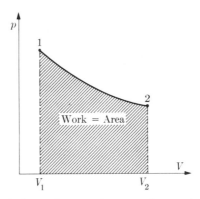

FIG. 16–1. The work done when a substance changes its volume and pressure is the area under the curve on a p-V diagram.

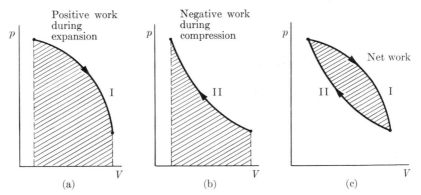

FIG. 16–2. The net work done in a cyclic process equals the area enclosed by the curve representing the process.

If, on the other hand, the pressure changes as the volume changes, then

$$W = \int_{V_1}^{V_2} p\, dV, \tag{16–3}$$

which may be interpreted graphically as the area under a curve on a p-V diagram, as shown in Fig. 16–1.

If a substance *expands* from 1 to 2 in Fig. 16–1, the area is regarded as positive and the work is positive. The *compression* from 2 to 1 gives rise to a negative area and a negative work.

In Fig. 16–2(a) the pressure and volume changes of a substance during expansion are indicated by curve I. The work is indicated by the shaded area under curve I. Similarly, for a compression, the work is represented by the shaded area under curve II in Fig. 16–2(b). In conformity with the sign convention for work, the area under I is positive, and that under II is negative. In Fig. 16–2(c), curves I and II are drawn together so that they constitute a series of processes whereby the substance is brought back to its initial state. Such a series of processes, represented by a closed figure, is called a *cycle*. The area within the closed figure is obviously the difference between the areas under curves I and II and therefore represents the *net* work done in the cycle. It should be noticed that the cycle is traversed in such a direction that the net work is positive. If the direction were reversed, the net work would be negative.

16–3 Work depends on the path. On the p-V diagram depicted in Fig. 16–3 an initial state 1 (characterized by pressure p_1 and volume V_1) and a final state 2 (characterized by pressure p_2 and volume V_2) are represented by the two points 1 and 2. There are many ways in which the system may be taken from 1 to 2. For example, the pressure may be kept constant from 1 to 3 (isobaric process) and then the volume kept constant from 3 to 2 (isochoric process), in which case the work is equal to the area under the line $1 \rightarrow 3$. Another possibility is the path $1 \rightarrow 4 \rightarrow 2$, in which case the work is the area under the line $4 \rightarrow 2$. The jagged line and the continuous curve from 1 to 2 represent other possibilities, in each of which the work is different. We can see, therefore, that *the work depends not only on the initial and final states but also on the intermediate states, i.e., on the path.*

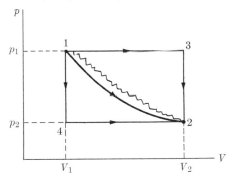

FIG. 16–3. Work depends on the path.

16–4 Work and heat. We have seen how a system may be caused to go from state 1 to state 2 by any number of processes, all of which involve the performance of work. There are other means, however, of changing the state of a system. Consider, for example, the four situations

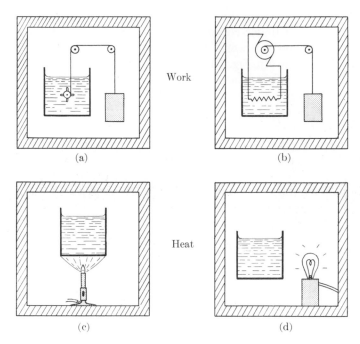

FIG. 16–4. Distinction between work and heat.

depicted in Fig. 16–4. In (a) the system is a composite one consisting of some water and a paddle wheel, which is caused to rotate and churn the water by means of a falling weight. In (b) both the water and an electric resistance wire embedded in the water constitute the system. An electric current in the resistor is maintained by a generator turned ·by means of a falling weight. In both cases the state of the system is caused to change and, since the agency for changing the state of the system is a falling weight, *both processes involve the performance of work.*

In (c) and (d), however, the situation is quite different. The system in both cases is some water in a heat-conducting container. In (c) the system is in contact with the burning gases from a Bunsen burner, i.e., with another body at a higher temperature, whereas in (d) the system is near but not in contact with an electric lamp whose temperature is much higher than that of the water. In both cases the state of the system is caused to change, but in neither case can the agency for the change be described by mechanical means. *In these cases we say that there is a flow of heat.*

   The flow of heat is a **nonmechanical energy transfer** *brought about by a temperature difference between two bodies.*

It is important to observe that the decision as to whether a particular change of state involves the performance of work or the transfer of heat requires first an unequivocal answer to the questions "What is the system?" and "What are the surroundings?" For example, in Fig. 16–4(b), if the resistor is regarded as the system and the water as the surroundings, then there is a transfer of heat from the resistor by virtue of the temperature difference between the resistor and the water. Also, if a small part of the water is regarded as the system, the rest of the water being the surroundings, then again there is a transfer of heat. If we consider, however, the *composite* system, composed of both the water and the resistor, the surroundings do not contain any object whose temperature differs from that of the system, and hence no heat is transferred between *this composite system* and its surroundings. The performance of work and the flow of heat are methods of supplying energy to a body or extracting energy from a body. We have seen that, in general, the work depends on the path by which the system was brought from the initial to the final state. Exactly the same is true of the heat transferred to or from a body. *Heat also depends on the path.*

It would be just as incorrect to refer to the "heat in a body" as it would be to speak about the "work in a body." For suppose we assigned an arbitrary value to "the heat in a body" in some standard reference state. The "heat in the body" in some other state would then equal the "heat" in the reference state plus the heat added when the body is carried to the second state. But the heat added depends entirely on the path by which we go from one state to the other, and since there are an infinite number of paths which might be followed, there are an infinite number of values which might equally well be assigned to the "heat in the body" in the second state. Since it is not possible to assign any one value to the "heat in the body" we conclude that this concept is meaningless.

16–5 Quantity of heat. Heat, like mechanical energy, is an intangible thing and a unit of heat is not something that can be preserved in a standards laboratory. The quantity of heat transferred in a process is measured by some change which accompanies the process, and a unit of heat is defined as the heat necessary to produce some standard, agreed-on change. Three such units are in common use, the calorie (cal), the kilogram·calorie (kcal), and the British thermal unit (Btu).

One calorie is the quantity of heat which must be supplied to one gram of water to raise its temperature through one celsius degree.

One kilogram·calorie is the quantity of heat which must be supplied to one kilogram of water to raise its temperature through one celsius degree.

*One Btu is the quantity of heat which must be supplied to one pound of water to raise its temperature through one fahrenheit degree.**

Evidently, 1 kilogram·calorie = 1000 calories.

Since 454 gm = 1 lb, and since 1 F° = $\frac{5}{9}$ C°, the Btu may be defined as the quantity of heat which must be supplied to 454 gm (0.454 kgm) of water to raise its temperature through $\frac{5}{9}$ C°, which is 454 × $\frac{5}{9}$ = 252 cal or 0.252 kcal. Hence

$$1 \text{ Btu} = 252 \text{ cal} = 0.252 \text{ kcal}.$$

The heat units here defined vary somewhat with the location of the degree, i.e., whether it is from 0° to 1°, 47° to 48°, etc. It is generally agreed to use the temperature interval from 14.5°C to 15.5°C (the "15° calorie"), and in English units to use the temperature interval from 63°F to 64°F. For most purposes this variation is small enough to be neglected.

It is essential that the distinction between "quantity of heat" and "temperature" shall be clearly understood. The terms are commonly misused in everyday life. Suppose that two pans, one containing a small and the other a large amount of water, are placed over identical gas burners and heated for the same length of time. It is obvious that at the end of this time the temperature of the small amount of water will have risen higher than that of the large amount. In this instance, equal quantities of heat have been supplied to each pan of water, but the increases in temperature are not equal.

On the other hand, suppose the two pans are both initially at a temperature of 60°F and that both are to be heated to 212°F. It is evident that more heat must be supplied to the pan containing the larger amount of water. The temperature change is the same for both but the quantities of heat supplied are very different.

We shall represent a quantity of heat by the letter Q.

16–6 The mechanical equivalent of heat. Energy in mechanical form is usually expressed in ergs, joules, or foot·pounds; energy in the form of heat is expressed in calories or Btu. The relative magnitudes of the "heat units" and the "mechanical units" can be found by an experiment in which a measured quantity of mechanical energy is completely converted into a measured quantity of heat. The first accurate experiments were performed by Joule, using an apparatus in which falling weights rotated

---

* In this part of the subject we shall depart from the engineering system of units which we used throughout mechanics, and adopt as a mass unit the *mass of the standard pound*. This unit is also called one pound, and is equal to a mass of 454 grams, or (about) $\frac{1}{32}$ slug. Also, for simplicity, we shall confine metric units chiefly to the cgs system.

a set of paddles in a container of water. The energy transformed was computed in mechanical units from a knowledge of the weights and their height of fall, and in heat units from a measurement of the mass of water and its rise in temperature. In more recent methods, which are also more precise, electrical energy is converted to heat in a resistance wire immersed in water. The best results to date give:

$$778 \text{ ft·lb} = 1 \text{ Btu,}$$
$$4.186 \text{ joules} = 1 \text{ cal,}$$
$$4186 \text{ joules} = 1 \text{ kcal.}$$

That is, 778 ft·lb of mechanical energy, when converted to heat, will raise the temperature of 1 lb of water through 1 F°, etc.

These relations are often expressed by the statement that *the mechanical equivalent of heat* is 4.186 joules/cal, or 778 ft·lb/Btu. The phraseology is a carryover from the early days when the equivalence of mechanical energy and heat was being established.

The precise value of the mechanical equivalent of heat depends on the particular temperature interval used in the definition of the calorie or Btu. To avoid this confusion, an international commission has agreed to *define* 1 kcal as *exactly* 1/860 kilowatt·hour. Then by definition, 1 cal = 4.18605 joules and 1 Btu = 778.26 ft·lb. It follows that 1 Btu = 251.996 cal.

16–7 Heat capacity. Specific heat. Materials differ from one another in the quantity of heat required to produce a given elevation of temperature in a given mass. Suppose that a quantity of heat Q is supplied to a given body, resulting in a temperature rise Δt. The ratio of the heat supplied to the corresponding temperature rise is called the *heat capacity* of the body.

$$\text{Heat capacity} = \frac{Q}{\Delta t}. \qquad (16\text{–}4)$$

Heat capacities are ordinarily expressed in calories per celsius degree, or Btu per fahrenheit degree. If we set $\Delta t = 1$ degree in Eq. (16–4), it will be seen that the heat capacity of a body is numerically equal to the quantity of heat which must be supplied to it to increase its temperature by one degree.

To obtain a figure that is characteristic of the material of which a body is composed, the *specific heat capacity*, abbreviated *specific heat*, of a material is defined as the *heat capacity per unit mass* of a body composed of the material. We shall represent specific heat capacity by the letter c.

$$c = \frac{\text{heat capacity}}{\text{mass}} = \frac{Q}{m \, \Delta t}. \qquad (16\text{–}5)$$

TABLE 16–1

SPECIFIC HEAT CAPACITIES

Substance	Specific heat, cal/gm·C°	Temperature interval
Aluminum	0.217	17–100°C
Brass	0.094	15–100
Copper	0.093	15–100
Glass	0.199	20–100
Ice	0.55	−10–0
Iron	0.113	18–100
Lead	0.031	20–100
Mercury	0.033	0–100
Silver	0.056	15–100

The specific heat capacity of a material is numerically equal to the quantity of heat which must be supplied to *unit mass* of the material to increase its temperature through 1 degree. The specific heat capacities of a few common materials are listed in Table 16–1. The units are cal/gm·C° or Btu/lb·F°.

It follows from Eq. (16–2) that the heat which must be supplied to a body of mass m, whose specific heat capacity is c, to increase its temperature through an interval Δt, is

$$Q = mc\,\Delta t = mc(t_2 - t_1). \qquad (16\text{–}6)$$

Strictly speaking, Eq. (16–5) defines the *mean* specific heat capacity over the temperature range Δt, since we know that the quantity of heat required to raise the temperature of a material through a small interval varies with the location of the interval in the temperature scale. The *true* specific heat capacity of a material at any temperature is defined from Eq. (16–5) by considering an infinitesimal temperature rise dt, and letting dQ be the heat required to produce this rise. We then have

$$\text{True specific heat } c = \frac{1}{m}\frac{dQ}{dt}, \qquad dQ = mc\,dt, \qquad Q = m\int_{t_1}^{t_2} c\,dt.$$

In general, c is a function of the temperature and must be so expressed to carry out the integration above.

At ordinary temperatures, and over temperature intervals which are not too great, however, specific heats may be considered constant. At extremely low temperatures, approaching absolute zero, all specific heats decrease and approach zero.

It should be pointed out that the significance of the word "capacity" in "heat capacity" is not the same as when one speaks of the "capacity" of a bucket. The bucket can hold just so much water and no more, while heat can be added to a body indefinitely with, of course, a corresponding rise in temperature.

For some purposes, particularly in dealing with gases, it is more convenient to express specific heat capacities on the basis of one gram·molecular weight rather than one gram. It was first noted in 1819 by Dulong and Petit that the specific heat capacities of the metals, expressed in this way, were all very nearly equal to 6 cal/gm·molecular wt·C°. This fact is known as the *Dulong and Petit law*. Since the number of molecules is the same in one gram·molecular weight of all substances, this means that the heat capacity of a metallic object depends only on the *number* of molecules it contains, not on the mass of each molecule.

16–8 Calorimetry. The term calorimetry relates to the measurement of quantities of heat. The water calorimeter in its simple form consists of a thin-walled metal can A (Fig. 16–5) whose capacity is about two liters, and whose outer surface is nickel-plated. The can contains a measured quantity of water, and is provided with a cover through which passes thermometer B. Heat losses are further reduced by surrounding the can with the heat-insulating jacket C. If the thermometer is read before and after an unknown quantity of heat Q is introduced into the calorimeter, Q may be found from the measured rise in temperature.

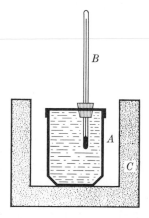

Fig. 16–5. The water calorimeter.

The water calorimeter may be used to measure specific heat as follows: a sample of the material whose specific heat is desired is heated in a furnace or steam bath to a known temperature, say t_s. Let the mass of the sample be m_s and its specific heat c_s.

The water in the calorimeter is thoroughly stirred and its temperature is measured. The sample is then quickly transferred to the calorimeter, the water is again thoroughly stirred, and the new temperature of the water is recorded. Let t_1 and t_2 be the initial and final temperatures of the water, m_w the mass of the water, m_c the mass of the calorimeter can, and c_c its specific heat.

If no heat is lost from the calorimeter during the experiment, energy is conserved. Therefore the heat given up by the sample in cooling from t_s to t_2 must equal the heat gained by the water and the calorimeter can. Hence

$$m_s c_s (t_s - t_2) = m_w \times 1(t_2 - t_1) + m_c c_c (t_2 - t_1)$$
$$= (m_w + m_c c_c)(t_2 - t_1)$$

and c_s may be found, since the other factors are known.

The effect of the heat capacity of the calorimeter, $m_c c_c$, is evidently equivalent to increasing the mass of the water by an amount $m_c c_c$ and using a calorimeter of zero heat capacity. The product $m_c c_c$ is called the *water equivalent* of the calorimeter.

Actually the calorimeter will gain (or lose) heat from its surroundings during an experiment unless special precautions are taken. One way of minimizing the heat transfer is to start with the calorimeter somewhat cooler than its surroundings and finish with its temperature higher than that of the surroundings by the same amount. Then the heat gained during the first part of the experiment offsets that lost in the latter part. Another method (the so-called "adiabatic jacket") is to heat the jacket by an electric heating coil so that its temperature rises at the same rate as does that of the calorimeter. If both temperatures are always equal there will be no gain or loss of heat.

It should be noted that this method of measuring specific heat gives only the *average* specific heat over the temperature range from t_s to t_2. Much more elaborate apparatus is required to measure the true specific heat at any desired temperature.

16–9 Change of phase. The term *phase* as used here relates to the fact that matter exists either as a solid, liquid, or gas. Thus the chemical substance H_2O exists in the *solid phase* as ice, in the *liquid phase* as water, and in the *gaseous phase* as steam. Provided they do not decompose at high temperatures, all substances can exist in any of the three phases under the proper conditions of temperature and pressure. Transitions

from one phase to another are accompanied by the absorption or liberation
of heat and usually by a change in volume.

As an illustration, suppose that ice is taken from a refrigerator where
its temperature was, say, −25°C. Let the ice be crushed quickly, placed
in a container, and a thermometer inserted in the mass. Imagine the
container to be surrounded by a heating coil which supplies heat to the
ice at a uniform rate, and suppose that no other heat reaches the ice.
The temperature of the ice would be observed to increase steadily, as shown
by the portion of the graph (Fig. 16–6) from a to b, or until the temperature has risen to 0°C. As soon as this temperature is reached, some liquid
water will be observed in the container. In other words, the ice begins
to melt. The melting process is a *change of phase*, from the solid phase
to the liquid phase. The thermometer, however, will show no *increase in
temperature*, and even though heat is being supplied at the same rate as
before, the temperature will remain at 0°C until all the ice is melted
(point c, Fig. 16–6). (The ice and water mixture must be kept thoroughly
stirred, otherwise the temperature of that part of the water closest to
the heater will rise above 0°C.)

As soon as the last of the ice has melted, the temperature begins to
rise again at a uniform rate (from c to d, Fig. 16–6) although this rate will
be slower than that from a to b because the specific heat of water is greater
than that of ice. When a temperature of 100°C is reached (point d),
bubbles of steam (gaseous water or water vapor) start to escape from the
liquid surface, or the water begins to boil. The temperature remains constant at 100°C until all the water has boiled away. Another change of
phase has therefore taken place, from the liquid phase to the gaseous
phase.

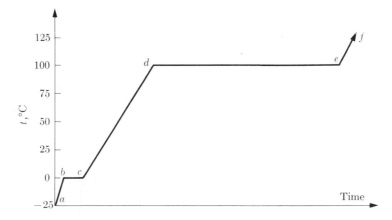

Fig. 16–6. The temperature remains constant during each change of phase.

If all the water vapor had been trapped and not allowed to diffuse away (a very large container would be needed), the heating process could be continued as from e to f. The gas would now be called "superheated steam."

Although water was chosen as an example in the process just described, the same type of curve as in Fig. 16–6 is obtained for many other substances. Some, of course, decompose before reaching a melting or boiling point, and others, such as glass or pitch, do not change state at a definite temperature but become gradually softer as their temperature is raised. Crystalline substances, such as ice or a metal, melt at definite temperatures. Glass and pitch are actually supercooled liquids of very high viscosity.

The temperature at which a crystalline solid melts when heat is supplied to it at atmospheric pressure is called its *normal melting point,* and the temperature at which a liquid boils when heat is supplied to it at atmospheric pressure is called its *normal boiling point.* The quantity of heat per unit mass that must be supplied to a material at its melting point to convert it completely to a liquid at the same temperature is called the *heat of fusion* of the material. The quantity of heat per unit mass that must be supplied to a material at its boiling point to convert it completely to a gas at the same temperature is called the *heat of vaporization* of the material. Heats of fusion and vaporization are expressed in calories per gram, or Btu per pound. Thus the heat of fusion of ice is about 80 cal/gm or 144 Btu/lb. The heat of vaporization of water (at 100°C) is 539 cal/gm or 970 Btu/lb. Some heats of fusion and vaporization are listed in Table 16–2.

TABLE 16–2

HEATS OF FUSION AND VAPORIZATION

Substance	Normal melting point		Heat of fusion, cal/gm	Normal boiling point		Heat of vaporization, cal/gm
	°K	°C		°K	°C	
Helium	3.5	−269.65	1.25	4.216	−268.93	5
Hydrogen	13.84	−259.31	14	20.26	−252.89	108
Nitrogen	63.18	−209.97	6.09	77.34	−195.81	48
Oxygen	54.36	−218.79	3.30	90.18	−182.97	51
Ethyl alcohol	159	−114	24.9	351	78	204
Mercury	234	− 39	2.82	630	357	65
Water	273.15	0.00	79.7	373.15	100.00	539
Sulphur	392	119	9.1	717.75	444.60	78
Lead	600.5	327.3	5.86	2023	1750	208
Antimony	903.65	630.50	39.4	1713	1440	
Silver	1233.95	960.80	21.1	2466	2193	558
Gold	1336.15	1063.00	15.4	2933	2660	377

When heat is removed from a gas its temperature falls, and at the same temperature at which it boiled, it returns to the liquid phase, or *condenses*. In so doing it gives up to its surroundings the same quantity of heat which was required to vaporize it. The heat so given up, per unit mass, is called the *heat of condensation* and is equal to the heat of vaporization. Similarly, a liquid returns to the solid phase, or freezes, when cooled to the temperature at which it melted, and gives up heat called *heat of solidification* exactly equal to the heat of fusion. Thus the melting point and the freezing point are at the same temperature, and the boiling point and condensation point are at the same temperature.

Whether a substance, at its melting point, is freezing or melting depends on whether heat is being supplied or removed. That is, if heat is supplied to a beaker containing both ice and water at 0°C, some of the ice will melt; if heat is removed, some of the water will freeze; the temperature in either case remains at 0°C so long as both ice and water are present. If heat is *neither supplied nor removed*, no change at all takes place and the relative amounts of ice and water, and the temperature, all remain constant.

This furnishes, then, another point of view which may be taken regarding the melting point. That is, the melting (or freezing) point of a substance is *that temperature at which both the liquid and solid phases can exist together*. At any higher temperature, the substance can only be a liquid; at any lower temperature, it can only be a solid.

The general term *heat of transformation* is applied both to heats of fusion and heats of vaporization, and both are designated by the letter L. Since L represents the heat absorbed or liberated in the change of phase of unit mass, the heat Q absorbed or liberated in the change of phase of a mass m is

$$Q = mL. \tag{16-7}$$

The household steam-heating system makes use of a boiling-condensing process to transfer heat from the furnace to the radiators. Each pound of water which is turned to steam in the furnace absorbs 970 Btu (the heat of vaporization of water) from the furnace, and gives up 970 Btu when it condenses in the radiators. (This figure is correct if the steam pressure is one atmosphere. It will be slightly smaller at higher pressures.) Thus the steam-heating system does not need to circulate as much water as a hot-water heating system. If water leaves a hot-water furnace at 140°F and returns at 100°F, dropping 40 F°, about 24 lb of water must circulate to carry the same heat as is carried in the form of heat of vaporization by one pound of steam.

Under the proper conditions of temperature and pressure, a substance can change directly from the solid to the gaseous phase without passing through the liquid phase. The transfer from solid to vapor is called *sub-*

limation, and the solid is said to *sublime.* "Dry ice" (solid carbon dioxide) sublimes at atmospheric pressure. Liquid carbon dioxide cannot exist at a pressure lower than about 73 lb/in^2.

Heat is absorbed in the process of sublimation, and liberated in the reverse process. The quantity of heat per unit mass is called the *heat of sublimation.*

16–10 Measurement of heats of fusion and vaporization.

The method of mixtures is used to measure heats of fusion and of vaporization. For example, the heat of fusion of ice may be found by dropping a weighed sample of ice at 0°C into a calorimeter containing a measured amount of water, and observing the temperature of the water before and after the addition of the ice. Let a mass m_i of ice at 0°C be dropped in a calorimeter containing a mass m_w of water, lowering the temperature of the water from t_1 to t_2. We shall assume that all the ice melts, and neglect the heat capacity of the calorimeter. Then if L represents the heat of fusion of the ice, the ice absorbs a quantity of heat $m_i L$ on melting (this converts it to water at 0°C) and a further quantity of heat $m_i t_2$ on warming up to the final temperature t_2. The water in the calorimeter gives up a quantity of heat $m_w(t_1 - t_2)$. Hence,

$$m_w(t_1 - t_2) = m_i(L + t_2),$$

so that L can be found if the other quantities are known.

The heat of condensation (= heat of vaporization) of steam can be measured in a similar way, by allowing steam from a boiler to condense within a calorimeter. The condensation usually takes place in a coiled tube immersed in the calorimeter, so that the amount of steam condensing may be found by weighing the coil before and after the experiment. We have:

Heat given up by condensing steam $= m_s L.$

$\left\{ \begin{array}{l} \text{Heat given up by condensed steam} \\ \quad \text{(water at 100°C) cooling to } t_2 \end{array} \right\} = m_s(100 - t_2).$

Heat absorbed by calorimeter $= m_w(t_2 - t_1).$

The heat of vaporization may be found by equating heat loss to heat gain.

16–11 Conduction of heat through a slab.

If one end of a metal rod is placed in a flame while the other is held in the hand, that part of the rod one is holding will be felt to become hotter and hotter, although it was not itself in direct contact with the flame. Heat is said to reach the cooler end of the rod by *conduction* along or through the material of the rod. The molecules at the hot end of the rod increase the violence of their vibration as the temperature of the hot end increases. Then, as they collide with their more slowly moving neighbors farther out on the rod, some of their energy of motion is shared with these neighbors and they in turn pass it along to those still farther out from the flame. Hence energy of thermal motion is passed along from one molecule to the next, while each individual molecule remains at its original position.

It is well known that metals are good conductors of electricity and also good conductors of heat. The ability of a metal to conduct an electric current is due to the fact that there are within it so-called "free" electrons, that is, electrons that have become detached from their parent molecules. The free electrons also play a part in the conduction of heat, and the reason metals are such good heat conductors is that the free electrons, as well as the molecules, share in the process of handing on thermal energy from the hotter to the cooler portions of the metal.

Conduction of heat can take place in a body only when different parts of the body are at different temperatures, and the direction of heat flow is always from points of higher to points of lower temperature. The phenomenon of heat flow is sometimes made the basis for the definition of temperature equality or inequality. That is, if heat flows from one body to another when the two are in contact, the temperature of the first, by definition, is higher than that of the second. If there is no heat flow, the temperatures are equal.

Figure 16–7 represents a slab of material of cross section A and thickness L. Let the whole of the left face of the slab be kept at a temperature t_2, and the whole of the right face at a lower temperature t_1. The direction of the heat current is then from left to right through the slab.

After the faces of the slab have been kept at the temperatures t_1 and t_2 for a sufficient length of time, the temperature at points within the slab is found to decrease uniformly with distance from the hot to the cold face. At each point, however, the temperature remains constant with time. The slab is said to be in a "steady state." (Nonsteady state problems in heat conduction involve mathematical methods beyond the scope of this book.)

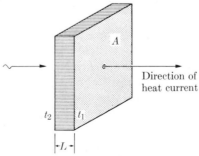

FIG. 16–7. Conduction of heat through a slab.

TABLE 16–3

THERMAL CONDUCTIVITY

Substance	K, cal/sec·cm·C°
Metals:	
Aluminum	0.49
Brass	0.26
Copper	0.92
Lead	0.083
Silver	0.97
Steel	0.12
Various solids:*	
Red brick	0.0015
Concrete	0.002
Cork	0.0001
Glass	0.002
Ice	0.004
Rock wool	0.0001
Wood	0.0003–0.0001
Gases:	
Air	0.000057
Hydrogen	0.00033
Oxygen	0.000056

* Representative values

It is found by experiment that the rate of flow of heat through the slab in the steady state is proportional to the area A, proportional to the temperature difference $(t_2 - t_1)$, and inversely proportional to the thickness L. Let H represent the quantity of heat flowing through the slab per unit time. Then

$$H \propto \frac{A(t_2 - t_1)}{L}.$$

This proportion may be converted to an equation on multiplication by a constant K whose numerical value depends on the material of the slab. The quantity K is called the *coefficient of thermal conductivity* or simply the thermal conductivity of the material.

$$H = \frac{KA(t_2 - t_1)}{L}. \tag{16–8}$$

The cgs unit of rate of heat flow, or heat current, is one calorie per second. Temperatures are expressed on the celsius scale. The units of A and L are obvious. The thermal conductivities of commercial insulating materials such as cork or rock wool are usually stated in a "hybrid" system in which areas are in square feet, temperatures in fahrenheit degrees, thicknesses in inches, and the rate of flow of heat in Btu per hour. In any system of units, H and K are numerically equal when $A =$ one unit of area, $t_2 - t_1 =$ one degree, and $L =$ one unit of length. Thus in the commercial system, the thermal conductivity of a material is numerically equal to the number of Btu that flow in one hour through a slab one inch thick and one square foot in cross section, when the temperature difference between the faces of the slab is one fahrenheit degree.

16–12 Convection. The term *convection* is applied to the transfer of heat from one place to another by the actual motion of hot material. The hot-air furnace and the hot-water heating system are examples. If the heated material is forced to move by a blower or pump, the process is called *forced convection;* if the material flows due to differences in density, the process is called *natural* or *free* convection. To understand the latter, consider a U-tube as illustrated in Fig. 16–8.

In (a), the water is at the same temperature in both arms of the U and hence stands at the same level in each. In (b), the right side of the U has been heated. The water in this side expands and therefore, being of smaller density, a longer column is needed to balance the pressure produced by the cold water in the left column. The stopcock may now be opened and water will flow from the top of the warmer column into the colder column. This increases the pressure at the bottom of the U pro-

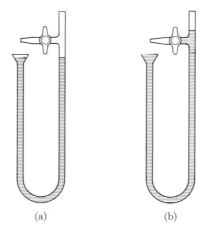

(a)   (b)

FIG. 16–8. Convection is brought about by differences in density.

duced by the cold column, and decreases the pressure at this point due to the hot column. Hence at the bottom of the U, water is forced from the cold to the hot side. If heat is continually applied to the hot side and removed from the cold side, the circulation continues of itself. The net result is a continual transfer of heat from the hot to the cold side of the column. In the common household hot-water heating system, the "cold" side corresponds to the radiators and the "hot" side to the furnace.

The anomalous expansion of water which was mentioned in Chapter 15 has an important effect on the way in which lakes and ponds freeze in winter. Consider a pond at a temperature of, say, 20°C throughout, and suppose the air temperature at its surface falls to −10°C. The water at the surface becomes cooled to, say, 19°C. It therefore contracts, becomes more dense than the warmer water below it, and sinks in this less dense water, its place being taken by water at 20°C. The sinking of the cooled water causes a mixing process, which continues until all the water has been cooled to 4°C. Now, however, when the surface water cools to 3°C, it expands, is less dense than the water below it, and hence floats on the surface. Convection and mixing then cease, and the remainder of the water can lose heat only by *conduction*. Since water is an extremely poor heat conductor, cooling takes place very slowly after 4°C is reached, with the result that the pond freezes first at its surface. Then, since the density of ice is even smaller than that of water at 0°C, the ice floats on the water below it, and further freezing can result only from heat flow upward by conduction.

The mathematical theory of heat convection is quite involved. There is no simple equation for convection as in the case of conduction. This arises from the fact that the heat lost or gained by a surface at one temperature in contact with a fluid at another temperature depends on many circumstances, such as:

1. Whether the surface is flat or curved.

2. Whether the surface is horizontal or vertical.

3. Whether the fluid in contact with the surface is a gas or a liquid.

4. The density, viscosity, specific heat, and thermal conductivity of the fluid.

5. Whether the velocity of the fluid is small enough to give rise to laminar flow or large enough to cause turbulent flow.

6. Whether evaporation, condensation, or formation of scale takes place.

16–13 Radiation. When one's hand is placed in direct contact with the surface of a hot-water or steam radiator, heat reaches the hand by *conduction* through the radiator walls. If the hand is held above the radiator but not in contact with it, heat reaches the hand by way of the upward-moving *convection* currents of warm air. If the hand is held at one side of the radiator it still becomes warm, even though conduction through the air is negligible and the hand is not in the path of the convection currents. Energy now reaches the hand by *radiation*.

The term radiation refers to the continual emission of energy from the surface of all bodies. This energy is called *radiant energy* and it is transmitted with the speed of light. When it falls on a body that is not transparent to it, it is absorbed and converted into heat. The study of radiant energy led to the the quantum theory of radiation, which is discussed at length in Chapter 37.

PROBLEMS

16–1. How many cubic feet of a coal gas, having a heat of combustion of 488 Btu/ft^3, must be burned to raise the temperature of 40 gal of water from 50°F to 150°F, assuming 25% stack loss? (There are 7.5 gal in a cubic foot.)

16–2. A certain Diesel engine consumes 20 lb of fuel oil per hour. The heat of combustion of the oil is 20,000 Btu/lb. If the over-all efficiency of the engine is 30%, (a) how many Btu/hr are converted into mechanical work? (b) How many Btu are wasted? (c) What horsepower does the engine develop?

16–3. An automobile weighing 2000 lb is traveling at 10 ft/sec. How many Btu are developed in the brakes when it is brought to rest?

16–4. (a) What quantity of heat, in Btu, is required to raise the temperature of the water in a 40-gal hot-water tank from 60°F to 140°F? (There are 7.5 gal in a cubic foot.) (b) If the water is heated by the combustion of gas (488 Btu/ft^3), how many cubic feet of gas must be burned if stack losses amount to 20%? (c) If the water is heated by an electric heater, how many kwh are required? The efficiency of the electric heater may be assumed 100%.

16–5. (a) A certain house burns 10 tons of coal in a heating season. If stack losses are 15%, how many Btu were actually used to heat the house? (Assume that the heat of combustion of the coal is 11,000 Btu/lb.) (b) In some localities large tanks of water are heated by solar radiation during the summer and the stored energy is used for heating during the winter. Find the required dimensions of the storage tank, assuming it to be a cube, to store

a quantity of energy equal to that computed in part (a). Assume that the water is heated to 120°F in the summer and cooled to 80°F in the winter.

16–6. An automobile engine whose output is 40 hp uses 4.5 gal of gasoline per hour. The heat of combustion of gasoline is 3×10^7 calories per gallon. What is the efficiency of the engine?

16–7. The electric power input to a certain electric motor is 0.50 kw, and the mechanical power output is 0.54 hp. (a) What is the efficiency of the motor? (b) How many Btu are developed in the motor in one hour of operation?

16–8. 400 gm of water are contained in a copper vessel of mass 200 gm. The water is heated by a friction device which dissipates mechanical energy, and it is observed that the temperature of the system rises at the rate of 3 C° per minute. Neglect heat losses to the surroundings. What power in watts is dissipated in the water?

16–9. If all the heat were converted to mechanical energy, how long could a 2000-hp motor be operated on the heat energy liberated by one cubic mile of ocean water when the temperature of the water is lowered by 1 C°? Why do we not utilize this tremendous reservoir of energy?

16–10. An aluminum can of mass 500 gm contains 117.5 gm of water at a temperature of 20°C. A 200-gm block of iron at 75°C is dropped into the can. Find the final temperature, assuming no heat loss to the surroundings.

16–11. A casting weighing 100 lb is taken from an annealing furnace where its temperature was 900°F and plunged into a tank containing 800 lb of oil at a temperature of 80°F. The final temperature is 100°F, and the specific heat of the oil is 0.5 Btu/lb·F°. What was the specific heat of the casting? Neglect the heat capacity of the tank itself and any heat losses.

16–12. Compute from Table 16–1 the heat capacities of one gram-molecular weight of Al, Cu, Pb, Hg, and Ag, and compare with the values predicted by the Dulong and Petit law.

16–13. Compare the heat capacities of equal *volumes* of water, copper, and lead.

16–14. A lead bullet, traveling at 350 m/sec, strikes a target and is brought to rest. What would be the rise in temperature of the bullet if none of the heat developed were lost to the surroundings?

16–15. A copper calorimeter whose mass is 300 gm contains 500 gm of water at a temperature of 15°C. A 560-gm block of copper, at a temperature of 100°C, is dropped into the calorimeter and the temperature is observed to increase to 22.5°C. Neglect heat losses to the surroundings. (a) Find the specific heat of copper. (b) What is the water equivalent of the calorimeter?

16–16. A 50-gm sample of a material, at a temperature of 100°C, is dropped into a calorimeter containing 200 gm of water initially at 20°C. The calorimeter is of copper and its mass is 100 gm. The final temperature of the calorimeter is 22°C. Compute the specific heat of the sample.

16–17. How much heat is required to convert 1 gm of ice at −10°C to steam at 100°C?

16–18. A beaker whose heat capacity is negligible contains 500 gm of water at a temperature of 80°C. How many grams of ice at a temperature of −20°C must be dropped in the water so that the final temperature of the system will be 50°C?

16–19. Ice cubes at 0°C are dropped into a jug of salt water at 0°C. It is observed that the temperature of the mixture drops below 0°C. What happens to the heat that is released by the salt water when its temperature decreases?

16–20. An open vessel contains 500 gm of ice at −20°C. The heat capacity of the container can be neglected. Heat is supplied to the vessel at the constant rate of 1000 cal/min for 100 min. Plot a curve showing the elapsed time as abscissa and the temperature as ordinate.

16–21. A copper calorimeter of mass 100 gm contains 150 gm of water and 8 gm of ice in thermal equilibrium at atmospheric pressure. 100 gm of lead at a temperature of 200°C are dropped into the calorimeter. Find the final temperature if no heat is lost to the surroundings.

16–22. 500 gm of ice at −16°C are dropped into a calorimeter containing 1000 gm of water at 20°C. The calorimeter can is of copper and has a mass of 278 gm. Compute the final temperature of the system, assuming no heat losses.

16–23. A tube leads from a flask in which water is boiling under atmospheric pressure to a calorimeter. The mass of the calorimeter is 150 gm, its heat capacity is 15 cal/C° and it contains originally 340 gm of water at 15°C. Steam is allowed to condense in the calorimeter until its temperature increases to 71°C, after which the total mass of calorimeter and contents is found to be 525 gm. Compute the heat of condensation of steam from these data.

16–24. An aluminum canteen whose mass is 500 gm contains 750 gm of water and 100 gm of ice. The canteen is dropped from an aircraft to the ground. After landing, the temperature of the canteen is found to be 25°C. Assuming that no energy is given to the ground in the impact, what was the velocity of the canteen just before it landed?

16–25. A calorimeter contains 500 gm of water and 300 gm of ice, all at a temperature of 0°C. A block of metal of mass 1000 gm is taken from a furnace where its temperature was 240°C and is dropped quickly into the calorimeter. As a result, all the ice is just melted. What would the final temperature of the system have been if the mass of the block had been twice as great? Neglect heat loss from the calorimeter, and the heat capacity of the calorimeter.

16–26. An ice cube whose mass is 50 gm is taken from a refrigerator where its temperature was −10°C and is dropped into a glass of water at 0°C. If no heat is gained or lost from outside, how much water will freeze onto the cube?

16–27. A copper calorimeter can, having a heat capacity of 30 cal/deg, contains 50 gm of ice. The system is initially at 0°C. Twelve gm of steam at 100°C and 1 atm pressure are run into the calorimeter. What is the final temperature of the calorimeter and its contents?

16–28. A vessel whose walls are thermally insulated contains 2100 gm of water and 200 gm of ice, all at a temperature of 0°C. The outlet of a tube leading from a boiler, in which water is boiling at atmospheric pressure, is inserted in the water. How many grams of steam must condense to raise the temperature of the system to 20°C? Neglect the heat capacity of the container.

16–29. A 2-kgm iron block is taken from a furnace where its temperature was 650°C and placed on a large block of ice at 0°C. Assuming that all the heat given up by the iron is used to melt the ice, how much ice is melted?

16–30. In a household hot-water heating system, water is delivered to the radiators at 140°F and leaves at 100°F. The system is to be replaced by a steam system in which steam at atmospheric pressure condenses in the radiators, the condensed steam leaving the radiators at 180°F. How many pounds of steam will supply the same heat as was supplied by 1 lb of hot water in the first installation?

16–31. A piece of ice falls from rest into a lake that is at 0°C, and one-half of one percent of the ice melts. Compute the minimum height from which the ice falls.

16–32. What must be the initial velocity of a lead bullet at a temperature of 25°C, so that the heat developed when it is brought to rest shall be just sufficient to melt it?

16–33. Inspect the following data sheet, which was prepared for an experiment to measure the heat of vaporization of water:

Mass of empty beaker	50 grams
Mass of filled beaker	150 grams
Mass of water	_____

Initial temperature of water	25°C
Final temperature of water	45°C
Change in temperature of water	_____

Mass of water, beaker, and condensed steam	154 grams
Mass of condensed steam	_____

CALCULATED HEAT OF
   VAPORIZATION OF
   WATER   _____

Describe the experiment performed. Fill in the blank spaces and use the data to calculate the heat of vaporization of water. What would you say about the experimental error?

16–34. A "solar house" has storage facilities for 4 million Btu. Compare the space requirements for this storage on the assumption (a) that the heat is stored in water heated from a minimum temperature of 80°F to a maximum at 120°F, and (b) that the heat is stored in Glauber salt ($Na_2SO_4 \cdot 10\ H_2O$) heated in the same temperature range.

Properties of Glauber salt:

Specific heat (solid)	0.46 Btu/lb·F°
Specific heat (liquid)	0.68 Btu/lb·F°
Specific gravity	1.6
Melting point	90°F
Heat of fusion	104 Btu/lb

16–35. An insulated aluminum calorimeter weighing 2 lb contains 20 lb of water. Both the water and the container are at 50°F. If 5 lb of ice at 32°F and 2 lb of steam at 212°F are added to the water, what is the final temperature of the system?

16–36. The specific heat capacity c of a substance is given by the empirical equation

$$c = a + bt^2,$$

where a and b are constants and t is the celsius temperature. (a) Compute the heat required to raise the temperature of a mass m of the substance from 0°C to t°C. (b) What is the mean specific heat of the substance in the temperature range between 0°C and t°C? (c) Compare this with the true specific heat at a temperature midway between 0°C and t°C.

16–37. At very low temperatures, in the neighborhood of absolute zero, the specific heat of solids is given by the Debye equation,

$$c = kT^3,$$

where T is the absolute or kelvin temperature and k is a constant, different for different materials. (a) Compute the heat required to raise the temperature of a mass m of a solid from 0°K to 10°K. (b) Compute the mean specific heat in the temperature range between 0°K and 10°K. (c) Compute the true specific heat at a temperature of 10°K.

16–38. A slab of a thermal insulator is 100 cm² in cross section and 2 cm thick. Its thermal conductivity is 2×10^{-4} cal/sec·cm·C°. If the temperature difference between opposite faces is 100°C, how many calories flow through the slab in one day?

16–39. One end of a copper bar 18 cm long and 4 cm² in cross section is in a steam bath and the other end is in a mixture of melting ice and water. Heat loss across the curved surface can be neglected. (a) What is the heat current in the bar? (b) What is the temperature at a point 4 cm from the cooler end?

16–40. A long rod, insulated to prevent heat losses, has one end immersed in boiling water (at atmospheric pressure) and the other end in a water-ice mixture. The rod consists of 100 cm of copper (one end in steam) and a length, L_2, of steel (one end in ice). Both parts of the rod are of cross-sectional area 5 cm². The temperature of the copper-iron junction is 60°C, after a steady state has been set up. (a) How many calories per second flow from the steam bath to the ice-water mixture? (b) How long is L_2?

16–41. A compound bar 2 meters long is constructed of a solid steel core 1 cm in diameter surrounded by a copper casing whose outside diameter is 2 cm. The outer surface of the bar is thermally insulated and one end is maintained at 100°C, the other at 0°C. (a) Find the total heat current in the bar. (b) What fraction is carried by each material?

16–42. One experimental method of measuring the thermal conductivity of an insulating material is to construct a box of the material and measure the power input to an electric heater, inside the box, which maintains the interior at a measured temperature above that of the outside surface. Suppose that in such an apparatus a power input of 120 watts is required to keep the interior of the box 70°C above the outside temperature. The total area of the box is 25,000 cm^2 and the wall thickness is 4 cm. Find the thermal conductivity of the material.

16–43. A container of wall area 5000 cm^2 and thickness 2 cm is filled with water in which there is a stirrer. The outer surface of the walls is kept at a constant temperature of 0°C. The thermal conductivity of the walls is 0.000478 cgs units, and the effect of edges and corners can be neglected. The power required to run the stirrer at an angular velocity of 1800 rev/min is found to be 100 watts. What will be the final steady-state temperature of the water in the container? Assume that the stirrer keeps the entire mass of water at a uniform temperature.

16–44. A boiler with a steel bottom 1.5 cm thick rests on a hot stove. The area of the bottom of the boiler is 1500 cm^2. The water inside the boiler is at 100°C, and 750 gm are evaporated every 5 minutes. Find the temperature of the lower surface of the boiler, which is in contact with the stove.

16–45. An icebox, having wall area of 2 m^2 and thickness 5 cm, is constructed of insulating material having a thermal conductivity of 10^{-4} cal/sec·cm·C°. The outside temperature is 20°C, and the inside of the box is to be maintained at 5°C by ice. The melted ice leaves the box at a temperature of 15°C. If ice costs one cent per kgm, what will it cost to run the icebox for one hour?

CHAPTER 17

THE LAWS OF THERMODYNAMICS

17-1 Internal energy. The temperature of a body may be increased by placing it in contact with a second body at a higher temperature, or by doing mechanical work on it. For example, the air in a bicycle pump becomes hotter when the piston is pushed down, although it could also be raised in temperature by placing it in a furnace. If one were given a sample of hot air, it would be impossible to tell by any tests whether it had been heated by compression or by heat flow from a hotter body. It therefore makes no sense to speak of the "heat in a body" or of the "work in a body."

Heat and work are two methods of adding energy to or subtracting energy from a system. They represent energy in transit and are the terms used when energy is moving. Once the transfer of energy is over, the body is said to have undergone a change in *internal energy*. It is impossible to separate or divide the internal energy into a mechanical and a thermal part. From the molecular point of view, the internal energy of a body is the sum of the kinetic and potential energies of its molecules, apart from any kinetic or potential energy of the body as a whole. To a first approximation, the internal energy of a gas at low pressure may be identified with the aggregate kinetic energy of its molecules.

17-2 The first law of thermodynamics. Suppose a system is caused to change from state 1 to state 2 along a definite path and that the heat absorbed, Q, and the work W are measured. Expressing both Q and W either in thermal units or in mechanical units, we may then calculate the difference $Q - W$. If now we do the same thing over again for many different paths (between the same states 1 and 2), the important result is obtained that $Q - W$ *is the same for all paths connecting 1 and 2*. But Q is the energy that has been added to a system by the transfer of heat and W is equal to the energy that has been extracted from the system by the performance of work. The difference $Q - W$, therefore, must represent the internal energy change of the system. It follows that *the internal energy change of a system is independent of the path*, and is therefore equal to the energy of the system in state 2 minus the energy in state 1, or $U_2 - U_1$.

$$U_2 - U_1 = Q - W.$$

If some arbitrary value is assigned to the internal energy in some standard reference state, its value in any other state is uniquely defined, since $Q - W$ is the same for all processes connecting the states.

The simple algebraic statement of these facts in the form

$$Q = U_2 - U_1 + W \qquad (17\text{--}1)$$

is known as *the first law of thermodynamics*. In applying the law in this form it must be remembered that (1) all quantities must be expressed in the same units, (2) Q is positive when heat goes into the system, (3) W is positive when the force *on* the system is opposite the displacement.

17–3 Adiabatic process. A process that takes place in such a manner that no heat enters or leaves a system is called an *adiabatic process*. This may be accomplished either by surrounding the system with a thick layer of heat insulating material (such as cork, asbestos, firebrick, or any light, porous powder) or by performing the process quickly. The flow of heat is a fairly slow process, so that any process performed quickly enough will be practically adiabatic. Applying the first law to an adiabatic process, we get

$$U_2 - U_1 = -W \quad \text{(Adiabatic process)}.$$

Thus the change in the internal energy of a system, in an adiabatic process, is equal in absolute magnitude to the work. If the work W is negative, as when a system is compressed, then $-W$ is positive, U_2 is greater than U_1, and the internal energy of the system increases. If W is positive, as when a system expands, the internal energy of the system decreases. An increase of internal energy is usually accompanied by a rise in temperature and a decrease in internal energy by a temperature drop.

The compression of the mixture of gasoline vapor and air that takes place during the compression stroke of a gasoline engine is an example of an approximately adiabatic process involving a temperature rise. The expansion of the combustion products during the power stroke of the engine is an approximately adiabatic process involving a temperature decrease. Adiabatic processes, therefore, play a very important role in mechanical engineering.

17–4 Isochoric process. If a substance undergoes a process in which the volume remains unchanged, the process is called *isochoric*. The rise of pressure and temperature produced by a flow of heat into a substance contained in a nonexpanding chamber is an example of an isochoric process. If the volume does not change, no work is done and, therefore, from the first law,

$$Q = U_2 - U_1 \quad \text{(Isochoric process)},$$

or all the heat that has been added has served to increase the internal energy. The very sudden increase of temperature and pressure accompanying the explosion of gasoline vapor and air in a gasoline engine may be treated mathematically as though it were an isochoric addition of heat.

17–5 Isobaric process. A process taking place at constant pressure is called an *isobaric process*. When water enters the boiler of a steam engine and is heated to its boiling point, vaporized, and then the steam is superheated, all these processes take place isobarically. Such processes play an important role in mechanical engineering and also in chemistry.

Consider the change of phase of a mass m of liquid to vapor at constant pressure and temperature. If V_L is the volume of liquid and V_V the volume of vapor, the work done in expanding from V_L to V_V at constant pressure p is

$$W = p(V_V - V_L).$$

The heat absorbed by each unit of mass is the heat of vaporization L. Hence

$$Q = mL.$$

From the first law,

$$mL = (U_V - U_L) + p(V_V - V_L). \tag{17–2}$$

EXAMPLE. One gram of water (1 cm^3) becomes 1671 cm^3 of steam when boiled at a pressure of 1 atm. The heat of vaporization at this pressure is 539 cal/gm. Compute the external work and the increase in internal energy.

$$
\begin{aligned}
\text{External work} &= p(V_V - V_L) \\
&= 1.013 \times 10^6 \text{ dynes/cm}^2 \,(1671 - 1) \text{ cm}^3 \\
&= 1.695 \times 10^9 \text{ ergs} \\
&= 169.5 \text{ joules} \\
&= 41 \text{ cal.}
\end{aligned}
$$

From Eq. (18–5)

$$U_V - U_L = mL - W = 539 - 41 = 498 \text{ cal.}$$

Hence the external work, or the external part of the heat of vaporization, equals 41 cal, and the increase in internal energy, or the internal part of the heat of vaporization, is 498 cal.

17–6 Free expansion. Imagine a vessel with rigid walls and covered with asbestos. Suppose the vessel is divided into two parts by a thin partition, and that one part contains a gas, while the other is evacuated. If the partition is suddenly broken, the gas rushes into a vacuum, undergoing what is known as a *free expansion*. Since the walls of the container are rigid, no external work is done, and since the vessel is heat-insulated, the process is adiabatic. Thus, $Q = 0$ and $W = 0$. Hence, from the first law,

$$U_1 = U_2 \quad \text{(Free expansion)},$$

or the initial and final internal energies are equal.

The magnitude of the temperature change (if any) that takes place as a result of a free expansion is of some theoretical interest and, as a result, many attempts have been made to perform an experiment of this sort. The experimental difficulties, however, are enormous and no one has really succeeded so far. From a practical point of view a free expansion is of no importance whatever.

17–7 Throttling process. A throttling process is one in which a fluid, originally at a constant high pressure, seeps through a porous wall or a narrow opening (needle valve or throttling valve) into a region of constant lower pressure, without a transfer of heat taking place. The experiment is sometimes called the porous plug experiment. Figure 17–1(a) will help to make the process clear. A fluid is discharged from a pump at a high pressure, then passes through a throttling valve into a pipe which leads directly to the intake or low-pressure side of the pump. Every successive element of fluid undergoes the throttling process in a continuous stream.

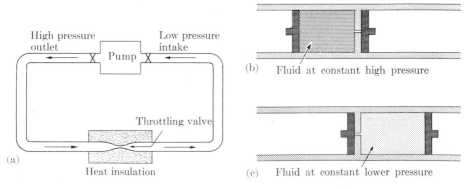

High pressure outlet   Low pressure intake   Pump

(b) Fluid at constant high pressure

Throttling valve

(a)

Heat insulation

(c) Fluid at constant lower pressure

FIG. 17–1. Throttling process.

Consider any element of fluid enclosed between the piston and throttling valve of Fig. 17–1(b). Suppose this piston to move toward the right and another piston on the other side of the valve to move to the right also at such rates that the pressure on the left remains at a constant high value and that on the right at a constant lower value. After all the fluid has been forced through the valve, the final state is that of Fig. 17–1(c).

The net work done in this process is the difference between the work done in forcing the right-hand piston out and the work done in forcing the left-hand piston in. Let

$$p_1 = \text{high pressure (on the left)},$$
$$V_1 = \text{volume of fluid at the high pressure},$$
$$p_2 = \text{lower pressure (on the right)},$$
$$V_2 = \text{volume of fluid at the low pressure}.$$

Since the low-pressure fluid changes in volume from zero to V_2 at the constant pressure p_2, the work is

$$p_2(V_2 - 0),$$

and since the high-pressure fluid changes in volume from V_1 to zero at the constant high pressure p_1, the work is

$$p_1(0 - V_1).$$

The net work W is therefore

$$W = p_2 V_2 - p_1 V_1.$$

Since the process is adiabatic, $Q = 0$, and hence from the first law,

$$0 = U_2 - U_1 + (p_2 V_2 - p_1 V_1)$$

or

$$U_1 + p_1 V_1 = U_2 + p_2 V_2. \tag{17–3}$$

This result is of great importance in steam engineering and in refrigeration. The sum $U + pV$, called the *enthalpy*, is tabulated for steam and for many refrigerants. The throttling process plays the main role in the action of a refrigerator, since this is the process that gives rise to the drop in temperature needed for refrigeration. Liquids that are about to evaporate (saturated liquids) always undergo a drop in temperature and partial vaporization as a result of a throttling process. Gases, however, may undergo either a temperature rise or drop, depending on the initial temperature and pressure and on the final pressure.

17–8 Differential form of the first law. Heat capacity. Up to this point we have used the first law of thermodynamics only in its finite form,

$$Q = U_2 - U_1 + W.$$

In this form the equation applies to a process in which states 1 and 2 differ in pressure, volume, and temperature by a finite amount. Suppose states 1 and 2 differ only infinitesimally. Then only an infinitesimal amount of heat dQ will be transferred, only an infinitesimal amount of work dW will be done, and the energy change dU is also infinitesimal. In these circumstances, the first law becomes

$$dQ = dU + dW.$$

If the system is of such a character that the only work possible is by means of expansion or compression, then $dW = p\,dV$, and

$$dQ = dU + p\,dV$$

is the *differential form of the first law*, applicable to solids, liquids, and gases.

The temperature of a substance may be raised under a variety of conditions. The volume may be kept constant, or the pressure may be kept constant, or both may be allowed to vary in some arbitrary manner. In each of these cases, the amount of heat necessary to cause unit rise of temperature, or the *heat capacity*, is different. In other words, a substance has many different heat capacities. Only two, however, are of practical use, namely, those at constant volume and at constant pressure.

Let us choose as a convenient unit of mass the number of grams equal to the molecular weight, that is, a mole. The corresponding heat capacity is called the *molar heat capacity*, represented by c_v. If we have n moles of a substance with a molar heat capacity at constant volume c_v and we raise its temperature at constant volume by an amount dT, then the heat transferred is $nc_v\,dT$ and the work done is zero. Using the first law of thermodynamics in its differential form,

$$dQ = dU + p\,dV,$$

we get

$$nc_v\,dT = dU,$$

or

$$c_v = \frac{1}{n}\left(\frac{dU}{dT}\right)_{\text{constant volume}}$$

For an isobaric process, $p\,dV$ is not zero, and the corresponding molar heat capacity, c_p, is larger than c_v.

17–9 The conversion of heat into work. The dominating feature of an industrial society is its ability to utilize, whether for wise or unwise ends, sources of energy other than the muscles of men or animals. Except for water power, where mechanical energy is directly available, most energy supplies are in the form of fuels such as coal or oil, where the energy is stored as internal energy. The process of combustion releases the internal energy and converts it to heat. In this form the energy may be utilized for heating habitations, for cooking, or for maintaining a furnace at high temperature in order to carry out other chemical or physical processes. But to operate a machine, or to propel a vehicle or a projectile, the heat must be converted to mechanical energy, and one of the problems of the mechanical engineer is to carry out this conversion with the maximum possible efficiency.

There is only one type of process in which internal energy can be converted directly to mechanical energy, and that is when the chemical substances can be combined in an electrolytic cell. All other methods involve the intermediate step of transforming internal energy into heat. The changes may be represented schematically by

$$\frac{\text{Internal}}{\text{energy}} \rightarrow \text{Heat} \rightarrow \frac{\text{Mechanical}}{\text{energy}}$$

The process represented by

$$\frac{\text{Internal}}{\text{energy}} \rightarrow \text{Heat}$$

presents few difficulties. The most common example is, of course, the combustion of coal, oil, or gas. The problem then reduces to

$$\text{Heat} \rightarrow \frac{\text{Mechanical}}{\text{energy}}$$

It is evident in the first place that this transformation always requires the services of some sort of *engine*, such as a steam engine, gasoline engine, or diesel engine.

At first sight the problem does not seem difficult, since we know that 1 Btu = 778 ft·lb, and it appears that every Btu of thermal energy should provide us with 778 ft·lb of mechanical energy. A pound of coal, for instance, develops about 13,000 Btu when burned, and might be expected to provide $13{,}000 \times 778$ ft·lb of mechanical work. Actual steam engines, however, furnish only from about 5% to about 30% of this value. What becomes of the remaining 70% to 95%?

Stack and friction losses account for only a small part, by far the largest part appearing as heat rejected in the exhaust. No one has ever constructed a heat engine which does not throw away in its exhaust a relatively large fraction of the heat supplied to it, and it is safe to say that no one ever will. The impossibility of constructing an engine which with no other outstanding changes will convert a given amount of heat *completely* into mechanical work is a fundamental law of Nature, known as *the second law of thermodynamics*. The first law, it will be recalled, is a statement of the principle of conservation of energy, and merely imposes the restriction that one can obtain *no more* than 778 ft·lb of mechanical work from every Btu of heat. It does not in itself restrict the fraction of a given amount of heat which an engine can convert into mechanical energy. The second law goes beyond the first, and states that 100% conversion is not possible by any form of engine. Of course, for that fraction of the heat supplied to it which an engine *does* convert to mechanical form, the equivalence expressed by the first law must hold true.

A young French engineer, Sadi Carnot, was the first to approach the problem of the efficiency of a heat engine from a truly fundamental standpoint. Improvements in steam engines, up to the time of Carnot's work in 1824, had either been along the lines of better mechanical design or, if more basic improvements had been made, they had come about by chance or inspiration and had not been guided by any knowledge of basic principles. Carnot's contribution was a "theoretical" one, but it had more influence on the development of our industrial society in the 19th Century than the work of any of the "practical" men who had preceded him in this field.

Briefly, what Carnot did was to disregard the details of operation of a heat engine and focus attention on its truly significant features. These are, first, the engine is supplied with energy, in the form of heat, at a relatively high temperature. Second, the engine performs mechanical work. Third, the engine rejects heat at a lower temperature. In Carnot's time the caloric theory of heat as an indestructible fluid was still generally accepted. It is difficult to ascertain from Carnot's published articles exactly what his beliefs were as to the nature of work and heat, largely because of his failure to give *precise* definitions of the terms used. But although Carnot himself may have intuitively understood the problem, most scientists of his time pictured the flow of heat through an engine, from a higher to a lower temperature, as analogous to the flow of water through a water wheel or turbine from a higher to a lower elevation. In any time interval, equal amounts of water enter the turbine and are discharged from it, but in the process some mechanical energy is abstracted from the water. Carnot believed that a similar process took place in a heat engine—some mechanical energy was abstracted from the heat but the amount of heat rejected by the engine in any time interval was equal to that delivered to the engine. We know now that this idea is incorrect, and that the heat rejected by the engine is less than the heat supplied to it by the amount that has been converted to mechanical work. In spite of his erroneous concept of the nature of heat, Carnot did in fact obtain the correct expression for the maximum efficiency of any heat engine operating between two given temperatures.

Since it is only heat and work that are of primary concern in a heat engine, we consider for simplicity an engine working in *closed cycles*. That is, the material that expands against a piston is periodically brought back to its initial condition so that in any one cycle the change in internal energy of this material, called the *working substance*, is zero. The condensing type of steam engine actually does operate in this way; the exhaust steam is condensed and forced back into the boiler so that the working substance (in this case, water) is used over and over again. The working substance then merely serves to transfer heat from one body to another and, by virtue of its changes in volume, to convert some of the heat to mechanical work.

The energy transformations in a heat engine are conveniently represented schematically by the *flow diagram* of Fig. 17–2. The engine itself is represented by the circle. The heat Q_2 supplied to the engine is proportional to the cross section of the incoming "pipeline" at the top of the diagram. The cross section of the outgoing pipeline at the bottom is proportional to that portion of the heat, Q_1, which is rejected as heat in the exhaust. The branch line to the right represents that portion of the heat supplied which the engine converts to mechanical work, W. Since the working substance is periodically returned to its initial state and the change in its internal energy in any number of complete cycles is zero, it follows from the first law of thermodynamics that

$$W = Q_2 - Q_1.$$

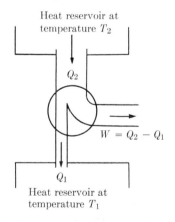

Heat reservoir at
temperature T_2

Q_2

$W = Q_2 - Q_1$

Q_1

Heat reservoir at
temperature T_1

Fig. 17–2. Schematic flow diagram of a heat engine.

That is, the mechanical work done equals the difference between the heat supplied and the heat rejected. (For convenience, W, Q_2, and Q_1 are all considered positive.)

The *thermal efficiency* E of the engine is the ratio of work output to heat input. The output is the mechanical work W. The exhaust heat is not considered a part of the output. The input is the heat Q_2. Hence

$$E = \frac{\text{Work output}}{\text{Heat input}} \rightarrow \frac{W}{Q_2},$$

$$E = \frac{Q_2 - Q_1}{Q_2}. \qquad (17\text{-}4)$$

In terms of the flow diagram, the most efficient engine is the one for which the branch pipeline representing the work obtained is as large as possible, and the exhaust pipeline representing the heat rejected is as small as possible, for a given incoming pipeline or quantity of heat supplied.

We shall now consider, without going into the mechanical details of their construction, the gasoline engine, the diesel engine, and the steam engine.

17–10 The gasoline engine. The common gasoline engine is of the four-cycle type, so called because four processes take place in each cycle. Starting with the piston at the top of its stroke, an explosive mixture of air and gasoline vapor is drawn into the cylinder on the downstroke, the inlet valve being open and the exhaust valve closed. This is the *intake* stroke. At the end of this stroke the inlet valve closes and the piston rises, performing an approximately adiabatic compression of the air-gasoline mixture. This is the *compression* stroke. At or near the top of this stroke a spark ignites the mixture of air and gasoline vapor, and combustion takes place very rapidly. The pressure and temperature increase at nearly constant volume.

The piston is now forced down, the burned gases expanding approximately adiabatically. This is the *power stroke* or *working stroke*. At the end of the power stroke the exhaust valve opens. The pressure in the cylinder drops rapidly to atmospheric and the rising piston on the *exhaust stroke* forces out most of the

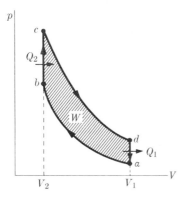

Fig. 17–3. $p\text{-}V$ diagram of the Otto cycle.

remaining gas. The exhaust valve now closes, the inlet valve opens, and the cycle is repeated.

For purposes of computation, the gasoline engine cycle is approximated by the *Otto* cycle illustrated in Fig. 17–3.

Starting at point *a*, air at atmospheric pressure is compressed adiabatically in a cylinder to point *b*, heated at constant volume to point *c*, allowed to expand adiabatically to point *d*, and cooled at constant volume to point *a*, after which the cycle is repeated. Line *ab* corresponds to the compression stroke, *bc* to the explosion, *cd* to the working stroke, and *da* to the exhaust of a gasoline engine. V_1 and V_2, in Fig. 17–3, are respectively the maximum and minimum volumes of the air in the cylinder. The ratio V_1/V_2 is called the *compression ratio*, and is about 7 for a gasoline engine.

The work output in Fig. 17–3 is represented by the shaded area enclosed by the figure *abcd*. The heat *input* is the heat supplied at constant volume along the line *bc*. The exhaust heat is removed along *da*. No heat is supplied or removed in the adiabatic processes *ab* and *cd*.

The heat input and the work output can be computed in terms of the compression ratio, assuming air to behave like an ideal gas. The result is

$$\mathrm{Eff}(\%) = 100 \left(1 - \frac{1}{(V_1/V_2)^{\gamma-1}}\right),$$

where γ is the ratio of the specific heat capacity at constant pressure to the specific heat capacity at constant volume, c_p/c_v. For a compression ratio of 7 and a value of $\gamma = 1.4$, the efficiency is about 54%. It will be seen that the higher the compression ratio, the higher the efficiency. Friction effects, turbulence, loss of heat to cylinder walls, etc., have been neglected. All these effects reduce the efficiency of an actual engine below the figure given above.

17–11 The diesel engine. In the diesel cycle, air is drawn into the cylinder on the intake stroke and compressed adiabatically on the compression stroke to a sufficiently high temperature so that fuel oil injected at the end of this stroke burns in the cylinder without requiring ignition by a spark. The combustion is not as rapid as in the gasoline engine, and the first part of the power stroke proceeds at essentially

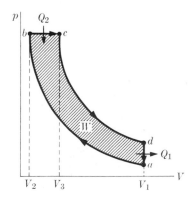

Fig. 17–4. *p-V* diagram of the diesel cycle.

constant pressure. The remainder of the power stroke is an adiabatic expansion. This is followed by an exhaust stroke which completes the cycle.

The idealized air-diesel cycle is shown in Fig. 17–4. Starting at point a, air is compressed adiabatically to point b, heated at constant pressure to point c, expanded adiabatically to point d, and cooled at constant volume to point a.

Since there is no fuel in the cylinder of a diesel engine on the compression stroke, pre-ignition cannot occur and the compression ratio V_1/V_2 may be much higher than that of an internal combustion engine. A value of 15 is typical. The *expansion* ratio V_1/V_3 may be about 5. Using these values, and taking $\gamma = 1.4$, the efficiency of the air-diesel cycle is about 56%. Hence somewhat higher efficiencies are possible than for the Otto cycle. Again, the actual efficiency of a real diesel must be smaller than the value given above.

17–12 The steam engine. The condensing type of steam engine performs the following sequence of operations. Water is converted to steam in the boiler, and the steam thus formed is superheated above the boiler temperature. Superheated steam is admitted to the cylinder, where it expands against a piston; connection is maintained to the boiler for the first part of the working stroke, which thus takes place at constant pressure. The inlet valve is then closed and the steam expands adiabatically for the rest of the working stroke. The adiabatic cooling causes some of the steam to condense. The mixture of water droplets and steam (known as "wet" steam) is forced out of the cylinder on the return stroke and into the condenser, where the remaining steam is condensed into water. This water is forced into the boiler by the feed pump, and the cycle is repeated.

An idealized cycle (called the rankine cycle) which approximates the actual steam cycle is shown in Fig. 17–5. Starting with liquid water at low pressure and temperature (point a), the water is compressed adiabatically to point b at boiler pressure. It is then heated at constant pressure to its boiling point (line bc), converted to steam (line cd), superheated (line de), expanded adiabatically (line ef), and cooled and condensed (along fa) to its initial condition.

The efficiency of such a cycle may be computed in the same way as was done in the previous examples, by finding the quantities of heat taken in and rejected along the lines be and fa. Assuming a boiler tem-

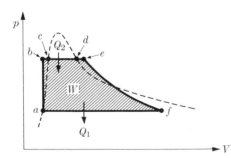

FIG. 17–5. The rankine cycle.

perature of 417°F (corresponding to a pressure of 300 lb/in^2), a super-heat of 63°F above this temperature (480°F), and a condenser temperature of 102°F, the efficiency of a rankine cycle is about 32%. Efficiencies of actual steam engines are, of course, considerably lower.

17–13 The second law of thermodynamics. Our experience with actual engines therefore leads us to the second law of thermodynamics, which may be stated rigorously as follows:

It is impossible to construct an engine that, operating in a cycle, will produce no effect other than the extraction of heat from a source and the conversion of this heat completely into work.

If the second law were not true, it would be possible to drive a steam-ship across the ocean by extracting heat from the ocean, or to run a power plant by extracting heat from the surrounding air. It should be noted that neither of these "impossibilities" violates the first law of thermodynamics. After all, both the ocean and the surrounding air contain an enormous store of internal energy which, in principle, may be extracted in the form of a flow of heat. There is nothing in the first law to preclude the possibility of converting this heat completely into work. The second law, therefore, is not a deduction from the first but stands by itself as a separate law of nature, referring to an aspect of nature different from that contemplated by the first law. The first law denies the possibility of creating or destroying energy; the second denies the possibility of utilizing energy in a particular way.

The fact that work may be dissipated completely into heat, whereas heat may not be converted entirely into work, expresses an essential one-sidedness of nature. All natural, spontaneous processes may be studied in the light of the second law, and in all such cases, this peculiar one-sidedness is found. Thus, heat always flows spontaneously from a hotter to a colder body; gases always seep through an opening spontaneously from a region of high pressure to a region of low pressure; gases and liquids left by themselves always tend to mix, not to unmix. Salt dissolves in water but a salt solution does not separate by itself into pure salt and pure water. Rocks weather and crumble; iron rusts; people grow old. These are all examples of *irreversible* processes that take place naturally in only one direction and, by their one-sidedness, express the second law of thermodynamics.

Irreversible, natural processes may be regarded from another point of view. A piece of pure salt and a volume of pure water represent an orderly arrangement of molecules. The solution of the salt in the water involves an increase in molecular disorder. If all the molecules of gas in a container were in one corner of the container, that would constitute an orderly arrangement. The uniform distribution throughout the container which actually exists is a much more disorderly arrangement. The sand that results from the weathering of rocks over a long period of time represents a greater disorder than the original well-formed rocks. Thus, the one-sidedness of nature may be redescribed by stating that *there is a tendency in nature to proceed toward a state of greater molecular disorder.*

17–14 The refrigerator. A refrigerator may be considered to be a heat engine operated in reverse. That is, a heat engine takes in heat from a *high* temperature source, converts a part of the heat into mechanical work output, and rejects the difference as heat in the exhaust at a *lower* temperature. A refrigerator takes in heat at a *low* temperature, the compressor supplies mechanical work *input*, and the sum is rejected as heat at a *higher* temperature.

The flow diagram of a refrigerator is given in Fig. 17–6. In terms of the processes in a household mechanical refrigerator, Q_1 represents the heat removed from the refrigerator by the cooling coils within it, W the work done by the motor, and Q_2 the heat delivered to the external cooling coils and removed by circulating air or water. It follows from the first law that

$$Q_2 = Q_1 + W.$$

That is, the circulating air or water must absorb both the heat "pumped" out of the refrigerator and the heat equivalent of the work done by the motor.

From an economic point of view, the best refrigeration cycle is one that removes the greatest amount of heat Q_1 from the refrigerator, for the least expenditure of mechanical work W. We therefore define the

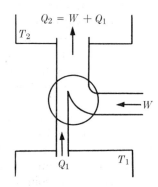

FIG. 17–6. Schematic flow diagram of a refrigerator.

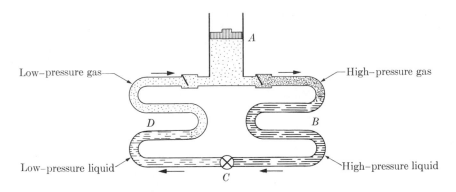

FIG. 17-7. Principle of the mechanical refrigeration cycle.

coefficient of performance (rather than the efficiency) of a refrigerator as the ratio Q_1/W, and since $W = Q_2 - Q_1$,

$$\text{Coefficient of performance} = \frac{Q_1}{Q_2 - Q_1}. \qquad (17\text{--}5)$$

The principles of the common refrigeration cycle are illustrated schematically in Fig. 17-7. Compressor A delivers gas (CCl_2F_2, NH_3, etc.) at high temperature and pressure to coils B. Heat is removed from the gas in B by water or air cooling, resulting in condensation of the gas to a liquid, still under high pressure. The liquid passes through the throttling valve or expansion valve C, emerging as a mixture of liquid and vapor at a lower temperature. In coils D, heat is supplied that converts the remaining liquid into vapor which enters compressor A to repeat the cycle. In a domestic refrigerator, coils D are placed in the ice compartment, where they cool the refrigerator directly. In a larger refrigerating plant, these coils are usually immersed in a brine tank and cool the brine, which is then pumped to the refrigerating rooms.

If no work were needed to operate a refrigerator, the coefficient of performance (heat extracted divided by work done) would be infinite. Coefficients of performance of actual refrigerators vary from about 2 to about 6. Experience shows that work is always needed to transfer heat from a colder to a hotter body. This negative statement leads to another statement of the second law of thermodynamics, namely:

It is impossible to construct a refrigerator that, operating in a cycle, will produce no effect other than the transfer of heat from a cooler to a hotter body.

At first sight, this and the previous statement of the second law appear to be quite unconnected, but it can be shown that they are in all respects equivalent. Any device that would violate one statement would violate the other.

17–15 The Carnot cycle. Although their efficiencies differ from one another, none of the heat engines which have been described has an efficiency of 100%. The question still remains open as to what is the maximum attainable efficiency, given a supply of heat at one temperature and a reservoir at a lower temperature for cooling the exhaust. An idealized engine which can be shown to have the maximum efficiency under these conditions was invented by Carnot and is called a *Carnot engine.* The *Carnot cycle,* shown in Fig. 17–8, differs from the Otto and diesel cycles in that it is bounded by two *isothermals* and two adiabatics. Thus all the heat input is supplied at a *single* high temperature and all the heat output is rejected at a *single* lower temperature. (Compare with Figs. 17–3 and 17–4, in which the temperature is different at all points of the lines *bc* and *da.*)

This, however, is not the only feature of the Carnot cycle. There are no "one-way" processes in the Carnot cycle, such as explosions or throttling processes. The isothermal and adiabatic processes of the Carnot cycle may be imagined to proceed in either direction. In the direction shown in Fig. 17–8, heat Q_2 goes in, heat Q_1 goes out, and work W is done by the engine. The arrows in the figure could be reversed, in which case the cycle would be a refrigeration cycle. Then heat Q_2 would go out, heat Q_1 would go in, and work W would have to be done on the refrigerator.

Suppose an engine (not a Carnot engine) were to operate between a source of heat at some temperature and a reservoir of heat at a lower

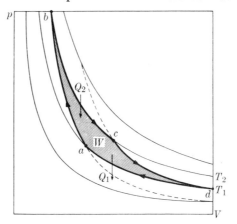

FIG. 17–8. The Carnot cycle.

temperature, thereby delivering to the outside an amount of work W.
Suppose this work W were used to operate a Carnot refrigerator which
extracted heat from the colder reservoir and delivered it to the warmer
source. It can be shown that if the first engine were more efficient than
the Carnot engine that would result by operating the Carnot refrigerator
backward, then the net effect would be a violation of the second law of
thermodynamics. Proceeding along these lines, it has been proved that:

*No engine operating between two given temperatures can be more
efficient than a Carnot engine operating between the same two temperatures,*

and also:

*All Carnot engines operating between the same two temperatures have
the same efficiency, irrespective of the nature of the working substance.*

17–16 The kelvin temperature scale. It was shown in the beginning of
this chapter that the efficiency of any engine is equal to

$$E = \frac{W}{Q_2} = \frac{Q_2 - Q_1}{Q_2} = 1 - \frac{Q_1}{Q_2}.$$

If, therefore, the efficiencies of all Carnot engines operating between the
same two temperatures are the same, irrespective of the working substance, the ratio Q_1/Q_2 must depend only on the two temperatures and
on nothing else. Lord Kelvin proposed that this fact be used to define
a temperature scale which would be independent of the properties of any
particular substance, unlike the gas thermometer scale described in
Chapter 15.

The kelvin temperatures of the reservoir and the source between which
a Carnot engine operates are defined by the relation

$$\boxed{\frac{Q_1}{Q_2} = \frac{T_1}{T_2},} \qquad (17\text{–}6)$$

where Q_1/Q_2 is the ratio of the heats rejected and absorbed, and T_1/T_2
is the ratio of the kelvin temperatures of the reservoir and the source.

At first thought it might seem that the ratio of two kelvin temperatures would be impossible to measure, since a Carnot engine is an ideal
engine, quite impossible to construct. The situation, however, is not
so bad as it seems. The ratio of two kelvin temperatures is the ratio
of two heats that are transferred during two isothermal processes bounded
by the same two adiabatics. The two adiabatic boundaries may be lo-

cated experimentally, and the heats transferred during two isothermal "nearly reversible" processes can be measured with considerable precision. As a matter of fact, this is one of the methods used in measuring temperatures below $1°K$.

To complete the definition of the kelvin scale we proceed, as in Chapter 15, to assign the arbitrary value of $273.16°K$ to the temperature of the triple point of water T_3. For a Carnot engine operating between reservoirs at the temperatures T and T_3, we have

$$\frac{Q}{Q_3} = \frac{T}{T_3}$$

or

$$T = 273.16°K\,\frac{Q}{Q_3}. \tag{17–7}$$

Comparing this with the corresponding expression for the ideal gas temperature, namely,

$$273.16°K\,\lim_{p_3\to 0}\left(\frac{p}{p_3}\right)_{\text{constant volume}},$$

it is seen that, in the kelvin scale, Q plays the role of a "thermometric property." This does not, however, have the objection attached to a coordinate of an arbitrarily chosen thermometer, inasmuch as the behavior of a Carnot engine is independent of the nature of the working substance.

The efficiency of a Carnot engine rejecting heat Q_1 to a reservoir at kelvin temperature T_1 and absorbing heat Q_2 from a source at kelvin temperature T_2 is, as usual,

$$E = 1 - \frac{Q_1}{Q_2}.$$

But, by definition of the kelvin scale,

$$\frac{Q_1}{Q_2} = \frac{T_1}{T_2}.$$

Therefore, the efficiency of a Carnot engine is

$$E\ (\text{Carnot}) = 1 - \frac{T_1}{T_2}. \tag{17–8}$$

Equation (17–8) points the way to the conditions which a real engine, such as a steam engine, must fulfill to approach as closely as possible the maximum attainable efficiency. These conditions are that the intake temperature T_2 must be made as high as possible and the exhaust temperature T_1 as low as possible.

The exhaust temperature cannot be lower than the lowest temperature available for cooling the exhaust. This is usually the temperature of the air, or perhaps of river water if this is available at the plant. The only recourse then is to raise the boiler temperature T_2. Since the vapor pressure of all liquids increases rapidly with increasing temperature, a limit is set by the mechanical strength of the boiler. Another possibility is to use, instead of water, some liquid with a lower vapor pressure. Successful experiments in this direction have been made with mercury vapor replacing steam. At a boiler temperature of 200°C, at which the pressure in a steam boiler would be 225 lb/in^2, the pressure in a mercury boiler is only 0.35 lb/in^2.

17–17 Absolute zero. It follows from Eq. (17–7) that the heat transferred isothermally between two given adiabatics decreases as the temperature decreases. Conversely, the smaller the value of Q, the lower the corresponding T. The smallest possible value of Q is zero, and the corresponding T is absolute zero. *Thus, if a system undergoes a reversible isothermal process without transfer of heat, the temperature at which this process takes place is called absolute zero.* In other words, at absolute zero, an isotherm and an adiabatic are identical.

It should be noted that the definition of absolute zero holds for all substances and is therefore independent of the peculiar properties of any one arbitrarily chosen substance. Furthermore, the definition is in terms of purely macroscopic concepts. No reference is made to molecules or to molecular energy. Whether absolute zero may be achieved experimentally is a question of some interest and importance. To achieve temperatures below 4.2°K, at which ordinary helium (mass number 4) liquefies, it is necessary to lower the vapor pressure by pumping away the vapor as fast as possible. The lowest temperature that has ever been reached in this way is 0.7°K, and this required larger pumps and larger pumping tubes than are usually employed in low-temperature laboratories. With the aid of the light isotope of helium (mass number 3) which liquefies at 3.2°K, vigorous pumping will yield a temperature of about 0.3°K. Still lower temperatures may be achieved magnetically, but it becomes apparent that, the closer one approaches absolute zero, the more difficult it is to go further. It is generally accepted as a law of Nature that, although absolute zero may be approached as close as we please, it is impossible actually to reach the zero of temperature. This is known as the *"unattainability statement of the third law of thermodynamics."*

PROBLEMS

17-1. A pound of water whose volume is 0.0190 ft^3 is converted into steam of volume 1.50 ft^3 at the constant pressure of 309 lb/in^2. How many foot·pounds of work are done?

17-2. A gas contained in a cylinder surrounded by a thick layer of felt is quickly compressed, the temperature rising several degrees. (a) Has there been a transfer of heat? (b) Has work been done?

17-3. A combustion experiment is performed by burning a mixture of fuel and oxygen in a constant-volume "bomb" surrounded by a water bath. During the experiment the temperature of the water is observed to rise. Regarding the mixture of fuel and oxygen as the system: (a) Has heat been transferred? (b) Has work been done? (c) What is the sign of ΔU?

17-4. A liquid is irregularly stirred in a well-insulated container and thereby undergoes a rise in temperature. Regarding the liquid as the system: (a) Has heat been transferred? (b) Has work been done? (c) What is the sign of ΔU?

17-5. A resistor, immersed in running water, carries an electric current. Consider the resistor as the system under consideration. (a) Is there a flow of heat into the resistor? (b) Is there a flow of heat into the water? (c) Is work done? (d) Assuming the state of the resistor to remain unchanged, apply the first law to this process.

17-6. In a certain process, 500 cal of heat are supplied to a system, and at the same time 100 joules of work are done. What is the increase in the internal energy of the system?

17-7. 200 Btu are supplied to a system in a certain process, and at the same time the system expands against a constant external pressure of 100 lb/in^2. The internal energy of the system is the same at the beginning and end of the process. Find the increase in volume of the system.

17-8. A substance undergoes a series of processes which bring it back to its initial state. In this cycle, heat Q_2 is absorbed by the substance and heat Q_1 is rejected. What is the net amount of work done?

17-9. An inventor claims to have developed an engine which takes in 100,000 Btu from its fuel supply, rejects 25,000 Btu in the exhaust, and delivers 25 kwh of mechanical work. Do you advise investing money to put this engine on the market?

17-10. A vessel with rigid walls and covered with asbestos is divided into two parts by an insulating partition. One part contains a gas at temperature T and pressure P. The other part contains a gas at temperature T' and pressure P'. The partition is removed. What conclusion may be drawn by applying the first law of thermodynamics?

17-11. A mixture of hydrogen and oxygen is enclosed in a rigid insulating container and exploded by a spark. The temperature and pressure both increase considerably. Neglecting the small amount of energy provided by the spark itself, what conclusion may be drawn by applying the first law of thermodynamics?

17-12. When water is boiled under a pressure of 2 atm, the heat of vaporization is 946 Btu/lb and the boiling point is 250°F. One lb of steam occupies a volume of 14 ft^3, and 1 lb of water a volume of 0.017 ft^3. (a) Compute the external work, in ft·lb and in

Btu, when 1 lb of steam is formed at this temperature. (b) Compute the increase in internal energy, in Btu.

17–13. When a system is taken from state a to state b, in Fig. 17–9, along the path acb, 80 Btu of heat flow into the system, and 30 Btu of work are done. (a) How much heat flows into the system along path adb if the work is 10 Btu? (b) When the system is returned from b to a along the curved path, the work is 20 Btu. Does the system absorb or liberate heat and how much? (c) If $U_a = 0$ and $U_d = 40$ Btu, find the heat absorbed in the processes ad and db.

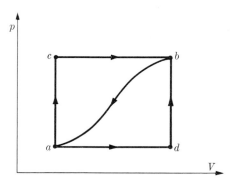

FIGURE 17–9

17–14. A steel cylinder of cross-sectional area 0.1 ft^2 contains 0.4 ft^3 of glycerin. The cylinder is equipped with a tightly fitting piston which supports a load of 6000 lb. The temperature of the system is increased from 60°F to 160°F. Neglect the expansion of the steel cylinder. Find (a) the increase in volume of the glycerin, (b) the mechanical work of the 6000-lb force, (c) the amount of heat added to the glycerin (specific heat of glycerin = 0.58 Btu/lb·F°), (d) the change in internal energy of the glycerin.

17–15. The efficiency of an Otto cycle is 50% and $\gamma = 1.50$. What is the compression ratio?

17–16. A Carnot engine whose high-temperature reservoir is at 127°C takes in 100 cal of heat at this temperature in each cycle, and gives up 80 cal to the low-temperature reservoir. Find the temperature of the latter reservoir.

17–17. A Carnot engine whose low-temperature reservoir is at 7°C has an efficiency of 40%. It is desired to increase the efficiency to 50%. By how many degrees must the temperature of the high-temperature reservoir be increased?

17–18. A Carnot engine is operated between two heat reservoirs at temperatures of 400°K and 300°K. (a) If in each cycle the engine receives 1200 cal of heat from the reservoir at 400°K, how many calories does it reject to the reservoir at 300°K? (b) If the engine is operated in reverse, as a refrigerator, and receives 1200 cal of heat from the reservoir at 300°K, how many calories does it deliver to the reservoir at 400°K? (c) How many calories would be produced if the mechanical work required to operate the refrigerator in part (b) were converted directly to heat?

17–19. What is the efficiency of an engine which operates by taking an ideal monatomic gas through the following cycle? Let $c_v = 3$ cal/gm-mole·C°. (a) Start with n moles at p_0, V_0, T_0. (b) Change to $2p_0$, V_0 at constant volume. (c) Change to $2p_0$, $2V_0$ at constant pressure. (d) Change to p_0, $2V_0$ at constant volume. (e) Change to p_0, V_0 at constant pressure.

17–20. A Carnot refrigerator takes heat from water at 0°C and discards it to the room at a temperature of 27°C. 100 kgm of water at 0°C are to be changed to ice at 0°C. (a) How many calories of heat are discarded to the room? (b) What is the required work in joules?

17–21. A cylinder contains air at a pressure of 2 atm. The volume is 3 liters and the temperature is 300°K. The air is carried through the following processes:

(1) Heated at constant pressure to 500°K.
(2) Cooled at constant volume to 250°K.
(3) Cooled at constant pressure to 150°K.
(4) Heated at constant volume to 300°K.

(a) Show each process on a p-V diagram, giving the numerical values of p and V at the end of each process.

(b) Calculate the net work done by the gas.

17–22. For the data in Problem 17–21 find (a) the number of gm-moles of air in the cylinder. (b) For air, $c_p = 7$ cal/gm-mole·C° and $c_v = 5$ cal/gm-mole·C°. Find the total heat input to the cylinder in processes (1) and (4). Express the answer in calories. (c) What is the efficiency of this device as a heat engine?

17–23. (a) What is the coefficient of performance of a Carnot refrigerator which removes heat from a reservoir at −10°C and delivers heat to a reservoir at 30°C? (b) How many kwh of energy would have to be supplied to the refrigerator to remove from the low-temperature reservoir an amount of heat equal to that required to melt 100 lb of ice? (c) What would be the cost of this energy, at 5 cents/kwh?

CHAPTER 18

THE IDEAL GAS AND THE ATOMIC VIEW OF MATTER

18-1 The ideal gas law. We know that the atoms of a gas are much more widely separated than are those of a liquid or solid; hence the forces between atoms are of less consequence and the behavior of a gas is governed by simpler laws than those applying to liquids and solids.

Robert Boyle, in 1660, reported on one of the first quantitative experiments relating to gaseous behavior. He found that if the temperature of a fixed mass of gas was held constant while its volume was varied over wide limits, the pressure exerted by the gas varied also, and in such a way that the product of pressure and volume remained approximately constant. This relation is known as *Boyle's law*. If p stands for the *absolute* pressure and V for the volume of any constant mass of gas, then Boyle's law may be written

$$pV = \text{constant} \begin{Bmatrix} \text{constant temperature} \\ \text{constant mass} \end{Bmatrix}. \qquad (18\text{-}1)$$

Many measurements of the pressure and volume of gases carried out since Boyle's time have shown that, at a temperature near that at which the gas condenses into a liquid, the product pV varies considerably. Only at temperatures far above the condensation point is Boyle's law obeyed. In the case of oxygen, nitrogen, air, hydrogen, and helium, Boyle's law is obeyed quite well in the neighborhood of room temperature and atmospheric pressure.

In describing the behavior of gases, it is very useful to use the *gram-mole* as a unit of mass. *A gram-mole of gas is M grams, where M is the molecular weight.* Thus, a mole of hydrogen, H_2, is 2 gm, a mole of oxygen, O_2, is 32 gm, etc. Suppose the pressure p, volume V, and the number of moles n of a gas are measured at constant temperature and the product pv (v is the volume per mole, V/n, or *molar volume*) is calculated. The remarkable property of gases that makes them so valuable in thermometry is displayed in Fig. 18-1, where the product pv is plotted against p for four different gases, all at the temperature of boiling sulfur in the top graph, all at the temperature of boiling water in the one beneath, all at the triple point of water in the next lower graph, and all at the temperature of solid CO_2 in the lowest. In each case it is seen that as the pressure approaches zero, *the product pv approaches the same value for all gases at the same temperature.*

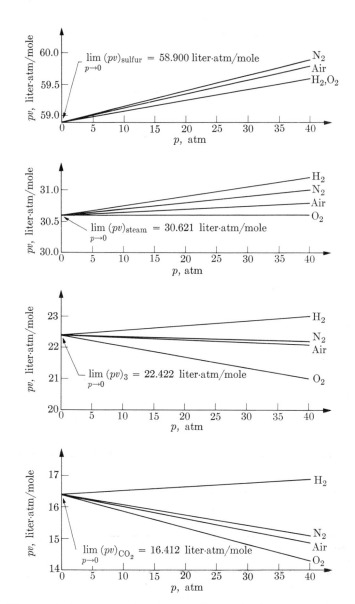

FIG. 18-1. The fundamental property of gases is that $\lim_{p \to 0} (pv)_T$ is independent of the nature of the gas and depends only on T.

According to the rules developed in Chapter 15, the kelvin temperature divided by T_3 ($T_3 = 273.16°K$) is obtained by taking the limiting value, as the pressure approaches zero, of the ratio p/p_3, *no matter what gas is chosen*. We have, therefore, two fundamental properties that hold *for all gases in the limit of low pressures*, thus:

$$pv = \text{constant} \qquad \text{(constant temperature)}, \qquad (18\text{–}2)$$

$$\frac{p}{p_3} = \frac{T}{T_3} \qquad \text{(constant volume)}. \qquad (18\text{–}3)$$

In Fig. 18–2, the relation between p and v at small values of p (Boyle's law) is plotted for two different temperatures: an arbitrary temperature T and the triple point temperature T_3.

At temperature T,

$$pv = k,$$

where k is a constant.

At temperature T_3,

$$(pv)_3 = k_3,$$

where k_3 is another constant.

Dividing the first equation by the second, we get that

$$\frac{pv}{(pv)_3} = \frac{k}{k_3} = \text{constant}, \qquad (18\text{–}4)$$

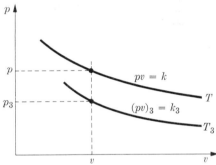

FIG. 18–2. The relation between p and v at small pressures and at two different temperatures.

which must hold for *any two points*, one on the upper curve and the other on the lower. If we apply this result to the two points shown in Fig. 18–2 *on the same constant volume line*, Eq. (18–4) reduces to

$$\frac{p}{p_3} = \frac{k}{k_3} \qquad \text{(constant } v\text{)}.$$

But p/p_3 is none other than the ratio T/T_3 as given in Eq. (18–3). It follows therefore that

$$\frac{k}{k_3} = \frac{T}{T_3},$$

and after substitution back into Eq. (18–4),

$$\frac{pv}{(pv)_3} = \frac{T}{T_3}.$$

Therefore, for all gases in the limit of low pressures,

$$pv = \left[\frac{(pv)_3}{273.16°}\right] \cdot T. \qquad (18\text{--}5)$$

The expression in brackets is called the *universal gas constant* and is denoted by R. The best value obtained so far for the limiting value of $(pv)_3$ is 22.4216 liters·atm/gm-mole, or 2271.87 joules/gm-mole. Hence

$$R = \frac{22.4216 \text{ liters·atm/gm-mole}}{273.16°K} = \frac{2271.87 \text{ joules/gm-mole}}{273.16°K},$$

$$R = \begin{cases} 0.08208 \text{ liter·atm/gm-mole·°K,} \\ 8.317 \times 10^7 \text{ ergs/gm-mole·°K} = 8.317 \text{ joules/gm-mole·°K,} \\ 8317 \text{ joules/kgm-mole·°K,} \\ 1.987 \text{ cal/gm-mole·°K} = 1.987 \text{ kcal/kgm-mole·°K.} \end{cases}$$

We may now write Eq. (18–5) as

$$pv = RT,$$

and replacing the molar volume v by the ratio of the total volume V to the number of moles n, we get finally

$$\boxed{pV = nRT.} \qquad (18\text{--}6)$$

Equation (18–6) expresses the behavior of real gases only at *low* pressures, where the forces of attraction among the molecules are very weak. If there were no forces whatever among the molecules, the equation would hold exactly. It is found useful to define an *ideal gas* as one that would obey Eq. (18–6) at *all* pressures, and hence this equation is called the *ideal gas law.*

18–2 Properties of an ideal gas. The relation between the pressure and molar volume of an ideal gas at constant temperature is shown by the curves of Fig. 18–2. The curves are equilateral hyperbolas, asymptotic to the p- and v-axes. Each curve corresponds to a different temperature. That is, while $pv = $ a constant at any one temperature, the constant is larger the higher the temperature.

Each of the curves in Fig. 18–2 can be considered to represent a *process* through which the gas is carried, for example a process in which the gas is compressed from a large to a small volume in a bicycle pump. We shall show later that to keep the temperature constant in such a compression it would be necessary to remove heat from the gas, and therefore the process would have to be carried out slowly in order to keep the temperature the same throughout the gas. Such a slow compression carries the gas through a series of states, each of which is very nearly an equilibrium state, and it is called a *quasi-static*, or a "nearly static" process. Unless stated otherwise, we shall assume in what follows that all processes are to be carried out in this way, so that at each stage of the process the gas is, for all practical purposes, in an equilibrium state.

Any process in which the temperature remains constant is called *isothermal*, and the curves in Fig. 18–2 are the isothermal curves or, more briefly, the *isotherms* of an ideal gas.

The first accurate statement of the law connecting the volume changes of a gas with changes in its temperature was published by Joseph Louis Gay-Lussac in 1802. Earlier work on the subject had been carried on by many other investigators, among them Jacques A. C. Charles, whose name is often associated with Gay-Lussac's in connection with the relation between volume and temperature of a gas at constant pressure. The proportionality between volume v and kelvin temperature T follows from the ideal gas law, Eq. (18–6). Thus

$$v = \text{constant } T \qquad (\text{constant } p) \qquad (18\text{--}7)$$

is the mathematical statement of Gay-Lussac's law. A graph of this law (not to scale) is shown in Fig. 18–3 for three different pressures. If an actual gas behaved like an ideal gas at very low temperatures, the straight lines shown in Fig. 18–3 would remain straight and pass through the origin. The absolute zero of temperature could then be defined as the temperature at which the volume of a gas held at constant pressure shrinks to zero! The stubborn fact remains, however, that at some low temperature, a gas maintained at constant pressure becomes a liquid, and Gay-Lussac's law breaks down.

Any process in which the pressure remains constant is called *isobaric*, and the lines in Fig. 18–3 are the isobaric lines or, more briefly, the *isobars* of an ideal gas.

The number of moles n in a sample of gas equals the mass m of the gas divided by its molecular weight. If the latter is represented by M, then $n = m/M$. Hence we may write,

$$pV = m\,\frac{R}{M}\,T. \qquad (18\text{--}8)$$

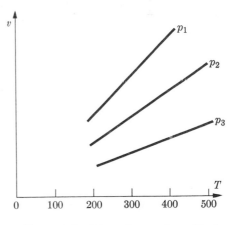

Fig. 18–3. The volume of an ideal gas is proportional to the kelvin temperature at constant pressure (Gay-Lussac's law).

TABLE 18–1

Gas	Density, gm/cm^3 at 1 atm, 0°C
Air	1.2929×10^{-3}
Argon	1.7832×10^{-3}
Carbon dioxide	1.9769×10^{-3}
Helium	0.1785×10^{-3}
Hydrogen	0.0899×10^{-3}
Nitrogen	1.2506×10^{-3}
Oxygen	1.4290×10^{-3}

Dividing both sides by V and remembering that the definition of the density ρ is m/V, we get

$$\rho = \frac{Mp}{RT}. \tag{18–9}$$

The density of a gas is seen to depend on its pressure and temperature as well as on its molecular weight. Hence in tabulating gas densities the pressure and temperature must be specified. The densities of a few common gases are listed in Table 18–1.

In numerical calculations on gases which may be assumed to be ideal, it is often necessary to compute a final value of p, V, T, or n in terms of given values. For this purpose we note that the quantity pV/nT has the constant value R at all stages of any process through which the gas may go. Hence if subscripts 1 and 2 refer to any two states,

$$\boxed{\frac{p_1 V_1}{n_1 T_1} = \frac{p_2 V_2}{n_2 T_2}.} \tag{18–10}$$

In this, as in all forms of the ideal gas equation, the temperature *must* be expressed either on the kelvin scale or on the rankine scale. A great advantage of Eq. (18–10) lies in the fact that no special units of p and V are needed, provided *both* p_1 and p_2 are expressed in the same units, and *both* V_1 and V_2 are expressed in the same units.

EXAMPLE 1. How many kilograms of O_2 are contained in a tank whose volume is 2 ft^3 when the gauge pressure is 2000 lb/in^2 and the temperature is 27°C?

Assume the ideal gas laws to hold. The molecular weight of oxygen is 32 gm/mole.

$$2 \text{ ft}^3 = 2 \times 28.3 = 56.6 \text{ liters.}$$

$$p_{\text{abs}} = 2015 \frac{\text{lb}}{\text{in}^2} = \frac{2015}{14.7} = 137 \text{ atm.}$$

$$T = t + 273 = 300°\text{K.}$$

Hence, from Eq. (18–6),

$$n = \frac{pV}{RT} = \frac{137 \text{ atm} \times 56.6 \text{ liters}}{0.082 \text{ liter·atm/gm-mole·°K} \times 300°\text{K}} = 315 \text{ gm-moles.}$$

$$m = 315 \times 32 = 10{,}100 \text{ gm} = 10.1 \text{ kgm.}$$

EXAMPLE 2. What volume would be occupied by this gas if it were allowed to expand to atmospheric pressure at a temperature of 50°C?
Since we are dealing with a fixed mass of gas, we may write

$$\frac{p_1 V_1}{T_1} = \frac{p_2 V_2}{T_2},$$

$$V_2 = V_1 \frac{p_1}{p_2} \frac{T_2}{T_1} = 2 \times \frac{137}{1} \times \frac{323}{300} = 295 \text{ ft}^3.$$

18–3 Thermodynamic surfaces. The equation of state of a substance is a relation among the three variables, p, V, and T. If these quantities are laid off on three mutually perpendicular axes, the equation of state defines a *surface* in the p-V-T space. All possible states of the substance are represented by points on this surface, and all processes through which the substance may be carried are represented by lines in the surface. An isothermal process is a line in the surface at all points of which T is constant; in other words, it is the intersection of the surface with a plane perpendicular to the temperature axis. Similarly, processes at constant pressure or volume are intersections of the surface with planes perpendicular to the pressure or volume axes. Such a surface is called a thermodynamic surface, although variables other than p, V, and T are often used.

Figure 18–4 illustrates the simplest of all p-V-T surfaces, that of an ideal gas. A few isotherms are indicated by the heavy lines. When this surface is viewed in a direction perpendicular to the p-V plane, the isotherms appear as in Fig. 18–2. Figure 18–5 is a photograph of the p-V-T surface of a real substance. It is not constructed to scale because of the large volume changes involved in vaporization.

In discussing the ideal gas law we have employed the macroscopic viewpoint, where we discuss the gross properties of the gas—pressure, tem-

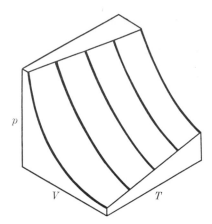

FIG. 18–4. p-V-T surface of an ideal gas.

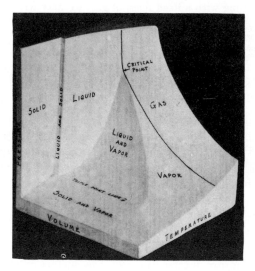

FIG. 18–5. p-V-T surface of a real substance. (Not to a uniform scale.)

perature, and volume. This same law can be derived from the microscopic viewpoint, where matter is regarded as a group of particles. The importance of the microscopic viewpoint cannot be overemphasized, and we next trace the development of this viewpoint, which was first used as a working hypothesis by chemists.

18–4 Chemical evidence for the atomic view of matter. The atomic view of matter had its first experimental verification in chemistry. The concepts of elements and compounds are obviously atomic concepts.

The kilogram-molecular (or atomic) weight of a material is the mass in kilograms of a particular number of the particles. This exact number is of relatively minor importance to chemistry and its magnitude was not even estimated until Loschmidt did so in 1865. We will discuss Perrin's method of determining it later in this chapter. Here is an interesting case where knowing the existence of a number was more important than knowing its magnitude. In physics and physical chemistry this number, called *Avogadro's number*, N_0, is of basic importance. It is almost inconceivably large; by modern measurements it is 6.025×10^{26} molecules per kilogram-mole. Only when Avogadro's number was known could the absolute mass of an atomic particle be computed.

18–5 Periodic table. Probably the most significant discovery in all chemistry, aside from the atomic nature of matter, was that of the periodic properties of the elements, now depicted in the familiar periodic table of the elements. The chemical properties of this table are probably familiar to most readers of this book; the physical properties will be discussed later. The table was proposed independently by Meyer and by Mendeléyev in 1869. Its usefulness lay both in its regularities and in its irregularities. One interesting irregularity in the original table was that in order to have the elements fall in positions consistent with their chemical properties, it was necessary to leave numerous spaces unoccupied. Mendeléyev suggested that these spaces would be filled with as yet undiscovered elements. Using his table, he was able to describe in considerable detail the properties these elements could be expected to have when they were discovered. It was nearly one hundred years before all these predictions of Mendeléyev were fulfilled.

Reflect, for a moment, on the vast simplification that the atomic view of matter provides. Looking about us, we see innumerable kinds of materials. The atomic view indicates that these materials are of discrete kinds whose number, however large, is not infinite. The discovery of elements is a further simplification in that the many materials we encounter are shown to be composed of only about one hundred chemically distinguishable materials, many of which are rare. It turns out that even these elements are not a heterogeneous group but are subject to further classification into a periodic table. The problems of chemistry are many, but it is easy to see that things are much simpler than might at first appear.

18–6 Physical evidence for the atomic view of matter. In chemistry, all atomic properties of matter are inferred from studies of gross matter. In 1827 the English botanist Robert Brown observed that microscopic pollen grains suspended in water appear to dance about in random fashion. At first the phenomenon was ascribed to the motions of living matter. In time, however, it was found that any kind of fine particles suspended in a liquid performed such a perpetual dance. Eventually it was realized that the molecules of a liquid are in constant motion and that the suspended particles recoiled (Brownian movement), when hit by the molecules of the liquid. Here for the first time effects that could be attributed to individual molecules were seen. What was observed was a collision process decidedly in the domain of physics. But what could mechanics, thus far concerned with solids, have to do with such collision processes?

The simplest kind of material to consider was a gas. The ideal gas law was a well-established *empirical* relationship, and its derivation was one of the objectives of physics. The application of classical physics to the mechanics of gases is called *the kinetic theory of gases.* It was developed between 1738 and 1900 by Bernoulli, Clausius, Maxwell, Boltzmann, Gibbs, and others.

18–7 Kinetic theory of gases. Molar heat capacity.

Early in our study of physics, we investigated the mechanics of bodies that can be regarded as particles. The study of extended bodies was treated by introducing certain averages, and the translational problem of extended bodies was solved by introducing the concept of a *center of mass* that moves as though it were a particle. The study of rotational properties of extended bodies was similarly facilitated by the introduction of another average property of the body, its *moment of inertia.* In the kinetic theory of gases, we assume that pressure, volume, temperature, etc., are averages of properties of gas molecules. Kinetic theory is a large and elegant subject. We can, however, derive a few useful relationships and convey its spirit.

Consider a cubical container of side L with its edges parallel to the x-, y-, and z-axes of a coordinate system, as shown in Fig. 18–6. The box contains molecules of only one kind, which we shall regard as very minute elastic spheres. All forces on these spheres are negligible except those which occur during collisions between the molecules or between the

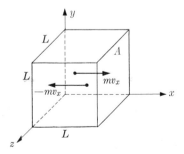

FIGURE 18–6

molecules and the sides of the box.* The total number of molecules, N, in the box is very great, but the molecules are so small that each collides with the walls much more frequently than it collides with other molecules. We assume that because of glancing collisions between molecules they will have no preferred direction of motion and that they will have a wide variety of speeds which, nevertheless, have some average value. There are several kinds of average velocity of the molecules that we could talk about. If we added all the velocities (vectorially) and divided by their number, we would get zero. This follows from the randomness we have assumed. The probability that one molecule has a certain velocity is the same as the probability that another molecule will have an equal and opposite velocity. If, on the other hand, we average the squares of the velocities, the result will not be zero, because the square of any real number is positive.

A particular molecule may have a velocity with rectangular components v_x, v_y, and v_z. In this case the square of its velocity is $v^2 = v_x^2 + v_y^2 + v_z^2$. If we calculate this for every individual molecule, add the results, and divide by N, the number of molecules in the box, we get

$$\frac{\sum_{i=1}^{N} v_i^2}{N} = \overline{v^2} = \overline{v_x^2} + \overline{v_y^2} + \overline{v_z^2}, \tag{18-11}$$

where the bar over a quantity indicates that we have averaged. Since there is no preferred direction of motion for the molecules, we can see that each of the three averages of the squares of the component velocities must equal the others, so that

$$\overline{v^2} = 3\overline{v_x^2}. \tag{18-12}$$

The square root of the quantity $\overline{v^2}$ is called the *root-mean-square speed*, v_{rms}.

A molecule of mass m hitting side A (Fig. 18–6) will have the x-component of its momentum changed from mv_x to $-mv_x$, causing a net change $2mv_x$ in the x-component of its momentum. We can compute how frequently this happens. A molecule can traverse the length of the box in the time L/v_x. The interval between collisions with side A is $2L/v_x$, and therefore the number of impacts per unit time on side A is $v_x/2L$. According to Newton's second law, the force exerted by the side of the box on the molecule is equal to the change of its momentum per unit time, and by Newton's third law, this force is equal and opposite to the force exerted

---

* The kinetic theory that we develop is valid not only for molecules, but for any other particles which conform to the stated assumptions.

by the molecule on the box. Therefore the average force on side A due to an individual molecule is

$$f_i = 2mv_{xi} \times \frac{v_{xi}}{2L} = \frac{mv_{xi}^2}{L}. \tag{18–13}$$

The total force for N molecules, each of mass m, is

$$F = \sum_{i=1}^{N} f_i = \frac{m}{L} \sum_{i=1}^{N} v_{xi}^2$$

$$= \frac{Nm}{L} \left(\frac{1}{N} \sum_{i=1}^{N} v_{xi}^2 \right) = \frac{Nm}{L} \overline{v_x^2}. \tag{18–14}$$

Since the pressure is the force per unit area, or F/L^2, we have

$$P = \frac{Nm\overline{v_x^2}}{L^3}. \tag{18–15}$$

But L^3 is the volume V of the box and Nm is the total mass of gas, M. Thus we obtain

$$PV = M\overline{v_x^2} = \tfrac{1}{3}M\overline{v^2}. \tag{18–16}$$

If we let the number of molecules in the box be the number of molecules in a mole (Avogadro's number, N_0), then M is the molecular weight of the gas.

This is not the result we sought, $PV = RT$, so we have as yet no justification for the many assumptions we have made. The result is interesting, however, because we did get the PV term, and the term $\tfrac{1}{3}M\overline{v^2}$ has a familiar look. If we write

$$\tfrac{1}{3}M\overline{v^2} = \tfrac{2}{3}(\tfrac{1}{2}M\overline{v^2}), \tag{18–17}$$

the quantity in parentheses is clearly the average translational kinetic energy of the molecules. We call this energy U, so that our result becomes

$$PV = \tfrac{2}{3}U. \tag{18–18}$$

We will have derived $PV = RT$ if we can show that $U = \tfrac{3}{2}RT$.

By 1850 Joule had demonstrated that heat is a form of energy. When a gas is heated at constant volume, the heat energy supplied causes a temperature change that must increase the energy of the gas. In fact, the molar heat capacity c_v at constant volume is dU/dT which, if we trust the unproved equation above, says that

$$c_v = \frac{dU}{dT} = \frac{3}{2} R. \tag{18–19}$$

Everything here is measurable, and we should now test our formula. The constant R in thermal units is 1.987 kcal/kgm-mole·C°; therefore $3R/2 = 2.97$ kcal/kgm-mole·C°. Compare this with the measured molar heat capacities at constant volume of the following gases and vapors:

Gas		c_v, kcal/kgm-mole·C°
Helium,	He	3.00
Argon,	A	3.00
Mercury,	Hg	3.00
Hydrogen,	H_2	4.82
Oxygen,	O_2	4.97
Chlorine,	Cl_2	6.01
Ether,	$(C_2H_5)_2O$	30.5

We see that three values agree very closely but that some are quite different. Both the agreements and the disagreements are interesting. The values which agree are those of monatomic gases and those that disagree are not. We shall have more to say about the apparent disagreements. The point here is to recall that in our discussion of kinetic theory we assumed that our molecules were isolated elastic spheres. We should not expect our result to apply to diatomic dumbbells or to complicated molecules.

18–8 Equipartition of energy. The agreement we have observed for monatomic molecules would not have been possible had there not been the number three in the expression $c_v = 3R/2$. Looking back over our derivation, we find that the three entered into the calculation from the statement $\overline{v^2} = 3\overline{v_x^2}$, that is, because the molecule was free to move in three-dimensional space. The expression for the average kinetic energy of translation of the molecules of a gas is composed of three equal parts, $R/2$ per degree of absolute temperature. The total energy is $3R/2$ because there are three independent directions in which the molecules can move. The principle of *equipartition of energy* states that if a molecule can have energy in several independent ways, the average energy associated with each of the ways is the same. The number of these ways is called the number of *degrees of freedom*. It is the number of coordinates necessary to specify the position of the molecule.

A diatomic molecule does not have its position completely specified by three coordinates. Since a diatomic molecule has extension, two more coordinates are required. A simple way to demonstrate this is to assign three cartesian coordinates, x, y, and z, to one of the atoms of the molecule.

If we assume the second atom is at a fixed distance from the first, its location is specified as being on a sphere with the first atom at its center. It requires but two additional coordinates to specify where on this sphere the second atom lies. Thus the addition of a second atom to the molecule adds two degress of freedom to the molecule. If our derivation for heat capacity had been based on *diatomic* instead of monatomic molecules, we would have obtained $5R/2$ instead of $3R/2$. We find that $5R/2 = 4.95$ kcal/kgm-mole·C°, which closely agrees with the measured molar heat capacities of such diatomic molecules as hydrogen and oxygen. Six coordinates are enough to specify the position of any *rigid* molecule, however complex, but if the molecules are composed of vibrating atoms, then the number of degrees of freedom may become very large. This accounts for the large molar heat capacity of ether. A fuller discussion of heat capacities requires the introduction of quantum theory, but classical kinetic theory reveals much, both qualitatively and quantitatively.

With the help of independent data from molar heat capacities we have found that the kinetic theory of matter provides a quantitative mechanical model for both the general gas law and the molar heat capacities. The equations derived lead to a very useful relation that can be obtained by substituting the value of RT from the general gas law, $PV = RT$, into Eq. (18–16). The result is

$$\tfrac{1}{2}M\overline{v^2} = \tfrac{3}{2}RT. \qquad (18\text{–}20)$$

This equation shows that the average kinetic energy of translation of the molecules of a gas depends only on the absolute temperature, and that at a given temperature, the lighter molecules have the greater speeds. The root-mean-square speed of hydrogen molecules at room temperature is about 1800 m/sec, or more than 1 mi/sec.

18–9 Maxwell's speed distribution law. We have found that $\overline{v^2}$ can be computed from the temperature of a gas. The speed thus determined is one of the important average properties of a gas. But an average can be misleading. For example, if a man who earns one million dollars a year is riding in a taxi, alone except for the driver, the average income of the occupants of the car is about $500,000. This true statement tends to imply that there are two wealthy men in the car. A fairer representation of the situation would be to state the income *distribution* of the occupants rather than the average income. This distribution would disclose that some incomes may be many orders of magnitude different from the average, and therefore economic analysis is better based on distribution of income than on average income.

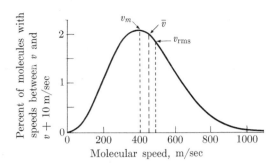

FIG. 18–7. Distribution of speeds for nitrogen molecules at 0°C.

We may rightly ask how individual molecular speeds vary from the average. With random collisions taking place, it is certain that some molecules will move much faster than others. Maxwell directed himself to this problem: given a certain gas at a known temperature, what fraction of the molecules will have speeds near any particular speed? Maxwell's solution is too difficult to present here, but the result is

$$\frac{\Delta N}{N} = \frac{4}{\sqrt{\pi}} \left(\frac{M}{2RT} \right)^{3/2} v^2 e^{-Mv^2/2RT} \, \Delta v. \qquad (18\text{–}21)$$

In this equation $\Delta N/N$ is the fraction of the number of molecules of the gas that have speeds between v and $v + \Delta v$, M is the molecular weight of the gas, T is its absolute temperature, and R is the gas constant per mole. This maxwellian distribution of speeds is shown graphically for a particular case in Fig. 18–7. The curve shows that the molecular speeds range from zero to infinity. The speed for which the curve is maximum is the *most probable speed*, v_m, since if we were to pick molecules at random, this speed would be found most often. The average speed obtained from the pressure calculation was $\sqrt{\overline{v^2}}$, or the root-mean-square speed v_{rms}. It is higher than the most probable speed because it is based on the square of the speeds, which gives high speeds more relative importance than small ones. Intermediate between these is the *average speed* $\bar{v}$. The relations between the characteristic speeds of gas molecules are as follows:

$$v_m = \sqrt{\frac{2}{3}} \, v_{\text{rms}} = 0.817 v_{\text{rms}},$$

$$\bar{v} = \sqrt{\frac{8}{3\pi}} \, v_{\text{rms}} = 0.921 v_{\text{rms}}, \qquad (18\text{–}22)$$

$$v_{\text{rms}} = \sqrt{\frac{3RT}{M}}.$$

EXAMPLE. Calculate (a) the root-mean-square speed of the molecules of nitrogen under standard conditions, and (b) the kinetic energy of translation of one of these molecules when it is moving with the most probable speed in a maxwellian distribution. (The required physical data can be found in Appendixes 7 and 8.)

(a) Using Eq. (18–20) and considering a kgm-mole of the gas, we have

$$\tfrac{1}{3}M\overline{v^2} = RT,$$

or

$$\overline{v^2} = 3RT/M,$$

$$\overline{v^2} = 3 \times 8.31 \times 10^3 \frac{\text{joule}}{{}^\circ\text{K}\cdot\text{mole}} \times 273{}^\circ\text{K} \times \frac{1\ \text{mole}}{28\ \text{kgm}} = 2.43 \times 10^5 \frac{\text{m}^2}{\text{sec}^2};$$

$$v_{\text{rms}} = \sqrt{\overline{v^2}} = \sqrt{2.43 \times 10^5\ \text{m}^2/\text{sec}^2} = 492\ \text{m/sec}.$$

This result can also be obtained from Eq. (18–16):

$$PV = \tfrac{1}{3}M\overline{v^2},$$

$$\overline{v^2} = \frac{3PV}{M}$$

$$= 3 \times 1.013 \times 10^5 \frac{\text{n}}{\text{m}^2} \times 22.42 \frac{\text{m}^3}{\text{mole}} \times \frac{1\ \text{mole}}{28\ \text{kgm}}$$

$$= 2.43 \times 10^5 \frac{\text{m}^2}{\text{sec}^2};$$

$$v_{\text{rms}} = \sqrt{\overline{v^2}} = \sqrt{2.43 \times 10^5\ \text{m}^2/\text{sec}^2} = 492\ \text{m/sec}.$$

(b) $$E_k = \tfrac{1}{2}mv_m^2.$$

The mass of a nitrogen molecule can be calculated from its molecular weight and Avogadro's number:

$$m = M/N_0$$

$$= 28 \frac{\text{kgm}}{\text{mole}} \times \frac{1\ \text{mole}}{6.03 \times 10^{26}\ \text{molecules}}$$

$$= 4.64 \times 10^{-26}\ \text{kgm/molecule}.$$

From Eq. (18–22) we have

$$v_m = \sqrt{\tfrac{2}{3}}\, v_{\text{rms}},$$

$$\therefore\ E_k = \tfrac{1}{2} \times 4.64 \times 10^{-26}\ \text{kgm} \times \tfrac{2}{3} \times 2.43 \times 10^5 \frac{\text{m}^2}{\text{sec}^2}$$

$$= 3.76 \times 10^{-21}\ \text{joule}.$$

Maxwell's distribution of speeds was employed to calculate other gas properties and was indirectly verified in terms of these secondary properties. A direct experimental verification was obtained by Zartman and Ko in 1930. They used an oven, shown in Fig. 18–8, containing bismuth vapor at a known high temperature (827°C). Bismuth molecules streamed from a slit in the oven into an evacuated region above.* The beam was made unidirectional by another slit, which admitted only properly directed molecules. Above the slit was a cylindrical drum that could be rotated in the vacuum about a horizontal axis perpendicular to the paper. A slit along one side of the drum had to be in a particular position to enable the beam of molecules to enter it. If the drum was stationary, so that the beam could enter, the beam moved along a

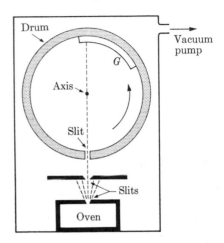

Fig. 18–8. Diagram of apparatus used by Zartman and Ko.

diameter of the drum and was deposited on a glass plate G mounted on the inside surface of the drum opposite the slit. During the experiment, the drum was rotated at a constant angular velocity, so that short bursts of molecules were admitted on each rotation. Because the speeds of the molecules varied, some crossed the diameter quickly and others took much more time, and since the drum was turning while the molecules were moving across it, they struck the cold glass plate at different places. Thus the distribution of speeds was translated by the apparatus into a distribution in space around the inside of the drum, as indicated by the darkening of the glass where the bismuth was deposited. The density of the deposit was measured optically, and comparison of the experimental distribution of speeds with Maxwell's theoretical value showed excellent agreement.

In this experiment all the apparatus except the oven was highly evacuated, so that there would be no gas molecules in the apparatus to cause collisions that would alter the direction and magnitude of the molecular velocities in the bismuth beam and thereby confuse the result.

---

* Fast molecules are more likely to escape from the oven than slow ones. Computation shows that if the oven is at a temperature T, the speed distribution of escaping molecules is the same as the speed distribution within an oven at a higher temperature, $4T/3$.

18–10 Collision probability. Mean free path. Let us now consider the factors which influence the likelihood of collisions between molecules. We define a collision as any contact between molecules, however slight. A collision occurs, then, whenever the separation of the centers of two molecules becomes equal to the sum of their radii. The specification as to whether a collision has occurred, therefore, depends both on the size of the moving molecule (bullet) and on the size of the target molecule. It does not matter whether the target is large and the bullet is small or conversely; the specification of a hit is based only on the sum of their radii. In the computations that follow, it is convenient to regard a bullet molecule as having no radius and to assign to each target molecule a pseudo radius equal to the radius r_b of the bullet molecule plus the radius r_t of the target molecule. The two cases are shown in Fig. 18–9. The shift in viewpoint makes no change in our criterion as to whether or not a hit has occurred. The target area that each such target molecule presents is called its *microscopic cross section*. It is usually denoted by the symbol σ (sigma). Thus

$$\sigma = \pi(r_t + r_b)^2 \tag{18–23}$$

is the cross-sectional area presented per target molecule for collisions with a particular type of bullet molecule. We shall make frequent use of this mutual collision cross section concept.

Let a thin square box of gas have dimensions l, l, and dx. If the number of molecules per unit volume is n, the box contains $nl^2\,dx$ molecules. Each of these molecules has a cross section σ, so that the group of molecules, assumed stationary, has a total cross section of $\sigma nl^2\,dx$. The area of a square side of the box is l^2. But within this square the molecules themselves present their total cross section. (It is assumed that the molecules cannot hide behind one another because dx, the thickness of the box, is too small.) The probability that a point bullet molecule that is incident normally on the square side will make a hit in passing through the box

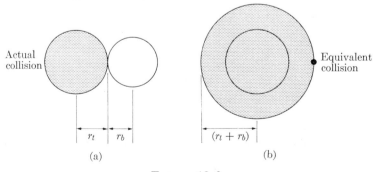

FIGURE 18–9

is the ratio of the area of all the molecular targets to the total area of incidence. Thus the collision probability is

$$\frac{\sigma n l^2 \, dx}{l^2} = n\sigma \, dx. \tag{18–24}$$

The product $n\sigma$, called the *macroscopic cross section*, will appear frequently. Note that its unit is reciprocal length, not area. If we think of coins instead of molecules, the probability of throwing "heads" is 1/2. On the average, then, the number of throws per "heads" is the reciprocal of 1/2 or 2. If the probability of a hit for a molecule going through our box is $n\sigma \, dx$, then the average number of times H that it must go through the box per hit is the reciprocal of the collision probability, or

$$H = \frac{1}{n\sigma \, dx}. \tag{18–25}$$

The average distance the particle must move through the gas per hit is $H \, dx$ or $1/n\sigma$. This average distance traveled between collisions is called the *mean free path*, L. Its value is

$$\boxed{L = \frac{1}{n\sigma}.} \tag{18–26}$$

The concept of mean free path may be visualized by thinking of a man shooting a rifle aimlessly into a forest. Most of his bullets will hit trees sooner or later, but some bullets will travel much farther than others. It is easy to see that the average distance the bullets go will be inversely proportional to both the size of the trees and the denseness of the woods.

In the above analysis, we assumed that the target molecules of the gas were at rest. This assumption is valid for a bullet molecule going through a solid, and we will meet this situation in Chapter 45 when we consider neutrons passing through a solid moderator in a nuclear reactor. Just now we are considering gases, however, and we have already found that gas pressure and specific heats can be regarded as manifestations of molecular kinetic energy. If the target molecules move, then the collision probability goes up, since there is now the possibility that the bullet molecule can be hit from the side. We should now recompute the mean free path, with the assumption that the molecules of the gas have speeds distributed according to Maxwell's law. Instead we shall do something much simpler, suggested by our calculation of pressure.

Let us consider a unit volume of gas and assume that a bullet molecule in it has the same speed as the target molecules and is really one of them. The molecules actually move in all directions, but let us further assume that as we view them $n/6$ move to our right, $n/6$ move to our left, $n/6$ move up, $n/6$ move down, $n/6$ move toward us, and $n/6$ move away from us. If the bullet molecule moves away from us, $n/6$ molecules move with the bullet molecule and therefore cause no collisions. Another $n/6$ molecules move against the bullet molecule. Relative to the approaching target molecules, the bullet molecule moves twice as fast and probably makes $2n\sigma/6$ or $n\sigma/3$ collisions per unit distance, on the average. The remaining $2n/3$ molecules move directly across the path of the bullet molecule. Relative to these molecules, the bullet molecule moves farther by a factor $\sqrt{2}$, since the bullet and target molecules move distances represented by the two legs of a right triangle. The probable number of collisions per unit distance with these cross-moving molecules is $\sqrt{2}(2n\sigma/3)$. The total probable number of collisions per unit distance for all these motions is $(\frac{1}{3} + 2\sqrt{2}/3)n\sigma = 1.276n\sigma$, and the mean free path L becomes $0.783/n\sigma$. If we had made this calculation using the maxwellian distribution of speeds, the result would have been

$$L = \frac{0.707}{n\sigma}. \qquad (18\text{--}27)$$

The apparatus used by Zartman and Ko, in the experiment described in the preceding section, was evacuated for testing Maxwell's law of distribution of speeds. This made n, the number of molecules per unit volume, so small that the mean free path was much greater than the diameter of the drum.

18–11 Faraday's law of electrolysis—skepticism. Another line of argument supporting the atomic view of matter came from the work of Faraday. In 1833 he observed that if the same electric charge is made to traverse different electrolytes, the masses of the materials deposited on the electrodes are proportional to the chemical equivalent weights of the materials. The quantity of electricity required to deposit an equivalent weight is called the *faraday*, F, equal to $(9.6522 \pm 0.0002) \times 10^7$ coulombs per kilogram equivalent weight. Like the simple proportionalities proposed by Dalton and Gay-Lussac, this also implied atomicity of matter. Faraday's law, however, brings electricity into the picture and implies that both electricity and matter are atomic.

We have traced a few highlights of the development of the atomic view of matter through most of the nineteenth century, but since no one had ever seen a molecule, the entire theory was still regarded with skepticism. Maxwell, who proposed the distribution of speeds already discussed, did his greatest work in electrical theory. It was he who found the relationship between electricity and light, and it is because of his work that we often call light "electromagnetic radiation." In his comprehensive book on electricity and magnetism (1873), after explaining Faraday's laws of electrolysis on the basis of the atomic theory of matter and electricity, Maxwell says, "It is extremely improbable that when we come to understand the true nature of electrolysis we shall retain in any form the theory of molecular charges, for then we shall have obtained a secure basis on which to form a true theory of electric currents and so become independent of these provisional theories."

As late as 1908 the physical chemist Wilhelm Ostwald and the physicist Ernst Mach opposed the atomic theory of matter. Their skepticism has an interesting explanation. These scientists were unwilling to accept purely indirect evidence. Mach makes their position clear in the following analogy: A long elastic rod held in a vise may be made to execute slow, perceivable vibrations. If the rod is shortened, the vibrations become a blur in which individual motions of the rod cannot be followed. If the rod is shortened further, the blur may be visually unobservable but a tone is heard. If the rod is made so short that we no longer experience a physical sensation from its behavior, we may still think of it as vibrating when struck. This, according to Mach, is a safe extrapolation of our ideas because it proceeds from the *directly* observable to the *indirectly* observable. Those who were skeptical about the atomic theory objected to the fact that the evidence was *entirely indirect*. The experiments described in the next section provided the observable events which made the indirect evidence we have given acceptable to everyone.

18–12 Perrin's verification of the atomic view of matter. Credit for removing the remaining skepticism of atomic theory goes to the French chemist Perrin. He had the idea that the suspended particles which dance about in a stationary liquid in Brownian movement behave like heavy gas molecules. His insight, skill, and patience makes a story in itself. Perrin prepared water suspensions of gamboge and mastic in which the suspended particles were remarkably uniform in size and mass. He observed that such a suspension of heavy particles did not settle out but assumed a distribution in height, with more particles per unit volume at the bottom of the container than at the top, and he measured this distribution of number as a function of height.

Consider a vertical column of gas (Fig. 18–10) which has a cross-sectional area a and which is at a uniform temperature. Through this column, let us take a horizontal slice of thickness dh. If the weight of the gas above this slice is w, then the weight of the gas above the bottom of the slice will be $w + dw = w + mgna\,dh$, where mg is the weight of a molecule, n is the average number of molecules per unit volume, and

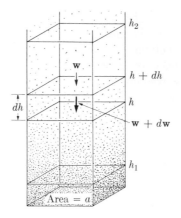

FIGURE 18–10

$a\, dh$ is the volume of the slice. (Note that we are employing an atomic view of the gas.) The difference of these weights per unit area, $mgn\, dh$, is the pressure difference due to the gas in the slice, that is, $dp = -mgn\, dh$. The minus sign denotes that the pressure decreases as the height increases. Since the molecules in the column of gas have weight, their paths between successive collisions are not straight lines but are curved downward in parabolas that are characteristic of projectile motion. Therefore the number of molecules per unit volume at a specified low level is greater than at a higher one. Because of this difference in concentration, there is a corresponding difference in the number of molecular collisions per unit time at the two levels and the column of gas comes to dynamic equilibrium. In this state, the weight of the molecules in any layer is just balanced by the net upward force caused by the difference between the number of molecular impacts per unit time on the lower and upper horizontal surfaces of the layer. We shall next seek an expression for the difference in pressure between two levels produced by a difference in molecular concentrations.

The equation $PV = RT$ holds for one mole of any gas that can be regarded as ideal. According to atomic theory, one mole of any gas contains a certain number of molecules, denoted by Avogadro's number N_0. We can obtain an expression that contains the concentration of the molecules by dividing the general gas law equation by Avogadro's number. Thus we have

$$\frac{PV}{N_0} = \frac{RT}{N_0} \quad \text{or} \quad P = \left(\frac{N_0}{V}\right)\left(\frac{R}{N_0}\right) T.$$

The quantity N_0/V is the average number of molecules per unit volume n, and therefore the gas law may now be written as $P = n(R/N_0)T$. Differentiation (recalling that R, N_0, and T are constant) yields $dP = (R/N_0)T\, dn$. When this expression for the difference of pressure due to the difference in molecular concentrations in the layer of height dh is equated to the difference due to the weight of the layer, we obtain

$$\frac{R}{N_0}T\, dn = -mgn\, dh,$$

or

$$\frac{dn}{n} = -\frac{mgN_0}{RT}\, dh. \qquad (18\text{–}28)$$

Upon integrating from level h_1 to level h_2, we obtain

$$\text{in } n_2 - \ln n_1 = -\frac{mgN_0(h_2 - h_1)}{RT},$$

or

$$n_2 = n_1 e^{-mgN_0(h_2-h_1)/RT}, \qquad (18\text{–}29)$$

which may be written as

$$n_2 = n_1 \exp\left[-\frac{mgN_0(h_2 - h_1)}{RT}\right]. \qquad (18\text{–}30)$$

Since the pressure of a gas is directly proportional to the number of molecules per unit volume, n_2 and n_1 in Eq. (18–29) can be replaced by p_2 and p_1, respectively. This equation is then called the *law of atmospheres*, since it gives the distribution in height of the pressure in a column of gas at constant temperature and subject to the force of gravity.

Equation (18–29) must be modified slightly to make it applicable to the study of Brownian movement. The effective weight of particles suspended in a fluid is reduced by Archimedes' buoyant force. A submerged particle of mass m and density ρ (rho) displaces a volume of liquid m/ρ. If the liquid displaced has a density ρ', the mass of liquid displaced is $\rho'm/\rho$, and the buoyant force it provides is $mg\rho'/\rho$. Thus the effective weight of the particle in the liquid becomes

$$mg - mg\frac{\rho'}{\rho} = mg\left(\frac{\rho - \rho'}{\rho}\right). \qquad (18\text{–}31)$$

When we replace the actual weight mg in Eq. (18–30) by the effective weight, we obtain

$$n_2 = n_1 \exp\left[-\frac{mg(\rho - \rho')N_0(h_2 - h_1)}{\rho RT}\right]. \qquad (18\text{–}32)$$

This is the equation for sedimentation equilibrium of an emulsion as a result of Brownian movement.

Perrin measured a series of n's at a series of h's. He verified that the particles of his suspension obeyed the sedimentation equation. Equally important, his measurements yielded a value for N_0, since all other quantities in the equation were known, and the very existence of Avogadro's number implies the correctness of the atomic theory.

It is interesting that Einstein, the greatest contributor to the development of modern physics, also had a part in the final establishment of the atomic theory. In 1905 he derived an equation which describes how a suspended particle should migrate through a liquid. His expression involved Avogadro's number, and Perrin's verification of the Einstein formula confirmed the value of this number. The results also showed that small particles suspended in a stationary liquid do move about in the manner predicted by the molecular-kinetic theory of heat.

Altogether, Perrin used four completely independent types of measurements, each of which was a visible verification of atomic theory and each of which gave a quantitative estimate of Avogadro's number. Since the publication of his results in 1908, no one has seriously doubted the atomic theory of matter.

18–13 Boltzmann's constant. Once N_0 was determined, it was possible to evaluate the frequently recurring quantity R/N_0. This is the universal gas constant *per molecule*, and is known as *Boltzmann's constant, k.* Its value is 1.380×10^{-23} joule/°K. Earlier in this chapter we computed the root-mean-square speed of gas molecules from $\frac{1}{3}M\overline{v^2} = RT$, Eq. (18–20), where M and R are the mass and gas constant *per mole*, respectively. Dividing this equation by N_0 and rearranging, we obtain

$$\boxed{\tfrac{1}{2}m\overline{v^2} = \tfrac{3}{2}kT,} \qquad (18\text{–}33)$$

where m and k are the mass and gas constant *per molecule*, respectively. Thus the average translational kinetic energy of any gas molecule depends only on its temperature (if indeed the word temperature has meaning for a single molecule), and the *average energy per degree of freedom* is $kT/2$.

Let us now return to Eq. (18–29), the law of atmospheres. In this equation N_0/R equals $1/k$ and $mg(h_2 - h_1)$ is the difference in gravitational potential energy, $E_{p_2} - E_{p_1}$, per particle between the two levels. If we set the potential energy of the particle at the first level equal to zero, as is usually done, and let n_0 and n be the number of particles per unit volume at the initial and final levels respectively, then, substituting in Eq. (18–29), we get

$$n = n_0 e^{-E_p/kT}. \tag{18–34}$$

This expression yields the relative number of particles per unit volume in two different energy states in terms of their difference of gravitational potential energy, E_p. It turns out that this same equation may be used for any case where the potential energy is a function of position. For two energy states of electrified particles, E_p would be the difference in their electrostatic potential energies. When all types or forms of energy are considered, we obtain the *Boltzmann distribution law*

$$n = n_0 e^{-E/kT}, \tag{18–35}$$

where E is the energy per degree of freedom. We will need this equation when we discuss the distribution of energy in a group of harmonic oscillators, in Chapter 37.

PROBLEMS

(Assume all gases to be ideal.)

18–1. A tank contains $1.5\ \mathrm{ft}^3$ of nitrogen at an absolute pressure of $20\ \mathrm{lb/in}^2$ and a temperature of $40°\mathrm{F}$. What will be the pressure if the volume is increased to $15\ \mathrm{ft}^3$ and the temperature raised to $440°\mathrm{F}$?

18–2. A tank having a capacity of $2\ \mathrm{ft}^3$ is filled with oxygen which has a gauge pressure of $60\ \mathrm{lb/in}^2$ when the temperature is $47°\mathrm{C}$. At a later time it is found that because of a leak the gauge pressure has dropped to $50\ \mathrm{lb/in}^2$ and the temperature has decreased to $27°\mathrm{C}$. Find (a) the mass of the oxygen in the tank under the first set of conditions, (b) the amount of oxygen that has leaked out.

18–3. A flask of volume 2 liters, provided with a stopcock, contains oxygen at $300°\mathrm{K}$ and atmospheric pressure. The system is heated to a temperature of $400°\mathrm{K}$, with the stopcock open to the atmosphere. The stopcock is then closed and the flask cooled to its original temperature. (a) What is the final pressure of the oxygen in the flask? (b) How many grams of oxygen remain in the flask?

18–4. A barrage balloon whose volume is $20{,}000\ \mathrm{ft}^3$ is to be filled with hydrogen at atmospheric pressure. If the hydrogen is stored in cylinders of volume $2\ \mathrm{ft}^3$ at an absolute pressure of $200\ \mathrm{lb/in}^2$, how many cylinders are required?

18–5. A bubble of air rises from the bottom of a lake, where the pressure is $3.03\ \mathrm{atm}$, to the surface, where the pressure is $1\ \mathrm{atm}$. The temperature at the bottom of the lake is $7°\mathrm{C}$ and the temperature at the surface is $27°\mathrm{C}$. What is the ratio of the size (i.e., the volume) of the bubble as it reaches the surface to the size of the bubble at the bottom?

18–6. (a) Two gm of nitrogen at $27°\mathrm{C}$ occupy a volume of 2 liters. What is the pressure? (b) If the pressure is doubled and the temperature raised to $127°\mathrm{C}$, calculate the final volume.

18–7. A liter of helium under a pressure of $2\ \mathrm{atm}$ and at a temperature of $27°\mathrm{C}$ is heated until both pressure and volume are doubled. (a) What is the final temperature? (b) How many grams of helium are there?

18–8. A flask contains 1 gm of oxygen at an absolute pressure of $10\ \mathrm{atm}$ and at a temperature of $47°\mathrm{C}$. At a later time it is found that because of a leak the pressure has dropped to $\frac{5}{8}$ of its original value and the temperature has decreased to $27°\mathrm{C}$. (a) What is the volume of the flask? (b) How many grams of oxygen leaked out between the two observations?

18–9. The submarine Squalus sank at a point where the depth of water was $240\ \mathrm{ft}$. The temperature at the surface is $27°\mathrm{C}$ and at the bottom it is $7°\mathrm{C}$. The density of sea water may be taken as $2\ \mathrm{slugs/ft}^2$. (a) If a diving bell in the form of a circular cylinder $8\ \mathrm{ft}$ high, open at the bottom and closed at the top, is lowered to this depth, to what height will the water rise within it when it reaches the bottom? (b) At what gauge pressure must compressed air be supplied to the bell while on the bottom to expel all the water from it?

18–10. A bicycle pump is full of air at an absolute pressure of $15\ \mathrm{lb/in}^2$. The length of stroke of the pump is

18 in. At what part of the stroke does air begin to enter a tire in which the gauge pressure is 40 lb/in^2? Assume the compression to be isothermal.

18–11. A vertical cylindrical tank 1 m high has its top end closed by a tightly fitting frictionless piston of negligible weight. The air inside the cylinder is at an absolute pressure of 1 atm. The piston is depressed by pouring mercury on it slowly. How far will the piston descend before mercury spills over the top of the cylinder? The temperature of the air is maintained constant.

18–12. A barometer is made of a tube 90 cm long and of cross section 1.5 cm^2. Mercury stands in this tube to a height of 75 cm. The room temperature is 27°C. A small amount of nitrogen is introduced into the evacuated space above the mercury and the column drops to a height of 70 cm. How many grams of nitrogen were introduced?

18–13. The simple barometer shown in Fig. 18–11 contains some air above

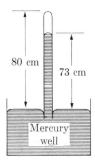

80 cm

73 cm

Mercury well

FIGURE 18–11

the mercury column so that it reads only 73 cm on a day when a true barometer reads 76 cm. (a) What would the false barometer read on another day when the true one reads 74 cm? (b) If, on the day the true

barometer reads 76 cm, the false barometer tube is pushed down into the mercury well until the volume of the air in it is one-half of its original volume, what will the height of the mercury in the false barometer then be?

18–14. An ideal gas at a pressure of 1 atm is heated at constant pressure until its volume is doubled, then heated at constant volume until its pressure is doubled, and finally allowed to expand isothermally until its pressure drops to 1 atm. Show the process in a p-V diagram.

18–15. (a) What would happen if the collisions between the molecules of a gas were not perfectly elastic? (b) What would happen to the shape of an air-filled spherical toy balloon if, on the average, the velocities of the gas molecules in one direction were to become greater than those in another?

18–16. Show that Eqs. (18–15), (18–16), and (18–20), collectively, are consistent with the statement that equal volumes of two different gases under the same conditions of temperature and pressure contain the same number of molecules.

18–17. (a) Show from Eq. (18–21) that the most probable speed in a maxwellian distribution is given by $v_m = \sqrt{2RT/M}$, and (b) then show from Eq. (18–20) that $v_m = \sqrt{\frac{2}{3}}\, v_{\mathrm{rms}}$.

18–18. Show that the ratio of the rms speeds of the molecules in two different gases at the same temperature is inversely proportional to the square root of their masses.

18–19. Find the ratio of the rms speed of hydrogen to that of oxygen in a mixture of these gases.

18–20. (a) At what temperature will the rms speed of oxygen molecules be twice their rms speed at 27°C? (b) At what temperature will the rms speed of nitrogen molecules equal the rms speed of oxygen molecules at 27°C?

18–21. Find the rms speed, the average speed, and the most probable speed of the molecules of gaseous hydrogen at a temperature of (a) 20°C and (b) 120°C.

18–22. The diameters of molecules can be computed from an equation derived by using the kinetic theory to explain the viscosity of a gas. The results show that the molecular diameters are about 2×10^{-10} m for all gases. Find (a) the microscopic cross section and (b) the macroscopic cross section of the molecules of hydrogen at a temperature of 20°C and a pressure of 1 atm.

18–23. (a) If the pressure is kept constant, at what temperature will the mean free path of the molecules of an ideal gas be twice that at 27°C? (b) If the temperature is kept constant, at what pressure in millimeters of mercury will the mean free path of the molecules of an ideal gas be 1000 times greater than that at a pressure of 1 atm?

18–24. Find the mean free path for a maxwellian distribution of speeds (Eq. 18–27) of the molecules of hydrogen gas when at a pressure of 1 atm and a temperature of (a) 20°C and (b) 120°C; and (c) when at a pressure of 100 atm and a temperature of 20°C. (Data for calculating the macroscopic cross section are given in Problem 18–22.) (d) How many collisions per second will a molecule moving with the average speed make in each of the preceding cases? (The time of contact during collisions is negligible.) (e) What is the ratio of the mean free path in part (a) to the wavelength of green light, $\lambda = 5500$ A?

18–25. Show that the kinetic energy of translation of a molecule having the most probable speed in a maxwellian distribution is equal to kT.

18–26. A neutron is a fundamental particle. Like ordinary gas molecules, neutrons have a distribution of speeds, and this distribution is of prime importance in the theory of nuclear reactors. A thermal neutron is defined as one having the most probable speed of a maxwellian distribution at 20°C. Find (a) the kinetic energy of translation and (b) the speed of a thermal neutron. (c) A thermal neutron is sometimes called a *"kT* neutron." Why?

18–27. In one of his experiments, using a water suspension of gamboge at 20°C, Perrin observed an average of 49 particles per unit area in a very shallow layer at one level and 14 particles per unit area at a level 60 microns higher. The density of the gamboge was 1.194 gm/cm^3 and each particle was a spherical grain having a radius of 0.212 micron. Find (a) the mass of each particle, (b) Avogadro's number, and (c) the molecular weight of a particle if each grain is regarded as a single giant molecule. Use the results from parts (a) and (b) to calculate (c).

CHAPTER 19

COULOMB'S LAW

19–1 Electric charges. It was known to the ancient Greeks as far back as 600 B.C. that amber, rubbed with wool, acquired the property of attracting light objects. In describing this property today, we say that the amber is *electrified*, or possesses an *electric charge*, or is *electrically charged*. These terms are derived from the Greek word *elektron*, meaning amber. It is possible to impart an electric charge to any solid material by rubbing it with any other material. Thus, an automobile becomes charged by virtue of its motion through the air; an electric charge is developed on a sheet of paper moving through a printing press; a comb is electrified in passing through dry hair. Actually, intimate contact is all that is needed to give rise to an electric charge. Rubbing merely serves to bring many points of the surfaces into good contact.

In lecture demonstrations hard rubber and fur are commonly used. If, after it is rubbed with fur, a rubber rod is placed in a dish containing tiny pieces of tissue paper, many of these will at first cling to the rod, but after a few seconds they will fly off. The initial attraction will be explained in Chapter 28; the subsequent repulsion is due to a force that is found to exist whenever two bodies are electrified in the same way. Suppose two small, very light pith balls are suspended near each other by fine silk threads. At first they will be attracted to an electrified rubber rod and will cling to it. A moment later, they will be repelled by the rubber and will also repel each other.

A similar experiment performed with a glass rod that has been rubbed with silk gives rise to the same result. Pith balls electrified by contact with such a glass rod are repelled not only by the glass rod but by each other. On the other hand, a pith ball that has been in contact with electrified rubber, when placed near one that has been in contact with electrified glass, is found to be attracted. We are therefore led to the conclusion that there are two kinds of electric charge—that possessed by hard rubber after being rubbed with fur, called a *negative charge*, and that possessed by glass after being rubbed with silk, called a *positive charge*. The words *negative* and *positive* are merely convenient labels, having no mathematical connotations whatever. As a matter of fact, as we shall see presently, a negatively charged body has acquired something extra, whereas a positively charged body has lost some of the same thing.

The experiments on pith balls described in the preceding paragraph lead to the fundamental results that (1) *like charges repel*, (2) *unlike charges attract*.

These repulsive or attractive forces, of electrical origin, exist in addition to the gravitational force of attraction and, in most situations with which we shall deal, are so much larger than the gravitational force that the latter may be completely neglected.

Suppose a rubber rod is rubbed with fur and then touched to a suspended pith ball. Both the rubber and the pith ball are negatively charged. If the fur is now brought near the pith ball, the ball will be attracted, indicating that the fur is positively charged. It follows that when rubber is rubbed with fur, opposite charges appear on the two materials. This is found to happen whenever any substance is rubbed with any other substance. Thus glass becomes positive, while the silk with which the glass was rubbed becomes negative. This suggests strongly that electric charges are not generated or created, but that the process of acquiring an electric charge consists of transferring something from one body to another, so that one body has an excess and the other a deficiency of that something.

19–2 Charging by contact. Ordinary matter contains equal amounts of positive and negative electricity. Hence ordinary matter does not exhibit electrical effects and is said to be electrically *neutral* or *uncharged*. If by some means the balance between positive and negative electricity is upset, a body is said to be *charged* and will be spoken of as a *charged body* or, for brevity, simply as a *charge*. There are many ways in which the normal balance between positive and negative charges can be altered. The oldest, historically, is the phenomenon of charging by friction, as described in Section 19–1. When rubber and fur are brought into contact there is a spontaneous transfer of negative charge from the fur to the rubber. The rubber therefore becomes negatively charged, while the fur is positively charged. Measurements show that the charge acquired by the rubber when it is brought into contact with the fur is exactly equal and opposite to that acquired by the fur. There is thus no *creation* of electric charge in the charging process, but simply a *transfer* of charge from one body to another.

A charged pith ball may be used as a test body to determine whether or not a second body is charged. A more sensitive test is afforded by the *leaf electroscope* (Fig. 19–1). Two strips of thin gold leaf or aluminum foil, A, are fastened at the end of a metal rod B which passes through a support C of rubber, amber, or sulfur. The surrounding case D is provided with windows through which the leaves can be observed and which serve to protect them from air currents. When the knob of the electroscope is touched by a charged body, the leaves acquire charges of the same sign and repel each other, their divergence being a measure of the quantity of charge they have received.

FIG. 19–1. The leaf electroscope.

If one terminal of a "B" battery of a few hundred volts potential difference is connected to the knob of an electroscope and the other terminal to the electroscope case, the leaves will diverge just as if they had been charged from a body electrified by contact. There is no difference between the "kinds" of charge given the leaves in the two processes and, in general, there is no distinction between "static electricity" and "current electricity." The term "current" refers to a flow of charge, while "electrostatics" is concerned for the most part with interactions between charges at rest.

19–3 Conductors and insulators.   Let one end of a copper wire be attached to the knob of an electroscope, its other end being supported by a glass rod, as in Fig. 19–2. If a charged rubber rod is touched to the far end of the wire, the electroscope leaves will immediately diverge. There has, therefore, been a transfer of charge along or through the wire, and the wire is called a *conductor*. If the experiment is repeated, using a silk thread or rubber band in place of the wire, no such deflection of the electroscope occurs and the thread or rubber is called an *insulator* or *dielectric*. The motion of charge through a material substance will be studied in more detail in Chapter 22, but for our present purposes it is sufficient to state that most substances fall into one or the other of the two classes above. Conductors permit the passage of charge through them, while insulators do not. Metals in general are good conductors, while nonmetals are insulators.

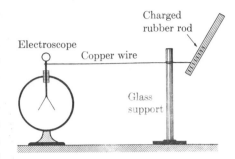

19–4 Charging a metal by induction. In charging a leaf electroscope by contact with, say, a rubber rod that has been rubbed with fur, some of the charge on the rubber is transferred to the electroscope, leaving the rubber with a smaller negative charge.

FIG. 19–2. Copper is a conductor of electricity.

After a while, the rubber rod will have to be recharged if it is to be used over and over again. There is, however, another way to use the rubber rod to charge other bodies, in which the rubber may impart a charge of opposite sign, and lose none of its own charge in the process. This is called *charging by induction*, and is explained with reference to Fig. 19–3. In part (a) of this figure are depicted schematically two neutral metal spheres in contact. It is understood that both metal spheres are supported on insulating stands. When a negatively charged rubber rod is brought *close* to one of the spheres, but without touching it, as in (b), some of the free charges in the metal spheres are separated. The excess of positive charge in the sphere nearer the rubber rod is known as an *induced positive charge*, and the excess of negative charge in the farther sphere is an *induced negative charge*. These induced charges will remain separated as long as the rubber is held nearby. If, however, the rod is removed, the charges will come together and the original neutral condition will be restored.

Suppose that the two spheres are separated slightly, as shown in part (c), while the rubber rod is nearby. If the rod is now removed, as in (d), we are left with two oppositely charged metal spheres. Since these charges attract each other, they remain as close together as possible. Only when the two spheres are separated by a great distance, as in (e), will the two charges be uniformly distributed. It should be noticed that the negatively charged rubber rod has lost none of its charge in the steps from (a) to (e).

The steps from (a) to (e) in Fig. 19–4 should be self-explanatory. In this figure, a single metal sphere (on an insulating stand) is charged by induction. The symbol lettered "ground" in part (c) simply means that the sphere is connected to the earth. The earth thus takes the place of the second sphere in Fig. 19–3. In step (c), negative charges are repelled to ground either through a conducting wire, or along the moist

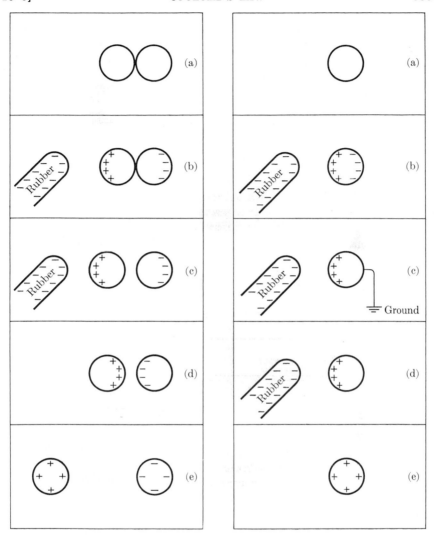

FIG. 19–3. By induction, equal and opposite charges are obtained on two metal spheres.

FIG. 19–4. Charging a single metal sphere by induction.

skin of a person who touches the sphere with his finger. The earth thus acquires a negative charge equal to the induced positive charge remaining on the sphere.

19–5 Coulomb's law. The first quantitative investigation of the law of force between charged bodies was carried out by Charles Augustin de Coulomb (1736–1806) in 1784, utilizing for the measurement of forces a

torsion balance of the type employed 13 years later by Cavendish in measuring gravitational forces. Coulomb found that the force of attraction
or repulsion between two "point charges," that is, charged bodies whose
dimensions are small compared with the distance r between them, is inversely proportional to the square of this distance.

The force also depends on the quantity of charge on each body. The
net charge of a body might be described by a statement of the excess number of electrons or protons in the body. In practice, however, the charge
of a body is expressed in terms of a unit much larger than the charge of
an individual electron or proton. We shall use the letter q or Q to represent the charge of a body, postponing for the present the definition of the
unit charge.

The concept of quantity of charge was not clearly appreciated in
Coulomb's time and no unit of charge or method of measuring it had been
devised. Thus, although Coulomb did not state his conclusions in this
form, his experiments showed that the force between two point charges
q and q' is proportional to the product of these charges. The complete
expression for the force between two point charges is therefore

$$F \propto \frac{qq'}{r^2} \tag{19-1}$$

or

$$F = k \frac{qq'}{r^2}, \tag{19-2}$$

where k is a proportionality constant whose magnitude depends on the
units in which F, q, q', and r are expressed. Equation (19-2) is the
mathematical statement of what is known today as *Coulomb's law: The
force of attraction or repulsion between two point charges is directly proportional to the product of the charges and inversely proportional to the square of
the distance between them.*

The best verification of Coulomb's law lies in the correctness of many
conclusions which have been drawn from it, rather than on direct experiments with point charges, which cannot be made with high precision.

If there is matter in the space between the charges, the net force acting
on each is altered because charges are "induced" in the molecules of the
intervening medium. This effect will be described later on. As a practical matter, the law can be used as it stands for point charges in air,
since even at atmospheric pressure the effect of the air is to alter the
force from its value in vacuum by only about one part in two thousand.

The same law of force holds whatever may be the sign of the charges
q and q'. If the charges are of like sign the force is a repulsion, if the
charges are of opposite sign the force is an attraction. Forces of the same
magnitude, but in opposite directions, are exerted on each of the charges.

Note that Coulomb's law has the same form as Newton's law of universal gravitation,

$$F = G \frac{mm'}{r^2}.$$

The electrical constant k corresponds to the gravitational constant G.

19–6 Quantity of charge. In our study of electricity and magnetism we shall express length, time, mass, force, etc., in the units of the mks system. We therefore wish to extend the mks system to include electrical and magnetic quantities. The first new unit we need is that of charge, and the mks unit of charge is the coulomb. The best definition of the coulomb is in terms of the ampere. (See Sections 22–1 and 26–3.) We temporarily define the coulomb as *that point charge which repels an equal charge of the same sign with a force of k newtons when the charges are one meter apart in a vacuum.* The best value of k is

$$k = 8.98742 \times 10^9 \ \frac{\text{n·m}^2}{\text{coul}^2},$$

but for most practical purposes k may be taken to be

$$k \approx 9 \times 10^9 \ \frac{\text{n·m}^2}{\text{coul}^2}.$$

It may seem odd that the definition of the coulomb should involve such a peculiar number. The answer lies in the fact that this is not the historic definition of the coulomb. Before the development of the mks system there was a system of electrical units known as the *practical* system. This system included many familiar units, like the volt, ampere, and coulomb. The mks system is a *basic* system of units which has been set up so as to incorporate the older practical units in which most electrical instruments are calibrated. This convenience far outweighs the disadvantage of the awkward value that had to be assigned to k.

The "natural" unit of electrical charge is the charge carried by the smallest portion of negative electricity, the electron. The most precise measurements up to the present time find this charge e to be

$$e = 1.601864 \times 10^{-19} \text{ coul}.$$

We will discuss the measurement of e in the next chapter.

When other equations are developed from Coulomb's law, it is found that the product $4\pi k$ frequently occurs. To avoid having to write the factor 4π, it is convenient to define a new constant, ϵ_0, by the relation

$$\epsilon_0 = \frac{1}{4\pi k}, \quad \text{or} \quad k = \frac{1}{4\pi \epsilon_0},$$

and write Coulomb's law as

$$F = \frac{1}{4\pi\epsilon_0} \frac{qq'}{r^2}.$$

(19–3)

From the numerical value of k given above, it follows that

$$\epsilon_0 = \frac{1}{4\pi k} = 8.85 \times 10^{-12} \frac{\text{coul}^2}{\text{n·m}^2},$$

while the factor $1/4\pi\epsilon_0$ is

$$\frac{1}{4\pi\epsilon_0} = k \approx 9 \times 10^9 \frac{\text{n·m}^2}{\text{coul}^2}.$$

In the *electrostatic* system of units (esu), forces are expressed in dynes, distances in centimeters, and the unit of charge is chosen of such magnitude that the proportionality constant in Coulomb's law is equal to unity. This law, with $k = 1$, then defines the unit charge in this system, the *statcoulomb*. *One statcoulomb is that charge which repels an equal charge of the same sign with a force of one dyne when the charges are separated by one centimeter*, the charges being carried by bodies whose dimensions are small compared with one centimeter. Coulomb's law takes the simpler form,

$$F = \frac{qq'}{r^2}.$$

The relation between the coulomb and the statcoulomb is

$$1 \text{ coulomb} = 2.99790 \times 10^9 \text{ statcoulombs}.$$

EXAMPLE. An α-particle is a nucleus of doubly ionized helium. It has a mass m of 6.68×10^{-27} kgm and a charge q of $+2e$ or 3.2×10^{-19} coul. Compare the force of electrostatic repulsion between two α-particles with the force of gravitational attraction between them.

The electrostatic force F_e is

$$F_e = \frac{1}{4\pi\epsilon_0} \frac{q^2}{r^2},$$

and the gravitational force F_g is

$$F_g = G \frac{m^2}{r^2}.$$

The ratio of the electrostatic to the gravitational force is

$$\frac{F_e}{F_g} = \frac{1}{4\pi\epsilon_0 G} \frac{q^2}{m^2} = 3.1 \times 10^{35}.$$

The gravitational force is evidently negligible compared with the electrostatic force.

PROBLEMS

19-1. Two positive point charges, each of magnitude q, are located on the y-axis at points $y = +a$ and $y = -a$. A third positive charge of the same magnitude is located at some point on the x-axis. (a) What is the force exerted on the third charge when it is at the origin? (b) What is the magnitude and direction of the force on the third charge when its coordinate is x? (c) Sketch a graph of the force on the third charge as a function of x, for values of x between $+4a$ and $-4a$. Plot forces to the right upward, forces to the left, downward. (d) For what value of x is the force a maximum?

19-2. A negative point charge of magnitude q is located on the y-axis at the point $y = +a$, and a positive charge of the same magnitude is located at $y = -a$. A third positive charge of the same magnitude is located at some point on the x-axis. (a) What is the magnitude and direction of the force exerted on the third charge when it is at the origin? (b) What is the force on the third charge when its coordinate is x? (c) Sketch a graph of the force on the third charge as a function of x, for values of x between $+4a$ and $-4a$.

19-3. A small ball having a positive charge q_1 hangs by an insulating thread. A second ball with a negative charge $q_2 = -q_1$ is placed at a horizontal distance a to the right of the first. (The distance a is large compared with the diameter of the ball.) (a) Show in a diagram all of the forces on the hanging ball in its final equilibrium position. (b) You are given a third ball having a positive charge $q_3 = 2q_1$. Find at least two points at which this ball can be placed so that the first ball will hang vertically.

19-4. Two small balls, each of mass 10 gm, are attached to silk threads 1 m long and hung from a common point. When the balls are given equal quantities of negative charge, each thread makes an angle of 4° with the vertical. (a) Draw a diagram showing all of the forces on each ball. (b) Find the magnitude of the charge on each ball.

19-5. A certain metal sphere of volume 1 cm^3 has a mass of 7.5 gm and contains 8.2×10^{22} free electrons. (a) How many electrons must be removed from each of two such spheres so that the electrostatic force of repulsion between them just balances the force of gravitational attraction? Assume the distance between the spheres is great enough so that the charges on them can be treated as point charges. (b) Express the number of electrons removed as a fraction of the total number of free electrons.

19-6. In the Bohr model of atomic hydrogen, an electron of mass 9.1×10^{-31} kgm revolves about a proton in a circular orbit of radius 5.3×10^{-11} m. The proton has a positive charge equal in magnitude to the negative charge on the electron and its mass is 1.67×10^{-27} kgm. (a) What is the radial acceleration of the electron? (b) What is its angular velocity?

19-7. One gram of monatomic hydrogen contains 6.02×10^{23} atoms, each consisting of an electron with charge -1.60×10^{-19} coul and a proton with charge $+1.60 \times 10^{-19}$ coul. (a) Suppose all these electrons could be located at the north pole of the earth and all the protons at the south pole. What would be the total force of attraction exerted on each group of charges by the other, in pounds? The diameter of the earth is 12,800 km. (b) What would be the magnitude and direction of the force exerted by the charges in part (a) on a third positive charge, equal in magnitude to the total charge at one of the poles and located at a point on the equator? Draw a diagram.

19–8. The dimensions of atomic nuclei are of the order of 10^{-13} m. Suppose that two α-particles are separated by this distance. (a) What is the force exerted on each α-particle by the other? (b) What is the acceleration of each? (See the example at the end of Section 19–6 for numerical data.)

19–9. The pair of equal and opposite charges in Problem 19–2 is called an *electric dipole.* (a) Show that when the x-coordinate of the third charge in Problem 19–2 is large compared with the distance a, the force on it is inversely proportional to the *cube* of its distance from the midpoint of the dipole. (b) Show that if the third charge is located on the y-axis, at a y-coordinate large compared with the distance a, the force on it is also inversely proportional to the cube of its distance from the midpoint of the dipole.

CHAPTER 20

THE ELECTRIC FIELD

20–1 The electric field. Figure 20–1(a) represents two positively charged bodies A and B, between which there is an electrical force of repulsion, **F**. Like the force of gravitational attraction, this force is of the action-at-a-distance type, making itself felt without the presence of any material connection between A and B. No one knows "why" this is possible—it is an experimental fact that charged bodies behave in this way. It is useful, however, to think of each of the charged bodies as modifying the state of affairs in the space around it, so that this state is different in some way from whatever it may be when the charged bodies are not present. Thus, let body B be removed. Point P, Fig. 20–1(b), is the point of space at which B was formerly located. The charged body A is said to produce or set up an *electric field* at the point P, and if the charged body B is now placed at P, one considers that a force is exerted on B *by the field*, rather than by body A directly. Since a force would be experienced by body B at all points of space around body A, the whole of space around A is an electric field.

One can equally well consider that body B sets up a field, and that a force is exerted on body A by the field of B.

The experimental test for the existence of an electric field at any point is simply to place a charged body, which will be called a *test charge*, at the point. If a force (of electrical origin) is exerted on the test charge, then an electric field exists at the point.

An electric field is said to exist at a point if a force of electrical origin is exerted on a charged body placed at the point.

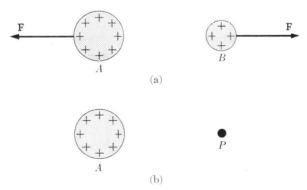

(a)

(b)

Fig. 20–1. The space around a charged body is an electric field.

Whether or not the force is of electrical origin can be determined by comparing the forces on the test body when it is charged and when it is uncharged. Any force that may be observed when the test body is charged, and which did not exist when it was uncharged, is a force of electrical origin.

Since force is a vector quantity, the electric field is a vector quantity also, having both magnitude and direction. The *magnitude* of the field at any point, represented by E, is defined as *the quotient obtained when the force F on a test charge placed at the point is divided by the quantity of charge q' on the test charge.* In other words, the magnitude of an electric field is the *force per unit charge.*

The *direction* of an electric field at any point is *the direction of the force on a positive test charge placed at the point.* The force on a negative charge, such as an electron, is therefore opposite to the direction of the field:

$$\mathbf{E} = \frac{\mathbf{F}}{q'}. \tag{20-1}$$

We shall refer to the electric field vector at a point as the *electric intensity* at the point. Several other terms are commonly used, for example electric field strength, electric field intensity, or merely field intensity. In the mks system, where forces are expressed in newtons and charges in coulombs, the unit of electric intensity is *one newton per coulomb.* Other units in which electric intensity may be expressed will be defined later.

Equation (20-1) may be written

$$\mathbf{F} = q'\mathbf{E}.$$

That is, the force exerted on a charge q' at a point where the electric intensity is $\mathbf{E}$ equals the product of the electric intensity and the charge.

20-2 Calculation of electric intensity. The preceding section describes an experimental method of measuring the electric intensity at a point. The method consists of placing a test charge at the point, measuring the force on it, and taking the ratio of the force to the charge. The electric intensity at a point may also be computed from Coulomb's law if the magnitudes and positions of all charges contributing to the field are known. Thus to find the magnitude of the electric intensity at a point of space P, at a distance r from a point charge q, imagine a test charge q' to be placed at P. The force on the test charge, by Coulomb's law, is

$$F = \frac{1}{4\pi\epsilon_0} \frac{qq'}{r^2},$$

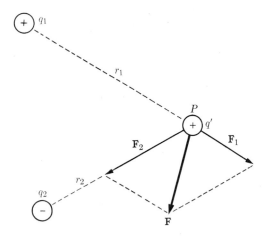

FIG. 20–2. The resultant force **F** on the test charge q' is the vector sum of forces $\mathbf{F}_1$ and $\mathbf{F}_2$.

and hence the electric intensity at P is

$$E = \frac{F}{q'} = \frac{1}{4\pi\epsilon_0}\frac{q}{r^2}.$$

The direction of the field is away from the charge q if the latter is positive, toward q if it is negative.

If a number of point charges q_1, q_2, etc., are at distances, r_1, r_2, etc., from a given point P, as in Fig. 20–2, each exerts a force on a test charge q' placed at the point and the resultant force on the test charge is the vector sum of these forces.

$$\mathbf{F} = \frac{1}{4\pi\epsilon_0}\frac{q_1 q'}{r_1^2} + \frac{1}{4\pi\epsilon_0}\frac{q_2 q'}{r_2^2} + \cdots \qquad \text{(vector sum)}$$

$$= \frac{1}{4\pi\epsilon_0}q'\left(\frac{q_1}{r_1^2} + \frac{q_2}{r_2^2} + \cdots\right) = \frac{1}{4\pi\epsilon_0}q'\sum\frac{q}{r^2} \qquad \text{(vector sum)}.$$

The electric intensity at the point,

$$\mathbf{E} = \frac{\mathbf{F}}{q'},$$

is therefore

$$\boxed{\mathbf{E} = \frac{1}{4\pi\epsilon_0}\sum\frac{q}{r^2}. \qquad \text{(Vector sum)}} \qquad (20\text{–}2)$$

In practice, electric fields are usually set up by charges distributed over the surfaces of conductors of finite size, rather than by point charges. The electric intensity is then calculated by dividing the distributed charges, in imagination, into infinitesimal charges dq. The sum in Eq. (20–2) then becomes an integral, and

$$\mathbf{E} = \frac{1}{4\pi\epsilon_0} \int \frac{dq}{r^2}. \quad \text{(Vector sum)}$$ (20–3)

Equation (20–1) defines the electric intensity at a point in terms of measurements that might be made at the point; it does not require any knowledge of the magnitude or position of the charges setting up the field. Equation (20–3) enables us to *compute* the intensity at a point without actually going to the point to make measurements, provided the distribution of charges setting up the field is known.

EXAMPLE 1. *Discrete charges.* An electric field is set up by two point charges q_1 and q_2, of the same magnitude but opposite sign, as in Fig. 20–3. What is the electric intensity at points a, b, and c?

At every point, the intensity due to the positive charge is directed radially away from that charge, and the intensity due to the negative charge is radially inward toward the charge.

At point a, the intensity due to each charge is directed toward the right. The resultant intensity $\mathbf{E}_a$ is also toward the right and its magnitude is the arithmetic sum of the individual intensities.

At point b, the intensity set up by q_1 is directed toward the left and that set up by q_2 is toward the right. The magnitude of the first is greater than that

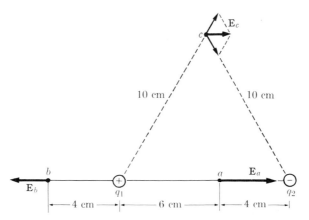

FIG. 20–3. Electric intensity at three points, a, b, and c, in the field set up by charges q_1 and q_2.

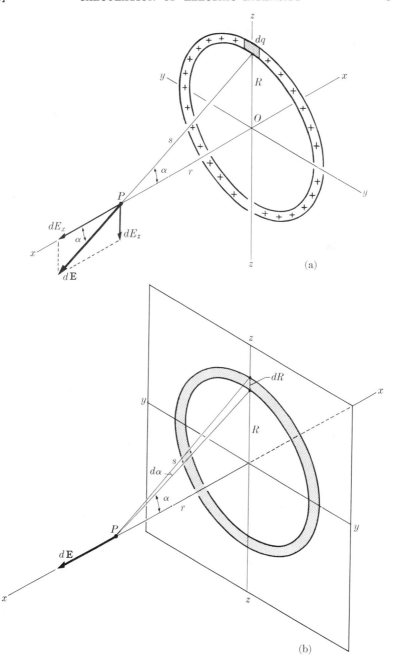

Fig. 20–4. (a) Electric intensity at a point on the axis of a ring of charge, due to the charge dq. (b) An infinitely large plane of charge is subdivided into narrow rings.

of the second. The resultant intensity $\mathbf{E}_b$ is toward the left and its magnitude is the difference between the individual intensities.

At point c, the individual intensities have the directions shown and the resultant intensity $\mathbf{E}_c$ is their vector sum. It is left to the reader to verify that if $q_1 = +12 \times 10^{-9}$ coul, $q_2 = -12 \times 10^{-9}$ coul, and the dimensions are as shown in the diagram, then

$$\mathbf{E}_a = 9.75 \times 10^4 \ \frac{\text{n}}{\text{coul}}, \text{ toward the right,}$$

$$\mathbf{E}_b = 6.20 \times 10^4 \ \frac{\text{n}}{\text{coul}}, \text{ toward the left,}$$

$$\mathbf{E}_c = 1.08 \times 10^4 \ \frac{\text{n}}{\text{coul}}, \text{ toward the right.}$$

EXAMPLE 2. *Charged ring.* In Fig. 20–4(a), a positively charged ring of radius R lies in the xz-plane. Compute the electric intensity at points on the axis of the ring.

The field is set up by a distributed charge and we must evaluate

$$\left(\frac{1}{4\pi\epsilon_0}\right)\int \frac{dq}{r^2}.$$

A short segment of the ring having a charge dq sets up at point P a field of intensity

$$dE = \frac{1}{4\pi\epsilon_0} \frac{dq}{s^2},$$

lying in the xz-plane and making an angle α with the x-axis. The resultant intensity cannot be obtained by integrating this expression, since integration is a process of algebraic, not vector, summation. The vector $d\mathbf{E}$, however, can be resolved into x- and z-components and the components can be integrated separately. It is seen from the diagram that when all segments of the ring are considered, the components dE_z will cancel by symmetry. The resultant field is therefore along the x-axis and is given by

$$E = \int dE_x = \int dE \cos \alpha = \int \frac{1}{4\pi\epsilon_0} \frac{dq}{s^2} \cos \alpha$$

$$= \frac{1}{4\pi\epsilon_0} \frac{\cos \alpha}{s^2} \int dq.$$

But $\int dq$ is the total charge q on the ring, so

$$E = \frac{1}{4\pi\epsilon_0} \frac{q \cos \alpha}{s^2}. \tag{20–4}$$

At the center of the ring, $\alpha = 90°$, $\cos \alpha = 0$, and $E = 0$, as is evident by symmetry. At distances large compared with R, the angle α is small, $\cos \alpha$

is approximately 1, and s^2 is nearly equal to r^2. Hence at large distances

$$E = \frac{1}{4\pi\epsilon_0}\frac{q}{r^2}.$$

In other words, at large distances the ring can be considered a point charge.

EXAMPLE 3. *Infinite plane sheet of charge.* In Fig. 20–4(b), positive charge is distributed uniformly over the entire yz-plane. Compute the electric intensity at points on the x-axis.

Subdivide the plane into narrow rings of radius R and width dR and use the results of the preceding example. Let σ represent the charge per unit area in the yz-plane. The area of the narrow ring is

$$dA = 2\pi R\, dR,$$

and the charge dq on the ring is

$$dq = \sigma\, dA = 2\pi\sigma R\, dR.$$

The vector $d\mathbf{E}$ in Fig. 20–4(b) represents the resultant field at P set up by the ring. From Eq. (20–4), replacing q by dq as given in the preceding equation, we get

$$dE = \frac{\sigma}{2\epsilon_0}\frac{R\cos\alpha}{s^2}\, dR.$$

The fields set up by the narrow rings of charge are all in the same direction, so the resultant field is the integral of the preceding expression. It is simpler to take α, rather than R, as the independent variable. We see from the diagram that

$$R = r\tan\alpha, \qquad s = r\sec\alpha.$$

Hence

$$dR = r\sec^2\alpha\, d\alpha$$

and

$$dE = \frac{\sigma}{2\epsilon_0}\sin\alpha\, d\alpha.$$

Now integrate with respect to α between the limits $\alpha = 0$ and $\alpha = \pi/2$.

$$E = \frac{\sigma}{2\epsilon_0}\int_0^{\pi/2}\sin\alpha\, d\alpha$$

$$= \frac{\sigma}{2\epsilon_0}\left[-\cos\alpha\right]_0^{\pi/2},$$

$$E = \frac{\sigma}{2\epsilon_0}. \tag{20–5}$$

Note that the distance r does not appear in the final result. This means that the intensity set up by an infinite plane of charge is independent of the

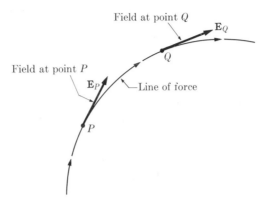

FIG. 20–5. The direction of the electric intensity at any point is tangent to the line of force through that point.

distance from the plane. In other words, the field is uniform and normal to the plane. Also, a field of the same magnitude but in the opposite sense is set up on the opposite side of the yz-plane.

20–3 Lines of force. The concept of lines of force was introduced by Michael Faraday (1791–1867) as an aid in visualizing electric (and magnetic) fields. A *line of force* (in an electric field) is *an imaginary line drawn in such a way that its direction at any point* (i.e., the direction of its tangent) *is the same as the direction of the field at that point.* (See Fig. 20–5.) Since, in general, the direction of a field varies from point to point, lines of force are usually curves.

Figure 20–6 shows some of the lines of force around a single positive charge; around two equal charges, one positive and one negative; and around two equal positive charges. The direction of the resultant intensity at every point in each diagram is along the tangent to the line of force passing through the point. Arrowheads on the lines indicate the direction in which the tangent is to be drawn.

No lines of force originate or terminate in the space surrounding a charge. Every line of force in an electrostatic field is a continuous line terminated by a positive charge at one end and a negative charge at the other. While sometimes for convenience we speak of an "isolated" charge and draw its field as in Fig. 20–6(a), this simply means that the charges on which the lines terminate are at large distances from the charge under consideration. For example, if the charged body in Fig. 20–6(a) is a small sphere suspended by a thread from the laboratory ceiling, the negative charges on which its force lines terminate would be found on the walls, floor, or ceiling, or on other objects in the laboratory.

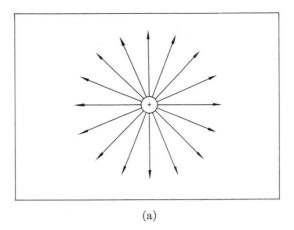

(a)

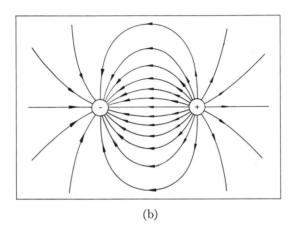

(b)

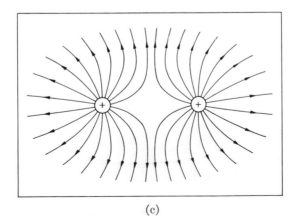

(c)

FIG. 20–6. The mapping of an electric field with the aid of lines of force.

At any one point in an electric field the field can have but one direction. Hence only one line of force can pass through each point of the field. In other words, lines of force never intersect.

It is, of course, possible to draw a line of force through every point of an electric field, but if this were done, the whole of space and the entire surface of a diagram would be filled with lines, and no individual line could be distinguished. By suitably limiting the number of force lines which one draws to represent a field, the lines can be used to indicate the magnitude of a field as well as its direction. This is accomplished by spacing the lines in such a way that *the number per unit area crossing a surface at right angles to the direction of the field is at every point proportional to the electric intensity.* In a region where the intensity is large, such as that between the positive and negative charges of Fig. 20–6(b), the lines of force are closely spaced, whereas in a region where the intensity is small, such as that between the two positive charges of Fig. 20–6(c), the lines are widely separated. If ΔN lines cross perpendicularly a small element of area ΔA, and if the electric intensity at the center of the element of area is E, then

$$\frac{\Delta N}{\Delta A_n} \propto E,$$

where the subscript n indicates that ΔA is normal to E. Many of the equations of electrostatics take a relatively simple form if we make this proportionality into an equation and choose ϵ_0 as the constant of proportionality. Thus, let us arbitrarily space the electric lines of force in such a way that, at any point, the number of lines per unit area and the electric intensity are connected by the relation

$$\boxed{\frac{\Delta N}{\Delta A_n} = \epsilon_0 E.} \qquad (20\text{--}6)$$

To understand why ϵ_0 is chosen as the constant of proportionality, consider the lines of force issuing from a positive point charge q, as shown in Fig. 20–6(a). Imagine a spherical surface of arbitrary radius r surrounding this point charge and concentric with it. The magnitude of the electric intensity at all points of the surface of this sphere is

$$E = \frac{1}{4\pi\epsilon_0} \frac{q}{r^2}.$$

The number of lines per unit area is therefore the same at all points of the surface and is given by

$$\epsilon_0 E = \frac{1}{4\pi} \frac{q}{r^2}.$$

Also, since the direction of E is radially outward, the lines of force cross the surface at right angles. The total area A_n of the spherical surface is $4\pi r^2$, so the total number of lines N crossing the surface is

$$N = \epsilon_0 E A_n = q.$$

We therefore see that if the spacing of the lines of force is chosen so that the number per unit area equals $\epsilon_0 E$, the total number of lines issuing from a positive point charge q is exactly equal to q.

20–4 Conclusions concerning the charge within a conductor. A conductor is a material within which there are free charges, that is, charges which are free to move provided a force is exerted on them by an electric field. If by any means an electric field is maintained within a conductor, there will be a motion of its free charges. (This motion is called a current.) On the other hand, if there is no field within a conductor there will be no motion of its free charges. We may now reverse the reasoning and conclude that if the charges in a conductor are known to be at rest, the electrostatic field within the conductor must be zero. With the help of this fact, we may now show that when a conductor is charged, the excess charge is confined entirely to the surface of the conductor.

Assume first that there are excess charges within a conductor. If there are excess charges, then there are lines of force terminating on those charges. If there are lines of force within the conductor, then there is a field within the conductor. It therefore follows that since there is no field within a conductor, there can be no excess charge within the conductor. If the conductor is not solid but is hollow, the same result holds true. Provided there are no charges within the cavity, the electric intensity in the cavity is zero and there are no charges on the inner wall of the conductor. The fact that the field within a closed conductor is zero is the basis of what is known as electrical or electrostatic *shielding*. Any device such as an electroscope can be isolated from the influence of other charges by surrounding it with a conductor. An interesting experiment is to surround an electroscope with a shield of wire mesh. The shield may be connected directly to one terminal of a static machine, and the electroscope will show practically no deflection when the machine is in operation. The wire mesh is not a continuous closed surface, but its shielding is nearly as effective as if it were.

Consider next an uncharged hollow conducting sphere with a small hole in its surface through which a body with a charge $+q$ may be introduced into the cavity, as shown in Fig. 20–7(a). At first the electric field set up by the charged body penetrates the walls of the hollow sphere, and a momentary rearrangement of the charges within the walls takes place. A negative induced charge appears on the inner surface of the sphere, and

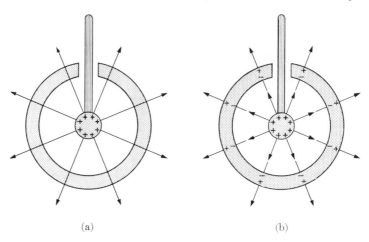

(a)   (b)

FIG. 20–7. Induced charges on the inner and outer surfaces of a hollow conductor.

a positive charge is induced on the outer surface, as shown in Fig. 20–7(b). Since the hollow sphere was originally uncharged, the positive charge on its outer surface is equal to the charge q within the cavity.

If the small charged body is moved around within the cavity, the *distribution* of induced charge on the inner surface changes but its magnitude remains the same. If, however, the charged body is touched to the inner wall of the hollow sphere, its positive charge will be completely neutralized by the equal induced negative charge on the inner wall, and the small body will therefore lose all of its original charge. An equal positive charge will be found on the outside wall of the hollow sphere.

Now that the outer surface of the hollow sphere is charged, suppose that the small body is withdrawn, recharged, and again introduced into the cavity. Again there is an induced charge on the inner wall, equal in magnitude to that of the charge q on the small body but of opposite kind. Since the *total* charge on the hollow sphere is not altered, the positive charge on its outer surface increases by an amount q. If the small body is again touched to the inner wall its charge will again be neutralized. Therefore by touching a charged body to the *inner* wall of a hollow conducting sphere, the charge on the body may, in effect, be *completely* transferred to the outer surface of the hollow sphere, no matter what charge already resides on this outer surface. This fact, which is the underlying principle of the Van de Graaff generator, will be discussed again in the next chapter after the concept of potential has been introduced.

20–5 Conclusions concerning the field outside a charged conductor. *Field around a charged sphere.* At the end of Section 20–3 we found that the number of lines issuing from a positive point charge q is exactly equal to q. If the point charge is isolated then there is no reason why these lines should issue in one direction more than in another, and so the lines must issue from the charge uniformly in all directions. If, now, there is an excess charge q on a sphere the same total number of lines must issue from the sphere. Since the sphere has perfect symmetry with respect to its center and since there is no reason why the excess charge should not distribute itself uniformly, there is no reason why these lines should issue in one direction more than in another. Therefore *the field outside an isolated charged conducting sphere is the same as though all of the charge were concentrated at the center of the sphere.* The field within the sphere is zero.

Field of an infinite charged conducting plate. When a metal plate is given a net charge, this charge distributes itself over the entire outer surface of the plate, and if the plate is of uniform thickness and is infinitely large (or if we are not too near the edges of a finite plate), the charge per unit area is uniform and is the same on both surfaces. Hence the field of such a charged plate arises from the superposition of the fields of *two* sheets of charge, one on each surface of the plate. By symmetry, the field is uniform and perpendicular to the plate. The field is away from the plate if the charge on it is positive. The magnitude of the electric intensity at any point can be found by using the results already derived for a sheet of charge.

Figure 20–8 shows a portion of a large charged conducting plate. Let σ represent the charge per unit area in the sheet of charge on *either* surface. At point a, outside the plate at the left, the component of electric intensity $\mathbf{E}_1$, due to the sheet of charge on the left face of the plate, is directed toward the left and its magnitude is $\sigma/2\epsilon_0$, from Eq. (20–5). The component $\mathbf{E}_2$ due to the sheet of charge on the right face of the plate is also toward the left and its magnitude is also $\sigma/2\epsilon_0$. The resultant intensity $\mathbf{E}$ is therefore

$$E = E_1 + E_2 = \frac{\sigma}{2\epsilon_0} + \frac{\sigma}{2\epsilon_0} - \frac{\sigma}{\epsilon_0}.$$

At point b, inside the plate, the two components of electric intensity are in opposite directions and their resultant is zero, as it must be in any conductor in which the charges are at rest. At point c the components again add and the magnitude of the resultant is σ/ϵ_0, directed toward the right.

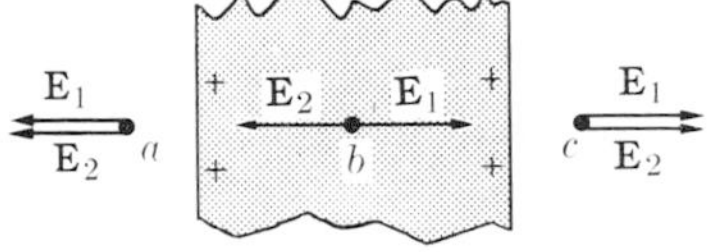

Field between oppositely charged parallel plates. When two plane parallel conducting plates, having the size and spacing shown in Fig. 20–9, are given equal and opposite

Fig. 20–8. Electric field inside and outside a charged conducting plate.

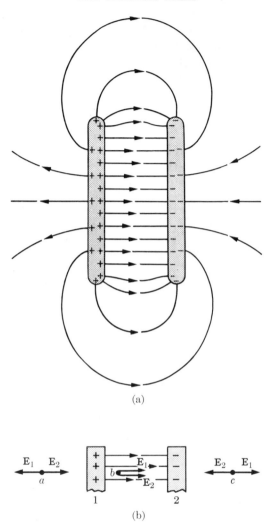

(a)

(b)

Fig. 20-9. Electric field between oppositely charged parallel plates.

charges, the field between and around them is approximately as shown in Fig. 20-9(a). While most of the charge accumulates at the opposing faces of the plates and the field is essentially uniform in the space between them, there is a small quantity of charge on the outer surfaces of the plates and a certain spreading or "fringing" of the field at the edges of the plates.

As the plates are made larger and the distance between them diminished, the fringing becomes relatively less. Such an arrangement of two oppositely charged plates separated by a distance small compared with their linear dimensions is encountered in many pieces of electrical equip-

TABLE 20–1

ELECTRIC FIELDS AROUND SIMPLE CHARGE DISTRIBUTIONS

Charge distribution responsible for the electric field	Arbitrary point in the electric field	Magnitude of the electric intensity at this point
Single point charge q	Distance r from q	$E = \dfrac{1}{4\pi\epsilon_0}\dfrac{q}{r^2}$
Several point charges, $q_1, q_2, \ldots$	Distance r_1 from q_1, r_2 from $q_2, \ldots$	$E = \dfrac{1}{4\pi\epsilon_0}\left(\dfrac{q_1}{r_1^2} + \dfrac{q_2}{r_2^2} + \cdots\right)$ (vector sum)
Charge q uniformly distributed on the surface of a conducting sphere of radius a	(a) Outside, $r > a$ (b) Inside, $r < a$	(a) $E = \dfrac{1}{4\pi\epsilon_0}\dfrac{q}{r^2}$ (b) $E = 0$
Two equally and oppositely charged conducting plates with charge per unit area σ	Any point between plates	$E = \dfrac{\sigma}{\epsilon_0}$

ment, notably in capacitors. In many instances the fringing is entirely negligible, and even if it is not, it is usually neglected for simplicity in computation. We shall therefore assume that the field between two oppositely charged plates is uniform, as in Fig. 20–9(b), and that the charges are distributed uniformly over the opposing surfaces.

The electric intensity at any point can be considered as the resultant of that due to two sheets of charge of opposite sign. Thus at points a and c in Fig. 20–9(b), the components $\mathbf{E}_1$ and $\mathbf{E}_2$ are each of magnitude $\sigma/2\epsilon_0$ but are oppositely directed, so their resultant is zero. At any point b between the plates the components are in the same direction and their resultant is σ/ϵ_0.

The results obtained so far are summarized in Table 20–1.

20–6 The ultimate unit of charge. The Millikan oil-drop experiment.
We have already mentioned in Section 18–11 that Faraday's law of electrolysis implies that electricity is atomic. In 1909 R. A. Millikan measured precisely the magnitude of the ultimate unit of charge, called the electronic charge, e.

An experiment to measure e must be carried out with a body having so few charges that the change of one charge makes a noticeable difference. Since the experiment must be done with very little charge, the force the body experiences will be small even though a large electric field is utilized. If the force on the charged body is very small, then the body itself must be very light. The force of gravity is always with us, and if the small electric force is not to be masked by a large gravitational force, then the mass of the body must be both small and known. If the body is small enough that the electric force on its charges is of the same order of magnitude as the gravitational force it experiences, then it may be that the gravitational force will be a useful standard of comparison rather than an annoying handicap.

Millikan used a drop of oil as his test body. It was selected from a mist produced by an ordinary atomizer. The drop was so small that it could not be measured optically, but with a microscope it could be seen as a bright spot because it scattered light from an intense beam, like a minute dust particle in bright sunlight.

When such a drop falls under the influence of gravity, it is hindered by the air it passes through. The way in which the fall of a small spherical body is hindered by air had been described by Stokes, who found that such a body experienced a resisting force **R** proportional to its velocity, or

$$R = kv. \tag{20–7}$$

The proportionality constant k was computed by Stokes to be

$$k = 6\pi\eta r, \tag{20–8}$$

where η is the coefficient of viscosity of the resisting medium and r is the radius of the body. (This law assumes that the resisting medium is homo-

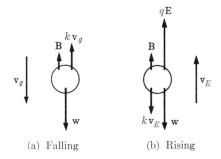

(a) Falling   (b) Rising

FIG. 20–10.   Forces acting on an oil drop (equilibrium conditions).

geneous. A more complicated law must be used if the size of the body is of the same order of magnitude as the mean free path of the molecules of the medium.) This is a friction equation very different from that introduced in mechanics to describe the force between two sliding bodies. In that case we assumed that the friction force depended only on the nature of the sliding surfaces and the normal force pressing the surfaces together. Hence in mechanics we discussed a force which did not depend on the speed of the motion. In the problem of a box sliding against friction down an inclined plane, the friction produced a constant force opposing the motion, but the acceleration was constant and the velocity increased continuously. A body subject to a frictional force like that given by Stokes' law will behave very differently.

A falling droplet of oil is acted on by its weight w, the buoyant force B of the air, and the resisting force $R = kv$ (Fig. 20–10). The resultant downward force F is

$$F = w - B - kv. \tag{20–9}$$

Initially, the velocity v is zero, the resisting force is zero, and the resultant downward force equals $w - B$. The drop therefore has an initial downward acceleration. As its downward velocity increases, the resisting force increases and eventually reaches a value such that the resultant force is zero. The drop then falls with a constant velocity called its *terminal velocity*, v_g. Since $F = 0$ when $v = v_g$, we have from Eq. (20–9),

$$w - B = kv_g. \tag{20–10}$$

Let ρ be the density of the oil and ρ_a the density of the air. Then

$$w = \tfrac{4}{3}\pi r^3 \rho g,$$
$$B = \tfrac{4}{3}\pi r^3 \rho_a g, \tag{20–11}$$

and inserting the value of k from Eq. (20–8), we get

$$\tfrac{4}{3}\pi r^3(\rho - \rho_a)g = 6\pi\eta r v_g. \tag{20–12}$$

All of the quantities in this equation except r are known or measurable. We can therefore solve for the drop radius r and hence can express the proportionality constant k in terms of known or measurable quantities. The result is

$$k = 18\pi\left[\frac{\eta^2 v_g}{2g(\rho - \rho_a)}\right]^{1/2}. \tag{20–13}$$

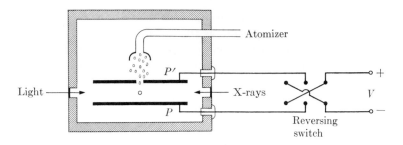

FIG. 20–11. Millikan's oil-drop experiment.

In the experiment, the oil drop is situated between two horizontal plates where a known strong electric field may be directed upward or downward or may be turned off (Fig. 20–11). The droplet has a small electric charge q which may be minus or plus, depending on whether it has an excess or deficiency of electrons. The droplet gets this charge from rubbing against the nozzle of the atomizer and from encounters with stray charges left in the air by cosmic rays, or deliberately produced by x-rays or by bringing a radioactive material nearby. In the electric field the drop will experience a force $q\mathbf{E}$, which can always be directed upward by the proper choice of the direction of $\mathbf{E}$. The experimenter must manipulate $\mathbf{E}$ so that the drop rises and falls in the region between the plates but never touches either.

The microscope with which the drop's movements are followed is equipped with two horizontal hairlines whose separation represents a known distance along the vertical line in which the drop travels. By timing the trips of the drop over this known distance, the terminal velocities of the drop are found. The velocities of fall, $\mathbf{v}_g$, are all the same, since oil does not evaporate and therefore the weight of the drop is constant. The velocity of rise, however, depends on the charge q. The resultant force on the drop while it is rising is

$$F = qE + B - w - kv. \qquad (20\text{--}14)$$

When the terminal velocity $\mathbf{v}_E$ is reached, the resultant force is zero, so

$$qE = w - B + kv_E. \qquad (20\text{--}15)$$

But from Eq. (20–10), $w - B = kv_g$, so finally

$$q = \frac{k}{E}\,(v_g + v_E). \qquad (20\text{--}16)$$

Since these terminal velocities are constant, they are relatively easy to measure.

This equation permits the evaluation of q, the charge on the drop. In the oil-drop experiment, the value of v_g is determined for a particular drop with the electric field off, and a whole series of v_E's for the same drop is observed with the field on. If we knew that the electronic charge was unique and that there was only one charge on the drop, then Eq. (20–16) would give the value of this charge at once. Since the nature of the electronic charge was not known, Millikan repeated the experiment with many different charges on the drop. This provided a set of q's which he found to be integral multiples of one charge which he took to be the ultimate unit of charge, e. Thus he established the *law of multiple proportions* for electric charges and concluded from it that electricity must be atomic in character.

Millikan made observations on oil drops of different sizes and also on drops of mercury. In one instance a drop was watched continuously for eighteen hours. The sets of observations always gave the same value of the electronic charge or "atom" of electricity. The best modern determination of e is $(1.601864 \pm 0.000025) \times 10^{-19}$ coulomb.

20–7 Electrical discharges. Cathode rays. In order to learn more about "particles of electricity," we turn to another line of investigation and consider the passage of electricity through gases. Although Benjamin Franklin's very dangerous experiment with kite and key was not a particularly convincing one, it nevertheless led to the correct conclusion that lightning is the discharge of electricity through a gas (air). Every electric spark is an example of this process. Since sparks are one of the most dramatic electric effects, it is natural that they should have been a subject of early study.

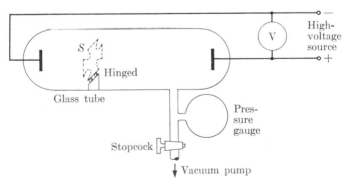

FIG. 20–12. Gas-discharge apparatus.

The passage of electricity through gases is a very complicated process and a great deal has been learned from it. There are many ways in which the character of an electrical discharge can be altered, but here we shall direct our attention to the effect of gas pressure. A typical discharge tube is shown in Fig. 20–12. This system has a gauge which measures the gas pressure and a pumping system which varies the pressure. Electrodes are sealed into the ends of the tube so that an electric field can be established between them.

When the pressure in the tube is atmospheric, a very large electric field is required to produce a discharge (about 3×10^6 volts/m for air). The discharge is a violent spark as the gas suddenly changes from an excellent insulator to a good conductor. As the pressure is reduced, the discharges are more easily established (Fig. 20–13), until, at very low pressures, they again become difficult to start. Discharges start most easily at a pressure of about 2 mm of mercury (although this will depend upon the kind of gas and the geometry of the electrodes). As the pressure is reduced, the discharge changes in character. With air in the tube, the bright spark changes to a purple glow filling the whole tube, and with neon, one obtains the red glow seen in many advertising signs. On further lowering of the pressure, the glow assumes a remarkable and complicated structure, with striations and dark spaces. At very low pressures the glow of the gas becomes dim and a new effect appears—the glass itself begins to glow. If the bulb has within it a device which is hinged so that it can be made to move into or out of the region between the electrodes by tipping the entire bulb (S in Fig. 20–12), then another effect may be seen. The greenish glow of the glass, which appears everywhere between the electrodes when the object S is out of the way, is partly obliterated when S is swung between the electrodes. If the object S has some distinctive shape, it may be seen clearly that it is casting a shadow. The shadow

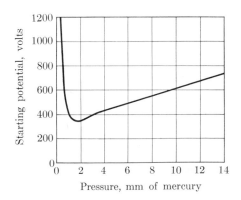

FIG. 20–13. Typical starting potential curve of gaseous discharge.

is on the side of S that is away from the negative electrode or cathode. If the cathode is small, the shadow is rather sharp. It is a simple deduction that the greenish glow is caused by some kind of rays from the cathode that cannot penetrate the obstruction S. These rays are called *cathode rays*. Many years ago it was observed that these rays could be deflected by both electric and magnetic fields, and the direction of these deflections showed that the rays were negatively charged.

Consider the motion of cathode rays in a uniform electric field such as that established between the two parallel plates P and P' shown in Fig. 20–14. The upper plate is positive and we will assume that the field is uniform over the length L of the plates.

The trajectory of a cathode ray is obtained in the same way that trajectories were found for projectiles in the gravitational field of force in mechanics. The only difference is that here the constant electric force is upward and is limited to the region between the plates. The gravitational force mg and the electrostatic force between two corpuscles are so small that they may be neglected.

If, in Fig. 20–14, the cathode rays enter the region between the plates at the origin O with a velocity v_x, this velocity will continue to be the horizontal component of the velocity of the rays. The general equation for displacement in uniformly accelerated motion is

$$s = s_0 + v_0 t + \tfrac{1}{2}at^2. \tag{20–17}$$

Applying Eq. (20–17) to the horizontal direction, we obtain

$$x = v_x t. \tag{20–18}$$

Between the plates, however, the rays experience an upward acceleration

$$a_y = \frac{qE}{m}. \tag{20–19}$$

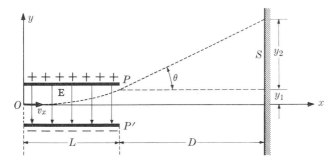

Fig. 20–14. Electrostatic deflection of cathode rays.

In this case **E** is constant, since fringing of the electric field is neglected, and it is equal to the potential difference between the deflection plates divided by their separation. Hence the general displacement equation becomes

$$y = \frac{qEt^2}{2m}. \tag{20–20}$$

Elimination of t between Eqs. (20–18) and (20–20) yields the equation for the parabolic trajectory,

$$y = \frac{qEx^2}{2mv_x^2}. \tag{20–21}$$

The quantity y_1, defined in Fig. 20–14, is the value of y when $x = L$.

Beyond the plates, the trajectory is a straight line because the charge is then moving in a field-free space. The value of y_2 is $D \tan \theta$, where D and θ are defined as in Fig. 20–14. The slope of this straight line is

$$\tan \theta = \left(\frac{dy}{dx}\right)_{x=L} = \left(\frac{qEx}{mv_x^2}\right)_{x=L} = \frac{qEL}{mv_x^2}. \tag{20–22}$$

The total deflection of the beam, y_E, is $y_1 + y_2$, so that

$$y_E = y_1 + y_2 = \frac{qEL^2}{2mv_x^2} + \frac{qELD}{mv_x^2} = \frac{qEL}{mv_x^2}\left(\frac{L}{2} + D\right). \tag{20–23}$$

———

EXAMPLE 1. When the terminals of a 100-volt battery are connected to two parallel plates 1 cm apart, the electric intensity in the space between the plates is 10^4 n/coul. Suppose we have a field of this intensity whose direction is vertically upward. Compute the force on an electron in this field and compare with the weight of the electron.

Electronic charge $e = 1.60 \times 10^{-19}$ coul.

Electronic mass $m = 9.1 \times 10^{-28}$ gm $= 9.1 \times 10^{-31}$ kgm.

$$F_{elec} = eE = 1.60 \times 10^{-19} \text{ coul} \times 10^4 \, \frac{\text{n}}{\text{coul}} = 1.60 \times 10^{-15} \text{ n.}$$

$$F_{grav} = mg = 9.1 \times 10^{-31} \text{ kgm} \times 9.8 \, \frac{\text{n}}{\text{kgm}} = 8.9 \times 10^{-30} \text{ n.}$$

The ratio of the electrical to the gravitational force is therefore

$$\frac{1.60 \times 10^{-15} \text{ n}}{8.9 \times 10^{-30} \text{ n}} = 1.8 \times 10^{14}!$$

It will be seen that the gravitational force is negligible.

EXAMPLE 2. If released from rest, what velocity will the electron of Example 1 acquire while traveling 1 cm? What will then be its kinetic energy? How long a time is required?

The force is constant, so the electron moves with a constant acceleration of

$$a = \frac{F}{m} = \frac{eE}{m} = \frac{1.60 \times 10^{-15}\,\text{n}}{9.1 \times 10^{-31}\,\text{kgm}} = 1.8 \times 10^{15}\,\frac{\text{m}}{\text{sec}^2}.$$

Its velocity after traveling 1 cm or 10^{-2} m is

$$v = \sqrt{2ax} = \sqrt{2 \times 1.8 \times 10^{15}\,\text{m/sec}^2 \times 10^{-2}\,\text{m}} = 6.0 \times 10^6\,\frac{\text{m}}{\text{sec}}.$$

Its kinetic energy is

$$\tfrac{1}{2}mv^2 = \tfrac{1}{2} \times 9.1 \times 10^{-31}\,\text{kgm} \times \left(6.0 \times 10^6\,\frac{\text{m}}{\text{sec}}\right)^2 = 1.6 \times 10^{-19}\,\text{joule}.$$

The time is

$$t = \frac{v}{a} = \frac{6.0 \times 10^6\,\text{m/sec}}{1.8 \times 10^{15}\,\text{m/sec}^2} = 3.3 \times 10^{-9}\,\text{sec}.$$

EXAMPLE 3. An electron moves in a vertical plane with a speed of 1.41×10^7 m/sec and enters a region where there is a uniform electric field of 3500 n/coul directed downward. Find (a) the coordinates of the electron 5×10^{-8} sec after it passes through the point of entry along a course directed at an angle of 30° below the horizontal, and (b) the direction of its velocity at this time.

Solution. (a) The field is uniform and directed downward, so there is a constant force on the electron directed upward along the positive y-axis. Therefore the acceleration of the electron is constant and its value is

$$a = \frac{F}{m} = \frac{Eq}{m} = \frac{Ee}{m} = \frac{3500\,\text{n/coul} \times 1.60 \times 10^{-19}\,\text{coul}}{9.11 \times 10^{-31}\,\text{kgm}} = 6.16 \times 10^{14}\,\frac{\text{m}}{\text{sec}^2}.$$

Referred to the point of entry O as the origin of coordinates, the equations of motion for the electron are

$$x = v_0 \cos\theta\, t = 1.41 \times 10^7\,\frac{\text{m}}{\text{sec}} \times 0.866 \times 5 \times 10^{-8}\,\text{sec}$$

$$= 0.61\,\text{m},$$

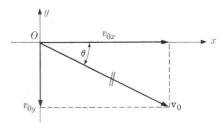

FIGURE 20–15

and

$$y = -v_0 \sin \theta \, t + \tfrac{1}{2} at^2$$

$$= -1.41 \times 10^7 \frac{m}{\sec} \times 0.500 \times 5 \times 10^{-8} \sec$$

$$+ \tfrac{1}{2} \times 6.16 \times 10^{14} \frac{m}{\sec^2} \times (5 \times 10^{-8} \sec)^2$$

$$= -0.35 \text{ m} + 0.77 \text{ m} = 0.42 \text{ m}.$$

(b)

$$v_x = v_0 \cos \theta$$

$$= 1.41 \times 10^7 \frac{m}{\sec} \times 0.866 = 1.22 \times 10^7 \frac{m}{\sec}.$$

$$v_y = -v_0 \sin \theta + at$$

$$= -1.41 \times 10^7 \frac{m}{\sec} \times 0.500 + 6.14 \times 10^{14} \frac{m}{\sec^2} \times 5 \times 10^{-8} \sec$$

$$= -0.71 \times 10^7 \frac{m}{\sec} + 3.07 \times 10^7 \frac{m}{\sec}$$

$$= 2.36 \times 10^7 \frac{m}{\sec}.$$

Let ϕ_x be the direction of motion with respect to the x-axis; then

$$\tan \phi_x = \frac{v_y}{v_x} = \frac{2.36 \times 10^7 \text{ m/sec}}{1.22 \times 10^7 \text{ m/sec}} = 1.94,$$

and

$$\phi_x = 62° 45'.$$

The direction of motion can also be obtained from the equation of the trajectory. Combining the x- and y-coordinate equations in part (a) by eliminating t gives

$$y = -x \tan \theta + \frac{1}{2} \frac{Ee}{m} \frac{x^2}{v_0^2 \cos^2 \theta}.$$

It is left to the reader to show that the slope of this curve at $x = 0.61$ m is 1.94.

PROBLEMS

$$\left(\epsilon_0 = 8.85 \times 10^{-12} \text{ coul}^2/\text{n·m}^2, \qquad \frac{1}{4\pi\epsilon_0} = 9 \times 10^9 \text{ n·m}^2/\text{coul}^2 \right)$$

20–1. A small object carrying a charge of -5×10^{-9} coul experiences a downward force of 20×10^{-9} n when placed at a certain point in an electric field. (a) What is the electric intensity at the point? (b) What would be the magnitude and direction of the force acting on an electron placed at the point?

20–2. What must be the charge on a particle of mass 2 gm for it to remain stationary in space when placed in a downward-directed electric field of intensity 500 n/coul?

20–3. In a rectangular coordinate system a charge of 25×10^{-9} coul is placed at the origin of coordinates, and a charge of -25×10^{-9} coul is placed at the point $x = 6$ m, $y = 0$. What is the electric intensity at (a) $x = 3$ m, $y = 0$; (b) $x = 3$ m, $y = 4$ m?

20–4. A charge of 16×10^{-9} coul is fixed at the origin of coordinates, a second charge of unknown magnitude is at $x = 3$ m, $y = 0$, and a third charge of 12×10^{-9} coul is at $x = 6$ m, $y = 0$. What is the magnitude of the unknown charge if the resultant field at $x = 8$ m, $y = 0$ is 20.25 n/coul directed to the right?

20–5. In a rectangular coordinate system, two positive point charges of 10^{-8} coul each are fixed at the points $x = +0.1$ m, $y = 0$, and $x = -0.1$ m, $y = 0$. Find the magnitude and direction of the electric intensity at the following points: (a) the origin; (b) $x = 0.2$ m, $y = 0$; (c) $x = 0.1$ m, $y = 0.15$ m; (d) $x = 0$, $y = 0.1$ m.

20–6. Same as Problem 20–5, except that one of the point charges is positive and the other negative.

20–7. How many excess electrons must be added to an isolated spherical conductor 10 cm in diameter to produce a field just outside the surface whose intensity is 1.3×10^{-3} n/coul?

20–8. The electric intensity in the region between a pair of oppositely charged plane parallel plates, each 100 cm^2 in area, is 10 n/coul. What is the charge on each plate? Neglect edge effects.

20–9. A small sphere whose mass is 0.1 gm carries a charge of 3×10^{-10} coul and is attached to one end of a silk fiber 5 cm long. The other end of the fiber is attached to a large vertical conducting plate which has a surface charge of 25×10^{-6} coul/m^2. Find the angle which the fiber makes with the vertical.

20–10. An "electric doublet" or "electric dipole" consists of a pair of electric charges of equal magnitude and opposite sign, as in Fig. 20–16. (a) Prove that the electric intensity set up by the doublet at point a is parallel to the x-axis and is approximately

$$E = \frac{1}{4\pi\epsilon_0} \frac{ql}{r^3} \quad \text{when } r \gg l.$$

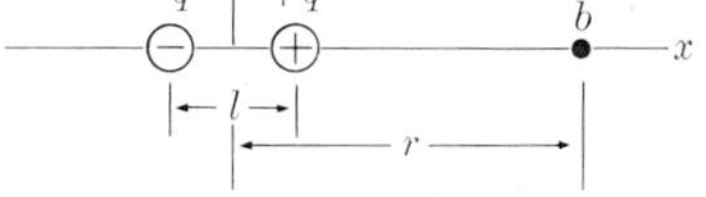

FIGURE 20–16

(b) Prove that the electric intensity at b is also parallel to the x-axis and is approximately

$$E = \frac{1}{4\pi\epsilon_0} \frac{2ql}{r^3} \quad \text{when } r \gg l.$$

20-11. An infinitely long straight wire has a uniform positive charge λ per unit length. (a) What is the charge dq on the element of length dx in Fig. 20-17? (b) What is the electric intensity dE set up at point P by this charge? (c) Show by integration that the magnitude of the resultant electric intensity at point P is

$$E = \lambda/2\pi\epsilon_0 r.$$

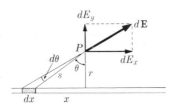

FIGURE 20-17

20-12. An oil droplet of mass 3×10^{-11} gm and of radius 2×10^{-4} cm carries 10 excess electrons. What is its terminal velocity (a) when falling in a region in which there is no electric field? (b) When falling in an electric field whose intensity is 3×10^5 n/coul directed downward? The viscosity of air is 180×10^{-7} n·sec/m². Neglect the buoyant force of the air.

20-13. A charged oil drop, in a Millikan oil-drop apparatus, is observed to fall through a distance of 1 mm in a time of 27.4 sec, in the absence of any external field. The same drop can be held stationary in a field of 2.37×10^4 n/coul. How many excess electrons has the drop acquired? The viscosity of air is 180×10^{-7}

n·sec/m². The density of the oil is 824 kgm/m³, and the density of air is 1.29 kgm/m³.

20-14. A charged oil drop falls 4.0 mm in 16.0 sec at constant speed in air in the absence of an electric field. The relative density of the oil is 0.80, that of the air is 1.30×10^{-3}, and the coefficient of viscosity of the air is 1.81×10^{-5} n·sec/m². Find (a) the radius of the drop and (b) the mass of the drop. (c) If the drop carries one electronic unit of charge and is in an electric field of 2×10^5 n/coul, what is the ratio of the force of the electric field on the drop to its weight?

20-15. When the oil drop in Problem 20-14 was in a constant electric field of 2×10^5 n/coul, several different times of rise over the distance of 4.0 mm were observed. The measured times were 36.0, 11.2, 17.7, 7.7, and 23.0 sec. Calculate (a) the velocity of fall under gravity, (b) the velocity of rise in each case, and (c) the sum of the velocity in part (a) and each velocity in part (b). (d) Show that the sums in part (c) are integral multiples of some number and interpret this result. (e) Calculate the value of the electronic charge from these data.

20-16. The maximum charge that can be retained by one of the spherical terminals of a large Van de Graaff generator is about 10^{-3} coul. Assume a positive charge of this magnitude, distributed uniformly over the surface of a sphere in otherwise empty space. (a) Compute the magnitude of the electric intensity at a point outside the sphere, 5 m from its center. (b) If an electron were released at this point, what would be the magnitude and direction of its initial acceleration?

20-17. The electric intensity in the region between the deflecting plates of a certain cathode-ray oscilloscope is

30,000 n/coul. (a) What is the force on an electron in this region? (b) What is the acceleration of an electron when acted on by this force?

20–18. A uniform electric field exists in the region between two oppositely charged plane parallel plates. An electron is released from rest at the surface of the negatively charged plate and strikes the surface of the opposite plate, 2 cm distant from the first, in a time interval of 1.5×10^{-8} sec. (a) Find the electric intensity. (b) Find the velocity of the electron when it strikes the second plate.

20–19. An electron is projected into a uniform electric field of intensity 5000 n/coul. The direction of the field is vertically upward. The initial velocity of the electron is 10^7 m/sec, at an angle of 30° above the horizontal. (a) Find the maximum distance the electron rises vertically above its initial elevation. (b) After what horizontal distance does the electron return to its original elevation? (c) Sketch the trajectory of the electron.

20–20. In Fig. 20–18, an electron is projected along the axis midway between the plates of a cathode-ray tube

with an initial velocity of 2×10^7 m/sec. The uniform electric field between the plates has an intensity of 20,000 n/coul and is upward. (a) How far below the axis has the electron moved when it reaches the end of the plates? (b) At what angle with the axis is it moving as it leaves the plates? (c) How far below the axis will it strike the fluorescent screen S?

20–21. An electron is projected with an initial velocity $v_0 = 10^7$ m/sec into the uniform field between the parallel plates in Fig. 20–19. The direction of the field is vertically downward, and the field is zero except in the space between the plates. The electron enters the field at a point midway between the plates. If the electron just misses the upper plate as it emerges from the field, find the magnitude of the electric intensity.

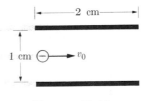

FIGURE 20–19

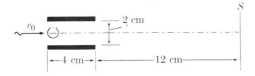

FIGURE 20–18

CHAPTER 21

POTENTIAL

21–1 Electrical potential energy. When a particle having a charge q' moves in an electric field, one of the forces on it is the electrical force, $q'\mathbf{E}$. The work of this force in a displacement $d\mathbf{s}$ is

$$dW_{\text{el}} = \mathbf{F} \cdot d\mathbf{s} = q'\mathbf{E} \cdot d\mathbf{s} \tag{21-1}$$

and the total work in a finite displacement from point 1 to point 2 is

$$W_{\text{el}} = q' \int_{s_1}^{s_2} \mathbf{E} \cdot d\mathbf{s}. \tag{21-2}$$

Let W' represent the work of all other forces. Then, from the work-energy principle,

$$W_{\text{el}} + W' = E_{k2} - E_{k1}, \tag{21-3}$$

where E_{k2} and E_{k1} are the final and initial kinetic energies of the particle.

We showed in Chapter 7 that if the work of a force depended only on the endpoints and not on the particular path between those points, this work could be transferred from the "work" side to the "energy" side of the work-energy equation (with sign reversed) and called an increase in potential energy. When this is the case, the force is called a *conservative* force.

The electrostatic force on a charged particle is a conservative force. To show this, consider first the special case of the radial electric field set up by a single fixed point charge q. The work of the electrical force, when a test charge q' undergoes any displacement, is computed in the same way as the work of a gravitational force (see Section 7–4). The only difference is that the gravitational force, Gmm'/r^2, is replaced by the electrical force, kqq'/r^2, or $qq'/4\pi\epsilon_0 r^2$. Also, while gravitational forces are always attractive, electrical forces between point charges may be either attractive or repulsive. Figure 21–1, which corresponds to Fig. 7–6, represents the electrical case. The work of the electrical force on the charge q', in the displacement $d\mathbf{s}$, is

$$dW = q'\mathbf{E} \cdot d\mathbf{s} = q'E \cos \theta \, ds.$$

But

$$E = \frac{q}{4\pi\epsilon_0 r^2}$$

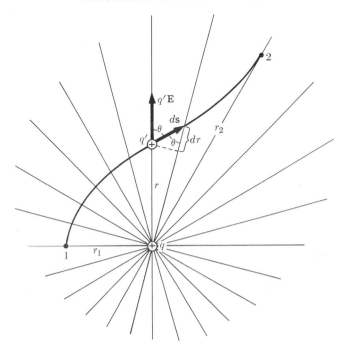

FIG. 21–1. Displacement of a test charge q' in the radial field of a point charge q.

and

$$ds \cos \theta = dr,$$

so

$$dW_{\text{el}} = \frac{qq'}{4\pi\epsilon_0} \int_{r_1}^{r_2} \frac{dr}{r^2}$$

and

$$W_{\text{el}} = -\frac{qq'}{4\pi\epsilon_0}\left(\frac{1}{r_2} - \frac{1}{r_1}\right). \tag{21–4}$$

The work therefore depends only on the radial distances r_2 and r_1, and not on the particular path between them, so the electrical force due to a point charge is conservative.

The work-energy principle, in this particular case, becomes

$$W' - \frac{qq'}{4\pi\epsilon_0}\left(\frac{1}{r_2} - \frac{1}{r_1}\right) = E_{k2} - E_{k1}$$

or

$$W' = E_{k2} - E_{k1} + \frac{qq'}{4\pi\epsilon_0 r_2} - \frac{qq'}{4\pi\epsilon_0 r_1}. \tag{21–5}$$

The potential energy of the charge q', at any distance r from the charge q, is therefore

$$E_p = \frac{qq'}{4\pi\epsilon_0 r}, \tag{21-6}$$

and Eq. (21-5) can be written as

$$W' = (E_{k2} - E_{k1}) + (E_{p2} - E_{p1}). \tag{21-7}$$

That is, the work of all forces *except* the electrical force equals the sum of the increases in kinetic and potential energy of the test charge q'.

When we set the potential energy equal to zero in Eq. (21-6), we find that $r = \infty$. That is, the reference level of potential energy of the test charge q' is at a point infinitely distant from the charge q. (It will be recalled that the same reference level was used for gravitational potential energy.) This choice is not *essential*, however. We could set the potential energy equal to zero at *any* arbitrary distance r_0 from the charge q. The potential energy at a distance r would then be

$$E_p = \frac{qq'}{4\pi\epsilon_0}\left(\frac{1}{r} - \frac{1}{r_0}\right).$$

The *change* in potential energy when the charge q' moves from a point r_1 to a point r_2 would, however, still be given by Eq. (21-4), since the terms in r_0 would cancel.

The distance r in Eq. (21-6) is always considered positive. The algebraic sign of the potential energy therefore depends on the signs of both of the charges q and q'. If these are both positive or both negative their product is positive and E_p is positive. That is, a positive charge q' in the field of another positive charge q (or a negative charge q' in the field of a negative charge q) has a positive potential energy relative to a point at infinity. As the charge q' moves away from the charge q its potential energy *decreases*.

If the charges q and q' are of opposite sign, their product is negative and E_p is negative. A negative charge q' in the field of a positive charge q has a negative potential energy, relative to a point at infinity. Its potential energy *increases* as it moves away from the charge q.

The latter case corresponds to that of gravitational potential energy, where the forces are attractive, like those between charges of opposite sign. The former case has no analogue in gravitation.

Now suppose that an electric field is set up by a number of fixed, discrete point charges $q_1, q_2, q_3, \ldots$, and that $r_1, r_2, r_3, \ldots$ are the distances from these charges to some point of the field. Each of the fixed charges exerts a force on a charge q' at the point. We can then calculate the works of each of these forces in any displacement of the test charge q', and since the work of each force depends only on the endpoints, the total work depends only on the endpoints also. Hence *any* electrostatic field is a conservative field, and Eq. (21–7) is true in general. The potential energy of a charge q' at any point is the *algebraic* sum (energy is a scalar quantity) of a number of terms like those in Eq. (21–6). That is,

$$E_p = \frac{q_1 q'}{4\pi\epsilon_0 r_1} + \frac{q_2 q'}{4\pi\epsilon_0 r_2} + \cdots$$

$$= \frac{q'}{4\pi\epsilon_0} \sum_i \frac{q_i}{r_i}. \tag{21–8}$$

If the charges setting up the field are distributed along lines, over surfaces, or throughout volumes, we must replace the sum by an integral:

$$E_p = \frac{q'}{4\pi\epsilon_0} \int \frac{dq}{r}. \tag{21–9}$$

21–2 Potential. In discussing electrostatic fields we found it convenient to consider, instead of the actual force $\mathbf{F}$ on a test charge q', the ratio of the force to the charge, or the *force per unit charge*. This is called the *electric intensity* $\mathbf{E}$:

$$\mathbf{E} = \frac{\mathbf{F}}{q'}, \qquad \mathbf{F} = q'\mathbf{E}. \tag{21–10}$$

Similarly, instead of the actual potential energy E_p of a test charge q' at a point of the field, it is more convenient to consider the ratio of the potential energy to the charge, or the *potential energy per unit charge*. This is called simply the *potential* at the point and is represented by V:

$$V = \frac{E_p}{q'}, \qquad E_p = q'V. \tag{21–11}$$

Unlike electric intensity, which is a vector quantity, potential is a *scalar*.

The unit of potential is evidently 1 joule/coulomb. This unit is called 1 *volt*, in honor of Alessandro Volta (1745–1827), an Italian scientist. He was the inventor of the "voltaic pile," the first electric cell.

The potential at a point in an electrostatic field is one volt if the ratio of the potential energy of a charge at the point, to the magnitude of the charge, is one joule per coulomb.

One one-thousandth of a volt is called one *millivolt* (mv), and one one-millionth of a volt is called a *microvolt* (μv). One thousand volts is a kilovolt (kv) and one million volts is a *megavolt* (Mv).

We have shown that the potential energy of a test charge q' at a distance r from a single fixed point charge q is

$$E_p = \frac{1}{4\pi\epsilon_0}\frac{qq'}{r}.$$

It follows that the potential V at this distance is

$$V = \frac{E_p}{q'} = \frac{1}{4\pi\epsilon_0}\frac{q}{r}. \tag{21–12}$$

At a point of the field set up by a number of discrete charges,

$$V = \frac{1}{4\pi\epsilon_0}\sum_i\frac{q_i}{r_i}, \tag{21–13}$$

and for distributed charges,

$$V = \frac{1}{4\pi\epsilon_0}\int\frac{dq}{r}. \tag{21–14}$$

In all these equations, the reference level of potential is a point at infinity. This is the most convenient point for problems in electrostatics. When dealing with electrical *circuits*, other reference levels are ordinarily used. The difference between the potentials at two points is, of course, the same whatever the choice of reference level.

The algebraic sign of the potential at a point is determined only by the signs of *the charges setting up the field*. For a single point charge q, the potential is positive (relative to a point at infinity) if q is positive, and is negative if q is negative.

The sign of the *potential energy* of a charge q' is determined by the signs of both q' and V, since $E_p = q'V$.

21–3 Potential difference. The difference between the potentials at two points of an electric field is of more interest than the absolute values of the potentials, because it is this difference that determines the change in potential energy of a charge when it moves from one point to the other. If the points are lettered a and b, the potential difference between them is simply $V_a - V_b$ or $V_b - V_a$. For brevity, we shall represent potential differences by a double subscript. Thus,

$$V_{ab} \equiv V_a - V_b,$$

$$V_{ba} \equiv V_b - V_a.$$

Evidently,

$$V_{ab} = -V_{ba}.$$

Since potentials are expressed in volts, potential differences are in volts also. Differences of potential may be measured by electroscopes, electrometers, and voltmeters. If the knob of a leaf electroscope is connected to a body at one potential and the case of the instrument to a body at a different potential, the divergence of the electroscope leaves is a rough measure of the potential difference between the bodies. Since there is no simple relation between the divergence of its leaves and the potential difference, the leaf electroscope is rarely used in quantitative work, some form of electrometer being preferred. The familiar pivoted coil voltmeter also measures the potential difference between its terminals, but being a current-operated instrument, it is not suitable for purely electrostatic measurements.

The potential difference between the terminals of a lead storage battery is about 12 volts, with the terminal marked + at the higher potential. If we call this terminal a and the other terminal b, then

$$V_{ab} = 12 \text{ volts}, \qquad V_{ba} = -12 \text{ volts}.$$

There is an electric field in the space between the battery terminals. If a positive charge moves from terminal a (+) to terminal b (−) its potential energy decreases by 12 joules/coul. This energy appears in some other form, such as heat in the filament of a headlight lamp or work in the starting motor.

A general expression for the potential difference between two points can be obtained by returning to Eq. (21–2). The work of the electrical force on a charge q', when the charge moves on any path from point a to point b, is

$$W_{\text{el}} = q' \int_a^b \mathbf{E} \cdot d\mathbf{s}.$$

This work is equal to the *decrease* in potential energy of the charge q', $E_{pa} - E_{pb}$. Thus

$$E_{pa} - E_{pb} = q' \int_a^b \mathbf{E} \cdot d\mathbf{s},$$

or

$$\frac{E_{pa}}{q'} - \frac{E_{pb}}{q'} = \int_a^b \mathbf{E} \cdot d\mathbf{s}.$$

But E_{pa}/q' is the potential V_a at point a, and E_{pb}/q' is the potential V_b at point b. Hence

$$V_{ab} \equiv V_a - V_b = \int_a^b \mathbf{E} \cdot d\mathbf{s}. \tag{21–15}$$

We therefore have two methods for calculating the potential difference between two points:

(1) If the magnitudes and positions of all charges setting up the field are known, we can (except for possible mathematical difficulties) compute the potentials at a and b from Eq. (21–13) or (21–14), and subtract one from the other.

(2) If the magnitude and direction of **E** are known at all points, we can evaluate the integral on the right side of Eq. (21–15).

EXAMPLE 1. An electric field is set up by two point charges q_1 and q_2, of the same magnitude but opposite sign, as in Fig. 21–2. What is the potential at points a, b, and c? (Compare Fig. 20–3.)

Potential is a scalar quantity; it has a magnitude (positive or negative) but not a direction. At every point, the potential due to the positive charge is positive and that due to the negative charge is negative.

At point a, the negative potential is greater than the positive potential and V_a is negative.

At point b, the positive potential exceeds the negative and V_b is positive.

At point c, equidistant from a and b, the positive and negative potentials are equal and $V_c = 0$. (Explain why V_c can be zero although $\mathbf{E}_c \neq 0$, as shown in Fig. 20–3.)

As a numerical example, let

$$q_1 = +12 \times 10^{-9} \text{ coul} \quad \text{and} \quad q_2 = -12 \times 10^{-9} \text{ coul.}$$

Then, if the dimensions are as shown in the diagram,

$$V_a = -900 \text{ volts}, \quad V_b = 1930 \text{ volts}, \quad V_c = 0.$$

EXAMPLE 2. By symmetry, the electric intensity E between two oppositely charged, closely spaced parallel plates is uniform and perpendicular to the plates. What is the potential difference between the plates (see Fig. 21–3)?

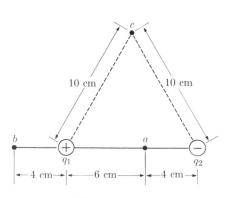

FIGURE 21–2

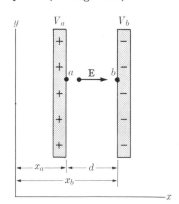

FIGURE 21–3

Take the x-axis parallel to the field, as in the diagram, and consider two points a and b at the inner surfaces of the plates. Then

$$V_{ab} = \int_a^b E \cos \theta \, ds.$$

But

$$E = \text{const}, \qquad \cos \theta = 1, \qquad ds = dx,$$

so

$$V_{ab} = E \int_{x_a}^{x_b} dx = E(x_b - x_a) = Ed,$$

and

$$E = \frac{V_{ab}}{d}, \tag{21–16}$$

where $d = x_b - x_a$ is the distance between the plates. *The electric intensity therefore equals the potential difference between the plates divided by the distance between them.* Equation (21–16) is a more useful expression for the electric intensity between parallel plates than is the equation $E = \sigma/\epsilon_0$, since the potential difference V_{ab} can be determined experimentally more readily than can the surface charge per unit area.

EXAMPLE 3. The electric intensity at a perpendicular distance r from an infinitely long straight wire having a charge λ per unit length is perpendicular to the wire and is given by the expression in Problem 20–11, namely,

$$E = \frac{1}{4\pi\epsilon_0} \frac{2\lambda}{r}.$$

Find the potential difference V_{ab} between two points at perpendicular distances r_a and r_b from the wire.

$$V_{ab} = \int_a^b E \cos \theta \, ds.$$

In this case, $ds = dr$ and $\cos \theta = 1$. Hence

$$V_{ab} = \frac{2\lambda}{4\pi\epsilon_0} \int_{r_a}^{r_b} \frac{dr}{r} = \frac{2\lambda}{4\pi\epsilon_0} \ln \frac{r_b}{r_a}.$$

21–4 Potential of a charged spherical conductor. The electric intensity *outside* a charged spherical conductor is the same as though all of the charge on the conductor were concentrated at its center. It follows that the potential at points outside the conductor is given by the same expression as that for a point charge, namely,

$$V = \frac{1}{4\pi\epsilon_0} \frac{q}{r}, \tag{21–17}$$

where r is equal to or greater than the radius of the sphere. At points *inside* the sphere the electric intensity is zero. Therefore from the general expression for the potential difference between two points, Eq. (21–15), it follows that the potential is the same at all internal points and is equal to the potential at the surface, namely,

$$V = \frac{1}{4\pi\epsilon_0} \frac{q}{a},\qquad (21\text{–}18)$$

where a is the radius of the sphere. Hence Eq. (21–17) gives the potential at points outside and Eq. (21–18) the potential at points inside the sphere.

Figure 21–4 shows a sphere of radius a having a positive charge q, together with graphs of the electric intensity E and the potential V at points along a line through the center of the sphere.

The maximum charge that can be retained by a conductor in air is limited by the fact that the air itself becomes conducting at an electric intensity of about 3×10^6 volts/m. In general, if E_m represents the upper limit of electric intensity, the maximum charge that can be retained by a spherical conductor in air is

$$q_m = 4\pi\epsilon_0 a^2 E_m.$$

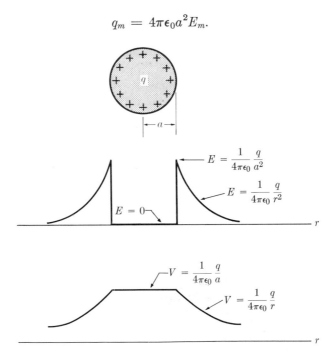

Fig. 21–4. Electric intensity E and potential V at points inside and outside a charged spherical conductor.

Hence the maximum *potential* to which a spherical conductor in air can be raised, from Eq. (21–18), is

$$V_m = aE_m.$$

For a sphere one centimeter in radius, $V_m = 0.01 \times 3 \times 10^6 = 30{,}000$ volts, and no amount of "charging" could raise the potential of a sphere of this size, in air, higher than about 30,000 volts.

It is this fact which necessitates the use of such large spherical terminals on high-voltage machines. If we make $a = 2$ meters, then

$$V_m = 2 \times 3 \times 10^6 = 6 \text{ million volts.}$$

At the other extreme is the effect produced by sharp points, a point being a portion of a surface of very small radius of curvature. Since the maximum potential is directly proportional to the radius, even relatively small potentials applied to sharp points in air will produce sufficiently high fields just outside the point to result in ionization of the surrounding air.

21–5 The work-energy principle. Let us now return to the work-energy principle as stated in Eq. (21–7),

$$W' = (E_{k2} - E_{k1}) + (E_{p2} - E_{p1}).$$

In this equation, W' represents the work of all forces on a charged particle *except* the electrical force. If *no* forces except the electrical force act on a particle, then $W' = 0$ and

$$E_{k2} + E_{p2} = E_{k1} + E_{p1}.$$

That is, the sum of the kinetic energy and the electrical potential energy of the particle is constant or is conserved. Writing out the explicit expressions for kinetic and electrical potential energy, we get

$$\tfrac{1}{2}mv_2^2 + qV_2 = \tfrac{1}{2}mv_1^2 + qV_1.$$

EXAMPLE. A simple type of vacuum tube known as a *diode* consists essentially of two electrodes within a highly evacuated enclosure. One electrode, the cathode, is maintained at a high temperature and emits electrons from its surface. A potential difference of a few hundred volts is maintained between the cathode and the other electrode, known as the anode or plate, with the anode at the higher potential. Suppose that in a certain diode the plate potential is 250 volts above that of the cathode, and an electron is emitted from the cathode with no initial velocity. What is its velocity when it reaches the anode?

Let V_k and V_p represent the cathode and anode potentials, respectively, and let the charge on the electron be e. The energy equation becomes

$$\tfrac{1}{2}mv_p^2 + eV_p = \tfrac{1}{2}mv_k^2 + eV_k.$$

Since $v_k = 0$,

$$v_p = \sqrt{\frac{2e(V_k - V_p)}{m}}.$$

From the given data,

$$e = -1.60 \times 10^{-19} \text{ coul},$$

$$V_p - V_k = 250 \text{ volts}, \qquad V_k - V_p = -250 \text{ volts}.$$

Hence

$$v_p = \sqrt{\frac{2 \times (-1.60 \times 10^{-19} \text{ coul}) \times (-250 \text{ volts})}{9.1 \times 10^{-31} \text{ kgm}}}$$

$$= 9.4 \times 10^6 \frac{m}{\text{sec}}.$$

Note that the shape or separation of the electrodes need not be known. The final velocity depends only on the difference of potential between the cathode and the anode. Of course, the time of transit from cathode to anode depends on the geometry of the tube.

21–6 Equipotential surfaces. The potential distribution in an electric field may be represented graphically by *equipotential surfaces*. An equipotential surface is one at all points of which the potential has the same value. While an equipotential surface may be constructed through every point of an electric field, it is customary to show only a few of the equipotentials in a diagram.

Since the potential energy of a charged body is the same at all points of a given equipotential surface, it follows that no (electrical) work is done when a charged body moves over such a surface. Hence the equipotential surface through any point must be at right angles to the direction of the field at that point. If this were not so, the field would have a component lying in the surface and work would be done by this component. The lines of force and the equipotential surfaces thus form a mutually perpendicular network. In general, the lines of force of a field are curves and the equipotentials are curved surfaces. For the special case of a uniform field, where the lines of force are straight and parallel, the equipotentials are parallel planes perpendicular to the lines of force.

The lines of force at the surface of a charged conductor are at right angles to the conductor if the charges on it are at rest. Hence the surface of such a conductor is an equipotential. Furthermore, since the field within a charged conductor is zero, the entire interior of the conductor is an equipotential *volume*, at the same potential as the surface of the conductor.

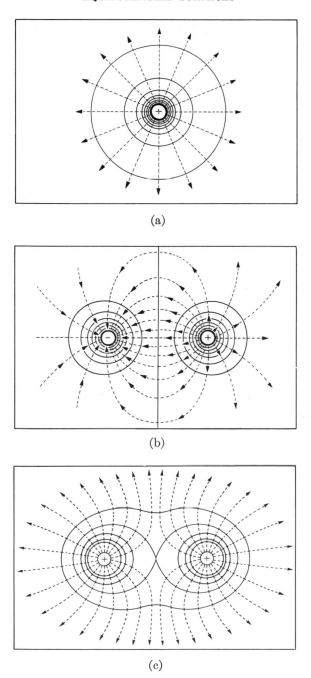

(a)

(b)

(c)

Fig. 21–5. Equipotential surfaces (solid lines) and lines of force (broken lines) in the neighborhood of point charges.

Figure 21–5 shows the same arrangements of charges as in Fig. 20–6. The lines of force have been drawn dotted and the intersections of the equipotential surfaces with the plane of the diagram are shown by the full lines. The actual field is, of course, three-dimensional.

21–7 Potential gradient. Let us return to the first equation in this chapter, Eq. (21–1), for the work of the electrical force on a particle having a charge q' in a displacement ds.

$$dW_{\text{el}} = q'\mathbf{E} \cdot d\mathbf{s} = q'E \cos \theta \, ds.$$

When both sides are divided by q', we get

$$\frac{dW}{q'} = \mathbf{E} \cdot d\mathbf{s} = E \cos \theta \, ds = E_s \, ds.$$

But dW/q', the work per unit charge of the electrical force, is equal to the *decrease* in potential energy of the charge, $-dV$. Hence

$$-dV = E_s \, ds$$

or

$$\boxed{E_s = -\frac{dV}{ds}.}$$
(21–19)

[This is merely the differential form of Eq. (21–15).]

The ratio dV/ds, or the rate of change of potential with distance in the direction of ds, is called the *potential gradient*, and E_s is the component of electric intensity in the direction of ds. Hence we have the important relation: *at any point in an electric field, the component of electric intensity in any direction is equal to the negative of the potential gradient in that direction.* In particular, if the direction of ds is the same as that of the electric intensity, the component of $\mathbf{E}$ in the direction of ds is equal to $\mathbf{E}$ and *the electric intensity is equal to the negative of the potential gradient in the direction of the field.*

Potential gradient is expressed in volts per meter, while electric intensity or force per unit charge is expressed in newtons per coulomb. However,

$$1\,\frac{\text{volt}}{\text{m}} = 1\,\frac{\text{joule/coul}}{\text{m}} = 1\,\frac{\text{n·m}}{\text{coul·m}} = 1\,\frac{\text{n}}{\text{coul}},$$

so that the volt/meter and the newton/coulomb are equivalent units.

As an example, we have shown that the potential at a radial distance r from a point charge q is

$$V = \frac{1}{4\pi\epsilon_0}\frac{q}{r}.$$

By symmetry, the electric intensity is in the radial direction, so

$$E = E_r = -\frac{dV}{dr}$$

$$= -\frac{d}{dr}\left(\frac{1}{4\pi\epsilon_0}\frac{q}{r}\right)$$

$$= \frac{1}{4\pi\epsilon_0}\frac{q}{r^2},$$

in agreement with Coulomb's law.

Suppose that a given electric field has been mapped by its network of lines of force and equipotential surfaces, with the (electrical) spacing between the equipotentials equal to some constant difference ΔV such as 1 volt or 100 volts. Let Δs represent the perpendicular distance between two equipotentials. Then Δs is in the direction of the field and it follows that

$$E = -\frac{\Delta V}{\Delta s}\text{ (approximately)}\qquad\text{or}\qquad \Delta s = -\frac{\Delta V}{E}.$$

That is, the greater the electric intensity E, the smaller the perpendicular distance Δs between the equipotentials. The equipotentials are therefore crowded close together in a strong field and are more widely separated in a weak field.

The geometrical relations between lines of force and equipotential surfaces afford a graphical method for determining the charge distribution and electric intensity in an arrangement of conductors where it would be difficult, if not impossible, to obtain an exact analytic expression for the desired result. Figure 21–6 is a sectional view of a long conductor perpendicular to the plane of the diagram. We know that the surface of the conductor is an equipotential, and also that at distances large compared with the dimensions of the body the equipotentials are cylindrical surfaces, since at a sufficiently great distance the body may be considered a line charge. Traces of the equipotentials may then be sketched, starting with one just outside the body and gradually altering the shape so that the trace approaches a circle. It will be found that the smaller the radius of curvature of the surface, the more closely must the equipotentials be spaced. The closest spacing occurs near the curved ends and the greatest spacing is outside the flat surfaces. The electric intensity is therefore greatest near the ends.

The lines of force may next be sketched in, making them everywhere perpendicular to the equipotentials, of which the surface of the conductor is one, and spacing them more closely together the smaller the separation of the equipotentials.

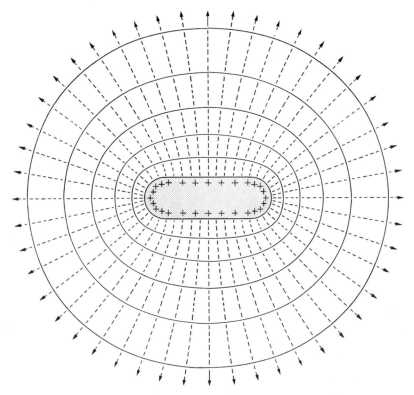

Fig. 21–6. Equipotential surfaces (solid lines) and lines of force (broken lines) about a conductor of irregular shape.

Finally, since the electric intensity just outside a surface is proportional to the surface density of charge, it follows that the surface density is greatest at the curved ends and least at the flat surfaces.

Note that although the surface density of charge is far from uniform over the surface of a body of irregular shape, the *potential* is necessarily constant over the entire surface.

21–8 The Van de Graaff generator. The Van de Graaff generator makes use of the fact that if a charged conductor is brought into *internal* contact with a second hollow conductor, *all* of its charge transfers to the hollow conductor no matter how high the potential of the latter may be. Thus, were it not for insulation difficulties, the charge, and hence the potential, of a hollow conductor could be raised to any desired value by successively adding charges to it by internal contact. Actually, since the conductor must be supported in some way, its maximum potential will be limited to that at which the rate of leakage of charge from it through

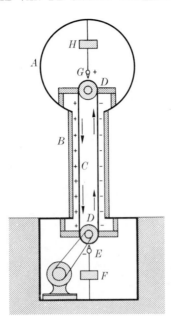

FIG. 21–7. Schematic diagram of a Van de Graaff generator.

its supports or through the surrounding air equals the rate at which charge is delivered to it.

The Van de Graaff generator is shown schematically in Fig. 21–7 and a photograph of the installation at M.I.T. in Fig. 21–8. Referring to Fig. 21–7, A is a hollow spherical conductor supported on an insulating hollow column B. A belt C passes over pulleys D, the lower pulley being driven by a motor while the upper one is an idler. Terminal E, which consists of a number of sharp points projecting from a horizontal rod, is maintained at a negative potential of some tens of thousands of volts relative to ground by the auxiliary source F. Terminal G, similarly constructed, is maintained at a positive potential with respect to the spherical terminal A. The air around the points becomes ionized and a "spray" of ions is repelled from each set of points, negative ions from E and positive ions from G. Some of these attach themselves to the surface of the moving belt, so that the upward moving half becomes negatively and the other half positively charged. The ion current at terminals E and G is adjusted so that, first, the charge carried toward either terminal is neutralized and, second, an equal charge of opposite sign is deposited on the belt.

The right-hand column in Fig. 21–8 encloses a giant x-ray tube some 20 ft long. The sphere at the top of this column houses the cathode of the tube. Electrons are driven down the tube by the potential difference

FIG. 21–8. Photograph of the Van de Graaff generator at the Massachusetts Institute of Technology. The column at the left houses an installation like that in Fig. 21–7. (Courtesy of M.I.T. News Service.)

between spheres and ground (about 2.5 million volts), and strike a metal anode mounted in a chamber below ground level. The anode then becomes a source of x-rays of short wavelength and great penetrating ability.

Van de Graaff generators are also used in nuclear physics research, where the large potential difference they can maintain is used to accelerate charged particles until they have enough energy to "smash" atomic nuclei. Atom smashers will be discussed again in Chapter 43.

Problems

21–1. A particle of charge $+3 \times 10^{-9}$ coul is situated in a uniform electric field directed to the left. In moving to the right a distance of 5 cm the work of an applied force is 6×10^{-5} joule and the change of kinetic energy is $+4.5 \times 10^{-5}$ joule. (a) What is the work of the electrical force? (b) What is the magnitude of the electric intensity?

21–2. A charge of 2.5×10^{-8} coul is placed in an upwardly directed uniform electric field whose intensity is 5×10^{4} n/coul. What is the work of the electrical force when the charge is moved (a) 45 cm to the right? (b) 80 cm downward? (c) 260 cm at an angle of 45° upward from the horizontal?

21–3. (a) Show that 1 n/coul = 1 volt/m. (b) A potential difference of 2000 volts is established across parallel plates in air. If the air becomes electrically conducting when the electric intensity exceeds 3×10^{6} n/coul, what is the minimum separation of the plates?

21–4. A small sphere of mass 0.2 gm hangs by a thread between two parallel vertical plates 5 cm apart. The charge on the sphere is 6×10^{-9} coul. What potential difference between the plates will cause the thread to assume an angle of 30° with the vertical?

21–5. Two positive point charges, each of magnitude q, are fixed on the y-axis at the points $y = +a$ and $y = -a$. (a) Draw a diagram showing the positions of the charges. (b) What is the potential V_0 at the origin? (c) Show that the potential at any point on the x-axis is

$$V = \frac{1}{4\pi\epsilon_0} \cdot \frac{2q}{\sqrt{a^2 + x^2}}.$$

(d) Sketch a graph of the potential on the x-axis as a function of x over the range from $x = +4a$ to $x = -4a$. (e) At what value of x is the potential one-half that at the origin?

21–6. Consider the same distribution of charges as in Problem 21–5. (a) Sketch a graph of the potential on the y-axis as a function of y, over the range from $y = +4a$ to $y = -4a$. (b) Discuss the physical meaning of the graph at the points $+a$ and $-a$. (c) At what point or points on the y-axis is the potential equal to that at the origin? (d) At what points on the y-axis is the potential equal to half its value at the origin?

21–7. Consider the same charge distribution as in Problem 21–5. (a) Suppose a positively charged particle of charge q' and mass m is placed precisely at the origin and released from rest. What happens? (b) What will happen if the charge in part (a) is displaced slightly in the direction of the y-axis? (c) What will happen if it is displaced slightly in the direction of the x-axis?

21–8. Again consider the charge distribution in Problem 21–5. Suppose a positively charged particle of charge q' and mass m is displaced slightly from the origin in the direction of the x-axis. (a) What is its velocity at infinity? (b) Sketch a graph of the velocity of the particle as a function of x. (c) If the particle is projected toward the left along the x-axis from a point at a large distance to the right of the origin, with a velocity half that acquired in part (a), at what distance from the origin will it come to rest? (d) If a negatively charged particle were released from rest on the x-axis, at a very large distance to the left of the origin, what would be its velocity as it passed the origin?

21–9. A positive charge $+q$ is located at the point $x = -a$, $y = -a$, and an equal negative charge $-q$ is located at the point $x = +a$, $y = -a$. (a) Draw a diagram showing the positions of the charges. (b) What is the potential at the origin? (c) What is the expression for the potential at a point on the x-axis, as a function of x? (d) Sketch a graph of the potential as a function of x, in the range from $x = +4a$ to $x = -4a$. Plot positive potentials upward, negative potentials downward.

21–10. In an apparatus for measuring the electronic charge e by Millikan's method, an electric intensity of 6.34×10^4 volts/m is required to maintain a charged oil drop at rest. If the plates are 1.5 cm apart, what potential difference between them is required?

21–11. A potential difference of 1600 volts is established across two parallel plates 4 cm apart. An electron is released from the negative plate at the same instant that a proton is released from the positive plate. (a) How far from the positive plate will they pass each other? (b) How do their velocities compare when they strike the opposite plates? (c) How do their energies compare when they strike the opposite plates?

21–12. (a) Prove that when a particle of constant mass and charge is accelerated from rest in an electric field, its final velocity is proportional to the square root of the potential difference through which it is accelerated. (b) Find the magnitude of the proportionality constant if the particle is an electron, the velocity is in m/sec, and the potential difference is in volts. (c) At velocities much greater than $\frac{1}{10}$ of

the velocity of light, the mass of a body becomes appreciably larger than its "rest mass" and cannot be considered constant. (The velocity of light is 3×10^8 m/sec.) Through what voltage must an electron be accelerated, assuming no change in its mass, to acquire a velocity $\frac{1}{10}$ that of light?

21–13. The potential at a certain distance from a point charge is 600 volts, and the electric field is 200 n/coul. (a) What is the distance to the point charge? (b) What is the magnitude of the charge?

21–14. Two point charges whose magnitudes are $+20 \times 10^{-9}$ coul and -12×10^{-9} coul are separated by a distance of 5 cm. An electron is released from rest between the two charges, 1 cm from the negative charge, and moves along the line connecting the two charges. What is its velocity when it is 1 cm from the positive charge?

21–15. A vacuum diode consists of a cylindrical cathode 0.05 cm in radius, mounted coaxially within a cylindrical anode 0.45 cm in radius. The potential of the anode is 300 volts above that of the cathode. An electron leaves the surface of the cathode with zero initial velocity. Find its velocity when it strikes the anode.

21–16. A vacuum triode may be idealized as follows. A plane surface (the cathode) emits electrons with negligible initial velocities. Parallel to the cathode and 3 mm away from it is an open grid of fine wire at a potential of 18 volts above the cathode. A second plane surface (the anode) is 12 mm beyond the grid and is at a potential of 15 volts above the cathode. Assume that the plane of the grid is an equipotential surface, and that the potential gradient between cathode and grid, and between grid and anode, are uniform. Assume also that the structure of the grid is sufficiently open for electrons to pass through it freely. (a) Draw a diagram of potential $vs.$ distance, along a line from cathode to anode. (b) With what velocity will electrons strike the anode?

21–17. What is the final velocity of an electron accelerated through a potential difference of 1136 volts if it has an initial velocity of 10^7 m/sec?

21–18. Suppose the potential difference between the spherical terminal of a Van de Graaff generator and the point at which charges are sprayed onto the upward moving belt is 2 million volts. If the belt delivers negative charge to the sphere at the rate of 2×10^{-3} coul/sec and removes positive charge at the same rate, what horsepower must be expended to drive the belt against electrical forces?

21–19. A positively charged ring of radius a is placed with its plane perpendicular to the x-axis and with its center at the origin. (a) Construct a graph of the potential V at points on the x-axis, as a function of x. (b) Construct in the same diagram a graph of the magnitude of the electric intensity E. (c) How is the second graph related geometrically to the first?

21–20. Consider the same charge distribution as in Problem 21–5. (a) Construct a graph of the potential energy of a positive point charge on the x-axis, as a function of x. (b) Construct a graph of the potential energy of a negative point charge on the x-axis, as a function of x. (c) What is the potential gradient at the origin, in the direction of the x-axis?

CHAPTER 22

CURRENT AND RESISTANCE

22-1 Current. In purely electrostatic problems such as those considered in the preceding chapters, one is concerned chiefly with the forces between charges, the final, steady-state distribution of charge brought about by these forces, and the motion of charged particles in empty space. We are next to discuss the motion of charge in a conductor when an electric field is maintained within the conductor. This motion constitutes a *current*.

A conductor, it will be recalled, is a material within which there are "free" charges which will move when a force is exerted on them by an electric field. The free charges in a *metallic* conductor are negative electrons. The free charges in an *electrolyte* are ions, both positive and negative. A *gas* under the proper conditions, as in a neon sign or a fluorescent lamp, is also a conductor and its free charges are positive and negative ions and negative electrons.

We have seen that when an isolated conductor is placed in an electric field the charges within the conductor rearrange themselves so as to make the interior of the conductor a field-free region throughout which the potential is constant. The motion of the charges in the rearranging process constitutes a current, but it is of short duration only and is called a *transient* current. If we wish to maintain a continuous current in a conductor, we must continuously maintain a field, i.e. a potential gradient, within it. If the field is always in the same direction, even though it may fluctuate in magnitude, the current is called *direct*. If the field reverses direction periodically, the flow of charge reverses also and the current is *alternating*. Direct and alternating currents are abbreviated to d-c and a-c respectively.

A number of electrical devices, which we shall discuss in detail later, have the property of maintaining their terminals continuously at different potentials. The most familiar of these are the dry cell, the storage battery, and the generator. If the ends of a wire are connected to the terminals of any one of these devices, a potential gradient or an electric field will be maintained within the wire and there will be a continuous motion of charge through it. To be specific, if the ends of a copper wire one meter long are connected to the terminals of a 6-volt storage battery, a potential gradient or electric field of intensity 6 volts/m or 6 n/coul is established and maintained along the wire.

When there is an electric field in a conductor the *free* charges within it are set in motion, positive charges moving in the same direction as the

438

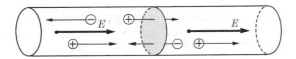

FIG. 22–1. Negative charges crossing a section from right to left are equivalent to positive charges crossing from left to right.

field, negative charges in the opposite direction. Figure 22–1 shows a portion of a conductor within which there is an electric field of intensity E. A few positive and negative free charges are also shown. In a given time interval a certain number of positive charges cross the shaded section from left to right, while negative charges cross it from right to left. Let q_+ represent the total positive charge crossing the section, and q_- the total negative charge crossing in the same time. The effect of positive charge crossing the section is to increase the net positive charge at the right of the section. But since *removal* of *negative* charge is equivalent to *addition* of *positive* charge, the negative charge crossing from right to left also increases the net positive charge at the right of the section. Therefore the total increase in positive charge q at the right of the section equals the *sum* of q_+ and q_-:

$$q = q_+ + q_- .$$

For example, if 4 coul of positive charge cross from left to right and 2 coul of negative charge cross from right to left, the total increase in positive charge at the right of the section is

$$q = 4 \text{ coul} + 2 \text{ coul} = 6 \text{ coul}.$$

The result is the same as if 6 coul of positive charge had crossed the section from left to right.

The *current* at the section, represented by the symbol i, is defined as the total rate of transfer of positive charge across the section, or as the total positive charge crossing per unit time. Thus, in the example above, if the time interval was 2 sec, the current was

$$i = \frac{6 \text{ coul}}{2 \text{ sec}} = 3 \frac{\text{coul}}{\text{sec}} .$$

More precisely, we should consider the total charge dq crossing the section in a time interval dt, and define the instantaneous current i as

$$i = \frac{dq}{dt} . \qquad (22\text{–}1)$$

The mks unit of current, *one coulomb per second*, is called one *ampere*, in honor of the French scientist André Marie Ampere (1775–1836), who developed many of the concepts of electricity and magnetism. Small currents are more conveniently expressed in milliamperes (ma) (1 milliampere $= 10^{-3}$ amp) or in microamperes (μa) (1 microampere $= 10^{-6}$ amp).

Since a current is a flow of charge, the common expression "flow of current" should be avoided, since literally it means "flow of flow of charge."

It might seem logical to define the *direction* of a current as the direction of motion of the free charges. We immediately come up against the difficulty, however, that in an electrolytic or gaseous conductor free charges of *both* signs are in motion in *opposite* directions. Whichever direction is assigned to the current, we would find charges moving in the opposite direction. Since some convention must be adopted, it has been agreed to speak of the direction of a current as if the carriers were all positive charges. In a *metallic* conductor, it is only the negative charges or free electrons which are mobile. Hence the entire current in a metallic conductor arises from the motion of negative charges, and *in a metallic conductor the electrons move in the opposite direction to the conventional current.* From now on we shall adopt this convention, and indeed shall often speak of the current in a metal as though it arose from the motion of positive charges alone.

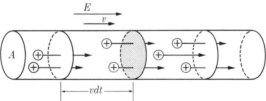

FIGURE 22–2

The current in a conductor can be expressed in terms of the velocity of the moving charges as follows. Consider a conductor of cross-sectional area A in which positively charged particles are moving from left to right, as in Fig. 22–2. Suppose there are n particles per unit volume, all moving with velocity v. In a time interval dt, each advances a distance $v\,dt$. The number of particles crossing any section such as that shaded is equal to the number contained in a portion of the conductor of length $v\,dt$ and of volume $vA\,dt$. This number is $nvA\,dt$, and if the charge on each is e, the total charge crossing the section is

$$dq = nevA\,dt.$$

The current is therefore

$$i = \frac{dq}{dt} = nevA. \tag{22-2}$$

In general, if any number of different kinds of charged particles are present, in different concentrations and moving with different velocities, the total charge crossing a section is

$$dq = A\ dt(n_1e_1v_1 + n_2e_2v_2 + \cdots)$$

and the current is

$$i = \frac{dq}{dt} = A\sum nev. \tag{22–3}$$

All of the *nev* products will have the same sign, since charges of opposite sign move in opposite directions.

If the charges in a conductor were perfectly free to move indefinitely, they would accelerate under the influence of the applied field, their velocities would continuously increase, and the current would continuously increase. This is not observed to happen; the current remains constant so long as the electric field is constant. This can be explained by assuming that after a momentary acceleration a moving particle collides with one of the fixed particles in the conductor and is slowed down or brought to rest, after which it again accelerates, and so on. It thus moves with a certain average velocity, called the *drift* velocity, which must be interpreted as the velocity v in the preceding equations. The collisions with the fixed particles result in a transfer of energy to them which increases their energy of vibration and results in the development of heat. This production of heat in a current-carrying conductor is discussed further in Section 22–7.

Let us estimate the drift velocity of the free electrons in a conductor. Consider a copper conductor of cross-sectional area 1 cm^2 or 10^{-4} m^2 in which the current is 200 amp. Previous calculations have shown that there are in copper about 8.5×10^{28} free electrons per cubic meter, on the assumption that each copper atom contributes two free electrons. Then

$$v = \frac{i}{enA}$$

$$= \frac{200\ \text{coul/sec}}{1.6 \times 10^{-19}\ (\text{coul/electron}) \times 8.5 \times 10^{28}\ (\text{electrons/m}^3) \times 10^{-4}\ \text{m}^2}$$

$$= 1.47 \times 10^{-4}\ \frac{\text{m}}{\text{sec}},$$

or about 0.02 cm/sec. The drift velocity is therefore quite small.

The drift velocity of the free electrons should not be confused with the velocity of propagation of an electromagnetic wave along the conductor, which, if the conductor is in vacuum, is the same as the velocity of light; that is, 3×10^8 m/sec or 186,000 mi/sec.

22–2 The complete circuit. When the ends of a wire are connected to two points maintained at fixed, but different, potentials, such as the terminals of a cell or generator, there will be a current in the wire but the potential of each point of the wire remains constant in time. Consider any short element of the wire bounded by two transverse planes and shown shaded in Fig. 22–3. If the electrons in the wire are moving from left to right, negative charge is entering the element at its left face and leaving it at its right face. The quantity of charge entering the element in any time interval must be exactly equal to that leaving, for if it were not, the quantity of charge in the element, and hence the potential of the element, would change. We conclude that the current must be the same at both faces of the element, and therefore must be the same at *all* sections of the wire. In this respect a flow of electrons is like the flow of an incompressible fluid.

The conducting wire and the cell or generator to which its ends are connected are said to form a complete circuit or a *closed circuit*. An electrolytic cell is represented by the symbol ⊣⊢ and a generator by ⊸○ᵗ, the + sign denoting the terminal which is normally at the higher potential. Figure 22–4 is a diagram of such a closed circuit. The light line marked with arrowheads indicates the direction of the conventional current. The electrons in the wire circulate in the opposite direction. The positive ions within the cell move in the same direction as the conventional current, the negative ions in the opposite direction.

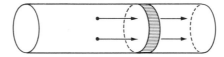

FIG. 22–3. Electric charge entering and leaving a small element of a wire.

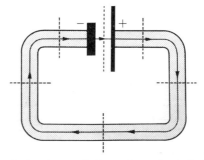

FIG. 22–4. A closed circuit consisting of an electrolytic cell and a wire.

A number of cross sections of the circuit are indicated by dotted lines. The current is the same at all these sections, including the one through the cell. *Current is not something which squirts out of the positive terminal of a cell and gets all used up by the time it reaches the negative terminal.* A steady current can exist only in a closed circuit equivalent to that of Fig. 22–4. If the wire is disconnected from the cell at either end, or if a break is made at any other point of the circuit, the current immediately ceases. The circuit is then said to be *open*.

Note carefully that the direction of the *conventional* current is "from plus to minus" *in the external circuit only*. Within the cell, the direction is from minus to plus.

22–3 Resistivity, resistance, and Ohm's law. The current i in a given conductor depends on the electric intensity E in the conductor. In a pure metal, the current is directly proportional to the electric intensity. For other materials, the relation between i and E is more complicated. In any case, we can define a property of a conductor called its *resistivity* ρ, as the ratio of the electric intensity to the current per unit cross-sectional area:

$$\rho = \frac{E}{i/A}. \tag{22–4}$$

Let V_a and V_b be the potentials at two points on a conductor separated by a length L. The electric intensity E in the conductor then equals the potential gradient $(V_a - V_b)/L$. Hence we can write Eq. (22–4) as

$$\rho = \frac{V_a - V_b}{iL/A},$$

or

$$i = \frac{V_a - V_b}{\rho L/A}. \tag{22–5}$$

The electrical *conductivity* of a material, σ, is defined as the reciprocal of the resistivity ρ. In terms of σ, we can write Eq. (22–5) in the form

$$i = \sigma A \frac{V_a - V_b}{L}.$$

It is then exactly analogous to the equation of steady-state heat conduction,

$$H = KA \frac{t_2 - t_1}{L}.$$

The electrical current i corresponds to the heat current H, the electrical conductivity σ to the thermal conductivity K, and the potential gradient $(V_a - V_b)/L$ to the temperature gradient $(t_2 - t_1)/L$.

The relation between the conduction of electricity and the conduction of heat is more than a mere mathematical analogy. The free electrons which are the carriers of charge in electrical conduction also play an important role in the conduction of heat, and hence a correlation can be expected between electrical and thermal conductivity. It is a familiar fact that good electrical conductors, such as the metals, are good conductors of heat, while poor electrical conductors are also poor conductors of heat.

The quantity $\rho L / A$ is called the *resistance R* of the conductor:

$$R = \frac{\rho L}{A}.$$

(22–6)

In terms of resistance, Eq. (22–5) becomes

$$i = \frac{V_a - V_b}{R} = \frac{V_{ab}}{R}.$$

(22–7)

If the current per unit area in a conductor is directly proportional to E, the resistivity ρ of the conductor is a constant and, therefore, for a conductor of given length L and area A, the resistance R is a constant also, independent of i and E. That is, for such a conductor, the current i is directly proportional to the potential difference V_{ab} or is a *linear* function of V_{ab}. The conductor is called a *linear* conductor, and Fig. 22–5(a) is a graph of i vs. V_{ab} for such a conductor.

This direct proportionality between the current in a metallic conductor and the potential difference between its terminals was discovered experimentally by the German scientist Georg Simon Ohm (1789–1854), and is known as *Ohm's law*.

From Eq. (22–7), the resistance R of any electrical device can be defined as the ratio of the potential difference between its terminals to the current through it:

$$R = \frac{V_{ab}}{i}.$$

(22–8)

The graphs in Fig. 22–5(b), (c), and (d) illustrate the behavior of *nonlinear* conductors, where resistance is not constant. In part (b) the resistance decreases with V_{ab}, in part (c) it increases, and in (d) it is first constant and then decreases.

The unit of resistance is the *volt per ampere*. A resistance of one volt per ampere is called one *ohm*. That is, *the resistance of a conductor is one ohm if the potential difference between the terminals of the conductor is one volt when the current in the conductor is one ampere.*

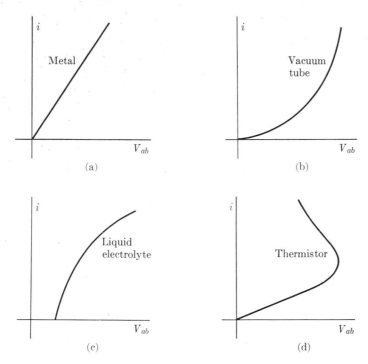

FIG. 22–5. Four examples of the relation between current and potential difference. (a) A metal, where R is constant. (b) A vacuum tube, where R decreases. (c) An electrolyte (liquid), where R increases. (d) A thermistor, where R is first constant and then decreases.

The Greek letter Ω (omega) is used to designate a resistance in ohms. Thus a resistance of 4.5 volts/amp or 4.5 ohms is written

$$4.5 \ \Omega.$$

Large resistances are more conveniently expressed in megohms (1 megohm $= 10^6$ ohms) and small resistances in microhms (1 microhm $= 10^{-6}$ ohm).

Resistance units constructed to introduce into a circuit lumped resistances large compared with those of leads and contacts are called *resistors*. A resistor is represented by the symbol ⌇⌇⌇.

Portions of a circuit of negligible resistance are shown by straight lines.

An adjustable resistor is called a *rheostat*. A common type is constructed by winding resistance wire on a porcelain or enamel tube, and making connections to one end and to a sliding contact. A rheostat is represented by ⌇⌇⌇ or simply ⌇⌇⌇ .

22–4 Calculation of resistance. The resistance of a homogeneous conductor of constant cross section is given by Eq. (22–6):

$$R = \frac{\rho L}{A}.$$

The resistance is proportional to the length of the conductor and inversely proportional to its cross section. If the conductor is of unit length and unit cross section, the ratio L/A is unity and the resistance R and the resistivity ρ are numerically equal. Hence the resistivity of a material is numerically equal to the resistance of a specimen of the material of unit length and unit cross-sectional area.

In the mks system, where the unit of length is the meter and the unit of area the square meter, the unit of resistivity is one *ohm·meter*. The resistivity of a material in ohm·meters is numerically equal to the resistance, in ohms, between opposite faces of a cube of the material one meter on a side. If the centimeter is used as a unit of length and the square centimeter as a unit of area, resistivities are expressed in *ohm·centimeters*.

It is evident from the significance of resistivity that materials having large resistivities are poor conductors or good insulators. Conversely, substances of small resistivity are good conductors. No perfect insulator ($\rho = \infty$) exists, nor does a perfect conductor* ($\rho = 0$). There is, however, a wide difference in the resistivities of different materials, so that in general they can be grouped into two classes, conductors and insulators. See Table 22–1.

The resistivity of a pure metal in a definite crystalline state and at a definite temperature is a quantity characteristic of the metal. Changes in the crystalline structure due to heat treatment or mechanical strain, or impurities alloyed with the metal even in minute quantities, may have a pronounced effect on its resistivity. For example, the resistivity of commercial annealed copper at 20°C is 1.72×10^{-8} ohm·m, that of hard drawn copper is 1.77×10^{-8} ohm·m.

EXAMPLE 1. What is the average electric intensity in the copper conductor referred to in the example in Section 22–1?

From Eq. (22–2), the electric intensity E is

$$E = \frac{\rho i}{A}.$$

---

* At extremely low temperatures, near absolute zero, some conductors lose the last vestige of resistance, a phenomenon known as *superconductivity*. A current once started in such a conductor will continue of itself so long as the temperature is maintained at the proper value.

RESISTIVITIES AT ROOM TEMPERATURE

Conductors	ρ, ohm·meters	Insulators	ρ, ohm·meters
Aluminum	2.63×10^{-8}	Amber	5×10^{14}
Carbon	3500×10^{-8}	Glass	$10^{10} - 10^{14}$
Constantan	49×10^{-8}	Lucite	$> 10^{13}$
Copper	1.72×10^{-8}	Mica	$10^{11} - 10^{15}$
Manganin	44×10^{-8}	Quartz (fused)	75×10^{16}
Nichrome	100×10^{-8}	Sulfur	10^{15}
Silver	1.47×10^{-8}	Teflon	$> 10^{13}$
Tungsten	5.51×10^{-8}	Wood	$10^{8} - 10^{11}$

From Table 22–1, the resistivity of copper is 1.72×10^{-8} ohm·m. Therefore,

$$E = \frac{1.72 \times 10^{-8} \text{ ohm·m} \times 200 \text{ amp}}{10^{-4} \text{ m}^2} = 0.0344 \frac{\text{volt}}{\text{m}}.$$

EXAMPLE 2. What is the potential difference between two points on the above wire 100 m apart?

(a) Since the electric intensity or potential gradient is 0.0344 volt/m, the potential difference between two points 100 m apart is

$$V_a - V_b = 0.0344 \frac{\text{volt}}{\text{m}} \times 100 \text{ m} = 3.44 \text{ volts.}$$

(b) The more common method of solution would be to first compute the resistance of the wire from $R = \rho L/A$ and then find the potential difference from $V_{ab} = Ri$. We have

$$R = \frac{1.72 \times 10^{-8} \text{ ohm·m} \times 100 \text{ m}}{10^{-4} \text{ m}^2} = 0.0172 \text{ ohm.}$$

Then

$$V_{ab} = 0.0172 \text{ ohm} \times 200 \text{ amp} = 3.44 \text{ volts,}$$

which is the same as the previous answer.

22–5 Measurement of current, potential difference, and resistance. Currents are measured by instruments called *galvanometers* or *ammeters*. The most common type makes use of the interaction between a current-carrying conductor and a magnetic field and is described in Chapter 25. For our present purposes it is sufficient to know that such instruments exist.

To measure the current at a point such as a, b, or c in Fig. 22–6(a), the circuit must be opened and the ammeter inserted at that point so that the current to be measured passes *through* the ammeter, as in Fig. 22–6(b). An ammeter is a low-resistance instrument, representative values being a few hundredths or thousandths of an ohm.

The potential difference between two points of a circuit might be measured with an electroscope or electrometer. It is more convenient, however, to use some type of *voltmeter*, the construction of which is described more fully in Chapter 25. Most voltmeters, unlike electroscopes and electrometers, are current operated. The voltmeter terminals are connected to the points between which the potential difference is to be measured. Figure 22–6(b) shows a voltmeter V connected so as to measure the potential difference between the terminals of the cell. If the details of its construction are disregarded, a voltmeter may be treated as a resistor which automatically indicates the potential difference between its terminals. Typical resistances, for a 100-volt instrument, are from 10,000 to 100,000 ohms.

The resistance of a conductor is the ratio of the potential difference between its terminals to the current in it. The most straightforward

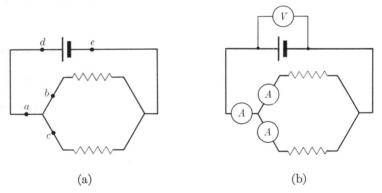

(a)   (b)

FIG. 22–6. Ammeter and voltmeter connections.

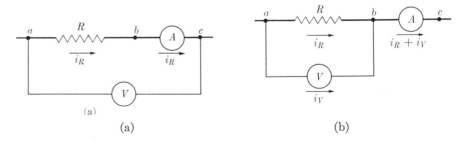

(a)   (b)

FIG. 22–7. Ammeter-voltmeter methods of measuring resistance.

method of measuring resistance is therefore to measure these two quantities and divide one by the other. The ammeter-voltmeter method for so doing is illustrated in Fig. 22–7. In circuit (a) the ammeter measures the current i_R in the resistor, but the voltmeter reads V_{ac} and not the potential difference V_{ab} between the terminals of the resistor. In circuit (b) the voltmeter reads V_{ab}, but the ammeter reads the *sum* of the currents in the resistor and in the voltmeter. Hence, whichever circuit is used, corrections must be made to the reading of one meter or the other, unless these corrections can be shown to be negligible.

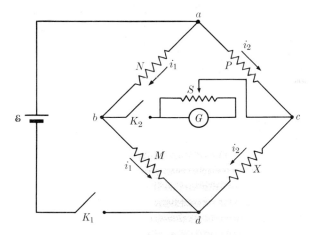

FIG. 22–8. Wheatstone bridge circuit.

22–6 The Wheatstone bridge. The Wheatstone bridge circuit, shown in Fig. 22–8, is widely used for the rapid and precise measurement of resistance. It was invented in 1843 by the English scientist Charles Wheatstone. M, N, and P are adjustable resistors which have been previously calibrated, and X represents the unknown resistance. To use the bridge, switches K_1 and K_2 are closed and the resistance of P is adjusted until the galvanometer G shows no deflection. Points b and c must then be at the same potential or, in other words, the potential drop from a to b equals that from a to c. Also, the drop from b to d equals that from c to d. Since the galvanometer current is zero, the current in M equals that in N, say i_1, and the current in P equals that in X, say i_2. Then, since $V_{ab} = V_{ac}$, it follows that

$$i_1 N = i_2 P,$$

and since $V_{bd} = V_{cd}$,

$$i_1 M = i_2 X.$$

When the second equation is divided by the first, we find

$$X = \frac{M}{N} P.$$

Hence if M, N, and P are known, X can be computed. The ratio M/N is usually set at some integral power of 10, such as 0.01, 1, 100, etc., for simplicity in computation.

During preliminary adjustments, when the bridge may be far from balance and V_{bc} large, the galvanometer must be protected by the shunt S. A resistor whose resistance is large compared with that of the galvanometer is permanently connected across the galvanometer terminals. When the sliding contact is at the left end of the resistor, none of the current in the path between b and c passes through the galvanometer. In a position such as that shown, that portion of the resistor at the right of the sliding contact is in series with the galvanometer, and this combination is shunted by that portion of the resistor at the left of the contact. Hence only a fraction of the current passes through the galvanometer. With the sliding contact at the right of the resistor, all the current passes through the galvanometer except the small fraction by-passed by the resistor. The galvanometer is therefore fully protected when the contact is at the left end of the resistor and practically full galvanometer sensitivity is attained when the contact is at the right end.

If any of the resistances are inductive, the potentials V_b and V_c may attain their final values at different rates when K_1 is closed, and the galvanometer, if connected between b and c, would show an initial deflection even though the bridge were in balance. Hence K_1 and K_2 are frequently combined in a double key which closes the battery circuit first and the galvanometer circuit a moment later, after the transient currents have died out.

Portable bridges are available having a self-contained galvanometer and dry cells. The ratio M/N can be set at any integral power of 10 between 0.001 and 1000 by a single dial switch, and the value of R can be adjusted by four dial switches.

22–7 Joule's law. The electronic motion in a conductor may be described as a series of accelerations, each of which is terminated by a collision with one of the fixed particles of the conductor. The electrons gain kinetic energy in the free paths between collisions, and give up to the fixed particles, in each collision, the same amount of energy they have gained. The energy acquired by the fixed particles (which are "fixed" only in the sense that their *mean* position does not change) increases their amplitude of vibration. In other words, it is converted to heat.

FIG. 22–9. Transfer of charge in a portion of a circuit.

To derive the expression for the rate of development of heat in a conductor, we first work out the general expression for the power input to any portion of an electric circuit. The rectangle in Fig. 22–9 represents a portion of a circuit in which there is a (conventional) current i from left to right. V_a and V_b are the potentials at terminals a and b. The nature of the circuit between a and b is immaterial—it may be a conductor, motor, generator, battery, or any combination of these. The power input, as we shall show, depends only on the magnitudes and relative directions of the current and the terminal potential difference.

In a time interval dt, a quantity of charge $dq = i\,dt$ enters the portion of the circuit under consideration at terminal a, and in the same time an equal quantity of charge leaves at terminal b. There has thus been a transfer of charge dq from a potential V_a to a potential V_b. The energy dW given up by the charge is

$$dW = dq(V_a - V_b) = i\,dt\,V_{ab},$$

and the *rate* at which energy is given up, or the power input P, is

$$P = \frac{dW}{dt} = iV_{ab}. \tag{22–9}$$

That is, the power is equal to the product of the current and the potential difference. If the current is in amperes or coul/sec and the potential difference in volts or joules/coul, the power is in joules/sec or watts, since

$$1\ \text{amp} \times 1\ \text{volt} = 1\,\frac{\text{coul}}{\text{sec}} \times 1\,\frac{\text{joule}}{\text{coul}} = 1\,\frac{\text{joule}}{\text{sec}} = 1\ \text{watt}.$$

Equation (22–9) is a perfectly general relation that holds whatever the nature of the circuit elements between a and b. We shall return to it later on.

In the special case in which the circuit between a and b is a pure resistance R, all of the energy supplied is irreversibly converted to heat, and in this special case the potential difference V_{ab} is given by

$$V_{ab} = iR.$$

Hence

$$P = iV_{ab} = i \times iR,$$

or

$$P = i^2 R. \tag{22–10}$$

To bring out more explicitly that in this special case the energy appears as heat, we may set $P = dH/dt$, where dH is the heat developed in time dt. Equation (22–10) then becomes

$$\frac{dH}{dt} = i^2 R.$$

(22–11)

If the conductor is linear, i.e., if R is a constant independent of i, Eq. (22–11) states that *the rate of development of heat is directly proportional to the square of the current*. This fact was discovered experimentally by Joule in the course of his measurements of the mechanical equivalent of heat, and it is known as *Joule's law*. Of course, it is a law only in the same sense as is Ohm's law, that is, it expresses a special property of certain materials rather than a general property of all matter. A material which obeys Ohm's law necessarily obeys Joule's law also, and the two are not independent relations.

If in Eq. (22–11) the resistance is expressed in ohms and the current in amperes, the rate of development of heat is in joules/sec or watts, since

$$1 \text{ amp}^2 \times 1 \text{ ohm} = 1 \text{ amp}^2 \times 1 \frac{\text{volt}}{\text{amp}} = 1 \text{ amp} \times 1 \text{ volt} = 1 \text{ watt}.$$

This can readily be converted to cal/sec from the relation 1 calorie = 4.186 joules.

Note that the *rate of development of heat* in a conductor is not the same thing as the *rate of increase of temperature* of the conductor. The latter depends on the heat capacity of the conductor and the rate at which heat can escape from the conductor by conduction, convection, and radiation. The rate of loss of heat increases as the temperature of the conductor increases, and the temperature of a current-carrying conductor will rise until the rate of loss of heat equals the rate of development of heat, after which the temperature remains constant. Thus when the circuit is closed through an incandescent lamp, the temperature of the filament rises rapidly until the rate of heat loss (chiefly by radiation) equals the rate of development of heat, $i^2 R$. On the other hand, a fuse is constructed so that when the current in it exceeds a certain predetermined value, the fuse melts before its final equilibrium temperature can be attained.

PROBLEMS

22-1. A silver wire 1 mm in diameter carries a charge of 90 coul in 1 hr and 15 min. Silver contains 5.8×10^{22} free electrons per cm^3. (a) What is the current in the wire? (b) What is the drift velocity of the electrons in the wire?

22-2. When a sufficiently high potential difference is applied between two electrodes in a gas, the gas ionizes, electrons moving toward the positive electrode and positive ions toward the negative electrode. (a) What is the current in a hydrogen discharge tube if in each second 4×10^{18} electrons and 1.5×10^{18} protons move in opposite directions past a cross section of the tube? (b) What is the direction of the current?

22-3. A vacuum diode can be approximated by a plane cathode and a plane anode, parallel to each other and 5 mm apart. The area of both cathode and anode is 2 cm^2. In the region between cathode and anode the current is carried solely by electrons. If the electron current is 50 ma, and the electrons strike the anode surface with a velocity of 1.2×10^7 m/sec, find the number of electrons per cubic millimeter in the space just outside the surface of the anode.

22-4. The belt of a Van de Graaff generator is one meter wide and travels with a speed of 25 m/sec. (a) Neglecting leakage, at what rate in coul/sec must charge be sprayed on one face of the belt to correspond to a current of 10^{-4} amp into the collecting sphere? (b) Compute the surface charge per unit area on the belt.

22-5. In the Bohr model of the hydrogen atom the electron makes about 0.6×10^{16} rev/sec around the

nucleus. What is the average current at a point on the orbit of the electron?

22-6. A wire 100 m long and 2 mm in diameter has a resistivity of 4.8×10^{-8} ohm·m. (a) What is the resistance of the wire? (b) A second wire of the same material has the same weight as the 100-meter length, but twice its diameter. What is its resistance?

22-7. (a) The following measurements of current and potential difference were made on a resistor constructed of Nichrome wire:

i (amp)	V_{ab} (volts)
0.5	2.18
1.0	4.36
2.0	8.72
4.0	17.44

Make a graph of V_{ab} as a function of i. Does the Nichrome obey Ohm's law? What is the resistance of the resistor, in ohms?

(b) The following measurements were made on a Thyrite resistor.

i (amp)	V_{ab} (volts)
0.5	4.76
1.0	5.81
2.0	7.05
4.0	8.56

Make a graph of V_{ab} as a function of i. Does Thyrite have constant resistance? What is the resistance of the resistor?

22-8. An aluminum bar 2.5 m long has a rectangular cross section 1 cm by 5 cm. (a) What is its resistance? (b) What would be the length of an iron wire 15 mm in diameter having the same resistance?

22–9. An electrical power line using No. 4 copper wire has a resistance of 0.248 ohm per 1000 ft and carries a current of 30 amp. If the potential at a point on the line is 250 volts, what is the potential at a point 5 miles farther along the line in the direction of the current?

22–10. A solid cube of silver has a mass of 84.0 gm. What is its resistance between opposite faces?

22–11. Refer to Fig. 22–5, where four different relations between current and potential difference are shown. Draw four corresponding graphs showing the qualitative relation between R and V_{ab}.

22–12. The international ampere is based on electrochemical measurements and equals 0.9998 abs amp. One international volt is equivalent to how many absolute volts?

22–13. A resistor develops heat at the rate of 40 watts when the potential difference across its ends is 60 volts. What is its resistance?

22–14. A motor operating on 120 volts draws a current of 2 amp. If heat is developed in the motor at the rate of 9 cal/sec, what is its efficiency?

22–15. No. 18 B and S rubber-covered copper wire has a diameter of 1.024 mm and an allowable carrying capacity of 3 amp. How many watts are dissipated per meter when the wire carries this current?

22–16. A "660-watt" electric heater is designed to operate from 120-volt lines. (a) What is its resistance? (b) What current does it draw? (c) What is the rate of development of heat, in cal/sec? (d) If the line voltage drops to 110 volts, what power does the heater take, in watts? (Assume the resistance constant. Actually, it will change somewhat because of the change in temperature.)

22–17. Express the rate of development of heat in a resistor in terms of (a) potential difference and current, (b) resistance and current, (c) potential difference and resistance.

22–18. The current in a wire varies with time according to the relation

$$i = 4 + 2t^2,$$

where i is in amperes and t in seconds. (a) How many coulombs pass a cross section of the wire in the time interval between $t = 5$ sec and $t = 10$ sec? (b) What constant current would transport the same charge in the same time interval?

22–19. The current in a wire varies with time according to the relation

$$i = 20 \sin 377t,$$

where i is in amperes, t in seconds, and $(377t)$ in radians. (a) How many coulombs pass a cross section of the wire in the time interval between $t = 0$ and $t = 1/120$ sec? (b) In the interval between $t = 0$ and $t = 1/60$ sec? (c) What constant current would transport the same charge in each of the intervals above?

CHAPTER 23

DIRECT-CURRENT CIRCUITS

23–1 Electromotive force. We have shown in the preceding chapter that in order to have a current in a conductor, an electric field must be maintained in the conductor. We have also shown that a continuous energy input is necessary to maintain the current, the energy being converted to heat in the conductor. The development of heat in a conductor is an "irreversible" process in the thermodynamic sense. That is, while energy is conserved in the process, the heat developed cannot be reconverted to electrical energy except under the restrictions imposed by the second law of thermodynamics.

We now wish to consider another type of energy transformation, one which is reversible in the thermodynamic sense. Devices in which such reversible transformations occur are the storage battery, the generator, and the motor. (There are other devices also, but they need not concern us at present.) Consider a storage battery which is operating the starting motor of an automobile. The internal energy of the materials in the battery is decreasing, and is converted to mechanical form available at the shaft of the starter motor. After the automobile engine starts, the starting motor is disconnected and the generator sends a reversed, charging current through the storage battery. The chemical reactions in the battery then proceed in the reversed direction and internal energy is developed at the expense of mechanical work that must be done by the automobile engine to drive the generator. Hence, depending on the direction of the current through it, we may have in the storage battery either of these transformations:

$$\text{Internal energy} \rightarrow \text{electrical energy,}$$

$$\text{Electrical energy} \rightarrow \text{internal energy.}$$

As contrasted with the *irreversible* conversion of electrical energy into heat via i^2R heating in a resistor, the conversion of electrical energy into internal energy in a storage battery is *reversible* in the sense that the internal energy can be completely recovered and converted to electrical form, with no outstanding changes in other bodies.*

---

* The fact that the recovery is not 100% in an actual storage battery under the conditions in which it is used does not vitiate the possibility of complete recovery under the proper conditions.

The mechanism of energy transformations in a motor or generator will be discussed in more detail in succeeding chapters. It will suffice for the present to state that in these devices we have conversion from electrical to mechanical (rather than internal) energy or vice versa, and that the conversion may be 100% in either direction.

Any device in which a reversible transformation between electrical energy and some other form of energy can take place is called a *seat of electromotive force.*

The magnitude of the electromotive force may be defined quantitatively as the energy converted from electrical to nonelectrical form, or vice versa (exclusive of energy converted irreversibly to heat), per unit of charge passing through the seat. More briefly, electromotive force may be defined as the *work per unit charge.* Electromotive force will be represented by the symbol $\mathcal{E}$, and is often abbreviated to emf.* Hence if dq is the charge crossing a section through the seat in time dt, and dW is the energy transformed in this time, the emf is

$$\mathcal{E} = \frac{dW}{dq}. \tag{23–1}$$

Since electromotive force is work per unit charge, the unit of emf in the mks system is *one joule per coulomb.* This is the same as the unit of potential and has been abbreviated to one volt. Hence emf's can be expressed in volts. It should be noted, however, that although emf and potential are expressible in the same unit, they relate to *different* concepts. The distinction will be made clearer as we proceed.

The work done by the seat in time dt is

$$dW = \mathcal{E}\,dq, \tag{23–2}$$

and the rate of doing work, or the power, is

$$P = \frac{dW}{dt} = \mathcal{E}\,\frac{dq}{dt} = \mathcal{E}i. \tag{23–3}$$

For example, the emf of an automobile storage battery is about 12 volts, or 12 joules/coul. This means that for every coulomb passing across a section through the battery (or across any section of a circuit to which the battery is connected) 12 joules of internal energy are converted to electrical form if the battery is discharging, or 12 joules of internal energy

---

* The use of the word "force" in connection with this concept is unfortunate, since an emf is not a force but work per unit charge. It has been suggested that "electromotance" would be a better term.

are developed at the expense of electrical energy if the battery is being charged. If the current in the battery is 10 amp, or 10 coul/sec, the rate of energy conversion is

$$P = \mathcal{E}i = 12 \text{ volts} \times 10 \text{ amp} = 120 \text{ watts.}$$

23–2 The circuit equation. Let us consider now a simple circuit (Fig. 23–1) in which a resistor of resistance R is connected by leads of negligible resistance to the terminals of a seat of emf such as a dry cell or storage battery. Let i represent the current in the circuit. When a number of circuit elements are connected as in Fig. 23–1 so as to provide only a single conducting path, they are said to be *in series*. Other types of connection will be considered later.

One minor point should be clarified at the start. Points p and a, in Fig. 23–1(a), are connected by a resistanceless conductor. The potential difference between two points of a conductor equals the product of the current and the resistance between the points. But since the resistance between p and a is zero, the potential difference between them is also zero or, in other words, points p and a are at the same potential. Hence p and a and, in fact, all points of the conductor connecting them, are *electrically* equivalent and separate letters need not be assigned to them. The same is evidently true of points b and q. The circuit is therefore relettered in Fig. 23–1(b).

If the direction of the current in the resistor is from a toward b, the potential V_a is higher than the potential V_b. The + sign at the terminal a of the cell indicates this fact.

Although, strictly speaking, emf is not a vector quantity, it is useful to assign to it a direction (or better, a sense). We shall arbitrarily consider the direction or sense of an emf to be from the − toward the + terminal of the seat, within the seat. This directed emf is indicated by an arrow in Fig. 23–1.

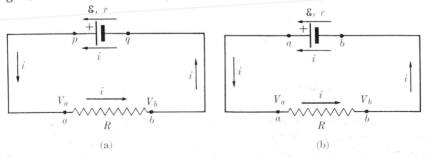

(a) (b)

FIG. 23–1. A seat of emf connected in series with a resistor by means of resistanceless connecting wires.

We now set down the expressions for the rates of energy transformation in the various parts of the circuit. Heat is developed in the external resistor at a rate Ri^2. It is also found, as might be expected, that every seat of emf has resistance. This is called *internal resistance* and we shall represent it by r. Hence the rate of development of heat in the cell is ri^2. The sum of Ri^2 and ri^2 is the rate at which energy is given up by the circulating charge in the form of heat, and the seat of emf must supply energy at an equal rate. Then, from Eq. (23–3),

$$\mathcal{E}i = Ri^2 + ri^2. \qquad (23\text{--}4)$$

After canceling and rearranging terms, we get

$$i = \frac{\mathcal{E}}{R + r}. \qquad (23\text{--}5)$$

The principle of conservation of energy therefore leads to this exceedingly useful relation between the current, the emf, and the resistance in a simple series circuit. It may be called the "circuit equation."

Consider next a circuit that contains a seat of emf within which work is done *by* the circulating charge. Examples are a motor, where the work done by the charge appears as mechanical energy, or a storage battery being "charged," where the work appears as internal energy. Figure 23–2 represents a circuit in which a motor, represented by the symbol ⊸O⊸ is being run by a battery. A resistance R is included for generality.

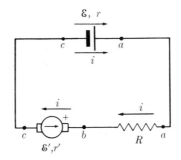

Fig. 23–2. A series circuit with two seats of emf.

The current in the motor is directed from right to left, or from b to c. Since the circulating charge gives up energy in passing through the motor, the potential V_b must be higher than the potential V_c. Hence a $+$ sign is attached to terminal b of the motor and the sense of its emf is from c toward b.

Let us represent the emf of the motor by $\mathcal{E}'$ and its internal resistance by r'. From the definition of electromotive force, the rate of conversion of energy to mechanical form by the motor is $\mathcal{E}'i$, and the rate of conversion to heat in the motor is $r'i^2$. The rates of development of heat in the external resistor and in the battery are Ri^2 and ri^2. The rate at which work is done on the circulating charge by the battery is $\mathcal{E}i$. Therefore

$$\mathcal{E}i = \mathcal{E}'i + r'i^2 + Ri^2 + ri^2$$

and

$$i = \frac{\mathcal{E} - \mathcal{E}'}{R + r + r'}, \tag{23–6}$$

or

$$i = \frac{\sum \mathcal{E}}{\sum R}. \tag{23–7}$$

This equation is evidently a generalization of Eq. (23–5) and may be stated: *the current* (in a series circuit) *equals the algebraic sum of the emf's in the circuit divided by the sum of the resistances in the circuit.*

It is necessary that a convention of sign be adopted when using Eq. (23–7). The simplest rule is to select an arbitrary direction around the circuit (clockwise or counterclockwise) as positive. Then currents and emf's are positive if they are in the direction selected, negative if in the opposite direction. Resistances are always considered positive. In writing Eq. (23–6), the clockwise direction was considered positive. If the opposite direction had been considered positive, the same equation would have been obtained with the signs of i, $\mathcal{E}$, and $\mathcal{E}'$ all reversed.

The *relative* directions of current and emf in the two seats in Fig. 23–2 lead to the following generalizations. When the current in a seat of emf is in the *same* direction as the emf, as it is in the battery, work is done *on* the circulating charge at the expense of energy of some other form. When the current in a seat of emf is *opposite* in direction to the emf, as in the motor, work is done *by* the circulating charge and energy of some other form appears. The emf in the latter case is often called a *back electromotive force.*

23–3 Potential difference between points in a circuit. We next deduce the general expression for the difference in potential between any two points in a series circuit. Figure 23–3 shows a portion of such a circuit in which the direction of the current i is from a toward b. The rate at which the circulating charge gives up energy to the portion of the circuit between a and b is iV_{ab}. In other words, this is the power input to this portion of the circuit, supplied by the seat or seats of emf in the remainder of the circuit (not shown). Power is also supplied *by* the first seat of emf (since

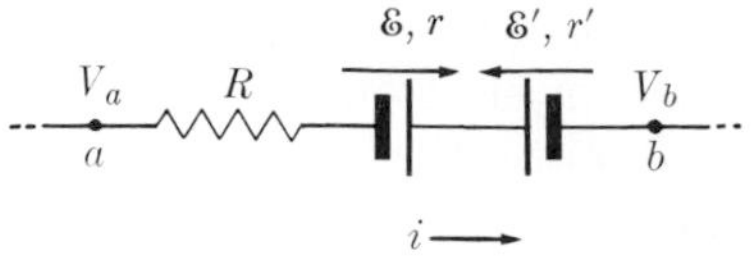

FIG. 23–3. Portion of a circuit with two seats of emf.

i and $\mathcal{E}$ are in the same direction) at a rate $\mathcal{E}i$. Power is supplied *to* the second seat of emf (i and $\mathcal{E}'$ are in opposite directions) at a rate $\mathcal{E}'i$. Heat is developed in the resistor and in the seats of emf at a total rate $(R + r + r')t^2$. Then, if we equate power input to power output,

$$iV_{ab} + \mathcal{E}i = \mathcal{E}'i + (R + r + r')i^2,$$

$$V_{ab} = (R + r + r')i - (\mathcal{E} - \mathcal{E}'), \qquad (23\text{–}8)$$

$$\boxed{V_{ab} = \sum Ri - \sum \mathcal{E}.} \qquad (23\text{–}9)$$

This is the desired general expression for the potential difference $V_{ab} \equiv V_a - V_b$ between any two points a and b of a series circuit.

Careful attention must be paid to algebraic signs. The direction from a toward b is always considered positive. Then currents and emf's are positive if their direction is from a toward b, negative if their direction is from b toward a. Resistances are always positive. The potential difference V_{ab} is positive if a is at a higher potential than b, negative if b is at a higher potential than a. It will be seen that the signs in Eq. (23–8) are consistent with these conventions.

Equation (23–9) was derived from conservation of energy and therefore it is completely general. It reduces, of course, to the familiar relation $V_{ab} = Ri$ for the special case where a and b are the terminals of a pure resistance. It also contains implicitly the general circuit equation, Eq. (23–7). That is, if points a and b coincide,

$$V_{ab} = 0 = \sum Ri - \sum \mathcal{E}, \qquad \text{and} \qquad i = \frac{\sum \mathcal{E}}{\sum R}.$$

We shall use Eq. (23–9) in later chapters also, when we encounter circuits where the current is a varying function of time.

EXAMPLE 1. Given that, in Fig. 23–4, $\mathcal{E}_1 = 12$ volts, $r_1 = 0.2$ ohm, $\mathcal{E}_2 = 6$ volts, $r_2 = 0.1$ ohm, $R_3 = 1.4$ ohms, $R_4 = 2.3$ ohms, compute (a) the current in the circuit, in magnitude and direction, and (b) the potential difference V_{ac}.

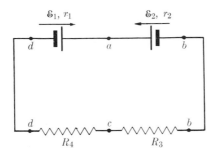

FIGURE 23–4

(a) It seems obvious that the current will be clockwise, since $\mathcal{E}_1 > \mathcal{E}_2$. However, to illustrate that one need not rely on intuition to find its direction, let us assume the counterclockwise direction to be positive. Then

$$\sum \mathcal{E} = -12 \text{ volts} + 6 \text{ volts} = -6 \text{ volts},$$

$$\sum R = 4 \text{ ohms} = 4 \frac{\text{volts}}{\text{amp}},$$

$$i = \frac{\sum \mathcal{E}}{\sum R} = \frac{-6 \text{ volts}}{4 \text{ volts/amp}} = -1.5 \text{ amp}.$$

The significance of the negative sign is that the current is in the negative, or clockwise, direction. Had we assumed the clockwise direction to be positive, we would have obtained

$$\sum \mathcal{E} = 12 \text{ volts} - 6 \text{ volts} = +6 \text{ volts},$$

$$\sum R = 4 \text{ ohms}, \qquad i = \frac{6 \text{ volts}}{4 \text{ ohms}} = +1.5 \text{ amp}.$$

So the same numerical value is obtained in either case, and the direction of the current need not be known in advance.

(b) The potential difference between a and c is $V_{ac} = \sum Ri - \sum \mathcal{E}$. We can proceed from a to c by two paths, and either may be used to compute V_{ac}. Let us first use path abc. We have already shown that the current is clockwise. The direction of the current in the path abc is from a toward c, hence i is positive and

$$\sum Ri = (0.1 \text{ ohm} + 1.4 \text{ ohms})(+1.5 \text{ amp}) = +2.25 \text{ volts}.$$

The direction of $\mathcal{E}_2$ is from b toward a, so

$$\sum \mathcal{E} = -6 \text{ volts}.$$

Hence

$$V_{ac} = +2.25 \text{ volts} - (-6 \text{ volts}) = +8.25 \text{ volts},$$

and since
$$V_{ac} \equiv V_a - V_c,$$
$$V_a - V_c = 8.25 \text{ volts}, \qquad V_a = V_c + 8.25 \text{ volts}.$$

That is, the potential at point a is 8.25 volts above that at point c.

If we proceed from a to c along path adc, the current term has a negative sign, since its direction is from c toward a. Hence

$$\sum Ri = (0.2 \text{ ohm} + 2.3 \text{ ohms})(-1.5 \text{ amp}) = -3.75 \text{ volts}.$$

The direction of $\mathcal{E}_1$ is from c toward a, so

$$\sum \mathcal{E} = -12 \text{ volts}.$$

Hence
$$V_{ac} = -3.75 \text{ volts} - (-12 \text{ volts}) = +8.25 \text{ volts},$$

and the same answer is obtained whichever path is used.

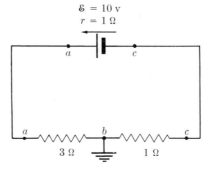

FIGURE 23–5

EXAMPLE 2. In practically all circuits, whether power distribution systems or small units such as radio amplifiers, one or more points of the circuit are connected to the earth or to "ground." In contrast to the reference level of potential used in general field theory (that of a point at infinity), when dealing with circuits the potential of the grounded points is assumed to be zero and the potential of any other point of the circuit is expressed relative to this reference level. Consider the simple circuit in Fig. 23–5, grounded at point b. Compute the potentials of points a and c.

The current in the circuit is

$$i = \frac{\sum \mathcal{E}}{\sum R} = \frac{10 \text{ volts}}{5 \text{ ohms}} = 2 \text{ amp}$$

and its direction is counterclockwise.

The potential differences V_{ab} and V_{bc} are

$$V_{ab} = Ri = 3 \text{ ohms} \times 2 \text{ amp} = 6 \text{ volts} = V_a - V_b,$$

$$V_{bc} = Ri = 1 \text{ ohm} \times 2 \text{ amp} = 2 \text{ volts} = V_b - V_c.$$

Since $V_b = 0$, it follows that

$$V_a = +6 \text{ volts}, \qquad V_c = -2 \text{ volts}.$$

That is, point a is 6 volts *above* ground and point c is 2 volts *below* ground. The potential difference V_{ac} can now be found by subtraction.

$$V_{ac} \equiv V_a - V_c = 6 \text{ volts} - (-2 \text{ volts}) = +8 \text{ volts}.$$

As a check, we may proceed from a to c through the cell, obtaining

$$V_{ac} = \sum Ri - \sum \mathcal{E} = 1 \text{ ohm} \times (-2 \text{ amp}) - (-10 \text{ volts}) = +8 \text{ volts}.$$

23–4 Terminal voltage of a seat of emf. It is convenient to develop the special form of Eq. (23–9) when points a and b are the terminals of a seat of electromotive force. There can be but two possibilities, shown in Fig. 23–6(a) and (b), namely, when the current and emf are in the same or opposite directions. Let us agree that point a shall always refer to the $+$ terminal and point b to the $-$ terminal of the seat. Then, since the direction from a to b in Eq. (23–9) is always positive, both $\mathcal{E}$ and i in Fig. 23–6(a) are negative and

$$V_{ab} = V_{+-} = \sum Ri - \sum \mathcal{E} = -ri - (-\mathcal{E}) = \mathcal{E} - ri.$$

In Fig. 23–6(b), $\mathcal{E}$ is negative but i is positive. Hence

$$V_{ab} = V_{+-} = ri - (-\mathcal{E}) = \mathcal{E} + ri.$$

The potential difference *between the $+$ and $-$ terminals* of a seat of emf is therefore equal to the emf of the seat, diminished by the product of the

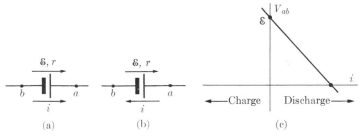

FIG. 23–6. (a) Current and emf in the same direction. (b) Current and emf in opposite directions. (c) Graph of terminal voltage of a seat of emf *vs.* current.

internal resistance and the current when emf and current are in the same direction, and increased by this product when the two are in opposite directions. (In the latter case we have a seat of back emf.) When the current in a seat of emf is zero, the terminal voltage equals the electromotive force. Therefore the emf of a seat may be found experimentally by measuring its terminal potential difference on open circuit.

If the terminal voltage is measured with the common type of voltmeter, care must be taken that the current in the circuit does not result in any appreciable lowering of the terminal voltage below the emf. Figure 23–7 shows a cell of emf ε and internal resistance r with a voltmeter of resistance R_V connected to its terminals. Since the voltmeter provides a conducting path, we have a closed circuit as soon as it is connected to the cell. The current in the circuit is

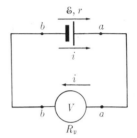

$$i = \frac{\varepsilon}{R_V + r}.$$

The terminal voltage is

$$V_{ab} = \varepsilon - ri = \varepsilon - r \frac{\varepsilon}{R_V + r}$$

$$= \varepsilon \left(\frac{1}{1 + r/R_V} \right).$$

FIG. 23–7. Measurement of the terminal voltage of a seat of emf by means of a voltmeter.

If $R_V \gg r$, the term in parentheses is nearly unity, and the voltmeter reading (V_{ab}) is nearly equal to the emf. It is evident, therefore, that a voltmeter should be a high-resistance instrument.

23–5 The potentiometer. The potentiometer is an instrument which can be used to measure the emf of a seat without drawing any current from the seat. It also has a number of other useful applications. Essentially, it balances an unknown potential difference against an adjustable, measurable potential difference.

The principle of the potentiometer is shown schematically in Fig. 23–8. A resistance wire ab is permanently connected to the terminals of a seat of emf ε_1. A sliding contact c is connected through the galvanometer G to a second cell whose emf ε_2 is to be measured. Contact c is moved along the wire until a position is found at which the galvanometer shows no deflection. (This necessitates that $V_{ab} \geq \varepsilon_2$.) If we then write the expression for V_{cb} for two paths between these points, we have

$$V_{cb} = iR_{cb}, \qquad \text{(Resistance wire path)}$$

$$V_{cb} = (r_g + r)i_2 - (-\varepsilon_2) = \varepsilon_2, \qquad \text{(Galvanometer path)}$$

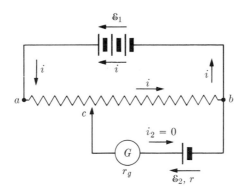

FIG. 23–8. Principle of the potentiometer.

where the last step is possible because *we have adjusted i_2 to be equal to zero.*

Hence iR_{cb} is *exactly* equal to the emf $\mathcal{E}_2$, and $\mathcal{E}_2$ can be computed if i and R_{cb} are known. No correction need be made for the "ir" term, since the current in $\mathcal{E}_2$ is zero.

23–6 Series and parallel connection of resistors. Most electrical circuits consist not merely of a single seat of emf and a single external resistor, but comprise a number of emf's, resistors, or other elements such as capacitors, motors, etc., interconnected in a more or less complicated manner. The general term applied to such a circuit is a *network*. We shall next consider a few of the simpler types of network.

Figure 23–9 illustrates four different ways in which three resistors having resistances R_1, R_2, and R_3 might be connected between points a and b. In part (a), the resistors provide only a single path between the points, and are said to be connected in *series* between these points. Any number of circuit elements such as resistors, cells, motors, etc., are similarly said to be in series with one another between two points if connected as in (a) so as to provide only a single path between the points.

The resistors in Fig. 23–9(b) are said to be in *parallel* between points a and b. Each resistor provides an alternative path between the points, and any number of circuit elements similarly connected are in parallel with one another.

In Fig. 23–9(c), resistors R_2 and R_3 are in parallel with each other, and this combination is in series with the resistor R_1. In Fig. 23–9(d), R_2 and R_3 are in series, and this combination is in parallel with R_1.

It is always possible to find a single resistor which could replace a combination of resistors in any given circuit and leave unaltered the

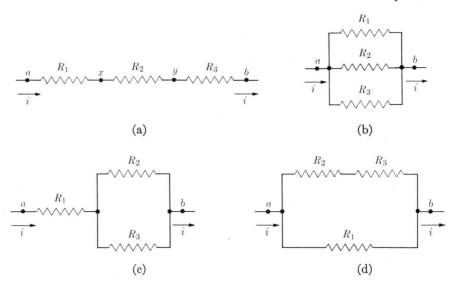

FIG. 23–9. Four different ways of connecting three resistors.

potential difference between the terminals of the combination and the current in the rest of the circuit. The resistance of this single resistor is called the *equivalent* resistance of the combination. If any one of the networks in Fig. 23–9 were replaced by its equivalent resistance R, we could write

$$V_{ab} = Ri \quad \text{or} \quad R = \frac{V_{ab}}{i},$$

where V_{ab} is the potential difference between the terminals of the network and i is the current at the point a or b. Hence the method of computing an equivalent resistance is to assume a potential difference V_{ab} across the actual network, compute the corresponding current i (or vice versa), and take the ratio of one to the other. The simple series and parallel connections of resistors are sufficiently common so that it is worth while to develop formulas for these two special cases.

If the resistors are in series, as in Fig. 23–9(a), the current in each must be the same and equal to the line current i. Hence

$$V_{ax} = iR_1, \qquad V_{xy} = iR_2, \qquad V_{yb} = iR_3,$$

$$V_{ax} + V_{xy} + V_{yb} = i(R_1 + R_2 + R_3).$$

But

$$V_{ax} = V_a - V_x, \qquad V_{xy} = V_x - V_y, \qquad V_{yb} = V_y - V_b,$$

$$V_{ax} + V_{xy} + V_{yb} = V_a - V_b = V_{ab}.$$

Hence

$$V_{ab} = i(R_1 + R_2 + R_3),$$

and

$$\frac{V_{ab}}{i} = R_1 + R_2 + R_3.$$

But V_{ab}/i is, by definition, the equivalent resistance R. Therefore

$$\boxed{R = R_1 + R_2 + R_3.}$$ (23–10)

Evidently the equivalent resistance of any number of resistors in series equals the sum of their individual resistances.

If the resistors are in parallel, as in Fig. 23–9(b), the potential difference between the terminals of each must be the same and equal to V_{ab}. If the currents in each are denoted by i_1, i_2, and i_3, respectively,

$$i_1 = \frac{V_{ab}}{R_1}, \qquad i_2 = \frac{V_{ab}}{R_2}, \qquad i_3 = \frac{V_{ab}}{R_3}.$$

Now charge is delivered to point a by the line current i, and removed from a by the currents i_1, i_2, and i_3. Since charge is not accumulating at a, it follows that

$$i = i_1 + i_2 + i_3,$$

or

$$i = \frac{V_{ab}}{R_1} + \frac{V_{ab}}{R_2} + \frac{V_{ab}}{R_3},$$

or

$$\frac{i}{V_{ab}} = \frac{1}{R_1} + \frac{1}{R_2} + \frac{1}{R_3}.$$

Since

$$\frac{i}{V_{ab}} = \frac{1}{R},$$

then

$$\boxed{\frac{1}{R} = \frac{1}{R_1} + \frac{1}{R_2} + \frac{1}{R_3}.}$$ (23–11)

Evidently, for any number of resistors in parallel, the *reciprocal* of the equivalent resistance equals the *sum of the reciprocals* of their individual resistances.

The equivalent resistances of the networks in Figs. 23–9(c) and (d) could be found by the same general method, but it is simpler to consider them as combinations of series and parallel arrangements. Thus in (c) the combination of R_2 and R_3 in parallel is first replaced by its equivalent resistance, which then forms a simple series combination with R_1. In (d), the combination of R_2 and R_3 in series forms a simple parallel combination with R_1. Not all networks, however, can be reduced to simple series-parallel combinations, and special methods must be used for handling such networks.

EXAMPLE. Compute the equivalent resistance of the network in Fig. 23–10, and find the current in each resistor.

Successive stages in the reduction to a single equivalent resistance are shown in parts (b) to (e) of the figure. For simplicity, the seat of emf has been omitted from all except the first and last diagrams. The 6-ohm and the 3-ohm resistor in parallel in (a) are equivalent to the single 2-ohm resistor which replaces them in (b). In (c) the 4- and the 2-ohm resistors in series are replaced by their equivalent 6-ohm resistor. Repetition of this process leads to the single equivalent 6-ohm resistor in (e).

We now work back up the series of diagrams and compute the currents. In the simple series circuit of (e) the current is $i = \sum \mathcal{E}/\sum R = $ 54 volts/6 ohms = 9 amp. Since the 6-ohm resistor in (e) replaces the 4-ohm and the 2-ohm resistors in series, the current in each of these in (d) is also 9 amp. In (c), the current in the 4-ohm resistor remains 9 amp but the currents in the 6-ohm and 3-ohm resistors divide as shown. Repetition of the process gives the current distribution in (a).

23–7 Power.

Since our analysis of circuits has been developed from considerations of energy and power, little can be added under this heading except by way of summary.

The power input to any portion of a circuit between points a and b is given by

$$P = iV_{ab}. \tag{23–12}$$

The power is expressed in watts when i is in amperes and V_{ab} in volts. Current is considered positive if its direction is from a toward b in the portion of the circuit considered. If the power input as computed by this equation has a negative sign, which will be the case if the current is from b toward a or if $V_a < V_b$, the portion of the circuit considered is actually supplying power to the remainder of the circuit and the magnitude of P represents the *power output*. Equation (23–12) is independent of the nature of the circuit between a and b, that is, the circuit may consist of resistors, motors, batteries, etc., arranged in any way.

If the circuit between a and b comprises resistance only, then $V_{ab} = Ri$ and

$$P = iV_{ab} = Ri^2 = dH/dt.$$

That is, the power input equals the rate of development of heat.

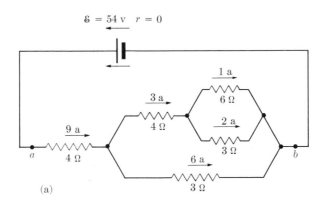

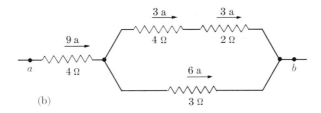

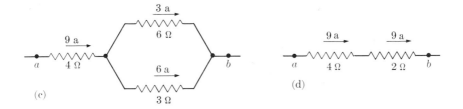

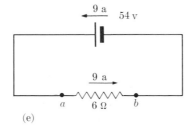

FIG. 23–10. Successive stages in the reduction of a network to a single equivalent resistance.

The rate of energy conversion in a seat of emf is equal to $\mathcal{E}i$. If $\mathcal{E}$ and i are in the same direction, electrical energy is developed at the expense of some other form. If $\mathcal{E}$ and i are in opposite directions (a seat of back emf), some other form of energy is developed at the expense of electrical energy.

EXAMPLE. Figure 23–11 shows a battery and a resistor in series. The current in the circuit is

$$i = \frac{12 \text{ volts}}{5.5 \text{ ohms} + 0.5 \text{ ohm}} = 2 \text{ amp.}$$

Point b is at a higher potential than point a, and

$$V_{ba} = iR = 2 \text{ amp} \times 5.5 \text{ ohms} = 11 \text{ volts,}$$

or

$$V_{ba} = \mathcal{E} - iR = 12 \text{ volts} - (2 \text{ amp} \times 0.5 \text{ ohm}) = 11 \text{ volts,}$$

and

$$V_{ab} = -V_{ba} = -11 \text{ volts.}$$

Consider first that part of the circuit within the upper dotted rectangle. The direction of the current through it is from a to b. Hence the power *input* to this portion is

$$\text{Power input} = iV_{ab} = 2 \text{ amp} \times (-11 \text{ volts}) = -22 \text{ watts.}$$

The minus sign means that this is actually a power output.

In the lower rectangle, the direction of the current is from b to a. Hence,

$$\text{Power input} = iV_{ab} = (-2 \text{ amp}) \times (-11 \text{ volts}) = +22 \text{ watts,}$$

and power is supplied to this part of the circuit.

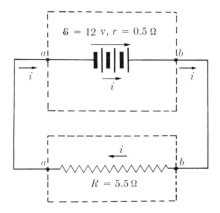

FIGURE 23–11

As a check, since the energy supplied to the resistor is converted to heat,

$$\frac{dH}{dt} = i^2 R = (2 \text{ amp})^2 \times 5.5 \text{ ohms} = 22 \text{ watts}.$$

The rate of conversion of nonelectrical to electrical energy in the seat of emf is

$$P = \mathcal{E}i = 12 \text{ volts} \times 2 \text{ amp} = 24 \text{ watts}.$$

The rate of development of heat in the seat of emf is

$$i^2 r = (2 \text{ amp})^2 \times 0.5 \text{ ohm} = 2 \text{ watts}.$$

The power output is therefore 24 watts — 2 watts = 22 watts, as previously computed.

To sum up:

The battery converts nonelectrical to electrical energy at the rate of 24 joules per second, or 24 watts.

The rate of heating in the battery is 2 watts.

The rate at which energy is supplied to the rest of the circuit by the battery is 24 — 2, or 22 watts.

This energy is transformed to heat in the resistor at the rate of 22 watts.

PROBLEMS

23–1. The internal resistance of a dry cell increases gradually with age, even though the cell is not used. The emf, however, remains fairly constant at about 1.5 volts. Dry cells are often tested for age at the time of purchase by connecting an ammeter directly across the terminals of the cell and reading the current. The resistance of the ammeter is so small that the cell is practically short-circuited. (a) The short-circuit current of a fresh No. 6 dry cell is about 30 amp. Approximately what is the internal resistance? (b) What is the internal resistance if the short-circuit current is only 10 amp? (c) The short-circuit current of a 6-volt storage battery may be as great as 1000 amp. What is its internal resistance?

23–2. An immersion heater has a resistance of 50 ohms and carries a current of 2.5 amp. What is the final temperature of 1500 gm of water initially at 20°C if the water absorbs all the heat given off by the heater during an interval of 3 minutes?

23–3. A closed series circuit consists of a 12-volt battery, a 3.7-ohm resistor, and a switch. The internal resistance of the battery is 0.3 ohm. The switch is opened. What would a high-resistance voltmeter read when placed (a) across the terminals of the battery, (b) across the resistor, (c) across the switch? Repeat (a), (b), and (c) for the case when the switch is closed.

23–4. In the circuit in Fig. 23–12, find (a) the rate of conversion of internal energy to electrical energy within the battery, (b) the rate of development of heat in the battery, (c) the rate of development of heat in the external resistor.

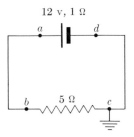

12 v, 1 Ω

FIGURE 23–12

23–5. A battery of emf $\mathcal{E}$ and internal resistance r is connected to an external resistance R. Prove that the power delivered to the external resistor is given by

$$P = \mathcal{E}^2 \frac{R}{(R + r)^2}.$$

By setting $dP/dR = 0$, show that P is maximum for $R = r$.

23–6. The power supplied to a motor is 180 watts at its rated voltage of 60 volts. (a) What series resistance should be used if the motor is to operate from a 110-volt line? (b) What power should the resistor be able to dissipate?

23–7. A single-layer cylindrical coil is wound of insulated wire 2 m long, successive windings touching each other. The insulation can withstand a maximum potential difference of 750 volts. What is the maximum diameter the coil may have to avoid breakdown between successive windings if a potential difference of 12,000 volts is applied across the ends of the coil?

23–8. (a) In the circuit shown in Fig. 23–13, what is the potential at point a? (b) What value resistor must be inserted in the circuit at c to make $V_a = 7.5$ volts? (c) A battery has an internal resistance of 1 Ω. What emf must it have to make $V_a = 2$ volts when the battery is inserted in the circuit at c? [The resistor of part (b) is removed.]

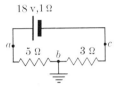

18 v,1 Ω

a　5 Ω　b　3 Ω　c

FIGURE 23–13

23–9. The external circuit of a battery has a resistance of 3 ohms and carries a current of 5 amp. When 5 ohms are added to the external circuit the current drops to 2.5 amp. (a) What is the emf of the battery? (b) What is its external resistance?

23–10. In the circuit of Fig. 23–14, calculate (a) V_{ag}, (b) V_{dg}, (c) V_{ch}.

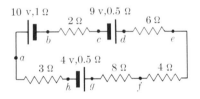

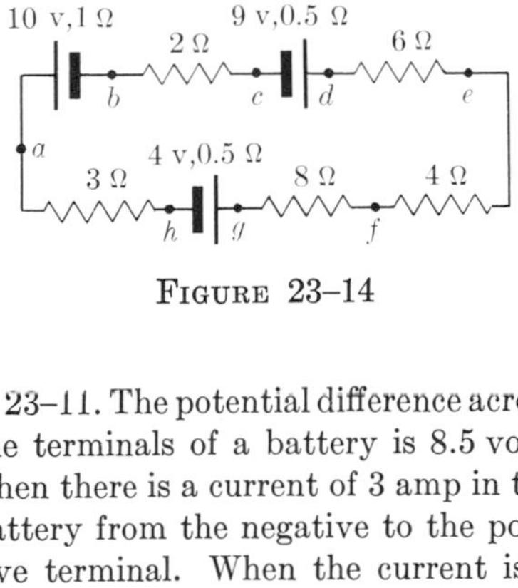

10 v,1 Ω　　9 v,0.5 Ω
　　　2 Ω　　　　　6 Ω
　　　b　　c　d　　　e
a
　　　4 v,0.5 Ω
3 Ω　　　　　8 Ω　　　4 Ω
　　h　g　　　　f

FIGURE 23–14

23–11. The potential difference across the terminals of a battery is 8.5 volts when there is a current of 3 amp in the battery from the negative to the positive terminal. When the current is 2 amp in the reverse direction, the potential difference becomes 11 volts. (a) What is the internal resistance of the battery? (b) What is the emf of the battery?

23–12. (a) What is the potential at point a in the circuit of Fig. 23–15? (b) What is the terminal voltage of the 4-volt battery? (c) A battery of emf

17 volts and internal resistance 1 ohm is inserted in the circuit at d, its positive terminal being the grounded side. What is now the difference of potential between the terminals of the 4-volt battery?

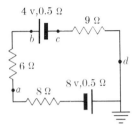

4 v,0.5 Ω
　　　　9 Ω
b　c
　　　　　　　　　d
6 Ω
　　　　8 v,0.5 Ω
a　8 Ω

FIGURE 23–15

23–13. A storage battery whose emf is 12 volts and whose internal resistance is 0.1 ohm (internal resistances of commercial storage batteries are actually only a few thousandths of an ohm) is to be charged from a 112-volt d-c supply. (a) Should the + or the − terminal of the battery be connected to the + side of the line? (b) What will be the charging current if the battery is connected directly across the line? (c) Compute the resistance of the series resistor required to limit the current to 10 amp. With this resistor in the circuit, compute (d) the potential difference between the terminals of the battery, (e) the power taken from the line, (f) the power wasted as heat in the series resistor, (g) the *useful* power input to the battery. (h) If electrical energy costs 3 cents per kwh, what is the cost of operating the circuit for 2 hours when the current is 10 amp?

23–14. Figure 23–16 represents a d-c generating plant G supplying electrical power to a distant factory along a transmission line. The terminal voltage of the generator, V_{ba}, is 230 volts, and the line current is 50 amp.   The resistances of the wires bc and ad are 0.1 ohm each. Point a is grounded. (a) What is the potential at point b? (b) What is the iR drop in each wire? (c) What is the potential at point c? (d) What is the potential at point d? (e) What is the line voltage at the load, that is, V_{cd}? (f) Show in a diagram how voltmeters should be connected to measure the potential differences in parts (b) and (e). (g) Compute the power output of the generator, the power loss in the line, and the power delivered to the factory. (h) Suppose the terminal voltage at the generator were doubled and the power delivered to the factory kept constant. Find the power output of the generator and the power loss in the line.

FIGURE 23–16

23–15. A 100-volt battery has an internal resistance of 5 ohms. (a) What is the reading of a voltmeter having a resistance of 500 ohms when placed across the terminals of the battery? (b) What maximum value may the ratio r/R_v have if the error in the reading of the emf of a battery is not to exceed 5%?

23–16. When switch S is open, the voltmeter V, connected across the terminals of the dry cell in Fig. 23–17, reads 1.52 volts. When the switch is closed the voltmeter reading drops to 1.37 volts and the ammeter reads 1.5 amp. Find the emf and internal resist-

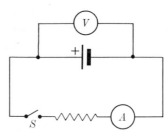

FIGURE 23–17

ance of the cell.   Neglect meter corrections.

23–17. In Fig. 23–18 is shown a potentiometer set up to measure the emf of cell x. B is a battery whose emf is approximately 3 volts and whose internal resistance is unknown. St is a standard cell of 1.0183 volts emf. The switch is set at point 2, placing the standard cell in the galvanometer circuit. When the tap b is 0.36 of the distance from a to c the galvanometer G reads zero. (a) What is the difference of potential across the entire length of resistor ac? (b) The switch is then set at point 1 and a new zero reading of the galvanometer obtained when b is 0.47 of the distance from a to c. What is the emf of cell x?

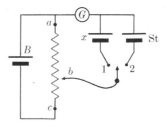

FIGURE 23–18

23–18. In Fig. 23–19 the "potentiometer" is a resistor with a movable tap. The galvanometer has a resistance of 90 ohms. P has a resistance of

75 ohms. At what point should the movable tap be placed if the current in the galvanometer is to be 1/3 the current in line *bc*?

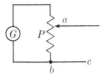

FIGURE 23–19

23–19. Prove that when two resistors are connected in parallel the equivalent resistance of the combination is always smaller than that of either resistor.

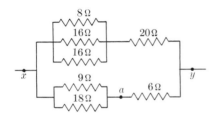

FIGURE 23–20

23–20. (a) Calculate the equivalent resistance of the circuit of Fig. 23–20 between *x* and *y*. (b) What is the potential difference between *x* and *a* if the current in the 8-ohm resistor is 0.5 amp?

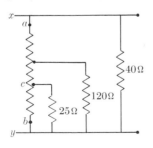

FIGURE 23–21

23–21. (a) The long resistor between *a* and *b* in Fig. 23–21 has a resistance of 300 ohms and is tapped at the one-third points. What is the equivalent resistance between *x* and *y*? (b) The potential difference between *x* and *y* is 320 volts. What is the potential difference between *b* and *c*?

23–22. The three resistors in Fig. 23–22 each have a resistance of 2 ohms and can dissipate a maximum of 18 watts without becoming excessively heated. What is the maximum power the circuit can dissipate?

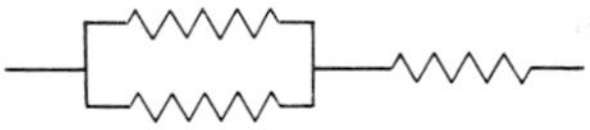

FIGURE 23–22

23–23. Two lamps marked "60 watts, 120 volts" and "40 watts, 120 volts" are connected in series across a 120-volt line. What power is consumed in each lamp? Assume that the resistance of the filaments does not vary with current.

23–24. Three equal resistors are connected in series. When a certain potential difference is applied across the combination the total power consumed is 10 watts. What power would be consumed if the three resistors were connected in parallel across the same potential difference?

23–25. (a) The power rating of a 10,000-ohm resistor is 2 watts. (The power rating is the maximum power the resistor can safely dissipate as heat without too great a rise in temperature.) What is the maximum allowable potential difference across the terminals of the resistor? (b) A 20,000-ohm resistor is to be connected across a potential difference of 300 volts. What power rating is required? (c) It is desired to connect a resistance of 1000 ohms across a potential difference of 200 volts. A number of 10-watt, 1000-ohm resistors are available. How should they be connected?

23–26. (a) Find the equivalent resistance of the external circuit in Fig. 23–23. (b) Find the readings of the ammeter A and the voltmeter V.

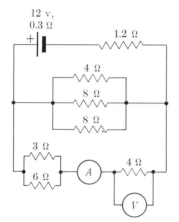

FIGURE 23–23

23–27. The resistance of a certain galvanometer is 30 ohms. (a) What resistance in shunt (i.e., in parallel) with the galvanometer will reduce the equivalent resistance to 10 ohms? (b) If the potential difference between the galvanometer terminals is 100 mv, find the current in the galvanometer and in the shunt.

23–28. In Fig. 23–24, find (a) the current in the battery, (b) the current in each resistor, (c) the potential difference between points a and b.

23–29. (a) Find the resistance of the network in Fig. 23–25, between the terminals a and b. (b) What potential difference between a and b will result in a current of 1 amp in the 4-ohm resistor?

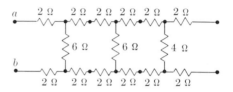

FIGURE 23–25

23–30. Two resistors A and B are in parallel with each other and in series with a 200-ohm resistor and a dry cell whose emf is 1.5 volts and whose internal resistance is negligible. The resistance of A is 100 ohms. When B is disconnected from A, an additional resistance of 50 ohms must be inserted in series in the circuit in order to keep the current through A unchanged. Find the resistance of B.

23–31. Find the potential difference between points a and b in Fig. 23–26.

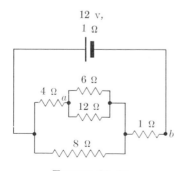

FIGURE 23–24

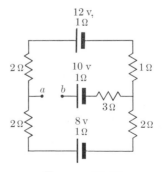

FIGURE 23–26

CHAPTER 24

THE MAGNETIC FIELD

24–1 Magnetism. The first magnetic phenomena to be observed were undoubtedly those associated with so-called "natural" magnets, rough fragments of an ore of iron found near the ancient city of Magnesia (whence the term "magnet"). These natural magnets have the property of attracting to themselves unmagnetized iron, the effect being most pronounced at certain regions of the magnet known as its *poles*. It was known to the Chinese as early as 121 A.D. that an iron rod, after being brought near a natural magnet, would acquire and retain this property of the natural magnet, and that such a rod when freely suspended about a vertical axis would set itself approximately in the north-south direction. The use of magnets as aids to navigation can be traced back at least to the eleventh century.

The study of magnetic phenomena was confined for many years to magnets made in this way. Not until 1819 was there shown to be any connection between electrical and magnetic phenomena. In that year the Danish scientist Hans Christian Oersted (1770–1851) observed that a pivoted magnet (a compass needle) was deflected when in the neighborhood of a wire carrying a current. Twelve years later, after attempts extending over a period of several years, Faraday found that a momentary current existed in a circuit while the current in a nearby circuit was being started or stopped. Shortly afterward followed the discovery that the motion of a magnet toward or away from the circuit would produce the same effect. Joseph Henry (1797–1878), an American scientist who later became the first director of the Smithsonian Institution, had anticipated Faraday's discoveries by about twelve months, but since Faraday was the first to publish his results he is usually assigned the credit for them. The work of Oersted thus demonstrated that magnetic effects could be produced by moving electric charges, and that of Faraday and Henry that currents could be produced by moving magnets.

It is believed at the present time that all so-called magnetic phenomena arise from forces between electric charges in motion. That is, moving charges exert "magnetic" forces on one another, over and above the purely "electrical" or "electrostatic" forces given by Coulomb's law. Since the electrons in atoms are in motion about the atomic nuclei, and since each electron appears to be in continuous rotation about an axis passing through it, all atoms can be expected to exhibit magnetic effects and, in fact, such is found to be the case. The possibility that the magnetic properties of matter were the result of tiny atomic currents was first suggested by Ampere in 1820. Not until recent years has the verification of these ideas been possible.

As with electrostatic forces, the medium in which the charges are moving may have a pronounced effect on the observed magnetic forces between them. In the present chapter we shall assume the charges or conductors to be in otherwise empty space. For all practical purposes the results will apply equally well to charges and conductors in air.

24–2 The magnetic field. Instead of dealing directly with the forces exerted on one moving charge by another, it is found more convenient to adopt the point of view that a moving charge sets up in the space around it a *magnetic field*, and that it is this field which exerts a force on another charge moving through it. The magnetic field around a moving charge exists in addition to the electrostatic field which surrounds the charge whether it is in motion or not. A second charged particle in these combined fields experiences a force due to the electric field whether it is in motion or at rest. The magnetic field exerts a force on the particle only if it is in motion.

A magnetic field is said to exist at a point if a force (over and above any electrostatic force) *is exerted on a moving charge at the point.*

The electric field set up by moving charges or by currents is, in many instances, so small that the electrostatic force on a moving charge can be neglected in comparison with the magnetic force.

There are two aspects to the problem of computing the magnetic force between moving charges. The first is that of finding the magnitude and direction of the magnetic field at a point, given the data on the moving charges that set up the field. The second is to find the magnitude and direction of the force on a charge moving in a given field. We shall take up the latter aspect of the problem first. That is, let us accept for the present the fact that moving charges and currents do set up magnetic fields, and study the laws that determine the force on a charge moving through the field.

The cathode-ray tube is a convenient experimental device for studying, at least in a qualitative way, the behavior of moving charges in a magnetic field. At one end of this tube is an electron gun which shoots out a narrow electron beam at a speed that can be controlled and calculated. At the other end is a fluorescent screen which emits light at the point where the electron beam strikes it. Let us suppose that our cathode-ray tube is small, that it is not surrounded by iron, and that it can be carried around the room easily. If the spot of light is always in the same place on the screen as we move the tube, we may conclude that there is no detectable

magnetic field. If, on the other hand, as we move the tube around the
room, the spot of light changes its position by virtue of the deflection of
the electron beam, we conclude that we are in a magnetic field. Since
the cathode-ray tube is imagined to be small, rotating the tube about any
axis through its center, without shifting the position of its center, will
provide information concerning the magnetic field in a small region at the
center or, roughly, the magnetic field at a point.

At a given point in a magnetic field, the electron beam will, in general,
be deflected. By rotating the cathode-ray tube, however, there will be
found one direction in which no deflection takes place. *The direction of
motion of a charge on which a magnetic field exerts no force is defined as the
direction of the magnetic field.* (The sense of the field will be defined later.)

Having determined the direction (but not the sense) of the magnetic
field, let us now place the cathode-ray tube so that the electron beam
moves in a plane perpendicular to this direction. Experiment shows that
a deflection always takes place in such a manner as to indicate a force
acting in this plane, but at right angles to the velocity of the electron
beam. That is, *when the velocity of the moving charge is perpendicular to
the magnetic field, the force is perpendicular to both the magnetic field and the
velocity.* The magnitude of this force is found to be directly proportional
to the velocity. If the velocity **v** of the moving charge is not perpendicular
to the direction of the magnetic field, but makes an angle ϕ with the field,
then the velocity vector **v** may be resolved into two components: $v \cos \phi$
in the direction of the field, and $v \sin \phi$ perpendicular to the field. In this
general case, *the force acting on the moving charge is perpendicular to both
the magnetic field and to $v \sin \phi$, and has a magnitude proportional to $v \sin \phi$,*
as shown in Fig. 24–1.

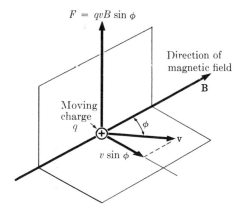

FIG. 24–1. The magnetic force **F** acting on a charge q moving with velocity **v**
is perpendicular to both the magnetic field and to $v \sin \phi$.

It is possible to conceive of a positive ion tube, with a positive ion source at one end and a detector at the other, so that deflection of the positive ion beam may be observed when the tube is placed in various positions in a magnetic field. By using different positive ions, it is possible to measure the force acting on positive charges of different magnitudes. Thus, with hydrogen ions (protons), the force on singly charged positive ions may be measured, and with other gases under proper conditions, forces on doubly and trebly charged positive ions may be measured. Experiment shows in all cases that *the force acting on a charge moving in a magnetic field is proportional to the magnitude of the charge.*

From these experimental observations we may define a vector quantity known as the *magnetic induction*, which characterizes a magnetic field in the same way that the vector **E** characterizes an electric field. The magnitude of the magnetic induction **B** at any point is defined as

$$B = \frac{F}{qv \sin \phi},$$
(24–1)

where q is the magnitude of the charge, v its velocity, ϕ the angle between v and the direction of the magnetic field, and F the force acting on a moving charge at the point.

When F is expressed in newtons, q in coulombs, and v in meters per second, B is said to be in *webers per square meter*. Thus, *one weber per square meter is the magnetic induction of a magnetic field in which one coulomb of charge, moving with a component of velocity perpendicular to the field* ($v \sin \phi$) *equal to one meter per second, is acted on by a force of one newton.* Hence,

$$1 \frac{\text{weber}}{\text{m}^2} = 1 \frac{\text{newton}}{\text{coul·m/sec}}$$

or, since one coulomb per second equals one ampere,

$$1 \frac{\text{weber}}{\text{m}^2} = 1 \frac{\text{newton}}{\text{amp·m}}.$$

In the cgs system, B is measured in *maxwells per square centimeter*, or in *gauss*. It can be shown that

$$1 \text{ gauss} = 1 \frac{\text{maxwell}}{\text{cm}^2} = 10^{-4} \frac{\text{weber}}{\text{m}^2},$$

or

$$1 \frac{\text{weber}}{\text{m}^2} = 10^4 \text{ gauss}.$$

The largest values of magnetic induction that can be produced in the laboratory are of the order of 10 w/m^2 or $100,000$ gauss, while in the

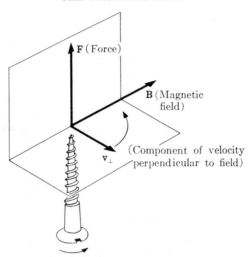

Fig. 24–2. The vectors $\mathbf{v}_\perp$, $\mathbf{B}$, and $\mathbf{F}$ form a mutually perpendicular set. If you rotate the vector $\mathbf{v}_\perp$ toward the vector $\mathbf{B}$, the vector $\mathbf{F}$ will point in the direction of advance of a right-hand screw.

magnetic field of the earth the induction is only a few hundred-thousandths of a weber per square meter, or a few tenths of a guass.

Up to this point we have defined the magnitude of the magnetic induction and its direction, but not its sense. The definition of the magnetic induction vector $\mathbf{B}$ may now be completed by specifying that *when the moving charge is positive*, the three vectors $\mathbf{v}_\perp$, $\mathbf{B}$, and $\mathbf{F}$ form a mutually perpendicular set, as shown in Fig. 24–2. In other words, both the magnitude and the direction of the force are correctly expressed by the relation

$$\mathbf{F} = q(\mathbf{v} \times \mathbf{B}), \qquad\qquad (24\text{–}2)$$

where $\mathbf{v} \times \mathbf{B}$ is the vector product of $\mathbf{v}$ and $\mathbf{B}$, first defined in Chapter 9 in connection with the concept of torque. $\mathbf{v} \times \mathbf{B}$ is the vector whose magnitude is $vB \sin \phi$ and whose direction is the direction of advance of a right-hand screw when rotated from $\mathbf{v}$ to $\mathbf{B}$. It may be seen that Eq. (24–2) conveys the information contained in Figs. 24–1 and 24–2.

EXAMPLE. An electron is projected into a magnetic field of flux density $B = 10 \text{ w/m}^2 = 10 \text{ n/(coul·m/sec)}$ with a velocity of 3×10^7 m/sec in a direction at right angles to the field. Compute the magnetic force on the electron and compare with the weight of the electron.

The magnitude of the magnetic force is

$$|\mathbf{F}| = |q(\mathbf{v} \times \mathbf{B})| = qvB \sin \theta$$

$$= 1.6 \times 10^{-19} \text{ coul} \times 3 \times 10^7 \frac{\text{m}}{\text{sec}} \times 10 \frac{\text{n}}{\text{coul·m/sec}} \times 1$$

$$= 4.8 \times 10^{-11} \text{ n}.$$

The gravitational force, or the weight of the electron, is

$$F = mg$$

$$= 9.1 \times 10^{-31} \text{ kgm} \times 9.8 \frac{\text{m}}{\text{sec}^2} = 8.8 \times 10^{-30} \text{ n.}$$

The gravitational force is therefore negligible in comparison with the magnetic force.

24–3 Lines of induction. Magnetic flux. A magnetic field, like an electric field, can be represented by lines called *lines of induction*, whose direction at every point is that of the magnetic induction vector. By convention, the number of these lines per unit area normal to the direction is made equal to the magnitude of the induction. The unit of induction was chosen to be one weber per square meter so that one weber would equal one line of induction. Similarly, in the cgs system, the unit of induction was chosen to be one maxwell per square centimeter so that one maxwell would equal one line.

In a uniform magnetic field, where the magnetic induction vector has a constant magnitude and direction at all points, the lines of induction are straight and equally spaced. If the pole pieces of an electromagnet are large and close together, there is a region between the poles where the magnetic field is approximately uniform. The lines of induction of various magnetic fields are shown in some of the figures in Chapter 26.

The total number of lines of induction threading through a surface is called the *magnetic flux* through the surface and is denoted by Φ (phi). In the special case where **B** is uniform and normal to a finite area A,

$$\Phi = BA. \tag{24–3}$$

Since B is in w/m^2 and A is in m^2, the flux is in *webers*.

More generally, the magnitude and direction of a magnetic field may vary from point to point of a surface. Then, the number of lines of induction $\Delta\Phi$ threading through an area ΔA is

$$\Delta\Phi = B \, \Delta A \cos \theta = B_n \, \Delta A,$$

and the total flux through a finite area is

$$\boxed{\Phi = \int B_n \, dA.} \tag{24–4}$$

Since the induction **B** at a point equals the flux per unit area, it is often referred to as the *flux density*.

24–4 Orbits of charged particles in magnetic fields. It is often necessary to represent pictorially a magnetic field perpendicular to the plane of the paper (or of the blackboard) directed either toward or away from the reader. This is usually done with a number of dots or crosses. The dots may be thought of as representing the points of arrows directed toward the reader, the crosses as the tail feathers of arrows directed away from the reader.

Let a positively charged particle at point O in a uniform magnetic field of flux density **B** be given a velocity **v** in a direction at right angles to the field (Fig. 24–3). An upward force **F**, equal to qvB, is exerted on the particle at this point. Since the force is at right angles to the velocity, it will not affect the magnitude of this velocity but will merely alter its direction. At points such as P and Q the directions of force and velocity will have changed as shown, the magnitude of the force remaining constant since the magnitudes of q, **v**, and **B** are constant. The particle therefore moves under the influence of a force whose magnitude is constant but whose direction is always at right angles to the velocity of the particle. The orbit of the particle is therefore a circle described with constant tangential speed v, the force **F** being the centripetal force. Since

$$\text{Centripetal acceleration} = \frac{v^2}{R},$$

we have, from Newton's second law,

$$qvB = m\,\frac{v^2}{R}$$

and the radius of the circular orbit is

$$R = \frac{mv}{Bq}. \qquad (24\text{–}5)$$

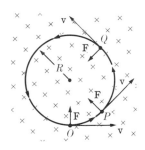

FIG. 24–3. The orbit of a charged particle in a uniform magnetic field is a circle when the initial velocity is perpendicular to the field.

If the direction of the initial velocity is not perpendicular to the field, the particle moves in a helix.

24–5 Thomson's measurement of q/m. We are now ready to consider how Thomson measured the ratio of charge to mass, q/m, for what he called "cathode corpuscles." His apparatus (Fig. 24–4) consisted of a highly evacuated glass tube into which several metal electrodes were sealed. Electrode C is the cathode from which the rays emerged. Electrode A is the anode, which was maintained at a high positive potential so that a discharge of cathode rays passed to it. Most of the rays hit A, but there was

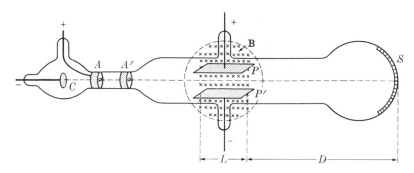

FIG. 24–4. Thomson's apparatus for measuring the ratio q/m for cathode rays.

a small hole in A through which some of the rays passed. These rays were further restricted by an electrode A' in which there was another hole. Thus a narrow beam of the rays passed into the region between the two plates P and P'. After passing between the plates, the rays struck the end of the tube, where they caused fluorescent material at S to glow. (We will discuss how this happens when we consider fluorescence in Chapter 38.)

The deflection plates P and P' were separated a known amount, so that when they were at a known difference of potential the electric field between them could be computed. We shall assume that the field was uniform for a distance L between the plates and zero outside them. When the upper plate P was made positive, the electric field deflected the negative cathode rays upward. After leaving the region between the plates, the electrons coast through the field-free region between the plates to the fluorescent screen at S. The deflection of the particles was discussed in detail in Chapter 20, where we obtained the result (Eq. 20–23)

$$y_E = \frac{qEL}{mv_x^2}\left(\frac{L}{2} + D\right).\qquad(24\text{–}6)$$

If q/m is regarded as a single unknown, then there are two unknowns in this equation. The initial velocity of the rays, v_x, must be determined before q/m can be found. We need another equation involving the initial velocity v_x, so that this unknown velocity can be eliminated between the new equation and Eq. (24–6).

Thomson obtained another equation by applying a magnetic field perpendicular to both the cathode-corpuscle beam and the electric field. It is represented in Fig. 24–4 as being into the page and uniform everywhere within the x-marked area. Thus the cathode rays experienced electric and magnetic forces in the same geometric space.

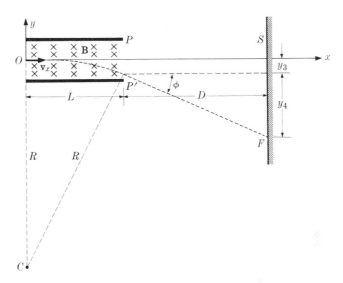

FIG. 24–5. Magnetic deflection of cathode rays.

Figure 24–5 shows the situation when the magnetic field alone is present. The negative cathode rays experience an initial force downward, but this force is not constant in direction, and so the cathode corpuscles move in a circular path according to Eq. (24–5). The equation of this path, taking the origin at C, the center of the curvature, is

$$R = \frac{mv_x}{qB},\tag{24–7}$$

where v_x is the initial velocity of the rays in the x-direction. Referred to the origin O, the equation of this circular path is

$$x^2 + (R + y)^2 = R^2.$$

Solving for R, we get

$$R = -\frac{x^2 + y^2}{2y} \approx -\frac{x^2}{2y}.\tag{24–8}$$

The approximation is good if the deflection is small compared with the distance the rays have moved into the magnetic field, that is, when $y^2 \ll x^2$.

Since the radius of curvature is difficult to measure, we eliminate R between Eqs. (24–8) and (24–7), and obtain

$$y = -\frac{qBx^2}{2mv_x}.\tag{24–9}$$

Therefore, for small deflections, the circular path may be approximated by the parabolic path of Eq. (24–9). The minus sign indicates that the curve is concave downward.

Just as in the electric case, we find that y_3 is the value of y for $x = L$. The rays again move in a straight line through the field-free region, so that

$$y_4 = D \tan \phi = D \left(\frac{dy}{dx} \right)_{x=L} . \qquad (24\text{–}10)$$

For the total magnetic deflection y_B, we have

$$y_B = y_3 + y_4,$$

or

$$y_B = - \frac{q}{m} \left(\frac{BL^2}{2v_x} + \frac{BLD}{v_x} \right) = - \frac{q}{m} \frac{BL}{v_x} \left(\frac{L}{2} + D \right). \qquad (24\text{–}11)$$

Equation (24–11) is similar to Eq. (24–6). It contains q/m and v_x together with measurable quantities, so that v_x can be eliminated and q/m found. It is interesting, however, to follow Thomson's procedure for determining v_x by considering the simultaneous application of the electric and the magnetic fields. If these are adjusted so that there is *no* deflection on the screen, then the force of the electric field on the charged particle is balanced by that of the magnetic field. For this condition of balance, we find that

$$F = qE - qv_x B = 0, \qquad (24\text{–}12)$$

or

$$\boxed{v_x = \frac{E}{B}.} \qquad (24\text{–}13)$$

This result can also be derived from Eqs. (24–6) and (24–11). When y_E and y_B are equal and opposite, the resultant deflection of the cathode-ray beam is zero, and we then have

$$y_E + y_B = \frac{q}{m} \frac{EL}{v_x^2} \left(\frac{L}{2} + D \right) - \frac{q}{m} \frac{BL}{v_x} \left(\frac{L}{2} + D \right) = 0. \qquad (24\text{–}14)$$

This expression is easily reduced to $E/v_x^2 = B/v_x$ or $v_x = E/B$.

For this particular ratio of the fields, the particle goes straight through both fields. It is undeflected, and therefore the measurement of v_x does not depend on the geometry of the tube. Since $y = 0$ at all times, the approximation in Eq. (24–8) is avoided. The velocity thus determined may be substituted into Eq. (24–6), which was derived without approximation.

Thomson measured q/m for cathode rays and found a unique value for this quantity which was independent of the cathode material and the residual gas in the tube. This independence indicated that cathode corpuscles are a common constituent of all matter. The modern accepted value of q/m is $(1.758897 \pm 0.000032) \times 10^{11}$ coulombs per kilogram. Thus Thomson is credited with discovery of the first subatomic particle, the electron. Because it was shown later that electrons have a unique charge e, the quantity he measured is now denoted by e/m. He also found that the velocity of the electrons in the beam was about one-tenth the velocity of light, much larger than any previously measured material particle velocity.

It was fortunate that the electrons Thomson studied had nearly equal velocities. If this had not been the case, the spot on the end of his experimental tube would have been seriously smeared. Both Eqs. (24–6) and (24–11) include the electron velocity and if all electrons had not had the same velocity, each would have undergone a different deflection. Thomson could tell that the electrons had a uniform velocity when he observed an undeflected spot upon proper adjustment of $\mathbf{E}$ and $\mathbf{B}$.

It is interesting to explore why the electrons in Thomson's apparatus had nearly uniform velocities. The electrons he studied came from the cathode and were accelerated toward the anode by a potential difference that we can call V. Since the energy required to separate the electrons from the cathode is negligibly small, the work done by the electric field on the charges went into kinetic energy.

In general, from the law of conservation of energy, the change of kinetic energy plus the change of electrical potential energy of a charge as it goes from point 1 to point 2 must equal zero because no work is done by external forces. Therefore we have

$$(\tfrac{1}{2}mv_2^2 - \tfrac{1}{2}mv_1^2) + (qV_2 - qV_1) = 0, \qquad (24\text{–}15)$$

or

$$\boxed{-q(V_2 - V_1) = \frac{m}{2}(v_2^2 - v_1^2).} \qquad (24\text{–}16)$$

The quantity $V_2 - V_1$ is the potential of the second electrode relative to the first.

If we apply Eq. (24–16) to Thomson's experiment, noting that the charges are negative, the accelerating voltage $V_2 - V_1$ is V, the initial velocity v_1 is zero, and the final velocity v_2 is v_x, we obtain

$$qV = \frac{m}{2}v_x^2,$$

or

$$q/m = e/m = v_x^2/2V. \qquad (24\text{–}17)$$

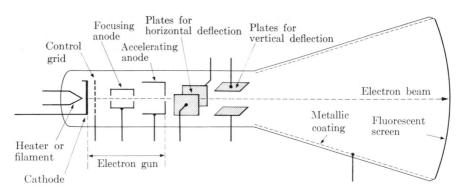

FIG. 24–6. Basic elements of a cathode-ray tube.

This is another equation relating e/m and v_x. It could have been used with either Eq. (24–6) or (24–11) to give e/m. Thomson could have measured the potential difference between the cathode and anode and been spared either the electric or magnetic deflection of the beam in the vicinity of P and P'. Indeed, other methods of measuring e/m utilize this principle.

Cathode-ray tubes such as Thomson used have been developed into important modern electronic components. Electrostatic deflection of an electron beam is used in the cathode-ray tube of modern oscilloscopes. Such tubes usually have two sets of deflecting plates (Fig. 24–6), so that the electron beam can be deflected right and left as well as up and down. These tubes utilize the fact that the deflection is proportional to the electric field between the plates, as shown by Eq. (24–6). Television tubes, on the other hand, commonly utilize magnetic deflection to cause the beam to sweep over the face of the picture area.

Anyone can demonstrate for himself that electric and magnetic fields deflect electron beams. Holding a strong permanent magnet near the face of a television picture produces weird distortions. Rubbing the face of a picture tube or even the plastic protective window with wool, silk, or nylon will produce strong electric fields when the humidity is low. Neither the magnetic nor electric fields thus produced are uniform or perpendicular to the beam, and the deflections they produce are striking in their unpredictability.

24–6 Mass of the electron. Avogadro's number. Since e/m and e are now known, it is only simple arithmetic to find the mass of the electron to be

$$m = (9.1084 \pm 0.0004) \times 10^{-31} \text{ kgm.}$$

Still another basic atomic constant may now be computed with precision by using the value of the electronic charge. The faraday is the amount of charge required to transport one equivalent weight of a material through an electrolyte. Dividing the faraday by e gives the number of electrons which have participated in this transport, or Avogadro's number, N_0. The result agrees with Perrin's value, which had finally established the atomic view of matter.

24–7 Positive rays. After the particle of negative electricity, the electron, had been identified, it was reasonable to ask about positive electricity. The search was made in a discharge tube very similar to that which disclosed cathode rays. In 1886, Goldstein observed that if the cathode of a discharge tube had slots in it, there appeared streaks of light in the gas on the side away from the anode. These channels of light, first called "canal rays," were easily shown to be due to charged particles. They moved in the direction of the electric field which was producing the discharge, and they were deflected by electric and magnetic fields in directions that proved that their charge was positive. Attempts were made to measure q/m, the ratio of the charge to the mass, of these *positive rays*. It was soon discovered that q/m for positive rays was much less than for electrons and that it depended on the kind of residual gas in the tube. The velocities of these positive rays were found to be nonuniform and much less than electron velocities.

Thomson devised a different method for measuring q/m of these positive rays having nonuniform velocities. Figure 24–7(a) shows the apparatus he used. The main discharge took place in the large bulb A at the left, where K is the cathode and D is the anode. The gas under study was slowly admitted through the tube at L and was simultaneously pumped out at F. Thus a very low gas pressure was maintained. Most of the positive rays produced in the bulb hit the cathode and heated it. The cathode had a "canal" through it, so that some of the positive rays passed into the right half of the apparatus. Just to the right of the cathode are M and N, the poles of an electromagnet. The pole pieces of this magnet were electrically insulated by sheets, I, so that the magnetic pole pieces could also be used as the plates of a capacitor for the establishment of an electric field. With neither electric nor magnetic fields, the positive rays passed straight through the chamber C to the sensitive layer at S. This layer was either the emulsion on a photographic plate or a fluorescent screen. The beam was well defined because of the narrow tunnel in the cathode through which it had to pass. Instead of crossed fields as in the electron apparatus, this apparatus has its fields perpendicular to the rays but parallel to each other. The electric field is directed downward and the magnetic induction is upward, so that in Fig. 24–7(b) the electric force is toward the bottom of the page along the y-axis and the magnetic force is out of the page toward the reader along the z-axis.

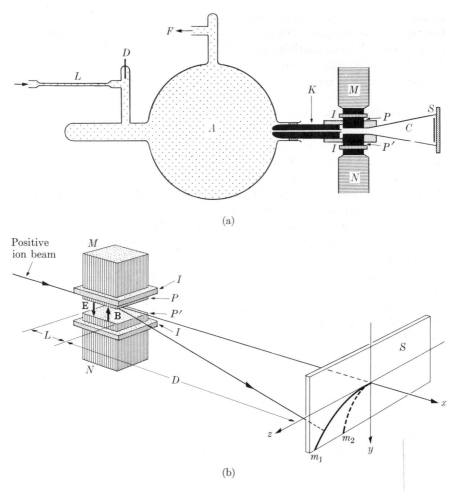

FIG. 24–7. (a) Diagram of Thomson's apparatus for positive-ray analysis. (b) Formation of positive-ray parabolas.

Let a particle of unknown q/m enter the region between the electric plates with an unknown velocity v_x along the x-axis. If the length of its path in each field between the plates is L, then the particle will acquire a downward acceleration, given by Eq. (20–19). It will undergo this acceleration for a time L/v_x, so that its downward velocity when leaving the plates is

$$v_y = \frac{qEL}{mv_x}. \qquad (24\text{–}18)$$

Since the particle is also moving in the magnetic field, it will be accelerated in the z-direction an amount qv_xB/m for a time L/v_x. It will therefore acquire a velocity in the z-direction given by

$$v_z = \frac{qv_xBL}{mv_x} = \frac{qBL}{m}. \qquad (24\text{–}19)$$

If the particle continues a distance D in the field-free space beyond the plates, then it will take D/v_x units of time to get there. Knowing the time and the velocities, we can compute the y- and z-coordinates of the point where the particle will hit. They are

$$y = \frac{qELD}{mv_x^2}, \qquad z = \frac{qBLD}{mv_x}. \qquad (24\text{–}20)$$

These are the parametric equations of a parabola, where v_x is the parameter. Since v_x is different for different particles of the same kind, the pattern on the screen is not a point but a locus of points. Elimination of v_x between these two equations leads to

$$z^2 = \frac{q}{m}\frac{B^2LD}{E}y, \qquad (24\text{–}21)$$

which is the equation of the parabola.

Actual parabolas obtained by Thomson's method are shown in Fig. 24–8. Examination of the figure reveals several things: Positive rays have distinct values of q/m, as is shown by the fact that the traces are clearly parabolas. That a single experiment discloses several values of q/m is evident from the fact that there are several parabolas. It is apparent that the method is not capable of great precision because the parabolas are not sharp.

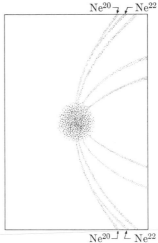

FIG. 24–8. The parabolas of neon.

Thomson assumed that each particle of the positive rays carried a charge equal and opposite to the electronic charge, and he attributed the divergent parabolas to differences in mass. He assumed that the positive rays were positive because each had lost one electron. Thomson could identify particular parabolas with particular ions (charged atoms or molecules are called *ions*). Thus for atomic hydrogen, he could verify that the q/m he measured was equal to the value one would expect from dividing the electronic charge by the mass per atom (the atomic weight of hydrogen divided by Avogadro's number). The reason that positive rays move more slowly than electrons and have lower values of q/m than electrons is now clear: the positive rays are much more massive. The largest q/m for positive rays is that for the lightest element, hydrogen. From the value of q/m it was found that the mass of the *hydrogen ion* or *proton* is 1836.13 ± 0.01 times the mass of an electron. Electrons contribute only a small amount to the mass of material objects.

24–8 Isotopes. The most striking thing that was shown by the Thomson parabolas was that certain chemically pure gases had more than one value of q/m. Most notable was the case of neon, of atomic weight 20.2. Neon exhibited a parabola situated to correspond to a particle of atomic weight 20, but it also had a parabola which indicated an atomic weight of 22. Since the next heavier element, sodium, has an atomic weight of 23.0, efforts to explain away the unexpected value of q/m failed at first. Finally, it was concluded that there must be two kinds of neon, with different masses but chemically identical. The proof of this interpretation was given by Aston, one of Thomson's students.

Aston used a principle which we discussed in Chapter 18. We pointed out there that the average kinetic energy of a molecule in a gas is $3kT/2$. Different gas molecules mixed together in a container must be at the same temperature, and hence the average kinetic energy of each kind of molecule must be the same. If the two gases have different molecular masses, the lighter molecules must have the higher average velocity, and these will make more collisions per unit time with the walls of the container than the heavier molecules. Therefore if these molecules are allowed to diffuse through a porous plug from a container into another vessel, the lighter molecules will have a higher probability of passing through than the heavier, slower ones. Aston took chemically pure neon gas and passed part of it through such a plug. Since one such pass accomplishes only a slight separation, the process had to be repeated many times. He ended with two very small amounts of gas. One fraction had been through the plug many times and the other had been "left behind" many times. He measured the atomic weight of each fraction and found values of 20.15 for the former and 20.28 for the latter. The difference was not great, but it was enough to show that there are indeed two kinds of neon. Many other elements have since been shown to exist in forms which are chemically identical but different in mass. Such forms of an element are called *isotopes*.

The discovery of isotopes solved several problems. It explained the two parabolas observed by Thomson. It also gave a logical explanation of the fact that the atomic weight of neon, 20.2, departs so far from an integral value. If chemical neon is a mixture of neon of atomic weight 20 and of neon of atomic weight 22, then there is some proportion of the two which, when mixed, will have an average atomic weight of 20.2.

24–9 Mass spectroscopy. A detailed search for the isotopes of all the elements required a more precise technique. Aston built the first of many instruments called mass spectrographs in 1919. His instrument had a precision of one part in 10,000, and he found that many elements have isotopes. Rather than discuss his instrument, however, we shall describe an elegant one built by Bainbridge. The Bainbridge mass spectrograph (Fig. 24–9) has a source of ions (not shown) situated above S_1. The ions under study pass through slits S_1 and S_2 and move down into the electric field between the two plates P and P'. In the region of the electric field there is also a magnetic induction $\mathbf{B}$, perpendicular to the paper. Thus the ions enter a region of crossed electric and magnetic fields like those used by Thomson to measure the velocity of electrons in his determination of e/m. Those ions whose velocity is E/B pass undeviated through this region, but ions with other velocities are stopped by the slit S_3. All ions which emerge from S_3 have the same velocity. The region of crossed fields is called a *velocity selector*. Below S_3 the ions enter a region where there is another magnetic field $\mathbf{B}'$, perpendicular to the page, but no electric field. Here the ions move in circular paths of radius R. From Eq. (24–5), we find that

$$m = \frac{qB'R}{v}. \tag{24–22}$$

Assuming equal charges on each ion, then, since B' and v are the same for all ions, we find that the masses of the ions are proportional to the radii

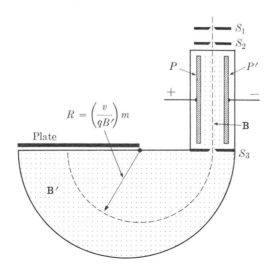

FIG. 24–9. Bainbridge's mass spectrograph, utilizing a velocity selector.

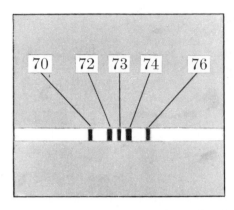

FIG. 24–10. The mass spectrum of germanium, showing the isotopes of mass numbers 70, 72, 73, 74, 76.

of their paths. Ions of different isotopes converge at different points on the photographic plate. The relative abundance of the isotopes is measured from the densities of the photographic images they produce. Figure 24–10 shows the mass spectrum of germanium. The numbers shown beside the isotope images are not the atomic weights of the isotopes but the integers nearest the atomic weights. These integers are called *mass numbers*, and isotopes are written with the mass number as a superscript to the chemical symbol. Thus the isotopes shown would be written Ge^{70}, Ge^{72}, etc. The mass number is represented by the letter A.

As in the case of neon, the discovery of the isotopes of the various elements largely accounted for the fact that many chemical atomic weights are not integers. If germanium has mass numbers 70, 72, 73, 74, and 76, it is no wonder that a mixture of isotopes of germanium has a chemical atomic weight of 72.6.

24–10 Physical atomic weights; atomic mass unit. One of the first discoveries in the field of mass spectroscopy was that oxygen, as found in air, oxides, sulphates, etc., is a mixture of three isotopes. The atomic weight of this mixture was arbitrarily assigned a value of exactly 16, and this number has served for many years as the basis for chemical atomic weights. The chemist continues to use atomic weights based on the chemical system because the relative proportions of the various isotopes in nature are nearly constant for most elements and, for his techniques, isotopes are indistinguishable.

In physics, however, where the relative abundance of isotopes, the separation of isotopes, and the properties of particular isotopes must be studied in great detail, the chemical system is inadequate. Until 1959, the physical system of atomic weights was based on assigning the number

16 to only the lightest, most abundant stable isotope of oxygen, the other two isotopes being designated by O^{17} and O^{18}. *Now, the basis of the physical system of atomic weights is the assignment of the number* 12 *to the lightest, most abundant stable isotope of carbon.* The physical unit of atomic masses, called the *atomic mass unit* (amu), is by definition $\frac{1}{12}$ of the mass of C^{12}. Since the mass of an atom is equal to its atomic weight divided by Avogadro's number, it follows from the definition that the amu is equal to the reciprocal of Avogadro's number. The mass of a neutral atom expressed in atomic mass units is called its *isotopic mass.* Values given in Appendix 4 are based on O^{16}. These are 0.0318 percent higher than values based on C^{12}.

The discovery of isotopes not only accounted for those chemical atomic weights which were far from integral, but also provided a new basis in terms of which the isotopic masses are very near to being integers. We shall see that the remaining discrepancy between isotopic masses and the integral mass numbers will prove to be of profound importance in nuclear physics.

24–11 The cyclotron. The cyclotron is an instrument developed in 1931 by Drs. Ernest O. Lawrence and M. Stanley Livingston at the University of California at Berkeley, for the purpose of securing a beam of charged atomic particles traveling at high speed. Despite its size and complexity, the basic theory of its operation is quite simple.

The heart of the cyclotron is a pair of metal chambers shaped like the halves of a pillbox that has been cut along one of its diameters. (See Fig. 24–11.) These hollow chambers, referred to as "dees" or "D's" because of their shape, have their diametric edges parallel and slightly separated from each other. A source of ions—the positively charged nuclei of heavy hydrogen (deuterons) are commonly used—is located near the midpoint of the gap between the dees. The latter are connected to the terminals of an electric circuit of the same sort as that used in a radio transmitter. The potential between the dees is thus caused to alternate rapidly, some millions of times per second, so the electric field in the gap between the dees is directed first toward one and then toward the other. But because of the electrical shielding effect of the dees, the space within each is a region of zero electric field.

The two dees are enclosed within, but insulated from, a somewhat larger cylindrical metal container from which the air is exhausted, and the whole apparatus is placed between the poles of a powerful electromagnet which provides a magnetic field whose direction is perpendicular to the ends of the cylindrical container.

Consider an ion of charge $+q$ and mass m, emitted from the ion source S at an instant when D_1 in Fig. 24–11 is positive. The ion is accelerated by the electric field in the gap between the dees and enters the (electric)

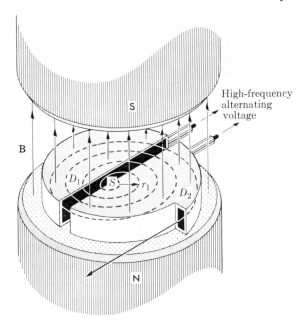

FIG. 24–11. Schematic diagram of a cyclotron.

field-free region within D_2 with a speed, say, of v_1. Since its motion is at right angles to the magnetic field, the ion will travel in a circular path of radius

$$r_1 = \frac{mv_1}{Bq}.$$

If now, in the time required for the ion to complete a half-circle, the *electric* field has reversed so that its direction is toward D_1, the ion will again be accelerated as it crosses the gap between the dees and will enter D_1 with a greater velocity v_2. It therefore moves in a half circle of larger radius within D_1 to emerge again into the gap.

The angular velocity ω of the ion is

$$\omega = \frac{v}{r} = B \frac{q}{m}.$$

Hence the angular velocity is *independent of the speed of the ion and of the radius of the circle* in which it travels, depending only on the magnetic induction and the charge-to-mass ratio (q/m) of the ion. If, therefore, the electric field reverses at regular intervals, each equal to the time required for the ion to make a half revolution, the field in the gap will always be in the proper direction to accelerate an ion each time the gap is crossed. It is this feature of the motion, that the time of rotation is independent of the radius, which makes the cyclotron feasible, since the regularly timed reversals are accomplished automatically by the "radio" circuit to which the dees are connected.

The path of an ion is a sort of spiral, composed of semicircular arcs of progressively larger radius connected by short segments along which the radius is increasing. If R represents the outside radius of the dees and v_{max} the speed of the ion when traveling in a path of this radius,

$$v_{max} = BR\frac{q}{m},$$

and the corresponding kinetic energy of the ion is

$$\frac{1}{2}mv_{max}^2 = \frac{1}{2}m\left(\frac{q}{m}\right)^2 B^2R^2.$$

The potential difference V which would be required to produce the same kinetic energy in a single step, as in the Van de Graaff generator, can be found from

$$\tfrac{1}{2}mv_{max}^2 = qV,$$

or

$$V = \frac{1}{2}\frac{q}{m}B^2R^2. \tag{24–23}$$

If the ions are deuterons,

$$\frac{q}{m} = 4.8 \times 10^7 \frac{\text{coul}}{\text{kgm}}.$$

In the M.I.T. cyclotron, B is about 1.8 w/m^2 and $R = 0.48$ m. Hence

$$V = \tfrac{1}{2} \times 4.8 \times 10^7 \times (1.8)^2 \times (0.48)^2$$
$$= 18 \times 10^6 \text{ volts, or 18 million volts,}$$

and the deuterons have the same speed as if they had been accelerated through a potential difference of 18 million volts.

Figure 24–12(a) is a photograph of the M.I.T. cyclotron, and Fig. 24–12(b) shows the dees removed from the gap between the poles of the electromagnet. The cover of the outer vacuum chamber has been removed in this photograph. The bar in the gap between the dees supports the ion source. Accelerated particles can be brought out of the chamber through a thin foil window in the short tube at the lower right.

Relativistic effects determine the maximum energy obtainable with the cyclotron. These will be discussed in Section 43–4.

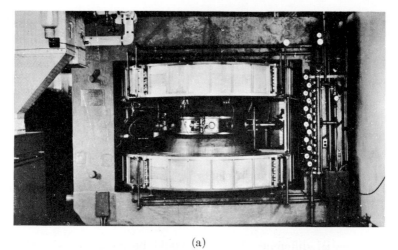

(a)

(b)

Fig. 24–12. The M.I.T. cyclotron.

PROBLEMS

24–1. The magnetic induction or flux density **B** in a certain region is 2 w/m^2 and its direction is that of the positive x-axis in Fig. 24–13. (a) What is the magnetic flux across the surface *abcd* in the figure? Express the answer in webers and in maxwells. (b) What is the magnetic flux across the surface *becf*? (c) What is the magnetic flux across the surface *aefd*?

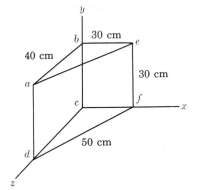

FIGURE 24–13

24–2. Each of the lettered circles at the corners of the cube in Fig. 24–14 represents a positive charge q moving with a velocity of magnitude v in the directions indicated. The region in the figure is a uniform magnetic field of

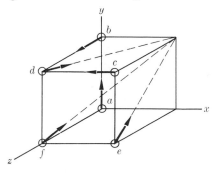

FIGURE 24–14

flux density **B**, parallel to the x-axis and directed toward the right. Copy the figure, find the magnitude and direction of the force on each charge, and show the force in your diagram.

24–3. A particle having a mass of 0.5 gm carries a charge of 2.5×10^{-8} coul. The particle is given an initial horizontal velocity of 6×10^4 m/sec. What is the magnitude and direction of the minimum magnetic field that will keep the particle moving in a horizontal direction?

24–4. A deuteron, an isotope of hydrogen whose mass is about 2 amu, travels in a circular path of radius 40 cm in a magnetic field of flux density 1.5 w/m^2. (a) Find the speed of the deuteron. (b) Find the time required for it to make one-half a revolution. (c) Through what potential difference would the deuteron have to be accelerated to acquire this velocity?

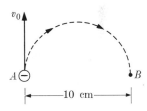

FIGURE 24–15

24–5. An electron at point A in Fig. 24–15 has a velocity v_0 of 10^7 m/sec. Find (a) the magnitude and direction of the magnetic induction that will cause the electron to follow the semicircular path from A to B; (b) the time required for the electron to move from A to B.

24–6. A particle carries a charge of 4×10^{-9} coul. When it moves with a velocity v_1 of 3×10^4 m/sec at 45°

above the x-axis in the xy-plane a uniform magnetic field exerts a force F_1 along the z-axis. When the particle moves with a velocity v_2 of 2×10^4 m/sec along the z-axis there is a force F_2 of 4×10^{-5} newton exerted on it along the x-axis. What are the magnitude and direction of the magnetic field? (See Fig. 24–16.)

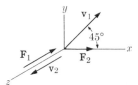

FIGURE 24–16

24–7. An electron moves in a circular path of radius 1.2 cm perpendicular to a uniform magnetic field. The velocity of the electron is 10^6 m/sec. What is the total magnetic flux encircled by the orbit?

24–8. An electron and an alpha particle (a doubly ionized helium atom) both move in circular paths in a magnetic field with the same tangential velocity. Compare the number of revolutions they make per second. The mass of the alpha particle is 6.68×10^{-27} kgm.

24–9. The magnetic induction in a cyclotron which is accelerating protons is 1.5 w/m². (a) How many times per second should the potential across the dees reverse? (b) The maximum radius of the cyclotron is 0.35 m. What is the maximum velocity of the proton? (c) Through what potential difference would the proton have to be accelerated to give it the maximum cyclotron velocity?

24–10. (a) What is the velocity of a beam of electrons when the simultaneous influence of an electric field of intensity 34×10^4 volts/m and a magnetic field of flux density 2×10^{-3} w/m², both fields being normal to the beam and to each other, produces no deflection of the electrons? (b) Show in a diagram the relative orientation of the vectors **v**, **E**, and **B**. (c) What is the radius of the electron orbit when the electric field is removed?

24–11. The electric field between the plates of the velocity selector in a Bainbridge mass spectrograph is 1200 volts/cm and the magnetic induction in both magnetic fields is 0.6 w/m². A stream of singly charged neon ions moves in a circular path of 7.28 cm radius in the magnetic field. Determine the mass number of the neon isotope.

24–12. A singly charged Li^7 ion has a mass of 1.16×10^{-23} gm. It is accelerated through a potential difference of 500 volts and then enters a magnetic field of flux density 0.4 w/m², moving perpendicular to the field. What is the radius of its path in the magnetic field?

24–13. Suppose the electric intensity between the plates P and P' in Fig. 24–9 is 150 volts/cm, and the magnetic induction in both magnetic fields is 0.5 w/m². If the source contains the three isotopes of magnesium, $_{12}Mg^{24}$, $_{12}Mg^{25}$, and $_{12}Mg^{26}$, and the ions are singly charged, find the distance between the lines formed by the three isotopes on the photographic plate. Assume the atomic weights of the isotopes equal to their mass numbers.

24–14. Two positive ions having the same charge q but different masses, m_1 and m_2, are accelerated horizontally from rest through a potential difference V. They then enter a region where there is uniform magnetic induction **B** normal to the plane of the trajectory. (a) Show that if the beam entered the magnetic field along the

x-axis, the value of the y-coordinate for each at any time t is

$$y = Bx^2(q/8mV)^{1/2}.$$

(b) Can this arrangement be used for isotope separation?

24–15. What must be the direction of the electric field $\mathbf{E}$ and the magnetic induction $\mathbf{B}$ in Fig. 24–7(b) so that the segment of the positive-ion parabola will be in (a) the lower right quadrant, (b) the upper right quadrant, and (c) the upper left quadrant as viewed from the right of the diagram?

24–16. (a) If the ion beam in Fig. 24–7(b) contains two types of ions having equal charges but different masses, which of the two parabolic segments will have those of greater mass? (b) If the masses are equal but the charges different, which segment will contain those having the larger charge?

24–17. For a particular parabola in Thomson's mass spectrograms, what physical quantity is different for the ions which land close to the origin than for those landing farther away? Why does this difference exist, since the accelerating voltage is the same for all the ions?

24–18. Deuterons in a cyclotron describe a circle of radius 32.0 cm just before emerging from the D's. The frequency of the applied alternating voltage is 10 Mc/sec. Find (a) the flux density of the magnetic field, and (b) the energy and speed of the deuterons upon emergence.

CHAPTER 25

MAGNETIC FORCES ON
CURRENT-CARRYING CONDUCTORS

25–1 Force on a current-carrying conductor. In the previous chapter we developed an expression for the force on a charge moving in a magnetic field. If the charge is infinitesimal then the force is infinitesimal, and we have from Eq. (24–1)

$$dF = dq(\mathbf{v} \times \mathbf{B}). \tag{25-1}$$

The velocity $\mathbf{v}$ is the displacement of the charge per unit time or $d\mathbf{l}/dt$. Upon substituting for $\mathbf{v}$ in Eq. (25–1) and taking the scalar quantity dt out of the parentheses, we have

$$dF = \frac{dq}{dt}\,(d\mathbf{l} \times \mathbf{B}) = i(d\mathbf{l} \times \mathbf{B}). \tag{25-2}$$

If the charge moves in a straight wire in a field which is uniform over the length of the wire, we can integrate over the length of the wire to obtain the force on a current:

$$\boxed{\mathbf{F} = i(\mathbf{l} \times \mathbf{B}).} \tag{25-3}$$

The vector $\mathbf{l}$ is parallel to the wire and has a positive sense in the direction of the conventional current. As the cross product indicates, the force is perpendicular to both $\mathbf{l}$ and $\mathbf{B}$ and has the direction of advance of a right-handed screw rotated from $\mathbf{l}$ into $\mathbf{B}$. The special case where $\mathbf{l}$ and $\mathbf{B}$ are also perpendicular to each other is illustrated in Fig. 25–1.

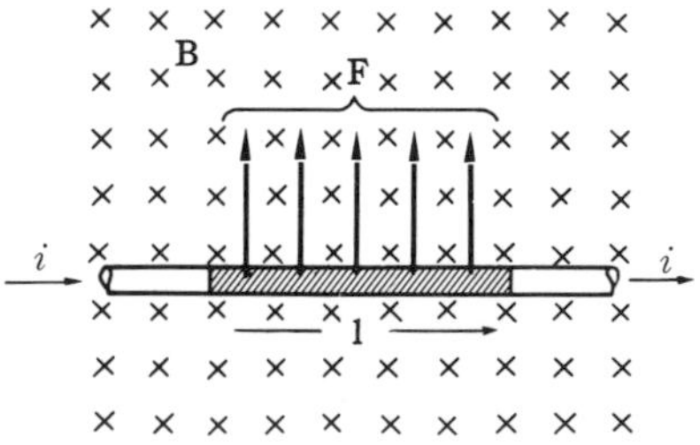

Fig. 25–1. Force on a straight conductor of length l at right angles to a magnetic field of flux density $\mathbf{B}$ directed away from the reader.

502

25–2 Force and torque on a complete circuit. The net force and torque on a complete circuit in a magnetic field can be found from Eq. (25–3). Three simple cases will be analyzed.

Rectangular loop. In Fig. 25–2 there is shown a rectangular loop of wire the lengths of whose sides are a and b. The normal to the plane of the loop makes an angle α with the direction of a uniform magnetic field. The loop is pivoted about an axis OO, and it carries a current i. (Provision must be made for leading the current into and out of the loop, or for inserting a seat of emf. This is omitted from the diagram for simplicity.)

Sides cd and ef of the loop are perpendicular to the field. Hence equal and opposite forces of magnitude

$$F = iaB$$

are exerted on them, vertically upward on cd, vertically downward on ef.

Sides ce and df make an angle ϕ with the field. Equal and opposite forces of magnitude

$$F' = ibB \sin \phi$$

are exerted on them, to the right on df and to the left on ce. [These forces are in reality distributed along each side of the loop. They are shown as single forces in Fig. 25–2(b).]

The resultant *force* on the loop is evidently zero, since the forces on opposite sides are equal and opposite. The resultant *torque*, however, is not zero, since the forces on sides cd and ef constitute a couple of moment

$$\Gamma = iaB \times b \sin \alpha. \tag{25–4}$$

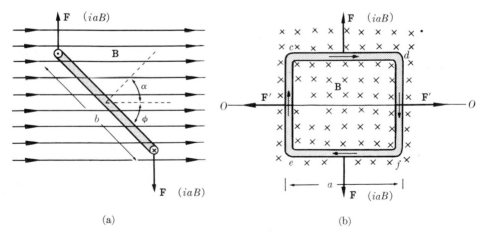

(a)   (b)

Fig. 25–2. Rectangular loop of wire carrying a current in a uniform magnetic field.

The couple is a maximum when $\alpha = 90°$ or when the plane of the coil is parallel to the field, and it is zero when $\alpha = 0$ and the plane of the coil is perpendicular to the field. The position of stable equilibrium is that in which side cd is uppermost.

Since ab is the area of the coil, A, Eq. (25–4) may be written

$$\Gamma = iAB \sin \alpha.$$

If the coil is a closely wound one having N turns, then evidently

$$\Gamma = NiAB \sin \alpha. \tag{25–5}$$

Circular loop. If we replace a circular loop by a very large number of small rectangular loops, then the sum of the areas of the rectangular loops may be made to approach the area of the circular one as closely as we please. Furthermore, the boundary of the rectangular loops will approximate the circular loop with any desired accuracy. Currents in the same sense in all the rectangular loops will give rise to forces which will cancel at all points except on the boundary. It can therefore be proved quite rigorously that, *not only for a circular loop, but for a loop of any shape whatever* carrying a current i in a magnetic field of flux density **B**, the torque is given by

$$\Gamma = iAB \sin \alpha,$$

where A is the area of the loop and α is the angle between the normal to the loop and the magnetic field.

Solenoid. A helical winding of wire is called a *solenoid*. If the solenoid is closely wound, it can be approximated by a number of circular turns lying in planes at right angles to its long axis. The total torque acting on a solenoid in a magnetic field is simply the sum of the torques on the individual turns. Hence for a solenoid of N turns in a uniform field of flux density **B**,

$$\Gamma = NiAB \sin \alpha,$$

where α is the angle between the axis of the solenoid and the direction of the field.

The torque is a maximum when the induction is parallel to the planes of the individual turns or perpendicular to the long axis of the solenoid. The effect of this torque, if the solenoid is free to turn, is to rotate it into a position in which each turn is perpendicular to the field and the axis of the solenoid is parallel to the field.

Although little has been said thus far regarding permanent magnets, everyone will probably recognize that the behavior of the solenoid as described above is the same as that of a bar magnet or compass needle, in that both the solenoid and the magnet will, if free to turn, set themselves with their axes parallel to a magnetic field. The behavior of a bar magnet or compass is usually explained by ascribing the torque on it to magnetic forces exerted on "poles" at its ends. We see, however, that no such interpretation is demanded in the case of the solenoid. May it not be, therefore, that the whirling electrons in a bar of magnetized iron are equivalent to the current in the windings of a solenoid, and that the observed torque arises from the same cause in both instances? We shall return to this question later.

25–3 The galvanometer. Any device used for the detection or measurement of current is called a *galvanometer*. The earliest form of galvanometer was simply the apparatus of Oersted, namely, a compass needle placed below the wire in which the current was to be measured. Wire and needle were both aligned in the north-south direction with no current in the wire. The deflection of the needle when a current was sent through the wire was then a measure of the current. The sensitivity of this form of galvanometer was increased by winding the wire into a coil in a vertical plane with the compass needle at its center, and instruments of this type were developed by Lord Kelvin in the 1890's to a point where their sensitivity is scarcely exceeded by any available at the present time.

Practically all galvanometers used today, however, are of the D'Arsonval moving-coil or pivoted-coil type, in which the roles of magnet and coil are interchanged. The magnet is made much larger and is stationary, while the moving element is a light coil swinging in the field of the magnet.* The construction of a moving-coil galvanometer is illustrated in Fig. 25–3. The magnetic field of a horseshoe magnet whose poles are designated by N and S is concentrated in the vicinity of the coil C by the soft iron cylinder A. The coil consists of from 10 to 20 turns, more or less, of insulated copper wire wound on a rectangular frame and suspended by a fine conducting wire or thin flat strip F which provides a restoring torque when the coil is deflected from its normal position, and which also serves as one current lead to the coil. The other terminal of the coil is connected to the loosely wound spiral S which serves as the second lead, but which exerts a negligible control on the coil.

When a current is sent through the coil, horizontal and oppositely directed side-thrusts are exerted on its vertical sides, producing a couple about a vertical axis through its center. The coil rotates in the direc-

---

* The magnetic field surrounding a permanent magnet is discussed more fully in Chapter 26. For our present purposes, we may take it for granted that in the region between the magnet poles of Fig. 25–3 there does exist a field whose general direction is from N to S.

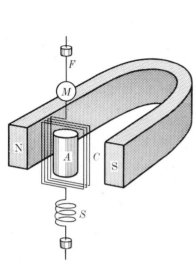

FIG. 25–3.   Construction of the D'Arsonval galvanometer.

FIG. 25–4.   D'Arsonval galvanometer. (Courtesy of Leeds and Northrup.)

tion of this couple and eventually comes to rest in such a position that the restoring torque exerted by the upper suspension equals the deflecting torque due to the side-thrust. The angle of deflection is observed with the aid of a beam of light reflected from a small mirror M cemented to the upper suspension, the light beam serving as a weightless pointer. Since light incident on the mirror is reflected at an angle of reflection equal to the angle of incidence, rotation of the mirror through an angle θ deflects the light beam through an angle 2θ. It is standard practice to observe the reflected beam on a scale at a distance of one meter from the galvanometer.

Because of the geometry of the field in which the moving coil swings, the deflections of a D'Arsonval galvanometer are not directly proportional to the current in the galvanometer coil except for relatively small angles. Hence these instruments are used chiefly as *null* instruments, that is, in connection with circuits such as those of a Wheatstone bridge or a potentiometer, in which other circuit elements are to be adjusted so that the galvanometer current is zero.

25–4 The pivoted-coil galvanometer. The pivoted-coil galvanometer, while essentially the same in principle as the D'Arsonval instrument, differs from the latter in two respects. One is that the moving coil, instead

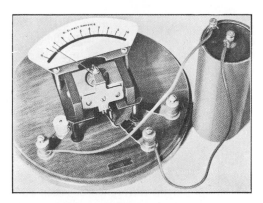

FIG. 25–5. Pivoted-coil galvanometer, modified for use as an ammeter or a voltmeter. Series resistor may be seen at left. (Courtesy of Houghton Mifflin Company.)

of being suspended by a fine fiber, is pivoted between two jewel bearings. The instrument may hence be used in any position and is much more rugged and conveniently portable. The second difference is that the permanent magnetic field is modified by the use of soft iron pole pieces attached to the permanent magnet as shown in Fig. 25–5, so that the coil swings in a field which is everywhere radial. The side-thrusts on the coil are therefore always perpendicular to the plane of the coil, and the angular deflection of the coil is directly proportional to the current in it. The restoring torque is provided by two hairsprings, which serve also as current leads. A length of aluminum tubing, flattened at its tip in a vertical plane, serves as a pointer.

The frictional torque of the jewel bearings, while small, is greater than that of a supporting fiber. Since the deflecting and restoring torques must both be considerably larger than the friction torque, pivoted-coil instruments cannot be made as sensitive as the D'Arsonval type. The smallest currents which can be read on such an instrument are of the order of magnitude of 0.1 microampere.

25–5 Ammeters and voltmeters. The coil of a pivoted-coil galvanometer is deflected because of the interaction between the field of the permanent magnet and the current in the coil. We shall assume that the deflection is proportional to this current. Since the coil and associated leads are metallic conductors obeying Ohm's law, the current in the coil is directly proportional to the potential difference between the terminals of the instrument. Hence the deflection of the instrument is proportional to the potential difference between its terminals as well as to the current through it, and it may be calibrated and used to measure either this potential difference or the current.

For example, suppose that the resistance of the coil and leads of a pivoted-coil galvanometer is 20 ohms, and that the galvanometer deflects full scale with a current in the coil of 10 ma or 0.010 amp. The potential difference between the terminals, with a current of 0.010 amp, is

$$V = iR = 0.010 \text{ amp} \times 20 \text{ ohms} = 0.20 \text{ volt.}$$

The scale of the instrument could therefore be calibrated to read either from zero to 0.010 amp, or from zero to 0.20 volt. Then if in some particular circuit the pointer were deflected by one-half the full-scale amount, one could conclude that the current through the instrument was 0.005 amp, and also that the potential difference between the terminals of the instrument was 0.10 volt.

It has been explained earlier that an ammeter must be inserted in series in a circuit and hence must be a low-resistance instrument, while a voltmeter, which is connected in parallel between the points whose potential difference is to be measured, needs to have a relatively high resistance. The physical limitations imposed on the size of the pivoted coil prevent the use of either very large wire, to obtain a low resistance, or a very large number of turns to obtain a high resistance. However, by inserting a low-resistance shunt in parallel with the pivoted coil, or a resistor of high resistance in series with it, any galvanometer may be modified to serve as an ammeter or a voltmeter.

As an illustration, consider the pivoted-coil galvanometer described in the preceding example, whose resistance was 20 ohms and which deflected full scale with a current of 0.010 amp through it. Suppose it is desired to convert this instrument to an ammeter which will be deflected full scale by a current of 10 amp. The coil and its shunt are shown schematically in Fig. 25–6. The line current is assumed to be 10.0 amp. Since the instrument is to deflect full scale with this line current, the current through the coil must be 0.010 amp. Hence the current in the shunt is

$$10 \text{ amp} - 0.010 \text{ amp} = 9.99 \text{ amp.}$$

Since the currents are inversely proportional to the resistances,

$$\frac{0.01}{9.99} = \frac{R_{\text{sh}}}{20}$$

and R_{sh}, the required shunt resistance, is 0.0200 ohm (to three significant figures).

The resistance R of the ammeter as a whole is

$$\frac{1}{R} = \frac{1}{R_{\text{coil}}} + \frac{1}{R_{\text{sh}}} = \frac{1}{20 \text{ ohms}} + \frac{1}{0.02 \text{ ohm}},$$

$$R = 0.020 \text{ ohm,}$$

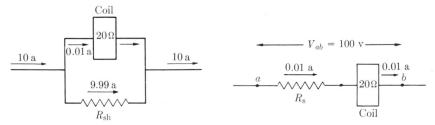

FIG. 25–6. Conversion of a galvanometer to an ammeter with the aid
of a shunt.

FIG. 25–7. Conversion of a galvanometer to a voltmeter with the aid
of a series resistor.

so that one has a low-resistance instrument which at the same time requires 10 amp for full-scale deflection. The shunt is ordinarily enclosed
within the case of the instrument, although in some instances external
shunts are provided.

Suppose next that it is desired to modify the same galvanometer for
use as a voltmeter which will deflect full scale with 100 volts across its
terminals. The coil and its series resistor are shown in Fig. 25–7. Assume
that $V_{ab} = 100$ volts. The current in the moving coil must then be 0.010
amp. Hence

$$0.010 \text{ amp} = \frac{100 \text{ volts}}{R_s + 20 \text{ ohms}},$$

and R_s, the required series resistance, is 9980 ohms.

The resistance of the voltmeter as a whole is 10,000 ohms, and one has
a high-resistance instrument which draws only 0.010 amp with a potential
difference of 100 volts between its terminals.

25–6 The ballistic galvanometer. A ballistic galvanometer is used for
measuring the *quantity of charge* displaced by a current of short duration,
as for example in the charging or discharging of a capacitor, to be discussed
in Chapter 28. While any moving-coil galvanometer can be used ballisti-
cally, instruments designed specifically for the purpose have coils with
somewhat larger moments of inertia, and suspensions with somewhat
smaller torque constants, than are found in instruments designed primarily
for current measurement.

The angular impulse exerted on a galvanometer coil during the passage
of a transient current produces an equal angular momentum of the coil.
The coil then proceeds to swing until its initial kinetic energy has been
converted to potential energy of the suspension. The maximum angle
of throw is observed, and this can be shown to be proportional to the
quantity of charge which passed through the coil. Note that the process
is entirely analogous to that which takes place when a ballistic pendulum
is struck by a bullet.

25–7 The direct-current motor. The direct-current motor is illustrated schematically in Fig. 25–8. The armature, A, is a cylinder of soft steel mounted on a shaft so that it can rotate about its axis. Embedded in longitudinal slots in the surface of the armature are a number of copper conductors C. Current is led into and out of these conductors through graphite brushes making contact with a cylinder on the shaft called the commutator (not shown in Fig. 25–8). The commutator is an automatic switching arrangement which maintains the currents in the conductors in the directions shown in the figure, whatever the position of the armature.

The current in the field coils F and F' sets up a magnetic field which because of the shape of the pole pieces P and P' is essentially radial in the gap between them and the armature. The motor frame M provides a path for the magnetic field. Some of the lines of induction are indicated by the dotted lines in the figure.

Application of the right-hand screw rule shows that with the relative directions of field and armature currents as shown, the side-thrust on each conductor is such as to produce a counterclockwise torque on the armature. When the motor is running, the armature develops mechanical energy at the expense of electrical energy. It must therefore be a seat of back emf. This is an "induced" emf and is discussed further in Chapter 27. The field windings, however, are static and behave like a pure resistance.

If the armature and the field windings are connected in series we have a *series* motor; if they are connected in parallel, a *shunt* motor. In some motors the field windings are in two parts, one in series with the armature and the other in parallel with it; the motor is then *compound*. The three corresponding electrical circuits are shown in Fig. 25–9.

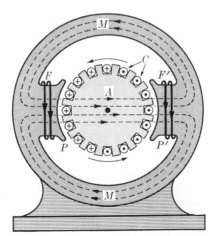

Fig. 25–8. Schematic diagram of a direct-current motor.

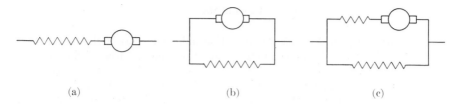

(a)   (b)   (c)

FIG. 25–9. Three ways of connecting the armature and field coils of a d-c motor. (a) Series, (b) shunt, (c) compound.

EXAMPLE. A series-wound d-c motor has an internal resistance of 0.2 ohm. When running at full load on a 120-volt line, a current of 40 amp is drawn.
(a) What is the emf in the armature?

$$V_{ab} = \Sigma ri - \Sigma \mathcal{E},$$
$$120 \text{ volts} = 0.2 \text{ ohm} \times 40 \text{ amp} - \mathcal{E},$$
$$\mathcal{E} = -112 \text{ volts}.$$

Since $\mathcal{E}$ is negative it is often called a "back emf."
(b) What is the power delivered to the motor?

$$P = iV_{ab}$$
$$= 40 \text{ amp} \times 120 \text{ volts} = 4800 \text{ watts}.$$

(c) What is the rate of generation of heat in the motor?

$$P = i^2 R$$
$$= (40 \text{ amp})^2 \times 0.2 \text{ ohm} = 320 \text{ watts}.$$

(d) What is the mechanical power developed?

Mechanical power = total power − rate of production of heat.
4800 watts − 320 watts = 4480 watts.

The mechanical power may also be calculated from the relation

Mechanical power = back emf × current
= 112 volts × 40 amp = 4480 watts.

PROBLEMS

25–1. The cube in Fig. 25–10, of sides 0.5 m, is in a uniform magnetic field of 0.6 w/m². The wire *abcde* carries a current of 4 amp in the direction indicated. Determine the magnitude and direction of the force acting on lengths *ab, bc, cd,* and *de.*

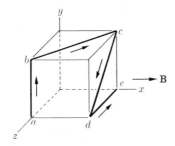

FIGURE 25–10

25–2. The plane of a rectangular loop of wire 5 cm × 8 cm is parallel to a magnetic field whose flux density is 0.15 w/m². (a) If the loop carries a current of 10 amp, what torque acts on it? (b) What is the maximum torque that can be obtained with the same total length of wire carrying the same current in this magnetic field?

25–3. The rectangular loop in Fig. 25–11 is pivoted about the *y*-axis and carries a current of 10 amp in the direc-

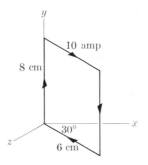

FIGURE 25–11

tion indicated. (a) If the loop is in a uniform magnetic field of flux density 0.2 w/m², parallel to the *x*-axis, find the force on each side of the loop, in dynes, and the torque in dyne·cm required to hold the loop in the position shown. (b) Same as (a) except the field is parallel to the *z*-axis. (c) What torque would be required if the loop were pivoted about an axis through its center, parallel to the *y*-axis?

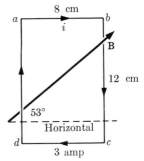

FIGURE 25–12

25–4. The rectangular coil of wire shown in Fig. 25–12 has 5 closely wound turns and carries a current of 3 amp. (a) What is the magnitude and direction of the force on each side of the coil when it is placed in a region where there is a uniform magnetic induction of 2×10^{-3} w/m² directed 53° above the horizontal? (b) What is the magnitude of the resultant torque of these forces about an axis parallel to *ad* in the plane of the loop?

25–5. What is the maximum torque on a galvanometer coil 5 × 12 cm, of 600 turns, when carrying a current of 10^{-5} amp in a field where the flux density is 0.10 w/m²?

25–6. The rectangular loop of wire in Fig. 25–13 has a mass of 0.1 gm per

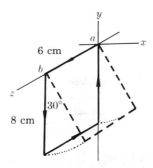

FIGURE 25-13

centimeter of length, and is pivoted about side ab as a frictionless axis. The current in the wire is 10 amp in the direction shown. (a) Find the magnitude and sense of the magnetic field, parallel to the y-axis, that will cause the loop to swing up until its plane makes an angle of 30° with the yz-plane. (b) Discuss the case where the field is parallel to the x-axis.

25-7. A 1-ma meter has a resistance of 33 ohms. (a) What value of resistor should be used, and how should it be connected to convert it into a meter reading 1 amp full scale? 10 amp full scale? (b) What maximum power must these resistors be able to dissipate?

25-8. A 50-ma meter has a resistance of 12 ohms. (a) What resistance multiplier is required to convert it into a meter reading 10 volts full scale? (b) If the actual resistance of the multiplier used is 2% greater than required, what is the percentage error in the full-scale reading of the 10-volt meter?

25-9. The coil of a pivoted-coil galvanometer has 50 turns and encloses an area of 6 cm². The magnetic induction in the region in which the coil swings is 0.01 w/m² and is radial. The torsional constant of the hairsprings is $k = 0.1$ dyne·cm/deg. Find the angular deflection of the coil for a current of 1 ma.

25-10. The resistance of a galvanometer coil is 25 ohms and the current required for full-scale deflection is 20 ma. (a) Show in a diagram how to convert the galvanometer to an ammeter reading 5 amp full scale, and compute the shunt resistance. (b) Show how to convert the galvanometer to a voltmeter reading 150 volts full scale, and compute the series resistance.

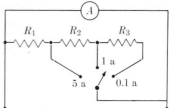

FIGURE 25-14

25-11. The 0.01-amp meter A in Fig. 25-14 has a resistance of 4 ohms. What must be the values of the resistors R_1, R_2, and R_3, connected as shown in the diagram, to convert the meter to one having the ranges 0.1 amp, 1 amp, and 5 amp?

25-12. An 0.2-amp meter has a moving coil consisting of 120 turns of wire. In repairing the meter 5 turns of wire were removed. How has the range of the meter been affected?

25-13. Figure 25-15 shows the internal wiring of a "three-scale" voltmeter whose binding posts are marked +, 3 v, 15 v, 150 v. The resistance of the moving coil, R_G, is 15 ohms, and a current

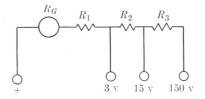

FIGURE 25-15

of 1 ma in the coil causes it to deflect full scale. Find the resistances R_1, R_2, R_3, and the over-all resistance of the meter on each of its ranges.

25–14. A certain d-c voltmeter is said to have a resistance of "one thousand ohms per volt." What current, in milliamperes, is required for full-scale deflection?

25–15. An ammeter reads 5 amp when connected across an unknown potential difference. A 10-ohm resistor is then inserted in series with the meter across the same potential difference, and the current drops to 3.5 amp. (a) What is the resistance of the ammeter? (b) What is the value of the unknown potential difference?

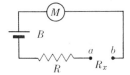

FIGURE 25–16

25–16. The circuit of a common type of ohmmeter is shown in Fig. 25–16. M is a 1-ma meter having a resistance of 100 ohms. The battery B has an emf of 3 volts and negligible internal resistance. R is so chosen that when the terminals a and b are shorted ($R_x = 0$) the meter reads full scale. When a and b are open ($R_x = \infty$) the meter reads zero. All intermediate values of R_x will be indicated by currents between 0 and 1 ma. (a) What should be the value of the resistor R? (b) What current would indicate a resistance R_x of 600 ohms? (c) What resistance R_x would be indicated when the meter reads 0.5 ma?

25–17. The resistance of the coil of a pivoted-coil galvanometer is 10 ohms, and a current of 0.02 amp causes it to

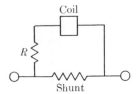

FIGURE 25–17

deflect full scale. It is desired to convert this galvanometer to an ammeter reading 10 amp full scale. The only shunt available has a resistance of 0.03 ohm. What resistance R must be connected in series with the coil? (See Fig. 25–17.)

25–18. A 150-volt voltmeter has a resistance of 20,000 ohms. When connected in series with a large resistance R across a 110-volt line, the meter reads 5 volts. Find the resistance R. (This problem illustrates one method of measuring large resistances.)

25–19. A potential difference of 110 volts is placed across a 12,000-ohm resistor ab. The voltmeter V has a resistance of 6000 ohms, and point c is $\frac{1}{4}$ of the distance from a to b. What is the reading of the voltmeter? (See Fig. 25–18.)

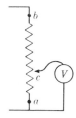

FIGURE 25–18

25–20. A voltmeter having a resistance of 1000 ohms is placed across the terminals of an unknown resistor, the two being inserted in series with an ammeter. When the ammeter reads 0.02 amp the voltmeter indicates 4 volts. What is the resistance of the unknown resistor?

25–21. A 600-ohm resistor and a 400-ohm resistor are connected in series across a 90-volt line. A voltmeter across the 600-ohm resistor reads 45 volts. (a) Find the voltmeter resistance. (b) Find the reading of the same voltmeter if connected across the 400-ohm resistor.

25–22. In Fig. 25–19, point a is maintained at a constant potential above ground. $R_1 = 20{,}000$ ohms, $R_2 = R_3 = 10{,}000$ ohms. A 150-volt voltmeter whose resistance is 15,000 ohms reads 45 volts when connected between point c and ground. (a) What is the potential of point a above ground? (b) What was the potential of point c above ground before the voltmeter was connected?

FIGURE 25–19

25–23. The ranges of a "three-scale" voltmeter (see Problem 25–13) are 1.5 v, 3 v, and 15 v. The resistance of the meter between its 15-volt terminals (i.e. between the + terminal and the terminal marked 15 v) is 1500 ohms. (a) What is the resistance between the 1.5-v terminals and between the 3-v terminals? (b) When a cell is connected across the 1.5-v terminals the meter reads 1.42 volts; when the same cell is connected across the 3-v ter-

minals the meter reads 1.48 volts. Compute the emf and internal resistance of the cell.

25–24. Two 150-volt voltmeters, one of resistance 15,000 ohms and the other of resistance 150,000 ohms, are connected in series across a 120-volt d-c line. Find the reading of each voltmeter.

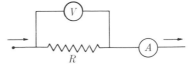

FIGURE 25–20

25–25. The voltmeter V in Fig. 25–20 reads 117 volts and the ammeter A reads 0.130 amp. The resistance of the voltmeter is 9000 ohms and the resistance of the ammeter is 0.015 ohm. Compute (a) the resistance R; (b) the power input to R.

25–26. The resistance of the moving coil of the galvanometer G in Fig. 25–21 is 25 ohms and it deflects full scale with a current of 0.010 amp. Find the magnitudes of the resistances R_1, R_2, and R_3, to convert the galvanometer to a multirange ammeter deflecting full scale with currents of 10 amp, 1 amp, and 0.1 amp.

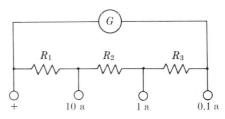

FIGURE 25–21

25–27. Find the efficiency of a certain motor from the following data, given on its name plate: 5 hp, 230 volts, 18 amp, 1200 rpm.

25–28. In a shunt-wound d-c motor the resistance of the field coils is 150 ohms and the resistance of the armature is 2 ohms. When a difference of potential of 120 volts is applied to the brushes, and the motor is running at full speed delivering mechanical power, the current supplied to it is 4.5 amp. (a) What is the current in the field coils? (b) What is the current in the armature? (c) What is the back emf developed by the motor? (d) How much mechanical power is developed by this motor?

25–29. A shunt-wound d-c motor is running at normal speed and developing 2 hp. The current in the armature is 7.0 amp when the impressed voltage is 220 volts. (a) What is the back emf of the motor? (b) At what rate is heat developed in the armature?

25–30. Figure 25–22 is a diagram of a shunt-wound d-c motor, operating from 120-volt d-c mains. The resistance of the field windings, R_f, is 240 ohms. The resistance of the armature, R_a, is 3 ohms. When the motor is running the armature develops a back emf $\mathcal{E}$ in the direction of the arrow. The motor draws a current of 4.5 amp from the line. Compute (a) the field current, (b) the armature current, (c) the back emf $\mathcal{E}$, (d) the rate of development of heat in the field windings, (e) the rate of development of heat in the armature, (f) the power input to the motor, (g) the efficiency of the motor, if friction and windage losses amount to 50 watts.

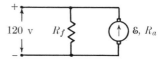

FIGURE 25–22

CHAPTER 26

MAGNETIC FIELD OF A CURRENT.
MAGNETIC PROPERTIES OF MATTER

26–1 Magnetic field of a current element. An electric charge in motion sets up, in the space around it, a magnetic field. A second charge, moving in a magnetic field, experiences a force. The two preceding chapters were devoted to the second aspect of the problem, that is, to the forces on moving charges or current-carrying conductors in magnetic fields. The existence of the field was taken for granted. In this chapter we return to the first part of the problem and correlate the magnitude and direction of a magnetic field with the motion of the charged particles responsible for it. In practice, the moving charges setting up a magnetic field are most commonly those constituting the current in a conductor. We shall therefore begin by discussing the magnetic field around a conductor in which there is a current.

The first recorded observations of magnetic fields set up by currents were those of Oersted, who discovered that a pivoted compass needle, beneath a wire in which there was a current, set itself with its long axis perpendicular to the wire. Later experiments by Biot and Savart, and by Ampere, led to a relation by means of which we can compute the flux density at any point of space around a circuit in which there is a current.

The circuit is to be divided, in imagination, into short elements of length dl, one of which is shown in Fig. 26–1. The moving charges in each element set up a field at all points of space, and the field of the entire circuit, at any point, is the resultant of the infinitesimal fields of all the elements of the circuit. The direction of the infinitesimal field $d\mathbf{B}$ set up at point P by the element of length dl is shown in Fig. 26–1. The vector $d\mathbf{B}$ lies *in* a plane perpendicular to the axis of dl, and is itself *perpendicular* to the plane determined by dl and the line joining P and dl. It follows that the lines of induction, to which the vectors are tangent, are circles lying in planes perpendicular to the axis of the element. The direction of these lines is clockwise when viewed along the direction of the conventional current in dl. A useful rule is to grasp the element (in imagination) in the right hand with the extended thumb pointing in the direction of the current. The fingers then encircle the element in the direction of the flux lines.

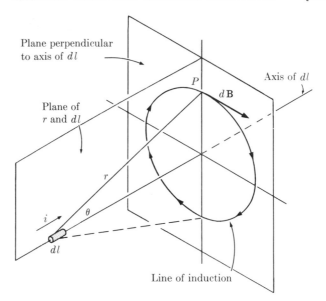

Fig. 26–1. Magnetic field due to a current element.

The magnitude of $d\mathbf{B}$ is given by the following relation:

$$dB = k' \frac{i \, dl \sin \theta}{r^2},\qquad\qquad (26\text{–}1)$$

where r is the distance between dl and the point P, and θ is the angle between $\mathbf{r}$ and $d\mathbf{l}$. This equation is often called *Ampere's formula*, or *Ampere's law*, but it should be credited to Biot, who first proposed it in 1820.

The factor k' in Eq. (26–1) is a proportionality constant whose magnitude, like that of the constant k in Coulomb's law, depends on the choice of units. If the units of flux density, current, and length are independently defined, then k' must be found by experiment. On the other hand, some arbitrary value may be assigned to k' and to the units of any two of the quantities in Eq. (26–1) and this equation may then be used to define the unit of the third quantity. The latter procedure is the one that is actually adopted. In the mks system, k' is set equal to exactly 10^{-7} w/amp·m, and Eq. (26–1) (or more precisely, an equation derived from it) is used to define the unit of current, the ampere.

For the sake of eliminating the factor 4π from other equations derived from the Biot law, and which are used more frequently than is the law itself, it is convenient to define a new proportionality constant μ_0 by the equation

$$\frac{\mu_0}{4\pi} = k', \qquad \mu_0 = 4\pi k'.$$

This procedure is analogous to replacing the proportionality constant k in Coulomb's law by the term $1/4\pi\epsilon_0$. To four significant figures,

$$\mu_0 = 4\pi k' = 12.57 \times 10^{-7} \ \frac{\text{w}}{\text{amp·m}},$$

$$\frac{\mu_0}{4\pi} = 10^{-7} \ \frac{\text{w}}{\text{amp·m}}.$$

The quantity μ_0 is called the permeability of free space.

By using the vector cross product we can now write the Biot law in one expression which gives the magnitude and direction of $d\mathbf{B}$ (see Fig. 26–2). We have

$$d\mathbf{B} = \frac{\mu_0}{4\pi} \, i \, \frac{d\mathbf{l} \times \hat{\mathbf{r}}}{r^2} \tag{26–2}$$

where $\hat{\mathbf{r}}$ is a new symbol representing a unit vector. A unit vector has the same direction as the vector with which it is associated but, by definition, it has a magnitude of unity. Figure 26–3 shows the unit vectors associated with vector $\mathbf{A}$, which is greater than unity, and vector $\mathbf{B}$, which is less than unity. Any vector is equal to its unit vector times its magnitude ($\mathbf{A} = A\hat{\mathbf{A}}$).

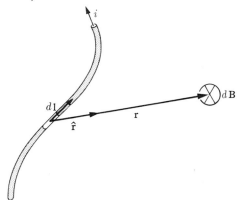

Fig. 26–2. Diagram for Biot's law in vector notation. The plane of the paper includes both $d\mathbf{l}$ and $\mathbf{r}$.

Fig. 26–3. $\hat{\mathbf{A}}$ is the unit vector of $\mathbf{A}$, which has a magnitude of 3. $\hat{\mathbf{B}}$ is the unit vector of $\mathbf{B}$, which has a magnitude of 0.5.

It follows from this equation that the flux density $d\mathbf{B}$ due to a current element is zero at all points on the axis of the element, since $\sin\theta = 0$ at all such points. At a given distance r from the element the flux density is a maximum in a plane passing through the element perpendicular to its axis, since $\theta = 90°$ and $\sin\theta = 1$ at all points in such a plane.

The expression for the resultant flux density at any point of space, due to a complete circuit, is obtained by forming the vector sum of all the values of $d\mathbf{B}$ due to all the elementary current elements. Thus

$$\mathbf{B} = \frac{\mu_0}{4\pi}\int \frac{i\,(d\mathbf{l} \times \hat{\mathbf{r}})}{r^2}. \qquad \text{(Vector sum)} \qquad (26\text{--}3)$$

Except in certain special cases, the evaluation of Eq. (26–3) is an elaborate mathematical problem. We shall be concerned in this book with three important simple applications: (1) the flux density at any point near a very long straight wire carrying a current, (2) the flux density on the axis of a circular loop, and (3) the flux density at a point near the center of a solenoid, or helix.

If there is matter in the space around a circuit, the flux density at a point will be due not entirely to currents in conductors, but in part to the magnetization of this matter. The magnetic properties of matter are discussed more fully in a later chapter. However, unless iron or some of the ferromagnetic materials are present, this effect is so small that, while strictly speaking Eq. (26–2) holds only for conductors in vacuum, as a practical matter it can be used without correction for conductors in air, or in the vicinity of any nonferromagnetic material.

26–2 Magnetic field of a long straight conductor. Let us use the Biot law to compute the magnetic induction at point P in Fig. 26–4, at a distance a from a long straight conductor coinciding with the x-axis. Construct x- and y-axes at an arbitrary point O. Let x be the distance from O to an element of length dx, r the distance from dx to P, and θ the angle between dx and r. Then in terms of the letters used in this diagram, Eq. (26–2) becomes

$$dB = \frac{\mu_0}{4\pi}\,i\,\frac{dx\sin\theta}{r^2}. \qquad (26\text{--}4)$$

The induction $d\mathbf{B}$ set up at P by any other element of the conductor is parallel to the vector shown in the diagram, so the resultant induction is the algebraic sum or integral of the dB's. Simplification will result if θ is chosen as the independent variable. It will be seen from the diagram that

$$r = a\csc\theta, \qquad x = a\cot\theta.$$

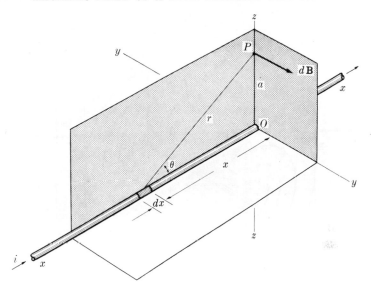

FIG. 26–4.   Magnetic field set up by the current in an element dx of a long straight conductor.

Hence

$$dx = -a \csc^2 \theta \, d\theta.$$

When these expressions for dx and r are inserted in Eq. (26–4), we get

$$dB = -\frac{\mu_0}{4\pi} \frac{i}{a} \sin \theta \, d\theta.$$

If the conductor is infinitely long (or very long in comparison with the distance a) the limits of integration of the original variable x are from $-\infty$ to $+\infty$. The corresponding limits of the angle θ are from π to 0. Hence

and

$$B = -\frac{\mu_0}{4\pi} \frac{i}{a} \int_\pi^0 \sin \theta \, d\theta = -\frac{\mu_0}{4\pi} \frac{i}{a} \left[-\cos \theta \right]_\pi^0,$$

$$B = \frac{\mu_0}{4\pi} \frac{2i}{a}.$$

This relation was deduced by Biot and Savart from experimental study of the field around a long straight conductor, before the differential form [Eq. (26–2)] had been discovered.   It is called the *Biot-Savart law*.

Unlike the electric field around a charged wire, which is radial, the lines of magnetic induction are *circles* concentric with the wire and lying

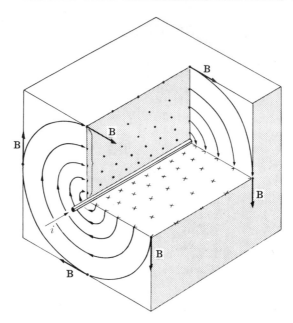

FIG. 26–5. Magnetic field around a long straight conductor.

in planes perpendicular to it. It will also be noted that in this idealized case each line of induction is a *closed* line, and that in this respect lines of induction differ from the lines of force in an electric field, which terminate on positive or negative charges.

A portion of the magnetic field around a long straight conductor is shown in the cutaway view in Fig. 26–5.

26–3 Force between parallel conductors. The ampere. Figure 26–6 shows a portion of two long straight parallel conductors separated by a distance a and carrying currents i and i' respectively in the same direction. Since each conductor lies in the magnetic field set up by the other, each will experience a force. The diagram shows some of the lines of induction set up by the current in the lower conductor. The magnitude of **B** at the upper conductor is

$$B = \frac{\mu_0}{4\pi} \frac{2i}{a}.$$

From Eq. (25–3), the force on a length l of the upper conductor is

$$F = i'Bl = \frac{\mu_0}{4\pi} l \frac{2ii'}{a},$$

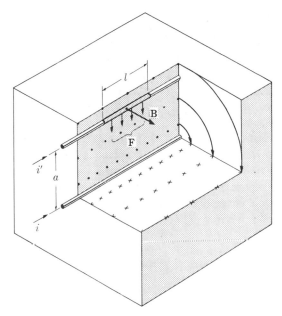

FIG. 26–6. Parallel conductors carrying currents in the same direction attract each other.

and the force per unit length is therefore

$$\frac{F}{l} = \frac{\mu_0}{4\pi} \frac{2ii'}{a}.$$

The direction of the force on the upper conductor is downward. There is an equal and opposite force per unit length on the lower conductor, as may be seen by considering the field around the upper conductor, or by Newton's third law. Hence the conductors attract each other.

If the direction of either current is reversed, the forces reverse also. Parallel conductors carrying currents in opposite directions repel each other.

The fact that two straight parallel conductors exert forces of attraction or repulsion on each other is made the basis of the definition of the ampere in the mks system. The ampere is defined as follows:

One ampere is that unvarying current which, if present in each of two parallel conductors of infinite length and one meter apart in empty space, causes each conductor to experience a force of exactly 2×10^{-7} newton per meter of length.

It follows from this definition and the preceding equation that the numerical value of μ_0 is exactly $4\pi \times 10^{-7}$ or, to four significant figures,

$$\mu_0 = 12.57 \times 10^{-7} \ \frac{\text{w}}{\text{amp·m}}.$$

Now the coulomb is defined not as in Section 19–6, but in terms of the ampere. It is the quantity of charge that in one second crosses a section of a circuit in which there is a constant current of one ampere. It follows that the unit of charge in the mks system is defined in terms of the force between *moving* charges, as contrasted with the electrostatic system, in which the statcoulomb is defined in terms of the electrostatic force between charges.

From the definition above, the ampere can be established, in principle, with the help of a meter stick and a spring balance. For the practical standardization of the ampere, coils of wire are used instead of straight wires and their separation is made only a few centimeters. The complete instrument, which is capable of measuring currents with a high degree of precision, is called a *current balance*.

26–4 Magnetic field of a circular turn. In many devices in which a current is used to establish a magnetic field, as in an electromagnet or a transformer, the wire carrying the current is wound into a coil of some sort. We therefore consider next the magnetic field set up by a single circular turn of wire carrying a current. This problem should be compared with Example 2 of Section 20–2, which is a similar analysis of the *electric* field on the axis of a charged ring.

Figure 26–7 shows a circular turn of radius R carrying a current i and lying in the yz-plane. Point P is on the axis of the turn, at a distance s

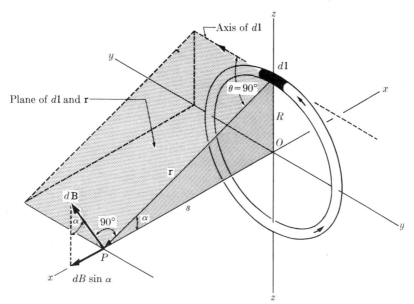

Fig. 26–7. Magnetic field set up by an element $d\mathbf{l}$ of a circular turn of wire carrying a current.

from its center O, and r is the distance from an element of the turn of length dl to point P. The plane determined by dl and $\mathbf{r}$ is shaded, and the induction $d\mathbf{B}$ set up at P by the current in the element dl is at right angles to this plane and lies in the xz-plane. The angle θ between dl and $\mathbf{r}$ is 90°, so in terms of the symbols used in this diagram the Biot law becomes

$$dB = \frac{\mu_0}{4\pi} \, i \frac{dl}{r^2}.$$

Let α represent the angle between r and the x-axis. The vector $d\mathbf{B}$ can then be resolved into a component $dB \sin \alpha$ along the x-axis and a component $dB \cos \alpha$ at right angles to it. It will be seen by symmetry that each element contributes an equal component $dB \sin \alpha$, but that the components $dB \cos \alpha$ set up by diametrically opposite elements will cancel out. Hence the resultant induction is along the x-axis, and is found by integration of the components $dB \sin \alpha$.

$$B = \int dB \sin \alpha = \frac{\mu_0}{4\pi} \frac{i \sin \alpha}{r^2} \int dl,$$

since $\sin \alpha$ and r are constants and may be taken outside the integral sign. The integral is merely the circumference of the turn, $2\pi R$, so finally

$$B = \frac{\mu_0}{2} \frac{iR \sin \alpha}{r^2}. \tag{26–5}$$

At the center of the turn, $\alpha = 90°$ and $r = R$, so at the center

$$B = \frac{\mu_0}{2} \frac{i}{R}. \tag{26–6}$$

If instead of a single turn, as in Fig. 26–7, we have a coil of N closely spaced turns all of essentially the same radius, each turn contributes equally to the field and Eq. (26–6) becomes

$$B = \frac{\mu_0}{2} \frac{Ni}{R}. \tag{26–7}$$

Some of the lines of induction surrounding a circular turn and lying in a plane through the axis are shown in Fig. 26–8. In reality, of course, the field is three-dimensional, and it may be visualized by imagining the plane to be rotated about the x-axis.

It was pointed out in Chapter 25 that a loop of wire of any shape and carrying a current is acted on by a torque when placed in an external magnetic field. The final position of equilibrium was seen to be one in

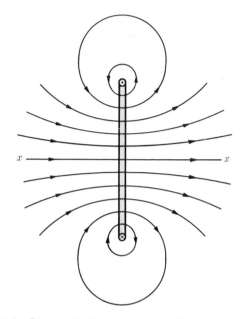

Fig. 26–8. Lines of induction surrounding a circular turn.

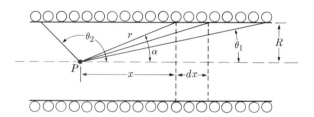

Fig. 26–9. Magnetic induction of a solenoid.

which the plane of the loop was perpendicular to the external field. Now we see that this position is such that, within the area enclosed by the loop, the induction of the loop's own field is in the same direction as that of the external field. In other words, a loop, if free to turn, will set itself in such a plane that the flux passing through the area enclosed by it has its maximum possible value. This is found to be true in all instances and is a useful general principle. For example, if a current is sent through an irregular loop of flexible wire in an external magnetic field, the loop will assume a circular form with its plane perpendicular to the field and with its own flux adding to that of the field. The same conclusion can, of course, be drawn by analyzing the side-thrusts on the elements of the conductor.

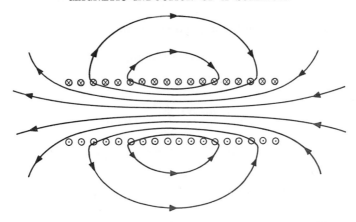

FIG. 26–10. Lines of induction surrounding a solenoid.

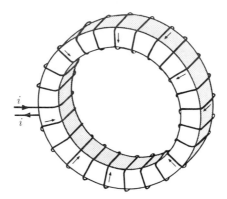

FIG. 26–11. A toroid.

26–5 Magnetic induction of a solenoid. The flux density produced at any point by a current in a solenoidal winding is simply the resultant of the flux densities set up at that point by each turn of the solenoid. To find the flux density at a point P on the axis of the solenoid (Fig. 26–9), consider an elementary length dx on the solenoid, at an axial distance x from P. Let l represent the length of the solenoid and N the number of turns in its winding. The number of turns per unit length is then N/l, and the number of turns in the length dx is $(N/l)\,dx$. (We are assuming that each turn can be considered to lie in a plane perpendicular to the axis of the solenoid.)

The flux density at P, set up by a current i in the element of length dx, is, from Eq. (26–5),

$$dB = \frac{\mu_0}{2}\frac{Ni}{l}\frac{R\sin\alpha}{r^2}\,dx.$$

Instead of x, let us use the angle α as the independent variable. Then

$$x = R \cot \alpha, \qquad dx = -R \csc^2 \alpha \, d\alpha, \qquad r^2 = R^2 \csc^2 \alpha$$

and

$$B = -\frac{\mu_0}{2} \frac{Ni}{l} \int_{\theta_1}^{\theta_2} \sin \alpha \, d\alpha$$

$$= \frac{\mu_0}{2} \frac{Ni}{l} (\cos \theta_1 - \cos \theta_2).$$

Note that this equation applies to any axial point and is not restricted to points within the solenoid.

At any axial point within a long solenoid and not too near either end, $\theta_1 = 0$ and $\theta_2 = 180°$. Hence at such a point

$$B = \mu_0 \frac{Ni}{l}. \tag{26–8}$$

At an axial point at one end of a long solenoid, $\theta_1 = 0$ and $\theta_2 = 90°$ (or vice versa). Hence, at either end,

$$B = \frac{\mu_0}{2} \frac{Ni}{l},$$

and the flux density at either end is one-half its magnitude at the center. However, the field is very nearly constant except close to the ends and the lines of induction enter and leave the solenoid in relatively small regions near its ends. (See Fig. 26–10.)

Although Eq. (26–8) was derived for a point on the axis of the solenoid, it is a good approximation for any point within the solenoid not too close to its ends.

A winding such as that sketched in Fig. 26–11 is called a *toroid*. It may be thought of as a solenoid which has been bent into a circular form so that its ends are joined together. Practically all the magnetic flux is confined to the interior of the toroid, and the flux density at any point within the winding is given by Eq. (26–8), where l is to be interpreted as the *mean circumference* of the toroid.

26–6 Magnetic properties of matter. We have discussed the magnetic fields set up by moving charges or by currents in conductors, when the charges or conductors are in air (or, strictly speaking, in a vacuum). However, pieces of technical equipment such as transformers, motors, and generators, which make use of the magnetic fields set up by a current, always incorporate iron or an iron alloy in their structures, both for the purpose of increasing the magnetic flux and for confining it to a desired region. Furthermore, by the use of permanent magnets, as in galvanometers or permanent magnet speakers, magnetic fields can be produced without any apparent circulation of charge.

We therefore turn next to a consideration of the magnetic properties which make iron and a few other ferromagnetic materials so useful. We shall find that magnetic properties are not confined to ferromagnetic materials but are exhibited (to a much smaller extent, to be sure) by *all* substances. From the standpoint of the electrical engineer, the ferromagnetic materials are of the greatest interest, but a study of the magnetic properties of other materials is of importance also, affording as it does another means of gaining an insight into the nature of matter in general.

The existence of the magnetic properties of a substance can be demonstrated by supporting a small spherically shaped specimen by a fine thread and placing it near the poles of a powerful electromagnet. If the specimen is of iron or one of the *ferromagnetic* substances, it will be attracted into the strong part of the magnetic field. Not so familiar is the fact that any substance whatever will be influenced by the field, although to an extent which is extremely small compared with a substance like iron. Some substances will, like iron, be forced into the strong part of the field, while others will be urged to move toward the weak part of the field. The first type is called *paramagnetic;* the second, *diamagnetic.* All substances, including liquids and gases, fall into one or the other of these classes. Liquids and gases must, of course, be enclosed within some sort of container, and due allowance must be made for the properties of the container as well as those of the medium (usually air) in which the specimens are immersed.

26–7 Magnetic permeability. All the formulas for magnetic fields that we have derived from the Biot law have included the constant μ_0, which we called the permeability of free space. If any of these coils were immersed in another medium the permeability would be different, and in the case of a ferromagnetic medium it would be very different. The permeability of any medium could be measured, in principle, by placing a long straight wire, or a circular turn, or a solenoid in the medium in question, measuring the resultant magnetic induction, and solving for the value of μ which would make the derived formulas valid. This is either an awkward or an inaccurate procedure, since the magnetic fields of most conductors, in principle at least, extend to infinity. It would be awkward to immerse a solenoid in a large piece of iron, and it is inaccurate to study a small piece of iron within a solenoid. A toroid, on the other hand, is a coil whose geometry is such that the entire magnetic field it produces is within the toroid. If we change the medium within a toroid we have changed the medium everywhere that the magnetic field exists. Therefore the simplest permeability measurements are made with a sample of the material under study in the form of a ring. This ring is then wrapped with wire, to form a toroidal winding. If this ring, called a Rowland ring, has N turns of wire, a mean circumferential length l, and carries a current i, we know that if the sample were absent the magnetic induction B_0 would be

$$B_0 = \frac{\mu_0 N i}{l}$$

With the sample inside the ring, we have

$$B = \frac{\mu N i}{l} \quad \text{or} \quad \mu = \frac{B l}{N i},$$

where μ is the permeability of the material. In practice B is measured by placing another winding about the toroid, as shown in Fig. 26–12, and by using the ballistic galvanometer method which will be developed in Section 27–7. If the material in the toroid is ferromagnetic, the measured μ is much greater than μ_0. The measured μ will be slightly larger than μ_0 if the sample is paramagnetic, and slightly smaller than μ_0 if the sample is diamagnetic. The permeabilities of para- and diamagnetic materials are so little different from μ_0 that the differences are difficult to detect by this method.

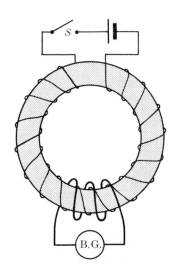

FIG. 26–12.   Magnetic specimen in the form of a ring with a toroidal winding.

Instead of remembering or tabulating the permeabilities of materials it is often convenient to relate these permeabilities to the permeability of free space. Thus we define the relative permeability K_m as

$$K_m = \frac{\mu}{\mu_0}.$$

Any equation we have written for the magnetic induction in free space can be applied to another medium if we replace μ_0 by either μ or $K_m\mu_0$.

K_m is $\begin{cases} \text{equal to 1 for a vacuum,} \\ \text{slightly larger than 1 for a paramagnetic substance,} \\ \text{slightly smaller than 1 for a diamagnetic substance,} \\ \text{often much larger than 1 for a ferromagnetic substance.} \end{cases}$

26–8 Magnetic intensity. All the expressions for **B** have involved the permeability μ of the medium, together with current and geometrical factors. It is useful to define a new vector $\mathbf{H} = \mathbf{B}/\mu$ which is independent of the medium and is called the *magnetic intensity*. Thus we have, from the Biot law,

$$d\mathbf{H} = \frac{1}{4\pi} i \frac{d\mathbf{l} \times \hat{\mathbf{r}}}{r^2}, \qquad (26\text{–}9)$$

and for the special case of a Rowland ring

$$H = \frac{Ni}{l}.$$

In more advanced treatments the magnetic intensity is introduced in a more sophisticated way and its significance is treated at length. From the Rowland ring formula it is easily seen that the unit of magnetic intensity is the *ampere per meter*, or *ampere·turns per meter* if one wishes to include the factor N in the units.

EXAMPLE. A Rowland ring, made of iron, of mean circumferential length 30 cm and cross section 1 cm^2, is wound uniformly with 300 turns of wire. Ballistic galvanometer measurements made with a search coil around the ring, as in Fig. 26–12, show that when the current in the windings is 0.032 amp, the flux in the ring is 2×10^{-6} weber. Compute (a) the flux density in the ring, (b) the magnetic intensity, (c) the permeability, (d) the relative permeability.

(a) Flux density $B = \dfrac{\Phi}{A} = \dfrac{2 \times 10^{-6}\ \text{w}}{10^{-4}\ \text{m}^2} = 2 \times 10^{-2}\ \dfrac{\text{w}}{\text{m}^2}.$

(b) Magnetic intensity $H = \dfrac{Ni}{l} = \dfrac{300 \times 0.032\ \text{amp}}{0.30\ \text{m}} = 32\ \dfrac{\text{amp}}{\text{m}}.$

(c) Permeability $\mu = \dfrac{B}{H} = \dfrac{2 \times 10^{-2} \text{ w/m}^2}{32 \text{ amp/m}} = 6250 \times 10^{-7} \dfrac{\text{w}}{\text{amp·m}}.$

(d) Relative permeability $K_m = \dfrac{\mu}{\mu_0} = \dfrac{6250 \times 10^{-7} \text{ w/amp·m}}{12.57 \times 10^{-7} \text{ w/amp·m}} = 498.$

26–9 Ferromagnetism. The flux density in a Rowland ring of iron may be hundreds or even thousands of times as great as that due to the magnetizing current alone. Furthermore, the flux density B is not a linear function of the magnetic intensity H or, in other words, the permeability μ is not a constant. To complicate matters even further, the permeability depends on the past history (magnetically speaking) of the iron, a phenomenon known as *hysteresis*. In fact, a flux may exist in the iron even in the absence of any external field; when in this state the iron is called a *permanent magnet*.

Any substance which exhibits the properties above is called *ferromagnetic*. Iron, nickel, and cobalt are the only ferromagnetic elements, but a number of alloys whose components are not ferromagnetic also show these effects.

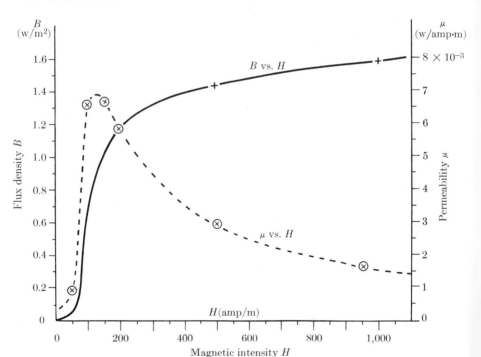

FIG. 26–13. Magnetization curve and permeability curve of annealed iron.

Because of the complicated relation between the flux density B and the magnetic intensity H in a ferromagnetic material, it is not possible to express B as an analytic function of H. Instead, the relation between these quantities is either given in tabular form or is represented by a graph of B vs. H, called the *magnetization curve* of the material.

The magnetization curve of a specimen of annealed iron is shown in Fig. 26–13 in the curve labeled B vs. H. The permeability μ, equal to the ratio of B to H, can be found at any point of the curve by dividing the flux density B, at the point, by the corresponding magnetic intensity H. For example, when $H = 150$ amp/m, $B = 1.01$ w/m^2 and

$$\mu = \frac{B}{H} = \frac{1.01 \text{ w/m}^2}{150 \text{ amp/m}} = 67,500 \times 10^{-7} \frac{\text{w}}{\text{amp·m}}.$$

It is evident that the permeability is not a constant. The curve labeled μ vs. H in Fig. 26–13 is a graph of μ as a function of H.

26–10 Hysteresis. A magnetization curve such as that in Fig. 26–13 expresses the relation between the flux density B in a ferromagnetic material and the corresponding magnetic intensity H, *provided the sample is initially unmagnetized and the magnetic intensity is steadily increased from zero.* Thus in Fig. 26–14, if the magnetizing current in the windings of an unmagnetized ring sample is steadily increased from zero until the magnetic intensity H corresponds to the abscissa Oe, the flux density B is given by the ordinate Of. If, starting from the same unmagnetized state, the magnetic intensity is first increased from zero to Og and then *decreased* to Oe, the magnetic state of the sample follows the path $Oabc$. The flux density, when the magnetic intensity has been reduced to Oe, is represented by the ordinate Oh rather than Of. If the magnetizing current is now reduced to zero, the curve continues to point d, where the flux density is Od.

The flux density in the sample is seen to depend not on the magnetic intensity alone, but on the magnetic history of the sample as well. It has a magnetic "memory," so to speak, and "remembers" that it has been magnetized to point b even after the magnetizing current has been cut off. At point d it has become a *permanent magnet*. This behavior of the ma-

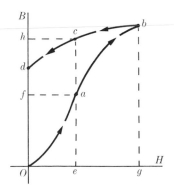

Fig. 26–14. Graph showing hysteresis.

terial, as evidenced by the fact that the *B–H* curve for decreasing *H* does not coincide with that for increasing *H*, is called *hysteresis*. The term means literally, "to lag behind."

In many pieces of electrical apparatus, such as transformers and motors, masses of iron are located in magnetic fields whose direction is continually reversing. That is, the magnetic intensity *H* increases from zero to a certain maximum in one direction, then decreases to zero, increases to the same maximum but in the opposite direction, decreases to zero, and continues to repeat this cycle over and over. The flux density *B* within the iron reverses also, but in the manner indicated in Fig. 26–15, tracing out a closed curve in the *B–H* plane, known as a *hysteresis loop*. Figure 26–14 may be considered as the start of such a hysteresis loop.

Positive values of *H* or *B* in Fig. 26–15 indicate that the respective directions of these quantities are, say, clockwise in a Rowland ring, while negative values mean that the directions are counterclockwise. The magnitude and direction of *H* are determined solely by the current in the winding, while those of *B* depend on the magnetic properties of the sample and its past history. Note that at points in the second and fourth quadrants, *B* and *H* are opposite in direction.

The ordinate *Ob* or *Oe* in Fig. 26–15 represents the flux density remaining in the specimen when the magnetic intensity has been reduced to zero. It is called the *retentivity* or *remanence* of the specimen and is designated by B_r. The abscissa *Oc* or *Of* represents the reversed magnetic intensity needed to reduce the flux density to zero after the specimen has been

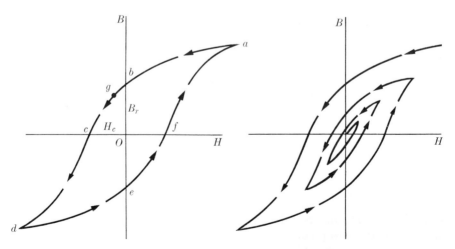

FIG. 26–15. Hysteresis loop.　　FIG. 26–16. Successive hysteresis loops during the operation of demagnetizing a ferromagnetic sample.

magnetized to saturation in the opposite direction, and it is called the *coercive force* or the *coercivity*, H_c. What is the permeability at points b, c, e, and f?

The magnetization curve Oab in Fig. 26–14 shows the sample initially unmagnetized. One may wonder how this can be accomplished, since cutting off the magnetizing current does not reduce the flux density in the material to zero. A sample may be demagnetized by reversing the magnetizing current a number of times, decreasing its magnitude with each reversal. The sample is thus carried around a hysteresis curve which winds more and more closely about the origin (see Fig. 26–16).

26–11 Ampere's theory of magnetism. The earliest speculations as to the origin of the magnetic properties of a piece of lodestone, or a permanent magnet, were that such a substance was composed of, or at least contained, a number of tiny particles each of which was endowed with two magnetic poles. The process of magnetizing a body consisted of aligning these elementary magnets with their like poles pointing the same way. When it was discovered that magnetic effects could also be produced by currents, Ampere proposed the theory that the magnetic properties of a body arose from a multitude of tiny closed current loops within the body. The currents in these loops were assumed to continue indefinitely, as if there were no resistance. In an unmagnetized body the loops were oriented at random. The magnetizing process consisted of aligning these loops with their planes parallel to one another and with the currents all circulating in the same direction.

At the time the theory was proposed it was highly speculative, since no currents were known that would continue indefinitely without any source of emf and without the production of heat. We now believe the theory to be essentially correct, the elementary current loops consisting of electrons spinning about their own axes or revolving in orbits around nuclei.

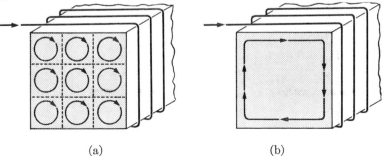

(a)   (b)

Fig. 26–17. (a) Alignment of atomic current loops. (b) Surface current equivalent to part (a).

Regardless of the origin of the current loops, a body in which the planes of all such loops are parallel to one another can be represented as in Fig. 26–17(a), where the loops are represented by small circles. At interior points the currents in adjacent loops are in opposite directions and their magnetic effects cancel. The outer portions of the outside loops, however, are uncompensated and the entire assembly of loops is equivalent to a current circulating around the outside of the conductor, as in Fig. 26–17(b). These equivalent surface currents have essentially the same shape as would a magnetizing winding around the specimen. The flux they produce adds to the flux produced by the current in an actual winding if the two circulate in the same direction, as in Fig. 26–17, or subtracts from it if they are in opposite directions.

26–12 Magnetic poles. A ring sample of magnetic material simplifies the presentation of most of the concepts associated with the magnetic properties of matter for the reason that the magnetic field of such a ring is confined entirely to its interior. We consider next the magnetization of a body whose field extends to the region surrounding it. The most common examples are a compass needle, or a bar or horseshoe magnet.

Consider a specimen of ferromagnetic material placed in the uniform magnetic field shown in Fig. 26–18(a). As soon as the specimen is introduced, the field becomes greatly distorted. The field at any point is the resultant of the original uniform field and the field set up by the orientation of the circulating currents [see Fig. 26–18(b)]. In picturesque language, we may say that the lines of induction "crowd" into the iron, leaving the field quite weak at certain places outside of the iron. If a watch (whose steel parts will not function properly when magnetized) is completely surrounded by an iron case, very few lines of induction of an external magnetic field will pass through the watch, most of them crowding into the iron case. This is known as *magnetic shielding.*

Upon removing the iron specimen from the field, all of the flux due to the electronic loops will disappear if the iron shows no hysteresis. Usually, however, hysteresis is present and the iron becomes a permanent magnet, with a magnetic field like that in Fig. 26–18(c). If the flux density is measured at various points outside the specimen, it will be found to be quite small at points near the center, but large near the two ends. The magnetic field set up in the space around the bar magnet appears as though the "cause" of the magnetism were concentrated at points near the ends, where the magnetic lines appear to originate at one point and terminate at the other. In fact, before the relations between electrical and magnetic effects were understood as well as they are today it was assumed that the magnetism actually was due to "magnetic charges," or, as they were called, magnetic "poles." The first evidence that an isolated magnetic

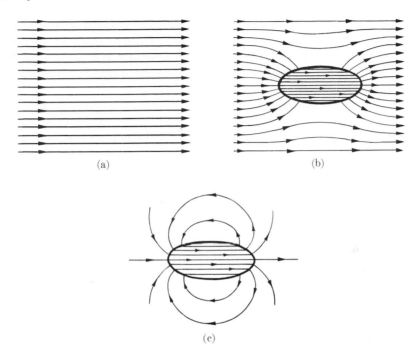

FIG. 26–18. (a) Original uniform magnetic field. (b) Field after insertion of specimen of iron. (c) Field of permanently magnetized specimen. The regions near the ends of the specimen, where most of the lines of induction enter or leave, are called *poles*.

pole does not exist was found when it was discovered that a bar magnet broken in two does *not* form two magnetic poles which can be separated like electric charges. Rather, a broken permanent magnet forms two complete magnets, each of which still has two equal and opposite poles. Although it is sometimes convenient to describe the field outside a permanent magnet or a solenoid as though it were due to "poles," we now know that unlike electric lines, which always begin at positive charges and end at negative ones, lines of magnetic induction are continuous.

26–13 Magnetic field of the earth. The first observation of the magnetic field of the earth was made with an instrument called a *compass*, a small bar magnet supported so as to be free to rotate in a horizontal plane. It was found that the magnet tends to assume an approximately north-south direction, and so the north-seeking pole of a compass was called a north pole and the south-seeking pole was called a south pole. Experimentation with two compasses quickly discloses that, in analogy with the electrical case, like magnetic poles repel and unlike magnetic poles attract. Thus a "north-seeking" pole seeks a south magnetic pole. This leads to the apparently paradoxical conclusion that the magnetic pole of the earth found in the northern hemisphere is a south magnetic pole, and the kind of magnetic pole found in the southern hemisphere is a north magnetic pole.

To a first approximation, the magnetic field of the earth is the same as that outside a uniformly magnetized sphere. Figure 26–19 represents a section through the earth. The heavy vertical line is its axis of rotation, and the *geographic* north and south poles are lettered N_G and S_G. The direction of the (presumed) internal magnetization makes an angle of about 15° with the earth's axis. The dotted line indicates the plane of the magnetic equator, and the letters N_M and S_M represent the so-called *magnetic* north and south poles. Note carefully that lines of induction emerge from the earth's surface over the entire southern magnetic hemisphere and enter its surface over the entire northern magnetic hemisphere. The north and south magnetic poles, considered as points on the earth's surface, are simply those points where the field is vertical. The former is located at latitude 70° N, longitude 96° W.

It is interesting to note that the same field at *external* points would result if the earth's magnetism were due to a short bar magnet near its center as in Fig. 26–19(b), with the south pole of the magnet pointing towards the north magnetic pole. The field within the earth is different in the two cases but for obvious reasons experimental verification of either hypothesis is impossible.

Except at the magnetic equator, the earth's field is not horizontal. The angle which the field makes with the horizontal is called the *angle of dip* or the *inclination*. At Cambridge, Mass. (about 45° N lat.), the mag-

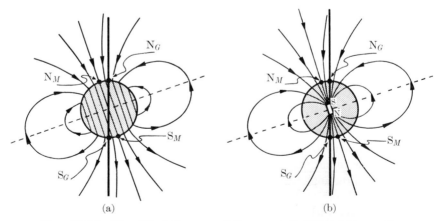

Fig. 26–19. Simplified diagram of the magnetic field of the earth.

nitude of the earth's field is about 5.8×10^{-5} w/m^2 and the angle of dip about 73°. Hence the horizontal component at Cambridge is about 1.7×10^{-5} w/m^2 and the vertical component about 5.5×10^{-5} w/m^2. In northern magnetic latitudes the vertical component is directed downward, in southern magnetic latitudes it is upward. The angle of dip is, of course, 90° at the magnetic poles.

The angle between the horizontal component and the true north-south direction is called the *variation* or *declination*. At Cambridge, Mass., the declination at present is about 15° W, that is, a compass needle points about 15° to the west of true north.

The magnetic field of the earth is not as symmetrical as one might be led to suspect from the idealized drawing of Fig. 26–19. It is in reality very complicated; the inclination and the declination vary irregularly over the earth's surface, and also vary with the time.

PROBLEMS

26–1. A long straight wire, carrying a current of 200 amp, runs through a cubical wooden box, entering and leaving through holes in the centers of opposite faces, as in Fig. 26–20. The length of each side of the box is 20 cm. Consider an element of the wire 1 cm long at the center of the box. Compute the magnitude of the magnetic induction ΔB produced by this element at the points lettered a, b, c, d, and e in Fig. 26–20. Points a, c, and d are at the centers of the faces of the cube, point b is at the midpoint of one edge, and point e is at a corner. Copy the figure and show by vectors the directions and relative magnitudes of the field vectors.

26–2. The wire in Fig. 26–21 carries a current of 8 amp. The cubical box has sides 25 cm in length. Determine the fields at P due to elements of the wire at a, b, and c, each of 0.5 cm length.

26–3. A long straight wire carries a current of 10 amp along the z-axis, as shown in Fig. 26–22. A uniform magnetic field whose flux density is 10^{-6} w/m² is directed parallel to the x-axis. What is the resultant magnetic field at the following points: (a) $x = 0$, $y = 2$ m, (b) $x = 2$ m, $y = 0$, (c) $x = 0$, $y = -0.5$ m?

26–4. A long straight wire carries a current of 1.5 amp. An electron travels with a velocity of 5×10^6 cm/sec par-

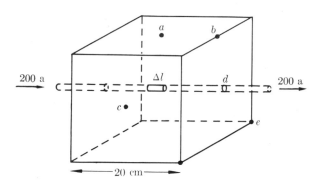

FIGURE 26–20

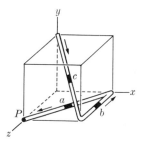

FIGURE 26–21

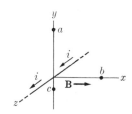

FIGURE 26–22

allel to the wire, 10 cm from it, and in the same direction as the current. What force does the magnetic field of the current exert on the moving electron?

26–5. Two long straight wires, A and B, are arranged in a vertical plane 10 cm apart, as in Fig. 26–23. B carries a current of 6 amp into the plane of the paper. (a) What must be the magnitude and direction of the current in A for the resultant induction at point a, 5 cm under A, to be zero? (b) What is then the resultant induction at b, 5 cm above B, and at c, 6 cm from A and 8 cm from B?

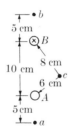

FIGURE 26–23

26–6. (a) What is the expression for the magnitude of the magnetic induction B on the axis of a circular turn of wire of radius R and carrying a current i, at a point at a distance x from the center of the turn? Compare your answer with the corresponding expression for the electric intensity E on the axis of a charged ring. (b) Sketch a graph of the magnitude of the magnetic induction as a function of x.

26–7. Two long parallel wires are hung by cords of 4 cm length from a common axis. The wires have a mass of 50 gm/m and carry equal currents in opposite directions. What is the current if the cords hang at an angle of 30° with the vertical?

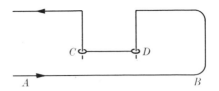

FIGURE 26–24

26–8. A long horizontal wire AB rests on the surface of a table. (See Fig. 26–24.) Another wire CD vertically above the first is 100 cm long and is free to slide up and down on the two vertical metal guides C and D. The two wires are connected through the sliding contacts and carry a current of 50 amp. The mass of the wire CD is 0.05 gm/cm. To what equilibrium height will the wire CD rise, assuming the magnetic force on it to be due wholly to the current in the wire AB?

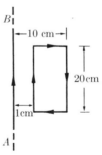

FIGURE 26–25

26–9. The long straight wire AB in Fig. 26–25 carries a current of 20 amp. The rectangular loop whose long edges are parallel to the wire carries a current of 10 amp. Find the magnitude and direction of the resultant force exerted on the loop by the magnetic field of the wire.

26–10. A closely wound coil has a diameter of 40 cm and carries a current of 2.5 amp. How many turns does it have if the magnetic induction at the center of the coil is 1.26×10^{-4} w/m^2?

26–11. A closely wound coil of 100 turns, 5 cm in radius, carries a current of 2 amp. Compute the magnetic flux density at the center of the coil.

26–12. A solenoid is 10 cm long and is wound with two layers of wire. The inner layer consists of 50 turns, the outer layer of 40 turns. The current is 3 amp, in the same direction in both layers. What is the magnetic induction at a point near the center of the solenoid?

26–13. A solenoid of length 20 cm and radius 2 cm is closely wound with 200 turns of wire. The current in the winding is 5 amp. Compute the magnetic induction at a point near the center of the solenoid.

26–14. A wooden ring whose mean diameter is 10 cm is wound with a closely spaced toroidal winding of 500 turns. Compute the flux density at a point on the mean circumference of the ring when the current in the windings is 0.3 amp.

26–15. The long straight wire AB in Fig. 26–26 carries a constant current i. (a) What is the flux density at the shaded area at a perpendicular distance x from the wire? (b) What is the magnetic flux $d\Phi$ through the shaded area? (c) What is the flux Φ through the rectangular area $CDEF$, in terms of i, l, a, and b?

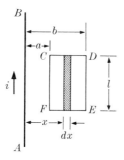

FIGURE 26–26

26–16. A long thin straight metallic strip whose width is b carries a constant current i. The current density is uniform. Derive the expression for the magnetic flux density at a point in the plane of the strip and at a distance a from the nearer edge of the strip.

26–17. A thin disk of dielectric material, having a total charge $+Q$ distributed uniformly over its surface, rotates n times per second about an axis perpendicular to the surface of the disk and passing through its center. Find the magnetic induction at the center of the disk.

26–18. A Rowland ring having 500 turns of wire and a mean diameter of 12 cm carries a current of 0.3 amp. The relative permeability of the core is

TABLE 26–1

MAGNETIC PROPERTIES OF SILICON STEEL

Magnetic intensity H, amp·turns/m	Flux density B, w/m^2
0	0
10	0.050
20	0.15
40	0.43
50	0.54
60	0.62
80	0.74
100	0.83
150	0.98
200	1.07
500	1.27
1,000	1.34
10,000	1.65
100,000	2.02
800,000	2.92

600. (a) What is the flux density in the core? (b) What is the magnetic intensity? (c) What part of the flux density is due to electronic loop currents in the core?

26–19. Table 26–1 lists corresponding values of H and B for a specimen of commercial hot-rolled silicon steel, a material widely used in transformer cores. (a) Construct graphs of B and μ as functions of H, in the range from $H = 0$ to $H = 1000$ amp·turns/m. (b) What is the maximum permeability? (c) What is the initial permeability $(H = 0)$? (d) What is the permeability when $H = 800,000$ amp·turns/m?

26–20. A bar magnet has a coercivity of 4×10^3 amp/m. It is desired to demagnetize it by inserting it inside a solenoid 12 cm long and having 60 turns. What current should be carried by the solenoid?

26–21. An electron moves on a horizontal line from east to west along the equator. What is the direction of the force exerted on it by the earth's magnetic field?

26–22. The horizontal component of the flux density of the earth's magnetic field at Cambridge, Mass., is 1.7×10^{-5} w/m². What is the horizontal component of the magnetic intensity?

CHAPTER 27

INDUCED ELECTROMOTIVE FORCE

27-1 Motional electromotive force. Our present-day large scale production and distribution of electrical energy would not be economically feasible if the only seats of emf available were those of a chemical nature, such as dry cells. The development of electrical engineering as we now know it began with Faraday and Henry, who independently and at nearly the same time discovered the principles of induced emf's and the methods by which mechanical energy can be converted directly to electrical energy.

Figure 27-1 represents a conductor of length l in a uniform magnetic field, perpendicular to the plane of the diagram and directed away from the reader. If the conductor is set in motion toward the right with a velocity **v**, perpendicular both to its own length and to the magnetic field, every charged particle within it experiences a force $F = qvB$ directed along the length of the conductor. The direction of the force on a negative charge is from a toward b in Fig. 27-1, while the force on a positive charge is from b toward a.

The state of affairs within the conductor is therefore the same as if it had been inserted in an electric field of intensity vB whose direction was

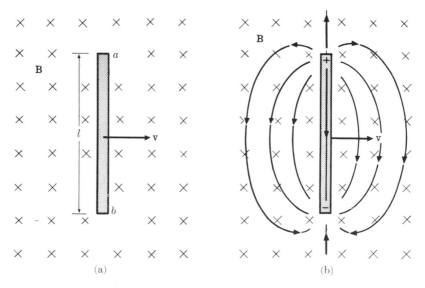

FIG. 27-1. Conductor moving in a uniform magnetic field.

544

from b toward a. The free electrons in the conductor will move in the direction of the force acting on them until the accumulation of excess charges at the ends of the conductor establishes an electrostatic field such that the resultant force on every charge within the conductor is zero. The general nature of this electrostatic field is indicated in Fig. 27-1(b). The upper end of the wire acquires an excess positive charge, and the lower end an excess negative charge.

That such a separation of charge actually takes place in a conductor moving in a magnetic field was shown by Barnet, who carried out experiments equivalent to cutting the rod at its center while it was still in motion, and then bringing it to rest. The upper half was found to be positively charged and the lower half negatively charged.

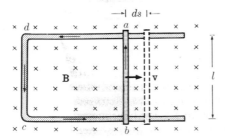

Fig. 27-2. Current produced by the motion of a conductor in a magnetic field.

Imagine now that the moving conductor slides along a stationary U-shaped conductor, as in Fig. 27-2. There is no magnetic force on the charges within the stationary conductor, but since it lies in the electrostatic field surrounding the moving conductor, a current will be established within it, the direction of this current (in the conventional sense) being counterclockwise, or from b toward a. As a result of this current the excess charges at the ends of the moving conductor are reduced, the electrostatic field within the moving conductor is weakened, and the magnetic forces cause a further displacement of the free electrons within it from a toward b. So long as the motion of the conductor is maintained there will, therefore, be a continual displacement of electrons clockwise around the circuit, or a conventional current in a counterclockwise direction. The moving conductor corresponds to a seat of electromotive force, and is said to have *induced* within it a *motional electromotive force*.

The magnitude of this emf can be found as follows. When a charge q moves from b to a through a distance l, the work of the force F is

$$W = Fl = vBql.$$

The emf $\mathcal{E}$ is the work per unit charge, so

$$\mathcal{E} = \frac{W}{q},$$

and

$$\boxed{\mathcal{E} = lvB} \qquad (27\text{--}1)$$

If B is expressed in w/m^2, l in meters, and v in m/sec, the emf is in joules per coulomb or volts, as may readily be verified. Equation (27–1) was derived for the special case of a conductor moving perpendicular to the lines of magnetic induction. If $\mathbf{l}$, $\mathbf{v}$, and $\mathbf{B}$ are not mutually perpendicular the emf is given by the *scalar product* of the two vectors $\mathbf{l}$ and $\mathbf{v} \times \mathbf{B}$,

$$\mathcal{E} = \mathbf{l} \cdot (\mathbf{v} \times \mathbf{B}).$$

The positive sense of $\mathcal{E}$ is the sense of the component of $\mathbf{v} \times \mathbf{B}$ parallel to $\mathbf{l}$.

An emf is presumed to develop in the rod even in the absence of any closed circuit, although of course there can be no steady current unless such a circuit is provided. If the conductor is part of a closed circuit, the resulting current is called an *induced current*.

EXAMPLE. The induction B in the region between the pole faces of an electromagnet is 0.5 w/m^2. Find the induced emf in a straight conductor 10 cm long, perpendicular to B, and moving perpendicular both to B and its own length with a velocity of 1 m/sec.

The induced emf is

$$\mathcal{E} = \mathbf{l} \cdot (\mathbf{v} \times \mathbf{B}) = lvB,$$

$$l = 0.10 \text{ m}, \quad v = 1 \text{ m/sec}, \quad B = 0.5 \text{ w/m}^2,$$

$$\mathcal{E} = 0.1 \times 1 \times 0.5 = 0.05 \text{ volt}.$$

27–2 The Faraday law. The induced emf in the circuit of Fig. 27–2 may be considered from another viewpoint. While the conductor moves toward the right a distance ds, the cross-sectional area of the closed circuit $abcd$ increases by

$$dA = l \, ds,$$

and the change in the magnetic flux through the area bounded by the circuit is

$$d\Phi = B \, dA = lB \, ds.$$

When both sides of this equation are divided by dt, we obtain

$$\frac{d\Phi}{dt} = lB\frac{ds}{dt} = lBv.$$

But the product lBv equals the induced emf $\mathcal{E}$, so the preceding equation states that *the induced emf in the circuit is numerically equal to the rate of change of the magnetic flux through it*. The right-hand screw convention of sign is usually used with this equation. If one faces the circuit, an emf is considered positive if it results in a conventional current in a clockwise direction, and $d\Phi/dt$ is considered positive if there is an increase in the flux directed away from the observer. (Then a decrease in flux away from the observer is negative, an increase in flux toward the observer is negative, and a decrease in flux toward the observer is positive.) In Fig. 27–2 the current is counterclockwise, so the emf is negative, while the flux is away from the observer and is increasing, so $d\Phi/dt$ is positive. A study of other possibilities shows that $\mathcal{E}$ and $d\Phi/dt$ always have opposite signs. Hence we write the equation for the instantaneous emf as

$$\mathcal{E} = -\frac{d\Phi}{dt}.$$

(27–2)

If the magnetic flux through a circuit changes by a finite amount $\Delta\Phi$ in a time interval Δt, the *average* induced emf is given by

$$\mathcal{E}_{av} = -\frac{\Delta\Phi}{\Delta t} = -\frac{\Phi_2 - \Phi_1}{t_2 - t_1}.$$

Equation (27–2) is known as *Faraday's law*. As it stands, it appears to be merely an alternative form of Eq. (27–1) for the emf in a moving conductor. It turns out, however, that the relation has a much deeper significance than might be expected from its derivation. That is, it is found to apply to any circuits through which the flux is caused to vary by any means whatever, even though there is no motion of any part of the circuit and hence no emf directly attributable to a force on a moving charge.

Suppose, for example, that two loops of wire are located as in Fig. 27–3. A current in circuit 1 sets up a magnetic field whose magnitude at all points is proportional to this current. A part of this flux passes through circuit 2, and if the current in circuit 1 is increased or decreased, the flux through circuit 2 will also vary. Circuit 2 is not moving in a magnetic field and hence no "motional" emf is induced in it, but there is a change in the flux through it, and it is found experimentally that an emf of magnitude $\mathcal{E} = d\Phi/dt$ appears in circuit 2.

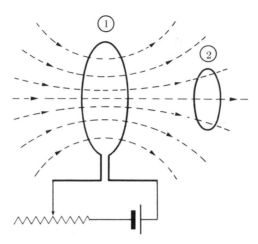

FIG. 27–3. As the current in circuit 1 is varied, the magnetic flux through circuit 2 changes.

In a situation such as that shown in Fig. 27–3 it is evident that no one portion of circuit 2 can be considered the seat of emf; the entire circuit constitutes the seat.

The problem cannot be reduced to one of a "motional" emf by saying that the flux lines set up by the current in circuit 1 move outward as the current in this circuit is increased and in doing so "cut" the conductor of circuit 2. There is no way of identifying one specific line of flux and saying that at a certain instant some one line passes through circuit 2, while a moment later the same line lies outside the circuit. The lines of flux are a figment of the imagination, in spite of the lines we draw to represent them, and it is meaningless to speak of a line as moving with a certain velocity. As the current in circuit 1 is increased the number of lines per square meter at every point increases, but the new lines are created in the process of increasing the current and did not get where they are by moving from somewhere else.

Another example may illustrate this point even more strikingly. Suppose we set up a magnetic field within the toroidal winding of Fig. 27–4, link the toroid with a conducting ring, and vary the current in the winding of the toroid, as discussed in Chapter 26. We have shown that the flux lines set up by a current in a toroidal winding are wholly confined to the space enclosed by the winding, so that not only is the ring not *moving* in a magnetic field, it is not even *in* a magnetic field. However, lines of flux do pass through the area bounded by the ring, and their number changes as the current in the winding changes. Equation (27–2) predicts an induced emf in the ring and we find by experiment that the emf actually exists. In case the reader has not identified the apparatus in Fig. 27–4

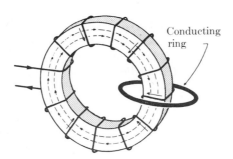

Fɪɢ. 27–4. An emf is induced in the ring when the flux in the toroid varies.

from the way it has been described, it may be pointed out that it is merely a transformer with a one-turn secondary, so that the phenomenon we are now discussing is the basis of the operation of every transformer.

To sum up, then, an emf is induced in a circuit whenever the flux through the circuit varies with time. The flux may be caused to vary in two ways, (1) by the motion of a conductor as in Fig. 27–2, or (2) by a change in the magnitude of the flux through a stationary circuit as in Fig. 27–3 or 27–4. For case (1), the emf may be computed either from

$$\mathcal{E} = 1 \cdot (\mathbf{v} \times \mathbf{B})$$

or from

$$\mathcal{E} = -\frac{d\Phi}{dt}.$$

For case (2), the emf may be computed only by

$$\mathcal{E} = -\frac{d\Phi}{dt}.$$

If we have a coil of N turns and the flux varies at the same rate through each, the induced emf's in the turns are in series, and the total emf is

$$\boxed{\mathcal{E} = -N\frac{d\Phi}{dt}.}$$

EXAMPLE. With a certain current in circuit 1 of Fig. 27–3, a flux of 5×10^{-4} w links with circuit 2. When circuit 1 is opened the flux falls to zero in 0.001 sec. What average emf is induced in circuit 2?

The average rate of decrease of flux in circuit 2 is

$$\frac{\Delta\Phi}{\Delta t} = \frac{5 \times 10^{-4}\ \text{w}}{0.001\ \text{sec}} = 0.5\ \frac{\text{w}}{\text{sec}}.$$

The average induced emf is therefore 0.5 volt.

27–3 Lenz's law. H. F. E. Lenz (1804–1864) was a German scientist who, without knowledge of the work of Faraday and Henry, duplicated many of their discoveries nearly simultaneously. The law which goes by his name is a useful rule for predicting the direction of an induced current. It states:

> *The direction of an induced current is such as to oppose the cause producing it.*

The "cause" of the current may be the motion of a conductor in a magnetic field, or it may be the change of flux through a stationary circuit. In the first case, the direction of the induced current in the moving conductor is such that the direction of the side-thrust exerted on the conductor by the magnetic field is opposite in direction to its motion. The motion of the conductor is therefore "opposed."

In the second case, the current sets up a magnetic field of its own which within the area bounded by the circuit is (a) *opposite* to the original field if this is *increasing*, but (b) is in the *same* direction as the original field if the latter is *decreasing*. Thus it is the *change in flux* through the circuit (not the flux itself) which is "opposed" by the induced current.

In order for there to be an induced current, we must have a closed circuit. If a conductor does not form a closed circuit, then we mentally complete the circuit between the ends of the conductor and use Lenz's law to determine the direction of the current. The polarity of the ends of the open-circuited conductor may then be deduced.

27–4 The betatron. The magnetic induction accelerator, or betatron is one of the family of instruments designed for the purpose of accelerating charged particles to high speeds. It was invented in 1940 by Donald W. Kerst of the University of Illinois. Kerst's original apparatus was capable of accelerating electrons to energies of 2 million electron volts. A second machine constructed by the General Electric Company developed 20 million electron volts, and in 1945 a third model was completed which can accelerate electrons to an energy of 100 million electron volts. The following description refers to the 100 million-volt machine.

An evacuated toroidal or doughnut-shaped glass tube of elliptical cross section, 74 inches in outside diameter and 58 inches in inside diameter, is placed horizontally in an air gap between the pole faces of an electromagnet. Alternating current at a frequency of 60 cycles/sec is sent through the windings of the electromagnet, so that the magnetic flux through the plane of the toroid reverses from a maximum in one direction to a maximum in the opposite direction in 1/120 sec. Electrons accelerated through approximately 50,000 volts by an electron gun are shot

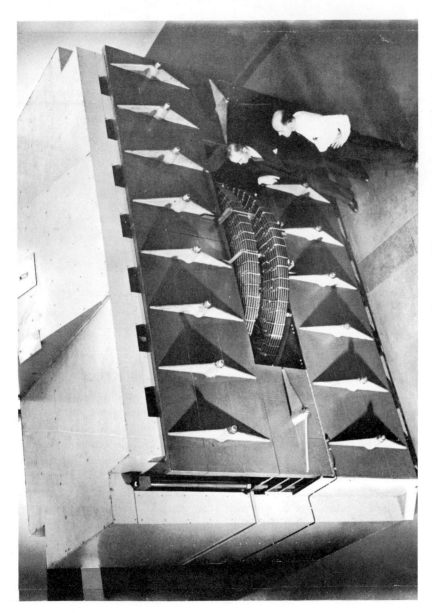

FIG. 27-5.   100 million-volt induction electron accelerator.   (Courtesy of General Electric Company.)

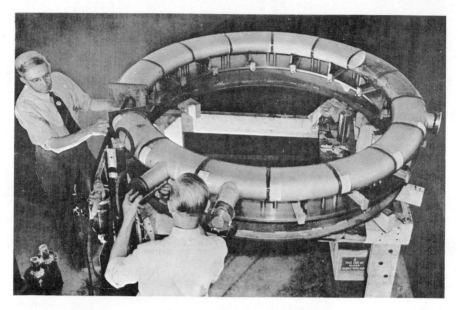

FIG. 27–6. Assembling the huge vacuum tube of the betatron. (Courtesy of General Electric Company.)

tangentially into the tube and are caused by the magnetic field to circle around within the tube in an orbit 66 inches in diameter. In each revolution they are accelerated through the same voltage (about 400 volts) as would be induced in a single turn of wire through which the flux varied at the same rate. The accelerator may be compared to an ordinary transformer, with the usual high-voltage secondary winding of many turns replaced by the electrons in the evacuated tube. The electrons are accelerated by the *changing* magnetic field and at the same time are forced to move in a circular orbit by the *existence* of the magnetic field. The velocity acquired is so great that an electron may make 250,000 revolutions in the time required for the flux to increase from zero to its maximum value. Since each revolution is equivalent to an acceleration through 400 volts, the final energy is 250,000 × 400 or 100 million electron-volts.

At any desired stage of the accelerating process an auxiliary coil can deflect the beam out of its circular path onto a target which then becomes a source of x-rays of extremely short wavelength and great penetrating ability.

Figure 27–5 is a front view of the accelerator. Figure 27–6 is a photograph showing the lower portion of the electromagnet, one of the energizing coils, and the vacuum tube.

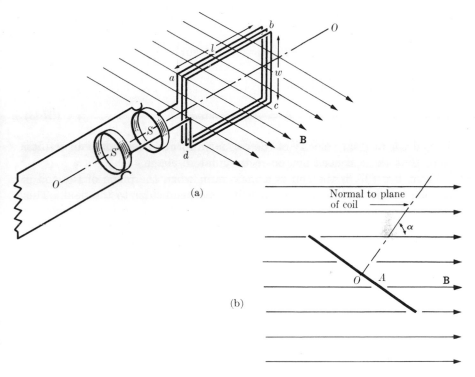

Fɪɢ. 27–7. Principle of the dynamo.

27–5 Induced emf in a rotating coil. The principle of the present-day form of dynamo is illustrated in Fig. 27–7. A closely wound rectangular coil *abcd* of N turns rotates about an axis OO which is perpendicular to a uniform magnetic field of flux density **B**. The terminals of the coil are connected to *slip rings* S-S concentric with the axis of the coil and rotating with it, but insulated from each other. Brushes bearing against these rings connect the coil to the external circuit. The magnetic field of a commercial dynamo is provided by an electromagnet and the coil itself is wound on an iron cylinder or *armature*. (The assembly of coil plus cylinder is also referred to as the armature.)

The magnitude of the emf induced in the coil of Fig. 27–7 may be computed either from the velocities of its sides transverse to the magnetic field or from the rate of change of flux through the coil. The flux through each turn of the coil of area A is

$$\Phi = BA \cos \alpha.$$

The instantaneous induced emf is

$$\mathcal{E} = -N \frac{d\Phi}{dt} = NBA \sin \alpha \, \frac{d\alpha}{dt},$$

but since $d\alpha/dt$ is ω, we have

$$\mathcal{E} = NBA\omega \sin \alpha. \qquad (27\text{--}3)$$

Thus if the angular velocity of the coil is uniform a sinusoidal emf results. Note that the coil need not be rectangular in shape.

From Eq. (27–3) the emf is a maximum when the plane of the coil is parallel to the field, and zero when it is perpendicular to the field. This is in agreement with the fact that in the parallel position the sides ab and cd are moving normally to the field, while in the perpendicular position their motion is parallel to the field. The maximum emf is

$$\mathcal{E}_{max} = NBA\omega.$$

Hence Eq. (27–3) can be written as

$$\mathcal{E} = \mathcal{E}_{max} \sin \alpha.$$

If ω is constant,

$$\alpha = \omega t \qquad \text{or} \qquad \alpha = 2\pi ft$$

and hence

$$\mathcal{E} = \mathcal{E}_{max} \sin \omega t = \mathcal{E}_{max} \sin 2\pi ft, \qquad (27\text{--}4)$$

which brings out explicitly the dependence of the instantaneous emf on the time t. A graph of Eq. (27–4) is given in Fig. 27–8. The rotating coil is the simplest form of *alternating-current generator* or *alternator*.

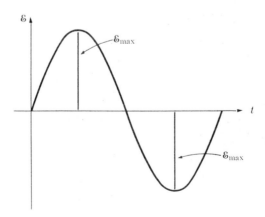

Fig. 27–8. Graph of the alternating emf induced in the coil of Fig. 27–7.

27–6 The direct-current generator. A coil of wire rotating in a magnetic field develops, as we have seen, a sinusoidal alternating emf. A unidirectional emf may be obtained by connecting each terminal of the coil to one side of a split ring or *commutator*. (See Fig. 27–9.) At the instant when the emf in the coil reverses, the connections to the external circuit are interchanged and the emf between the terminals, although pulsating, is always in the same direction, as shown in Fig. 27–10.

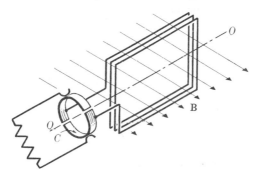

Fig. 27–9. Split ring, or commutator, for unidirectional emf.

If it is desired to generate an emf that is not only unidirectional but also practically constant, a first step might be to wind a large number of coils on the generator armature, bringing the terminals of each coil out to its own pair of small commutator segments. The brushes would thus make connection to each coil during a short period when the emf in that coil was near its maximum value. The emf in the external circuit would thus have only a very slight ripple. This method, however, is very wasteful because, at the moment when the commutator segments belonging to one coil are in contact with the brushes, the other coils arc completely inactive.

To avoid this, a large number of conductors are set in slots in the armature and connected in series in such a way that the entire armature is a closed coil with a net emf equal to zero. Connections are made to commutator segments (whose number is one-half that of the conductors) so that at any moment the emf across the brushes is the resultant of the emf's in half the conductors. With enough conductors,

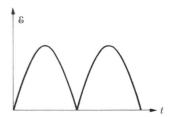

Fig. 27–10. Graph of the unidirectional pulsating emf in the external circuit of Fig. 27–9.

this emf is not only unidirectional but also practically constant. The connections are complicated, and a discussion of them properly belongs in a text on d-c machinery.

We are now in a position to understand why the armature of a motor is a seat of back emf, a fact which was stated without proof in Chapter 25. A motor armature is simply a coil (or coils) in continuous rotation in a magnetic field. The armature is forced to rotate by the side-thrust on the current maintained in it by the external seat of emf to which its terminals are connected. The fact that it does rotate results in the generation of an emf within it, opposite to the external emf. Every motor is therefore necessarily a generator also.

27–7 Search-coil method of measuring magnetic flux. A useful experimental method of measuring the flux density at a point in a magnetic field will now be described. The apparatus consists of a ballistic galvanometer connected by flexible leads to the terminals of a small, closely wound coil called a *search coil* or a *snatch coil*. Assume first, for simplicity, that the search coil is placed with its plane perpendicular to a magnetic field of flux density B. If the area enclosed by the coil is A, the flux Φ through it is $\Phi = BA$. Now if the coil is quickly given a one-quarter turn about one of its diameters so that its plane becomes parallel to the field, or if it is quickly snatched from its position to another where the field is known to be zero, the flux through it decreases rapidly from BA to zero. During the time that the flux is decreasing, an emf of short duration is induced in the coil and a "kick" is imparted to the ballistic galvanometer. The maximum deflection of the galvanometer is noted.

The galvanometer current at any instant is

$$i = \frac{\varepsilon}{R},$$

where R is the combined resistance of galvanometer and search coil, ε is the instantaneous induced emf, and i the instantaneous current. Since $\varepsilon = -N\,(d\Phi/dt)$, the instantaneous current is

$$i = -\frac{N}{R}\frac{d\Phi}{dt},$$

and

$$i\,dt = -\frac{N}{R}\,d\Phi,$$

$$\int_0^t i\,dt = -\frac{N}{R}\int_\Phi^0 d\Phi.$$

But

$$\int_0^t i\,dt = q, \qquad \int_\Phi^0 d\Phi = -\Phi,$$

so

$$q = \frac{N\Phi}{R}, \qquad \Phi = \frac{Rq}{N}, \qquad (27\text{--}5)$$

and

$$B = \frac{\Phi}{A} = \frac{Rq}{NA}. \qquad (27\text{--}6)$$

The maximum deflection of a ballistic galvanometer is proportional to the quantity of charge displaced through it. (See Section 25–6.) Hence, if this proportionality constant is known, q may be found, and from q we can obtain Φ and B.

In some cases, such as that of the Rowland ring, the search coil is not moved but the flux through it is changed in some way. In such cases this method gives the change of flux through the coil.

Strictly speaking, while this method gives correctly the total flux through the coil, it is only the *average* flux density over the area of the coil which is measured. However, if the area is sufficiently small, this approximates closely the flux density at, say, the center of the coil.

The preceding discussion assumed the plane of the coil to be initially perpendicular to the direction of the field. If one is "exploring" a field whose direction is not known in advance, the same apparatus may be used to find the direction by performing a series of experiments in which the coil is placed at a given point in the field in various orientations, and snatched out of the field from each orientation. The deflection of the galvanometer will be a maximum for the particular orientation in which the plane of the coil was perpendicular to the field. Thus both the magnitude and direction of an unknown field can be found by this method.

PROBLEMS

27–1. The cube in Fig. 27–11, one meter on a side, is placed in a uniform magnetic field of flux density 0.2 w/m² directed along the x-axis. Wires A, C, and D move in the directions indicated, each at the rate of 50 cm/sec. Determine the emf induced in each wire.

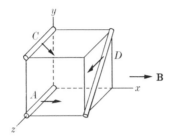

FIGURE 27–11

27–2. A slender rod one meter long rotates about an axis through one end and perpendicular to the rod, with an angular velocity of 2 rev/sec. The plane of rotation of the rod is perpendicular to a uniform magnetic field of 0.5 w/m² flux density. What emf is induced across the ends of the rod?

27–3. A conducting rod AB in Fig. 27–12 makes contact with the metal rails CA and DB. The apparatus is in a uniform magnetic field of flux density 500 milliwebers/m², perpendicular to the plane of the diagram. (a) Find the

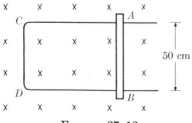

FIGURE 27–12

magnitude and direction of the emf induced in the rod when it is moving toward the right with a velocity of 4 m/sec. (b) If the resistance of the circuit $ABCD$ is 0.2 ohm (assumed constant), find the force required to maintain the rod in motion. Neglect friction. (c) Compare the rate at which mechanical work is done by the force (F_v) with the rate of development of heat in the circuit (i^2R).

27–4. Figure 27–13 is a side view of the same rod and metal rails as in Fig. 27–12, except that the magnetic induction makes an angle of 60° with the plane of the loop $ABCD$. Find the induced emf. The flux density is 500 milliwebers/m² and the velocity of the rod is 4 m/sec toward the right.

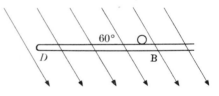

FIGURE 27–13

27–5. A closely wound rectangular coil of 50 turns has dimensions of 12 cm × 25 cm and is in a uniform magnetic field of flux density 2 w/m². In 0.1 sec the plane of the coil is rotated from a position where it makes an angle of 37° with the magnetic field, through the small angle to a position perpendicular to the field. What is the average emf induced in the coil?

27–6. A coil of 1000 turns enclosing an area of 20 cm² is rotated from a position where its plane is perpendicular to the earth's magnetic field to one where its plane is parallel to the field, in 0.02 sec. What average emf is induced if the flux density of the earth's magnetic field is 6×10^{-5} w/m²?

27–7. A flat square coil of 10 turns has sides of length 12 cm. The coil rotates in a magnetic field whose flux density is 0.025 w/m². (a) What is the angular velocity of the coil if the maximum emf produced is 20 mv? (b) What is the average emf at this velocity?

27–8. A cardboard tube is wound with two windings of insulated wire, as in Fig. 27–14. Terminals a and b of winding A may be connected to a seat of emf through a reversing switch.

State whether the induced current in the resistor R is from left to right, or from right to left, in the following circumstances: (a) the current in winding A is from a to b and is increasing; (b) the current is from b to a and is decreasing; (c) the current is from b to a and is increasing.

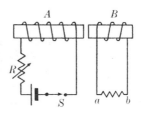

FIGURE 27–15

opened, (b) coil B is brought closer to coil A, (c) the resistance of R is decreased.

27–11. The orbit of an electron in a betatron is a circle of radius R. Suppose the electron is revolving in this orbit with a tangential velocity v. (a) What flux density is required to maintain the electron in this orbit if the magnitude of its velocity is constant? (b) If the flux density is uniform over the plane of the orbit, and is increasing at a rate dB/dt, what is the equivalent voltage accelerating the electron in each revolution?

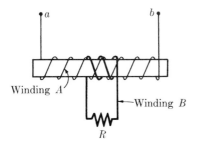

Winding A

Winding B

R

FIGURE 27–14

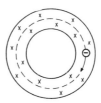

FIGURE 27–16

27–9. A solenoid has 96 turns of wire, a length of 8 cm, a cross-sectional area of 6 cm², and carries a current of 0.25 amp. A "secondary" of 2 turns is wound around the solenoid. When a switch is opened the magnetic field of the solenoid becomes zero in 0.05 sec. What emf is induced in the 2 turns?

27–10. Using Lenz's law, determine the direction of the current in resistor ab of Fig. 27–15 when (a) switch S is

27–12. In the diagram of the toroidal tube of the betatron, Fig. 27–16, a magnetic field is directed into the plane of the diagram and is increasing. An electron is moving clockwise. (a) Show that the emf induced around the electron's orbit is such as to accelerate the electron. (b) Show that the increasing radial force on the electron due to the magnetic field tends to prevent the electron from going to larger orbits.

27-13. A rectangular coil of wire rotates with its axis of rotation perpendicular to a magnetic field whose flux density is 0.60 w/m^2 [see Fig. 27-7(a)]. The coil is 6 cm × 8 cm and has 250 turns. (a) At what speed must the coil rotate to generate an average emf of 100 volts during each quarter revolution? (b) What is the maximum emf at this speed?

27-14. Assume a rectangular coil of wire having 10 turns and dimensions of 20 cm × 30 cm to be rotating at a constant speed of 600 rev/min in a magnetic field in which the flux density is 0.10 w/m^2. The axis of rotation is perpendicular to the field. Find the maximum emf produced.

27-15. A coil of 5 turns has dimensions 9 cm × 7 cm. It rotates at the rate of 15π rad/sec in a uniform magnetic field whose flux density is 0.8 w/m^2. (a) What maximum emf is induced in the coil? (b) What is the emf 1/90 sec after it reaches the value of zero? (c) Sketch a curve of $\mathcal{E}$ vs. t for one rotation of the coil, and on the same graph, a curve of $\mathcal{E}$ vs. t if the angular velocity of the coil is doubled.

27-16. A circular turn of wire 4 cm in radius rotates with an angular velocity of 1800 rev/min about a diameter which is perpendicular to a uniform magnetic field of flux density 0.5 w/m^2. What is the instantaneous induced emf in the turn when the plane of the turn makes an angle of 30° with the direction of the flux?

27-17. A closely wound search coil has an area of 4 cm^2, 160 turns, and a resistance of 50 ohms. It is connected to a ballistic galvanometer whose resistance is 30 ohms. When the coil is rotated quickly from a position parallel to a uniform magnetic field to one perpendicular to the field, the galvanometer indicates a charge of 4×10^{-5} coul. What is the flux density of the field?

27-18. A solenoid 50 cm long and 8 cm in diameter is wound with 500 turns. A closely wound coil of 20 turns of insulated wire surrounds the solenoid at its midpoint, and the terminals of the coil are connected to a ballistic galvanometer. The combined resistance of coil, galvanometer, and leads is 25 ohms. (a) Find the quantity of charge displaced through the galvanometer when the current in the solenoid is quickly decreased from 3 amp to 1 amp. (b) Draw a sketch of the apparatus, showing clearly the directions of winding of the solenoid and coil, and of the current in the solenoid. What is the direction of the current in the coil when the solenoid current is decreased?

27-19. The cross-sectional area of a closely wound search coil having 20 turns is 1.5 cm^2 and its resistance is 4 ohms. The coil is connected through leads of negligible resistance to a ballistic galvanometer of resistance 16 ohms. Find the quantity of charge displaced through the galvanometer when the coil is pulled quickly out of a region where $B = 1.8$ w/m^2 to a point where the magnetic field is zero. The plane of the coil, when in the field, made an angle of 90° with the magnetic induction.

27-20. The wire AB in Fig. 26-26 carries a varying current i, given by

$$i = I_m \sin \omega t,$$

where i is the instantaneous current I_m the maximum current, and ω is a constant. Find the expression for the instantaneous induced emf in the loop $CDEF$.

CHAPTER 28

CAPACITANCE. PROPERTIES OF DIELECTRICS

28–1 Capacitors. If a number of charged conductors are in the vicinity of one another, the potential of each is determined not only by its own charge but by the magnitude and sign of the charges on the other conductors and by their shapes, sizes, and locations. For example, the potential of a positively charged sphere is lowered if a second, negatively charged sphere is brought near the first.

An important special case arises in practice when two conductors in the same vicinity are given equal amounts of charge of opposite sign. This is usually accomplished by connecting the conductors, both initially uncharged, to the terminals of a battery, which results in a transfer of charge from one conductor to the other. We shall see later that the energy taken from the battery is reversibly stored in the electric field surrounding the conductors. Thus the charged conductors constitute a seat of emf. Such an arrangement of two conductors is called a *capacitor*. The fact that each conductor is in the vicinity of another carrying a charge of opposite sign makes possible the transfer of relatively large quantities of charge from one conductor to the other, with relatively small differences of potential.

The capacitance C of a capacitor is defined as the ratio of the charge Q on either conductor to the potential difference V_{ab} between the conductors:

$$C = \frac{Q}{V_{ab}}. \qquad (28\text{–}1)$$

The net charge on the capacitor as a whole, of course, is zero, and "the charge on a capacitor" is understood to mean the charge on *either* conductor, without regard to sign. We see from its definition that capacitance is expressed in *coulombs per volt*. Since one volt is equivalent to one joule per coulomb, one coulomb per volt is equivalent to one coul^2/joule. A capacitance of one coulomb per volt is called one *farad* (in honor of Michael Faraday). That is, *the capacitance of a capacitor is one farad if one coulomb is transferred from one conductor to the other, per volt of potential difference between the conductors.*

A capacitor is represented by the symbol

Capacitors find many applications in electrical circuits. A capacitor is used to eliminate sparking when a circuit containing inductance is suddenly opened. The ignition system of every automobile engine contains a capacitor for this purpose. Capacitors are used in radio circuits for tuning, and for "smoothing" the rectified current delivered by the power supply. The efficiency of alternating-current power transmission can often be increased by the use of large capacitors.

The term "condenser" has long been used for the piece of apparatus we have described as a "capacitor." But "capacitor" is to be preferred, both because nothing is actually "condensed" in a "condenser," and also because of the corresponding usage of the terms resistance and resistor. That is, a resistor is a device that has resistance, and a capacitor is a device that has capacitance.

28–2 The parallel-plate capacitor. The most common type of capacitor consists of two conducting plates parallel to each other and separated by a distance which is small compared with the linear dimensions of the plates (see Fig. 28–1). Practically the entire field of such a capacitor is localized in the region between the plates, as shown. There is a slight "fringing" of the field at its outer boundary, but the fringing becomes relatively less as the plates are brought closer together. If the plates are sufficiently close, the fringing may be neglected, the field between the plates is uniform, and the charges on the plates are uniformly distributed over their opposing surfaces. This arrangement is known as a *parallel-plate capacitor*.

Let us assume first that the plates are in vacuum. It has been shown that the electric intensity between a pair of closely spaced parallel plates in vacuum is

$$E = \frac{1}{\epsilon_0}\sigma = \frac{1}{\epsilon_0}\frac{Q}{A},$$

where A is the area of each plate and Q is the charge on *either* plate. Since the electric intensity or potential gradient between the plates is uniform, the potential difference between the plates is

$$V_{ab} = Ed = \frac{1}{\epsilon_0}\frac{Qd}{A},$$

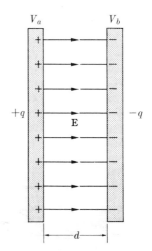

Fig. 28–1. Parallel-plate capacitor.

where d is the separation of the plates. Hence the capacitance of a parallel-plate capacitor in vacuum is

$$C = \frac{Q}{V_{ab}} = \epsilon_0 \frac{A}{d}. \qquad (28\text{-}2)$$

Since ϵ_0, A, and d are constants for a given capacitor, the capacitance is a constant independent of the charge on the capacitor, and is directly proportional to the area of the plates and inversely proportional to their separation. If mks units are used, A is to be expressed in square meters and d in meters. The capacitance C will then be in farads.

As an example, let us compute the area of the plates of a one-farad parallel-plate capacitor if the separation of the plates is one millimeter and the plates are in vacuum.

$$C = \epsilon_0 \frac{A}{d},$$

$$A = \frac{Cd}{\epsilon_0} = \frac{1 \text{ farad} \times 10^{-3} \text{ m}}{8.85 \times 10^{-12} \text{ coul}^2/\text{n·m}^2} = 1.13 \times 10^8 \text{ m}^2.$$

This corresponds to a square 10,600 meters, or 34,600 ft, or about $6\frac{1}{2}$ miles on a side!

Since the farad is such a large unit of capacitance, units of more convenient size are the *microfarad* (1 μf $= 10^{-6}$ farad), and the *micro-micro-farad* (1 $\mu\mu$f $= 10^{-12}$ farad). For example, a common radio set contains in its power supply several capacitors whose capacitances are of the order of ten microfarads, while the capacitances of the tuning capacitors are of the order of a few hundred micro-microfarads.

Variable capacitors whose capacitance may be varied at will (between limits) are widely used in the tuning circuits of radio receivers. These are usually air capacitors of relatively small capacitance and are constructed of a number of fixed parallel metal plates connected together and constituting one "plate" of the capacitor, while a second set of movable plates also connected together forms the other "plate" (Fig. 28-2). By rotating a shaft on which the movable plates are mounted, the second set may be caused to interleave the first to a greater or lesser extent. The effective area of the capacitor is that of the interleaved portion of the plates only.

A variable capacitor is represented by the symbol

While parallel-plate capacitors are the simplest and cheapest to construct, capacitors consisting of concentric spheres and of coaxial cylinders are sometimes used in standards laboratories, since the corrections for the "fringing" fields can be made more readily and the capacitance can be

FIG. 28–2. Variable air capacitor. (Courtesy of General Radio Company.)

accurately calculated from the dimensions of the apparatus. Problems involving a spherical and a cylindrical capacitor will be found at the end of the chapter.

EXAMPLE. The plates of a parallel-plate capacitor are 5 mm apart and 2 m² in area. The plates are in vacuum. A potential difference of 10,000 volts is applied across the capacitor. Compute (a) the capacitance, (b) the charge on each plate, and (c) the electric intensity in the space between them.

(a)
$$C = \epsilon_0 \frac{A}{d}$$

$$= 8.85 \times 10^{-12} \frac{\text{coul}^2}{\text{n·m}^2} \times \frac{2 \text{ m}^2}{5 \times 10^{-3} \text{ m}}$$

$$= 3.54 \times 10^{-9} \frac{\text{coul}^2}{\text{n·m}}.$$

But

$$1 \frac{\text{coul}^2}{\text{n·m}} = 1 \frac{\text{coul}^2}{\text{joule}} = 1 \frac{\text{coul}}{\text{joule/coul}} = 1 \frac{\text{coul}}{\text{volt}} = 1 \text{ farad},$$

so

$$C = 3.54 \times 10^{-9} \text{ farad}.$$

(b) The charge on the capacitor is

$$Q = CV_{ab} = 3.54 \times 10^{-9} \frac{\text{coul}}{\text{volt}} \times 10^4 \text{ volts}$$

$$= 3.54 \times 10^{-5} \text{ coul}.$$

(c) The electric intensity is

$$E = \frac{\sigma}{\epsilon_0} = \frac{Q}{\epsilon_0 A} = \frac{3.54 \times 10^{-5} \text{ coul}}{8.85 \times 10^{-12} \text{ (coul}^2/\text{n·m}^2) \times 2 \text{ m}^2}$$

$$= 20 \times 10^5 \frac{\text{n}}{\text{coul}}.$$

Or, since the electric intensity equals the potential gradient,

$$E = \frac{V_{ab}}{d} = \frac{10^4 \text{ volts}}{5 \times 10^{-3} \text{ m}} = 20 \times 10^5 \frac{\text{volts}}{\text{m}}.$$

Of course, the newton/coulomb and the volt/meter are equivalent units.

28–3 Capacitors in series and in parallel. Circuits often contain two or more capacitors. Consider the three capacitors connected as in Fig. 28–3, where it is possible to proceed from point a to point d along only one path, $abcd$. When this is the case, the capacitors are said to be connected in *series* between points a and d. In Fig. 28–4, on the other hand, it is possible to go from a to b along three different paths, and the capacitors are said to be connected in *parallel* between points a and b.

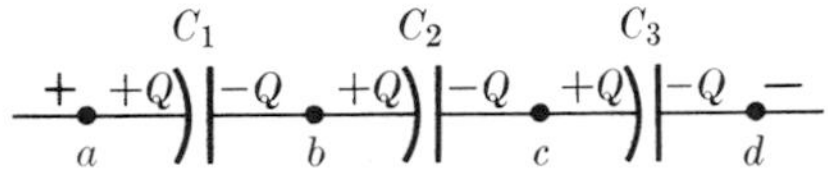

FIG. 28–3. Capacitors in series. The charge on each capacitor is the same.

The capacitance of a capacitor is defined as the ratio of the charge Q on either plate to the potential difference between the capacitor terminals. The charge Q may be described as the charge displaced past any point of the external circuit in the process of charging the capacitor.

The *equivalent* capacitance of a capacitor network is similarly defined as the ratio of the displaced charge to the potential difference between the terminals of the network. Hence the method of computing the equivalent capacitance of a network is to assume a potential difference between the terminals of the network, compute the corresponding charge, and take the ratio of the charge to the potential difference.

Let the capacitances of the three capacitors in Fig. 28–3 be C_1, C_2,

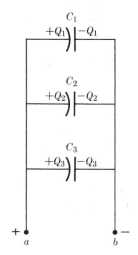

FIG. 28–4. Capacitors in parallel. The potential difference across each capacitor is the same.

and C_3, and suppose that the terminals a and d are maintained at a potential difference V_{ad}. If the left plate of capacitor 1 receives a charge $+Q$, an equal negative charge $-Q$ will be induced on the right plate. At the same time, a charge $+Q$ appears on the left plate of capacitor 2, since the conductor consisting of the right plate of capacitor 1, the left plate of capacitor 2, and the wire connecting them was originally uncharged and is insulated from the rest of the circuit. Thus each capacitor receives a charge of *magnitude* Q on each of its plates. Then

$$Q = C_1 V_{ab}, \qquad Q = C_2 V_{bc}, \qquad Q = C_3 V_{cd},$$

and

$$V_{ad} = V_{ab} + V_{bc} + V_{cd}.$$

Let C represent the *equivalent* capacitance of the arrangement, that is, the capacitance of the single capacitor that would become charged with the same charge Q when the potential difference across its terminals is V_{ad}. Then

$$V_{ad} = \frac{Q}{C}$$

and

$$\frac{Q}{C} = \frac{Q}{C_1} + \frac{Q}{C_2} + \frac{Q}{C_3},$$

whence

$$\boxed{\frac{1}{C} = \frac{1}{C_1} + \frac{1}{C_2} + \frac{1}{C_3}.} \qquad (28\text{-}3)$$

That is, when any number of capacitors are connected in series, the reciprocal of the equivalent capacitance equals the sum of the reciprocals of the individual capacitances.

Next, let a potential difference V_{ab} be applied across the terminals a and b of the parallel network in Fig. 28-4. The potential difference across each capacitor is then V_{ab}, but the charges on each are different. Thus

$$Q_1 = C_1 V_{ab}, \qquad Q_2 = C_2 V_{ab}, \qquad Q_3 = C_3 V_{ab}.$$

The total charge Q on the parallel network is

$$Q = Q_1 + Q_2 + Q_3.$$

Again defining the equivalent capacitance C as that of a single capacitor which would acquire the same total charge Q with the same potential difference V_{ab}, we have

$$Q = C V_{ab}$$

and hence

$$CV_{ab} = C_1 V_{ab} + C_2 V_{ab} + C_3 V_{ab}$$

or

$$\boxed{C = C_1 + C_2 + C_3.}$$ (28–4)

Hence when any number of capacitors are connected in parallel, the equivalent capacitance equals the sum of the individual capacitances.

EXAMPLE. Refer to Fig. 28–5. If point b is grounded and point a is maintained at a potential of $+1200$ volts, find the charge on each capacitor and the potential of point c.

The 4-μf and the 2-μf capacitors are in parallel, and are hence equivalent to a single capacitor of capacitance

$$C_4 = 4\ \mu f + 2\ \mu f = 6\ \mu f.$$

This equivalent capacitor is in series with the 3-μf capacitor. Hence the equivalent capacitance C of the network is

$$\frac{1}{C} = \frac{1}{C_1} + \frac{1}{C_4} = \frac{1}{3\ \mu f} + \frac{1}{6\ \mu f} = \frac{1}{2\ \mu f}$$

or

$$C = 2\ \mu f.$$

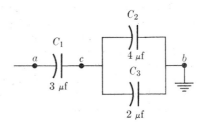

FIG. 28–5. Simple network of capacitors.

The charge on the equivalent capacitor is

$$Q = CV_{ab} = 2 \times 10^{-6}\ \text{farad} \times 1200\ \text{volts} = 2.4 \times 10^{-3}\ \text{coul.}$$

This must equal the charge on the 3-μf capacitor, and the sum of the charges on the 4-μf and 2-μf capacitors. Now

$$V_{ac} = \frac{Q_1}{C_1} = \frac{2.4 \times 10^{-3}\ \text{coul}}{3 \times 10^{-6}\ \text{farad}} = 800\ \text{volts,}$$

$$V_{ac} \equiv V_a - V_c = 800\ \text{volts,} \quad V_a = 1200\ \text{volts,} \quad \therefore V_c = 400\ \text{volts}$$

and

$$V_{cb} \equiv V_c - V_b = 400\ \text{volts} - 0 = 400\ \text{volts.}$$

Hence

$$Q_2 = C_2 V_{cb} = 4 \times 10^{-6}\ \text{farad} \times 400\ \text{volts} = 1.6 \times 10^{-3}\ \text{coul,}$$

$$Q_3 = C_3 V_{cb} = 2 \times 10^{-6}\ \text{farad} \times 400\ \text{volts} = 0.8 \times 10^{-3}\ \text{coul,}$$

$$Q_2 + Q_3 = (1.6 + 0.8) \times 10^{-3}\ \text{coul} = 2.4 \times 10^{-3}\ \text{coul.}$$

28–4 Energy of a charged capacitor. The process of charging a capacitor consists of transferring charge from the plate at lower potential to the plate at higher potential. The charging process therefore requires the expenditure of energy. Imagine the charging process to be carried out by starting with both plates completely uncharged, and then repeatedly removing small positive charges from one plate and transferring them to the other plate. At a stage of this process when the total quantity of charge transferred has reached an amount q, the potential difference between the plates is

$$V_{ab} = \frac{q}{C},$$

The work dW required to transfer the next small charge dq is

$$dW = V_{ab}\, dq = \frac{1}{C}\, q\, dq.$$

The total work done in the charging process, while the charge increases from zero to its final value Q, is

$$W = \int dW = \frac{1}{C} \int_0^Q q\, dq,$$

or

$$W = \frac{1}{2}\frac{Q^2}{C}. \tag{28–5}$$

Since the farad is equivalent to the coul^2/joule, the energy is expressed in joules when Q is in coulombs and C in farads.

Since $V_{ab} = Q/C$, Eq. (28–5) is equivalent to

$$W = \tfrac{1}{2}CV_{ab}^2 = \tfrac{1}{2}QV_{ab}, \tag{28–6}$$

where V_{ab} now represents the potential difference across the capacitor when its charge is Q. This energy stored in the capacitor is reversibly reconvertible into some other form if the capacitor is discharged. Thus, unlike a resistor, a capacitor is a seat of emf, and so long as we limit our discussion to ideal or perfect capacitors we could substitute the symbol ε wherever we have used V. In the next chapter we shall treat a capacitor as a seat of emf.

———————

EXAMPLE. A 1-μf capacitor is charged to 100 volts and a 2-μf capacitor to 200 volts. They are then connected in parallel, positive plate to positive plate. Determine the initial and final energies and account for the difference.

The initial energy of the 1-μf capacitor is

$$(W_1)_i = \tfrac{1}{2}C_1 V_1^2 = \tfrac{1}{2} \times 10^{-6}\ \text{farad} \times 10^4\ \text{volts} = 0.005\ \text{joule},$$

and the initial energy of the 2-μf capacitor is

$$(W_2)_i = \tfrac{1}{2}C_2 V_2^2 = \tfrac{1}{2} \times 2 \times 10^{-6} \text{ farad} \times 4 \times 10^4 \text{ volts} = 0.04 \text{ joule}.$$

The total initial energy of both capacitors is

$$(W_1 + W_2)_i = 0.005 \text{ joule} + 0.04 \text{ joule} = 0.045 \text{ joule}.$$

When the two capacitors are connected in parallel, $+$ to $+$, the resulting combination has a capacitance C_f of 3 μf and a charge Q_f equal to the sum of the two separate charges.

Thus,

$$Q_f = Q_1 + Q_2 = C_1 V_1 + C_2 V_2$$

$$= 1 \times 10^{-6} \text{ farad} \times 100 \text{ volts} + 2 \times 10^{-6} \text{ farad} \times 200 \text{ volts}$$

$$= 5 \times 10^{-4} \text{ coul}.$$

The final energy of the combination is therefore

$$W_f = \frac{1}{2} \frac{Q_f^2}{C_f} = \frac{(5 \times 10^{-4} \text{ coul})^2}{2 \times 3 \times 10^{-6} \text{ farad}} = 0.0417 \text{ joule}.$$

The final energy is seen to be less than the initial energy, the difference being the energy that must have been converted into another form. If the connecting wires that were used to make the parallel combination were extremely thin (large resistance), the energy was converted into heat. If, on the other hand, these wires were quite thick (negligible resistance), much of the energy was radiated in the form of radiowaves.

28-5 Dielectric coefficient. Permittivity. Most capacitors utilize a solid, nonconducting material or *dielectric* between their plates. A common type is the paper and foil capacitor, in which strips of metal foil form the plates and a sheet of paper impregnated with wax is the dielectric. By rolling up such a capacitor, a capacitance of several microfarads can be obtained in a relatively small volume. The "Leyden jar," constructed by cementing metal foil over a portion of the inside and outside surfaces of a glass jar, is essentially a parallel-plate capacitor, with the glass forming the dielectric.

Electrolytic capacitors utilize as their dielectric an extremely thin layer of nonconducting oxide between a metal plate and a conducting solution. Because of the small thickness of the dielectric, electrolytic capacitors of relatively small dimensions may have a capacitance of the order of 50 μf.

The function of a solid dielectric between the plates of a capacitor is threefold. First, it solves the mechanical problem of maintaining two large metal sheets at an extremely small separation but without actual

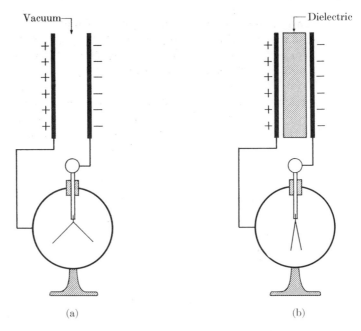

FIG. 28–6. Effect of a dielectric between the plates of a parallel-plate capacitor. (a) With a given charge, the potential difference is V_0. (b) With the same charge, the potential difference V is smaller than V_0.

contact. Second, since its dielectric strength is larger than that of air, the maximum potential difference which the capacitor can withstand without breakdown is increased. Third, it is found that the capacitance of a capacitor of given dimensions is several times larger with a dielectric separating its plates than if the plates were in vacuum. This effect can be demonstrated as follows. Figure 28–6(a) illustrates a parallel-plate capacitor whose plates have been given equal and opposite charges of magnitude Q. The plates are assumed to be in vacuum and the potential difference V_0 between the plates is indicated by an electroscope. If a sheet of dielectric, such as glass, bakelite, or hard rubber, is now inserted between the plates as in Fig. 28–6(b), just filling the space between them, the potential difference is observed to decrease to a smaller value V. If the dielectric is removed, the potential difference returns to its original value, showing that the original charges on the plates were not affected by insertion of the dielectric.

With a vacuum between its plates, the electric intensity E_0 in the region between the plates of a parallel-plate capacitor is

$$E_0 = \frac{V_0}{d} = \frac{\sigma}{\epsilon_0}. \qquad (28\text{–}7)$$

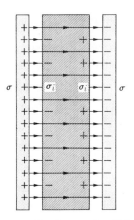

Fig. 28–7. Induced charges on the faces of a dielectric in an external field.

The observed reduction in potential difference, when a dielectric is inserted between the plates, implies a reduction in the electric intensity, which in turn implies a reduction in the charge per unit area. Since no charge has leaked off the plates, such a reduction could be caused only by charges of opposite sign appearing on the two surfaces of the dielectric. That is, the dielectric surface adjacent to the positive plate must have an induced negative charge and that adjacent to the negative plate an induced positive charge of equal magnitude, as shown in Fig. 28–7. The field set up by the induced charges is opposite to the original field, therefore the electric intensity E in the dielectric is smaller than the original intensity E_0.

Let us define a quantity ϵ by the equation

$$E = \frac{V}{d} = \frac{\sigma}{\epsilon}, \qquad (28\text{–}8)$$

where ϵ is greater than ϵ_0 since, by observation, V is less than V_0. We call ϵ the *permittivity* of the dielectric and ϵ_0 may therefore be called the "permittivity of a vacuum."

The ratio of ϵ to ϵ_0 is called the *relative permittivity* or the *dielectric coefficient* of the dielectric and is represented by K (a pure number).

$$K = \frac{\epsilon}{\epsilon_0}. \qquad (28\text{–}9)$$

Some representative values of K are listed in Table 28–1. Evidently, $K = 1$ for a vacuum, and K for air is so nearly equal to 1 that for most purposes an air capacitor is equivalent to one in vacuum. The properties of a parallel-plate capacitor in vacuum and with a dielectric between its plates are compared in Table 28–2.

TABLE 28–1

DIELECTRIC COEFFICIENT K

($\epsilon_0 = 8.85 \times 10^{-12}$ coul^2/n·m^2)

Material	t, °C	K
Vacuum		1
Glass	25	5–10
Mica	25	3–6
Hevea rubber	27	2.94
Neoprene	24	6.70
Bakelite	27	5.50
	57	1.80
	88	18.2
Plexiglas	27	3.40
Polyethylene	23	2.25
Vinylite	20	3.18
	47	3.60
	76	3.92
	96	6.60
	110	9.9
Teflon	22	2.1
Germanium	20	16
Strontium titanate	20	310
Titanium dioxide (rutile)	20	173($\perp$), 86($\parallel$)
Water	25	78.54
Glycerin	25	42.5
Liquid ammonia	−77.7	25
Benzene	20	2.284
Air (1 atm)	20	1.00059
Air (100 atm)	20	1.0548

If the area of the capacitor plates is A, then $\sigma = Q/A$ and, from Eq. (28–8), the capacitance of a parallel-plate capacitor with a dielectric between its plates is

$$C = \epsilon \frac{A}{d} = K\epsilon_0 \frac{A}{d}. \qquad (28\text{–}10)$$

This reduces to Eq. (28–2) for a capacitor in vacuum, where $\epsilon = \epsilon_0$ and $K = 1$. It follows from Eqs. (28–2) and (28–10) that

$$K = \frac{C}{C_0}. \qquad (28\text{–}11)$$

TABLE 28–2

PARALLEL-PLATE CAPACITOR

With vacuum	With dielectric
$C_0 = \epsilon_0 \dfrac{A}{d}$	$C = \epsilon \dfrac{A}{d}$
$E_0 = \dfrac{\sigma}{\epsilon_0}$	$E = \dfrac{\sigma}{\epsilon} = \dfrac{\sigma - \sigma_i}{\epsilon_0}$
$K = 1$	$K = \dfrac{\epsilon}{\epsilon_0}$
$V_0 = E_0 d$	$V = Ed$

The induced charge per unit area on the surfaces of the dielectric, σ_i, can be computed as follows. The field E_i set up by this charge is

$$E_i = \frac{\sigma_i}{\epsilon_0},$$

and the resultant field E is

$$E = E_0 - E_i = \frac{\sigma}{\epsilon_0} - \frac{\sigma_i}{\epsilon_0}.$$

But

$$E = \frac{\sigma}{\epsilon} = \frac{\sigma}{K\epsilon_0},$$

so

$$\sigma_i = \sigma \frac{K - 1}{K}. \qquad (28\text{–}12)$$

EXAMPLE. The parallel plates in Fig. 28–6 have an area of 2000 cm^2 or 2×10^{-1} m^2, and are 1 cm or 10^{-2} m apart. The original potential difference between them, V_0, is 3000 volts, and it decreases to 1000 volts when a sheet of dielectric is inserted between the plates. Compute (a) the original capacitance C_0, (b) the charge Q on each plate, (c) the capacitance C after insertion of the dielectric, (d) the dielectric coefficient K of the dielectric, (e) the permittivity ϵ of the dielectric, (f) the induced charge Q_i on each face of the dielectric, (g) the original electric intensity E_0 between the plates, (h) the electric intensity E after insertion of the dielectric.

(a) $C_0 = \epsilon_0 \dfrac{A}{d} = 8.85 \times 10^{-12} \dfrac{\text{coul}^2}{\text{n·m}^2} \times \dfrac{2 \times 10^{-1}\,\text{m}^2}{10^{-2}\,\text{m}} = 17.7 \times 10^{-11}$ farad.

(b) $Q = C_0 V_0 = 17.7 \times 10^{-11}$ farad $\times\, 3 \times 10^3$ volts $= 53.1 \times 10^{-8}$ coul.

(c) $C = \dfrac{Q}{V} = \dfrac{53.1 \times 10^{-8} \text{ coul}}{10^3 \text{ volts}} = 53.1 \times 10^{-11} \text{ farad.}$

(d) $K = \dfrac{C}{C_0} = \dfrac{53.1 \times 10^{-11} \text{ farad}}{17.7 \times 10^{-11} \text{ farad}} = 3.$

(e) $\qquad\qquad \epsilon = K\epsilon_0 = 3 \times 8.85 \times 10^{-12} \dfrac{\text{coul}^2}{\text{n·m}^2}$

$$= 26.6 \times 10^{-12} \dfrac{\text{coul}^2}{\text{n·m}^2}.$$

(f) $Q_i = Q\left(\dfrac{K-1}{K}\right) = 53.1 \times 10^{-8} \text{ coul} \left(\dfrac{3-1}{3}\right) = 35.4 \times 10^{-8} \text{ coul.}$

(g) $\qquad\qquad E_0 = \dfrac{V_0}{d} = \dfrac{3000 \text{ volts}}{10^{-2} \text{ m}} = 3 \times 10^5 \dfrac{\text{volts}}{\text{m}}.$

(h) $\qquad\qquad E = \dfrac{V}{d} = \dfrac{1000 \text{ volts}}{10^{-2} \text{ m}} = 1 \times 10^5 \dfrac{\text{volts}}{\text{m}},$

or

$$E = \frac{\sigma}{\epsilon} = \frac{Q}{A\epsilon} = \frac{53.1 \times 10^{-8} \text{ coul}}{2 \times 10^{-1} \text{ m}^2 \times 26.6 \times 10^{-12} \text{ coul}^2/\text{n·m}^2} = 1 \times 10^5 \frac{\text{volts}}{\text{m}},$$

or

$$E = \frac{\sigma - \sigma_i}{\epsilon_0} = \frac{Q - Q_i}{A\epsilon_0} = \frac{(53.1 - 35.4) \times 10^{-8} \text{ coul}}{2 \times 10^{-1} \text{ m}^2 \times 8.85 \times 10^{-12} \text{ coul}^2/\text{n·m}^2}$$

$$= 1 \times 10^5 \frac{\text{volts}}{\text{m}}.$$

PROBLEMS

28–1. A capacitor has a capacitance of 8.5 μf. How much charge must be removed to lower the potential difference of its plates by 50 volts?

28–2. Three capacitors having capacitances of 8, 8, and 4 μf are connected in series across a 12-volt line. (a) What is the charge on the 4-μf capacitor? (b) What is the total energy of all three capacitors? (c) The capacitors are disconnected from the line and reconnected in parallel with the positively charged plates connected together. What is the voltage across the parallel combination? (d) What is the energy of the combination?

28–3. The capacitance of all the capacitors shown in Fig. 28–8 are in μf. (a) What is the equivalent capacitance between x and y? (b) If the charge on the 5-μf capacitor is 120 μcoul, what is the potential difference between x and a?

each capacitor, (c) the final energy of the system, (d) the decrease in energy when the capacitors are connected.

28–6. A 1-μf capacitor and a 2-μf capacitor are connected in series across a 1200-volt supply line. (a) Find the charge on each capacitor and the voltage across each. (b) The charged capacitors are disconnected from the line and from each other, and reconnected with terminals of like sign together. Find the final charge on each and the voltage across each.

28–7. A 1-μf capacitor and a 2-μf capacitor are connected in parallel across a 1200-volt supply line. (a) Find the charge on each capacitor and the voltage across each. (b) The charged capacitors are then disconnected from the line and from each other, and reconnected with terminals of unlike sign together. Find the final charge on each and the voltage across each.

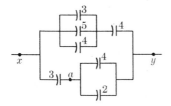

FIGURE 28–8

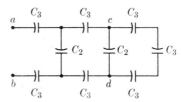

FIGURE 28–9

28–4. A 500-μf capacitor is charged to 120 volts. How many calories are produced on discharging the capacitor if all of the energy goes into heating the wire?

28–5. A 20-μf capacitor is charged to a potential difference of 1000 volts. The terminals of the charged capacitor are then connected to those of an uncharged 5-μf capacitor. Compute (a) the original charge of the system, (b) the final potential difference across

28–8. In Fig. 28–9, each capacitance $C_3 = 3$ μf and each capacitance $C_2 = 2$ μf. (a) Compute the equivalent capacitance of the network between points a and b. (b) Compute the charge on each of the capacitors nearest a and b, when $V_{ab} = 900$ volts. (c) With 900 volts across a and b, compute V_{cd}.

28–9. The capacitance of a variable radio capacitor can be changed from 50 μμf to 950 μμf by turning the dial from 0° to 180°. With the dial set at 180° the capacitor is connected to a 400-volt battery. After charging, the capacitor is disconnected from the battery and the dial is turned to 0°. (a) What is the charge on the capacitor? (b) What is the potential difference across the capacitor when the dial reads 0°? (c) What is the energy of the capacitor in this position? (d) How much work is required to turn the dial, if friction is neglected?

28-10. An air capacitor, consisting of two closely spaced parallel plates, has a capacitance of 1000 $\mu\mu$f. The charge on each plate is 1 microcoulomb. (a) What is the potential difference between the plates? (b) If the charge is kept constant, what will be the potential difference between the plates if the separation is doubled? (c) How much work is required to double the separation?

28-11. (a) The permittivity of diamond is 1.46×10^{-10} coul^2/n·m^2. What is the dielectric coefficient of diamond? (b) What is the dielectric coefficient of a metal?

28-12. Two parallel plates of 100 cm^2 area are given equal and opposite charges of 10^{-7} coul. The space between the plates is filled with a dielectric material, and the electric intensity within the dielectric is 3.3×10^5 volts/m. (a) What is the dielectric coefficient of the dielectric? (b) What is the total induced charge on one face of the dielectric?

28-13. Two parallel plates have equal and opposite charges. When the space between the plates is evacuated, the electric intensity is 2×10^5 volts/m. When the space is filled with dielectric, the electric intensity is 1.2×10^5 volts/m. What is the induced charge density on the surface of the dielectric?

28-14. A potential difference of 100 volts exists between the plates of a parallel-plate capacitor in which the dielectric is air. (a) What will be the difference in potential between the plates if a dielectric sheet having a dielectric coefficient of 2.5 is inserted between the plates, the charge on the plates remaining constant? (b) With the air dielectric the capacitance of the capacitor was 100 μf. Find the energy in the capacitor for each dielectric. (c) Assume that there is no friction between the dielectric and the plates. How much work would be required to withdraw the dielectric from the plates?

28-15. A parallel-plate capacitor is to be constructed using as a dielectric rubber, having a dielectric coefficient of 3 and a dielectric strength of 2×10^5 volts/cm. The capacitor is to have a capacitance of 0.15 μf and must be able to withstand a maximum potential difference of 6000 volts. What is the minimum area the plates of the capacitor may have?

28-16. A capacitor consists of two parallel plates of area 25 cm^2 separated by a distance of 0.2 cm. The material between the plates has a dielectric coefficient of 5. The plates of the capacitor are connected to a 300-volt battery. (a) What is the capacitance of the capacitor? (b) What is the charge on either plate? (c) What is the energy in the charged capacitor?

28-17. Two oppositely charged conducting plates, having numerically equal quantities of charge per unit area, are separated by a dielectric 5 mm thick, of dielectric coefficient 3. The resultant electric intensity in the dielectric is 10^6 volts/m. Compute: (a) the free charge per unit area on the conducting plates, (b) the induced charge per unit area on the surfaces of the dielectric.

28–18. The paper dielectric, in a paper and foil capacitor, is 0.005 cm thick. Its dielectric coefficient is 2.5 and its dielectric strength is 50×10^6 volts/m. (a) What area of paper, and of tinfoil, is required for a 0.1-μf capacitor? (b) If the electric intensity in the paper is not to exceed one-half the dielectric strength, what is the maximum potential difference that can be applied across the capacitor?

28–19. A spherical capacitor consists of an inner metal sphere of radius r_a supported on an insulating stand at the center of a hollow metal sphere of inner radius r_b. There is a charge $+Q$ on the inner sphere and a charge $-Q$ on the outer. (a) What is the potential difference V_{ab} between the spheres? (b) Prove that the capacitance is

$$C = 4\pi\epsilon_0 \frac{r_b r_a}{r_b - r_a}.$$

28–20. A coaxial cable consists of an inner solid cylindrical conductor of radius r_a supported by insulating disks on the axis of a thin-walled conducting tube of inner radius r_b. The two cylinders are oppositely charged with a charge λ per unit length. The potential difference V_{ab} between the conductors is

$$V_{ab} = \frac{2\lambda}{4\pi\epsilon_0} \ln \frac{r_b}{r_a}.$$

Prove that the capacitance of a length l of the cable is

$$C = l \frac{2\pi\epsilon_0}{\ln(r_b/r_a)}.$$

Neglect any effect of the supporting disks.

28–21. The plates of a parallel-plate capacitor in vacuum have charges $+Q$ and $-Q$ and the distance between the plates is x. The plates are disconnected from the charging voltage and pulled apart a short distance dx. (a) What is the change dC in the capacitance of the capacitor? (b) What is the change dW in its energy? (c) Equate the work $F\,dx$ to the increase in energy dW and find the force of attraction F between the plates. (d) Explain why F is not equal to QE, where E is the electric intensity between the plates.

CHAPTER 29

INDUCTANCE AND TRANSIENT CURRENTS

29-1 Self-inductance. We have shown that an emf is induced in a stationary circuit whenever the magnetic flux linking the circuit is increasing or decreasing. In the preceding examples, the source of the magnetic field has been considered to be independent of the circuit in which the induced emf appears. But whenever there is a current in any circuit, this current sets up a magnetic field which itself links with the circuit and which varies when the current varies. Hence any circuit in which there is a varying current has induced in it an emf, because of the variation in its own magnetic field. Such an emf is called a *self-induced electromotive force*. For example, Fig. 29-1 shows in a schematic way a coil of N turns connected in series with a seat of emf and a rheostat and linked by Φ lines of induction. As the rheostat slider is moved the flux linking the coil varies and thus induces an emf in the circuit.

The number of flux linkages per unit current is called the *self-inductance* of the circuit, L:

$$L = \frac{N\Phi}{i}. \qquad (29\text{--}1)$$

The unit of self-inductance is evidently the *weber-turn per ampere*. For brevity, one weber-turn per ampere is called one *henry*, in honor of Joseph Henry.

The self-inductance of a circuit depends on its size, shape, number of turns, etc. It also depends on the magnetic properties of the material in which a magnetic field exists. For example, the self-inductance of a solenoid

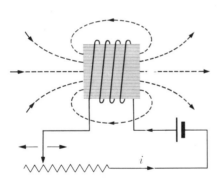

FIG. 29-1. A flux of Φ lines of induction linking a coil of N turns. When the current in the circuit changes, the flux changes also, and a self-induced emf appears in the circuit.

of given dimensions is much greater if it has an iron core than if it is in vacuum. If no *ferro*magnetic materials are present, the self-inductance is a constant, independent of the current, since then the flux density at any point is directly proportional to the current. When ferromagnetic materials are present, the self-inductance varies in a complicated way as the current varies, because of the variations in permeability. For simplicity, we shall consider only circuits of constant self-inductance.

Equation (29–1) can be written as

$$N\Phi = Li.$$

Differentiating both sides with respect to t gives

$$N\frac{d\Phi}{dt} = L\frac{di}{dt},$$

and since the self-induced emf $\mathcal{E}$ is

$$\mathcal{E} = -N\frac{d\Phi}{dt},$$

it follows that

$$\boxed{\mathcal{E} = -L\frac{di}{dt}.} \qquad (29\text{–}2)$$

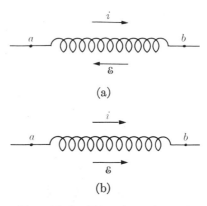

(a)

(b)

Fig. 29–2. Direction of a self-induced emf. (a) i increasing, $\mathcal{E}$ opposite to i, point a at a higher potential than b. (b) i decreasing, $\mathcal{E}$ and i in the same direction, b at higher potential than a. ($R = 0$.)

The self-inductance of a circuit may therefore be regarded also as *the self-induced emf per unit rate of change of current.* When $\mathcal{E}$ is expressed in volts and di/dt in amperes per second, L is in henrys. Hence *the self-inductance of a circuit is one henry if an emf of one volt is induced in the circuit when the current in the circuit changes at the rate of one ampere per second.*

A circuit or part of a circuit which has inductance is called an *inductor.* An inductor is represented by the symbol ⟶〰〰〰〰⟶

The direction of a self-induced emf is found from Lenz's law. The "cause" of the emf is an increasing or decreasing current. If the current is increasing, the direction of the induced emf is opposite to that of the current. If the current is decreasing, the emf and the current are in the same direction. Thus it is the *change* in current, not the current itself, which is "opposed" by the induced emf (see Fig. 29–2).

EXAMPLE 1. Compute the self-inductance of the toroid in Fig. 26–11 if it is wound with 100 turns of wire on a form of mean circumference 20 cm, cross-sectional area 1 cm², and relative permeability $K_m = 1000$ (assumed constant).

Assume an arbitrary current i in the windings. The flux density B in the core is

$$B = \mu H = K_m \mu_0 \frac{Ni}{l}$$

$$= \frac{1000 \times 4\pi \times 10^{-7} \ (\text{w/amp·m}) \times 100 \text{ turns} \times i}{0.20 \text{ m}}$$

$$= 0.63i \ \frac{\text{w}}{\text{amp·m}^2}.$$

The total flux Φ is

$$\Phi = BA = 0.63i\ \frac{\text{w}}{\text{amp·m}^2} \times 10^{-4}\ \text{m}^2 = 6.3 \times 10^{-5}i\ \frac{\text{w}}{\text{amp}}.$$

The number of flux linkages is

$$N\Phi = 100\ \text{turns} \times 6.3 \times 10^{-5}\ i\ \frac{\text{w}}{\text{amp}} = 6.3 \times 10^{-3}i\ \frac{\text{weber-turn}}{\text{amp}}.$$

The self-inductance is

$$L = \frac{N\Phi}{i} = 6.3 \times 10^{-3}\ \frac{\text{weber-turn}}{\text{amp}} = 6.3 \times 10^{-3}\ \text{henry}.$$

EXAMPLE 2. If the current in the coil above increases uniformly from zero to 1 amp in 0.1 sec, find the magnitude and direction of the self-induced emf.

$$\mathcal{E} = -L\,\frac{di}{dt} = -6.3 \times 10^{-3}\ \text{h} \times \frac{1\ \text{amp}}{0.1\ \text{sec}} = -0.063\ \text{volt}.$$

Since the current is increasing, the direction of this emf is opposite to that of the current.

29–2 Energy associated with an inductor. Consider an inductor carrying a current i which is increasing at the rate di/dt. This changing current results in a back emf $L(di/dt)$, so that power P is supplied to the inductor, where

$$P = Li\,\frac{di}{dt}. \tag{29–3}$$

The energy dW supplied in time dt is $P\,dt$, or

$$dW = Li\,di, \tag{29–4}$$

and the total energy supplied while the current increases from zero to I is

$$W = \int dW = L\int_0^I i\,di,$$

or

$$\boxed{W = \tfrac{1}{2}LI^2.} \tag{29–5}$$

After the current has reached its final steady value, $di/dt = 0$, and the power input is zero. The energy that has been supplied to the inductor is used to establish the magnetic field around the inductor, where it is "stored" as a form of potential energy so long as the current is maintained. When the circuit is opened the magnetic field collapses and this energy is returned to the circuit. It is this release of energy that maintains the arc often seen when a switch is opened in an inductive circuit.

Thus the energy stored in an inductor, like that stored in a capacitor, is reversibly convertible. Since the energy stored in an inductor can be reconverted to the energy of an electric current, an inductor is a seat of emf.

29–3 Circuit containing inductance and resistance. An inductor in which there is an increasing current is a seat of emf whose direction is opposite to that of the current. As a consequence of this back emf, the current in an inductive circuit will not rise to its final value at the instant when the circuit is closed, but will grow at a rate which depends on the inductance and resistance of the circuit.

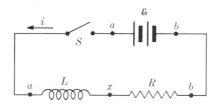

FIG. 29–3.   Series circuit containing resistance and self-inductance (R-L circuit).

Figure 29–3 shows a series circuit consisting of a resistanceless inductor, a noninductive resistor, a battery of emf $\mathcal{E}$ and negligible internal resistance, and a switch S. At some instant after the switch is closed, let i represent the current in the circuit and di/dt its rate of increase. The potential difference across the inductor is

$$\mathcal{E}_{ax} = -L \frac{di}{dt},$$

and we can use the general series circuit relation, Eq. (23–9). When the switch is closed both i and di/dt are counterclockwise in Fig. 29–3 and we have

$$V_{aa} = \Sigma Ri - \Sigma \mathcal{E} = 0 = Ri - \left(\mathcal{E} - L \frac{di}{dt} \right), \qquad (29\text{--}6)$$

or

$$\frac{\mathcal{E}}{R} = \frac{L}{R} \frac{di}{dt} + i, \qquad (29\text{--}7)$$

and

$$\frac{di}{(\mathcal{E}/R) - i} = \frac{R}{L} dt.$$

Since $i = 0$ when $t = 0$, we integrate between limits, as follows:

$$\int_0^i \frac{di}{(\mathcal{E}/R) - i} = \frac{R}{L} \int_0^t dt,$$

and get

$$-\ln \frac{(\mathcal{E}/R) - i}{\mathcal{E}/R} = \frac{Rt}{L}.$$

Hence

$$\frac{\mathcal{E}}{R} - i = \frac{\mathcal{E}}{R} e^{-Rt/L}$$

and, finally,

$$i = \frac{\mathcal{E}}{R} - \frac{\mathcal{E}}{R} e^{-Rt/L}.$$

The first term on the right, $\mathcal{E}/R$, is constant, while the second term depends on the time. At time $t = 0$, the second term equals $\mathcal{E}/R$ and the current i is zero. As time goes on, the second term *decreases* and approaches zero. The current therefore *increases* and approaches the constant value $\mathcal{E}/R$ given by the first term. The second term is called a *transient* current and the first term the *steady-state* current. The steady-state current does not depend on the self-inductance and is the same as it would be in a pure resistance R connected to a cell of emf $\mathcal{E}$. If I represents the steady-state current $\mathcal{E}/R$, the previous equation may be written as

$$i = I(1 - e^{-Rt/L}). \tag{29-8}$$

Figure 29–4(a) is a graph of Eq. (29–8). The instantaneous current i first rises rapidly, then increases more slowly and approaches asymptotically the final value $I = \mathcal{E}/R$. The *time constant* of the circuit is defined as the time at which $Rt/L = 1$, or when

$$t = \frac{L}{R}.$$

If L is expressed in henrys [1 henry = 1 volt/(amp/sec)] and R is in ohms (1 ohm = 1 volt/amp), the time constant is in seconds. When $t = L/R$,

$$i = I \ (1 - e^{-1}) = I \ [1 - (1/2.718)] = I \ [1 - 0.369] = 0.631 \ I,$$

or about 63% of I.

For a circuit with a given resistance, this time is longer the larger the inductance, and vice versa. Thus although the graph of i vs. t has the same general shape whatever the inductance, the current rises rapidly to

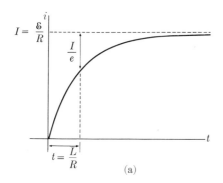
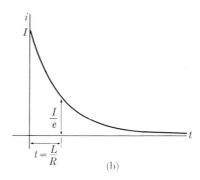

FIG. 29–4. (a) Growth of a current in a circuit containing inductance and resistance. (b) Decay of current in a circuit containing inductance and resistance.

its final value if L is small, and slowly if L is large. For example, if $R = 100$ ohms and $L = 10$ henrys,

$$\frac{L}{R} = \frac{10\text{ h}}{100\text{ ohms}} = 0.1\text{ sec},$$

and the current increases to about 63% of its final value in 0.1 sec. On the other hand, if $L = 0.01$ henry,

$$\frac{L}{R} = \frac{0.01\text{ h}}{100\text{ ohms}} = 10^{-4}\text{ sec},$$

and only 10^{-4} sec is required for the current to increase to 63% of its final value.

If there is a steady current I in the circuit of Fig. 29–3 and the battery is short-circuited, the decay of the current depicted in Fig. 29–4(b) follows a curve which is the exact inverse of Fig. 29–4(a). The equation of the decaying current is

$$i = Ie^{-Rt/L}, \tag{29–9}$$

and the time constant, L/R, is the time for the current to decrease to $1/e$th of its original value.

———

EXAMPLE. An inductor of inductance 3 henrys and resistance 6 ohms is connected to the terminals of a battery of emf 12 volts and of negligible internal resistance. (a) Find the initial rate of increase of current in the circuit. (b) Find the rate of increase of current at the instant when the current is one ampere. (c) What is the instantaneous current 0.2 sec after the circuit is closed? (d) What is the final steady-state current?

(a) From Eq. (29–7),

$$\frac{di}{dt} = \frac{\mathcal{E}}{L} - \frac{R}{L}\,i.$$

The initial current is zero. Hence the initial rate of increase of current is

$$\frac{di}{dt} = \frac{\mathcal{E}}{L} = \frac{12 \text{ volts}}{3 \text{ h}} = 4\,\frac{\text{amp}}{\text{sec}}.$$

(b) When $i = 1$ amp,

$$\frac{di}{dt} = \frac{12 \text{ volts}}{3 \text{ h}} - \frac{6 \text{ ohms}}{3 \text{ h}} \times 1 \text{ amp} = 2\,\frac{\text{amp}}{\text{sec}}.$$

(c) From Eq. (29–8),

$$i = \frac{\mathcal{E}}{R}\,(1 - e^{-Rt/L}) = \frac{12 \text{ volts}}{6 \text{ ohms}}\,(1 - e^{-6 \times 0.2/3}) = 2 \text{ amp}\,(1 - e^{-0.4})$$

$$= 2 \text{ amp}\,(1 - 0.672) = 0.65 \text{ amp}.$$

(d) The final steady-state current is

$$I = \frac{\mathcal{E}}{R} = \frac{12 \text{ volts}}{6 \text{ ohms}} = 2 \text{ amp}.$$

29–4 Circuit containing capacitance and resistance. When the switch S in Fig. 29–5 is closed, the charge on the capacitor does not increase instantaneously to its final value, but approaches this value in the same way as does the current in a circuit containing inductance and resistance.

Let q represent the charge on the capacitor at a certain instant after the switch S is closed, and i the current in the circuit at that instant. The instantaneous emf of the capacitor is $\mathcal{E}_{ax} = -q/C$, and we may use the general series circuit equation to obtain

$$V_{aa} = \Sigma Ri - \Sigma \mathcal{E} = 0 = Ri - \left(\mathcal{E} - \frac{q}{C}\right). \qquad (29\text{--}10)$$

Since $i = dq/dt$, we obtain

$$\mathcal{E} = \frac{q}{C} + R\,\frac{dq}{dt},$$

or

$$C\mathcal{E} = RC\,\frac{dq}{dt} + q.$$

This equation has exactly the same form as Eq. (29–7) and therefore has the same solution, namely,

$$q = C\mathcal{E} - C\mathcal{E}e^{-t/RC}, \qquad (29\text{--}11)$$

where the solution has steady-state and transient parts, as before.

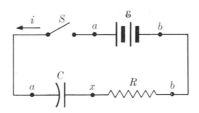

FIG. 29–5. Series circuit containing capacitance and resistance (*R-C* circuit).

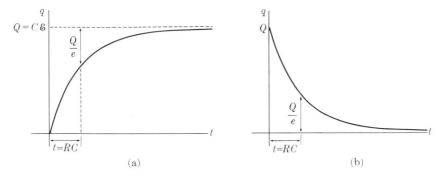

FIG. 29–6. Charge and discharge of a capacitor through a resistor.

After a sufficiently long time has elapsed, the term $e^{-t/RC}$ becomes negligibly small and the charge q approaches the value $Q = C\mathcal{E}$. Hence we can also write

$$q = Q(1 - e^{-t/RC}). \qquad (29\text{–}12)$$

Figure 29–6(a) is a graph of this equation. The charge approaches its final value asymptotically and an infinite time is required for the capacitor to become fully charged. The time constant of the circuit is equal to RC. For example, if $R = 1$ megohm $= 10^6$ ohms and $C = 1\,\mu f = 10^{-6}$ farad, the time constant is 1 sec and the charge on the capacitor increases to 63% of its final value in 1 sec.

If the capacitor is originally charged and is then discharged through a resistance R, the charge decreases with time according to the relation

$$q = Qe^{-t/RC}, \qquad (29\text{–}13)$$

as shown in Fig. 29–6(b). The time constant RC is the time for the charge to decrease to $1/e$th of its original value.

The curves in Fig. 29–6 also show the way in which the potential difference across the capacitor changes, since the potential difference is proportional to the charge.

29–5 Electrical oscillations. When the discharge of a capacitor through a resistor was discussed in Section 29–4, the effect of inductance in the circuit was ignored. We now consider how the discharge is affected by inductance, taking up first a circuit in which the resistance is negligible.

Figure 29–7(a) represents schematically a charged capacitor, a switch, and an inductor of negligible resistance. At the instant when the circuit is closed, the capacitor starts to discharge through the inductor. At a later instant, represented in Fig. 29–7(b), the capacitor has completely discharged and the potential difference between its terminals (and those of the inductor) has decreased to zero. The current in the inductor has meanwhile established a magnetic field in the space around it. This magnetic field now decreases, inducing an emf in the inductor in the same direction as the current. The current therefore persists, although with diminishing magnitude, until the magnetic field has disappeared and the capacitor has been charged in the opposite sense to its initial polarity, as in Fig. 29–7(c). The process now repeats itself in the reversed direction, and in the absence of energy losses the charges on the capacitor will surge back and forth indefinitely. This process is called an *electrical oscillation.*

The frequency of the electrical oscillations of a circuit containing inductance and capacitance only (a so-called *L-C* circuit) may be calculated in exactly the same way as the frequency of oscillation of a body suspended from a spring. (See Chapter 11.)

In the mechanical problem, a body of mass m is attached to a spring of force constant k. Because the system is conservative, the sum of the kinetic and elastic potential energies is constant and is equal to the elastic potential energy when the body has its maximum displacement A. The steps in the derivation of the equation of motion are given in the left

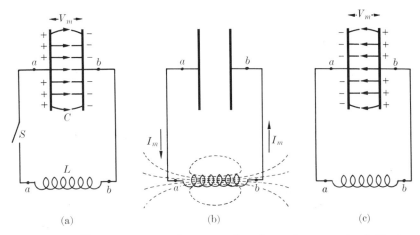

(a)   (b)   (c)

FIG. 29–7. Energy transfer between electric and magnetic fields in an oscillating circuit (*L-C* circuit).

TABLE 29–1

OSCILLATION OF A MASS ON A SPRING COMPARED WITH THE
ELECTRICAL OSCILLATION IN AN L-C CIRCUIT

Mass on a spring	Circuit containing inductance and capacitance
$\dfrac{1}{2}mv^2 + \dfrac{1}{2}kx^2 = \dfrac{1}{2}kA^2$	$\dfrac{1}{2}Li^2 + \dfrac{1}{2}\dfrac{q^2}{C} = \dfrac{1}{2}\dfrac{Q^2}{C}$
$v = \sqrt{\dfrac{k}{m}}\sqrt{A^2 - x^2}$	$i = \sqrt{\dfrac{1}{LC}}\sqrt{Q^2 - q^2}$
$v = \dfrac{dx}{dt}$	$i = \dfrac{dq}{dt}$
$\displaystyle\int \dfrac{dx}{\sqrt{A^2 - x^2}} = \sqrt{\dfrac{k}{m}}\int dt$	$\displaystyle\int \dfrac{dq}{\sqrt{Q^2 - q^2}} = \sqrt{\dfrac{1}{LC}}\int dt$
$\sin^{-1}\dfrac{x}{A} = \sqrt{\dfrac{k}{m}}\,t$	$\sin^{-1}\dfrac{q}{Q} = \sqrt{\dfrac{1}{LC}}\,t$
$x = A\sin\sqrt{\dfrac{k}{m}}\,t$	$q = Q\sin\sqrt{\dfrac{1}{LC}}\,t$
$\omega = 2\pi f = \sqrt{\dfrac{k}{m}}$	$\omega = 2\pi f = \sqrt{\dfrac{1}{LC}}$
$x = A\sin\omega t$	$q = Q\sin\omega t$

column of Table 29–1. The motion is simple harmonic, with an angular frequency ω given by

$$\omega = \sqrt{\dfrac{k}{m}}.$$

The electrical circuit in Fig. 29–7 is also a conservative system, provided the resistance of the circuit is zero. The sum of the energy associated with the magnetic field of the inductor, $\frac{1}{2}Li^2$, and the energy associated with the electric field of the capacitor, $\frac{1}{2}(q^2/C)$, is constant and equal to the energy of the capacitor when it has its maximum charge Q. The way in which the charge on the capacitor varies with time is given in the right column of Table 29–1. The angular frequency of the electrical oscillations is

$$\omega = \sqrt{\dfrac{1}{LC}}. \qquad (29\text{–}14)$$

This is called the *natural frequency* of the L-C circuit.

The parallelism between the mechanical and electrical systems displayed in Table 29–1 is only one of many such examples in physics. So close is the parallelism between electrical and mechanical (and acoustical) systems that it has been found possible to solve complicated mechanical and acoustical problems by setting up analogous electrical circuits and measuring the currents and voltages which correspond to the desired mechanical and acoustical "unknowns."

The effect of resistance in an oscillatory circuit is to drain away the energy of the circuit and convert it to heat. Resistance, in other words, plays the same role in an electrical circuit as friction does in a mechanical system. Oscillations may be sustained in a circuit if some provision is made for returning energy at the same rate as it is removed. The most common method of doing this at present is to utilize the amplifying properties of a thermionic tube.

PROBLEMS

29–1. (a) Show that the two expressions for self-inductance, namely,

$$\frac{N\Phi}{i} \quad \text{and} \quad \frac{\mathcal{E}}{di/dt},$$

have the same units. (b) Show that L/R and RC both have the units of time.

FIGURE 29–8

29–2. Two capacitors are charged in series by a 12-volt battery (Fig. 29–8). (a) What is the time constant of the charging circuit? (b) After being closed for the length of time determined in (a) the switch S is opened. What is the voltage across the 6-μf capacitor?

29–3. A coil has a resistance of 25 ohms and a time constant of 0.075 sec. What is its inductance?

29–4. The resistance of a 10-henry inductor is 200 ohms. The inductor is suddenly connected across a potential difference of 10 volts. (a) What is the final steady current in the inductor? (b) What is the initial rate of increase of current? (c) At what rate is the current increasing when its value is one-half the final current? (d) At what time after the circuit is closed does the current equal 99% of its final value? (e) Compute the current at the following times after the circuit is closed: 0, 0.025 sec, 0.05 sec, 0.075 sec, 0.10 sec. Show the results in a graph.

29–5. An inductor of resistance R and self-inductance L is connected in series with a noninductive resistor of resistance R_0 to a constant potential difference $\mathcal{E}$ (Fig. 29–9). (a) Find the expression for the potential difference V_{cb} across the inductor at any time t after switch S_1 is closed. (b) Let $\mathcal{E} = 20$ volts, $R_0 = 50$ ohms, $R = 150$ ohms, $L = 5$ henrys. Compute a few points, and construct graphs of V_{ac} and V_{cb} over a time interval from zero to twice the time constant of the circuit.

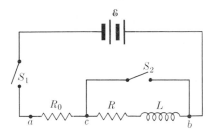

FIGURE 29–9

29–6. After the current in the circuit of Fig. 29–9 has reached its final steady value the switch S_2 is closed, thus short-circuiting the inductor. What will be the magnitude and direction of the current in S_2, 0.01 sec after S_2 is closed?

29–7. Refer to the inductor in the example at the end of Section 29–3. (a) What is the power input to the inductor at the instant when the current in it is 0.5 amp? (b) What is the rate of development of heat at this instant? (c) What is the rate at which the energy of the magnetic field is increasing? (d) How much energy is stored in the magnetic field when the current has reached its final steady value?

29–8. A 10-μf capacitor is connected through a 1-megohm resistor to a constant potential difference of 100 volts. (a) Compute the charge on the capacitor at the following times after the connections are made: 0, 5 sec, 10 sec, 20 sec, 100 sec. (b) Compute the charging current at the same instants. (c) How long a time would be required for the capacitor to acquire its final charge if the charging current remained constant at its initial value? Compare with the time constant of the circuit. (d) Find the time required for the charge to increase from zero to 5×10^{-4} coul. (e) Construct graphs of the results of parts (a) and (b) for a time interval of 20 sec.

29–9. A capacitor of capacitance C is charged by connecting it through a resistance R to the terminals of a battery of emf $\mathcal{E}$ and of negligible internal resistance. (a) How much energy is supplied by the battery in the charging process? (b) What fraction of this energy appears as heat in the resistor?

29–10. The maximum capacitance of a variable air capacitor is 35 $\mu\mu$f. (a) What should be the self-inductance of a coil to be connected to this capacitor if the natural frequency of the L-C circuit is to be 550×10^3 cycles/sec, corresponding to one end of the broadcast band? (b) The frequency at the other end of the broadcast band is 1550×10^3 cycles/sec. What must be the minimum capacitance of the capacitor if the natural frequency is to be adjustable over the range of the broadcast band?

CHAPTER 30

ALTERNATING CURRENTS AND ELECTROMAGNETIC WAVES

30–1 The alternating-current series circuit. A coil of wire, rotating with constant angular velocity in a uniform magnetic field, develops a sinusoidal alternating emf as explained in Section 27–5. This simple device is the prototype of the commercial alternating-current generator, or alternator, the field and armature structure of which are illustrated in Fig. 30–1. A number of pairs of poles are spaced around the inner circumference of the *stator*. As each conductor on the surface of the armature or *rotor* sweeps across the magnetic field, a motional emf is induced in it, in one direction as the conductor passes a north pole and in the opposite direction as it passes a south pole. The induced emf is therefore alternating, the number of complete cycles in each revolution equaling the number of *pairs* of poles. This multipole structure enables a sufficiently high frequency to be attained without an unduly high angular velocity of the rotor.

The induced emf of a commercial alternator may differ slightly from a purely sinusoidal form but we shall assume in this chapter that we have to do with an alternator which maintains between its terminals a sinusoidal potential difference given by

$$v = V_m \sin 2\pi f t = V_m \sin \omega t, \qquad (30\text{–}1)$$

where v is the instantaneous potential difference, V_m the maximum potential difference, and f is the frequency, equal to the number of revolu-

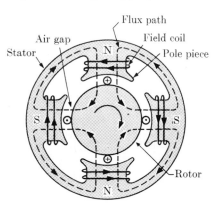

FIG. 30–1. Schematic diagram of a four-pole commercial alternating-current generator.

591

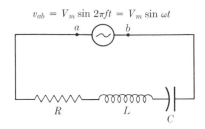

$$v_{ab} = V_m \sin 2\pi f t = V_m \sin \omega t$$

FIG. 30–2. Series circuit of a resistor, an inductor, and a capacitor.

tions per second of the rotor multiplied by the number of pairs of poles. For many of the a-c generators in this country, $f = 60$ cycles/sec and $\omega = 2\pi f \approx 377$ rad/sec.

We now proceed to investigate the current in a circuit when a sinusoidal alternating potential difference is maintained across its terminals. Let a series circuit composed of a resistor, an inductor, and a capacitor be connected to the terminals of an alternator as in Fig. 30–2. The instantaneous potential difference between a and b may be computed from the general equation for potential difference, Eq. (23–9). We have

$$V_m \sin \omega t = Ri - \left(-L \frac{di}{dt} - \frac{q}{C} \right) = Ri + L \frac{di}{dt} + \frac{q}{C},$$

where i, di/dt, and q are respectively instantaneous current, its rate of change, and the charge on the capacitor. Differentiating this equation with respect to t, and replacing dq/dt by i, we find

$$\omega V_m \cos \omega t = R \frac{di}{dt} + L \frac{d^2 i}{dt^2} + \frac{1}{C} i.$$

This is a differential equation of the second order.

The solution consists of the sum of a *steady-state* current and a *transient* current. The transient current dies out exponentially, like the charging current of a capacitor, and while in practice transient currents and potential differences may be of importance, we shall consider only the steady-state solution, which is

$$i = \frac{V_m}{\sqrt{R^2 + [\omega L - (1/\omega C)]^2}} \sin (\omega t - \phi),$$

where

$$\phi = \tan^{-1} \frac{\omega L - (1/\omega C)}{R}.$$

The solution can be verified by calculating di/dt and $d^2 i/dt^2$ and substituting in the differential equation.

The steady-state current, like the terminal voltage, is seen to vary sinusoidally with the time. Its maximum value is

$$I_m = \frac{V_m}{\sqrt{R^2 + [\omega L - (1/\omega C)]^2}}.$$

The steady-state current may hence be written

$$i = I_m \sin (\omega t - \phi). \tag{30-2}$$

The frequency of the current is the same as that of the voltage, but the two differ in phase, or are out of phase, by the angle ϕ.

Let us introduce the following abbreviations:

$$\omega L = X_L, \qquad \frac{1}{\omega C} = X_C,$$

$$\omega L - \frac{1}{\omega C} = X_L - X_C = X,$$

$$\sqrt{R^2 + X^2} = Z.$$

Then

$$I_m = \frac{V_m}{\sqrt{R^2 + (X_L - X_C)^2}} = \frac{V_m}{\sqrt{R^2 + X^2}} = \frac{V_m}{Z}, \tag{30-3}$$

$$\phi = \tan^{-1} \frac{X}{R}. \tag{30-4}$$

The quantity Z is called the *impedance* of the circuit; X, the *reactance;* and X_L and X_C, the *inductive reactance* and *capacitive reactance* respectively. Impedances and reactances are expressed in ohms. The general term for a device possessing reactance is a *reactor*.

The maximum current is seen to be related to the maximum potential difference by an equation having the same form as Ohm's law for steady currents, impedance Z corresponding to resistance R.

———————

EXAMPLE. A 1000-ohm resistor is in series with an 0.5-henry inductor and an 0.2-μf capacitor. Compute the impedance of the circuit (a) at an angular frequency $\omega = 2\pi f = 2000$ rad/sec, (b) at an angular frequency $\omega = 5000$ rad/sec.

(a) When $\omega = 2000$ rad/sec,

$$X_L = \omega L = 2000 \frac{\text{rad}}{\text{sec}} \times 0.5 \frac{\text{volt}}{\text{amp/sec}} = 1000 \text{ ohms,}$$

$$X_C = \frac{1}{\omega C} = \frac{1}{2000 \text{ rad/sec} \times 0.2 \times 10^{-6} \text{ coul/volt}} = 2500 \text{ ohms,}$$

$$X = X_L - X_C = 1000 \text{ ohms} - 2500 \text{ ohms} = -1500 \text{ ohms},$$

$$Z = \sqrt{R^2 + X^2} = \sqrt{(1000 \text{ ohms})^2 + (-1500 \text{ ohms})^2} = 1800 \text{ ohms}.$$

(b) When $\omega = 5000$ rad/sec,

$$X_L = \omega L = 5000 \frac{\text{rad}}{\text{sec}} \times 0.5 \frac{\text{volt}}{\text{amp/sec}} = 2500 \text{ ohms},$$

$$X_C = \frac{1}{\omega C} = \frac{1}{5000 \text{ rad/sec} \times 0.2 \times 10^{-6} \text{ coul/volt}} = 1000 \text{ ohms},$$

$$X = X_L - X_C = 2500 \text{ ohms} - 1000 \text{ ohms} = 1500 \text{ ohms},$$

$$Z = \sqrt{R^2 + X^2} = \sqrt{(1000 \text{ ohms})^2 + (1500 \text{ ohms})^2} = 1800 \text{ ohms}.$$

30–2 Effective values. The instantaneous value of an alternating current, emf, or potential difference varies continuously from a maximum in one direction through zero to a maximum in the opposite direction, and so on. The behavior of a simple series circuit as given by Eq. (30–3) is expressed in terms of maximum values I_m and V_m. It is found more convenient to describe alternating currents and voltages by their effective values than by their maximum values. The effective value of a varying current is defined as that steady current which would develop the same quantity of heat in the same time in the same resistance.

The rate of development of heat in a resistance R, carrying a sinusoidal alternating current $i = I_m \sin \omega t$, is

$$i^2 R = I_m^2 R \sin^2 \omega t.$$

The total heat developed in a time T equal to one period is

$$H = \int_0^T i^2 R \, dt = I_m^2 R \int_0^T \sin^2 \omega t \, dt, = \tfrac{1}{2} I_m^2 R T.$$

The heat developed by a constant current I_{eff} in the same time is

$$H = I_{\text{eff}}^2 R T.$$

Since by definition of I_{eff} the quantities of heat are equal,

$$I_{\text{eff}}^2 R T = \tfrac{1}{2} I_m^2 R T,$$

$$I_{\text{eff}} = \frac{I_m}{\sqrt{2}}.$$

Hence, *if a current varies sinusoidally*, its effective value is $1/\sqrt{2} = 0.707$ times its maximum value. Similarly, the effective value of a sinusoidally varying voltage is $1/\sqrt{2}$ times its maximum value. For example, when it is stated that the alternating potential difference between the supply mains of a household power line is 110 volts, this means that the effective potential difference is 110 volts, and hence the maximum potential difference is $110 \times \sqrt{2} = 155$ volts.

When the first and last terms of Eq. (30–3) are divided by $\sqrt{2}$, we obtain

$$\frac{I_m}{\sqrt{2}} = \frac{V_m/\sqrt{2}}{Z},$$

or

$$I_{\text{eff}} = \frac{V_{\text{eff}}}{Z}. \tag{30–5}$$

It will be understood from now on that the letters I, $\mathcal{E}$, or V, without subscripts, refer to the effective values of the corresponding quantities. Equation (30–5) will therefore be written

$$I = \frac{V}{Z}.$$

30–3 Resonance. The impedance of an a-c series L–R–C circuit depends on the frequency, since the inductive reactance is directly, and the capacitive reactance is inversely, proportional to the frequency. Note that there is one particular frequency at which X_L and X_C are numerically equal. At this frequency, $X = X_L - X_C$ is zero. Hence the impedance Z, equal to $\sqrt{R^2 + X^2}$, is a minimum at this frequency, and is equal to the resistance R.

If the circuit is connected to a generator of constant effective terminal voltage but of variable frequency, the effective current will be a maximum at the frequency for which the impedance is a minimum. This frequency is called the *resonant frequency* of the circuit. The resonant frequency ω_0 is easily computed, since at this frequency $X_L = X_C$. Hence

$$\omega_0 L = \frac{1}{\omega_0 C},$$

$$\omega_0 = 2\pi f_0 = \sqrt{\frac{1}{LC}}. \tag{30–6}$$

Note that this is equal to the natural frequency of oscillation of an L–C circuit, as discussed in Section 29–5.

If the self-inductance L or the capacitance C of a circuit can be varied, the resonant frequency can be varied also. This is the procedure by which a radio receiving set may be "tuned" to the desired station.

30–4 The transformer. For reasons of efficiency it is desirable to transmit electrical power at high voltages and small currents, with consequent reduction of I^2R heating in the transmission line. On the other hand, considerations of safety and of insulation of moving parts require relatively low voltages in generating equipment and in motors and household appliances. One of the most useful features of a-c circuits is the ease and efficiency with which voltages (and currents) may be changed from one value to another by means of transformers.

In principle, the transformer consists of two coils electrically insulated from each other and wound on the same iron core (Fig. 30–3). An alternating current in one winding sets up an alternating magnetic flux in the core. Most of this flux links with the other winding and induces in it an alternating emf. Power is thus transferred from one winding to the other via the flux in the core. The winding to which power is supplied is called the *primary,* that from which power is delivered is called the *secondary.* Either winding may be used as the primary. The symbol for an iron-core transformer is ⊒‖⫤

In any actual transformer the flux lines are not confined entirely to the iron but some of them return through the air, as indicated in Fig. 30–3. That part of the flux which links both the primary and secondary windings is called the *mutual* flux. The part linking the primary only is the *primary leakage flux* and the part linking the secondary only is the *secondary leakage flux.*

The power output of a transformer is necessarily less than the power input because of unavoidable losses in the form of heat. These losses consist of I^2R heating in the primary and secondary windings (the copper losses) and hysteresis and eddy current heating in the core (the core losses). Hysteresis is minimized by the use of iron having a narrow hysteresis loop, and eddy currents are minimized by laminating the core.

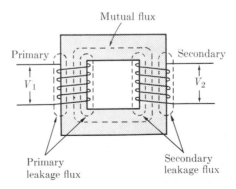

Fig. 30–3. An iron-core transformer.

In spite of these losses, transformer efficiencies are usually well over 90% and in large installations may reach 99%.

For simplicity, we shall consider an idealized transformer in which there are no losses and no leakage flux. Let the secondary circuit be open. The primary winding then functions merely as an inductor. The primary current is out of phase with the primary voltage by 90° ($\phi = \pi/2$) and therefore the average power taken over any integral number of cycles is zero. The core flux is in phase with the primary current. Since the same flux links both primary and secondary, the induced emf *per turn* is the same in each. The ratio of primary to secondary induced emf is therefore equal to the ratio of primary to secondary turns, or

$$\frac{\mathcal{E}_2}{\mathcal{E}_1} = \frac{N_2}{N_1}.$$

In the idealized case assumed, the induced emf's $\mathcal{E}_1$ and $\mathcal{E}_2$ are numerically equal to the corresponding terminal voltages V_1 and V_2. Hence by properly choosing the turn ratio N_2/N_1, any desired secondary voltage may be obtained from a given primary voltage. If $V_2 > V_1$, we have a *step-up* transformer; if $V_2 < V_1$, a *step-down* transformer.

Consider next the effect of closing the secondary circuit. The secondary current I_2 and its phase angle ϕ_2 will, of course, depend on the nature of the secondary circuit. As soon as the secondary circuit is closed, some power must be delivered by the secondary (except when $\phi_2 = 90°$) and from energy considerations an equal amount of power must be supplied to the primary. The process by which the transformer is enabled to draw the requisite amount of power is as follows. When the secondary circuit is open, the core flux is produced by the primary current only. But when the secondary circuit is closed, both primary and secondary currents set up a flux in the core. The secondary current, by Lenz's law, tends to weaken the core flux and therefore to decrease the back emf in the primary. But (in the absence of losses) the back emf in the primary must equal the primary terminal voltage, which is assumed to be fixed. The primary current therefore increases until the core flux is restored to its original no-load magnitude.

30–5 Electromagnetic waves. We conclude our discussion of electricity with a brief account of one of the most elegant pieces of work in all theoretical physics. Electricity and magnetism were once considered separate subjects. Our discussion has shown, however, that these two fields are strongly interdependent. We have seen that moving charges produce magnetic fields and that changing magnetic fields produce electric fields. In 1864 James Clerk Maxwell succeeded in putting the laws of electricity and magnetism into general mathematical form. He found that taken together these laws led to differential equations of wave motion. Maxwell was able to compute the velocity of these waves in terms of characteristics of the transmitting medium, much as we did for mechanical waves in Chapter 12. He found this velocity to be $1/\sqrt{\mu\epsilon}$, which for free space becomes $1/\sqrt{\mu_0\epsilon_0}$ and which has the value 3×10^8 m/sec. *This is the free space velocity of light!* Thus, in expressing the laws of electromagnetism in rigorous mathematical form, Maxwell discovered the intimate relation between electromagnetism and light.

Maxwell's theory was verified in 1888 when Hertz demonstrated that oscillating currents in an electric circuit can radiate energy through space to another similar circuit. Hertz used a circuit containing inductance and capacitance, hence capable of oscillating. Whenever a spark jumped across a gap in the active (transmitting) circuit, electromagnetic waves were radiated from the region in which the electric discharge occurred. (Modifications of this first transmitter were used for radio communication until the advent of vacuum tubes.) The passive or receiving circuit was a resonant circuit containing a gap. When energy was transferred from one circuit to the other, sparks jumped across the receiver gap. Hertz's experiments showed that the radiation generated by electric circuits obeyed the known laws of optics.

30–6 Electrodynamics. It is unfortunate that we do not have time to develop here the methods of Maxwell's electrodynamics. We can, however, develop qualitatively the idea that the ultimate source of radiation is an accelerated electric charge.

Every electric charge produces an electric field whose lines of force extend radially from the charge through all space. When this charge is in motion, a magnetic field is produced in accordance with Biot's law, and the magnetic field lines are circles concentric with the current. According to the viewpoint of Maxwell's field theory, it is the motion of the electric lines of force that sets up the magnetic field transverse to them. A steady electric current is accompanied by steady electric and magnetic

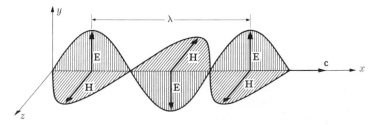

FIG. 30–4. A plane polarized electromagnetic wave of wavelength λ showing the relation of the vectors **E**, **H**, and **c**.

fields; however, a varying current (i.e., one composed of accelerated charges) will produce changes in both the fields associated with it. These changes are propagated outward from the accelerated charges through space with the speed of light. The acceleration of a charge produces a pulse of electromagnetic radiation which consists of an electric field component and a magnetic field component that are perpendicular to each other and to their direction of propagation. If the charge oscillates with a simple periodic motion, an electromagnetic wave like that in Fig. 30–4 will be produced.

The energy transmitted by the electromagnetic waves in a radiation field may be specified either in terms of the intensity or of the energy density of the wave motion. The *intensity* of the radiation is defined as the energy transmitted per unit time and per unit area, across an area normal to the direction of propagation of the waves. The mks unit of intensity is 1 watt per square meter. The *energy density* or volume density of the radiation is defined as the amount of radiant energy per unit volume of space. The mks unit of energy density is 1 joule per cubic meter. It is evident that the energy density is equal to the intensity divided by the velocity of propagation of the wave. The term energy density is particularly useful in discussing the radiation within an enclosure.

Our discussion has implied a linear acceleration but, according to Maxwell's theory, radiation occurs whenever an electric charge is accelerated in any manner. For example, a charge moving with constant speed in a circular path will be a source of radiation. This case is equivalent to two mutually perpendicular simple periodic motions with equal amplitudes and frequencies, but with a phase difference of 90°.

Every radio transmission is a refined repetition of Hertz's original experiments verifying Maxwell's proposition. Instead of involving the physical motion of charged bodies, however, a radio transmitter causes electrons to move back and forth in an antenna which is physically at rest. These accelerated electrons produce radiation. The electric field in this radiation will exert force on any charges it encounters. Thus the electrons in a receiving antenna respond to the radiation by being accelerated, and their motion constitutes an electric current. A modern radio receiver amplifies these currents and makes them easy to observe. Hertz had no amplifiers, so the voltage induced in the receiver had to be large enough to cause visible sparks.

30–7 The unity of radiation. The many forms of radiation—heat, light, radar, radio, etc.—differ from one another in frequency but not in kind. The so-called "kinds" of radiation are characterized by the techniques used to produce and detect them; actually, they all travel through free

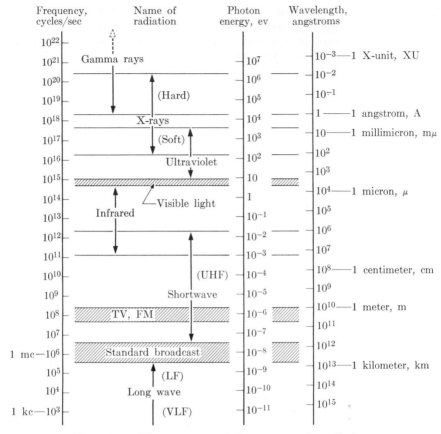

FIG. 30–5. The spectrum of electromagnetic radiation.

space with the same velocity and should all be understood in terms of the same theory. The tremendous range of the electromagnetic spectrum is shown in Fig. 30–5 (photon energy, mentioned in the figure, will be discussed in Section 37–9). The classical theory of Maxwell applies to all these radiations and all are due ultimately to the acceleration of electrical charges. Except for differences due to frequency, an observation made on one "kind" of radiation must also be true of all other kinds.

PROBLEMS

30–1. (a) At what frequency would a 5-henry inductor have a reactance of 4000 ohms? (b) At what frequency would a 5-μf capacitor have the same reactance?

30–2. What is the reactance of an 0.015-μf capacitor at (a) 1 cycle/sec? (b) 5 kilocycles/sec? (c) 2 megacycles/sec?

30–3. (a) What is the reactance of a 1-henry inductor at a frequency of 60 cycles/sec? (b) What is the inductance of an inductor whose reactance is 1 ohm at 60 cycles/sec? (c) What is the reactance of a 1-μf capacitor at a frequency of 60 cycles/sec? (d) What is the capacitance of a capacitor whose reactance is 1 ohm at 60 cycles/sec?

30–4. (a) Compute the reactance of a 10-henry inductor at frequencies of 60 cycles/sec and 600 cycles/sec. (b) Compute the reactance of a 10-μf capacitor at the same frequencies. (c) At what frequency is the reactance of a 10-henry inductor equal to that of a 10-μf capacitor?

30–5. A series circuit consists of a 25-ohm resistor, a 10-μf capacitor, and an inductor having a resistance of 12 ohms and inductance 0.1 henry. Determine for frequencies of 100 cycles/sec and 1000 cycles/sec (a) the impedance of the circuit, (b) the impedance of the inductor.

30–6. A capacitor has a reactance of 40 ohms at 60 cycles/sec. What percentage change in frequency will cause an increase of 20% in the reactance?

30–7. A tone control circuit consists of a 100-ohm resistor in series with a capacitor. The circuit is designed to have twice the impedance at 100 cycles/sec that it has at 300 cycles/sec. What size capacitor is required?

30–8. A length of wire bent in the form of a narrow U carries a current whose frequency is 60 cycles/sec. What is the frequency of vibration of the sides of the U? What is the cause of the vibration of loose laminations in the core of a transformer?

30–9. A $6\frac{2}{3}$-μf capacitor is connected in series with a coil to an a-c supply of 1.2 volts and of controllable frequency. By adjusting the frequency it is observed that the current reaches its largest effective value of 0.2 amp when the angular frequency $\omega = 2\pi f$ is 50,000 rad/sec. (a) Find the resistance and inductance of the coil. (b) What is the current when $\omega = 150,000$ rad/sec?

30–10. The capacitance C in an L-C circuit is 300 $\mu\mu$f. What should be the inductance L if the resonant frequency of the circuit is 1 megacycle/sec (10^6 cycles/sec)?

30–11. An inductor having a reactance of 25 ohms gives off heat at the rate of 2.39 cal/sec when it carries a current of 0.5 amp. What is the impedance of the inductor?

30–12. The efficiency of a transformer is 92%. When 150 volts are impressed across the primary winding it carries a current of 2 amp. What is the voltage across the secondary winding when 0.1 amp is drawn from it?

30–13. The range of wavelengths allocated to the "broadcast band" is from about 190 m to 556 m. A given station operates within a channel 10 kilocycles wide. What is the maximum number of stations that may operate in this band if no overlapping of wavelengths is to take place?

30–14. What is the frequency of electromagnetic waves (in free space) of the following wavelengths: 10^{-8} cm (x-rays); 5×10^{-5} cm (yellow light); 10 cm (microwaves); 300 m (broadcast band)?

CHAPTER 31

THE NATURE AND PROPAGATION OF LIGHT

31-1 The nature of light. Until about the middle of the 17th century, it was generally believed that light consisted of a stream of corpuscles. These corpuscles were emitted by light sources, such as the sun or a candle flame, and traveled outward from the source in straight lines. They could penetrate transparent materials and were reflected from the surfaces of opaque materials. When the corpuscles entered the eye, the sense of sight was stimulated.

By the middle of the 17th century, while most workers in the field of optics accepted the corpuscular theory, the idea had begun to develop that light might be a wave motion of some sort. Christian Huygens, in 1678, showed that the laws of reflection and refraction could be explained on the basis of a wave theory and that such a theory furnished a simple explanation of the recently discovered phenomenon of double refraction. The wave theory failed of immediate acceptance, however. For one thing, it was objected that if light were a wave motion one should be able to see around corners, since waves can bend around obstacles in their path. We know now that the wavelengths of light waves are so short that the bending, while it does actually take place, is so small that it is not ordinarily observed. As a matter of fact, the bending of a light wave around the edges of an object, a phenomenon known as diffraction, was noted by Grimaldi as early as 1665, but the significance of his observations was not realized at the time.

In the first quarter of the 19th century the experiments of Thomas Young and Augustin Fresnel, on interference, and the measurements of the velocity of light in liquids by Leon Foucault at a somewhat later date, conclusively demonstrated the existence of optical phenomena for whose explanation a corpuscular theory was inadequate. The phenomena of interference and diffraction will be discussed further in Chapter 35, where it will be shown that they are only what would be expected if light is a wave motion. Young's experiments enabled him to measure the wavelength of the waves and Fresnel showed that the rectilinear propagation of light, as well as the diffraction effects observed by Grimaldi and others, could be accounted for by the behavior of waves of short wavelength.

The next great forward step in the theory of light was the work of Maxwell, discussed in the previous chapter. We shall have more to say about the nature of light in later chapters.

31–2 Waves and rays.   Most of our work in optics will have to do with the propagation of light and the formation of images by mirrors and lenses.   All of these effects can be interpreted in terms of a wave theory.   When waves spread out from a small source in a uniform medium, the wavefronts are spheres concentric with the source.   At large distances from the source, the radii of the spheres become so large that the wavefronts can be considered plane.   Figure 30–4 is a diagram of the electromagnetic fields in a plane electromagnetic wave.   Such a diagram can be simplified by drawing only those wavefronts in which the electric and magnetic intensities are a maximum in one direction or the other, and which are therefore separated from one another by one-half a wavelength. Thus, *a wavefront is the locus of points where the waves have the same phase,* and the *phase velocity* is the velocity of propagation of these surfaces of common phase.

A train of light waves may be represented even more simply by *rays* than by wavefronts.   In a corpuscular theory a ray is simply the path followed by a light corposcle.   From the wave viewpoint, a ray is an imaginary line drawn in the direction in which the wave is traveling. At a boundary surface between two substances, such as the surface between a glass plate and the air outside it, the direction of a ray may change suddenly, but it is a straight line both in the air and in the glass. If a substance is not homogeneous the rays, in general, are curved but are still normal to the wavefronts.   This is the case in the earth's atmosphere, where the density of the air, and hence the velocity, vary with elevation.

The wavelength of electromagnetic waves capable of affecting the sense of sight lies between 0.00004 cm and 0.00007 cm.   Because these wavelengths are so small, it is convenient to express them in terms of a small unit of length.

Three such units are commonly used: the *micron,* the *millimicron,* and the *angstrom.*   One micron (1 μ) is a millionth of a meter, one millimicron (1 mμ) is one one-thousandth of a micron, and one angstrom (1 A) is one ten-thousandth of a micron:

$$1\,\mu = 10^{-6}\,\text{m} = 10^{-4}\,\text{cm},$$

$$1\,\text{m}\mu = 10^{-9}\,\text{m} = 10^{-7}\,\text{cm},$$

$$1\,\text{A} = 10^{-10}\,\text{m} = 10^{-8}\,\text{cm}.$$

Most workers in the fields of optical instrument design, color, and physiological optics express wavelengths in *millimicrons.*   For example, the wavelength of the yellow light from a sodium flame is 0.0000589 cm or 589 mμ.

31–3 Sources of light. The energy of electromagnetic radiation, or *radiant energy*, emitted per unit time depends upon the temperature and the nature of the surface of a body. This radiation is a mixture of different wavelengths. At a temperature of 300°C the most intense of these waves has a wavelength of 5000×10^{-9} m or 5000 mμ, which is in the *infrared* region. At a temperature of 800°C a body emits enough visible radiant energy to be self-luminous and appears "red hot." By far the larger part of the energy emitted, however, is still carried by infrared waves. At 3000°C, which is about the temperature of an incandescent lamp filament, the radiant energy contains enough of the "visible" wavelengths, between 400 mμ and 700 mμ, so that the body appears nearly "white hot."

In modern incandescent lamps, the filament is a coil of fine tungsten wire. An inert gas such as argon is introduced to reduce evaporation of the filament. Incandescent lamps vary in size from one no larger than a grain of wheat to one with a power input of 5000 watts, used for illuminating airfields.

The brightest source of light is the *carbon arc*. Rods of carbon from 6 to 12 inches in length and from $\frac{1}{4}$ to $\frac{1}{2}$ inch in diameter are placed either horizontally, as shown in Fig. 31–1(a), or at an angle, as shown in Fig. 31–1(b). Carbon arcs are used in all motion picture theaters, where they operate on from 50 to several hundred amperes.

A common laboratory source of light is provided by a mercury arc. A glass or quartz tube has tungsten electrodes sealed in each end, and a pool of mercury surrounds the negative electrode. A difference of potential is established across the electrodes and the tube is tilted until the mercury makes contact between the two electrodes. Some mercury is vaporized, and when the tube is restored to its vertical position an electric discharge is maintained by electrons and positive mercury ions. When the mercury is at low pressure the mercury atoms emit a characteristic light consisting of only yellow, green, blue, and violet. A didymium filter may be used to absorb the yellow, and a yellow glass filter to absorb the blue and violet, leaving an intense green light consisting of a very small band of wavelengths whose average value is 546 mμ. Low-pressure mercury arcs containing only one isotope of mercury, of atomic weight 198, are obtainable from the United States National Bureau of Standards. The green light from these lamps consists of an extremely narrow band of wavelengths, and is a very close approach to *monochromatic* light.

An intense source of yellow light of average wavelength 589.3 mμ is provided by a sodium arc lamp. This is usually made of a special kind of glass that is not attacked by sodium and into which electrodes are sealed. Each electrode is a filament for providing electrons to maintain an electric discharge through an inert gas. After the inert gas discharge

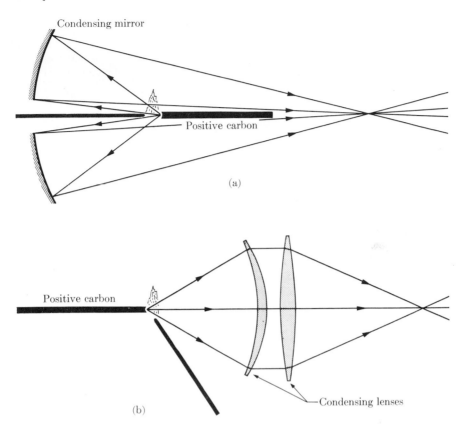

Fɪɢ. 31–1. Two types of carbon arcs. (a) With condensing mirror, for moderately sized motion picture theaters. (b) With condensing lenses, for large motion picture theaters.

has taken place for a few minutes, the temperature rises to a value at which the vapor pressure of the sodium is great enough to provide sufficient sodium atoms to emit the characteristic yellow sodium light. Sodium lamps are often used for street lighting because of their economy and because great visual acuity results when almost monochromatic light is used.

31–4 Shadows. Probably one of the first optical phenomena to be noted was that the shadow of an object illuminated by a source of small dimensions has the same shape as the object and that the edges of the shadow are extensions of straight lines from the source, tangent to the edges of the object. Point O in Fig. 31–2(a) represents a *point source* of light. That is, the dimensions of the source are small in comparison with other distances involved. S is a screen, and P is a circular obstacle

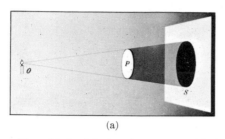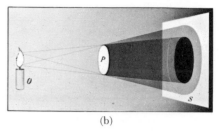

(a)   (b)

FIG. 31–2. (a) A point source of light casts a sharply defined shadow. (b) If the source is not a point, the shadow consists of a central umbra surrounded by a penumbra.

between source and screen. The portion of the screen bounded by rays from the source tangent to the edges of the obstacle is called the *geometrical shadow* of the obstacle.

If the source is not sufficiently small to be considered a point, the shadow consists of two portions, as in Fig. 31–2(b). The inner portion, which receives no light from the source, is called the *umbra*. Surrounding the umbra is the *penumbra*, within which a part of the source is screened by the obstacle. An observer within the umbra cannot see any part of the source; one within the penumbra can see a portion of the source; while from points outside the penumbra the entire source can be seen.

31–5 The velocity of light. The velocity of light in free space is one of the fundamental constants of nature. Its magnitude is so great (about 186,000 mi/sec or 3×10^8 m/sec) that it evaded experimental measurement until 1676. Up to that time it was generally believed that light traveled with an infinite velocity.

The first attempt to measure the velocity of light involved a method proposed by Galileo. Two experimenters were stationed on the tops of two hills about a mile apart. Each was provided with a lantern, the experiment being performed at night. One man was first to uncover his lantern and, observing the light from this lantern, the second was to uncover his. The velocity of light could then be computed from the known distance between the lanterns and the time elapsing between the instant when the first observer uncovered his lantern and when he observed the light from the second. While the experiment was entirely correct in principle, we know now that the velocity is too great for the time interval to be measured in this way with any degree of precision.

Eight years later, in 1676, the Danish astronomer Olaf Roemer, from astronomical observations made on one of the satellites of the planet Jupiter, obtained the first definite evidence that light is propagated with a finite velocity. Jupiter has twelve small satellites or moons, four of

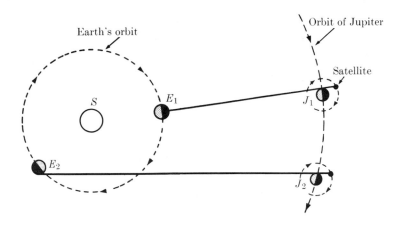

Fɪɢ. 31–3. Roemer's method for deducing the velocity of light.

which are sufficiently bright to be seen with a moderately good telescope or a pair of field glasses. The satellites appear as tiny bright points at one side or the other of the disk of the planet. These satellites revolve about Jupiter just as does our moon about the earth and, since the plane of their orbits is nearly the same as that in which the earth and Jupiter revolve, each is eclipsed by the planet during a part of every revolution.

Roemer was engaged in measuring the time of revolution of one of the satellites by taking the time interval between consecutive eclipses (about 42 hrs). He found, by a comparison of results over a long period of time, that while the earth was receding from Jupiter the periodic times were all somewhat longer than the average, and that while it was approaching Jupiter the times were all somewhat shorter. He concluded rightly that the cause of these variations was the varying distance between Jupiter and the earth.

Figure 31–3, not to scale, illustrates the case. Let observations be started when the earth and Jupiter are in the positions E_1 and J_1. Since Jupiter requires about 12 years to make one revolution in its orbit, then by the time the earth has moved to E_2 (about five months later) Jupiter has moved only to J_2. During this interval the distance between the planets has been continually increasing. Hence at each eclipse, the light from the satellite must travel a slightly greater distance than at the preceding eclipse, and the observed time of revolution is slightly larger than the true time.

Roemer concluded from his observations that a time of about 22 minutes was required for light to travel a distance equal to the diameter of the earth's orbit. The best figure for this distance, in Roemer's time, was about 172,000,000 miles. Although there is no record that Roemer actually

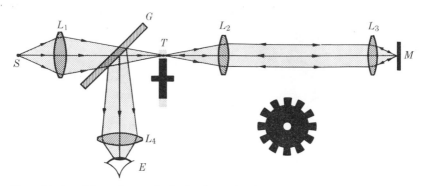

FIG. 31–4. Fizeau's toothed-wheel method for measuring the velocity of light. S is a light source, L_1, L_2, L_3, and L_4 are lenses, T is the toothed wheel, M is a mirror, and G is a glass plate.

made the computation, had he used the data above he would have found a velocity of about 130,000 mi/sec or 2.1×10^8 m/sec.

The first successful determination of the velocity of light from purely terrestrial measurements was made by the French scientist Fizeau in 1849. A schematic diagram of his apparatus is given in Fig. 31–4. Lens L_1 forms an image of the light source S at a point near the rim of a toothed wheel T, which can be set into rapid rotation. G is an inclined plate of clear glass. Suppose first that the wheel is stationary and the light passes through one of the openings between the teeth. Lenses L_2 and L_3, which are separated by about 8.6 km, form a second image on the mirror M. The light is reflected from M, retraces its path, and is in part reflected from the glass plate G through the lens L_4 into the eye of an observer at E.

If the wheel T is set in rotation, the light from S is "chopped up" into a succession of wave trains of limited length. If the speed of rotation is such that by the time the front of one wave train has traveled to the mirror and returned, an opaque segment of the wheel has moved into the position formerly occupied by an open portion, no reflected light will reach the observer E. At twice this angular velocity, the light transmitted through any one opening will return through the next and an image of S will again be observed. From a knowledge of the angular velocity and radius of the wheel, the distance between openings, and the distance from wheel to mirror, the velocity of light may be computed. Fizeau's measurements were not of high precision. He obtained a value of 3.15×10^8 m/sec.

Fizeau's apparatus was modified by Foucault, who replaced the toothed wheel with a rotating mirror. By introducing between the wheel and the mirror a tube filled with water, he proved that the velocity of light in water is less than in air. A corpuscular theory demands that it shall be greater, and at the time these measurements were made they were taken as conclusive proof that a corpuscular theory was untenable.

The most precise measurements by the Foucault method were made by the American physicist Albert A. Michelson (1852–1931). His first experiments were performed in 1878 while he was on the staff of the Naval Academy at Annapolis. The latest, which were under way at the time of his death, were completed in 1935 by Pease and Pearson.

In an analysis of all measurements up to 1953, DuMond and Cohen report that the best value is

$$c = 2.997929 \times 10^8 \text{ m/sec},$$

which they believe correct within $\pm 0.000008 \times 10^8$ m/sec.

The most accurate direct experimental determination of ϵ_0 was made by Rosa and Dorsey at the United States National Bureau of Standards. Using the equation discussed in Section 30–5,

$$c = \sqrt{1/\epsilon_0\mu_0},$$

they obtained the value

$$c = (2.9979 \pm 0.0001) \times 10^8 \text{ m/sec},$$

which is seen to be in excellent agreement with the value reported by DuMond and Cohen.

31–6 Index of refraction. With a few exceptions, the velocity of light in a material substance, which we shall represent by v, is less than the velocity in free space. Furthermore, while light of all wavelengths travels with the same velocity in empty space, the velocity in material substances is different for different wavelengths. This effect is known as *dispersion*. The ratio of the velocity of light in a vacuum to the *phase* velocity of light of a particular wavelength in any substance is called the *index of refraction* of the substance for light of that particular wavelength. We shall designate index of refraction by n, stating, if necessary, the particular wavelength to which it refers. If no wavelength is stated, the index is usually assumed to be that corresponding to the yellow light from a sodium flame, of wavelength 589 mμ. Index of refraction is evidently a pure number (the ratio of two velocities) and in most instances is numerically greater than unity:

$$n = \frac{c}{v}. \tag{31–1}$$

The velocity of light in a gas is nearly equal to its velocity in free space and the dispersion is small. For example, the index of refraction of air at standard conditions, for violet light of wavelength 436 mμ, is 1.0002957, while for red light of wavelength 656 mμ, the index is 1.0002914. It follows that for most purposes the velocity of light in air can be assumed equal to its velocity in free space and the index of refraction of air can be assumed unity. The index of refraction of a gas increases uniformly as the density of the gas is increased.

The index of refraction of most of the common glasses used in optical instruments lies between 1.46 and 1.96. There are only a very few substances having indices larger than this value, diamond being one, with an index of 2.42, and rutile (synthetic crystalline titanium dioxide), with an index of 2.7, another. The values for a number of solids and liquids are given in Table 31–1.

TABLE 31–1

INDEX OF REFRACTION FOR YELLOW SODIUM LIGHT
(λ = 589 mμ)

Substance	Index of refraction
Solids:	
Ice (H_2O)	1.309
Fluorite (CaF_2)	1.434
Rock salt (NaCl)	1.544
Quartz (SiO_2)	1.544
Zircon ($ZrO_2 \cdot SiO_2$)	1.923
Diamond (C)	2.417
Fabulite ($SrTiO_3$)	2.409
Rutile (TiO_2)	$\begin{cases} 2.616 \\ 2.903 \end{cases}$
Liquids at 20°C:	
Methyl alcohol (CH_3OH)	1.3290
Water (H_2O)	1.3330
Ethyl alcohol (C_2H_5OH)	1.3618
Carbon tetrachloride (CCl_4)	1.4607
Turpentine	1.4721
Glycerine	1.4730
Benzene	1.5012
Carbon disulfide (CS_2)	1.6276

31–7 Huygens' principle. Huygens' principle is a geometrical method for finding, from the known shape of a wavefront at some instant, what the shape will be at some later instant. The principle states that every point of a wavefront may be considered the source of small secondary wavelets, which spread out in all directions with a velocity equal to the velocity of propagation of the waves. The new wavefront is then found by constructing a surface tangent to the secondary wavelets or, as it is called, the *envelope* of the wavelets. If the velocity of propagation is not the same at all portions of the wavefront, the appropriate velocity must be used for the various wavelets.

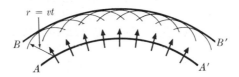

FIG. 31–5. Huygens' principle.

Huygens' principle is illustrated in Fig. 31–5. The original wavefront, AA', is traveling as indicated by the small arrows. We wish to find the shape of the wavefront after a time interval t. Let v represent the velocity of propagation. Construct a number of circles (traces of spherical wavelets) of radius $r = vt$, with centers along AA'. The trace of the envelope of these wavelets, which is the new wavefront, is the curve BB'. The velocity v has been assumed the same at all points and in all directions.

Huygens' principle and all other wave phenomena, like reflection, refraction, interference, and diffraction (to be discussed in later chapters), apply equally well to any kind of waves: light waves, radio waves, sound waves, etc. This statement applies until we come to polarization (Chapter 36), where the waves under discussion must be transverse.

31–8 Atmospheric refraction. The density of the earth's atmosphere is greatest at the surface of the earth and decreases with increasing elevation. As a result of this, light rays entering the earth's atmosphere from the sun or the stars are continuously deviated so as to follow a curved path, as is shown in Fig. 31–6(a). The cause of the deviation may be seen by considering the wavefronts, which, if coming from astronomical objects, may be assumed plane when reaching the earth. The lower portion of a wavefront such as AA', Fig. 31–6(b), is always traveling in air of a greater density than the upper portion A'. Greater density means greater index of refraction or smaller velocity. Hence the lower portion of the wave always travels more slowly than the upper portion and

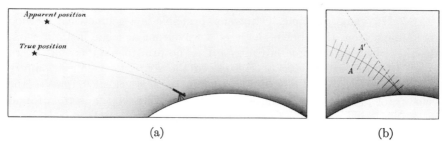

(a)   (b)

FIG. 31–6. Deviation of a ray by the earth's atmosphere.

Huygens' construction leads to the shift in the direction of the wavefront as shown. An observer at the earth's surface sees the light source in the direction of the tangent to the rays when they reach the earth and concludes that the object is nearer the zenith than its true position.

Another phenomenon produced by atmospheric refraction is the mirage, illustrated in Fig. 31–7. The conditions necessary for its production require that the air nearer the surface of the ground shall be less dense than that above, a situation which is sometimes found over an area intensely heated by the sun's rays. Light from the upper portion of an object may reach the eye of an observer by the two paths shown in the figure, with the result that the object is seen in its actual position, together with its inverted image below it, as though a reflecting surface lay between the object and observer. The weary traveler in the desert interprets the reflecting surface as a body of water. This same phenomenon accounts for the "wet" appearance of the surface of a smooth highway under a hot sun, when it is seen at a glancing angle.

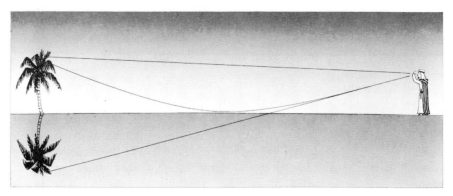

FIG. 31–7. The mirage.

PROBLEMS

31-1. What is the wavelength in meters, microns, millimicrons, and angstrom units of (a) soft x-rays of frequency 2×10^{17} cycles/sec? (b) green light of frequency 5.6×10^{14} cycles/sec?

31-2. The visible spectrum includes a wavelength range from about 400 mμ to about 700 mμ. Express these wavelengths in inches.

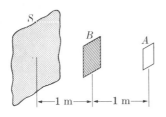

FIGURE 31-8

31-3. In Fig. 31-8, A is an extended light source in the form of a square 2 cm on a side. B is an opaque square sheet parallel to A, and 3 cm on a side. (a) What is the area of the umbra of the shadow of B on screen S? (b) What is the area of the penumbra on S?

31-4. Repeat Problem 31-3 when A is replaced by a point source of light at its center.

31-5. (a) What is the velocity of light of wavelength 500 mμ (in vacuum), in glass whose index at this

wavelength is 1.50? (b) What is the wavelength of these waves in the glass?

31-6. A glass plate 3 mm thick, of index 1.50, is placed between a point source of light of wavelength 600 mμ (in vacuum) and a screen. The distance from source to screen is 3 cm. How many waves are there between source and screen?

31-7. The velocity of light of wavelength 656 mμ in heavy flint glass is 1.60×10^8 m/sec. What is the index of refraction of this glass?

31-8. Light of a certain frequency has a wavelength in water of 442 mμ. What is the wavelength of this light when it passes into carbon disulfide?

31-9. Assuming the radius of the earth's orbit to be 92,900,000 miles, and taking the best value of the velocity of light, compute the time required for light to travel a distance equal to the diameter of the earth's orbit. Compare with Roemer's value of 22 minutes.

31-10. Fizeau's measurements of the velocity of light were continued by Cornu, using Fizeau's apparatus but with the distance between mirrors increased to 22.9 km. One of the toothed wheels used was 40 mm in diameter and had 180 teeth. Find the angular velocity at which it should rotate so that light transmitted through one opening will return through the next.

CHAPTER 32

REFLECTION AND REFRACTION AT PLANE SURFACES

32–1 Reflection of light. Most of the objects we see are visible because they reflect light into our eyes. In the most common class of reflection, called *diffuse reflection*, light is reflected in all directions. A book on a table in a room lighted only by a point source of light can be seen from any part of the room. This type of reflection occurs whenever the roughness of the reflecting body has "dimensions" large compared with the wavelength of the reflected wave. In the other class of reflection, called *regular* or *specular reflection*, a narrow beam or *pencil* of light is reflected in one direction only. This type of reflection occurs from smooth surfaces whose irregularities are small compared with the wavelength of the reflected wave. For example, reflection from a bed sheet is diffuse, whereas reflection from a mirror is specular. Reflection from a polished automobile is intermediate, in that the reflected light is both diffuse and specular. Our main interest is in specular reflection, and in what follows the word "reflection" will mean "specular reflection."

32–2 Reflection of a plane wave at a plane surface. Consider the trace of a plane wave surface AA' (Fig. 32–1) which is just making contact with the reflecting surface MM' along a line through A perpendicular to the plane of the diagram. The planes of the wave surface and the reflecting surface are also normal to the plane of the figure. The position of the wave surface after a time interval t may be found by applying Huygens' principle. With points on AA' as centers, draw a number of secondary

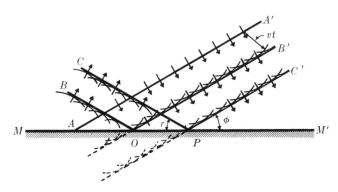

Fig. 32–1. Successive positions of a plane wave AA' as it is reflected from a plane surface.

wavelets of radius vt, where v is the velocity of propagation in the medium above the surface. Those wavelets originating near the upper end of AA' spread out unhindered, and their envelope gives that portion of the new wave surface OB'. The wavelets originating near the lower end of AA', however, strike the reflecting surface. If the latter had not been there, they would have occupied the positions shown by the dotted circular arcs. The effect of the reflecting surface is to reverse the direction of travel of those wavelets which strike it, so that that part of a wavelet which would have penetrated below the surface actually lies above it, as shown by the full lines. The envelope of these reflected wavelets is then that portion of the wave surface OB. The trace of the entire wave surface at this instant is the broken line BOB'. A similar construction gives the line CPC' for the wave surface after another interval t.

The angle ϕ between the incident wave and the surface is called the *angle of incidence;* that between the reflected wave and the surface, r, is called the *angle of reflection.* To find the relation between these angles, consider Fig. 32–2, which is the same as a portion of Fig. 32–1. From O, draw $OP = vt$, perpendicular to AA'. Now OB, by construction, is tangent to a circle of radius vt with center at A. Hence if AQ is drawn from A to the point of tangency, the triangles APO and AQO are equal. (Right triangles with the side AO in common and with $AQ = OP$.) The angle ϕ therefore equals the angle r,

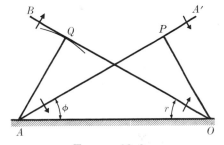

FIGURE 32–2

and we have the *law of reflection: a plane wave is reflected from a plane surface with the angle of reflection equal to the angle of incidence.*

32–3 Refraction of a plane wave at a plane surface. Whenever a train of light waves traveling in one transparent medium strikes the surface of a second transparent medium whose index differs from that of the first (that is, in which the velocity differs from that in the first), two new wave trains are found to originate at the interface. One, the reflected wave, travels back into the original medium, while the other, called the *refracted* wave, is propagated into the second medium. The direction of the reflected wave is given by the law of reflection deduced in Section 32–2. We now proceed to find the direction of travel of the refracted wave.

Consider the trace of a plane wave surface AA' (Fig. 32–3) which is just making contact with the surface MM' along a line through A perpendicular to the plane of the diagram. MM' represents a boundary surface between two transparent media of different indices of refraction.

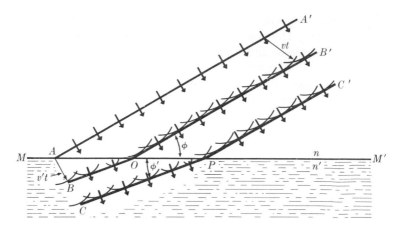

FIG. 32–3. Successive positions of a plane wavefront AA' as it is refracted by a plane surface.

Let n be the index of the medium above MM', and n' that of the medium below. Assume that $n' > n$. The reflected waves are not shown in the figure, as they proceed exactly as in Fig. 32–1. Let us apply Huygens' principle to find the position of the refracted wave surface after a time t.

With points on AA' as centers, draw a number of secondary wavelets. Those originating near the upper end of AA' travel with velocity $v = c/n$ and after a time interval t are spherical surfaces of radius vt. The wavelet originating at point A, however, is traveling in the lower medium with speed $v' = c/n'$ and in time t is a spherical surface of radius $v't$. The envelope of the wavelets from the original wave surface is the plane whose trace is the broken line BOB'. A similar construction leads to the trace CPC' after a second interval t.

The angles ϕ and ϕ' between the surface and the incident and refracted wave surfaces are called respectively the *angle of incidence* and the *angle of refraction*. To find the relation between these angles refer to Fig. 32–4, which is the same as a portion of Fig. 32–3. Draw $OQ = vt$, perpendicular to AQ, and draw $AB = v't$, perpendicular to BO. From the right triangle AOQ,

$$\sin \phi = \frac{vt}{AO},$$

and from the right triangle AOB,

$$\sin \phi' = \frac{v't}{AO}.$$

Hence

$$\frac{\sin \phi}{\sin \phi'} = \frac{v}{v'}. \qquad (32\text{–}1)$$

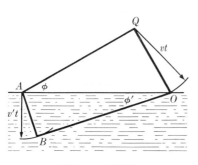

FIGURE 32–4

That is, when a train of plane waves strikes the boundary surface between two transparent media, *the ratio of the sine of the angle of incidence to the sine of the angle of refraction is equal to the ratio of the velocities in the two media.*

Since by definition

$$n = \frac{c}{v} \quad \text{and} \quad n' = \frac{c}{v'},$$

where c is the velocity of light in free space, it follows that

$$\frac{v}{v'} = \frac{n'}{n},$$

and Eq. (32–1) may be written

$$\frac{\sin \phi}{\sin \phi'} = \frac{n'}{n},$$

or

$$n \sin \phi = n' \sin \phi'. \tag{32–2}$$

This equation is more useful than Eq. (32–1), since the index of refraction of a substance is the property which is usually tabulated, rather than the velocity of light in that substance. Since for any given pair of substances the ratio n'/n is a constant, Eq. (32–2) is equivalent to

$$\frac{\sin \phi}{\sin \phi'} = \text{constant.}$$

The discovery that the sines of the angles of incidence and refraction stand in a constant ratio to each other is usually credited to Willebrord Snell, in 1621, although there seems to be some doubt whether it was actually discovered by him. In accord with common usage, however, we shall refer to Eq. (32–2) as *Snell's law.*

32–4 Ray treatment of reflection and refraction. It is possible to analyze the passage of light through any optical system by successive applications of Huygens' principle to the wave surfaces, as was done in the preceding section at a single surface. However, it is often much simpler to trace a few rays through the system. The wave surfaces may then be constructed at right angles to the rays.

The simple case of reflection and refraction of plane waves at a plane surface is illustrated in Fig. 32–5. In Fig. 32–5(a) there is shown a train of plane waves incident on a plane boundary surface, together with the reflected and refracted waves. In Fig. 32–5(b) the same wave trains are represented by rays. Figure 32–5(c) shows a single incident ray together with the refracted ray and the reflected ray. The angle between any

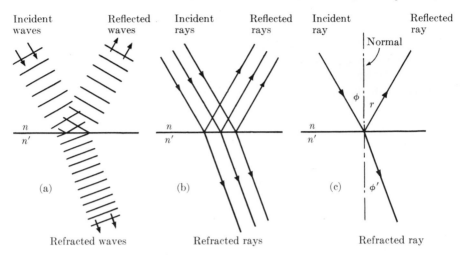

FIG. 32–5. (a) A train of plane waves is in part reflected and in part re-fracted at the boundary between two media. (b) The waves in (a) are repre-sented by rays. (c) For simplicity, only a single incident, reflected, and refracted ray are drawn.

wave surface and the *reflecting surface* is equal to the angle between the cor-responding *ray* and the *normal* to the reflecting surface, since the sides of the angles are mutually perpendicular. Thus in Fig. 32–5(c), ϕ is equal to the angle of incidence, ϕ' is equal to the angle of refraction, and r is equal to the angle of reflection. The planes of the incident and refracted waves and the plane of the boundary surface are all perpendicular to the plane of the diagram. It follows that the corresponding rays and the surface normal, which are perpendicular to these planes, *all lie in the same plane,* that is, the plane of the diagram. In general, the plane determined by an incident ray and the normal to the surface at the point of incidence is called the *plane of incidence.*

It is evident from Snell's law that the angle of refraction is always less than the angle of incidence for a ray passing from a medium of smaller into one of larger index, as from air into glass. In such a case the ray is bent *toward* the normal. If the light is traveling in the opposite direction, the reverse is true and the ray is bent *away from* the normal.

To summarize the laws of reflection and refraction in terms of rays:

When a ray of light is reflected, the angle of reflection is equal to the angle of incidence. The incident ray, the reflected ray, and the normal to the surface at the point of incidence, all lie in the same plane.

When a ray of light is refracted, $n \sin \phi = n' \sin \phi'$. The incident ray, the refracted ray, and the normal to the surface at the point of incidence, all lie in the same plane.

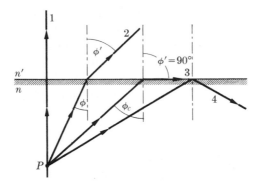

FIG. 32–6. Total internal reflection. The angle of incidence ϕ_c, for which the angle of refraction is 90°, is called the critical angle.

32–5 Total internal reflection. Figure 32–6 shows a number of rays diverging from a point source P in a medium of index n and striking the surface of a second medium of index n', where $n > n'$. From Snell's law,

$$\sin \phi' = \frac{n}{n'} \sin \phi.$$

Since n/n' is greater than unity, $\sin \phi'$ is larger than $\sin \phi$ and evidently equals unity (i.e., $\phi' = 90°$) for some angle ϕ less than 90°. This is illustrated by ray 3 in the diagram, which emerges just grazing the surface at an angle of refraction of 90°. The angle of incidence for which the refracted ray emerges tangent to the surface is called the *critical angle* and is designated by ϕ_c in the diagram. If the angle of incidence is greater than the critical angle, the sine of the angle of refraction, as computed by Snell's law, is greater than unity. This may be interpreted to mean that beyond the critical angle the ray does not pass into the upper medium but is *totally internally reflected* at the boundary surface. Total internal reflection can occur only when a ray is incident on the surface of a medium whose index is *smaller* than that of the medium in which the ray is traveling.

The critical angle for two given substances may be found by setting $\phi' = 90°$ or $\sin \phi' = 1$ in Snell's law. We then have

$$\boxed{\sin \phi_c = \frac{n'}{n}.} \tag{32–3}$$

The critical angle of an air-glass surface, taking 1.50 as a typical index of refraction of glass, is

$$\sin \phi_c = \frac{1}{1.50} = 0.67, \qquad \phi_c = 42°.$$

This angle, very conveniently, is slightly less than 45°, which makes possible the use in many optical instruments of prisms of angles 45°–45°–90° as totally reflecting surfaces. The advantages of totally reflecting prisms over metallic surfaces as reflectors are, first, that the light is *totally* reflected, while no metallic surface reflects 100% of the light incident on it, and second, the reflecting properties are permanent and not affected by tarnishing. Offsetting these is the fact that there is some loss of light by reflection at the surfaces where light enters and leaves the prism, although recently discovered methods of coating the surfaces with so-called "nonreflecting" films can reduce this loss considerably.

The simplest type of reflecting prism is shown in Fig. 32–7. Its angles are 45°–45°–90°. Light incident normally on one of the shorter faces strikes the inclined face at an angle of incidence of 45°. This is greater than the critical angle, so the light is totally internally reflected and emerges from the second of the shorter faces after undergoing a deviation of 90°.

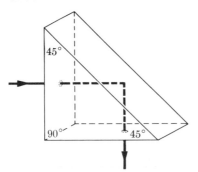

FIG. 32–7. A totally reflecting prism.

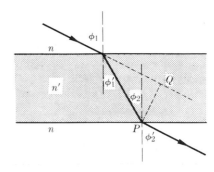

FIG. 32–8. Refraction by a parallel plate.

32–6 Refraction by a plane parallel plate. Suppose light is incident at an angle ϕ_1 (as in Fig. 32–8) on the upper surface of a transparent plate, the surfaces of the plate being plane and parallel to one another. Let ϕ_1' be the angle of refraction at the upper surface, and ϕ_2 and ϕ_2' the angles of incidence and refraction at the lower surface. Let n be the index of the medium on either side of the plate, and let the index of the plate be n'. The figure is drawn with $n' > n$. From Snell's law,

$$n \sin \phi_1 = n' \sin \phi_1',$$

$$n' \sin \phi_2 = n \sin \phi_2'.$$

But, as is evident from the diagram,

$$\phi_1' = \phi_2.$$

Combining these relations, we find

$$\phi_1 = \phi_2'.$$

That is, the emergent ray is parallel to the incident ray. It is not deviated in passing through the plate but is *displaced* by the distance PQ. It will be left as an exercise to show that a ray of light passing through any number of plane parallel plates of different index is not deviated but only displaced from its original path, provided it emerges into a medium of the same index as that in which it was originally traveling.

32–7 Refraction by a prism. The prism, in one or another of its many forms, is second only to the lens as the most useful piece of optical apparatus. Totally reflecting prisms have been mentioned briefly. We consider now the *deviation* and the *dispersion* produced by a prism.

Consider a light ray incident at an angle ϕ on one face of a prism, as in Fig. 32–9(a). Let the index of the prism be n, the included angle at the apex be A, and let the medium on either side of the prism be air. It is desired to find the *angle of deviation, δ*. This is a straightforward problem in surveying. One has only to apply Snell's law at the first surface, compute the angle of refraction, then by geometry find the angle of incidence at the second surface, and from a second application of Snell's law find the angle of refraction at the second surface. The direction of the emergent ray is then known and the angle of deviation may be found.

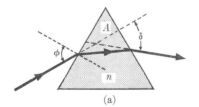 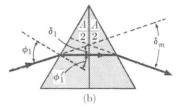

(a)   (b)

FIG. 32 9. (a) Deviation by a prism. (b) The deviation is a minimum when the ray passes through the prism symmetrically.

While the method is simple enough, the expression for the angle δ turns out in the general case to be rather complicated. However, as the angle of incidence is, say, decreased from a large value, the angle of deviation decreases at first and then increases, and is a minimum when the ray passes through the prism symmetrically as in Fig. 32–9(b). The angle δ_m is then called the angle of *minimum deviation* and in this special case it is related to the angle of the prism and its index by the equation

$$n = \frac{\sin (A + \delta_m)/2}{\sin A/2}. \tag{32–4}$$

To derive Eq. (32–4), we have from Fig. 32–9(b),

$$\phi_1' = \frac{A}{2} \text{ (sides mutually perpendicular)},$$

$$\delta_1 = \frac{\delta_m}{2} \text{ (half the deviation takes place at each surface)},$$

$$\phi_1 = \phi_1' + \delta_1 = \frac{A}{2} + \frac{\delta_m}{2} = \frac{A + \delta_m}{2},$$

$$\sin \phi_1 = n \sin \phi_1',$$

$$\therefore \sin \frac{A + \delta_m}{2} = n \sin \frac{A}{2}, \text{ which is Eq. (32–4)}.$$

By making use of the equation derived above, the index of refraction of a transparent solid may be measured. The specimen whose index is desired is ground into the form of a prism. The angle of the prism A and the angle of minimum deviation δ_m are measured with the aid of a spectrometer. Since these angles may be determined with a high degree of precision, this method is an extremely accurate one and by means of it indices of refraction may be measured to the sixth place of decimals.

If the angle of the prism is small, the angle of minimum deviation is small also and we may replace the sines of the angles by the angles. One then obtains

$$n = \frac{A + \delta_m}{A},$$

or

$$\delta_m = (n - 1)A, \tag{32–5}$$

a useful approximate relation.

32–8 Dispersion. Most light beams are a mixture of waves whose wavelengths extend throughout the visible spectrum. While the velocity of light waves in a vacuum is the same for all wavelengths, the velocity in a material substance is different for different wavelengths. Hence the index of refraction of a substance is a function of wavelength. A substance in which the velocity of a wave varies with wavelength is said to exhibit *dispersion*. Figure 32–10 is a diagram showing the variation of index of refraction with wavelength for a number of the more common optical materials.

Consider a ray of white light, a mixture of all visible wavelengths, incident on a prism as in Fig. 32–11. Since the deviation produced by the prism increases with increasing index of refraction, violet light is deviated most and red least, with other colors occupying intermediate positions.

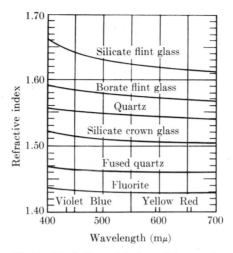

FIG. 32–10. Variation of index with wavelength.

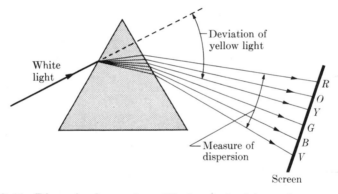

FIG. 32–11. Dispersion by a prism. The band of colors on the screen is called a spectrum.

On emerging from the prism, the light is spread out into a fan-shaped beam as shown. The light is said to be *dispersed* into a spectrum.

When white light is dispersed by a prism, it can be seen from Fig. 32–11 that the whole fan-shaped beam is deviated from the incident direction. A convenient measure of this deviation is provided by the angle of deviation of yellow light, since yellow is roughly midway between red and violet. A simple measure of the dispersion is provided by the angular separation of the red and violet rays. Since deviation and index of refraction are related, the deviation of the entire spectrum is controlled by the index of refraction for yellow light, whereas the dispersion depends on the difference between the index for violet light and that for red light.

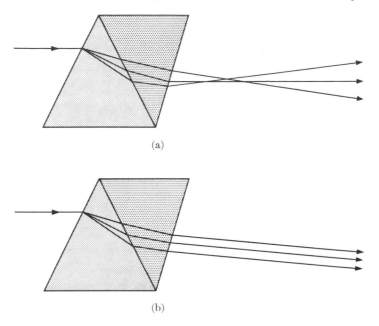

(a)

(b)

FIG. 32–12. (a) A direct-vision prism. (b) An achromatic prism.

From the graphs of Fig. 32–10 it can be seen that for a substance like fluorite, whose index for yellow light is small, the difference between the indices for red and violet is also small. On the other hand, in the case of silicate flint glass, both the index for yellow light and the difference between extreme indices are large. In other words, for most transparent materials the greater the deviation, the greater the dispersion.

The brilliance of diamond is due in part to its large dispersion. In recent years synthetic crystals of titanium dioxide and of strontium titanate, with about eight times the dispersion of diamond, have been produced.

Because of the shape of the curves in Fig. 32–10, the dispersions produced by two prisms of equal angles are not exactly proportional to the mean deviations. It is therefore possible to combine two (or more) prisms of different materials in such a way that there is no net deviation of a ray of some chosen wavelength, while there remains an outstanding dispersion of the spectrum as a whole. Such a device, illustrated in Fig. 32–12(a), is known as a *direct-vision prism*. Two prisms may also be designed so that the dispersion of one is offset by the dispersion of the other, although the deviation is not. A compound prism of this sort is called *achromatic* (without color). See Fig. 32–12(b).

625

PROBLEMS

32–1. Prove that a ray of light reflected from a plane mirror rotates through an angle 2θ when the mirror rotates through an angle θ about an axis perpendicular to the plane of incidence.

32–2. Prove that a ray of light travels the shortest possible distance in going from point A to point B after reflection from the plane mirror M in Fig. 32–13. [*Hint:* Draw a straight line connecting B and the image of A.]

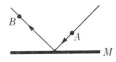

FIGURE 32–13

32–3. A parallel beam of light makes an angle of 30° with the surface of a glass plate having a refractive index of 1.50. (a) What is the angle between the refracted beam and the surface of the glass? (b) What should be the angle of incidence ϕ with this plate for the angle of refraction to be $\phi/2$?

32–4. Light strikes a glass plate at an angle of incidence of 60°, part of the beam being reflected and part refracted. It is observed that the reflected and refracted portions make an angle of 90° with each other. What is the index of refraction of the glass?

32–5. A ray of light is incident on a plane surface separating two transparent substances of indices 1.60 and 1.40. The angle of incidence is 30° and the ray originates in the medium of higher index. Compute the angle of refraction.

32–6. A point light source is 2 in. below a water-air surface. Compute the angles of refraction of rays from

the source making angles with the normal of 10°, 20°, 30°, and 40°, and show these rays in a carefully drawn full-size diagram.

32–7. A parallel-sided plate of glass having a refractive index of 1.60 is held on the surface of water in a tank. A ray coming from above makes an angle of incidence of 45° with the top surface of the glass. (a) What angle does the ray make with the normal in the water? (b) How does this angle vary with the refractive index of the glass?

32–8. A glass cube in air has a refractive index of 1.50. Parallel rays of light enter the top obliquely and then strike a side of the cube. Is it possible for the rays to emerge from this side?

32–9. A point source of light is 8 in. below the surface of a body of water. Find the diameter of the largest circle at the surface through which light can emerge from the water.

32–10. The index of refraction of the prism shown in Fig. 32–14 is 1.56. A ray of light enters the prism at point a and follows in the prism the path ab which is parallel to the line cd. (a) Sketch carefully the path of the ray from a point outside the prism at the left, through the glass, and out some distance into the air again. (b) Compute the angle between the original and final directions in air. (Dotted lines are construction lines only.)

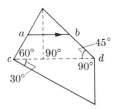

FIGURE 32–14

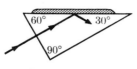

FIGURE 32–15

32–11. Light is incident normally on the short face of a 30°-60°-90° prism, as in Fig. 32–15. A drop of liquid is placed on the hypotenuse of the prism. If the index of the prism is 1.50, find the maximum index the liquid may have if the light is to be totally reflected.

32–12. A 45°-45°-90° prism is immersed in water. What is the minimum index of refraction the prism may have if it is to reflect totally a ray incident normally on one of its shorter faces?

32–13. The velocity of a sound wave is 1100 ft/sec in air and 4400 ft/sec in water. (a) What is the critical angle for a sound wave incident on the surface between air and water? (b) Which medium has the higher "index of refraction" for sound?

32–14. A light ray strikes a parallel-sided glass plate of thickness t at an angle of incidence ϕ. Show that the lateral displacement D of the emergent beam is given by the relation

$$D = t\,\frac{\sin(\phi - \phi')}{\cos\phi'},$$

where ϕ' is the angle of refraction of the ray within the glass.

32–15. A ray of light is incident at an angle of 60° on one surface of a glass plate 2 cm thick, of index 1.50. The medium on either side of the plate is air. Find the transverse displacement between the incident and emergent rays.

32–16. The prism of Fig. 32–16 has a refractive index of 1.414, and the angles A are 30°. Two light rays m and n are parallel as they enter the prism. What is the angle between them after they emerge?

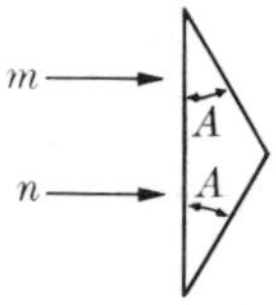

FIGURE 32–16

32–17. What is the angle of minimum deviation of an equiangular prism having a refractive index of 1.414?

32–18. An equiangular prism is constructed of the silicate flint glass whose index of refraction is given in Fig. 32–10. Find the angles of minimum deviation for light of wavelength 400 mμ and 700 mμ.

32–19. A silicate crown prism of apex angle 15° is to be combined with a prism of silicate flint so as to result in no net deviation of light of wavelength 550 mμ. (See Fig. 32–10 for indices of refraction.) Find the angle of the flint prism. Assume that light passes through both prisms at the angle of minimum deviation.

CHAPTER 33

REFLECTION AND REFRACTION AT A SINGLE SURFACE

33–1 Introduction. In the preceding chapter we discussed the reflection and refraction of rays of light at a surface separating two substances of different index, but considered only a single ray or bundles of parallel rays. We now take up the problem of tracing the paths of a large number of rays, all of which diverge from some one point of an object which is either self-luminous or has a rough surface capable of reflecting light in all directions. Such a point is represented by P in Fig. 33–1. At the right of P is a plane surface like that of a block of glass. A ray incident on any point of the surface is in part transmitted and in part reflected. The direction of the reflected ray is given by the law of reflection and that of the transmitted or refracted ray by Snell's law. These two principles suffice to determine the directions of all rays after they encounter a surface of any shape. We shall first consider the reflected rays only, from both plane and spherical surfaces, and then discuss refraction at plane and spherical surfaces. Surfaces other than plane and spherical are used only rarely in optical instruments, since these are the only shapes that can be produced by machine methods at reasonable cost.

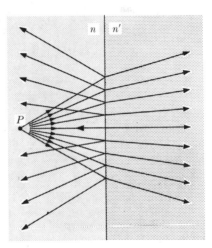

Fig. 33–1. Reflection and refraction of rays at a plane surface.

33–2 Reflection at a plane mirror. While some light is reflected at any surface separating two substances of different index, it is often desirable that the fraction reflected shall be as large as possible. By making the surface of highly polished metal, or by applying a thin metallic coat to a polished surface, the fraction of the light reflected can be made nearly 100%. A highly reflecting smooth surface is called a *mirror*, and we shall speak of the reflecting surfaces in the sections to follow as mirrors, although the equations to be derived will apply also to smooth surfaces from which the light is only partially reflected, such as the surface of a pane of window glass, or that of a lens.

627

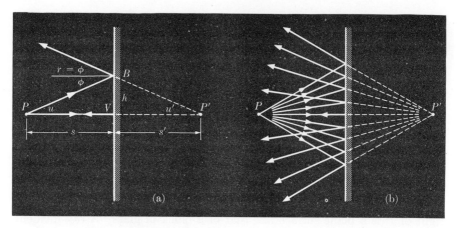

FIG. 33–2. Rays diverging from point P appear to diverge from point P' after reflection at a plane surface.

Figure 33–2(a) shows two rays diverging from a point P at a distance s at the left of a plane mirror. We call P the *object point* and s the *object distance*. In measuring the object distance we shall always *start at the reflecting surface and proceed toward the object point. If this direction is opposite the direction of the oncoming light, the object distance s is positive.* In Fig. 33–2(a) it is evident that s is positive. The ray PV, incident normally on the mirror, returns along its original path. The ray PB, making an arbitrary angle u with PV, strikes the mirror at an angle of incidence $\phi = u$ and is reflected at an angle $r = \phi = u$.

Extend the reflected rays by dotted lines at the right of the mirror, as shown. These dotted lines intersect at P', at a distance s' to the right of the mirror. We shall prove in a moment that *all* rays diverging from P will give rise to reflected rays which, when prolonged backwards into the region behind the mirror, intersect at the point P', as shown in Fig. 33–2(b). If one looks toward the mirror from the left, his eye treats the diverging reflected rays as if they had actually originated at the point P'. We say that P' is the *image* of point P and we call s' the *image distance*. In measuring the image distance we shall always *start at the reflecting surface and proceed toward the image point. If this direction is the same as that of the ongoing (reflected) light, the image distance s' is positive.*

In Fig. 33–2(a) it is evident that s' is negative. The angle u' is equal to r and hence is equal to u. Let h represent the distance VB. Then from the triangles PBV and $P'BV$,

$$\tan u = \frac{h}{s}, \qquad \tan u' = \frac{h}{-s'},$$

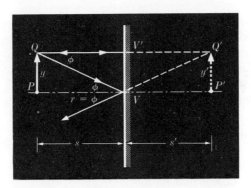

FIG. 33–3. Construction for determining the height of an image formed by reflection at a plane surface.

and since $u = u'$, it follows that

$$s = -s'. \tag{33–1}$$

This result is true whatever the value of the angle u. For the special case of a plane mirror, we see that the image of an object point lies on the extension of the normal from the object point to the mirror, and that the object distance and image distance are equal in absolute value.

Now consider an object of finite size and parallel to the mirror, represented by the arrow PQ in Fig. 33–3. Point P', the image of P, is found as in Fig. 33–2(a). Two of the rays from Q are shown in Fig. 33–3, and all rays from Q appear to diverge from its image Q' after reflection. Other points of the object PQ are imaged between P' and Q'. Let y and y' represent the lengths of object and image, respectively. These lengths are *measured from the axis PP', and are positive when this direction is up.* The ratio y'/y is called the *magnification m:*

$$m = \frac{y'}{y}.$$

From the triangles PQV and $P'Q'V$,

$$\tan \phi = \frac{y}{s} = \frac{y'}{-s'},$$

and since $s = -s'$, it follows that $y' = y$ and hence for a plane mirror the magnification is unity.

The image $P'Q'$ in Fig. 33–3 is called *virtual*, meaning that the reflected rays *appear* to diverge from the image, although they do not actually do so. Virtual images are represented by dashed lines.

The three-dimensional virtual image of a three-dimensional object, formed by a plane mirror, is shown in Fig. 33–4. The image of every object point lies on the normal from that point to the mirror, and the distances from object and image to the mirror are equal. Thus while the images $P'Q'$ and $P'S'$ are parallel to their objects, $P'R'$ is reversed relative to PR. The object and its image are related in the same way as are a left hand and a right hand. To verify this, point your thumbs along

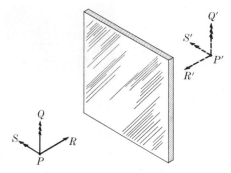

FIG. 33–4. A plane mirror forms a three-dimensional perverted image of a three-dimensional object.

PR and $P'R'$, your forefingers along PQ and $P'Q'$, and your middle fingers along PS and $P'S'$. When an object and image are related in this way the image is called *perverted*. When the transverse dimensions of object and image are in the same direction, the image is *erect*. Thus a plane mirror forms an erect but perverted image.

33–3 Reflection at a spherical mirror. Figure 33–5 shows a spherical mirror of radius of curvature R, with its concave side toward the left. The center of curvature of the surface is at C. In measuring the radius of curvature we shall always *start at the reflecting surface and proceed toward the center of curvature. If this direction is the same as that of the ongoing (reflected) light, the radius of curvature is positive.* In Fig. 33–5, R is positive. Point P is an object point. Since the direction from the mirror to P is opposite that for the oncoming light, the object distance s is positive. The ray PV, passing through C, strikes the mirror normally and is reflected back along itself. Point V is called the *vertex*, and the line PCV the *axis*.

Ray PB, at an arbitrary angle u with the axis, strikes the surface at B, where the angle of incidence is ϕ and the angle of reflection is $r = \phi$. The rays reflected at V and B intersect at the image point P' at a distance s' from the mirror. Since the direction from the mirror to P' is the same as that of the ongoing light, s' is positive. We wish to derive an expression for s'.

Making use of the fact that an exterior angle of a triangle equals the sum of the two opposite interior angles, and considering the triangles PBC and $P'BC$ of Fig. 33–5, we have

$$\theta = u + \phi, \qquad u' = \theta + \phi.$$

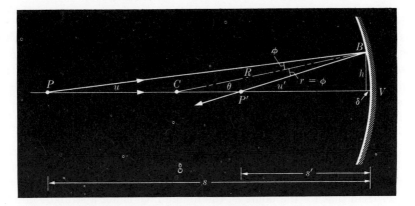

FIG. 33–5. Construction for finding the position of the image P' of a point object P, formed by a concave spherical mirror.

Eliminating ϕ between these equations gives

$$u + u' = 2\theta. \tag{33-2}$$

Let h represent the height of B above the axis, and δ the short distance from V to the foot of this vertical line. Now write the expressions for the tangents of u, u', and θ:

$$\tan u = \frac{h}{s - \delta}, \qquad \tan u' = \frac{h}{s' - \delta}, \qquad \tan \theta = \frac{h}{R - \delta}.$$

Evidently, these trigonometric equations cannot be solved as simply as the corresponding equations for a plane mirror. However, if the angle u is small, the angles u' and θ will be small also. Since the tangent of a small angle is nearly equal to the angle (in radians), we can replace tan u' by u', etc., in the equations above. Also, if u is small, the distance δ can be neglected compared with s', s, and R. Hence *approximately, for small angles,*

$$u = \frac{h}{s}, \qquad u' = \frac{h}{s'}, \qquad \theta = \frac{h}{R}.$$

Substituting in Eq. (33–2) and canceling h, we get

$$\boxed{\frac{1}{s} + \frac{1}{s'} = \frac{2}{R}} \tag{33-3}$$

as a general relation among the three quantities s, s', and R. The significant feature of the equation above is that *it does not contain the angle* u.

This means that *all* rays from P making sufficiently small angles with the axis will, after reflection, intersect at P'. Such rays, nearly parallel to the axis, are called *paraxial* rays. As the angle increases, the point P' moves closer to the vertex, and a spherical mirror, unlike a plane mirror, does not form a point image of a point object. This property of a spherical mirror is called *spherical aberration*.

If $R = \infty$ the mirror becomes plane and Eq. (33–3) reduces to Eq. (33–1), previously derived for this special case.

Now suppose we have an object of finite size, represented by the arrow PQ in Fig. 33–6, perpendicular to the axis PV. The image of P formed by paraxial rays is at P'. Since the object distance for point Q is a trifle greater than that for the point P, the image $P'Q'$ is not a straight line but is curved, another aberration of spherical surfaces, called *curvature of field*. However, if the height PQ is not too great, the image is nearly straight and perpendicular to the axis, and we shall assume this to be the case.

We now compute the magnification m. The ray QCQ', incident normally, is reflected back on itself. The ray QV makes an angle of incidence ϕ and an angle of reflection $r = \phi$. From the triangles PQV and $P'Q'V$,

$$\tan \phi = \frac{y}{s} = \frac{-y'}{s'}.$$

Hence

$$\boxed{m = \frac{y'}{y} = -\frac{s'}{s}.} \tag{33–4}$$

For a plane mirror, $s = -s'$ and hence $y' = y$, as we have already shown.

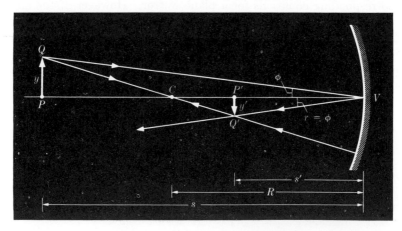

FIG. 33–6. Construction for determining the height of an image formed by a concave spherical mirror.

33-4 Sign conventions. In the sections to follow we shall see that in general an object point may lie on either side of a reflecting or refracting surface. The same is true of an image point, and of the center of curvature of a spherical surface. (If the latter lies at the left of the surface, the concave side of the surface faces toward the left.) Also, objects and images of finite size may extend either above or below the axis of a surface. By adopting a convention of algebraic signs for s, s', R, y, and y', it becomes unnecessary to derive special formulas for a large number of special cases. A single formula can cover all cases and the algebraic sign of a quantity will tell us whether it lies at the right or left of a surface, etc. Many sign conventions are in common use. The one that we have been using is due to R. E. Worley and applies equally well to reflecting and refracting surfaces, giving rise to the same relation between s and s' for both a mirror and a lens. In summary:

1. All distances are measured along the axis *from* the reflecting or refracting surface to the point in question.

2. An object distance (from the surface to the object) against the *oncoming* light is positive.

3. An image distance (from the surface to the image) with the *ongoing* light is positive.

4. A radius of curvature (from the surface to the center of curvature) with the *ongoing* light is positive.

5. An object or image dimension *above* the axis is positive.

To illustrate the use of these conventions, let us derive for a convex mirror the relation between object and image distance, and the expression

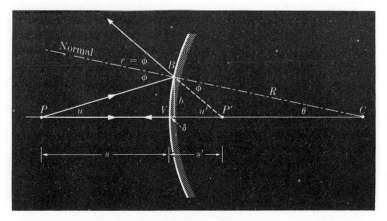

FIG. 33-7. Construction for finding the position of the image P' of a point object P, formed by a convex spherical mirror.

for the magnification. In Fig. 33–7 we make use of the triangles PBC and $P'BC$ and get

$$\phi = u + \theta, \qquad u' = \phi + \theta$$

or

$$u - u' = -2\theta. \tag{33–5}$$

Also

$$\tan u = \frac{h}{s + \delta}, \qquad \tan u' = \frac{h}{-s' - \delta}, \qquad \tan \theta = \frac{h}{-R - \delta}.$$

Assuming the angles u, u', and θ to be small (rays are paraxial) and that δ is very small compared with s, s', and R, the preceding equations become

$$u = \frac{h}{s}, \qquad u' = \frac{h}{-s'}, \qquad \theta = \frac{h}{-R},$$

and when these are substituted into Eq. (33–5), we get

$$\frac{1}{s} + \frac{1}{s'} = \frac{2}{R},$$

which is exactly the same formula as that obtained for a concave mirror (Eq. 33–3).

Figure 33–8 shows the image of a finite object formed by a convex mirror. From the triangles PQV and $P'Q'V$,

$$\tan \phi = \frac{y}{s} = \frac{y'}{-s'}.$$

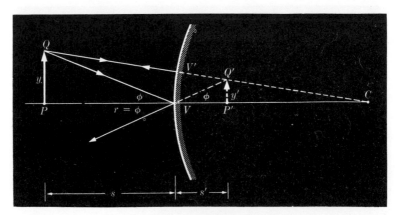

FIG. 33–8. Construction for determining the height of an image formed by a convex spherical mirror.

Hence, just as for a concave mirror (Eq. 33–4),

$$m = \frac{y'}{y} = -\frac{s'}{s}.$$

The image $P'Q'$ formed by the concave mirror in Fig. 33–6 is determined by actual rays of light that intersect at all the points lying between P' and Q'. Such an image is a *real image* and may be formed on a screen. In Fig. 33–8, however, the image formed by the convex mirror consists of points from which the reflected rays of light appear to be coming. Actually no real light exists in the space behind the mirror. This image is therefore a *virtual image*.

EXAMPLE 1. (a) What type of mirror is required to form an image, on a wall 3 m from the mirror, of the filament of a headlight lamp 10 cm in front of the mirror? (b) What is the height of the image if the height of the object is 5 mm?

(a) $s = 10$ cm, $s' = 300$ cm.

$$\frac{1}{10 \text{ cm}} + \frac{1}{300 \text{ cm}} = \frac{2}{R},$$

$$R = 19.4 \text{ cm}.$$

Since the radius is positive, a concave mirror is required.

(b) $m = -\frac{s'}{s} = -\frac{300 \text{ cm}}{10 \text{ cm}} = -30.$

The image is therefore inverted (m is negative) and is 30 times the height of the object, or $30 \times 5 = 150$ mm.

EXAMPLE 2. A small object lies 4 in. to the left of the vertex of a concave mirror of radius of curvature 12 in. Find the position and magnification of the image.

$$s = 4 \text{ in.}, \qquad R = 12 \text{ in.},$$

$$\frac{1}{4 \text{ in.}} + \frac{1}{s'} = \frac{2}{12 \text{ in.}},$$

$$s' = -12 \text{ in.},$$

$$m = -\frac{s'}{s} = -\frac{-12 \text{ in.}}{4 \text{ in.}} = 3.$$

The image is therefore 12 in. to the right of the vertex (s' is negative), is virtual (s' is negative), erect (m is positive), and 3 times the height of the object. See Fig. 33–9.

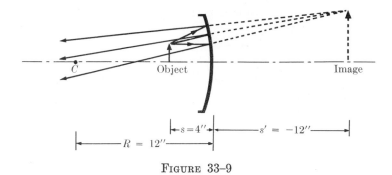

FIGURE 33-9

33-5 Focal point and focal length. When an object point is at a very large distance from a mirror, all rays from that point that strike the mirror are parallel to one another. The object distance $s = \infty$, and from Eq. (33-3)

$$\frac{1}{\infty} + \frac{1}{s'} = \frac{2}{R}, \qquad s' = \frac{R}{2}.$$

The image distance s' then equals one-half the radius of curvature and has the same sign as R. This means that if R is positive, as in Fig. 33-10(a), the image point F lies to the left of the mirror and is real, while if R is negative, as in (b), the image point F lies at the right of the mirror and is virtual.

Conversely, if the image distance s' is very large, the object distance s is

$$\frac{1}{s} + \frac{1}{\infty} = \frac{2}{R}, \qquad s = \frac{R}{2}.$$

The object distance then equals half the radius of curvature. If R is positive, as in Fig. 33-11(a), s is positive. If R is negative, as in Fig. 33-11(b), s is negative and the *object is behind* the mirror. That is, rays previously made converging by some other surface are converging toward F.

The point F in Figs. 33-10 and 33-11 is called the *focal point* of the mirror. It may be considered either as the image point of an infinitely distant object point on the mirror axis, or as the object point of an infinitely distant image point. Thus the mirror of an astronomical telescope forms at its focal point an image of a star on the axis of the mirror.

The distance between the vertex of a mirror and the focal point is called the *focal length* of the mirror and is represented by f. The magnitude of the focal length, from the preceding discussion, equals one-half the radius of curvature. We shall see in the next chapter that a lens also has a focal length, and that the focal length of a lens which *converges* parallel rays to a real image is also a positive quantity. A concave mirror, which

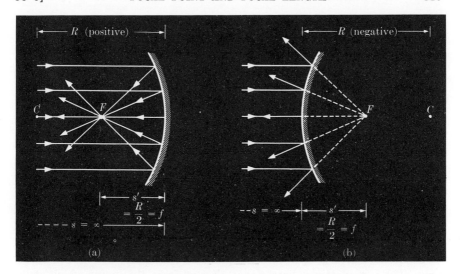

FIG. 33–10. Incident rays parallel to the axis (a) converge to the focal point F of a concave mirror, (b) diverge as though coming from the focal point F of a convex mirror.

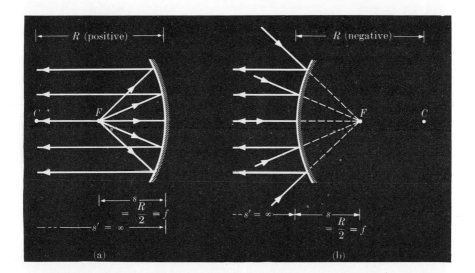

FIG. 33–11. Rays from a point object at the focal point of a spherical mirror are parallel to the axis after reflection. The object in part (b) is virtual.

behaves like a converging lens, has a positive focal length:

$$f = \frac{R}{2}.$$

(33–6)

The relation between object and image distances for a mirror may now
be written as

$$\frac{1}{s} + \frac{1}{s'} = \frac{1}{f}.$$

(33–7)

33–6 Graphical methods. The position and size of the image formed
by a mirror may be found by a simple graphical method. This method
consists of finding the point of intersection, after reflection from the mirror,
of a few rays diverging from some point of the object *not* on the mirror
axis. Then (neglecting aberrations) *all* rays from this point which strike

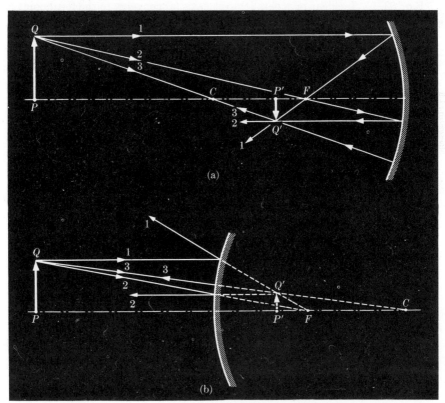

FIG. 33–12. Rays used in the graphical method of locating an image.

the mirror will intersect at the same point. Three rays whose paths may readily be traced are shown in Fig. 33–12.

1. *A ray parallel to the axis.* After reflection, this ray passes through the focal point of a concave mirror or appears to come from the focal point of a convex mirror.

2. *A ray from (or proceeding toward) the focal point.* This ray is reflected parallel to the axis.

3. *A ray along the radius* (extended if necessary). This ray intersects the surface normally and is reflected back along its original path.

Having found the position of the image point by means of the intersection of any two of the rays 1, 2, 3, the paths of all other rays from the same point may be drawn.

EXAMPLE. A concave mirror has a radius of curvature of magnitude 20 in. Find graphically the image of an object in the form of an arrow perpendicular to the axis of the mirror and at the following object distances: 30 in., 20 in., 10 in., 5 in. Check the construction by computing the size and magnification of the image.

The graphical construction is indicated in the four parts of Fig. 33–13. [Note that in (b) and (c) only two of the three rays can be used.] The calculations are given below.

The radius of curvature is $R = 20$ in., and the focal length $f = R/2 = 10$ in. Hence

$$\frac{1}{s} + \frac{1}{s'} = \frac{1}{f} = \frac{1}{10 \text{ in.}}.$$

(a)
$$\frac{1}{30 \text{ in.}} + \frac{1}{s'} = \frac{1}{10 \text{ in.}}, \qquad s' = 15 \text{ in.},$$

$$m = -\frac{s'}{s} = -\frac{15 \text{ in.}}{30 \text{ in.}} = -\frac{1}{2}.$$

(b)
$$\frac{1}{20 \text{ in.}} + \frac{1}{s'} = \frac{1}{10 \text{ in.}}, \qquad s' = 20 \text{ in.},$$

$$m = -\frac{s'}{s} = -\frac{20 \text{ in.}}{20 \text{ in.}} = -1.$$

(c)
$$\frac{1}{10 \text{ in.}} + \frac{1}{s'} = \frac{1}{10 \text{ in.}}, \qquad s' = \infty,$$

$$m = -\frac{s'}{s} = -\frac{\infty}{10 \text{ in.}} = -\infty.$$

(d)
$$\frac{1}{5 \text{ in.}} + \frac{1}{s'} = \frac{1}{10 \text{ in.}}, \qquad s' = -10 \text{ in.},$$

$$m = -\frac{s'}{s} = -\frac{-10 \text{ in.}}{5 \text{ in.}} = 2.$$

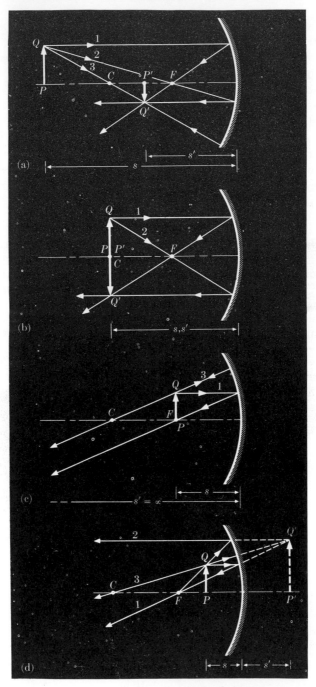

FIG. 33-13. Image of an object at various distances from a concave mirror.

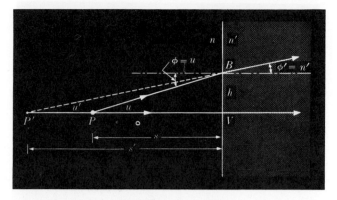

FIG. 33–14. Construction for finding the position of the image P' of a point object P, formed by refraction at a plane surface.

33–7 Refraction at a plane surface. The method of finding the image of a point object formed by rays refracted at a plane or spherical surface is essentially the same as for reflection, the only difference being that Snell's law replaces the law of reflection. In every case, we let n represent the index of the medium at the left of the surface and n' that of the medium at the right. The same convention of signs is used as in reflection.

Consider first a plane surface, shown in Fig. 33–14, and assume $n' > n$. A ray from the object point P toward the vertex V is incident normally and passes into the second medium without deviation. A ray making an angle u with the axis is incident at B with an angle of incidence $\phi = u$. The angle of refraction, ϕ', is found from Snell's law,

$$n \sin \phi = n' \sin \phi'.$$

The two rays both appear to come from point P' after refraction. From the triangles PVB and $P'VB$,

$$\tan \phi = \frac{h}{s}, \qquad \tan \phi' = \frac{h}{-s'}. \tag{33–8}$$

(We must write $-s'$, since this quantity is negative in the diagram.)

If the angle u is small, the angles ϕ, u', and ϕ' are small also, and therefore, approximately,

$$\tan \phi = \sin \phi, \qquad \tan \phi' = \sin \phi'.$$

Then Snell's law can be written as

$$n \tan \phi = n' \tan \phi',$$

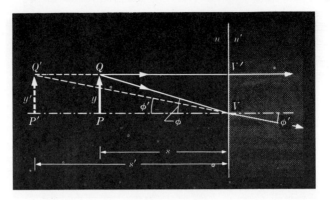

FIG. 33–15. Construction for determining the height of an image formed by refraction at a plane surface.

and from Eq. (33–8), after canceling h, we have

$$\frac{n}{s} = - \frac{n'}{s'},$$

or

$$\frac{s'}{s} = - \frac{n'}{n}. \tag{33–9}$$

This is an *approximate* relation, *good for paraxial rays only.* That is, a plane refracting surface does *not* image all rays from a point object at the same image point.

Consider next the image of a finite object, as in Fig. 33–15. The two rays shown diverging from point Q appear to diverge from its image Q' after refraction. From the triangles PQV and $P'Q'V$,

$$\tan \phi = \frac{y}{s}, \qquad \tan \phi' = \frac{y'}{-s'}.$$

Combining with Snell's law and using the small-angle approximation, $\sin \phi = \tan \phi$, $\sin \phi' = \tan \phi'$, we get

$$\frac{ny}{s} = - \frac{n'y'}{s'},$$

and hence

$$m = \frac{y'}{y} = - \frac{ns'}{n's}. \tag{33–10}$$

However, from Eq. (33–9), $ns' = -n's$, so

$$m = \frac{y'}{y} = 1 \quad \text{(plane refracting surface)},$$

in agreement with Fig. 33–15. The image distance is greater than the object distance, but image and object are the same size.

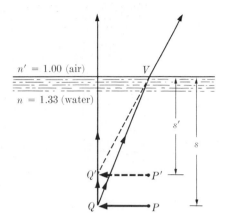

FIG. 33–16. Arrow $P'Q'$ is the image of the underwater object PQ.

A common example of refraction at a plane surface is afforded by looking vertically downward into the quiet water of a pond or a swimming pool; the apparent depth is less than the actual depth. Figure 33–16 illustrates this case. Two rays are shown diverging from a point Q at a distance s below the surface. Here, n' (air) is less than n (water) and the ray incident at V is deviated *away* *from* the normal. The rays after refraction appear to diverge from Q', and the arrow PQ, to an observer looking vertically downward, appears lifted to the position $P'Q'$. From Eq. (33–9),

$$s' = -\frac{n'}{n}s = -\frac{1.00}{4/3}s = -\frac{3}{4}s.$$

The apparent depth s' is therefore only three-fourths of the actual depth s. The same phenomenon accounts for the apparent sharp bend in an oar when a portion of it extends below a water surface. The submerged portion appears lifted above its actual position.

33–8 Refraction at a spherical surface. Finally, we consider refraction at a spherical surface. In Fig. 33–17, P is an object point at a distance s to the left of a spherical surface of radius R. The indices at the left and right of the surface are n and n', respectively. Ray PV, incident normally, passes into the second medium without deviation. Ray PB, making an angle u with the axis, is incident at an angle ϕ with the normal and is refracted at an angle ϕ'. These rays intersect at P' at a distance s' to the right of the vertex. From the triangles PBC and $P'BC$,

$$\phi = \theta + u, \qquad \theta = u' + \phi'. \tag{33–11}$$

From Snell's law,

$$n \sin \phi = n' \sin \phi'.$$

Also, the tangents of u, u', and θ are

$$\tan u = \frac{h}{s + \delta}, \qquad \tan u' = \frac{h}{s' - \delta}, \qquad \tan \theta = \frac{h}{R - \delta}. \tag{33–12}$$

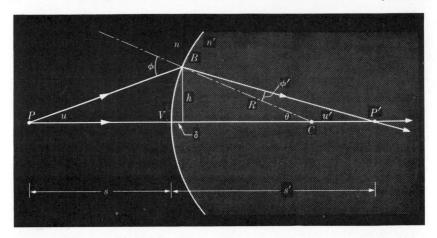

FIG. 33–17. Construction for finding the position of the image P' of a point object P, formed by refraction at a spherical surface.

For paraxial rays we may approximate both the sine and tangent of an angle by the angle itself, and neglect the small distance δ. Snell's law then becomes

$$n\phi = n'\phi',$$

and combining with the first of Eqs. (33–11), we get

$$\phi' = \frac{n}{n'}\,(u + \theta).$$

Substituting this in the second of Eqs. (33–11) gives

$$nu + n'u' = (n' - n)\theta.$$

Using the small-angle approximations of Eqs. (33–12) and canceling h, this becomes

$$\boxed{\frac{n}{s} + \frac{n'}{s'} = \frac{n' - n}{R}\,.} \qquad (33\text{–}13)$$

If $R = \infty$ and the surface is plane, this equation reduces to Eq. (33–9), already derived for the special case of a plane surface.

The magnification is found from the construction in Fig. 33–18. From point Q draw two rays, one through the center of curvature C and the other incident at the vertex V. From the triangles PQV and $P'Q'V$,

$$\tan\phi = \frac{y}{s}, \qquad \tan\phi' = \frac{-y'}{s'},$$

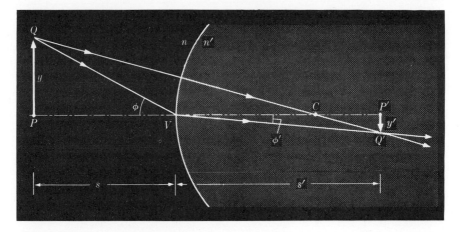

Fig. 33–18. Construction for determining the height of an image formed by refraction at a spherical surface.

and from Snell's law,

$$n \sin \phi = n' \sin \phi'.$$

For small angles,

$$\tan \phi = \sin \phi, \qquad \tan \phi' = \sin \phi',$$

and hence

$$\frac{ny}{s} = -\frac{n'y'}{s'},$$

or

$$m = \frac{y'}{y} = -\frac{ns'}{n's}, \qquad (33\text{–}14)$$

which agrees with the relation previously derived for a plane surface.

Equations (33–13) and (33–14) can be applied to both convex and concave refracting surfaces when a consistent sign convention is used, and they apply whether n' is greater or less than n. The reader should construct diagrams like Figs. 33–17 and 33–18, when R is negative and $n' < n$, and use them to derive Eqs. (33–13) and (33–14).

The concepts of focal point and focal length can also be applied to a refracting surface. Such a surface is found to have two focal points. The first is the object point when the image is at infinity, the second is the image point of an infinitely distant object. These points lie on opposite sides of the surface and at different distances from it, so that a single refracting surface has two focal lengths. The positions of the focal points can readily be found from Eq. (33–13) by setting s or s' equal to infinity.

33-9 Summary. The results of this chapter are conveniently summarized in Table 33-1. Note that by letting $R = \infty$, the equation for a plane surface follows immediately from the appropriate equation for a curved surface.

TABLE 33-1

	Plane mirror	Curved mirror	Plane refracting surface	Curved refracting surface
Object and image distances	$\dfrac{1}{s} + \dfrac{1}{s'} = 0$	$\dfrac{1}{s} + \dfrac{1}{s'} = \dfrac{2}{R} = \dfrac{1}{f}$	$\dfrac{n}{s} + \dfrac{n'}{s'} = 0$	$\dfrac{n}{s} + \dfrac{n'}{s'} = \dfrac{n' - n}{R}$
Magnification	$m = -\dfrac{s'}{s} = 1$	$m = -\dfrac{s'}{s}$	$m = -\dfrac{ns'}{n's} = 1$	$m = -\dfrac{ns'}{n's}$

EXAMPLE 1. One end of a cylindrical glass rod (Fig. 33–19) is ground to a hemispherical surface of radius $R = 20$ mm. Find the image distance of a point object on the axis of the rod, 80 mm to the left of the vertex. The rod is in air.

$$n = 1, \qquad n' = 1.5, \qquad R = +20 \text{ mm}, \qquad s = +80 \text{ mm}.$$

$$\frac{1}{80 \text{ mm}} + \frac{1.5}{s'} = \frac{1.5 - 1}{+20 \text{ mm}},$$

$$s' = +120 \text{ mm}.$$

The image is therefore formed at the right of the vertex (s' is positive) and at a distance of 120 mm from it. Suppose that the object is an arrow 1 mm high, perpendicular to the axis. Then

$$n = 1, \qquad n' = 1.5, \qquad s = +80 \text{ mm}, \qquad s' = +120 \text{ mm}.$$

Hence

$$m = -\frac{ns'}{n's} = -\frac{1 \times 120 \text{ mm}}{1.5 \times 80 \text{ mm}} = -1.$$

That is, the image is the same height as the object, but is inverted.

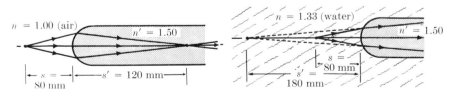

FIGURE 33-19   FIGURE 33-20

EXAMPLE 2. Let the same rod be immersed in water of index 1.33, the other quantities having the same values as before. Find the image distance (Fig. 33–20).

$$\frac{1.33}{80 \text{ mm}} + \frac{1.5}{s'} = \frac{1.5 - 1.33}{+20 \text{ mm}},$$

$$s' = -180 \text{ mm}.$$

The fact that s' is a negative quantity means that the rays, after refraction by the surface, are not converging but appear to diverge from a point 180 mm to the left of the vertex. We have met a similar case before in the refraction of spherical waves by a plane surface and have called the point a *virtual image*. In this example, then, the surface forms a virtual image 180 mm to the left of the vertex.

PROBLEMS

33–1. What is the size of the smallest vertical plane mirror in which an observer standing erect can see his full-length image?

33–2. The image of a tree just covers the length of a 2-in. plane mirror when the mirror is held 1 ft from the eye. The tree is 300 ft from the mirror. What is its height?

33–3. An object is placed between two mirrors arranged at right angles to each other. (a) Locate all of the images of the object. (b) Draw the paths of rays from the object to the eye of an observer.

33–4. An object 1 cm high is 20 cm from the vertex of a concave spherical mirror whose radius of curvature is 50 cm. Compute the position and size of the image. Is it real or virtual? Erect or inverted?

33–5. A concave mirror is to form an image of the filament of a headlight lamp on a screen 4 m from the mirror. The filament is 5 mm high, and the image is to be 40 cm high. (a) What should be the radius of curvature of the mirror? (b) How far in front of the vertex of the mirror should the filament be placed?

33–6. The diameter of the moon is 2160 mi and its distance from the earth is 240,000 mi. Find the diameter of the image of the moon formed by a spherical concave telescope mirror of focal length 12 ft.

33–7. A spherical concave shaving mirror has a radius of curvature of 1 ft. What is the magnification when the face is 4 in. from the vertex of the mirror?

33–8. A concave spherical mirror has a radius of curvature of 10 cm. Make a diagram of the mirror to scale, and show rays incident on it parallel to the axis and at distances of 1, 2, 3, 4, and 5 cm from it. Using a protractor, construct the reflected rays and indicate the points at which they cross the axis.

33–9. An object is 6 in. from the center of a silvered spherical glass Christmas tree ornament 3 in. in diameter. What is the position and magnification of its image?

33–10. A tank whose bottom is a mirror is filled with water to a depth of 20 cm. A small object hangs motionless 8 cm under the surface of the water. What is the apparent depth of its image when viewed at normal incidence?

33–11. A ray of light in air makes an angle of incidence of 45° at the surface of a sheet of ice. The ray is refracted within the ice at an angle of 30°. (a) What is the critical angle for the ice? (b) A speck of dirt is embedded $\frac{3}{4}$ in. below the surface of the ice. What is its apparent depth when viewed at normal incidence?

33–12. A microscope is focused on the upper surface of a glass plate. A second plate is then placed over the first. In order to focus on the bottom surface of the second plate, the microscope must be raised 1 mm. In order to focus on the upper surface it must be raised 2 mm *further*. Find the index of refraction of the second plate. (This problem illustrates one method of measuring index of refraction.)

33–13. A layer of ether ($n = 1.36$) 2 cm deep floats on water ($n = 1.33$) 4 cm deep. What is the apparent distance from the ether surface to the bottom of the water layer, when viewed at normal incidence?

33–14. The end of a long glass rod 8 cm in diameter has a hemispherical surface 4 cm in radius. The refractive index of the glass is 1.50. Determine each position of the image if an object is placed on the axis of the rod at the following distances from its end: (a) infinitely far, (b) 16 cm, (c) 4 cm.

33–15. The rod of Problem 33–14 is immersed in a liquid. An object 60 cm from the end of the rod and on its axis is imaged at a point 100 cm inside the rod. What is the refractive index of the liquid?

33–16. What should be the index of refraction of a transparent sphere in order that paraxial rays from an infinitely distant object will be brought to a focus at the vertex of the surface opposite the point of incidence?

33–17. The left end of a long glass rod 10 cm in diameter, of index 1.50, is ground and polished to a convex hemispherical surface of radius 5 cm. An object in the form of an arrow 1 mm long, at right angles to the axis of the rod, is located on the axis 20 cm to the left of the vertex of the convex surface. Find the position and magnification of the image of the arrow formed by paraxial rays incident on the convex surface.

33–18. A transparent rod 40 cm long is cut flat at one end and rounded to a hemispherical surface of 12 cm radius at the other end. A small object is embedded within the rod along its axis and halfway between its ends. When viewed from the flat end of the rod the apparent depth of the object is 12.5 cm. What is its apparent depth when viewed from the curved end?

33–19. A solid glass hemisphere having a radius of 10 cm and a refractive index of 1.50 is placed with its flat face downward on a table. A parallel beam of light of circular cross section 1 cm in diameter travels directly downward and enters the hemisphere along its diameter. What is the diameter of the circle of light formed on the table?

33–20. A small tropical fish is at the center of a spherical fish bowl 1 ft in diameter. Find its apparent position and magnification to an observer outside the bowl. The effect of the thin walls of the bowl may be neglected.

33–21. A solid glass sphere of radius R and index 1.50 is silvered over one hemisphere, as in Fig. 33–21. A small object is located on the axis of the sphere at a distance $2R$ from the pole of the unsilvered hemisphere. Find the position of the final image formed after all refractions and reflections have taken place.

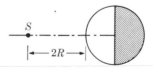

FIGURE 33–21

CHAPTER 34

LENSES

34–1 Images as objects. Most optical systems include more than one reflecting or refracting surface. The image formed by the first surface serves as the object for the second; the image formed by the second surface serves as the object for the third; etc. Figure 34–1 illustrates the various situations which may arise, and the following discussion of them should be thoroughly understood.

In Fig. 34–1, the arrow at point O represents a small object at right angles to the axis. A narrow cone of rays diverging from the head of the arrow is traced through the system. Surface 1 forms a real image of the arrow at point P. Distance V_1O is the object distance for the first surface and distance V_1P is the image distance. Both of these are positive.

The image at P, formed by surface 1, serves as the object for surface 2. The object distance is V_2P and is positive, since the direction from V_2 to P is opposite that of the oncoming light. The second surface forms a virtual image at point Q. The image distance is V_2Q and is negative because the direction from V_2 to Q is opposite that of the ongoing light.

The image at Q, formed by surface 2, serves as the object for surface 3. The object distance is V_3Q and is positive. The image at Q, although virtual, constitutes a real object so far as surface 3 is concerned. The rays incident on surface 3 are rendered converging and, except for the interposition of surface 4, would converge to a real image at point R. Even though this image is never formed, distance V_3R is the image distance for surface 3 and is positive.

The rays incident on surfaces 1, 2, and 3 have all been diverging and the object distance has been the distance from the point from which the rays were actually or apparently diverging to the vertex of the surface.

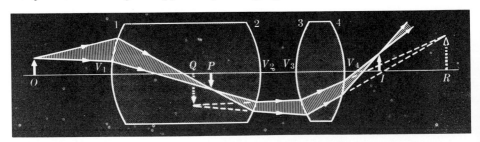

Fig. 34–1. The object for each surface, after the first, is the image formed by the preceding surface.

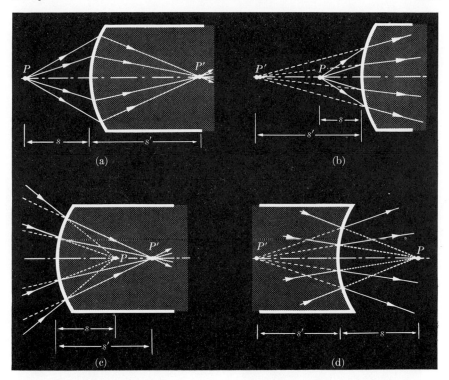

Fig. 34–2. (a) A real image of a real object. (b) A virtual image of a real object. (c) A real image of a virtual object. (d) A virtual image of a virtual object.

The rays incident on surface 4, however, are *converging* and there is no point at the left of the vertex from which they diverge or appear to diverge. *The image at R, toward which the rays are converging,* is the object for surface 4, and since this image is reached by proceeding in the direction of the oncoming light, the object distance V_4R is negative. The image at R is called a *virtual object* for surface 4. In general, whenever a *converging* cone of rays is incident on a surface, the point toward which the rays are converging serves as the object, the object distance is negative, and the point is called a virtual object.

Finally, surface 4 forms a real image at I, the image distance being V_4I and positive.

The meaning of virtual object and of virtual image are further exemplified by Fig. 34–2.

34–2 The thin lens. A lens is an optical system bounded by two refracting surfaces having a common axis. The general problem of refraction by a lens is solved by applying the methods of Section 34–1 to each

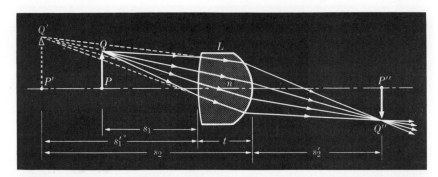

FIG. 34–3. The image formed by the first surface of a lens serves as the object for the second surface.

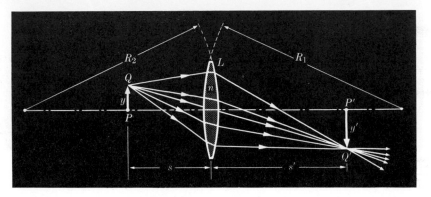

FIG. 34–4. A thin lens.

surface in turn, the object for the second surface being the image formed by the first. Figure 34–3 shows a pencil of rays diverging from point Q of an object PQ. The first surface of lens L forms a virtual image of Q at Q'. This virtual image serves as a real object for the second surface of the lens, which forms a real image of Q' at Q''. Distance s_1 is the object distance for the first surface; s_1' is the corresponding image distance. The object distance for the second surface is s_2, equal to the sum of s_1' and the lens thickness t, and s_2' is the image distance for the second surface.

If, as is often the case, the lens is so thin that its thickness t is negligible in comparison with the distances s_1, s_1', s_2, and s_2', we may assume that s_1' equals s_2, and measure object and image distances from either vertex of the lens. We shall also assume the medium on both sides of the lens to be air, with index of refraction 1.00. For the first refraction, Eq. (33–13) becomes

$$\frac{1}{s_1} + \frac{n}{s_1'} = \frac{n-1}{R_1}.$$

Refraction at the second surface yields

$$\frac{n}{s_2} + \frac{1}{s_2'} = \frac{1 - n}{R_2}.$$

Adding these two equations, and remembering that the lens is so thin that $s_2 = -s_1'$, we get

$$\frac{1}{s_1} + \frac{1}{s_2'} = (n - 1)\left(\frac{1}{R_1} - \frac{1}{R_2}\right).$$

Since s_1 is the object distance for the thin lens and s_2' is the image distance, the subscripts may be omitted, and we get finally

$$\frac{1}{s} + \frac{1}{s'} = (n - 1)\left(\frac{1}{R_1} - \frac{1}{R_2}\right). \qquad (34\text{–}1)$$

The usual sign conventions apply to this equation. Thus, in Fig. 34–4, s, s', and R_1 are positive quantities, but R_2 is negative.

The *focal length f* of a thin lens may be defined either as (a) the object distance of a point object on the lens axis whose image is at infinity, or (b) the image distance of a point object on the lens axis at an infinite distance from the lens. When we set either s or s' equal to infinity in Eq. (34–1) we find for the focal length

$$\frac{1}{f} = (n - 1)\left(\frac{1}{R_1} - \frac{1}{R_2}\right), \qquad (34\text{–}2)$$

which is known as the *lensmaker's equation.*

Substituting Eq. (34–2) in Eq. (34–1), the thin lens equation becomes

$$\frac{1}{s} + \frac{1}{s'} = \frac{1}{f}. \qquad (34\text{–}3)$$

This is known as the *gaussian* form of the thin lens equation, after the mathematician, Karl F. Gauss. Note that it has exactly the same form as the equation for a spherical mirror.

The object point for which the image is at infinity is called the *first focal point* of the lens and is lettered F in Fig. 34–5(a). The image point for an infinitely distant object is called the *second focal point* and is lettered

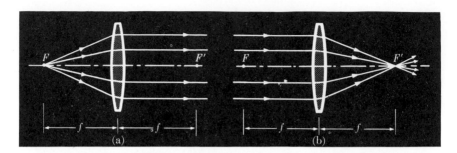

FIG. 34–5. First and second focal points of a thin lens.

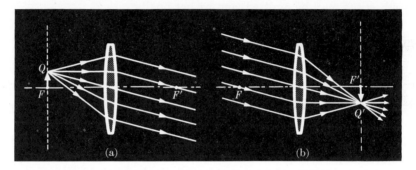

FIG. 34–6. Planes through the focal points of a lens are called *focal planes*.

F' in Fig. 34–5(b). The focal points of a thin lens lie on opposite sides of the lens at a distance from it equal to its focal length.

Figure 34–6 corresponds to Fig. 34–5, except that it is drawn for object and image points not on the axis of the lens. Planes through the first and second focal points of a lens, perpendicular to the axis, are called the first and second *focal planes*. Paraxial rays from point Q in Fig. 34–6(a), in the first focal plane of the lens, are parallel to one another after refraction. In other words, they converge to an infinitely distant image of point Q. In Fig. 34–6(b) a bundle of parallel rays from an infinitely distant point, not on the lens axis, converges to an image Q' lying in the second focal plane of the lens.

The three-dimensional image of a three-dimensional object, formed by a lens, is shown in Fig. 34–7. Since point R is nearer the lens than point P, its image, from Eq. (34–3), is farther from the lens than is point P', and the image $P'R'$ points in the same direction as the object PR. Arrows $P'S'$ and $P'Q'$ are reversed in space, relative to PS and PQ. Although we speak of the image as "inverted," only its transverse dimensions are reversed.

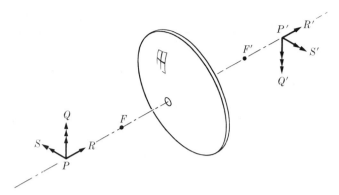

Fig. 34–7. A lens forms a three-dimensional image of a three-dimensional object.

Figure 34–7 should be compared with Fig. 33–4, showing the image formed by a plane mirror. Note that the image formed by a lens, although it is inverted, is not perverted. That is, if the object is a left hand, its image is a left hand also. This may be verified by pointing the left thumb along PR, the left forefinger along PQ, and the left middle finger along PS. A rotation of 180° about the thumb as an axis then brings the fingers into coincidence with $P'Q'$ and $P'S'$. In other words, inversion of an image is equivalent to a rotation of 180° about the lens axis.

The magnification produced by a lens is the product of the magnification at each of its surfaces. The magnification due to the first refraction is, from Eq. (33–14),

$$m_1 = -\frac{1 \times s_1'}{n s_1},$$

and that due to the second refraction is

$$m_2 = -\frac{n s_2'}{1 \times s_2}.$$

The over-all magnification m of the lens is therefore

$$m = \left(-\frac{1 \times s_1'}{n s_1}\right)\left(-\frac{n s_2'}{1 \times s_2}\right).$$

Since the lens is thin, $s_2 = -s_1'$, and

$$\boxed{m = -\frac{s'}{s}.}$$

$$(34\text{–}4)$$

A simpler derivation of this equation may be obtained merely by inspection of Fig. 34–4, where the object PQ, the image $P'Q'$, and the lines PP' and QQ' form two similar triangles. Hence

$$\frac{-y'}{y} = \frac{s'}{s},$$

and since m, as usual, is y'/y, we get

$$m = -\frac{s'}{s},$$

in agreement with Eq. (34–4).

Although Eqs. (34–3) and (34–4) were derived for the special case of rays making small angles with the axis and, in general, do not apply to rays making large angles, they may be used for any lens which has been corrected so that all rays are imaged at the same point. They are therefore two of the most important equations in geometrical optics.

34–3 Diverging lenses. A bundle of parallel rays incident on the lens shown in Figs. 34–5 and 34–6 converges to a real image after passing through the lens. The lens is called a *converging lens*. Its focal length, as computed from Eq. (34–2), is a positive quantity and therefore the lens is also called a *positive lens*.

A bundle of parallel rays incident on the lens in Fig. 34–8 becomes diverging after refraction and the lens is called a *diverging lens*. Its focal length, computed by Eq. (34–2), is a negative quantity and therefore the lens is also called a *negative lens*. The focal points of a negative lens are reversed, relative to those of a positive lens. The second focal point, F', of a negative lens is the point from which rays, originally parallel to the axis, appear to diverge after refraction, as in Fig. 34–8(a). Incident rays

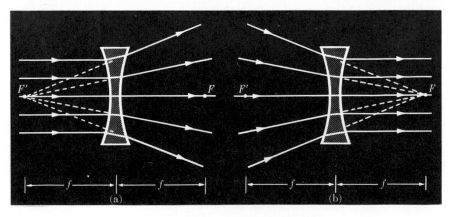

Fig. 34–8. Focal points of a diverging lens.

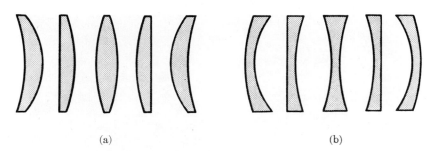

FIG. 34–9. (a) Meniscus, plano-convex, and double-convex converging lenses. (b) Meniscus, plano-concave, and double-concave diverging lenses.

converging toward the first focal point F, as in Fig. 34–8(b), emerge from the lens parallel to its axis. That is, just as for a positive lens, the second focal point is the (virtual) image of an infinitely distant object on the axis of the lens, while the first focal point is the object point (a virtual object if the lens is diverging) for which an image is formed at infinity. Equations (34–2) through (34–6) apply both to negative and to positive lenses. Various types of lenses, both converging and diverging, are illustrated in Fig. 34–9.

In addition to lenses having spherical surfaces, use is frequently made of *cylindrical* lenses, particularly in spectacles, to correct a defect of vision known as *astigmatism*. One or both surfaces of a cylindrical lens are portions of cylinders (Fig. 34–10). Since defects of vision other than astigmatism are frequently present also, a spectacle lens may be cylindrical at one surface and spherical at the other, or one of its surfaces may be a combined sphere and cylinder.

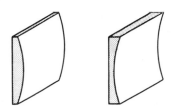

FIG. 34–10. Cylindrical lenses.

34–4 Graphical methods. The position and size of the image of an object formed by a thin lens may be found by a simple graphical method. This method consists of finding the point of intersection, after passing through the lens, of a few rays diverging from some chosen point of the object. Then (neglecting lens aberrations) all rays from this point which pass through the lens will intersect at the same point. In using the

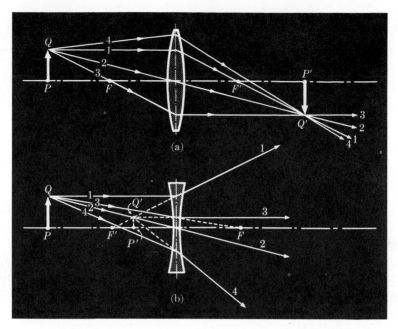

FIG. 34–11. Graphical method of locating an image.

graphical method, the entire deviation of any ray is assumed to take place at a plane through the center of the lens. Three rays whose paths may readily be traced are shown in Fig. 34–11.

1. *A ray parallel to the axis.* After refraction by the lens, this ray passes through the second focal point of a converging lens, or appears to come from the second focal point of a diverging lens.

2. *A ray through the center of the lens.* This ray is not appreciably deviated, since the two lens surfaces through which the central ray passes are very nearly parallel if the lens is thin. We have seen that a ray passing through a plate with parallel faces is not deviated, but only displaced. For a thin lens, the displacement may be neglected.

3. *A ray through (or proceeding toward) the first focal point.* This ray emerges parallel to the axis.

Having found the position of the image point by means of the intersection of any two of the rays 1, 2, 3, the paths of all other rays from the same point, such as ray 4 in Fig. 34–11, may be drawn. A few examples of this procedure are given in Fig. 34–12.

34–5 Images as objects for lenses. It was shown in Section 34–1 and Fig. 34–1 how the image formed by any one *surface* in an optical system

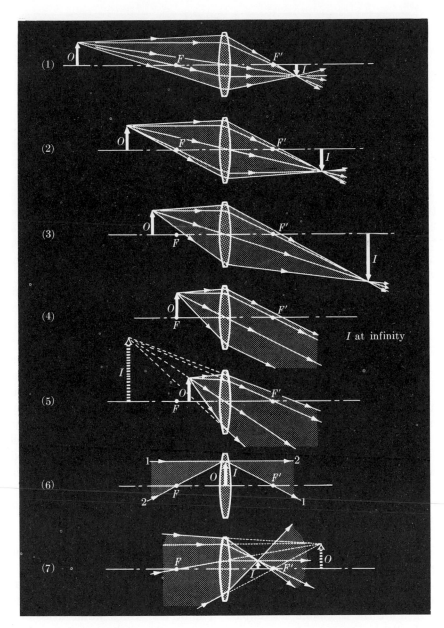

FIG. 34–12. Formation of an image by a thin lens.

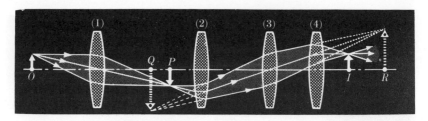

Fɪɢ. 34–13. The object for each lens, after the first, is the image formed by the preceding lens.

serves as the object for the next surface. In the majority of optical systems employing lenses, more than one lens is used and the image formed by any one *lens* serves as the object for the next lens. Figure 34–13 illustrates the various possibilities. Lens 1 forms a real image at P of a real object at O. This real image serves as a real object for lens 2. The virtual image at Q formed by lens 2 is a real object for lens 3. If lens 4 were not present, lens 3 would form a real image at R. Although this image is never formed, it serves as a virtual object for lens 4, which forms a final real image at I.

34–6 Lens aberrations. The relatively simple equations we have derived connecting object and image distances, focal lengths, radii of curvature, etc., were based upon the approximation that all rays made small angles with the axis. In general, however, a lens is called upon to image not only points on its axis, but points which lie off the axis as well. Furthermore, because of the finite size of the lens, the cone of rays which forms the image of any point is of finite size. Nonparaxial rays proceeding from a given object point do not, in general, all intersect at the same point after refraction by a lens. Consequently, the image formed by these rays is not a sharp one. Furthermore, the focal length of a lens depends upon its index of refraction, which varies with wavelength. Therefore, if the light proceeding from an object is not monochromatic, a lens forms a number of colored images which lie in different positions and are of different sizes, even if formed by paraxial rays.

The departures of an actual image from the predictions of simple theory are called *aberrations*. Those caused by the variation of index with wavelength are the *chromatic aberrations*. The others, which would arise even if the light were monochromatic, are the *monochromatic aberrations*. Lens aberrations are not caused by any faulty construction of the lens, such as the failure of its surfaces to conform to a truly spherical shape, but are simply consequences of the laws of refraction at spherical surfaces.

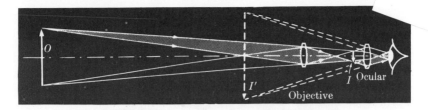

FIG. 34–14. The astronomical telescope.

34–7 The telescope. An *astronomical* telescope is illustrated in Fig. 34–14. The objective lens forms a real, reduced image I of the object O. I' is the virtual image of I formed by the ocular. The image I' may be formed anywhere between the near and far points of the eye.

In practice, the objects examined by a telescope are at such large distances from the instrument that the image I is formed very nearly at the second focal point of the objective. Furthermore, if the image I' is at infinity, the image I is at the first focal point of the ocular. (This is not the case in Fig. 34–14, which has been drawn to show all the essential elements in a finite diagram.) The distance between objective and ocular, or the length of the telescope, is therefore the sum of the focal lengths of objective and ocular, $f_1 + f_2$.

The angular magnification of a telescope is defined as the ratio of the angle subtended at the eye by the final image I', to the angle subtended at the (unaided) eye by the object. This ratio may be expressed in terms of the focal lengths of objective and ocular as follows. The shaded bundle of rays in Fig. 34–15 corresponds to that in Fig. 34–14, except that the object and the final image are both at infinity. The ray passing through F_1, the first focal point of the objective, and through F'_2, the second focal point of the ocular, has been emphasized. The object (not shown) subtends an angle u at the objective and would subtend essentially the same

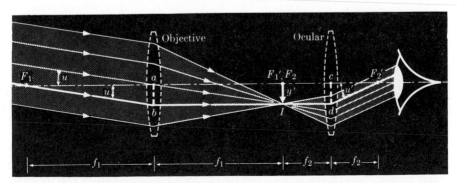

FIG. 34–15. Telescope, final image at infinity.

FIG. 34–16. The prism binocular. (Courtesy of Bausch & Lomb Optical Co.)

angle at the unaided eye. Also, since the observer's eye is placed just to
the right of the focal point F'_2, the angle subtended at the eye by the final
image is very nearly equal to the angle u'. The distances ab and cd are
evidently equal to each other and to the height y' of the image I. Since
both u and u' are small, they may be approximated by their tangents.
From the right triangles F_1ab and F'_2cd, $u = -y'/f_1$, $u' = y'/f_2$. Hence

$$M = \frac{u'}{u} = -\frac{y'/f_2}{y'/f_1} = -\frac{f_1}{f_2}. \qquad (34\text{–}5)$$

The angular magnification of a telescope is therefore equal to the ratio
of the focal length of the objective to that of the ocular. The minus sign
denotes an inverted image. While an inverted image is not a disadvantage
if the instrument is to be used for astronomical observations, it is desirable
that a terrestrial telescope shall form an erect image. This is accomplished in the *prism binocular*, of which Fig. 34–16 is a cutaway view,
by a pair of 45°-45°-90° totally reflecting prisms inserted between objective
and ocular. The image is inverted by the four reflections from the inclined
faces of the prisms.

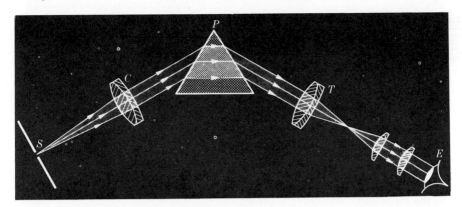

FIG. 34-17. Principle of the prism spectrometer.

34-8 The prism spectrometer. Optical instruments may be grouped into two general classes, *image-forming* instruments and *analyzing* instruments. Instruments of the former class serve to form the image of some given object; those of the latter class are used to determine the composition, intensity, or state of polarization of a beam of light. The prism spectrometer is an analyzing instrument, used primarily to discover what wavelengths are present in a given light beam.

The essential elements of a prism spectrometer are illustrated in Fig. 34-17. A narrow slit S, illuminated by the light to be analyzed, is located at the first focal point of the lens C, called the *collimator*. The parallel beam of light emerging from the collimator falls on the prism P, is deviated, and the emergent light examined by the telescope T. Since, as we have seen, the index of refraction of optical materials varies with wavelength, the various wavelengths present in the light are deviated by different angles.

The observer E sees a number of images of the slit side by side, each formed by light of a particular wavelength. If the source emits light of all wavelengths, the images form a continuous succession, called a *continuous spectrum*. If the source emits only a few definite wavelengths, the images of the slit are separated from one another and appear as a series of bright lines, each the color of the light producing it. The spectrum is then called a *line spectrum*.

PROBLEMS

34–1. A thin-walled glass sphere of radius R is filled with water. An object is placed a distance $3R$ from the surface of the sphere. Determine the position of the final image. The effect of the glass wall may be neglected.

34–2. A transparent rod 40 cm long is cut flat at one end and rounded to a hemispherical surface of 12 cm radius at the other end. An object is placed on the axis of the rod, 10 cm from the hemispherical end. (a) What is the position of the final image? (b) What is its magnification? Assume the refractive index to be 1.50.

34–3. Both ends of a glass rod 10 cm in diameter, of index 1.50, are ground and polished to convex hemispherical surfaces of radius 5 cm at the left end and radius 10 cm at the right end. The length of the rod between vertices is 60 cm. An arrow 1 mm long, at right angles to the axis and 20 cm to the left of the first vertex, constitutes the object for the first surface. (a) What constitutes the object for the second surface? (b) What is the object distance for the second surface? (c) Is the object real or virtual? (d) What is the position of the image formed by the second surface? (e) What is the height of the final image?

34–4. The same rod as in Problem 34–3 is now shortened to a distance of 10 cm between its vertices, the curvatures of its ends remaining the same. (a) What is the object distance for the second surface? (b) Is the object real or virtual? (c) What is the position of the image formed by the second surface? (d) Is the image real or virtual? Erect or inverted, with respect to the original object? (e) What is the height of the final image?

34–5. A glass rod of refractive index 1.50 is ground and polished at both ends to hemispherical surfaces of 5 cm radius. When an object is placed on the axis of the rod and 20 cm from one end the final image is formed 40 cm from the opposite end. What is the length of the rod?

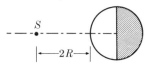

FIGURE 34–18

34–6. A solid glass sphere of radius R and index 1.50 is silvered over one hemisphere, as in Fig. 34–18. A small object is located on the axis of the sphere at a distance $2R$ from the pole of the unsilvered hemisphere. Find the position of the final image after all refractions and reflections have taken place.

34–7. A narrow beam of parallel rays enters a solid glass sphere in a radial direction. At what point outside the sphere are these rays brought to a focus? The radius of the sphere is 3 cm and its index is 1.50.

34–8. A glass plate 1 in. thick, of index 1.50, having plane parallel faces, is held with its faces horizontal and its lower face 4 in. above a printed page. Find the position of the image of the page, formed by rays making a small angle with the normal to the plate.

34–9. (a) Show that the equation $(1/s) + (1/s') = 1/f$ is that of an equilateral hyperbola having as asymptotes the lines $x = f$ and $y = f$. (b) Construct a graph with object distance (s) as abscissa, and image distance (s') as ordinate, for a lens of focal length f, and for object distances from 0 to ∞. (c) On the same set of axes construct a graph of magnification (ordinate) *vs.* object distance.

34–10. A converging lens has a focal length of 10 cm. For object distances of 30 cm, 20 cm, 15 cm, and 5 cm determine (a) image position, (b) magnification, (c) whether image is real or virtual, (d) whether image is erect or inverted.

34–11. Sketch the various possible thin lenses obtainable by combining two surfaces whose radii of curvature are, in absolute magnitude, 10 cm and 20 cm. Which are converging and which are diverging? Find the focal length of each lens if made of glass of index 1.50.

34–12. The radii of curvature of the surfaces of a thin lens are $+10$ cm and $+30$ cm. The index is 1.50. (a) Compute the position and size of the image of an object in the form of an arrow 1 cm high, perpendicular to the lens axis, 40 cm to the left of the lens. (b) A second similar lens is placed 160 cm to the right of the first. Find the position of the final image. (c) Same as (b) except the second lens is 40 cm to the right of the first. (d) Same as (c) except the second lens is diverging, of focal length -40 cm.

34–13. An object is placed 18 cm from a screen. (a) At what points between object and screen may a lens of 4 cm focal length be placed to obtain an image on the screen? (b) What is the magnification of the image for these positions of the lens?

34–14. An object is imaged by a lens on a screen placed 12 cm from the lens. When the lens is moved 2 cm farther from the object the screen must be

moved 2 cm closer to the object to refocus it. What is the focal length of the lens?

34–15. Three thin lenses, each of focal length 20 cm, are aligned on a common axis and are separated by 30 cm. Find the position of the image of a small object on the axis, 60 cm to the left of the first lens.

34–16. An equiconvex thin lens made of glass of index 1.50 has a focal length in air of 30 cm. The lens is sealed into an opening in one end of a tank filled with water (index $= 1.33$). At the end of the tank opposite the lens is a plane mirror, 80 cm distant from the lens. Find the position of the image formed by the lens-water-mirror system, of a small object outside the tank on the lens axis and 90 cm to the left of the lens. Is the image real or virtual? Erect or inverted?

34–17. For a thin converging lens, (a) what is the minimum distance between an object and its image if the image is real? (b) What is the minimum distance if the image is virtual?

34–18. A diverging meniscus lens of 1.48 refractive index has spherical surfaces whose radii are 2.5 and 4 cm. What would be the position of the image if an object were placed 15 cm in front of the lens?

34–19. A plano-convex lens is 2 cm thick along its axis. The refractive index is 1.50 and the radius of curvature of the convex surface is 10 cm. The convex surface faces toward the left. (a) Find the distance from the first focal point to the vertex of the convex surface. (b) Find the distance from the vertex of the plane surface to the second focal point.

34–20. When an object is placed at the proper distance in front of a converging lens, the image falls on a screen 20 cm from the lens. A diverging lens is now placed halfway between the converging lens and the screen, and it is found that the screen must be moved 20 cm farther away from the lens to obtain a clear image. What is the focal length of the diverging lens?

34–21. (a) Prove that when two thin lenses of focal lengths f_1 and f_2 are placed *in contact*, the focal length f of the combination is given by the relation

$$1/f = (1/f_1) + (1/f_2).$$

(b) A converging meniscus lens has an index of refraction of 1.50 and the radii of its surfaces are 5 and 10 cm. The concave surface is placed upward and filled with water. What is the focal length of the water-glass combination?

34–22. Two thin lenses, both of 10 cm focal length, the first converging, the second diverging, are placed 5 cm apart. An object is placed 20 cm in front of the first (converging) lens. (a) How far from this lens will the image be formed? (b) Is the image real or virtual?

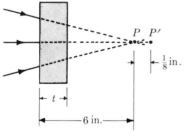

FIGURE 34–19

34–23. Rays from a lens are converging toward a point image P, as in Fig. 34–19. What thickness t of glass of index 1.50 must be interposed as in the figure in order that the image shall be formed at P'?

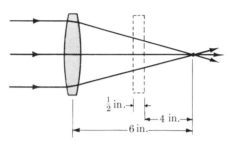

FIGURE 34–20

34–24. An object 10 ft in front of a camera lens is sharply imaged on a photographic film 6 in. behind the lens. A glass plate 0.5 in. thick, of index 1.50, having plane parallel faces, is interposed between lens and plate as shown in Fig. 34–20. (a) Find the new position of the image. (b) At what distance in front of the lens will an object be in sharp focus on the film with the plate in place, the distance from lens to film remaining 6 in.? Consider the lens as a simple thin lens.

34–25. An ocular consists of two similar positive thin lenses having focal lengths of 2 in., separated by a distance of 1 in. Where are the focal points of the ocular?

CHAPTER 35

INTERFERENCE AND DIFFRACTION

35–1 Principles of interference. Coherent sources. We have seen that the position and magnification of the image formed by a mirror or lens can be computed on the assumption that light travels in a straight line in a homogeneous medium, and that rays of light are deviated through definite angles at the surfaces separating two different media. The location of an image was seen to be a problem in geometry, and the methods used are those of *geometrical optics*.

In this chapter we shall discuss the phenomena of interference and diffraction, for whose understanding the principles of geometrical optics do not suffice. Instead, we must return to the more fundamental point of view that light is a wave motion, and that the effect of a number of wave trains arriving at one point on a screen depends upon the phases of the waves as well as upon their amplitudes. This part of the subject is called *physical optics*.

At any point where two or more trains of waves cross one another they are said to *interfere*. This does not mean that any wave train is impeded by the presence of the others, but refers to the combined effect of them all at the point in question. The *principle of superposition* states that the resultant displacement at any point and at any instant may be found by adding the instantaneous displacements that would be produced at the point by the individual wave trains if each were present alone. The term "displacement" as used here is a general one. If one is considering surface ripples on a liquid, the displacement means the actual displacement of the surface above or below its normal level. If the waves are sound waves, the term refers to the excess or deficiency of pressure. If the waves are electromagnetic, the displacement means the magnitude of the electric or magnetic field intensity.

The fundamental problem under consideration is the effect at one point on a screen when light waves coming from different sources arrive at this point. Suppose, for the sake of simplicity, that we have two sources. If the waves leaving these sources start in phase, travel different paths, and then come together on a screen, they *may* arrive in phase. If this is the case, they will reenforce each other. But this reenforcement may last only a very short time, for one of the sources may undergo a sudden phase shift, after which the two wave trains from the two sources will not start in phase. When these new waves arrive together at the screen, they may not reenforce. It is a fundamental property of the atoms or molecules of a source of light that they are continually undergoing transitions which produce frequent haphazard phase changes in the light which they emit.

To produce observable interference effects, *it is necessary to have two sources emitting light waves which, at the start, are always in phase. This can never be accomplished with two separate sources.* Even if the light waves from separate sources were in phase at one moment, they would shortly get out of phase. To ensure the existence of two light waves leaving two points always in phase, *it is necessary to start with only one light wave* and to split this wave into two parts, each of which travels a different path, the two waves eventually meeting at the same point on a screen. In these circumstances, any haphazard changes of phase which the original light wave undergoes are shared by the two parts, which therefore leave their respective starting points always in phase. Two points of this sort are called *coherent sources*.

Let S_2 and S_3 in Fig. 35-1 represent two coherent *point* sources on the line xO, and P a point in a vertical plane for which the path difference $PS_2 - PS_3$ is some whole number of wavelengths $m\lambda$. The vibrations at P due to the two waves will therefore be in phase and the two waves will reenforce each other at this point. Reenforcement will also take place at point P' in a horizontal plane if $P'S_2 = PS_2$ and $P'S_3 = PS_3$. In fact, at all points of the circle through P and P', with center at O, the

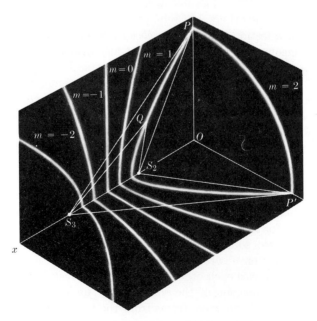

Fig. 35-1. Curves of maximum intensity in the interference pattern of two monochromatic point sources.

waves from the two sources will reenforce, and a bright circular *interference fringe* will appear on a vertical screen through P and P', perpendicular to the line xO.

Point Q in Fig. 35–1 is another point for which the path difference $QS_2 - QS_3$ is also $m\lambda$, and the curve passing through P and Q is the locus of all such points in the vertical plane. This curve is a hyperbola, a curve which has the property that the difference between the distances from any point on it to two fixed points is a constant. If we imagine this hyperbola to be rotated about the line xO as an axis, it sweeps out a surface called a *hyperboloid*, and we see that the waves from S_2 and S_3 will arrive at *all* points of this surface so as to reenforce each other.

The diagram of Fig. 35–1 has been drawn for the simple case where the distance from S_2 to S_3 is 3λ, and where the path difference $PS_2 - PS_3 = 2\lambda$ $(m = 2)$. The hyperbola lettered $m = 1$ is the locus of points in a vertical plane for which the path difference is λ. The locus of all points for which the path difference is zero $(m = 0)$ is a line passing through the midpoint of S_2S_3. Hyperbolas for which $m = -1$ and $m = -2$ are also shown. Rotation of these curves about xO gives rise, in this case, to five hyperboloids. Bright lines will appear on a screen in any position, along those curves where the hyperboloids intersect the screen.

If the distance between the sources is many wavelengths, there will be a large number of surfaces over which the waves reenforce, and a large number of alternate bright and dark hyperbolic (almost straight) fringes will be formed on a screen parallel to the line joining the sources. Also, a great number of alternate bright and dark circular fringes will be formed on a screen perpendicular to the line joining the sources.

The experimental realization of these ideas will be described in the next section.

35–2 Young's experiment and Pohl's experiment. One of the earliest demonstrations of the fact that light can produce interference effects was performed in 1802 by the English scientist Thomas Young. The experiment was a crucial one at the time, since it added further evidence to the growing belief in the wave nature of light. A corpuscular theory was quite inadequate to account for the effects observed.

Young's apparatus is shown in Fig. 35–2(a). Light from a source at the left (not shown) falls on a narrow slit S_1. Two more slits, S_2 and S_3, are parallel to S_1 and equidistant from it. When a screen is placed at the right of these slits, a number of alternate bright and dark bands are observed on it, parallel to the slits, as shown in the lower part of Fig. 35–3. If either of the slits S_2 or S_3 is covered, the dark lines disappear, and the screen is illuminated in a broad band, as shown in the upper part of Fig. 35–3. A corpuscular theory cannot account for the fact that a point

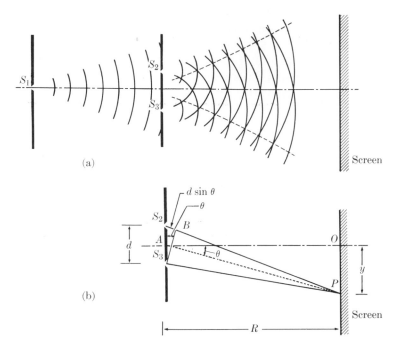

(a)

(b)

FIG. 35-2. Interference of light waves passing through two slits. Young's experiment.

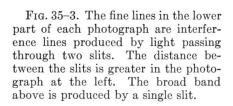

FIG. 35-3. The fine lines in the lower part of each photograph are interference lines produced by light passing through two slits. The distance between the slits is greater in the photograph at the left. The broad band above is produced by a single slit.

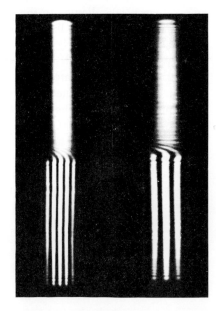

on the screen, bright when only one slit is exposed, becomes dark when both slits are exposed. The explanation in terms of the wave theory follows.

According to Huygens' principle, cylindrical wavelets spread out from slit S_1 and reach slits S_2 and S_3 at the same instant. A train of Huygens wavelets diverges from both of these slits, which therefore act as coherent sources. Let d represent the distance between the slits, and consider a point P on the screen, in a direction making an angle θ with the axis of the system [Fig. 35–2(b)]. With P as a center and PS_3 as radius, strike an arc intersecting PS_2 at B. If the distance R from slits to screen is large in comparison with the distance d between the slits, the arc S_3B can be considered a straight line at right angles to PS_3, PA, and PS_2. Then the triangle BS_2S_3 is a right triangle, similar to POA, and the distance S_2B equals $d \sin \theta$. This latter distance is the difference in path length between the waves reaching P from the two slits. The waves spreading out from S_2 and S_3 necessarily start in phase, but they will not be in phase at P because of this difference in length of path. According to the principles discussed in the preceding section, complete reenforcement will take place at the point P, that is, P will lie at the center of a bright fringe when the path difference $d \sin \theta$ is some integral number of wavelengths, say $m\lambda$ (m = 0,1,2,3, etc.). Thus

$$d \sin \theta = m\lambda,$$

or

$$\sin \theta = \frac{m\lambda}{d}.$$

Now λ is of the order 5×10^{-5} cm, while d cannot be made much smaller than about 10^{-2} cm. As a rule, only the first five to ten fringes are bright enough to be seen, so that m is at most, say, 10. Therefore the very largest value of $\sin \theta$ is

$$\sin \theta \text{ (maximum)} = \frac{10 \times 5 \times 10^{-5} \text{ cm}}{10^{-2} \text{ cm}} = 0.05,$$

which corresponds to an angle of only 3°.

The central bright fringe at point O, or zeroth fringe (m = 0), corresponds to zero path difference, or $\sin \theta = 0$. If point P is at the center of the mth fringe, the distance y from the zeroth to the mth fringe is, from Fig. 35–2(b),

$$y = R \tan \theta.$$

Since, however, the angle θ for all values of m is extremely small,

$$y = R \sin \theta.$$

Therefore

$$y = R \frac{m\lambda}{d},$$

and

$$\lambda = \frac{yd}{mR}. \qquad (35\text{–}1)$$

Hence by measuring the distance between the slits, the distance to the screen, and the distance from the central fringe to some fringe on either side, the wavelength of the light producing the interference pattern may be computed.

EXAMPLE. With two slits spaced 0.2 mm apart, and a screen at a distance of one meter, the third bright fringe is found to be displaced 7.5 mm from the central fringe. Find the wavelength of the light used.

Let λ be the unknown wavelength in centimeters. Then

$$\lambda = \frac{yd}{mR} = \frac{0.75 \text{ cm} \times 0.02 \text{ cm}}{3 \times 100 \text{ cm}} = 5 \times 10^{-5} \text{ cm} = 500 \text{ m}\mu.$$

Circular interference fringes may be produced very easily with the aid of simple apparatus suggested by Robert Pohl, professor of physics at the University of Göttingen. A small mercury arc lamp S_1 is placed a few

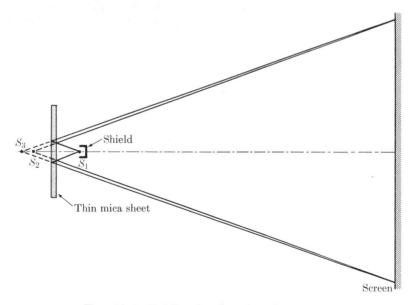

FIG. 35–4. Pohl's mica-sheet interferometer.

FIG. 35–5.   Circular interference fringes produced by Pohl's mica inter-ferometer.   The dark rectangle is the shadow of the mercury arc housing. (Photographed by I. Antman.)

centimeters away from a sheet of mica of thickness about 0.002 inch, as shown in Fig. 35–4.   Some light is reflected from the first surface, as though it were issuing from the virtual image S_2.   An approximately equal amount of light is reflected from the back surface as though it were com-ing from the virtual image S_3.   The circular interference fringes formed by the light issuing from these two coherent sources may be thrown on the entire wall of a room, as shown in Fig. 35–5.

35–3 Phase changes in reflection.   A very important fact concerning the reflection of light from a surface of higher index of refraction than that in which it is originally traveling is demonstrated with the aid of an interferometer known as *Lloyd's mirror*.   This is depicted in Fig. 35–6. In this arrangement, the two coherent sources are the actual slit source S_1 and its virtual image S_2.   The fringes formed by interference between the light waves from these coherent sources may be viewed on a ground glass screen placed anywhere beyond the mirror.   If, instead of viewing the fringes on a screen, an ocular is used to view the fringes that form in space

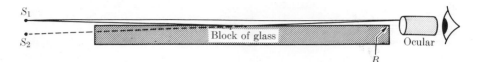

FIG. 35–6. Lloyd's mirror. When the ocular is focused on the edge B of the glass block, the fringe nearest the edge is black.

in a plane passing through the edge B, the fringe nearest this edge is seen to be black. This is the fringe corresponding to zero path difference, and if the two wave trains giving rise to this fringe had both traveled in air or had both been reflected from glass, this fringe would have been bright. Of the two wave trains forming the zeroth fringe, however, one had undergone reflection from the glass and one had proceeded directly from S_1. The fact that the zeroth fringe is black indicates that *the waves reflected from glass have undergone a phase shift of 180°.* In other words, the wave train has gained (or lost) half a wavelength in the process of reflection.

35–4 Interference in thin films. The brilliant colors that are often seen when light is reflected from a soap bubble or from a thin layer of oil floating on water are produced by interference effects between the two trains of light waves reflected at opposite surfaces of the thin films of soap solution or of oil. In Fig. 35–7, the line ab is one ray in a beam of mono- chromatic light incident on the upper surface of a thin film. The lines at right angles to ab indicate the wave surfaces in the incident beam. A part of the incident light is reflected at the first surface, as indicated by ray bc, and a part, represented by bd, is transmitted. At the second surface a part is again reflected and of this a part emerges as represented by ray ef. Lines at right angles to bc and ef represent wave surfaces. If

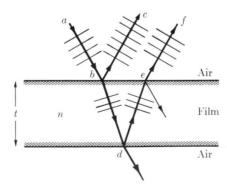

FIG. 35–7. Interference between light waves reflected from the upper and lower surfaces of a thin film.

the beam has appreciable width, the wave surfaces will overlap and the reflected wave trains can produce interference effects.

For simplicity, we shall assume that light is incident at right angles to the film. Let t represent the thickness of the film and n its index of refraction. If λ is the wavelength of the light waves in air, the wavelength in the film is λ/n, and the number of waves contained in the path length through the film and back, or $2t$, is $2t/(\lambda/n)$. Suppose this is some integral number. Then a wave surface in the light that has traveled through the film and back emerges from the film at the same time that a wave surface in the incident wave train arrives at and is reflected from the film. If no other considerations were involved, the waves reflected from the two surfaces would be in the correct relation to interfere *constructively*, that is, their displacements would add. However, at the upper surface the light is reflected from a medium of index greater than that in which it is traveling, while the reverse is true at the lower surface. As was shown with Lloyd's mirror, when a train of waves is reflected at the surface of a medium of higher index, the reflected wave train loses (or gains) half a wavelength. Hence the waves that have traveled through the film and back are exactly out of phase with the waves reflected at the upper surface and the wave trains interfere *destructively*. In other words, if the path length through the film and back contains an integral number of waves, no light is reflected. It can be seen without further detailed explanation that if the path length through the film and back contains some integral number of waves *plus half a wave*, conditions are right for constructive interference and there will be strong reflection.

If the film is extremely thin compared with the wavelength of light, the path length through the film and back is negligible and the only outstanding effect is the loss of half a wavelength in the waves reflected at the first surface. Then, regardless of wavelength, the waves reflected from the two surfaces are out of step and destroy one another. Hence no light is reflected and the film appears black by reflected light. (There is no violation of the principle of conservation of energy in destructive interference, since whatever energy is absent in the reflected light is found in the transmitted light.)

If the film is in the shape of a thin wedge of narrow angle, and is viewed by reflected monochromatic light, it will appear to be crossed by parallel bright bands of the color of the light used, separated by dark bands. At the apex, the film will be dark. At a distance from the apex such that the film thickness is one-quarter of a wavelength, it will be bright. Where the thickness equals one-half a wavelength it will be dark, and so on. If the film is illuminated first by blue, then by red light, the spacing of the red bands is greater than that of the blue, as is to be expected from the greater wavelength of the red light. The bands produced by intermediate wavelengths occupy intermediate positions. If the film is illuminated by white light, its color at any point is that due to the mixture of those colors which may be reflected at that point, while the colors for which the thickness is such as to result in destructive interference are absent. Just those colors which are absent in the reflected light, however, are found to predominate in the transmitted light. At any point, the color of the film by reflected light is complementary to its color by transmitted light.

The phenomenon of interference is utilized in the production of so-called "nonreflecting" glass. A thin layer or film of transparent material is deposited on the surface of the glass, as in Fig. 35–8. If the index of this material is properly chosen at some value intermediate between that of air and the glass, equal quantities of light will be reflected from its outer surface, and from the boundary surface between it and the glass. Furthermore, since in both reflections the light is reflected from a medium of greater index than that in which it is traveling, the same phase change occurs in each reflection. It follows that if the film thickness is one-quarter wavelength (normal incidence is assumed), the light reflected from the first surface will be 180° out of phase with that reflected from the second, and complete destructive interference will result.

The thickness can, of course, be one-quarter wavelength for one particular wavelength only. This is usually chosen in the yellow-green portion of the spectrum, where the eye is most sensitive. Some reflection then takes place at both longer and shorter wavelengths and the reflected light has a purple hue. The over-all reflection from a lens or prism surface can be reduced in this way from 4 or 5 percent to a fraction of 1 percent. The treatment is extremely effective in eliminating stray reflected light and increasing the contrast in an image formed by highly corrected lenses having a large number of air-glass surfaces.

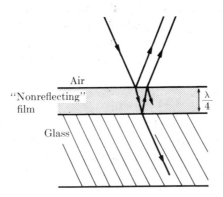

Fig. 35–8. Destructive interference results when the film thickness is one-quarter of a wavelength.

35–5 Newton's rings. If the convex surface of a lens is placed in contact with a plane glass plate, as in Fig. 35–9, a thin film of air is formed between the two surfaces. The thickness of this film is very small at the point of contact, gradually increasing as one proceeds outward. The loci of points of equal thickness are circles concentric with the point of contact. Such a film is found to exhibit interference colors, produced in the same way as the colors in a thin soap film. The interference bands are circular, concentric with the point of contact. When viewed by reflected light, the center of the pattern is black, as is a thin soap film. Note that in this case there is no phase reversal of the light reflected from the upper surface of the film (which here is of smaller index than that of the medium in which the light is traveling before reflection), but the phase of the wave reflected from the lower surface is reversed. When viewed by transmitted light, the center of the pattern is bright. If white light is used, the color of the light reflected from the film at any point is complementary to the color transmitted.

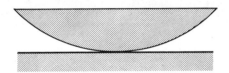

FIG. 35–9. Air film between a convex and a plane surface.

These interference bands were studied by Newton, and are called after him, *Newton's rings.* Figure 35–10 is a photograph of Newton's rings, formed by the air film between a convex and a plane surface.

The surface of an optical part which is being ground to some desired curvature may be compared with that of another surface, known to be correct, by bringing the two in contact and observing the interference fringes. For example, if a plane surface (an "optical flat") is desired, a glass plate whose lower surface is accurately plane is placed over the surface to be tested. If both surfaces are accurately plane, and if contact between them is made at one edge, a series of straight interference fringes, parallel to the line of contact, will be observed. If the surface being ground is not plane, the interference bands will be curved. By noting the shape and separation of the fringes, the departure of the surface from the desired form may be determined.

Figure 35–11 is a photograph made at one stage of the process of manufacturing a telescope objective. The lower, larger diameter, thicker disk is the master. The smaller upper disk is the objective under test. The "contour lines" are Newton's interference fringes, and each one indicates an additional departure of the specimen from the master of one-half a

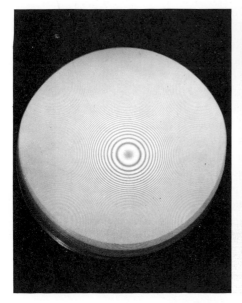

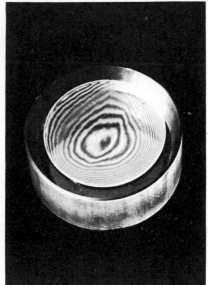

FIG. 35–10. Newton's rings formed by interference in the air film between a convex and a plane surface. (Courtesy of Bausch & Lomb Optical Co.)

FIG. 35–11. The surface of a telescope objective under inspection during manufacture. (Courtesy of Bausch & Lomb Optical Co.)

wavelength of light. That is, at 10 lines from the center spot the space between the specimen and master is 5 wavelengths, or about 0.0002 inch. This specimen is very poor.

35–6 Diffraction. According to geometrical optics, if an opaque object is placed between a point light source and a screen, as in Fig. 35–12, the edges of the object will cast a sharp shadow on the screen (the penumbra will be negligible if the source is sufficiently small). No light will reach the screen at points within the geometrical shadow, while outside the shadow the screen will be uniformly illuminated. The photograph repro-

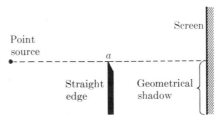

FIG. 35–12. Geometrical shadow of a straight edge.

FIG. 35–13. Shadow of a razor blade.

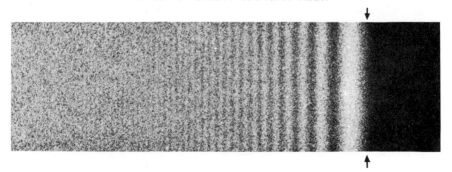

FIG. 35–14. Shadow of a straight edge.

duced in Fig. 35–13 was made by placing a razor blade halfway between a pinhole illuminated by monochromatic light and a photographic film, so that the film made a record of the shadow cast by the blade. Figure 35–14 is an enlargement of a region near the shadow of an edge of the blade. The boundary of the *geometrical* shadow is indicated by the short arrows. Note that a small amount of light has "bent" around the edge, into the geometrical shadow, which is bordered by alternate bright and dark bands. Note also that in the first bright band, just outside the geometrical shadow, the illumination is actually greater than in the region of uniform illumination at the extreme left.

This simple experimental setup serves to give some idea of the true complexity of what is often considered the most elementary of optical phenomena, the shadow cast by a small source of light.

The reason that a diffraction pattern like that of Fig. 35–13 is not commonly observed in the shadow of an object is merely that most light sources are not point sources. If a shadow of a razor blade is cast by a frosted bulb incandescent lamp, for example, the light from every point of the surface of the lamp forms its own diffraction pattern, but these overlap to such an extent that no individual pattern can be observed.

The term *diffraction* is applied to problems in which one is concerned with *the resultant effect produced by a limited portion of a wave surface.* Since in most diffraction problems some light is found within the region of geometrical shadow, diffraction is sometimes defined as "the bending of light around an obstacle." It should be emphasized, however, that the process by which diffraction effects are produced is going on continuously in the propagation of every wave. Only if a part of the wave is cut off by some obstacle are the effects commonly called "diffraction effects" observed. But since every optical instrument does in fact make use of only a limited portion of a wave (a telescope, for example, utilizes only that portion of a wave admitted by the objective lens), it is evident that a clear comprehension of the nature of diffraction is essential for a complete understanding of practically all optical phenomena.

The main features observed in diffraction effects can be predicted with the help of Huygens' principle, according to which every point of a wave surface can be considered the source of a secondary wavelet which spreads out in all directions. However, instead of finding the new wave surface by the simple process of constructing the envelope of all the secondary wavelets, we must combine these wavelets according to the principles of interference. That is, at every point we must combine the displacements that would be produced by the secondary wavelets, taking into account their amplitudes and relative phases. The mathematical operations required are not simple (one must find the combined effect of an infinite number of infinitesimal wavelets) and it must suffice here to indicate only the general ideas involved, and describe the results.

35–7 Fraunhofer diffraction by a single slit. In the drawing of Fig. 35–15, a beam of parallel monochromatic light is incident from the left on an opaque plate in which there is a narrow horizontal slit. According to the principles of geometrical optics, the transmitted beam would have the same cross section as the slit, and a screen in the path of the beam would be illuminated uniformly over an area of the same size and shape as the slit, as in part (a) of the figure. Actually, what one observes on the screen is the diffraction pattern shown in part (b). The beam spreads

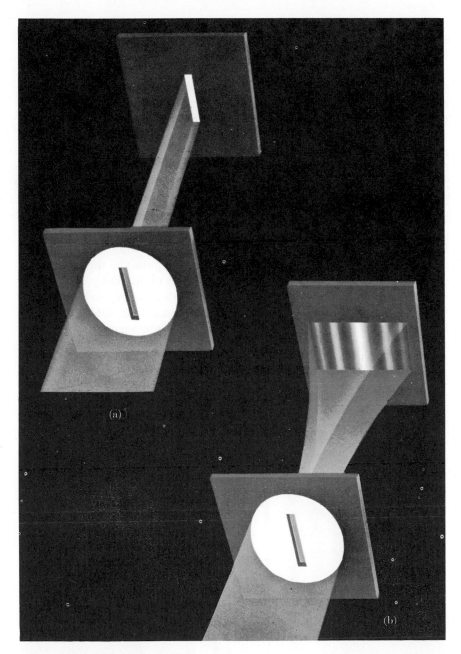

FIG. 35–15. (a) Geometrical "shadow" of a slit. (b) Diffraction pattern of a slit. The slit width has been greatly exaggerated.

out laterally after passing through the slit, and the diffraction pattern consists of a central bright band, which may be much wider than the slit width, bordered by alternating dark bands and bright bands of decreasing intensity. A diffraction pattern of this nature can readily be observed by looking at a point source such as a distant street light through a narrow slit formed between two fingers in front of the eye. The retina of the eye then corresponds to the screen in Fig. 35–15.

The width of the slit in Fig. 35–15 has been greatly exaggerated for clarity. To obtain a lateral spread having the proportions shown in the figure, the slit width would have to be of the order of 5 wavelengths of light. There is also a small horizontal spreading of the beam, which has been omitted in the diagram for simplicity.

Figure 35–16 is an enlargement of a photograph made by placing a photographic film in the plane of the screen in a setup like that in Fig. 35–15(b).

Let us now apply Huygens' principle to compute the distribution of light on the screen. Small elements of area are obtained by subdividing the wave surface passing through the slit into narrow strips, parallel to the long edges of the slit. A section through the slit is shown in Fig. 35–17(a). The division of the wave surface into narrow strips, which are seen end on, is indicated by the short lines across the wave surface. From each of these strips, secondary wavelets spread out in all directions, as shown.

In Fig. 35–17(b), a screen is placed at the right of the slit and P is one point on a line in the screen, the line being parallel to the long edges of the slit and perpendicular to the plane of the diagram. The light reaching a point on the line is calculated by applying the principle of superposition to all the wavelets arriving at the point, from all the elementary

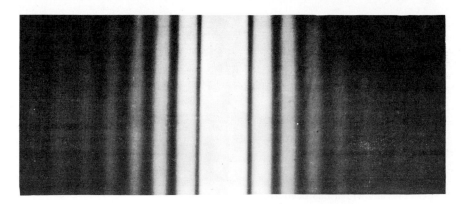

FIG. 35–16. Diffraction pattern of a single slit.

strips of the original wave surface. Because of the varying distances to the point, and the varying angles with the original direction of the light, the amplitudes and phases of the wavelets at the point will be different.

The problem is greatly simplified when the screen is sufficiently distant, or the slit sufficiently narrow, so that all rays from the slit to a point on the screen can be considered parallel, as in Fig. 35–17(c). The former case, where the screen is relatively close to the slit (or the slit is relatively wide) is referred to as *Fresnel* diffraction, the latter as *Fraunhofer* diffraction, named, respectively, after Augustin Jean Fresnel, French physicist, 1788–1827, and Joseph von Fraunhofer, Bavarian optician, 1787–1826. There is, of course, no difference in the nature of the diffraction process in the two cases, and Fresnel diffraction merges gradually into Fraunhofer diffraction as the screen is moved away from the slit, or as the slit width is decreased.

Fraunhofer diffraction occurs also if a lens is placed just beyond the slit, as in Fig. 35–17(d), since the lens brings to a focus, in its second focal plane, all light traveling in a specified direction. That is, the lens forms in its focal plane a reduced image of the pattern that would appear on an infinitely distant screen in the absence of the lens.

The photograph in Fig. 35–16 is a Fraunhofer diffraction pattern.

Some of the important aspects of Fraunhofer diffraction by a slit can

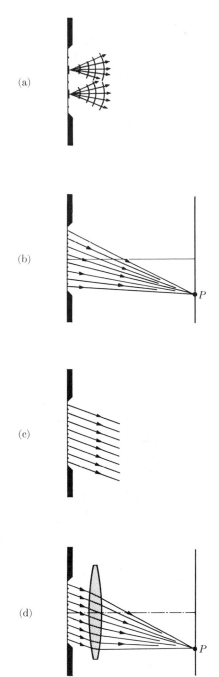

(a)

(b)

(c)

(d)

FIG. 35–17. Diffraction by a slit.

be deduced very easily. Consider the two extremely narrow strips in the wave passing through a slit, one just below the upper edge of the slit and the other just below its centerline, as in Fig. 35–18, and the wavelets from these strips that travel in a direction making an angle α with the direction of the incident light. The two wave trains start out from the plane of the original wave surface in phase, but the upper one has to travel a greater distance than the lower before reaching the screen. This additional distance, from Fig. 35–18, is

$$\frac{D}{2}\sin\alpha,$$

where D is the slit width.

For those points on the screen that lie on a line through O, opposite the center of the slit, the angle α is zero and the path difference is zero. The wavelets from *all* strips on the transmitted wave surface therefore reach points on this line in phase with one another, their amplitudes add, and the center of the diffraction pattern is bright. As we consider points farther and farther out from the center, the angle α increases and the path difference increases. When the path difference has become equal to one-half a wavelength, the wavelets from the two strips in Fig. 35–18 reach the screen out of phase and complete destructive interference results. The path difference between the wavelets from the two strips next below those in Fig. 35–18 is also one-half wavelength, so that these two wavelets cancel each other also. Proceeding in this way, it is seen that the light from each element in the upper half of the slit is canceled by the light from the corresponding element in the lower half. Hence no light reaches the

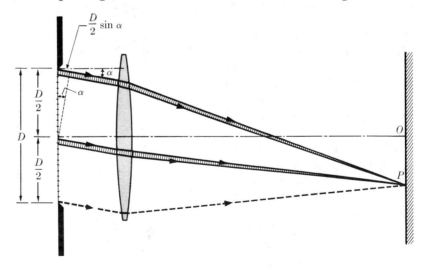

Fig. 35–18. Diffraction by a single slit.

screen at a point such as P, provided that

$$\frac{D}{2} \sin \alpha = \frac{\lambda}{2},$$

or

$$\sin \alpha = \frac{\lambda}{D}.$$

By dividing the slit into quarters, sixths, etc., one can show by similar reasoning that the screen is again dark when

$$\sin \alpha = \frac{2\lambda}{D}, \quad \frac{3\lambda}{D}, \quad \text{etc.} \tag{35–2}$$

The angle corresponding to the first minimum at either side of the center is called the *half-angular breadth* of the central band. The angular breadth of the entire central band is twice as great. The half-angular breadth is proportional to the wavelength λ and inversely proportional to the slit width D. It was stated earlier that in order to obtain a divergence of the diffracted beam like that shown in Fig. 35–15(b), the slit width should be about 5 wavelengths. We can now justify this statement. If the slit width D equals 5 wavelengths, the half-angular breadth of the central band is

$$\sin \alpha = \frac{\lambda}{D} = \frac{\lambda}{5\lambda} = 0.20,$$

$$\alpha = 12° \text{ (very nearly)},$$

which is approximately the angular divergence shown in Fig. 35–15. When the slit width is just one wavelength,

$$\sin \alpha = 1, \quad \alpha = 90°,$$

and the central band spreads out over an angle of 180°.

35–8 The plane diffraction grating. Suppose that instead of a single slit, or two slits side by side as in Young's experiment, we have a very large number of parallel slits all of the same width and spaced at regular intervals. Such an arrangement, known as a *diffraction grating*, was first constructed by Fraunhofer. The earliest gratings were of fine wires, 0.04 mm to 0.6 mm in diameter, spaced at intervals of from 0.0528 mm to 0.6866 mm. Gratings are now made by ruling, with a diamond point, a large number of equidistant grooves on a glass or metal surface.

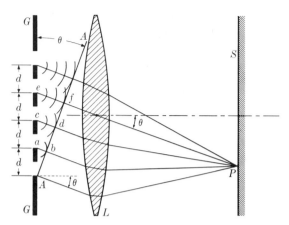

FIG. 35–19. The plane diffraction grating.

Let GG, in Fig. 35–19, represent the grating, the slits of which are perpendicular to the plane of the paper. While only five slits are shown in
the diagram, an actual grating contains several thousand, with a grating
spacing d of the order of one ten-thousandth of an inch. Let a train of
plane waves be incident normally on the grating from the left. The
problem of finding the intensity of the light transmitted by the grating
then combines the principles of interference and diffraction. That is, each
slit gives rise to a diffracted beam whose nature, as we have seen, depends
on the slit width. These diffracted beams then interfere with one another
to produce the final pattern.

Let us assume that the slits are so narrow that the diffracted beam
from each spreads out over a sufficiently wide angle for it to interfere with
all the other diffracted beams. Consider first the light proceeding from
elements of infinitesimal width at the lower edges of each opening, and
traveling in a direction making an angle θ with that of the incident beam,
as in Fig. 35–19. A lens at the right of the grating forms in its focal plane
a diffraction pattern similar to that which would appear on a screen at
infinity.

Suppose the angle θ in Fig. 35–19 is taken so that the distance $ab = \lambda$,
the wavelength of the incident light. Then $cd = 2\lambda$, $ef = 3\lambda$, etc. The
waves from all of these elements, since they are in phase at the plane of
the grating, are also in phase along the plane AA and therefore reach the
point P in phase. The same holds true for any set of elements in corresponding positions in the various slits.

If the angle θ is increased slightly, the disturbances from the grating
elements no longer arrive at AA in phase with one another, and even an
extremely small change in angle results in almost complete destructive

interference between them, provided there are a large number of slits in the grating. Hence the maximum at the angle θ is an extremely sharp one, differing from the rather broad maxima and minima which result from interference or diffraction effects with a small number of openings.

As the angle θ is still further increased, a position is eventually reached in which the distance ab in Fig. 35–19 becomes equal to 2λ. Then cd equals 4λ, cf equals 6λ, and so on. The disturbances at AA are again all in phase, the path difference between them now being 2λ, and another maximum results. Evidently still others will appear when $ab = 3\lambda$, $4\lambda, \ldots$ Maxima will also be observed at corresponding angles on the opposite side of the grating normal, as well as along the normal itself, since in the latter position the phase difference between disturbances reaching AA is zero.

The angles of deviation for which the maxima occur may readily be found from Fig. 35–20. Consider the right triangle Aba. Let d be the distance between successive grating elements, called the "grating spacing." The necessary condition for a maximum is that $ab = m\lambda$, where $m = 0, 1, 2, 3$, etc. It follows that

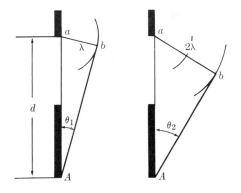

$$\sin \theta = m \frac{\lambda}{d} \qquad (35\text{–}3)$$

Fig. 35–20. First-order maximum when $ab = \lambda$, second-order maximum when $ab = 2\lambda$.

is the necessary condition for a maximum. The angle θ is also the angle by which the rays corresponding to the maxima have been *deviated* from the direction of the incident light.

In practice, the parallel beam incident on the grating is usually produced by a lens at the first focal point of which is a narrow illuminated slit. Each of the maxima is then a sharp image of the slit, of the same color as that of the light illuminating the slit, assumed thus far to be monochromatic. If the slit is illuminated by light consisting of a mixture of wavelengths, the lens will form a number of images of the slit in different positions, every wavelength in the original light giving rise to a set of slit images deviated by the appropriate angles. If the slit is illuminated with white light, a continuous group of images is formed side by side or, in other words, the white light is dispersed into continuous spectra. In contrast with the single spectrum produced by a prism, a grating forms a number of spectra on either side of the normal. Those which correspond to $m = 1$ in Eq. (35-3) are called *first-order*, those which correspond to $m = 2$ are called *second-order*, and so on. Since for $m = 0$ the deviation is zero, all colors combine to produce a white image of the slit in the direction of the incident beam.

In order that an appreciable deviation of the light may be produced, it is necessary that the grating spacing be of the same order of magnitude as the wavelength of light. Gratings for use in or near the visible spectrum are ruled with from 10,000 to 30,000 lines per inch.

The diffraction grating is widely used in spectroscopy, instead of a prism, as a means of dispersing a light beam into spectra. If the grating spacing is known, then from a measurement of the angle of deviation of any wavelength, the value of this wavelength may be computed. In the case of a prism this is not so; the angles of deviation are not related in any simple way to the wavelengths but depend on the characteristics of the material of which the prism is constructed. Since the index of refraction of optical glass varies more rapidly at the violet than at the red end of the spectrum, the spectrum formed by a prism is always spread out more at the violet end than it is at the red. Also, while a prism deviates red light the least and violet the most, the reverse is true of a grating, since in the latter case the deviation increases with increasing wavelength.

EXAMPLE 1. The limits of the visible spectrum are approximately 400 mμ to 700 mμ. Find the angular breadth of the first-order visible spectrum produced by a plane grating having 15,000 lines per inch, when light is incident normally on the grating.

The grating spacing, d, in centimeters, is

$$d = \frac{2.54 \text{ cm/in.}}{15,000 \text{ lines/in.}} = 1.69 \times 10^{-4} \text{ cm.}$$

The angular deviation of the violet is

$$\sin \theta = \frac{4 \times 10^{-5} \text{ cm}}{1.69 \times 10^{-4} \text{ cm}} = 0.237,$$

$$\theta = 13° 40'.$$

The angular deviation of the red is

$$\sin \theta = \frac{7 \times 10^{-5} \text{ cm}}{1.69 \times 10^{-4} \text{ cm}} = 0.415,$$

$$\theta = 24° 30'.$$

Hence the first-order visible spectrum includes an angle of

$$24° 30' - 13° 40' = 10° 50'.$$

EXAMPLE 2. Show that the violet of the third-order visible spectrum overlaps the red of the second-order spectrum.

The angular deviation of the third-order violet is

$$\sin \theta = \frac{3 \times (4 \times 10^{-5}\,\text{cm})}{d}$$

and of the second-order red it is

$$\sin \theta = \frac{2 \times (7 \times 10^{-5}\,\text{cm})}{d}.$$

Since the first angle is smaller than the second, whatever the grating spacing, the third order will always overlap the second.

35–9 Fresnel diffraction due to a circular obstacle. A circular *opening* in an opaque screen transmits only a small circular patch of a wave surface; the remainder of the wave is obscured. An interesting effect is observed if we reverse this procedure and insert a small circular *obstacle* in the light from a distant point source. A small circular patch of the

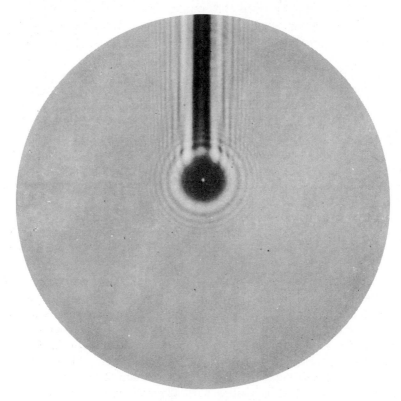

FIG. 35–21. Shadow of a ball bearing.

wave is then obscured, while the remainder is allowed to proceed. Figure 35–21 is a photograph of the shadow of a small ball bearing, supported from the tip of a magnetized sewing needle. Constructive interference of the wavelets from the unobstructed portion of the incident wave results in the small bright spot at the center of the geometrical shadow.

35–10 The resolving power of optical instruments. The expressions for the magnification of a telescope or a microscope (except for certain numerical factors) involved only the focal lengths of the lenses making up the optical system of the instrument. It appears at first sight as though any desired magnification might be attained by a proper choice of these focal lengths. Beyond a certain point, however, while the image formed by the instrument becomes larger (or subtends a larger angle) it does not gain in detail, even though all lens aberrations have been corrected. This limit to the useful magnification is set by the fact that light is a wave motion and the laws of geometrical optics do not hold strictly for a wave surface of limited extent. Physically, the image of a point source is not the intersection of *rays* from the source, but the diffraction pattern of those *waves* from the source that pass through the lens system.

It is an important experimental fact that the light from a point source, diffracted by a circular opening, is focused by a lens not as a geometrical point, but as a disk of finite radius surrounded by dark and bright rings. The larger the wave surface admitted (i.e., the larger the lenses or diaphragms in an optical system), the smaller the diffraction pattern of a point source and the closer together may two point sources be before their diffraction disks overlap and become indistinguishable. An optical system is said to be able to *resolve* two point sources if the corresponding diffraction patterns are sufficiently small or sufficiently separated to be distinguished. The numerical measure of the ability of the system to resolve two such points is called its *resolving power*.

Figure 35–22(a) is a photograph of four point sources made with the camera lens "stopped down" to an extremely small aperture. The nature of the diffraction patterns is clearly evident and it is obvious that further magnification, or enlargement of the picture, would not aid in resolving the sources. What is necessary is not to make the image *larger*, but to make the diffraction patterns *smaller*. Figures 35–22(b) and (c) show how the resolving power of the lens is increased by increasing its aperture. In (b) the diffraction patterns are sufficiently small for all four sources to be distinguished. In (c) the full aperture of the lens was utilized.

An arbitrary criterion proposed by Lord Rayleigh is that two point sources are just resolvable if the central maximum of the diffraction pattern of one source just coincides with the first minimum of the other. Let P_1 and P_2 in Fig. 35–23 be two point objects and let P_1' and P_2' be

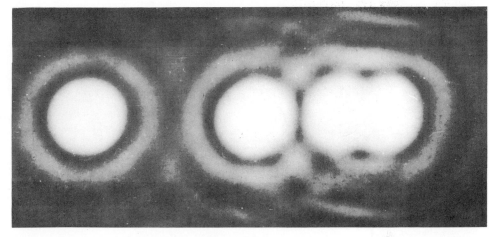

(a)

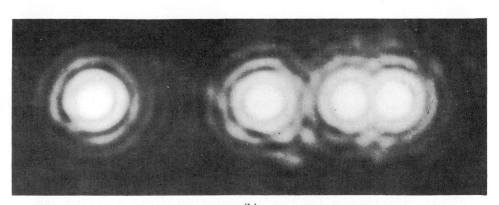

(b)

(c)

FIG. 35–22.   Diffraction patterns of four "point" sources, with a circular opening in front of the lens.   In (a), the opening is so small that the patterns at the right are just resolved, by Rayleigh's criterion.   Increasing the aperture decreases the size of the diffraction patterns, as in (b) and (c).

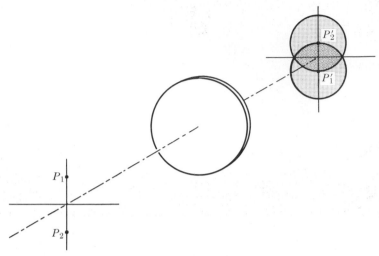

FIG. 35–23. Two point sources are just resolvable if the first minimum of the diffraction pattern of one coincides with the center of the other.

the centers of their diffraction patterns, formed by some optical instrument such as a microscope or telescope, which for simplicity is represented in the diagram as a single lens. If the images are just resolved, that is, if according to Rayleigh's criterion the first minimum of one pattern coincides with the center of the other, the separation of the centers of the patterns equals the radius of the central bright disk. From a knowledge of the focal lengths and separations of the lenses in any particular instrument, one can compute the corresponding distance between the two point objects. This distance, the minimum separation of two points that can just be resolved, is called the *limit of resolution* of the instrument. The smaller this distance, the greater is said to be the *resolving power*. The resolving power increases with the solid angle of the cone of rays intercepted by the instrument, and is inversely proportional to the wavelength of the light used. It is as if the light waves were the "tools" with which our optical system is provided, and the smaller the tools the finer the work which the system can do.

PROBLEMS

35-1. Two slits are spaced 0.3 mm apart and are placed 50 cm from a screen. What is the distance between the second and third dark lines of the interference pattern when the slits are illuminated with light of 600 mμ wavelength?

35-2. Light of wavelength 500 mμ is incident perpendicularly from air on a film 10^{-4} cm thick and of 1.375 refractive index. Part of the light enters the film and is reflected back at the second face. (a) How many waves are contained along the path of this light in the film? (b) What is the phase difference between these waves as they leave the film and as they enter it?

35-3. A glass plate 0.40 micron thick is illuminated by a beam of white light normal to the plate. The index of refraction of the glass is 1.50. What wavelengths within the limits of the visible spectrum ($\lambda = 40 \times 10^{-6}$ cm to $\lambda = 70 \times 10^{-6}$ cm) will be intensified in the reflected beam?

35-4. Two rectangular pieces of plane glass are laid one upon the other on a table. A thin strip of paper is placed between them at one edge so that a very thin wedge of air is formed. The plates are illuminated by a beam of sodium light at normal incidence. Bright and dark interference bands are formed, there being ten of each per centimeter length of wedge measured normal to the edges in contact. Find the angle of the wedge.

35-5. What is the thinnest film of 1.40 refractive index in which destructive interference of the violet component (400 mμ) of an incident white beam in air can take place by reflection? What is then the residual color of the beam?

35-6. A sheet of glass 10 cm long is placed in contact with a second sheet, and is held at a small angle with it by a metal strip 0.1 mm thick placed under one end. The glass is illuminated from above with light of 546 mμ wavelength. How many dark interference fringes are observed per cm in the reflected light?

35-7. The surfaces of a prism of index 1.52 are to be made "nonreflecting" by coating them with a thin layer of transparent material of index 1.30. The thickness of the layer is such that at a wavelength of 500 mμ (in vacuum), light reflected from the first surface is one-half a wavelength out of phase with that reflected from the second surface. Find the thickness of the layer.

35-8. The radius of curvature of the convex surface of a plano-convex lens is 30 cm. The lens is placed convex side down on a plane glass plate, and illuminated from above with red light of wavelength 650 mμ. Find the diameter of the third bright ring in the interference pattern.

35-9. A slit of width D was placed in front of a lens of focal length 80 cm. The slit was illuminated by light of wavelength 600 mμ and the diffraction pattern of Fig. 35-16 was formed on a screen in the second focal plane of the lens. If the photograph of Fig. 35-16 represents an enlargement to twice the actual size, what was the slit width?

35-10. Plane monochromatic waves of wavelength 600 mμ are incident normally on a plane transmission grating having 500 lines/mm. Find the angles of deviation in the first, second, and third orders.

35-11. A plane transmission grating is ruled with 4000 lines/cm. Compute

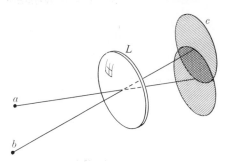

FIGURE 35–24

the angular separation in degrees, in the second-order spectrum, between the α and δ lines of atomic hydrogen, whose wavelengths are respectively 656 mμ and 410 mμ. Assume normal incidence.

35–12. (a) What is the wavelength of light which is deviated in the first order through an angle of 20° by a transmission grating having 6000 lines/cm? (b) What is the second-order deviation of this wavelength? Assume normal incidence.

35–13. What is the longest wavelength that can be observed in the fourth order for a transmission grating having 5000 lines/cm? Assume normal incidence.

35–14. In Fig. 35–24, two point sources of light, a and b, at a distance of 50 m from lens L and 6 mm apart, produce images at c which are just resolved by Rayleigh's criterion. The focal length of the lens is 20 cm. What is the diameter of the diffraction circles at c?

CHAPTER 36

POLARIZATION

36–1 Polarization. The phenomena of interference and diffraction can occur with any sort of waves, such as sound waves or surface waves on a liquid. In this chapter we consider some optical phenomena that depend not merely on the fact that light is a wave motion, but that the waves are *transverse*. These are called *polarization* effects. They can be observed only with transverse waves and cannot be duplicated with sound waves because the latter are longitudinal.

Let us consider for a moment the nature of the electromagnetic waves radiated by a radio antenna. Suppose the antenna is vertical, and we consider a portion of a wavefront in a vertical plane and not too near the antenna, as in Fig. 36–1. The electric field intensity **E** at all points of this wavefront is in a vertical direction, as indicated. If in the wavefront in the diagram the electric intensity is a maximum in the upward direction, then in wavefronts one-half a wavelength ahead of or behind this one the intensity is a maximum in a downward direction. At all points of any plane fixed in space, the electric vector oscillates up and down along a vertical line and the wave is said to be *linearly* polarized. (Waves of this sort are also described as plane polarized, or merely as polarized.)

To avoid confusion, the magnetic intensity **H** is not shown in Fig. 36–1. It is always at right angles to the electric intensity **E**.

The "antennas" that radiate light waves are the molecules of which light sources are composed. The electrically charged particles in the molecules acquire energy in some way, and radiate this energy as electromagnetic waves of short wavelength. Presumably the waves from any

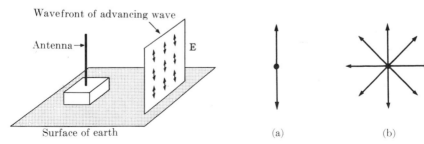

FIG. 36–1. The electromagnetic waves radiated by an antenna are linearly polarized.

FIG. 36–2. Schematic diagrams of (a) linearly polarized light, and (b) ordinary light.

one molecule are linearly polarized, like those from a radio antenna. But since any actual light source contains a tremendous number of molecules, oriented at random, the light emitted is a mixture of waves linearly polarized in all possible transverse directions. Let the plane of the diagram in Fig. 36–2(a) represent a wavefront in a beam of light advancing toward the reader, and the dot an end view of one ray in this beam. A linearly polarized light wave is represented schematically by the double arrow, which indicates that the electric field oscillates in the vertical direction only. A beam of natural light is represented as in part (b), in which the arrows indicate a mixture of waves, linearly polarized in all possible transverse directions.

36–2 Polarization by reflection. There are a number of methods by which the vibrations in one particular direction can be "sorted out," in whole or in part, from a beam of natural light. One of these is the familiar process of reflection. When natural light strikes a reflecting surface, there is found to be a preferential reflection for those waves in which the electric vector is vibrating perpendicular to the plane of incidence. (The plane of incidence is the plane containing the incident ray and the normal to the surface. See Fig. 36–3.) An exception is that at normal incidence all directions of polarization are reflected equally. At one particular angle of

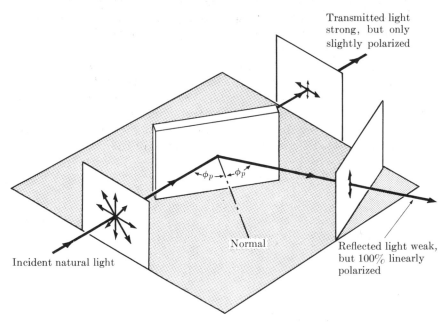

Fig. 36–3. When light is incident at the polarizing angle, the reflected light is linearly polarized.

incidence, known as the *polarizing angle*, no light whatever is reflected except that in which the electric vector is perpendicular to the plane of incidence. This case is illustrated in Fig. 36–3.

The situation depicted in Fig. 36–3 calls for somewhat more explanation. The heavy double arrow lettered **E** in Fig. 36–4 represents the amplitude of the electric field in a linearly polarized wave advancing toward the reader, the direction

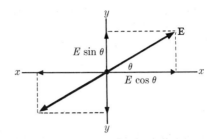

FIG. 36–4. Linearly polarized light resolved into two linearly polarized components.

of vibration making an angle θ with the x-axis. This wave can be resolved into two component waves (that is, it is equivalent to these two waves) linearly polarized along the x- and y-axes, and of amplitudes $E \cos \theta$ and $E \sin \theta$. In the same way, each linearly polarized component in the incident beam of natural light in Fig. 36–3, as represented by the "star" of vectors, can be resolved into two components, one perpendicular and the other parallel to the plane of incidence.

We can describe the reflection of light at the surface by stating what happens to each component of an arbitrary linearly polarized wave in the

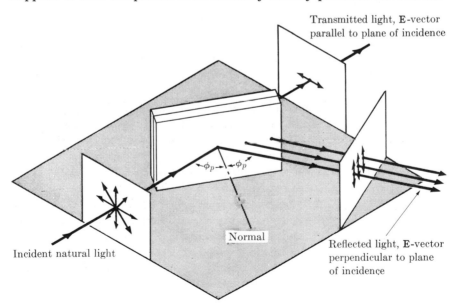

FIG. 36–5. Separation of natural light into two beams of linearly polarized light by reflection from a pile of plates.

incident light. When incident at the polarizing angle, *none* of the components parallel to the plane of incidence are reflected; that is, they are 100% transmitted in the *refracted* beam. Of the components perpendicular to the plane of incidence, about 15% are reflected if the reflecting surface is glass. (The fraction reflected depends on the index of the reflecting material.) Hence the *reflected* light is weak and *completely* linearly polarized. The *refracted* light is a mixture of the parallel components, all of which are refracted, and the remaining 85% of the perpendicular component. It is therefore strong, but only *partially* polarized.

At angles of incidence other than the polarizing angle some of the components parallel to the plane of incidence are reflected, so that except at the polarizing angle the reflected light is not completely linearly polarized.

To increase the intensity of the reflected light, a pile of thin glass plates is often used, as shown in Fig. 36–5. Due to the many rays reflected at the polarizing angle from the various surfaces, there is not only an increase in intensity of the reflected light, but also an increase in the polarization of the transmitted light, which now contains much less of the perpendicular component.

If n is the index of the material in which the light is traveling before reflection, and n' is the index of the reflecting material, the polarizing angle ϕ_p is given by

$$\tan \phi_p = \frac{n'}{n}. \tag{36–1}$$

This equation is known as *Brewster's law*, after Sir David Brewster, who discovered it experimentally in 1812.

36–3 Double refraction. The progress of a wave train through a homogeneous isotropic medium, such as glass, may be determined graphically by Huygens' construction. The secondary wavelets in such a medium are spherical surfaces. There exist, however, many transparent crystalline substances which, while homogeneous, are *anisotropic*. That is, the velocity of a light wave in them is not the same in all directions. Crystals having this property are said to be *doubly refracting*, or *birefringent*. *Two* sets of Huygens wavelets propagate from every wave surface in such a crystal, one set being spherical and the other ellipsoidal. The two sets are tangent to each other in one direction, called the *optic axis* of the crystal.

Figure 36–6(a) shows the traces of the Huygens wavelets from a point source within a doubly refracting crystal. The complete wave surfaces are obtained by rotating the diagram about axis AA. The direction of line ASA is the optic axis. (The optic axis is a *direction* in the crystal, not just one line. Any other line parallel to ASA is also an optic axis.)

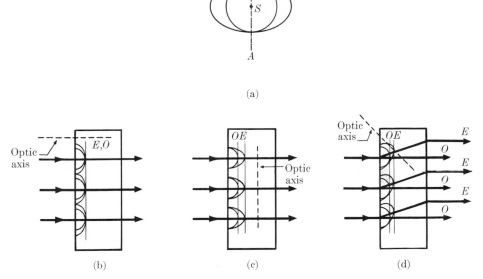

(a)

(b)   (c)   (d)

FIG. 36–6. (a) Spherical and ellipsoidal waves diverge from point S in a doubly refracting crystal. (b) Light traveling in the direction of the optic axis, (c) perpendicular to the optic axis, and (d) at an arbitrary angle to the optic axis.

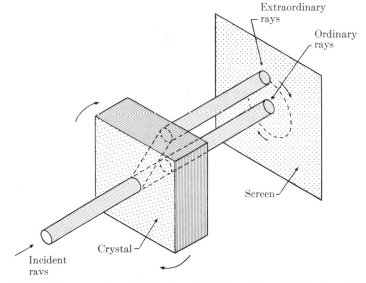

FIG. 36–7. A narrow beam of natural light can be split into two beams by a doubly refracting crystal.

Parts (b), (c), and (d) of Fig. 36–6 show the wavefronts in three sections cut from the crystal in different directions, when light is incident normally on the surface of the section. It will be seen that two sets of waves travel through the crystal, one formed by the tangents to the spheres and the other by the tangents to the ellipsoids.

It may be seen in Fig. 36–6(d) that a ray incident normally is broken up into two rays in traversing the crystal. The ray which corresponds to wave surfaces tangent to the spherical wavelets is undeviated and is called the *ordinary ray O*. The ray corresponding to the wave surfaces tangent to the ellipsoids is deviated even though the incident ray is normal to the surface, and is called the *extraordinary ray E*. If the crystal is rotated about the incident ray as an axis, the ordinary ray remains fixed but the extraordinary ray revolves around it, as shown in Fig. 36–7. Furthermore, for angles of incidence other than 90°, Snell's law (i.e., $\sin \phi / \sin \phi' =$ constant) holds for the ordinary but *not* for the extraordinary ray, since evidently the velocity of the latter is different in different directions.

The index of refraction for the extraordinary ray is therefore a function of direction. It is customary to state the index for the direction at right angles to the optic axis, in which the velocity is a maximum or a minimum. Some values of n_O and n_E, the indices for the ordinary and extraordinary rays, are listed in Table 36–1.

Figure 36–6 is drawn for a crystal in which the velocity of the ellipsoidal waves is greater than that of the spherical waves, except in the direction of the optic axis. In some crystals the velocity of the ellipsoidal waves is less than that of the spherical waves except along the optic axis, where the two are equal. Both this type of crystal and that described above are called *uniaxial*. In some crystals there are two different directions in which the velocities are equal. These crystals are called *biaxial*, but since all of the doubly refracting crystals used in optical instruments (chiefly quartz and calcite) are uniaxial, we shall consider only this type.

TABLE 36–1

INDICES OF REFRACTION OF DOUBLY REFRACTING CRYSTALS
(For light of wavelength 589 mμ)

Material	n_O	n_E
Calcite	1.6583	1.4864
Quartz	1.544	1.553
Tourmaline	1.64	1.62
Ice	1.306	1.307

36–4 Polarization by double refraction. Experiment shows that the ordinary and extraordinary waves in a doubly refracting crystal are linearly polarized in mutually perpendicular directions. Consequently, if some means can be found to separate one wave from the other, a doubly refracting crystal may be used to obtain linearly polarized light from natural light. There are a number of ways in which this separation may be accomplished.

One method of separating the two components is by means of a *Nicol prism* or one of its modifications. The Nicol prism is a crystal of Iceland spar or calcite ($CaCO_3$), whose natural shape is shown by the full lines in Fig. 36–8(a). To make a Nicol prism, the end faces of the crystal are cut at a more obtuse angle, as shown by the dotted lines. The crystal is then cut along the shorter diagonal $b'd'$ and cemented together again with Canada balsam. The index of Canada balsam has such a value that the ordinary ray is totally reflected, while the extraordinary ray is transmitted as in Fig. 36–8(b).

Certain doubly refracting crystals exhibit *dichroism;* that is, one of the polarized components is absorbed much more strongly than the other. Hence if the crystal is cut of the proper thickness, one of the components is practically extinguished by absorption, while the other is transmitted in appreciable amount, as indicated in Fig. 36–9. Tourmaline is one example of such a dichroic crystal.

A recent development in polarizing materials is polaroid, one type of which consists of a thin layer of tiny needlelike dichroic crystals of hera-

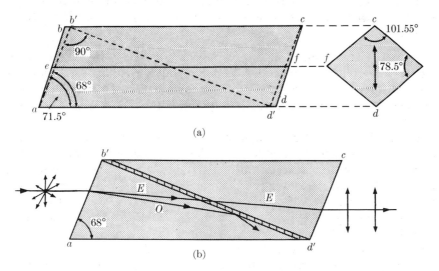

FIG. 36–8. (a) Natural crystal of Iceland spar. (b) A Nicol prism.

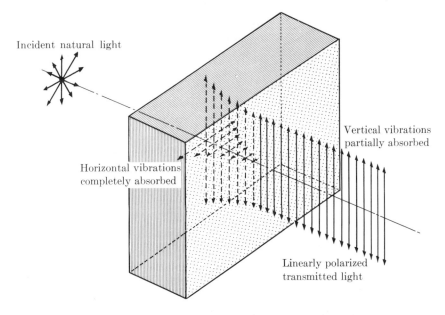

Incident natural light

Vertical vibrations
partially absorbed

Horizontal vibrations
completely absorbed

Linearly polarized
transmitted light

Fig. 36–9. Linearly polarized light transmitted by a dichroic crystal.

pathite (iodoquinine sulfate), in parallel orientation, embedded in a plastic
matrix and enclosed for protection between two transparent plates. This
method of construction makes possible the manufacture of polarizing
plates or sheets of large area. While the transmitted light is slightly
colored and not completely polarized, the large area of such plates and
their moderate cost has already opened up many new applications of
polarized light.

36–5 The scattering of light. The sky is blue. Sunsets are red. Skylight is largely linearly polarized, as can readily be verified by looking at
the sky directly overhead through a polarizing plate. It turns out that
one and the same phenomenon is responsible for all three of the effects
noted above.

In Fig. 36–10, sunlight (unpolarized) comes from the left along the
z-axis and passes over an observer looking vertically upward along the
y-axis. One of the molecules of the earth's atmosphere is located at
point O. The electric field in the beam of sunlight sets the electric charges
in the molecule in vibration. Since light is a transverse wave, the direction of the electric field in any component of the sunlight lies in the xy-plane
and the motion of the charges takes place in this plane. There is no
field, and hence no vibration, in the direction of the z-axis.

An arbitrary component of the incident light, vibrating at an angle θ
with the x-axis, sets the electric charges in the molecule vibrating in the

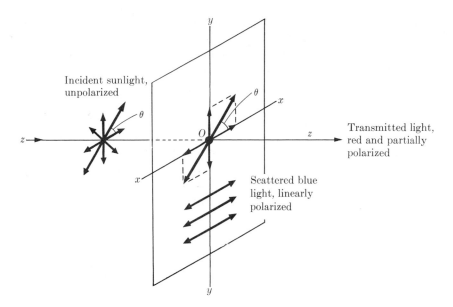

Fɪɢ. 36–10. Scattered light is linearly polarized.

same direction, as indicated by the heavy line through point O. In the usual way, we can resolve this vibration into two, one along the x- and the other along the y-axis. The result, then, is that each component in the incident light produces the equivalent of two molecular "antennas," oscillating with the frequency of the incident light and lying along the x- and y-axes.

The antenna along the y-axis does not send any light to the observer directly below it. It does, of course, send out light in other directions. The only light reaching the observer comes from the component of vibration along the x-axis and, as is the case with the waves from any antenna, this light is linearly polarized with the electric field parallel to the antenna. The vectors on the y-axis below point O show the direction of vibration of the light reaching the observer.

The process described above is called *scattering*. The energy of the scattered light is abstracted from the original beam, which becomes weakened in the process.

The vibration of the charges in the molecule is a *forced* vibration, like the vibration of a mass on a spring when the upper end of the spring is moved up and down with simple harmonic motion. It is well known that the closer the driving frequency approaches the natural frequency of vibration of the spring-mass system, the greater is the amplitude of the forced vibrations. Now the natural frequency of the electric charges in a molecule lies in the ultraviolet region. The frequencies of the waves in visible light are less than the ultraviolet frequencies, but the higher the frequency of the incident light, the closer is the driving frequency to the natural frequency, and the greater the amplitude of vibration, the greater the intensity of the scattered light. In other words, blue light is scattered more than red, with the result that the hue of the scattered light is blue.

Toward evening, when sunlight has to travel a large distance through the earth's atmosphere to reach a point over or nearly over an observer, a large proportion of the blue light in sunlight is removed from it by scattering. White light minus blue light is yellow or red in hue. Thus when sunlight, with the blue component removed, is incident on a cloud, the light reflected from the cloud to the observer has the yellow or red hue so commonly seen at sunset.

From the explanation above, it follows that if the earth had no atmosphere we would receive no skylight at the earth's surface, and the sky would appear as black in the daytime as it does at night. This conclusion is borne out by observations at high altitudes, where there is less atmosphere above the observer.

36–6 Circular and elliptic polarization. Linearly polarized light represents a special and relatively simple type of polarization. When the ordinary and extraordinary rays in a doubly refracting crystal are separated, each ray taken alone is linearly polarized, but with the directions of vibration at right angles. When, however, the crystal is cut with its faces parallel to the optic axis, so that light, incident normally on one of its faces, traverses the crystal in a direction perpendicular to the optic axis, as shown in Fig. 36–6(c), the ordinary and extraordinary rays are not separated. *They traverse the same path, but with different speeds.* Upon emerging from the second face of the crystal, the ordinary and extraordinary rays are out of phase with each other and give rise to either elliptically polarized, circularly polarized, or linearly polarized light, depending upon a number of factors which we shall proceed to discuss now.

Since in the ordinary ray the direction of vibration is perpendicular to that in the extraordinary ray, we have to consider a fundamental problem which, for the sake of simplicity, may be discussed in mechanical terms: What sort of vibration results from the combination of two simple harmonic vibrations at right angles to each other and differing in phase? The solution may be reached in a variety of ways: (1) with the aid of mechanical equipment, (2) by using two circles of reference for plotting two simple harmonic motions at right angles, and (3) by establishing alternating potential differences on the horizontal and vertical plates of a cathode-ray oscilloscope.

FIG. 36–11. Vibrations which result from the combination of a horizontal and a vertical simple harmonic motion of the same frequency and the same amplitude, for various values of the phase difference.

In Fig. 36–11 are shown the results obtained by combining a horizontal and a vertical simple harmonic motion of the same frequency and the same amplitude, for nine different phase differences. It is at once evident that *two simple harmonic motions at right angles to each other never produce destructive interference, no matter what the phase difference.*

1. When the phase difference is 0, 2π, or any even multiple of π, the result is a linear vibration at 45° to both original vibrations.

2. When the phase difference is π, 3π, or any odd multiple of π, the result is also a linear vibration, but at right angles to those corresponding to even multiples of π.

3. When the phase difference is $\pi/2$, $3\pi/2$, or any odd multiple of $\pi/2$, the resulting vibration is a circle.

4. At all other phase differences, the resulting vibration is an ellipse.

With these facts in mind, consider the optical apparatus shown in Fig. 36–12. After unpolarized light traverses the polarizer, it is linearly polarized, with the vibration direction along the dotted line drawn on the polarizer. This linearly polarized light then enters a crystal plate cut so that the light travels in a direction perpendicular to the optic axis. The crystal plate has been rotated about the light beam until the optic axis makes an angle of 45° with the direction of vibration of the polarized light incident upon it. Since the E-vibration is, in this case, parallel to the optic axis, and the O-vibration is perpendicular to it, it follows that the amplitudes of the E and O beams are identical. The E and O beams travel through the crystal along the same path but with different speeds and, as they are about to emerge from the second crystal face, they combine to form one of the vibrations depicted in Fig. 36–11, depending on the phase difference.

The phase difference between the E- and O-vibrations at the second face of the crystal depends on the following: (1) the frequency of the light, (2) the indices of refraction of the crystal for E and O light, (3) the thickness of the crystal.

If a given crystal has such a thickness as to give rise to a phase difference of $\pi/2$ for a given frequency, then, according to Fig. 36–11, a circular vibration results and the light emerging from this crystal is said to be *circularly polarized light.* The crystal itself is called a *quarter-wave plate.*

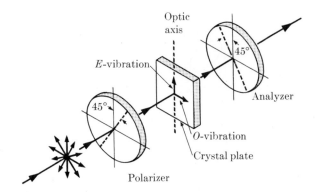

FIG. 36–12. Crystal plate between crossed polaroids. Since the optic axis makes an angle of 45° to the vibration direction of the linearly polarized light transmitted by the polarizer, the amplitudes of the O- and E-vibrations in the crystal are equal.

If the crystal plate shown in Fig. 36–12 is a quarter-wave plate, the intensity of light transmitted by the analyzer will remain unvaried as the analyzer is rotated. In other words, if an analyzer alone is used to analyze circularly polarized light, it will give the same result as when used to analyze unpolarized light.

A quarter-wave plate for, say, green light, is not a quarter-wave plate for any other color. Other colors have different frequencies, and since the E and O indices are different for these frequencies the phase difference would not be $\pi/2$.

If the crystal has such a thickness as to give rise to a phase difference of π for a given frequency, then, according to Fig. 36–11, a linear vibration perpendicular to the incident vibration direction results. The light that emerges from this crystal is linearly polarized and, by rotating the analyzer, a position of the analyzer may be found at which this light will be completely stopped. A crystal plate of this sort is called a *half-wave plate* for the given frequency of light. For any other frequency it would not be a half-wave plate.

If the phase difference produced by a crystal plate is such as to produce an elliptical vibration, the emerging light is said to be *elliptically polarized*.

36–7 Optical activity. When a beam of linearly polarized light is sent through certain types of crystals and certain liquids, the direction of vibration of the emerging linearly polarized light is found to be different from the original direction. This phenomenon is called *rotation of the plane of polarization*, and substances which exhibit the effect are called *optically active*. Those which rotate the plane of polarization to the right, looking along the advancing beam, are called dextrorotatory or right-handed; those which rotate it to the left, laevorotatory or left-handed.

Optical activity may be due to an asymmetry of the molecules of a substance, or it may be a property of a crystal as a whole. For example, solutions of cane sugar are dextrorotatory, indicating that the optical activity is a property of the sugar molecule. The rotation of the plane of polarization by a sugar solution is used commercially as a method of determining the proportion of cane sugar in a given sample. Crystalline quartz is also optically active, some natural crystals being right-handed and others left-handed. Here the optical activity is a consequence of the crystalline structure, since it disappears when the quartz is melted and allowed to resolidify into a glassy noncrystalline state called fused quartz.

Problems

36–1. A beam of light is incident on a liquid of 1.40 refractive index. The reflected rays are completely polarized. What is the angle of refraction of the beam?

36–2. The critical angle of light in a certain substance is 45°. What is the polarizing angle?

36–3. At what angle above the horizontal must the sun be in order that sunlight reflected from the surface of a calm body of water shall be completely polarized?

36–4. A parallel beam of "natural" light is incident at an angle of 58° on a plane glass surface. The reflected beam is completely linearly polarized. (a) What is the angle of refraction of the transmitted beam? (b) What is the refractive index of the glass?

36–5. Canada balsam has a refractive index of 1.528. What is the minimum angle of incidence that the ordinary ray may make with the Canada balsam layer of a Nicol prism to be totally reflected at this layer?

36–6. A parallel beam of linearly polarized light of wavelength 589 mμ (in vacuum) is incident on a calcite crystal, as in Fig. 36–6(c). Find the wavelengths of the ordinary and extraordinary waves in the crystal.

36–7. A beam of light, after passing through the Nicol prism N_1 in Fig. 36–13, traverses a cell containing a scattering medium. The cell is observed at right angles through another Nicol, N_2. Originally, the Nicols are oriented until the brightness of the field seen by the observer is a maximum. (a) Prism N_2 is rotated through 90°. Is extinction produced? (b) Prism N_1 is now rotated through 90°. Is the field bright or dark? (c) Prism N_2 is then restored to its original position. Is the field bright or dark?

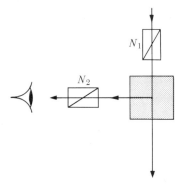

FIGURE 36–13

36–8. The phase difference δ between the E and O rays after traversing a crystal plate such as that in Fig. 36–12 is given by

$$\delta = \frac{2\pi}{\lambda} t(n_O - n_E),$$

where λ is the wavelength in air and t is the thickness of the crystal. (a) Show that the minimum thickness of a quarter-wave plate is given by $t = \lambda/4(n_O - n_E)$. (b) What is this minimum thickness for a quarter-wave calcite plate and light of 589 mμ wavelength?

CHAPTER 37

QUANTUM THEORY OF RADIATION

37–1 Introduction. In 1864 James Clerk Maxwell announced the results of his efforts to put the laws of electricity into good mathematical form. He had succeeded in this formulation and found in addition an important by-product: the laws could be combined to form differential equations whose solutions are waves. He showed, furthermore, that the velocity of these waves is the *velocity of light!* Thus in one dramatic move he put the theory of electricity in order and incorporated all optics into that theory.

Maxwell's theory was verified in 1888 when Hertz demonstrated that oscillating currents in an electric circuit can radiate energy through space to another similar circuit. Hertz used a circuit containing inductance and capacitance, hence capable of oscillating. Whenever a spark jumped across a gap in the active (transmitting) circuit, electromagnetic waves were radiated from the region in which the electric discharge occurred. (Modifications of this first transmitter were used for radio communication until the advent of vacuum tubes.) The passive or receiving circuit was a loop of wire containing a gap. When energy was transferred from one circuit to the other, sparks jumped across the receiver gap. Hertz's experiments showed that the radiation generated by electric circuits obeyed the known laws of optics. It thus appeared that the theory of light was in a very satisfactory and elegant state.

Yet the last word on this subject had not been said. Hertz noted that the induced spark was more easily produced when the terminals of the receiving gap were illuminated by light from the sparks in the transmitter gap. This effect was studied more fully by one of Hertz's students, Hallwachs, who showed that a negatively charged clean plate of zinc loses its charge when illuminated by ultraviolet light. Thus Hertz's verification of Maxwell's wave theory of light led almost simultaneously to the discovery of the photoelectric effect which, as we shall see, led in turn to a profound reinterpretation of the wave theory of radiation.

37–2 Thermal radiation. We all know that a body will emit visible radiation if it is hot enough. A close relation between temperature and radiation is further indicated by the fact that a white-hot body is hotter than a red-hot one. We might explore this matter further by passing the radiation from a hot body through some dispersive instrument such as a prism or grating spectrometer. If we measure the radiant energy emitted

709

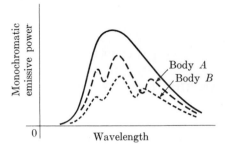

FIG. 37–1. The radiation spectrum of several hot bodies.

by a hot body, A, for a whole series of radiant frequencies, we might obtain a graph similar to the dashed curve of Fig. 37–1. The ordinate of this curve is called the *monochromatic emissive power*, which is the amount of energy radiated per unit time per unit area of emitter in a unit wavelength range; the abscissa is the wavelength rather than the frequency. Repeating the same experiment for another body B of a different material but at the same temperature, we might now obtain the dotted curve of Fig. 37–1. It is clear from the figure that at most wavelengths the first body is a more efficient emitter at the given temperature than the second. Although the two curves differ, they have the same general character. They come to their highest points at about the same wavelength. Upon studying a great variety of substances all at the same temperature, we would obtain a great variety of emission curves, but none of these would ever have a greater monochromatic emissive power than the envelope curve (solid line) in Fig. 37–1. Let us attempt to find or make an emitter which has an emission curve identical to the solid curve of Fig. 37–1.

37–3 Emission and absorption of radiation. It may be wondered why it is, if the surfaces of all bodies are continually emitting radiant energy, that all bodies do not eventually radiate away all their internal energy and cool down to a temperature of absolute zero. The answer is that they would do so if energy were not supplied to them in some way. In the case of a Sunbowl heater element or the filament of an electric lamp, energy is supplied electrically to make up for the energy radiated. As soon as this energy supply is cut off, these bodies do, in fact, cool down very quickly to room temperature. The reason that they do not cool further is that their surroundings (the walls, and other objects in the room) are also radiating, and some of this radiant energy is intercepted, absorbed, and converted into internal energy. The same thing is true of all other objects in the room—each is both emitting and absorbing radiant energy simultaneously. If any object is hotter than its surroundings, its rate of emission will exceed its rate of absorption. There will thus be a net loss of energy and the body will cool down unless heated by some other method. If a body is at a lower temperature than its surroundings, its rate of absorption will be larger than its rate of emission and its temperature will rise. When the body is at the same temperature as its surroundings the two rates become equal, there is no net gain or loss of energy, and no change in temperature.

Imagine that the walls of an enclosure are kept at the temperature T and a number of different bodies are suspended one after another within the enclosure. Regardless of their temperatures when they were inserted, it will be found that eventually each comes to the same temperature as that of the walls, T, even if the enclosure is evacuated. If the bodies are small compared with the size of the enclosure, radiant energy from the walls strikes the surface of each body at the same rate. Of this energy, a part is reflected and the remainder absorbed. In the absence of any other process, the energy absorbed will raise the temperature of the absorbing body, but since the temperature is observed *not* to change, each body must *emit* radiant energy at the same rate as it *absorbs* it. Hence *a good absorber is a good emitter, and a poor absorber is a poor emitter*.

Since a good absorber is a good emitter, the *best* emitter will be that surface which is the best absorber. But no surface can absorb more than all the radiant energy which strikes it. Any surface which does absorb all the incident energy will be the best emitting surface possible.

37-4 Blackbody radiation. In acoustics, an open window is taken to be a perfect absorber of sound, since an open window reflects virtually no sound back into the room. In optics, there are few things darker than the keyhole of a windowless closet, since what little light gets into the closet bounces around against absorbing surfaces before it is redirected out the keyhole. Painting the inside of the closet black may increase the darkness of the keyhole, but the essential darkness of the hole is due to the geometry of the cavity rather than to the absorptivity of its surfaces. A small hole in a cavity of opaque material is the most perfect absorber of radiant energy man has found. Conversely, a small hole in a cavity is the most perfect emitter man has devised. We can conclude this from the proof above or we can understand it more thoroughly from the following. If we look into a hole in a heated cavity, we can see the radiation from the inside wall just opposite to the hole. In addition, we see some radiation from other parts of the inside of the cavity which was directed toward the spot of wall we are looking at and is reflected to us by that spot. The absorption and emission of radiation by a hole in a hollow tungsten cylinder is shown in Fig. 37-2. The light streak across the center of the figure is an incandescent filament maintained at a constant color temperature for comparison purposes. When the cylinder is cold, the

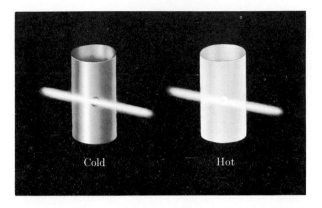

FIG. 37–2. Radiation from a hollow tungsten cylinder.

hole is darker than any other part and actually appears black, but when the cylinder is heated sufficiently, the hole is brighter than the body of the tube and matches the reference filament. Such a hollow absorber-emitter is called a *blackbody*.

The reader can demonstrate for himself that blackbodies can be made from bright objects. A bundle of sewing needles held with their points directed toward the eye look remarkably black. A pile of razor blades at least $\frac{1}{16}$ inch thick also looks black when viewed from the sharp side.

We now return to the question of the spectrum of the radiation emitted by a hot body. If we take a blackbody as our sample, we can measure the emission from the hole as we did the material samples in getting the data for Fig. 37–1. This experiment shows that the emission of the blackbody gives at once the smooth solid curve of Fig. 37–1, which, unlike the other curves in the figure, is independent of the material used to make the emitter. This confirms what we might have suspected before, that the solid curve portrays a general characteristic of thermal radiation at a given temperature. A study of this curve should give information about radiation itself. With consideration of the material composing the cavity eliminated, the remaining important variable is the temperature of the radiation source. Mathematically, the total energy radiated per unit time per unit area of emitter is proportional to the area under the curve, and Stefan found empirically that this area is directly proportional to the fourth power of the absolute temperature, $E = \sigma T^4$. (Here σ is the Stefan-Boltzmann constant.) This is called the "fourth-power law." It was derived theoretically by Boltzmann, who used a thermodynamic argument. Wien found that as the temperature of any blackbody is changed the curve retains its general shape, but that the maximum of the curve shifts with temperature so that the wavelength of the most intense radiation is inversely proportional to the absolute temperature, or $\lambda_{max} = \text{constant}/T$. This is a special case of Wien's displacement law, which states that at corresponding wavelengths the monochromatic energy density (energy per unit volume) of the radiation in the cavity of a blackbody varies directly as the fifth power of the absolute temperature. The relation defining corresponding wavelengths at temperatures T_1 and T_2 is $\lambda_1 T_1 = \lambda_2 T_2$. The displacement law enables us to predict the entire curve at *any* temperature, given the entire curve at *one* particular temperature. Neither of these radiation laws, however, treats the basic problem of why the energy radiated from a blackbody has this particular wavelength distribution.

37–5 The Wien and Rayleigh-Jeans laws. A comparison of the blackbody radiation curves of Fig. 37–3 and the Maxwell distribution of speeds in a gas shown in Fig. 18–7 shows a remarkable similarity. Wien noted this similarity and tried to fit a function such as Maxwell had derived for the speed distribution to the blackbody wavelength distribution. There is more than the similarity of the curves to justify this approach. If the molecules of the blackbody are thermally agitated, then their distribution of speeds may be somewhat like that derived by Maxwell. The accelerations of these molecules should be related to their velocities.

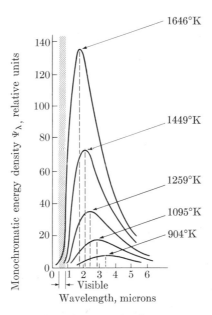

FIG. 37–3 The distribution of energy in the spectrum of the radiation from a blackbody at different temperatures.

These molecules contain charges which are therefore thermally accelerated, and we have shown that classical electrodynamics indicates that
radiation results from accelerated charges.   This argument is hardly
rigorous, but it is a plausible explanation of the relationship between the
similar curves.   The expression that Wien obtained for the monochromatic energy density Ψ_λ within an isothermal blackbody enclosure in
the wavelength range λ to $\lambda + d\lambda$ is

$$\Psi_\lambda \, d\lambda = \frac{c_1 \lambda^{-5}}{e^{c_2/\lambda T}} \, d\lambda, \tag{37–1}$$

where λ is the wavelength, T is the absolute temperature, and e is the
base of natural logarithms.   This formula is essentially empirical and
contains two adjustment constants c_1 and c_2, called the first and second
radiation constants, respectively.   Wien chose these constants so that
the fit he obtained was rather good except at long wavelengths.   The
graph of Wien's law is shown dashed in Fig. 37–4.   But a "pretty good
fit" is not good enough, and a formula which is essentially empirical
tells us nothing about the nature of radiation.
    Lord Rayleigh set out to derive the radiation distribution law in a
rigorous way.   We shall not repeat his argument here except to mention
that he concentrated attention on the radiation itself.   He said that the
electromagnetic radiation inside an isothermal blackbody cavity is reflected back and forth by the walls to form a system of standing waves
for each frequency present.   Thus these waves should resemble the standing waves on a violin string or, even more closely, the standing sound
waves within an acoustic cavity.   Just as a string can vibrate to produce

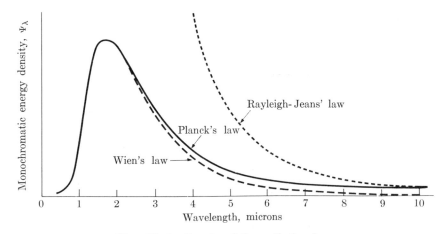

FIG. 37–4. Graphs of the radiation laws.

a fundamental and a whole series of overtones, so there should be many modes of vibration present in the standing waves of radiation in the cavity space. It is a small sample of this radiation that streams out of a hole in a blackbody for spectrum analysis. Because the system is in thermal equilibrium, the radiation from the cavity absorbed by the interior walls must equal that emitted to the cavity by the atomic oscillators in the walls. Each mode of vibration introduces two degrees of freedom, one for the potential energy of the oscillator and one for its kinetic energy. In Section 18–9 we found that the energy per degree of freedom was $\frac{1}{2}kT$, and thus each mode of vibration has a total energy kT associated with it.

We cannot reproduce here Rayleigh's involved derivation of the number of modes of vibration within the cavity. The result he obtained for the number of modes of vibration, dn_λ, per unit volume of space in the wavelength range λ to $\lambda + d\lambda$, is

$$dn_\lambda = 8\pi \frac{d\lambda}{\lambda^4}. \qquad (37\text{--}2)$$

If we accept this result, we need only multiply the energy per mode of vibration, kT, by the number of modes per unit volume of space within the wavelength interval $d\lambda$ to obtain the Rayleigh-Jeans law. The result is

$$\Psi_\lambda \, d\lambda = 8\pi kT \frac{d\lambda}{\lambda^4}. \qquad (37\text{--}3)$$

This equation is also plotted in Fig. 37–4. At first glance, this law appears vastly inferior to Wien's. Although it fits well for long wavelengths, at short wavelengths or high frequencies it heads toward infinity in what has been dramatically called the "ultraviolet catastrophe." Theoretically, however, the Rayleigh law must be taken far more seriously than Wien's. It was derived rigorously on the basis of classical physics. It involves no arbitrary constants, and where it does fit the experimental curve, it fits exactly. Whereas the failure of the Wien law was "too bad," the failure of the Rayleigh law presented a crisis. It indicated that classical theory was unable to account for an important experimental observation. This was the situation to which Max Planck directed himself.

37–6 Planck's law; emission quantized. Planck's first step was essentially empirical. He found that by putting a mere minus one into the denominator of the Wien formula and by adjusting Wien's constants, he could get a formula which reduced to the Rayleigh formula at long wavelengths and which fitted the experimental curve everywhere. He knew that he had found a correct formula and that it should be derivable. Planck's position was a little like that of a student who has peeked at the answer in the back of the book and is now faced with the task of showing how that answer can be logically computed. Planck tried by every method he could conceive to derive this correct formula from classical physics. He was finally forced to conclude that there was no flaw in Rayleigh's derivation and that the flaw must lie in classical theory itself.

Planck had to eliminate the "ultraviolet catastrophe" which came into Rayleigh's derivation because of the assumption that the radiation standing waves had a fundamental and also an infinite number of harmonic modes of vibration. Each of these was assumed to have an average energy kT. Instead of taking the average energy per mode to be kT directly, Planck examined this matter in more detail.

The average we seek will be found by taking the sum of the products of the number of oscillators in each energy state and the energy of that state, and then dividing this sum by the total number of oscillators in all the states.

Let the energy which is associated with each of the degrees of freedom of an oscillator be some integral multiple m of a small unit of energy u. We can later make this as small as we choose and allow it to approach zero. (The method at this point is following a procedure used by Boltzmann, in 1877, to determine the distribution of kinetic energy among the molecules in a gas.) The number of oscillators having the energy mu, as given by the Boltzmann distribution law (Eq. 18–35), is

$$n_m = n_0 e^{-mu/kT}. \tag{37–4}$$

The energy contributed by the n_m oscillators is obviously

$$mun_m = mun_0 e^{-mu/kT}. \tag{37–5}$$

Therefore the average energy $\overline{w}$ of an oscillator is

$$\overline{w} = \frac{\sum_{m=0}^{\infty} mun_0 e^{-mu/kT}}{\sum_{m=0}^{\infty} n_0 e^{-mu/kT}}. \tag{37–6}$$

Since m is an integer, Eq. (37–6) becomes

$$\overline{w} = \frac{0 + ue^{-u/kT} + 2ue^{-2u/kT} + 3ue^{-3u/kT} + \cdots}{1 + e^{-u/kT} + e^{-2u/kT} + e^{-3u/kT} + \cdots}. \tag{37–7}$$

Let $x = e^{-u/kT}$. Then Eq. (37–7) can be written as

$$\overline{w} = ux \frac{1 + 2x + 3x^2 + \cdots}{1 + x + x^2 + \cdots}. \tag{37–8}$$

The limits of these convergent series can be found by the usual methods (note that $x < 1$). The convergence limit of the series in the numerator is $1/(1 - x)^2$. This can be checked by expanding it according to the binomial theorem. The denominator is a simple geometric progression converging to $1/(1 - x)$. Upon substituting these limits in Eq. (37–8), we have

$$\overline{w} = ux \frac{1/(1 - x)^2}{1/(1 - x)} = \frac{ux}{1 - x} = \frac{u}{(1/x) - 1}. \tag{37–9}$$

When x is replaced by its equivalent, the result is

$$\overline{w} = \frac{u}{e^{u/kT} - 1}. \tag{37–10}$$

If we now multiply Eq. (37–10) by the number of modes of vibration in a unit volume of cavity space, from Eq. (37–2), we obtain the energy density in a wavelength range $d\lambda$,

$$\Psi_\lambda \, d\lambda = \frac{8\pi}{\lambda^4} \frac{u}{e^{u/kT} - 1} d\lambda. \tag{37–11}$$

Recall that in this derivation the energy of an oscillator has been assumed to be an integer, m, times some small energy, u. Classical physics says the energy may have any value. This is equivalent to saying u may be exceedingly small and, in the limit, approach zero. If we set $u = 0$, Eq. (37–10) is indeterminate, $0/0$. If we apply L'Hospital's rule, differentiating both numerator and denominator with respect to u before letting $u = 0$, we find

$$\overline{w} = kT, \tag{37–12}$$

which is in complete agreement with Rayleigh's classical assumption.

The relation given in Eq. (37–11) begins to look like Wien's law, Eq. (37–1), if u is not zero. Indeed, the denominators of these two equations become identical (except for the minus one) if a value of u is chosen so that the powers of the exponential terms are the same. To obtain this value of u, we let

$$\frac{c_2}{\lambda T} = \frac{u}{kT}, \tag{37–13}$$

or

$$u = \frac{c_2 k}{\lambda} = \frac{c_2 k}{c} f. \tag{37–14}$$

In this last equation, c is the free-space velocity of light and f is the frequency of the oscillator and therefore also the frequency of the radiation it emits. If we replace the constants $c_2 k/c$ by another constant h, we have

$$u = \frac{hc}{\lambda} = hf. \tag{37--15}$$

When the value of u from Eq. (37–15) is substituted in Eq. (37–11), we obtain Planck's law for the energy density of blackbody or cavity radiation. This law is

$$\Psi_\lambda \, d\lambda = \frac{8\pi ch\lambda^{-5}}{e^{ch/\lambda kT} - 1} \, d\lambda. \tag{37--16}$$

This equation does agree with the experimental results. It is plotted in Fig. 37–4.

The new constant h is called *Planck's constant.* We have seen that it could be determined from Wien's constant c_2, but it is better evaluated from the photoelectric effect discussed later in this chapter. Its value is $h = (6.6253 \pm 0.0003) \times 10^{-34}$ joule·second. (Note that the units are those of angular momentum.)

Thus Planck was led to his startling, nonclassical assumption that the energy states of an oscillator must be an *integral* multiple of the product of the constant h and the frequency f of the radiation it emits. If E represents the smallest permissible energy change, Planck's famous quantum* equation is

$$\boxed{E = hf.} \tag{37--17}$$

Planck introduced the quantum concept in 1900, and it eventually led to the conclusion that radiation is not emitted in continuous amounts but in discrete bundles of energy each equal to hf. These bundles or packets of radiant energy are now called *quanta* or *photons.* This was the beginning of the atomic theory of radiation, which has grown to become the quantum theory. It is obvious, however, that quanta of radiation of different frequencies have different "sizes" (energies), and that they are atomic only in the sense that they are discrete. Planck thought at first that his *ad hoc*† hypothesis applied only to the oscillators and, possibly, to the emitted radiation in their immediate neighborhood and that, at most, it was a slight modification of Maxwell's theory of radiation. However, we shall see that he initiated a series of events which have changed our whole concept of the interaction of electromagnetic radiation with matter.

---

* Quantum is the Latin word for *how much* or *how great.*

† *Ad hoc* means literally *to this,* and is used to describe a hypothesis which is applicable to but one (this) situation.

EXAMPLE. What is the energy in a quantum of radiation having a wavelength of 5000 A?

$$E = hf = \frac{hc}{\lambda}$$

$$= 6.63 \times 10^{-34}\ \text{j·sec} \times 3 \times 10^{8}\ \frac{\text{m}}{\text{sec}} \times \frac{1}{5000\ \text{A}} \times \frac{1\ \text{A}}{10^{-10}\ \text{m}}$$

$$= 3.98 \times 10^{-19}\ \text{j}.$$

37–7 The photoelectric effect. We now turn from thermal radiation to another portion of the electromagnetic spectrum and consider an effect which is due to radiation of higher frequency. We mentioned earlier that even before the discovery of the electron Hallwachs observed that zinc irradiated with ultraviolet light lost negative charge. He proposed that somehow the radiation caused the zinc to eject negative charge. In 1899 Lenard showed that the radiation caused the metal to emit electrons.

This phenomenon, called the photoelectric effect, can be studied in detail with the apparatus shown in Fig. 37–5. In this figure, S is a source of radiation of variable and known frequency f and intensity I, E is an emitting electrode of the material being studied, and C is a collecting electrode. Both electrodes are contained in an evacuated glass envelope with a quartz window that permits the passage of ultraviolet and visible light. The electric circuit allows the electrodes to be maintained at different known potentials and permits the measurement of any current between the electrodes. We first make the collecting electrode positive with respect to the emitting electrode, so that any electrons ejected will be quickly swept away from the emitter. About 10 volts is enough to do this but not enough to free electrons from the negative electrode by positive ion bombardment as was the case in the early cathode-ray tubes. If the tube is dark, no electrons are emitted and the microammeter indicates no current. If ultraviolet light is allowed to fall on the emitting elec-

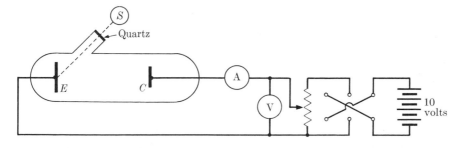

FIG. 37–5. Apparatus for investigating the photoelectric effect.

trode, electrons are liberated and the current is measured by the micro-ammeter. It is found that the rate of electron emission is proportional to the light intensity. By holding the frequency f of the light and the accelerating potential V constant, we can obtain data like that represented in Fig. 37-6.

It is hardly surprising that if a little light liberates a few electrons, more light liberates many. If we vary either the frequency of the light or the material irradiated, only the slope of the line changes.

We can now experiment by keeping the light intensity constant and varying the frequency. The graphs of these data are shown in Fig. 37-9, where A and B represent two different irradiated materials. The significant thing about these curves is that for every substance irradiated there is a limiting frequency below which no photoelectrons are produced. This frequency, called the *threshold frequency*, f_0, is a characteristic of the material irradiated. The wavelength of light corresponding to the threshold frequency is the *threshold wavelength*, λ_0. No photoelectrons are emitted for wavelengths greater than this.

The existence of a threshold frequency is difficult to explain on the basis of the wave theory of light. If we think of light as consisting of a pulsating electromagnetic field, we can imagine that that field is sometimes directed so as to tend to eject electrons from a metallic surface. We might even feel it reasonable that certain frequencies of light would resonate with the electrons of the metal so that, for a particular metal, there might be preferred light frequencies which would cause emission more efficiently. The striking thing about these data is that for each material there is a frequency below which no photoelectrons are emitted and above which they are emitted. This effect is independent of the intensity of the light.

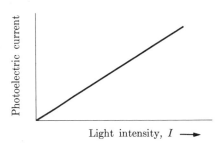

FIG. 37-6. Photoelectric current as a function of the intensity of the light. The frequency of the light and the accelerating potential are kept constant.

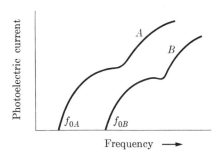

FIG. 37-7. Photoelectric current for two materials as a function of the frequency of the light. The intensity of the light and the accelerating potential are kept constant.

In 1905 Einstein proposed a daring but simple explanation. He centered attention on the energy aspect of the situation. Whereas Planck had proposed that radiation was composed of energy bundles only in the neighborhood of the emitter, Einstein proposed that these energy bundles *preserve their identity throughout their life*. Instead of spreading out like water waves, Einstein conceived that the emitted energy bundle stays together, and carries an amount of energy equal to hf. For Einstein, the significance of the light frequency was not so much an indication of the frequency of a pulsating electric field as it was a measure of the energy of a bundle of light called a *photon*. His interpretation of the data of Fig. 37–7 would be that a quantum of light below the threshold frequency just does not have enough energy to remove an electron from the metal, but light above that frequency does.

The threshold frequency is dependent on the nature of the material irradiated because there is for each material a certain minimum energy necessary to liberate an electron. The *photoelectric work function* of a material is the *minimum* energy required to free a photoelectron from that material. Less energy is needed to free an electron from, or near, the surface of a material than from the interior.

In a third photoelectric experiment let us hold both the frequency and intensity of the light constant. The variable is the potential difference across the photoelectric cell. Starting with the collector at about 10 volts positive, we reduce this potential to zero and then run it negative until the photocurrent stops entirely. Curve I_1 of Fig. 37–8 shows the type of curve we might expect for this particular substance. This curve requires careful interpretation.

When the potential difference across the tube is about 10 volts or more, *all* the emitted electrons travel across the tube. This stream of charges is called the *saturation* current, and it is obvious that an increase in the potential of the collector cannot cause an increase in current. As the accelerating potential is reduced, the velocities of the electrons in the space between the electrodes become smaller and there are more electrons per unit volume of space. This concentration of negative charge is called *space charge*, and it lowers the potential in the vicinity of the emitting surface. Indeed, the potential in this region usually falls below the potential of the emitter. Thus, although the accelerating potential is still positive, this potential barrier due to space charge can turn back electrons emitted with low kinetic energy and thereby reduce the electron current. However, those high-energy electrons that get beyond this barrier caused by space charge arrive at the anode collector with the same energy they would have had if the space charge had been absent, since the total potential difference from emitter to collector is independent of the space charge. The net work done on the collected electrons depends

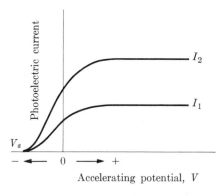

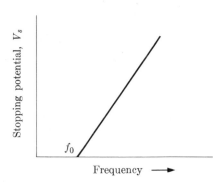

FIG. 37-8. Photoelectric current as a function of the accelerating potential for light of different intensities having a two-to-one ratio. The frequency of the light is constant.

FIG. 37-9. Stopping potential as a function of the frequency of the light. Results are independent of intensity.

only on the net potential difference. As the accelerating potential is reduced from positive values through zero to negative values, the tube current reduces both because of space charge and the applied retarding potential. Eventually, there are so few electrons in the space that the space-charge effect becomes negligible compared with the retarding potential itself, which finally stops the current completely.

The *stopping potential V_s* is the value of the retarding potential difference that is just sufficient to halt the *most energetic* photoelectron emitted. Therefore the product of the stopping potential and the electronic charge, $V_s e$, is equal to the maximum kinetic energy that an emitted electron can have. Since this stopping potential has a definite value, it indicates that the emitted electrons have a definite upper limit to their kinetic energy. Doubling the intensity of the light doubles the current at each potential, as in I_2 of Fig. 37-8, but the stopping potential is *independent* of the intensity.

If, however, the experiment is repeated with a series of different light frequencies, it is found that the stopping potential increases linearly with the frequency. This is best shown by plotting the stopping potential against the frequency, as shown in Fig. 37-9. Below the threshold frequency no electrons are emitted and the stopping potential is of course zero; however, as the frequency is increased above the threshold, the stopping potential increases linearly with the frequency.

To see how fully the data of Fig. 37-9 confirm the Einstein photon interpretation of the photoelectric effect, we now interpret the graph of Fig. 37-9 as he would have. For light frequency between zero and the threshold frequency there are no photoelectrons produced, since the incident photons have less energy than the work function of the material. For light above the threshold frequency, photoelectrons are emitted. The energy of these emitted electrons may vary greatly, since some may have been emitted from inside the metal and may have required more than the work-function energy to be liberated. According to the Einstein view, however, there must be an upper limit to the energy of the emitted photoelectrons. No photoelectrons can have energy in excess of the energy of the incoming photon less the minimum energy to free an electron, the work function. Since the photon energy is proportional to frequency and since the stopping potential measures the maximum kinetic energy of the emitted photoelectrons, the graph of stopping potential against frequency should be a straight line. This is precisely what Fig. 37–9 shows. The quantitative check of the Einstein interpretation is that the slope of the straight line provides a method of determining the way in which photon energy depends on photon frequency, which is Planck's constant.

A final and decisive experiment consists of making the irradiating light extremely weak. In this case, the number of photoelectrons is very small and special techniques are required to detect them. The significant result of this experiment is that dim light causes emission of photoelectrons which, however few, are emitted *instantaneously* and with the same maximum kinetic energy as for bright light of the same frequency.

According to the wave theory of light, pulsating electromagnetic fields spread out from their source. Dim light corresponds to waves of small amplitude and small energy. If dim light spreads over a surface, conservation of energy requires that either no photoelectrons should be emitted or the electrons must store energy over long periods of time before gathering enough energy to become free of the metal. The fact that high-energy photoelectrons appear immediately can be explained only by assuming that the light energy falls on the surface in concentrated bundles. According to Einstein, the dim light consists of a few photons each having energy depending only on the light frequency. This energy is not spread over the surface uniformly as required by the wave theory. A photon that is absorbed gives all its energy to one electron, and that electron will be emitted violently even though the number of such events is small.

If a man dives into a swimming pool, his energy is partly converted into waves which agitate other swimmers in the pool. If it were observed that when a man dives into a pool another swimmer is suddenly ejected from the pool onto a diving board, we would be forced to conclude that the energy provided by the diver did not spread out in an expanding wavefront, but was somehow transferred in concentrated form to the ejected swimmer. A swimming party held in such a superquantum pool would be a very odd affair compared with one in a classical pool.

To summarize Einstein's interpretation of the photoelectric effect, we equate the energy of an incident photon of frequency f to the sum of the work function of the emitter $(W = hf_0)$ and the maximum kinetic energy that an ejected photoelectron can acquire. We then have

$$hf = hf_0 + \tfrac{1}{2}mv_{max}^2,$$

or

$$\tfrac{1}{2}mv_{max}^2 = hf - hf_0,$$

or

$$\boxed{V_s e = hf - W.}$$

(37–18)

This is a linear equation. It is the equation of the graph in Fig. 37–9. It is evident that the slope of the curve of V_s plotted as a function of f is equal to h/e, that f_0 is the f-axis intercept, and that W/e is the intercept of the extrapolated curve on the V_s-axis. Note that if $f < f_0$, v is imaginary. The physical meaning is that photoelectric emission is then impossible. Einstein's photoelectric equation was first verified with precision in 1916 by Millikan, who made careful measurements of the photoemission from many different substances.

37–8 Summary of the atomic view of radiation. We described how Maxwell strengthened Huygens' wave theory when he showed that electromagnetic waves were a consequence of the laws of electricity and magnetism. We reported that Hertz demonstrated that electric circuits could be made to produce the electromagnetic waves Maxwell predicted. But we also mentioned that Hertz observed that he could produce sparks more easily when his spark gap was illuminated. Thus Hertz's work, which supported Maxwell's theory, also contained the first observation of the photoelectric effect. Although the wave theory of light accounts beautifully for many optical phenomena, it fails to account for either the blackbody radiation or the photoelectric effect, where light appears to possess marked particle aspects. It is hardly satisfactory to regard light as a wave motion part of the time and a particle phenomenon at other times. We shall return to the question of the resolution of this conflict of viewpoint in Chapter 41. At this point it is clear, however, that the resolution of this paradox can never eliminate the idea that light is emitted and absorbed in bundles of energy called photons, and that now radiation must join matter and electricity in having a basically atomic character. The fact that radiant energy is quantized is a radical departure from classical physics and will require us to re-examine the whole energy concept from the quantum point of view. Establishing this fact has been the main business of this chapter. Before closing the chapter, however, we shall consider two related topics.

37–9 The electron volt. In the Einstein equation, we measured the maximum kinetic energy of the emitted electrons by noting the potential energy difference $(V_s e)$, which was equivalent to the electron kinetic energy. This method of determining and expressing electron energies is a particularly convenient one, and it suggests a new unit of energy. This new unit of energy is called the *electron volt*, ev, which is defined as the amount of energy equal to the change in energy of one electronic charge when it moves through a potential difference of one volt. Since the electron volt is an energy unit, it is in the same category as the foot-pound, the British thermal unit, and the kilowatt-hour.

Energies in joules can be converted to electron volts by dividing by $e_c = 1.60 \times 10^{-19}$. In this case e_c is *not a charge* but a *conversion factor* having the units of joules per electron volt. The Einstein equation, Eq. (37–18), is valid in any consistent system of units. If we choose mks units and divide Eq. (37–18) by the factor e_c, we obtain the same relation in electron volts:

$$E_{k(\text{max})} \ (\textit{numerically equal to } V_s) = \frac{hf}{e_c} - \frac{W}{e_c}. \qquad (37\text{–}19)$$

In words, this equation states that the maximum kinetic energy of a photo-electron in electron volts equals the energy of the photon in electron volts minus the work function in electron volts.

When the electron volt is too small a unit, it is convenient to use 10^3 ev = 1 kev (kilo electron volts), 10^6 ev = 1 Mev (mega electron volts), and 10^9 ev = 1 Bev (billion electron volts).

It is also useful to express photon energies in electron volts. In terms of photon frequency,

$$E = \frac{hf}{e_c} = 6.63 \times 10^{-34} \text{ j·sec} \times \frac{1 \text{ ev}}{1.60 \times 10^{-19} \text{ j}} \times f$$

$$= 4.14 \times 10^{-15} f \ (\text{sec·ev}). \qquad (37\text{–}20)$$

Or, since $f = c/\lambda$, we get

$$E = 4.14 \times 10^{-15} \text{ sec·ev} \times 3 \times 10^8 \frac{\text{m}}{\text{sec}} \times \frac{1}{\lambda}$$

$$= \frac{1.24 \times 10^{-6}}{\lambda} \ (\text{m·ev}). \qquad (37\text{–}21)$$

If the wavelength is expressed in angstroms instead of meters, we have

$$E = \frac{1.24 \times 10^{-6}}{\lambda} \ (\text{m·ev}) \times \frac{1 \text{ A}}{10^{-10} \text{ m}},$$

or

$$E = \frac{1.24 \times 10^4}{\lambda} \ (\text{ev·A}). \tag{37-22}$$

If data having five significant figures are used, the result is

$$E = \frac{12396}{\lambda} \ (\text{ev·A}). \tag{37-23}$$

We shall use Eq. (37–22) *frequently*.

EXAMPLE. Light having a wavelength of 5000 A falls on a material having a photoelectric work function of 1.90 ev. Find (a) the energy of the photon in ev, (b) the kinetic energy of the most energetic photoelectron in ev and in joules, and (c) the stopping potential.

(a) From Eq. (37–22)

$$E = \frac{1.24 \times 10^4 \ \text{ev·A}}{\lambda} = \frac{12400 \ \text{ev·A}}{5000 \ \text{A}} = 2.47 \ \text{ev}.$$

(b) The law of conservation of energy gives

Maximum kinetic energy = photon energy — work function

or

$$E_k = 2.47 \ \text{ev} - 1.90 \ \text{ev} = 0.57 \ \text{ev}.$$

Also

$$E_k = 0.57 \ \text{ev} \times \frac{1.60 \times 10^{-19} \ \text{j}}{1 \ \text{ev}} = 9.11 \times 10^{-20} \ \text{j}.$$

(c)

$$V_s = \frac{0.57 \ \text{ev}}{1 \ \text{electronic charge}} = 0.57 \ \text{volt}.$$

37–10 Thermionic emission. We have already considered two ways in which electrons can be released from a metal. In Chapter 20 we discussed the discharge of electricity through gases. The electrons that participate in cold-cathode discharges are obtained from the cathode while it is bombarded by the positive ions produced in the residual gas in the tube. In this chapter we have considered another emission process, called photoelectric emission. There is still another kind of electron emission, which we shall now discuss briefly.

If a metal is heated, the thermal agitation of the matter may give electrons enough energy to exceed the work function of the material. Thus the space around a heated metal is found to contain many electrons.

A study of this effect shows that the *thermionic work function* is very nearly the same as the photoelectric work function—a most satisfying result.

Since a fine wire can be heated easily by passing an electric current through it, thermionic emission is one of the most convenient electron sources. Most radio-type vacuum tubes use a heated cathode as their electron source. Thermal emission of negative charges from a hot wire in a vacuum was first observed by Edison in 1883 when he was making incandescent lamps, and such thermal emission is called the *Edison effect*. In 1899, J. J. Thomson showed that the thermions in this effect are electrons.

PROBLEMS

37-1. Predict from the curves in Fig. 37–3 the sequence of colors which would be seen if a piece of iron were heated from 20°C to 2500°C in a dark room.

37-2. Radiant energy with wavelengths longer than visible radiation (infrared region) is often called "heat radiation." (a) Can shorter wavelengths heat a body on which the radiation falls? (b) To what extent is it proper to call infrared rays heat rays? (See Fig. 37–3.)

37-3. If 5% of the energy supplied to an incandescent light bulb is radiated as visible light, how many visible quanta are emitted per second by a 100-watt bulb? Assume the wavelength of all the visible light to be 5600 A.

37-4. The directions of emission of photons from a source of radiation are random. According to the wave theory, the intensity of radiation from a point source varies inversely as the square of the distance from the source. Show that the number of photons from a point source passing out through a unit area is also given by an inverse square law.

37-5. Show that Planck's radiation law, Eq. (37–16), reduces to Wien's law for short wavelengths, and to the Rayleigh-Jeans' law for long ones. [*Hint:* Express the exponential term as

a series to obtain the second of these laws.]

37-6. Since it has been shown that matter, electricity, and radiant energy are discrete or "atomic" in character, is it strictly correct to write their differentials dm, dq, and dE respectively? Explain.

37-7. Show that Planck's constant h has the same physical units as angular momentum.

37-8. How many quanta of radiation having a wavelength of 912 A are required to furnish an electron with 13.6 ev of energy?

37-9. (a) In Problem 18–26 it was found that a thermal neutron has a velocity of 2200 m/sec. What is a thermal neutron's kinetic energy in ev? (b) What is the increase in kinetic energy in ev of each water molecule in a stream which goes down a 450-ft (137.1 m) waterfall?

37-10. The fissioning of a U^{235} atom yields 200 Mev of energy. How many such atoms must fission to provide an amount of energy equal to that required to lift a mosquito one inch? The mass of an average mosquito is 0.90 mgm.

37-11. (a) Calculate the energy released in ev per atom or molecule in the complete combustion of each of the following compounds:

Compound	Atomic or molecular weight	Heat of combustion
1. Coal	12 (carbon)	14,000 Btu/lb (7,780 kcal/kgm)
2. Ethyl alcohol	46	327.6 kcal/gm-mole
3. Starch	162 (assumed)	4,179 kcal/kgm
4. Trinitrotoluene (TNT)	227	821 kcal/gm-mole
5. Gasoline	100 (n-heptane)	20,750 Btu/lb (11,530 kcal/kgm)

(b) The fissioning of a U^{235} atom releases 200 Mev of energy. What is the ratio of this energy to that released per molecule of the compounds in the first part of this problem? (c) What is the ratio of the energy released per unit mass of uranium to the energy released per unit mass of each of the compounds?

37–12. At 200 Mev per fission per atom of U^{235} find, on the basis of the energy released in complete combustion (data given in Problem 37–11), (a) the number of grams of uranium needed to furnish a megawatt-day (24 hr) of energy, (b) the number of tons of coal equivalent to 1 lb of uranium, and (c) the number of pounds of uranium which equal the blast effect of a megaton of TNT. [*Note:* Only about 30% of the energy of combustion of TNT goes into its blast or explosive effect. Assume that the blast efficiency of the uranium is 100%.] It is very useful in nuclear engineering to remember the relations or conversion factors calculated in parts (a) and (b).

37–13. The light-sensitive compound on most photographic films is silver bromide, AgBr. We will assume that a film is exposed when the light energy absorbed dissociates this molecule into its atoms. (The actual process is more complex, but the quantitative result does not differ greatly.)

The energy of or heat of dissociation of AgBr is 23.9 kcal/gm-mole. Find (a) the energy in ev, (b) the wave-length, and (c) the frequency of the photon which is just able to dissociate AgBr. (d) Explain the fact that light from a firefly can expose a photographic film, whereas the radiation from a TV station transmitting 50,000 watts at 100 megacycles cannot. (e) Will photographic films stored in a light-tight container be ruined (exposed) by the radio waves constantly passing through them? Explain.

37–14. When a certain photoelectric surface is illuminated with light of different wavelengths, the stopping potentials given in the table below are observed.

Plot the stopping potential as ordinate against the frequency of the light as abscissa. Determine (a) the threshold frequency, (b) the threshold wavelength, (c) the photoelectric work function of the material, and (d) the value of Planck's constant h (the value of e being known).

37–15. The photoelectric work function of potassium is 2.0 ev. If light having a wavelength of 3600 A falls on potassium, find (a) the stopping potential, (b) the kinetic energy in ev of the most energetic electrons ejected, and (c) the velocities of these electrons.

37–16. What will be the change in the stopping potential for photoelectrons emitted from a surface if the wavelength of the incident light is reduced from 4000 A to 3980 A? (Assume that the decrease in wavelength is so small that it may be considered a differential.)

λ, A	3660	4050	4360	4920	5460	5790
V_s, volts	1.48	1.15	0.93	0.62	0.36	0.24

CHAPTER 38

THE ATOMIC MODELS OF RUTHERFORD AND BOHR

38–1 Introduction. We have traced how matter, electricity, and radiation came to be regarded as atomic in character. We have established the existence of some elementary particles that are more fundamental than the chemical elements. Electrons, for example, are common to all elements and are a common building block of all matter. Our discussion of positive rays and mass spectroscopy showed that matter also has positive constituents which are much more massive than electrons. Thomson, who made the first quantitative measurements on electrons and positive rays, assumed that a normal chemical atom consists of a mixture of constituents. This mixture came to be called the "plum-pudding" atomic model: the atom was regarded as a cluster of heavy positive particles, well seasoned with an equal number of electronic plums.

38–2 The Rutherford nuclear atom. A very different atomic model was indicated by an experiment performed by Rutherford in 1911.

We shall discuss radioactivity at some length in Chapter 42, but in order to be able to discuss the Rutherford experiment a few observations need to be made now. Certain atoms are unstable and fly apart of their own accord. The nature of these disintegrations depends on the element that is disintegrating, but in every case the fragments ejected consist either of electrons, here called beta rays, or of doubly ionized helium atoms, called alpha particles. These disintegration fragments usually are ejected with high energies from a radioactive substance and are often accompanied by very short-wavelength photon radiation called gamma rays. Radium, for example, is an excellent source of high-energy alpha particles. These alpha particles can travel through a few centimeters of air before they are stopped, and in a vacuum they travel long distances without losing energy. When they strike certain materials, they cause visible fluorescent light flashes.

Radiolight watch dials are painted with a paste containing fluorescent material and a trace of radium. Under a microscope the glow of the dial can be seen to be a multitude of flashes, called scintillations, which remind one of the twinkling of the stars on a summer night. The effect may be seen through a 4-power magnifier, but it is better to use two or three times this magnification. The light is less likely to appear continuous if there is very little radioactive material on

730

the dial. Observations must be made in a completely darkened room and it may be necessary to wait about five minutes for the eyes to become dark-adapted. This time delay will also permit any phosphorescence to die out. Both fluorescence and phosphorescence will be discussed in Section 38–10.

———————

Rutherford studied how these alpha particles from radium were absorbed by matter. He found they were absorbed very easily by sheets of metal a few hundredths of a millimeter thick, but that they could penetrate thin gold foil. (Gold is the most malleable substance known. It can be hammered or rolled extremely thin without tearing.) Rutherford's apparatus is shown schematically in Fig. 38–1. Radium was placed in a cavity at the end of a narrow tunnel in a lead block. Alpha particles were emitted in random directions by this source and the lead absorbed all except those emitted along the axis of the tunnel. In this way Rutherford obtained a collimated beam of alpha particles which streamed toward the gold foil. Particles that went through the foil produced flashes on the fluorescent screen.

Many of the alpha particles did go straight through the foil or were deflected only by very small amounts. Surprisingly, however, some particles were deflected through large angles. It was observed that a few alpha particles were even deflected back to the side of the gold from which they came. Rutherford could not, then, interpret his observations on the basis of the plum-pudding model of the atom. It appeared to him that the thin gold leaf must be primarily empty space in order to account for the fact that most alpha particles passed through the gold undeflected. But to understand the large scattering angles through which some of the alpha particles were deflected, he had to assume that they had encountered something small and relatively massive. He proposed that the plum-pudding model (which was only intuitive anyway) be replaced by a model in which the massive positive charges of atoms were concentrated in a very small region of the whole atom. He postulated that the rest of the atom consisted of a mist of negative electrons whose

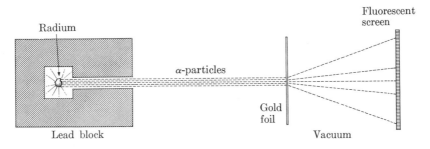

Fig. 38–1. Schematic diagram of Rutherford's alpha-particle scattering apparatus.

total negative charge was equal to the concentrated positive charge. Rutherford neglected interactions between the alpha particles and the electrons, both because the negative electronic charge was diffuse and because the electrons had so little mass.

The significant interaction, then, was between the doubly charged alpha particle ($+2e$) and the positive core having an integral number Z of positive charges of electronic magnitude $+Ze$. Rutherford assumed that these two charges acted on each other with a coulomb force which in this case was repulsive. The equation for this force in rationalized units is

$$F = \frac{1}{4\pi\epsilon_0} \frac{2e \cdot Ze}{r^2} = \frac{2Ze^2}{4\pi\epsilon_0 r^2}. \qquad (38\text{--}1)$$

This force is inversely proportional to the square of the distance between the bodies. In advanced mechanics it is shown that such a force always results in an orbit that is a conic section. When the force is attractive, like the gravitational force between the sun and planets of the solar system, the orbits must be parabolas, ellipses, or, in special cases, circles or straight lines. When the inverse square force is repulsive, however, the conic section must be the far branch of a hyperbola or its degenerate form, a straight line.

Of course the alpha particle and the atom core of the scattering metallic foil both experience the force given by Eq. (38–1). But since the gold atom is much more massive than the alpha particle, we shall assume that the gold atom remains fixed.

Consider, now, an alpha particle aimed perfectly at the core of an atom of a metal. The repelling force tends to slow the alpha particle, and since this force becomes greater as the particle nears the core, the alpha particle must finally stop. After this momentary pause, the alpha particle will be accelerated away from the atom along the same line by which it approached. In this case the path of the particle is a straight

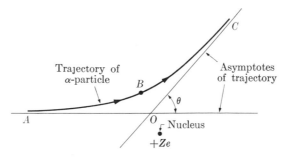

Fig. 38–2. Scattering of an alpha particle by the Rutherford nuclear atom.

line. Obviously, this case is rare, since it requires that the alpha particle move directly toward the atom core.

In general, the alpha particle will not be perfectly aimed. If an alpha particle is aimed so as to pass near the core (Fig. 38–2), then it will begin its approach at A, moving parallel to a line which is one asymptote of the hyperbolic orbit. Because the repulsive force is radial whereas the particle's motion is not, the alpha particle is forced to move away from this asymptote of its trajectory. At its point of nearest approach, B, the velocity of the alpha particle is entirely tangential, and beyond this point the path straightens out, becoming parallel to another asymptote through C. The alpha particle is scattered through the angle θ between these two asymptotes. In the rare case of perfect aim θ is 180°, whereas for the most common case of a wide miss it is 0°. Between these extremes the angle of scattering depends on the initial speed of the alpha particle, the charge on the core, and the aiming of the alpha particle.

In a given experimental situation the first two of these variables are constant, while the third is impossible to measure or control. But the very randomness of the aim makes it possible to treat this variable statistically, and Rutherford could compute what fraction of the alpha-particle deflections should lie between one angle and another.

In 1913, Geiger and Marsden carried out an exhaustive test of the Rutherford theory, using gold and silver foils. The agreement between the theory and their experimental results was excellent. Their technique was not very sensitive to the core charge Z, but they estimated that it was about half the atomic weight. Later, Chadwick made more refined measurements with copper, silver, and platinum foils. He showed that the integer Z is very near the atomic number. In Chapter 40 we shall discuss the work of Moseley, who showed that the number of core charges is *exactly* the atomic number.

The Rutherford theory assumes that alpha particles are scattered by stationary point charges. This theory also gives a way of estimating the size of the "point." The required equation for the special case of an alpha particle aimed directly at the nucleus is readily derived from the law of conservation of energy. Let M be the mass of the alpha particle, $+2e$ its charge, and v its initial velocity. At its distance of closest approach d to the core charge $+Ze$, the particle is momentarily at rest, so that all of its kinetic energy must then have been converted into electrical potential energy. Thus we have

$$\tfrac{1}{2}Mv^2 = \frac{1}{4\pi\epsilon_0}\frac{2e \cdot Ze}{d}, \tag{38–2}$$

or

$$d = \frac{Ze^2}{\pi\epsilon_0 Mv^2}. \tag{38–3}$$

For the metals studied, the "radius" of the nucleus, d, is about 10^{-14} m. This is far less than the radius of the space the atom occupies as computed from the density of the metal and Avogadro's number or from the kinetic theory of matter. This atomic radius is about 10^{-10} m. Furthermore, the distance of nearest approach is only an upper limit on the size of the core.

Since aluminum is a light metal with a rather low atomic number, aluminum should repel alpha particles less readily than the heavier metals do. Equation (38–3) shows that for smaller Z the distance of nearest approach is less. For aluminum, d can be as small as 0.8×10^{-14} m. But it has been found that the Rutherford formulas do not fit perfectly for aluminum. The deviations can be explained by assuming that at very small distances from the force center, the force of repulsion is actually less than that computed from Coulomb's law. This suggests that a very short-range attractive force is competing with the repulsive electric force. This force cannot be gravitational. Not only is the gravitational force many magnitudes too small, but also it is an inverse square force which varies with distance, exactly as the coulomb force does. This new force must depend on distance more strongly than does an inverse square force. If we define the size of the atomic core to be the region where this new, short-range force is significant compared with the coulomb force, then the radius of the core is about 10^{-14} m.

The success of Rutherford's theory of alpha-particle scattering gives him the distinction of having discovered the *atomic nucleus*. He probed matter with alpha particles and found it mostly empty space. He found the most massive part of the atom concentrated in a region of density about 10^{16} kgm/m^3 (relative density about 10^{13}). This massive part contains positive particles which must repel one another with large electric forces. But nuclear stability and the fact that the coulomb law is not accurate for short distances indicate that there is some entirely *new short-range force* that binds nuclear particles together. The Rutherford model raised many questions about how atoms are held apart and how solid bodies can retain their rigid structure. The answers to these questions come from the structure of the electronic "mist" outside the nucleus. To study this electron arrangement, we next direct our attention to atomic spectra.

38–3 Spectra. Readers of this book have studied light and know that spectrographs are instruments which analyze light according to its distribution of frequency or color. These instruments always have an entrance slit and lens, a dispersive component which may be a prism or grating, and an optical system that forms an image of the slit on a detector that is usually a photographic plate. The instrument forms an image of the slit for each frequency of light present, so that light which is continuous in its frequency distribution forms a wide image which is a continuous succession of slit images. Light which is discontinuous in frequency distribution forms a discrete set of slit images that are called spectral lines.

In our earlier study of light, attention was particularly directed toward the theory of operation of spectrographs, but it was pointed out at that time that the light from any element in gaseous form produces a discontinuous line spectrum. Each element has its own characteristic frequency distribution or spectrum, so that each element can be identified by the light that it emits. The most dramatic instance of such identification occurred when the element helium was "discovered" in the spectrum of the sun before it was chemically isolated here on earth.

Our present interest in spectroscopy goes far deeper than an interest in instruments or a technique for analysis. Our concern lies in what the light emitted by an element can tell about the structure of that element. Our situation is like that of a man from Mars who might attempt to learn the structure of a piano by analyzing the sounds it can make.

38–4 The hydrogen spectrum. The obvious place to start the study of spectra is with the spectrum of hydrogen. It is not surprising that this lightest element has the simplest spectrum and probably the simplest structure. The hydrogen spectrum is shown in Fig. 38–3. The regularity of the spectral lines is immediately evident, and it appears obvious that there is some interrelationship among them. In 1885, a Swiss high-school mathematics teacher by the name of Balmer took the wavelengths of these lines as a problem in numbers. He set out to find a formula which would show their interrelation. He hit upon a formula which could be made to give these wavelengths very precisely. The Balmer formula is

$$\lambda \text{ (angstroms)} = \frac{3645.6n^2}{n^2 - 4}. \qquad (38\text{–}4)$$

Each different wavelength is obtained by putting into the formula different values of the running integers n, which are $n = 3$, $n = 4$, $n = 5$, etc.

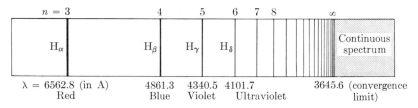

FIG. 38–3. Diagram of the Balmer series of atomic hydrogen. (The wavelengths are the values in air.)

The success of the Balmer formula led Rydberg to attempt a formulation which would apply to heavier elements. He proposed an equation of the form

$$\bar{f} = \frac{1}{\lambda} = A - \frac{R}{(n + \alpha)^2}, \tag{38-5}$$

where $\bar{f}$ is the *wave number*, R is the *Rydberg constant* which is equal to $1.09678 \times 10^7 \text{ m}^{-1}$, and n is a running integer. A and α are adjustment constants which depend on the element and the part of the spectrum or spectral series to which the formula is applied. Rydberg found that this formula, which can be regarded as a generalization of the Balmer formula, could be fitted to many spectral series, and further that the value of R was nearly the same when the formula was applied to different elements.

The wave number is the number of waves per unit length, that is, reciprocal wavelength. One might suppose that the logical quantity to use for the reciprocal form of wavelength would be the frequency, c/λ. In spectroscopy, the wave number is used because in order to compute the frequency without losing the remarkable precision of wavelength measurements, it would be necessary to know the velocity of light to an equal precision. Wave numbers can be computed without knowing the velocity of light and so they retain all the accuracy of spectroscopic wavelength measurements. However, the wave number is not an absolute constant for a given spectral line because its wavelength depends upon the index of refraction of the medium in which the measurements are made. The wavelength in air is corrected to vacuum by means of the relation $\lambda_{\text{vac}} = \mu\lambda_{\text{air}}$, where μ is the index of refraction of air for the particular wavelength. In the visible region, λ_{vac} is approximately 2.5×10^{-2} percent greater than λ_{air}.

In 1908, Ritz noted that the wave numbers of many spectral lines are the differences between the wave numbers of other spectral lines, and that the A term of the Rydberg formula was really a particular value of a term, like the second term of the Rydberg formula. Using this "combination principle," Ritz rewrote the Rydberg formula as

$$\bar{f} = \frac{R}{(m + \beta)^2} - \frac{R}{(n + \alpha)^2}, \tag{38-6}$$

where α and β are adjustment constants which depend on the element. For different spectral series of a given element, m takes on different integral values. The different lines within a series are computed by changing the running integer n. It is easily shown that for $\alpha = \beta = 0$ and $m = 2$, Eq. (38-6) reduces to the Balmer formula for hydrogen.

In the same year, 1908, Paschen found another hydrogen series of lines in the infrared region to which Eq. (38-6) could be fitted by making

$\alpha = \beta = 0$, $m = 3$, and $n = 4$, 5, 6, etc. Thus, both the then-known hydrogen series could be represented by

$$\bar{f} = R\left(\frac{1}{m^2} - \frac{1}{n^2}\right). \tag{38-7}$$

This gives the Balmer series when $m = 2$ and $n = 3$, 4, 5, etc., and correctly predicts the Paschen series for $m = 3$ and $n = 4$, 5, 6, etc.

38–5 The Bohr model and theory of the atom. Equation (38–7) represented the entire known hydrogen spectrum with great precision, but it was an empirical formula. At this point we have a correct but underived formula for the hydrogen spectrum. In 1913, Niels Bohr succeeded in deriving this important relation.

Bohr extended Rutherford's model of the atom. He retained the small core or nucleus of the atom and proposed, in addition, that there were electrons moving in orbits around the nucleus. In the case of hydrogen, Bohr proposed that the nucleus consisted of one proton with one electron revolving about it. This is a planetary model of the atom where the heavy positive nucleus is like the sun and the light, negative electron is like the planet earth. In this model, hydrogen is a tiny, one-planet solar system with the gravitational force of the solar system replaced by the electrostatic force of attraction between the oppositely charged particles. The general equations for the gravitational force and the electrostatic force are, respectively,

$$F = G\frac{MM'}{r^2} \quad \text{and} \quad F = \frac{1}{4\pi\epsilon_0}\frac{qq'}{r^2}. \tag{38-8}$$

Both forces are inversely proportional to the square of the distance between the particles. The planets of the solar system have elliptical orbits which are nearly circular. Bohr assumed that the planetary electron of hydrogen moves in a circular orbit, which makes the analysis of the classical aspects of the problem straightforward. Let v be the tangential speed of a mass M' that is revolving around a very large mass M in a circular orbit of radius r. Revolution occurs around the center of mass of the system which, in effect, is at the center of the large, massive body. The centripetal force acting on M' is the gravitational force of attraction due to M. Thus we have

$$F = G\frac{MM'}{r^2} = M'a = \frac{M'v^2}{r}, \tag{38-9}$$

from which we obtain

$$v^2 = \frac{GM}{r}. \tag{38-10}$$

In Bohr's model of the atom, an electron of mass m and tangential speed v revolves in a circular orbit of radius r around a massive nucleus having a positive charge Ze. In this case, too, the center of the orbit is essentially at the center of the heavy nucleus. The centripetal force acting on the orbiting electron is the electrostatic force of attraction due to the nuclear charge, and therefore the force equation is

$$F = \frac{1}{4\pi\epsilon_0} \frac{Ze \cdot e}{r^2} = ma = \frac{mv^2}{r}. \tag{38–11}$$

From this equation we find that

$$v^2 = \frac{Ze^2}{4\pi\epsilon_0 mr}. \tag{38–12}$$

(For hydrogen, the atomic number Z equals one. We include Z for generality.) Each of the equations (38–10) and (38–12) provides a relationship between the variables v and r. If one is known, the other can be found. In the gravitational case, any pair of values of v and of r which satisfy Eq. (38–10) may actually occur. In the electrical case, classical physics imposes no limitation on the number of solutions there can be for Eq. (38–12). For the case of the hydrogen atom, Bohr introduced a restrictive condition which is known as the first Bohr postulate. He assumed that not all the possible orbits that can be computed from Eq. (38–12) are found in hydrogen. Bohr's *first postulate* is that *only those orbits occur for which the angular momenta of the planetary electron are integral multiples of $h/2\pi$*, that is, $nh/2\pi$. Here n is any integer and h is Planck's constant.

The 2π in this expression has no particular physical significance. This factor could have appeared in quantum theory, although this was not pointed out in our discussion of it. Planck said the energy of a photon is $E = hf$. If, instead of using the frequency in cycles per second, he had used the angular frequency, $\omega = 2\pi f$, in radians per second, then his constant would have been $h/2\pi$, a quantity often written $\hbar$ and read "h-bar." In terms of $\hbar$, the energy of a photon is $E = \hbar\omega$, and the angular momentum of Bohr's first postulate is $n\hbar$. (Similarly, $\bar{\lambda}$ means $\lambda/2\pi$.)

Bohr's first postulate introduces the integer idea that appears in the Ritz formula and also introduces Planck's constant, which we have seen plays an important role in the atomic view of radiation. Stated mathematically, this first postulate is

$$I\omega = \frac{nh}{2\pi}, \tag{38–13}$$

where I is the moment of inertia of the electron about the center, ω is its angular velocity, and $n = 1, 2, 3, \ldots$ For the revolving electron, the quantity $I\omega = mr^2\omega = mvr$. From this we obtain an equation that expresses Bohr's first postulate in a very useful form:

$$mvr = \frac{nh}{2\pi}. \tag{38–14}$$

The product mvr is usually called the moment of momentum of the electron.

The orbiting electron in hydrogen must simultaneously satisfy the conditions expressed by Eqs. (38–12) and (38–14). After eliminating v between these two equations, we find that the orbits which exist or are "permitted" in the hydrogen atom are only those that have radii

$$r = \frac{\epsilon_0 h^2 n^2}{\pi m Z e^2}. \tag{38–15}$$

Since we must next consider the energy of the planetary electron and since it may seem odd that it proves convenient to consider the electron energy as being negative, we now review some basic energy concepts that were presented in Chapter 7. The energy concept is useful in calculations only when there is an exchange of energy. Fundamentally, every energy calculation is the result of an integration that always involves either an initial and a final state (evaluation of a definite integral) or an arbitrary constant (evaluation of an indefinite integral). As a matter of convenience we arbitrarily assign a certain energy to a particular state. Thus, in considering kinetic energy, we usually say that a body at rest has no kinetic energy. A man on a moving train has no kinetic energy relative to himself, but an observer on the ground regards the man on the train as moving and having kinetic energy. Each is correct in terms of *his* arbitrary definition of zero energy. This arbitrary choice of reference level is more familiar in the case of potential energy. When we say the gravitational potential energy of a mass m is mgy, it is necessary to state what is meant by $y = 0$.

In discussing the energy of a planetary electron, we shall use the usual convention of field theory, namely, that the electron has no energy when it is at rest infinitely far from its nucleus. Because an electron can do work as it moves nearer the positive nucleus, it loses electric potential energy. Since the electron starts from rest at infinity with zero energy, its potential energy must become more negative as it approaches the nucleus.

To obtain an expression for the electric potential energy of an electron, we integrate the product of the electrostatic force of the nuclear charge on the electron and a differential displacement along the line of action of the force. The limits of integration are infinity and r, the radius of an orbit. Therefore we have

$$E_p = \int_\infty^r F\, dr = \int_\infty^r \frac{1}{4\pi\epsilon_0} \frac{Ze^2}{r^2}\, dr = -\frac{Ze^2}{4\pi\epsilon_0 r}. \qquad (38\text{--}16)$$

Note that the potential energy of the electron in this case is zero at infinity and negative elsewhere. We can use Eq. (38–12) to find its kinetic energy:

$$E_k = \tfrac{1}{2}mv^2 = \frac{Ze^2}{8\pi\epsilon_0 r}. \qquad (38\text{--}17)$$

The total energy of the planetary electron is the sum of the potential and kinetic energies:

$$E = E_k + E_p = \frac{Ze^2}{8\pi\epsilon_0 r} - \frac{Ze^2}{4\pi\epsilon_0 r} = -\frac{Ze^2}{8\pi\epsilon_0 r}. \qquad (38\text{--}18)$$

We have computed the total energy as a function of r. But we have seen that r can have only those values given by Eq. (38–15). Using this equation to eliminate r, we find

$$E_n = -\frac{me^4 Z^2}{8\epsilon_0^2 h^2 n^2}, \qquad (38\text{--}19)$$

where $n = 1, 2, 3, \ldots$ for the energy states that it is possible for the electron to have. The integer n is called the *total* or *principal* quantum number and it can have any of the series of values, $1, 2, 3, \ldots$ The values of n determine the energies of the states. When n is large, the energy is large, that is, less negative than for small integers. The energy required to remove an electron from a particular state to infinity is called the *binding energy* of that state. It is numerically equal to E_n.

In calling E the energy of the electron, we are not precise. We have assumed that the electron does all the moving, while the nucleus remains at rest. Since the mass M of the proton is 1836 times the mass m of the electron, the latter has most of the kinetic energy of the atomic system. A detailed treatment would require us to consider the movement of each particle about their common center of mass. There is a theorem in mechanics which states that in a two-body problem such as this, the motion of one body may be neglected if the mass of the other body is taken to be the *"reduced mass,"* which is the product of the two masses over their sum, $mM/(m + M) = m/(1 + m/M)$. If, in Eq. (38–19) and elsewhere, we *replace* the electron mass m by the reduced mass, then our equations correctly describe the atomic system *as a whole*.

We now consider how Bohr used this set of energies to account for the hydrogen spectrum. In Chapter 30 we described how classical electrodynamics predicts that energy will be radiated whenever a charged particle is accelerated. We were careful to point out that the acceleration could be due to a change of direction of motion as well as due to a change of speed. According to classical theory, an orbital electron should radiate energy because of its centripetal acceleration. In order to preserve his atomic model of planetary electron orbits, Bohr had to devise a theory which would violate this classical prediction since, according to it, any electron that separated from the nucleus would soon radiate away its energy and fall back into the nucleus. Bohr's second break with classical physics is contained in his *second postulate*, which states that *no electron radiates energy so long as it remains in one of the orbital energy states; and that radiation occurs only when an electron goes from a higher energy state to a lower one, the energy of the quantum of radiation, hf, being equal to the difference of the energy states.* Let the quantum number $n = n_2$ represent a higher energy state and $n = n_1$ represent a lower energy state $(n_1 < n_2)$; then the second Bohr postulate can be written as

$$hf = E_{n_2} - E_{n_1}. \tag{38–20}$$

Substituting for the energies from Eq. (38–19), we have for the frequency of the emitted radiation

$$f = \frac{me^4 Z^2}{8\epsilon_0^2 h^3}\left(\frac{1}{n_1^2} - \frac{1}{n_2^2}\right) \tag{38–21}$$

or, in terms of the wave number,

$$\bar{f} = \frac{1}{\lambda} = \frac{me^4 Z^2}{8\epsilon_0^2 h^3 c}\left(\frac{1}{n_1^2} - \frac{1}{n_2^2}\right), \tag{38–22}$$

where c is the velocity of light in a vacuum. Comparing Eq. (38–22) with Eq. (38–7) shows that both have the same form.

Equally impressive is the fact that the constant factor of the Bohr formula is the Rydberg constant, R. Again comparing Eqs. (38–7) and (38–22), we find

$$R = \frac{me^4 Z^2}{8\epsilon_0^2 h^3 c} = 1.09678 \times 10^7 \text{ m}^{-1}. \tag{38–23}$$

The R given here is R_∞, which would be correct if the mass of the nucleus were infinite compared with the mass of an electron. If the motion of the

TABLE 38-1

THE SPECTRAL SERIES OF HYDROGEN

Values of n_1	Name of series	Values of n_2
1	Lyman	2, 3, 4, etc.
2	Balmer	3, 4, 5, etc.
3	Paschen	4, 5, 6, etc.
4	Brackett	5, 6, 7, etc.
5	Pfund	6, 7, 8, etc.

nucleus is taken into account, m must be replaced by the reduced mass. Therefore, in general, $R = R_\infty/(1 + m/M)$. This accounts for the slight variation of R from element to element noted by Rydberg. It is a triumph of the Bohr model and theory that the slight differences between the spectra of ordinary hydrogen and its isotope, heavy hydrogen (deuterium), can be attributed to the influence of the nuclear mass. In fact, heavy hydrogen was discovered spectroscopically by Urey in 1932.

The Bohr formula gives the Balmer series for $n_1 = 2$ and the Paschen series for $n_1 = 3$, as we have seen before. But the Bohr theory places no restrictions on n_1 and his result suggested that there might be additional hydrogen series not yet found experimentally. In 1916 Lyman found a series in the far ultraviolet, in 1922 Brackett found a new series in the infrared, and in 1924 Pfund located another in the same region. Table 38-1 summarizes the five hydrogen series.

38-6 Evaluation of the Bohr theory of the atom. Bohr's successful derivation of the Rydberg-Ritz formula opened the door to an understanding of the extra-nuclear structure of atoms which is now virtually complete. The student may feel that anyone can get the right answer to a problem if he is permitted to write his own postulates and break the rules of the game—especially when he knows the answer before he starts. Upon reflection, however, it is remarkable that Bohr could get the right answer without being more arbitrary than he was. There is no harm in introducing a new constant into physics as Planck did, but it is a great achievement to find that an empirical constant like the Rydberg constant is expressible in terms of basic constants already known. It is true that Bohr did work backwards in order to know that in his first postulate he should let the angular momentum be $nh/2\pi$. The impressive thing is that he found something so simple. There was no need to set the angular momentum to n times an arbitrary number. In view of later developments, it is surprising that Bohr could retain as much classical theory as he did.

38–7 Energy levels. Bohr's second postulate that there are only certain discrete energy levels in the hydrogen atom is especially important because it has been found to have wide application throughout atomic physics. Energy levels are most conveniently expressed in electron volts. Equation (38–19) gives the energy states of a one-electron atom in basic units. If E_n is in joules, it may be converted into electron volts by dividing by the conversion factor e_c: 1.60×10^{-19} j/ev. For this case we have

$$E \text{ (ev)} = \frac{E_n}{e_c} = -\frac{1}{e_c} \cdot \frac{me^4 Z^2}{8\epsilon_0^2 h^2} \cdot \frac{1}{n^2} \cdot \qquad (38\text{–}24)$$

Upon substituting the values of the constants in this equation and letting $Z = 1$, we find that the energy levels of the hydrogen atom are given by

$$E \text{ (ev)} = -\frac{13.6}{n^2} \cdot \qquad (38\text{–}25)$$

These energy levels can now be represented graphically as in Fig. 38–4. The quantum numbers are shown at the left and the corresponding energies of hydrogen in electron volts are given at the right. In this array of energies, the higher (less negative) energies are at the top while the lower (more negative) are toward the bottom. In a normal unexcited hydrogen atom, the electron is in its lowest energy state at the bottom, with $n = 1$. An electron in this *ground state* is stable and moves in this orbit continuously without emitting or absorbing energy. The "excitement" begins when the electron absorbs energy in some way. There are a variety of ways in which this may be brought about. If the hydrogen is in an electric discharge, a free electron which has been accelerated by the electric field may hit it.* If the hydrogen is heated, the electron may be excited by a thermal-motion collision. If the hydrogen is illuminated, it may absorb energy from a photon. Suppose the electron in hydrogen absorbs about 20 ev of energy in one of these ways. This is enough energy to lift the electron to $n = \infty$ (13.6 ev) with 6.4 ev left over. In this case, the electron is made entirely free of its home nucleus and is given 6.4 ev of kinetic energy besides. If the electron absorbs just 13.6 ev, it is merely freed from its home nucleus and drifts about with only its thermal kinetic energy. In either of these cases the remaining nucleus is an ion. If the electron absorbs less than 13.6 ev of energy, it may absorb only just enough to leave it in one of the permitted energy levels. This energy in electron

---

* We use the word "hit" loosely. We saw in the discussion of alpha-particle scattering that a collision between charged bodies does not involve physical contact in the usual sense.

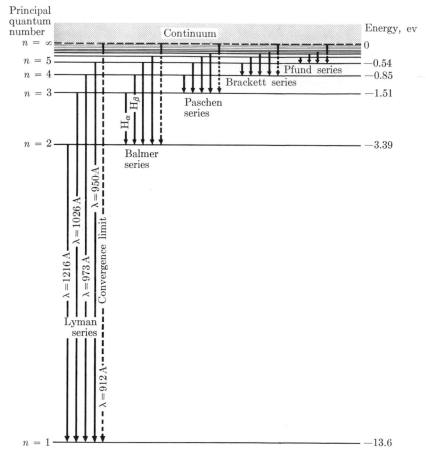

FIG. 38–4. Energy-level diagram of the hydrogen atom.

volts is *numerically* equal to the *excitation potential* of that state in volts. This atom has been excited but not ionized.

The excited electron next returns to its normal state. If it was excited to $n = 4$, it may jump from 4 to 1 in one step. It may also go 4, 2, 1 or 4, 3, 1 or 4, 3, 2, 1. In each step of the return trip, the electron must lose an amount of energy equal to the difference of the energy levels. The only mechanism available for this energy loss is through the emission of electromagnetic radiation. Thus, in Fig. 38–4 we have represented graphically the second Bohr postulate, given in Eq. (38–20). When we see the light from a hydrogen discharge, we are "seeing" the electrons go from excited states to their ground states.

The electron transitions which end on $n = 1$ constitute the Lyman series, on $n = 2$, the Balmer series, on $n = 3$, the Paschen series, etc.

From the energy-level diagram we can see that the Lyman transitions involve the largest changes of energy, produce the highest frequencies, and provide the "bluest" (ultraviolet) light.

The shaded region at the top of Fig. 38–4 represents the fact that electrons at infinity may have kinetic energy, so that their energy there is not zero but positive. If an electron of hydrogen is completely removed from its nucleus, then one of these electrons at infinity having *any* energy may fall into any one of the energy levels. Such an electron undergoes a change of energy equal to its energy at infinity minus the negative energy of the level to which it falls. The "double negative" in the last sentence enables us to conclude that the energy radiated by such a transition is the sum of the electron's kinetic energy at infinity and that involved in the transition from $n = \infty$ to the final level. The energy radiated will have a value greater than that involved in the transition from $n = \infty$ to the final level. Since there is a wide distribution of the energies among the electrons at infinity, there is a continuous spectrum below the short-wavelength convergence limit of any series.

38–8 Ionization potentials. Confirmation of the energy level concept is convincingly given by a consideration of ionization potential. Consider a radio-type tube (Fig. 38–5) which contains a filament-heated cathode, a plate as anode, and the gas being studied. If the anode has its potential increased from zero to several volts positive relative to the cathode, it is found that the current is proportional to the three-halves power of the potential difference. This is the Child-Langmuir law. In mathematical form, it is $I = kV^{3/2}$. The number of electrons emitted per unit area from a cathode depends on the cathode composition and temperature. In ionization potential experiments, the cathode is operated hot enough so that the tube current is not limited by cathode emission. The k in the equation $I = kV^{3/2}$ is determined by tube geometry and the volume density of the charges between the electrodes. The 3/2 power of V comes from considering the space-charge effect of the electrons between cathode and anode, discussed in Section 37–7.

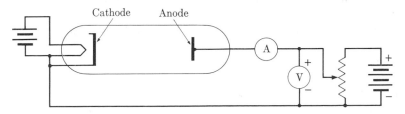

Fig. 38–5. Apparatus for determining ionization potential.

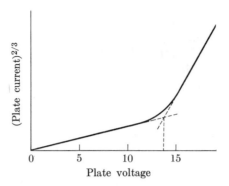

FIG. 38–6. Plate current in hydrogen-filled tube.

As the potential difference is increased, however, it is found that at a certain potential the current begins to increase much more rapidly, as shown in Fig. 38–6. When the plate potential reaches this critical value, some electrons bumping their way from cathode to anode acquire enough energy to knock electrons off the gas atoms that are present. These electrons contribute to the plate current and the positive ions cancel some of the space charge. Thus ionization causes a marked increase in the tube current. If the gas under study is hydrogen, the ionization potential is found to be 13.6 volts. It is a remarkable confirmation of the energy-level idea that there should be excellent agreement for the ionization potential as measured by the very different techniques of spectroscopy and electronics. Since the electrons are emitted from the cathode with an initial velocity distribution, some of them acquire enough energy to produce ionization at lower accelerating potentials than others. This accounts for the curved section joining the two straight-line portions of the graph in Fig. 38–6. Except for this short curved part, the break in the line is quite abrupt. This sudden change of slope would not occur if several low-energy electrons could combine in their efforts to ionize the atom of hydrogen.

38–9 Resonance potentials. The experiment just described was set up to measure the potential through which electrons must be accelerated before they can lift orbital electrons from their lowest energy state (ground state) to infinity. This ionization was detected by an increase in the current through the tube. But before the bombarding electrons have enough energy to take the atom apart by removing an electron, they have enough energy to lift an electron to an excited state. Orbital electrons in the gas can be transferred from their lowest energy state to any of the higher states. As implied earlier, the quantum conditions which require an orbital electron to emit only certain frequencies as radiation apply also to the absorption process. These electrons can absorb only energies represented by transitions between energy levels. If an orbital electron is hit by a bombarding electron with insufficient energy to produce an energy transition, the orbital electron absorbs no energy from the bombarding electron and *the collision is perfectly elastic.* If the orbital electron is hit by a high-energy bombarding electron, then the orbital electron can absorb energy by making a transition. This leaves the bombarding electron with that much less energy. *Such a collision is inelastic,* since the bombarding electron is left with less energy than it had before the collision. Such an inelastic collision puts the orbital electron in one of the excited states, and hence it can radiate energy in returning to a lower state.

Consider again the ionization experiment. As the potential difference across the tube is slowly increased, the electrons from the heated cathode are accelerated to higher and higher velocities. At low speeds, these electrons make completely elastic collisions with the electrons of the gas, so that they are deviated but not slowed by the collision process. As the potential difference across the tube is increased, however, a potential is reached where energy can be transferred to an orbital electron. Consider the case of hydrogen, with its ionization potential of 13.6 volts. A look at Fig. 38–4 discloses that the least amount of energy the normal orbital electron can absorb is 13.6 − 3.40 or 10.2 ev. A bombarding electron with 10.2 ev of energy can "resonate" with hydrogen and transfer its energy to the hydrogen. This produces no ionization, so the current through the tube is not changed, but after making such collisions the bombarding electrons proceed more slowly and the hydrogen shows its "excitement" by radiating. The hydrogen will not glow visibly because this resonance radiation is one line of the Lyman series, which is in the ultraviolet region, but ultraviolet spectroscopy confirms that the radiation is there.

In order to demonstrate the resonance phenomenon electronically, we need a more elaborate tube, such as that used by Franck and Hertz, who originated this experiment in 1913. The principal parts of such a

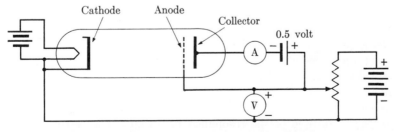

Fig. 38–7. Apparatus for determining resonance potential of a gas.

tube are shown schematically in Fig. 38–7. From the standpoint of electronics, the effect of resonance is that the bombarding electrons are slowed down, and we need a device which will measure the energy of the bombarding electrons after they have made collisions. Suppose that the anode of the ionization tube is perforated or made of wire mesh. In this case, some of the bombarding electrons will pass through the electrode rather than hit it. We now need to know the energy with which the bombarding electrons arrive at the anode.

In our consideration of the photoelectric effect, we measured the energy of photoelectrons by making them move against the force action of an electric field, and the energy of the photoelectrons was given by the stopping potential. Here we use much the same technique and insert into the tube another electrode beyond the anode. This collector electrode is maintained less positive than the anode, say 0.5 volt, so that any electrons that pass through the anode will be slowed by the field between the electrodes. Electrons which reach this last electrode must have passed the anode with an energy of at least 0.5 ev.

The experimental procedure consists of measuring the collector current as a function of the anode potential with respect to the cathode, and typical results are shown in Fig. 38–8. From $V = 0$ to $V = 0.5$ volt, there is no collector current, since no electrons can reach the anode if they have less than 0.5 ev of energy. Above $V = 0.5$ volt, the collector current rises because the

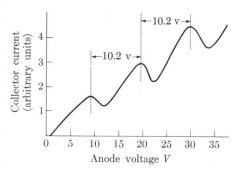

FIG. 38–8. Resonance potential curve for hydrogen.

number of electrons having at least this minimum energy increases. When V reaches the resonance potential of the gas, the collector current begins to decrease because some of the bombarding electrons are slowed by inelastic collisions with orbital electrons in the gas. The current rises again as V is further increased since, in the stronger field, bombarding electrons can make inelastic collisions early and still undergo enough acceleration to surmount the 0.5-volt barrier.

The second dip is not due to a new energy transition, because very few electrons ever get enough energy to excite the next transition. The second dip occurs at twice the resonance potential and is caused by the bombarding electrons suffering two inelastic collisions of the same kind. Thus each peak of the curve signifies more collisions and each peak is an integral multiple of the resonance potential. The separation of successive resonance peaks is 10.2 volts for hydrogen. (Since this gas ionizes at 13.6 volts, the second resonance peak will be masked by other effects if the tube shown in Fig. 38–7 is used. Actually, a more complicated tube which differentiates the resonance and ionization effects is used. This important experimental detail does not in any way alter the principle discussed in this section.) Again these electronic data corroborate the spectrographic observations, and the experiment further strengthens the energy-level concept.

38–10 Fluorescence and phosphorescence. Another application of the energy-level concept is in the explanation of fluorescence. The fluorescent lamps used for modern lighting work in the following way. The electric discharge within the lamp is through mercury vapor. The spectrum of mercury has some lines in the visible region, but most of the emitted radiation is concentrated in a line in the ultraviolet. If the tube were made of quartz, which can transmit ultraviolet light, this radiation would be able to get out of the tube, where it could be used for air sterilization or to produce "sunburn." But a clear tube is a poor source of visible light. Therefore the inside of a fluorescent lamp is coated with a material which absorbs the invisible ultraviolet light. Thus the atoms of this fluorescent material become excited. If the excited electrons fell back to their normal state in one step, they would re-emit the ultraviolet light, which would still be invisible. But the excited electrons return to their normal state in more than one step. Each step produces radiation of less energy than the original excitation, so that the energy of the ultraviolet light is converted into visible light. The various tints that different lamps have are controlled by the nature of the fluorescent material used.

Some materials have what are called *metastable* states. When an electron is excited into one of these states, it does not return to its normal state at once, but may remain excited for an appreciable time. Such materials have a persistent light, called *phosphorescence,* which may last several hours after all external excitation is removed. These materials are sometimes used on the screens of cathode-ray tubes, and they are sometimes used to make light switches glow, so that they may be found in the dark. Most fluorescent tubes have some phosphorescence. It may be observed in a dark room a few minutes after the light is turned off.

38–11 Many-electron atoms. We have stated that the Bohr theory is successful only for one-electron atoms, which pretty well limits application of the theory to hydrogen, heavy hydrogen, and ionized helium.

In our solar system, the various planets interact with one another only very slightly. The motion of the planets is understood by first considering that each planet experiences only the gravitational force of the sun.   When these problems are solved for each planet, the weak planet-to-planet forces are treated as minor perturbations.   The solar analogy is fruitful in understanding hydrogen, since hydrogen has but one electron.   When an atom has two or more electrons, the interelectron interactions are not small and the simple planetary model breaks down. But one can sense what is in fact found: that a multiplicity of energy levels exists in these cases and so there are many lines in the spectra. Furthermore, the whole treatment so far has been of an *isolated* atom, that is, atoms in the gaseous state.   In the liquid and solid states, the interactions between the electronic systems of the closely packed atoms introduce so many additional energy levels that the spectrum is now continuous.   Thus if the electrodes for an electric arc are copper rods, the spectrum of the light from the incandescent rods is continuous, whereas that from the gaseous copper ions in the arc between the elec- trodes is a line spectrum.

Although the Bohr theory is unable to give a quantitative explanation of the spectra of more complicated atoms, it provided a conceptual frame- work in terms of which the spectra of many-electron atoms could be understood.   It developed that in complex atoms no more than two elec- trons may have the quantum number n equal to one.   Thus, for example, unexcited beryllium, with four electrons, has two electrons with $n = 1$ and two with $n = 2$.   There may be up to eight electrons in an atom for which $n = 2$.   Thus unexcited aluminum, with thirteen electrons, has two with $n = 1$, eight with $n = 2$, and three with $n = 3$.   The number of electrons that may have a particular value of n becomes much greater for larger values of n, but there is a definite number for each value.   All electrons in any given atom which have a particular value of n have *about* the same energy, but for each value of n there is a group of energy states which require a total of four different quantum numbers to specify.

TABLE 38–2

Shell name	Principal quantum number	Maximum occupancy
K	1	2
L	2	8
M	3	8
N	4	18
O	5	18
P	6	32
Q	7	16 known

A group of electrons in an atom all having about the same energy and all having the same value for the principal quantum number n is called a *shell*. These shells are given alphabetical names. The innermost shell, with $n = 1$, has up to two electrons and is called the K-shell. The next shell, with $n = 2$, has up to eight electrons and is called the L-shell. Similarly, the M-, N-, O-, P-, and Q-shells have n's equal to 3, 4, 5, 6, and 7. Each shell may have electrons up to the number listed in Table 38–2.

In any given element the electrons of the unexcited atom occupy the lowest possible shells. Thus tin, which has fifty electrons, has its K-, L-, M-, and N-shells completely filled, and the O-shell is only partly filled, with 14 electrons.

This scheme, which can be deduced from spectroscopic data, is confirmed by the chemical and physical properties of the atoms. For example, all elements with the highest shell completely filled are inert gases. The shells we have been discussing correlate closely with the periodic table of the elements.

38–12 The status of Bohr's model and theory of the atom. In this chapter we have seen how Rutherford's discovery of the nucleus led Bohr to propose a model for the hydrogen atom and devise a theory which accounted for the spectral lines that hydrogen emits. Unfortunately, the Bohr model of the atom suffers from serious defects. In the first place it applies only to one-electron atoms, principally hydrogen. But even for this simple element, Sommerfeld found it necessary to postulate elliptical orbits and to consider the relativistic mass change (see Chapter 39) of the revolving electron in order to account for the details in the fine structure of the spectral lines. Attempts to apply Bohr theory to heavier elements were moderately successful in a few cases. The next heavier element, helium, has two electrons, but when one of these is removed by ionization, the remaining ion has but one electron and is hydrogenlike. The alkaline metals share with hydrogen the same column in the periodic table and their spectra are also hydrogenlike when ionized until only one orbital electron remains. But the Bohr model is not a general solution to the problem of atomic structure.

Furthermore, the Bohr model does not answer all the questions we can raise about hydrogen. A complete analysis should not only reveal the frequency of the emitted light, but also the relative intensity of the different spectral lines. In Chapter 41 we will discuss wave mechanics, which has replaced the Bohr analysis. But we need not be dismayed with Bohr's work simply because it has been replaced by something better. Road maps are far less accurate than topographical survey maps. But on a cross-country trip, road maps are a better guide because the survey maps are cumbersome and contain details that are often irrelevant. The

Bohr theory of hydrogen is like a road map which we use even when we know a more precise map exists.

Despite its shortcomings the Bohr model was a conceptual "breakthrough" that facilitated many empirical observations about the electronic structure of the heavier atoms to which Bohr's work did not apply directly. We shall find Bohr's conceptual scheme very useful in describing the x-ray spectra of heavy elements. Although wave mechanics has replaced the Bohr model, wave mechanics confirms and builds upon the energy-level concept that he introduced.

PROBLEMS

38–1. Derive the equation for the radii of the Bohr orbits, Eq. (38–15), from Eqs. (38–11) and (38–13).

38–2. Show that the tangential speed of an electron in its orbit is $v = Ze^2/2\epsilon_0 nh$, and its angular speed is $\omega = \pi m Z^2 e^4/2\epsilon_0^2 n^3 h^3$.

38–3. (a) Calculate the radii of the first, second, and third "permitted" electron orbits in hydrogen, in angstroms. (b) What is the diameter of the hydrogen atom in the ground state?

38–4. Suppose one has a tank of atomic hydrogen at a temperature of 20°C and a pressure of 1 atm. If each of the atoms and also the average distance between them were expanded until the diameter of each nucleus is 1 inch, what would then be (a) the radius of the smallest electron orbit in feet, and (b) the average distance to the nearest atomic neighbor in miles? (Assume that the nuclear diameter is 2×10^{-14} m, and that the distance between atomic neighbors is 9×10^{-5} cm. This is four times the mean free path calculated for molecular hydrogen in Problem 18–22.) (c) What would be the distance between neighbors on this expanded scale if the gas pressure were reduced to 1 mm of mercury? (d) If the gas were liquefied so that the atoms "touched," would there still be open space in the world of hydrogen atoms?

38–5. Calculate the binding energy of the electron in hydrogen in joules and in ev when $n = 1, 2, 3,$ and infinity.

38–6. An alpha particle having a kinetic energy of 7.68 Mev is projected directly toward the nucleus of a copper atom. What is their distance of closest approach? The mass of an alpha particle is four times that of the proton and the atomic number of copper is 29.

38–7. Evaluate the Rydberg constant for hydrogen from atomic constants, assuming a nucleus of infinite mass.

38–8. Rearrange and alter the Balmer formula, Eq. (38–4), so that the left side is the wave number in reciprocal meters. Show that the result agrees with Eq. (38–19) when the Rydberg constant is substituted in the latter equation and when $n_1 = 2$ and $n_2 = n$.

38–9. Calculate (a) the frequency, (b) the wavelength, and (c) the wave number of the H_β line of the Balmer series for hydrogen. This line is emitted in the transition from $n_2 = 4$ to $n_1 = 2$. Assume that the nucleus has infinite mass.

38–10. Using the reduced mass equations, calculate the wavelength of the H_β line (see Problem 38–9) in the Balmer series for the three isotopes of hydrogen: H^1; deuterium, H^2; and tritium, H^3.

38–11. The Rydberg constants (reduced mass form) for hydrogen and singly ionized helium are 10967757.7 m^{-1} and 10972226.6 m^{-1} respectively. For the nuclei of these atoms, $M_{He} = 3.9726 M_H$. From the given data, calculate the ratio of the mass of the proton to that of the electron to four significant figures.

38–12. For each of the series listed in Table 38–1, calculate the short-wavelength limit and find the energy of the quantum in ev for each.

38–12. Calculate the short-wavelength limit of each of the series listed in Table 38–1, and find the energy of the quantum in ev for each.

38–13. Some of the energy levels of a hypothetical one-electron atom (not hydrogen) are as follows:

n	1	2	3	4	5	∞
E_n, ev	-15.60	-5.30	-3.08	-1.45	-0.80	0

Draw the energy-level diagram and find (a) the ionization potential, (b) the short-wavelength limit of the series terminating on $n = 2$, (c) the excitation potential for the state $n = 3$, and (d) the wave number of the photon emitted when the atomic system goes from the energy state $n = 3$ to the ground state. (e) What is the minimum energy that an electron will have after interacting with this unexcited atom if the initial kinetic energy of the electron is (1) 6 ev, (2) 11 ev?

38–14. (a) What is the least amount of energy in ev that must be given to a hydrogen atom so that it can emit the H_β line (see Problem 38–9 and Fig. 38–4) in the Balmer series? (b) How many different possibilities of spectral line emission are there for this atom when the electron goes from $n = 4$ to the ground state?

38–15. Neglecting reduced mass corrections, show that (a) the short-wavelength limit of the Lyman series ($n = 1$) of hydrogen is the same as that of the "Balmer" series ($n = 2$) of ionized helium, and (b) that the wavelength of the first line of this helium series is 1.35 times the wavelength of the first line of the Lyman series of hydrogen.

38–16. (a) Show that the frequency of revolution of an electron in its circular orbit in the Bohr model of the atom is $f = mZ^2e^4/4\epsilon_0^2 n^3 h^3$.

(b) Show that when n is very large, the frequency of revolution equals the radiated frequency calculated from Eq. (38–21) for a transition from $n_2 = n + 1$ to $n_1 = n$. (This problem illustrates Bohr's *correspondence principle*, which is often used as a check on quantum calculations. When n is small, quantum physics gives results which are very different from those of classical physics. When n is large, the differences are not significant and the two methods then "correspond.")

38–17. A 10-kgm satellite circles the earth once every 2 hr in an orbit having a radius of 8000 km. (a) Assuming that Bohr's angular momentum postulate applies to satellites just as it does to an electron in the hydrogen atom, find the quantum number of the orbit of the satellite. (b) Show from Bohr's first postulate and Newton's law of gravitation that the radius of an earth-satellite orbit is directly proportional to the square of the quantum number, $r = kn^2$, where k is the constant of proportionality. (c) Using the result from part (b), find the distance between the orbit of the satellite in this problem and its next "allowed" orbit. (d) Comment on the possibility of observing the separation of the two adjacent orbits. (e) Do quantized and classical orbits correspond for this satellite? Which is the "correct" method for calculating the orbits?

CHAPTER 39

RELATIVITY

39–1 Importance of viewpoint. What one observes often depends on one's viewpoint. An election will be interpreted differently by Democrats and Republicans. A change in college rules may be viewed differently by students and administration. What scientists observe also depends on their viewpoint. Consider the interpretations of physical events that might be made by a person of high I.Q. born and brought up on a merry-go-round. He would experience a force somewhat like the force of gravity. It would be downward at the center of rotation, and, because of the centrifugal component, it would be directed downward and out at points away from the center. Our observer could learn to live happily with this force. He might even seek to write a quantitative description of it and express its nature in terms of mathematical equations. Though we express the force of gravity we experience as $F = mg$ (always downward), our observer would have a harder time of it, since his force is not constant in either magnitude or direction. If our merry-go-round observer were to have the genius to devise a whole system of mechanics, the mechanics he would devise would not be the mechanics of Newton. Newton said that a moving body subject to no forces will continue to move with a constant speed in a constant direction. But an airplane which flew "straight" over the merry-go-round would appear to move in a curved path to our special observer.

The situation described appears far-fetched, but the earth turns, and we were all born and brought up on a merry-go-round! The acceleration of gravity is complicated by the rotation of the earth, and there are many other effects, like cyclonic storms, which are a direct result of the rotation. Newton knew of this complication. The earth turns rather slowly compared with a regular merry-go-round, and the effects of the earth's rotation are small enough that most of the time we can neglect them. But, strictly speaking, Newton's laws just do not hold precisely for an observer who is earthbound. For Newton's laws to be valid precisely, we must observe events from what is called an inertial frame or a Galilean-Newtonian coordinate system. Such a system is one which has no acceleration.

The whole structure of classical physics, then, is based on the assumption that we interpret all events as they would be interpreted by an observer who is either at rest in an inertial frame or moving with constant linear velocity with respect to it. The man on the merry-go-round would have a physics far from Newtonian. By stepping onto the earth he would find his physics more nearly Newtonian. The genius of Newton is, in part, that although he never could step off the earth physically, he did step off the earth mentally. He interpreted events as though he had no acceleration. Because of this shift in his viewpoint, he was able to write his laws of mechanics in the particularly simple form that he did.

But Newton never really knew where he projected himself to, and this worried him. He excluded the earth as a vantage point because the earth not only rotates but revolves about the sun. The sun offered possibilities, but even the sun moves and is probably accelerated through space. The stellar constellations were named by the ancients and the stability of their arrangement led to their being called the "fixed" stars. Yet it would be the strangest of coincidences if the "fixed" stars really were fixed. Any velocity looks small when seen from far enough away, and from modern astronomical measurements we know that the constellations are slowly changing.

It would seem, however, that if we locate a frame of reference so that it is fixed relative to the stars, this vantage point will be sufficiently steady for Newton's laws to serve well enough for every practical purpose. Such a vantage point is good enough for the practical men who want to fly aircraft, build rocket engines, or communicate via television. But for a philosopher or physicist whose primary concern is the understanding of the nature of things and whose goal is the discovery of truth, uncertainty about the frame of reference represented a serious flaw in the logical structure of classical physics. *It is an amazing fact that concern over this seemingly minor point led ultimately to the discovery of how to release the energy of the nucleus of the atom.*

39–2 The search for a frame of reference—the ether. The search for something more fixed than the stars went something like this. As we pointed out in Chapter 30, James Clerk Maxwell demonstrated that electricity and light are related phenomena. Starting with known properties of electricity and magnetism, Maxwell derived equations which are identical in form to the equations which describe many wave phenomena. He could demonstrate, furthermore, that the velocity of the waves he discovered was the same as the velocity of light. He could derive many other properties of light, and it was soon accepted that he had put the wave theory of light on a firm foundation. In this theory, light is an electromagnetic wave motion.

Every wave motion has something that "waves." Sound waves have air and water waves have water. Surely, it was argued, light waves must involve the waving of something even in free space. No one knew what it was, but it was given the name "luminiferous ether."

Light passes through many kinds of materials. It passes through relatively heavy materials like glass and it passes through the nearly perfect vacuum that must lie between the stars and the earth. Thus ether must permeate all of space. Light is a transverse wave motion. This comes out of Maxwell's theory and from many experimental observations, particularly those on polarized light. This implies that the ether is a solid. Transverse waves involve shear forces and can occur only in solids which can support shear. Sound waves in air must be longitudinal because of this fact. Furthermore, the ether must be a rigid solid. The propagation velocity of mechanical waves in various materials depends on the elastic constants of the material. These are much greater for steel than for air. The very great velocity of light thus implies that the ether must have a very large shear modulus. It is rather hard on the imagination to suppose that all space is filled with this rigid solid and that all material objects move through this solid without resistance, yet it was supposed to exist. However fanciful it may seem to us, physicists felt that this ether might be just the thing to which to attach a Newtonian coordinate system. It was conceived that Newton's laws would hold exactly for an observer moving without acceleration *relative to the ether*.

If the ether is assumed to be at rest, then the interesting question is: How fast are we moving through the ether? Since all speculations about the ether stem from its properties as a medium for carrying light, an optical experiment is indicated. It is not hard to compute how sensitive the apparatus must be in order to measure the ether drift. Assuming, for the sake of argument, that the sun has no ether drift, the velocity of the earth through the ether must be its orbital velocity. If the sun has an ether drift, then the drift of the earth will be even greater than its orbital velocity at some seasons. Knowing that the radius of the earth's orbit is about 93 million miles, we can find the orbital velocity to be about 18.5 mi/sec. By performing the experiment at the best season of the year, we know that we should be able to find an ether drift of at least 18.5 mi/sec. The velocity of light is 186,000 mi/sec. Great as our orbital velocity is, it is only about 10^{-4} times the velocity of light; so it is evident that a very sensitive instrument is required.

39–3 The Michelson interferometer. A device of sufficient sensitivity was made and used in the United States by Michelson and Morley in 1887. The principle of their apparatus is brought out by the following analogy. Suppose two equally fast swimmers undertake a race in a river between floats anchored to the river bed. Two equal courses, each having a total length $2L$, are laid out from the starting point, float A, shown in Fig. 39–1. One course is AD, parallel to the flow of the river relative to the earth, and the other is AC, perpendicular to it. How will the times compare if

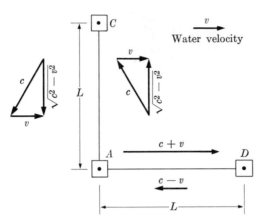

Fig. 39–1. Swimming analogy to the Michelson-Morley experiment.

each of the swimmers goes out and back on his course? Let the speed of each swimmer relative to the water be c, and let the water drift or velocity with respect to the earth be v. When the swimmer on the parallel course goes downstream, his velocity will add to that of the water, giving him a resultant velocity of $(c + v)$ with respect to the earth. The time required for him to swim the distance L from A to D is $L/(c + v)$. On his return, he must overcome the water drift. His net velocity then is $(c - v)$, and his return time is $L/(c - v)$. His total time is the sum of these two times. This is seen to depend upon the velocity of the water, and is given by

$$t_{\parallel} = \frac{L}{c + v} + \frac{L}{c - v} = \frac{2Lc}{c^2 - v^2}. \tag{39–1}$$

The other swimmer, going perpendicular to the water drift, spends the same time on each half of his trip, but he must head upstream if he is not to be carried away by the current. The component of his velocity that carries him toward his goal is $\sqrt{c^2 - v^2}$ with respect to the earth. The total time for his trip also depends on the water drift, and is

$$t_{\perp} = \frac{2L}{\sqrt{c^2 - v^2}}. \tag{39–2}$$

To see how these two times compare, we divide the parallel course time, Eq. (39–1), by the perpendicular course time, Eq. (39–2), and obtain

$$\frac{t_{\parallel}}{t_{\perp}} = \frac{2Lc}{c^2 - v^2} \cdot \frac{\sqrt{c^2 - v^2}}{2L} = \frac{1}{\sqrt{1 - (v^2/c^2)}}. \tag{39–3}$$

In still water $v = 0$, the ratio of the times is unity, and the race is a tie, as we would expect. In slowly moving water, the ratio is greater than unity and the swimmer on the perpendicular course wins; or, put differ-

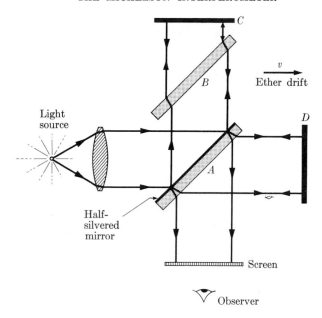

FIG. 39-2. The Michelson interferometer.

ently, if the swimmers are stroking in phase when they leave float A, they will be out of phase when they return to it. If the velocity of the river increases to nearly that of the swimmer, then the ratio tends toward infinity. If the river velocity exceeds the swimmer velocity, the entire analysis breaks down. The ratio becomes imaginary and both swimmers are swept off the course by the current. The point is that, by observing the race, the velocity of the water relative to the system of anchored floats can be measured.

The optical equivalent of the above situation is to have a race between two light rays over identical courses, one parallel and one perpendicular to the ether drift. The instrument used, called a Michelson interferometer, is shown schematically in Fig. 39-2.

Light enters the apparatus from the source at the left. At A it strikes a glass mirror which has a half-silvered surface. Half the light is reflected up toward B and C, while the other half refracts at both surfaces of A and emerges parallel to the original beam and goes on to D. Both C and D are full-silvered, front-surface mirrors which turn their beams back toward A. The beam from C is partly reflected at A, but part of that beam refracts through A and goes to the observer. The beam from D partially refracts through A and is lost, but part of that beam is also reflected toward the observer. The plate of glass at B has the same thickness and inclination as that at A, so that the two light paths from source to observer pass through the same number of glass thicknesses. If the light from the slit did not diverge and remained very narrow in going through the apparatus, the observer would see a line of light. The brightness of this line would depend on the difference in the optical length* of the two light paths. If these differed by any whole number of wavelengths of the light (including zero), the line would be bright. If the paths differed by an odd number of half-wavelengths, then the line would be dark. Between these extremes every brightness gradation would be observed. In practice, the light does diverge in the apparatus, and there are a great many slightly different paths being traversed simultaneously. Consequently the observer does not see one line but a multiplicity of lines. The loci of points where the paths differ by whole wavelengths are bright, and where the paths differ by an odd number of half-wavelengths there is darkness. Thus, as one path length is varied, the observer sees fringes, like the teeth of a comb, move across the field, rather than a single line becoming lighter and darker. It is fortunate that the optical system works as it does, since it is easier for the eye to detect differences in position than differences in intensity.

The precision of this device is remarkable. If yellow light from sodium is used, the wavelength is 5.893×10^{-7} m. Moving the mirror C away from A one-half this distance will increase one path length by a whole wavelength and cause the pattern to move an amount equal to the separation of two adjacent dark lines. If we can estimate to hundredths of fringes, then the smallest detectable motion is only 2.9×10^{-9} m. Upon moving a mirror one-thousandth of an inch, 86 fringes would go by. (One way of defining a meter is to say that it is the length of 1,553,164 red cadmium wavelengths.)

The similarity between the Michelson interferometer and the swimming race should be evident. Light corresponds to the swimmers and has the free-space velocity, c, with respect to its ether medium. The ether drift corresponds to the water current drift and has the velocity v with respect to the earth. Just as we could learn about the river flow by seeing the outcome of the swimmers' race, so we wish to measure the ether drift by conducting a "light race" over equal paths parallel and perpendicular to the ether drift.

Suppose that instead of taking the ratio of the times for the two paths of the river race we now take their difference; then

---

* Two paths have the same optical length if light traverses both in the same time. The optical lengths of the interferometer paths can be changed by changing their physical length, by changing the index of refraction of the region through which the light passes, or, if the swimming analogy applies, by moving the apparatus relative to the light-carrying medium.

$$\Delta t = \frac{2Lc}{c^2 - v^2} - \frac{2L}{\sqrt{c^2 - v^2}} = \frac{2L}{c}\left[\left(1 - \frac{v^2}{c^2}\right)^{-1} - \left(1 - \frac{v^2}{c^2}\right)^{-1/2}\right].$$

$$(39\text{--}4)$$

Using the first two terms of the binomial expansion, we have, to a good approximation if $v \ll c$, that

$$\Delta t = \frac{2L}{c}\left[\left(1 + \frac{v^2}{c^2}\right) - \left(1 + \frac{v^2}{2c^2}\right)\right] = \frac{Lv^2}{c^3}. \qquad (39\text{--}5)$$

In the interferometer, the time difference should appear as a fringe shift from the position the fringes would have if there were *no* ether drift. The distance light moves in a time Δt is $d = c\,\Delta t$ and if this distance represents n waves of wavelength λ, then $d = n\lambda$. Therefore the fringe shift would be

$$\boxed{n = \frac{Lv^2}{\lambda c^2}.} \qquad (39\text{--}6)$$

Thus if the light race is carried out with light of speed c and wavelength λ in an interferometer whose arms are of length L, one of which is parallel to the ether drift of velocity v, then Eq. (39–6) gives the number of fringes that should be displaced because of the motion of the earth through the ether compared with their positions if the earth were *at rest* in the ether.

39–4 The Michelson-Morley experiment. The apparatus used was large and had its effective arm length increased to about 10 m by using additional mirrors to fold up the path. The entire apparatus was floated on mercury so that it could be rotated at constant speed without introducing strains that would deform the apparatus. *Rotation was necessary* in order to make the fringes shift, and by rotating through 90°, first one arm and then the other could be made parallel to the drift, thereby *doubling* the fringe displacement of Eq. (39–6). We can now estimate whether this instrument should be sensitive enough to detect the ether drift. Recall that at some time of the year the ether drift v was expected to be at least the orbital velocity of the earth, which is about $10^{-4}\,c$. Thus we expect v/c to be at least 10^{-4}. Using light of wavelength 5×10^{-7} m, the computed shift is $n = 0.4$ fringe. Michelson and Morley estimated that they could detect a shift of one-hundredth of a fringe. Sensitivity to spare!

Measurements were made over an extended period of time at all seasons of the year, but no significant fringe shift was observed. Thinking that the earth might drag a little ether along with it, just as a boat carries a thin layer of water when it glides, Michelson and Morley took the entire apparatus to a mountain laboratory in search of a site which would project into the drifting ether. Again a diligent search failed to measure an ether drift. The experiment "failed."

Few experimental "failures" have been more stimulating than this. The negative result of the Michelson-Morley experiment presented a challenge to explain its failure. Fitzgerald and Lorentz proposed an *ad hoc* explanation. They pointed out that there might be an interaction between the ether and objects moving relative to it, such that the object became shorter in all its dimensions parallel to the relative velocity. Recall that in the flowing-river analogy the ratio of the times of the swimmers in Eq. (39–3) was

$$\frac{1}{\sqrt{1 - v^2/c^2}}.$$

If the route parallel to the flow had been shorter by this factor, then the ratio of the times would have been one and the race would have been a tie. A similar shortening of the parallel interferometer arm would account for the tie race Michelson and Morley always observed. The shortening could never be measured because any rule used to measure it would also be moving relative to the ether and would shorten also. Whether you accept the Fitzgerald-Lorentz contraction hypothesis or not, the Michelson-Morley experiment indicates that all observers who measure the velocity of light will get the same result regardless of their own velocity through space.

39–5 The constant velocity of light. Speed trials of cars, boats, and airplanes are never official unless they are made in the following way. The record contender must drive his craft in opposite directions over a measured course and the speed attained is calculated to be the double distance divided by the total time spent between markers. This technique is used to make any wind, water, or other conditions which may be helpful in one direction be cancelled out by their hindrance on the reverse trip. Measurements of the speed of light are similarly made by timing a flash of light as it goes to a distant mountain and returns. This technique is rather good and, *to a first approximation,* the influence of a moving medium does cancel out. But the cancellation is not perfect and *to a second approximation,* the effect of a moving medium does *not* cancel. This becomes obvious if the medium moves faster than the speed under test. In this case, the test cannot be made, since the thing tested is carried away. The fact that Fizeau, in France, and others obtained consistent results for the velocity of light at a variety of times, places, and in different directions was in itself evidence that the speed of the earth through the ether (if any) was small compared with the velocity of light. It is highly significant that the

Michelson-Morley interferometer was sensitive enough to detect the second-order term. Referring back to Eq. (39–5), you will note that the first terms (the ones) cancel out and the significant result remains only because the second terms do not cancel. The Michelson-Morley experiment was sensitive to the second-order terms because, instead of trying to measure the times of transit of light through their apparatus, they measured the *difference* of times. Michelson and Morley found that the speed of the earth through space made *no difference* in the speed of light relative to them. The inference is clear either that the earth moves in some way through the ether space more slowly than it moves about the sun, or that *all observers must find that their motion through space makes no difference in the speed of light relative to them.*

The above inference was clear, at least to Einstein, who took the second alternative and made it a cornerstone of his special theory of relativity. Relativity together with the atomic view of matter and energy underlie all the great new vistas that physics brings to the twentieth century.

Recall that the Michelson-Morley experiment was carried out to measure the speed of the earth relative to the ether in order to establish a frame of reference relative to which Newton's laws would hold. The failure of that experiment meant that the search for the fixed reference system must be made by another technique or abandoned altogether. Einstein explored the alternative of abandonment. He asked himself where he would stand (both literally and figuratively) if there were no "Newtonian" frame of reference. In this case there could be no absolute velocities, for every velocity would have to be measured relative to an origin that might and probably would be moving. Since there can be no preferred frame of reference, any frame must be as good as any other. To be universal, the laws of physics must be the same for all observers regardless of any motion they may have. Contrary to the first paragraphs of this chapter, one's viewpoint *must make no difference* in one's interpretation of events observed. If he is to be correct, the man born and brought up on a merry-go-round must deduce the same laws of physics as anyone else.

39–6 General and special theories of relativity. Relativity is divided into two branches. One is called the general theory of relativity and the other is the special, or restricted, theory of relativity. In the general theory, proposed in 1915, Einstein treats the class of problems that arise when one frame of reference is accelerated relative to another. This class includes the problem of our man in the merry-go-round, since his objects experience a centripetal acceleration relative to the earth. In the special theory, proposed in 1905, Einstein treats problems that arise when one frame of reference moves with a *constant linear velocity* relative to another.

The general theory is quite difficult. Fortunately, the special theory is sufficient for discussing most atomic and nuclear phenomena. It contains much "uncommon sense" and many ideas which tease the imagination. But the mathematics is simple enough that we can derive several interesting relationships which are basic to an understanding of the material which follows.

39–7 Classical relativity. Let us begin by considering the relativity of physical quantities in classical or Galilean-Newtonian physics, and ask how events in one system, S, moving with constant linear velocity, appear from another system S', also moving with constant linear velocity.

No generality will be lost if one of the systems, say S, is regarded as being at rest, and the other, S', as moving with a uniform velocity v. Our problem, then, is like that of comparing the observations of a man on the ground with those of a man on a uniformly moving train.

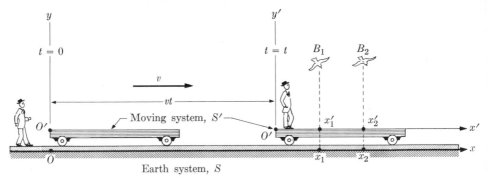

Fig. 39–3. Coordinate systems S and S'.

In Fig. 39–3 the earth observer considers himself to be at the origin O of his system S and he chooses an x-axis parallel to the track. The train observer in S' likewise measures distances from himself at O' and chooses his x'-axis parallel to the track. Let us measure time from the moment when the two observers are exactly opposite each other. Suppose that at some later time t each observer decides to measure the separation of two birds, B_1 and B_2, which happen to be hovering over the track. The observer at O' observes that the positions of B_1 and B_2 are the small distances x'_1 and x'_2. The observer at O finds the positions of B_1 and B_2 are the larger distances x_1 and x_2. The observer at O can compute the O' observations by noting that the observer at O' has moved a distance vt, with the result

$$x'_1 = x_1 - vt \qquad \text{and} \qquad x'_2 = x_2 - vt. \qquad (39\text{–}7)$$

The observer on the train (who may think the train is at rest with the earth moving under it) can account for the difference in their observations by observing that O has drifted away from him a distance vt. He obtains

$$x_1 = x_1' + vt \quad \text{and} \quad x_2 = x_2' + vt. \tag{39–8}$$

These are transformation equations in that they transform observations from one system to the other. By solving either set of equations for the separation of the birds, we get

$$x_2 - x_1 = x_2' - x_1' \quad \text{or} \quad \Delta x = \Delta x'. \tag{39–9}$$

This shows that the two observers agree on how far apart the two birds are. Note that the relative velocity v of the observers need not be known. Similarly, the time t since the two observers were opposite each other need not be known, but all observations must be *simultaneous*—even if the birds cooperate by staying the same distance apart.

What we have just shown is that *distance* or length is an *invariant* quantity when transformed from one Newtonian coordinate system to another.

We now compare results by the same two observers for a velocity measurement. Suppose that one bird flies from position B_1 at time t_1 to position B_2 at time t_2. The transformation equations of the positions of the bird are of the same form except for the difference of time, thus

$$x_1' = x_1 - vt_1, \qquad x_2' = x_2 - vt_2. \tag{39–10}$$

To solve for the average observed velocity u', we take the difference between the two transformation equations and divide by the time interval, obtaining

$$x_2' - x_1' = (x_2 - vt_2) - (x_1 - vt_1) = (x_2 - x_1) - v(t_2 - t_1), \tag{39–11}$$

or

$$\Delta x' = \Delta x - v\,\Delta t. \tag{39–12}$$

Therefore the velocity relation is

$$u' = \frac{\Delta x'}{\Delta t} = \frac{\Delta x}{\Delta t} - v = u - v. \tag{39–13}$$

Thus the *velocities* measured by the two observers are *not* the same. They are *not invariant* under a transformation between Galilean-Newtonian coordinate systems.

Suppose the bird again cooperates and swoops over the train with different velocities at positions 1 and 2. Each observer could measure the velocity at each position. Using the result just derived, we find that the velocity transformation equations are

$$u'_1 = u_1 - v \quad \text{and} \quad u'_2 = u_2 - v. \qquad (39\text{--}14)$$

If the observers also measured the time Δt it took the bird to get from one position to the other, they could solve for the average acceleration. Taking the difference between the velocity transformations gives

$$u'_2 - u'_1 = u_2 - u_1. \qquad (39\text{--}15)$$

Dividing by Δt, we have $a' = a$, which shows that velocity difference and *acceleration* are *invariant* under transformation between Newtonian inertial frames of reference.

The transformation equations we have just derived formally are fairly obvious. The most complicated result, the *variant* velocity transformation, was used without formal proof in the study of impact and Doppler effect, and was used in our recent discussion of the Michelson-Morley experiment. In fact, the problem presented by the negative result of that experiment was that, contrary to the Newtonian transformation, observers *must* find the velocity of light the *same* whether the observers are moving or not.

The classical transformation equations just derived apply only for reference frames moving with *constant linear velocity* with respect to one another. It is their failure in cases involving uniform motion that leads us into Einstein's special theory of relativity. We have not treated the classical transformation equations which deal with accelerated or rotating frames of reference, since these much more complicated equations would lead us into a discussion of general relativity, which we shall not explore.

In the derivations above we have tacitly made the *classical assumption* that time intervals are the same for all observers. Actually, there is no *a priori* reason* for assuming that time or any other physical quantity is invariant under a transformation of coordinates. Whether or not an assumption is correct is determined solely by the experimental verification of the results predicted with its aid. We will find later in this chapter that the invariance of time interval will have to be abandoned, when the invariance of the free-space velocity of light is assumed.

39–8 Einsteinian relativity. The Michelson-Morley experiment was carried out to measure the velocity of the earth through the ether in the hope that the ether would provide a fixed frame of reference relative to which Newton's laws would hold exactly. Einstein assumed that all experiments designed to locate a fixed frame of reference would fail. Since he assumed

---

*An *a priori* reason is one deduced from previous assumptions or known causes.

that a fixed frame of reference could never be found, he went to the other extreme and postulated that the laws of physics should be so stated that they apply relative to any frame of reference.

If the laws of physics took different forms for different moving observers, then the different forms of the laws would provide a method for determining the nature of an observer's motion. This would take us back to the Newtonian view that there is a unique frame of reference for which the laws of physics are Newton's laws. Going back to our man on the merry-go-round, it is hard to see how the laws of motion could ever seem the same to him as they seem to a man standing on the earth. We have pointed out, however, that this is a problem in general relativity. For special or restricted relativity, we need only face the problem of making the laws of physics take the same form for all observers *translating* relative to each other with *constant* velocity. Limiting ourselves to special relativity, we may state the first postulate as follows:

(1) *The laws of physics apply equally well for any two observers moving with constant linear velocity relative to each other or, in other words, the observations on one reference frame are not preferred above those on any other.*

The Michelson-Morley experiment was based on the assumption that since the classical velocity transformation is not invariant, it should be possible to measure the velocity of light in the ether relative to the earth. That experiment demonstrated that at least one velocity is invariant— the velocity of light. Einstein accepted this as a second fundamental assumption of his special theory of relativity. He postulated that:

(2) *All observers must find the same value of the free-space velocity of light regardless of any motion they may have.*

39–9 Relativistic space-time transformation equations. The equations we are about to derive were first obtained by Fitzgerald and Lorentz. We mentioned earlier that they obtained an *ad hoc* explanation of the negative result of the Michelson-Morley experiment by supposing that the interferometer shortened along its velocity vector through the ether. But we shall derive the relativistic transformation equations as consequences of Einstein's two postulates.

We return to our two observers at O and O' in systems S and S'. We ask the observer at O' to go back and pass the observer at O again. This time—just as O is opposite O'—we fire a photographic flashbulb. Thus at time $t = 0$, each observer is at the source of a spherical light wave. If we endow each observer with a supernatural power so that each can "see" the light spread out into space, then *each* observer must feel that *he* is at the center of the growing sphere of light. This must be the case, since we are now imposing the condition that the velocity of light is the same for all observers even if the velocity of an object is not.

The equation of the expanding sphere seen by the observer at O is

$$x^2 + y^2 + z^2 = c^2 t^2, \tag{39–16}$$

where c is the velocity of light. Similarly, the observer at O' writes for his equation of the sphere

$$x'^2 + y'^2 + z'^2 = c^2 t'^2. \tag{39–17}$$

Clearly, the relativistic transformation equations must be different from the classical ones if both observers are *each* to seem to be at the center of the same sphere.

As we consider what the new transformation equations are to be, we find that we are somewhat limited. These new equations must be linear. Any quadratic equation has two solutions and higher-order equations have more solutions. Surely any observations from the system S must have a unique interpretation in the system S'. There must be a "one-to-one" correspondence between what each observer "sees." The transformation equations must be linear in the space coordinates and in the times. Since the classical transformation equations were found to be $x' = x - vt$ and $x = x' + vt'$, let us here assume the next simplest linear equations,

$$x' = k(x - vt) \qquad \text{and} \qquad x = k'(x' + vt'), \tag{39–18}$$

where the k's are transformation quantities to be determined. Note that our notation t and t' admits the possibility that time intervals may not be identical for the two observers. Note further that k and k' must be equal if, as required by Einstein's first postulate, there is to be no preferred reference system. Hereafter we shall let k represent both k and k'.

We now seek to transform Eq. (39–17) so that the observer at O' "sees" what the observer at O would see. Mathematically, this requires that we eliminate x', y', z', and t' by using the assumed transformation equations. The coordinates y, y', z, and z' are perpendicular to the relative velocity of the observers, so that $y' = y$ and $z' = z$.* We have assumed a transformation equation for x', but we need some manipulation before we can eliminate t'. To get t' in terms of unprimed quantities, we work with our two assumed transformation equations in Eq. (39–18). Solving the second for t' and using the first to eliminate x', we obtain

$$t' = k \left[\frac{x}{v} \left(\frac{1}{k^2} - 1 \right) + t \right]. \tag{39–19}$$

---

* If this conclusion seems hasty, one can write $y = k_y(y - v_y t)$. Since the only relative velocity is along the x-axis, we have $v_y = 0$. This leaves $y = k_y(y)$, which we could carry into our subsequent derivation. If we did so, it would be obvious immediately that $k_y = 1$. A similar argument applies to the z-transformation. In order to make these simplifications in our derivations, we assumed the relative velocity to be parallel to the x-axis.

We can now transform the observation from O' into the observation from O by eliminating the primed quantities from Eq. (39–17). We obtain

$$k^2(x - vt)^2 + y^2 + z^2 = c^2k^2\left[\frac{x}{v}\left(\frac{1}{k^2} - 1\right) + t\right]^2. \quad (39\text{–}20)$$

Upon expanding and collecting terms, we have

$$\left[k^2 - \frac{c^2k^2}{v^2}\left(\frac{1}{k^2} - 1\right)^2\right]x^2 - \left[2vk^2 + \frac{2c^2k^2}{v}\left(\frac{1}{k^2} - 1\right)\right]xt$$

$$+ y^2 + z^2 = [c^2k^2 - v^2k^2]t^2. \quad (39\text{–}21)$$

This equation represents the expanding sphere of light as seen by the observer at O' whose observations have been interpreted (transformed) by the observer at O. This equation must be identical to the direct observation of the expanding sphere as seen from O, namely Eq. (39–16). For this to be the case, it is necessary that the quantities within brackets in Eq. (39–21) equal 1, 0, and c^2 respectively.*

Since the quantity within the third pair of brackets appears the simplest, we set it equal to c^2, obtaining

$$c^2 = c^2k^2 - v^2k^2 = k^2(c^2 - v^2). \quad (39\text{–}22)$$

From this we get

$$k^2 = \frac{c^2}{c^2 - v^2}$$

or

$$\boxed{k = \frac{1}{\sqrt{1 - v^2/c^2}}.} \quad (39\text{–}23)$$

We choose the positive value of the square root, so that relativistic and classical physics correspond at low velocities.

Setting the quantity in the second pair of brackets in Eq. (39–21) equal to zero and solving for k, we again get the same result. This is encouraging. It appears possible that the transformation we have assumed can indeed allow each observer to consider himself to be at the center of the expanding sphere of light. The final check is to determine whether the value of k we have obtained makes the coefficient of x^2 become unity.

---

* In the $x = 0$ plane, the sphere becomes a circle, so that the sphere of Eq. (39–16) degenerates to $y^2 + z^2 = c^2t^2$ and the same sphere described by Eq. (39–21) degenerates to $y^2 + z^2 = [c^2k^2 - v^2k^2]t^2$. Since these equations describe the same circle, they must be identical, and to be identical, the quantity within the brackets must equal c^2.

Upon substituting for k, we find that the quantity within the first pair of brackets becomes

$$k^2 - \frac{c^2 k^2}{v^2}\left(\frac{1}{k^2} - 1\right)^2 = \frac{c^2}{c^2 - v^2} - \frac{c^2 c^2}{v^2(c^2 - v^2)}\left(\frac{c^2 - v^2}{c^2} - 1\right)^2$$

$$= \frac{c^2}{c^2 - v^2} - \frac{c^4}{v^2(c^2 - v^2)}\left(\frac{c^2 - v^2 - c^2}{c^2}\right)^2$$

$$= \frac{c^2}{c^2 - v^2} - \frac{v^2}{c^2 - v^2} = 1.$$

The consistency of these results means that mathematically it is possible to devise linear transformation equations which permit the transformation of one velocity to be invariant. We have chosen that one velocity to be the free-space velocity of light by assuming our two observers to be "watching" an expanding light wave. We need only modify the classical transformation equations by the inclusion of $k = 1/\sqrt{1 - v^2/c^2}$ and note that time, which was the same for all Newtonian observers, must now be transformed along with the space coordinates. Knowing k, we can simplify Eq. (39–19) to

$$t' = k\left[t - \frac{vx}{c^2}\right]. \qquad (39\text{--}24)$$

We can now summarize both Newtonian and relativistic transformation equations for two observers having a relative velocity v parallel to the x-axis as follows:

Galilean-Newtonian	Einsteinian-relativistic
$x' = x - vt$	$x' = k(x - vt)$
$y' = y$	$y' = y$
$z' = z$	$z' = z$
$t' = t$	$t' = k\left(t - \dfrac{vx}{c^2}\right),$

$$(39\text{--}25)$$

where

$$k = \frac{1}{\sqrt{1 - v^2/c^2}}.$$

Note that if $v \ll c$, then k is nearly 1 and the relativistic transformation equations reduce to the Newtonian forms. Thus Newtonian physics can be regarded as a special case of relativistic physics. Recall that the tremendous velocity of the earth about the sun is 18 mi/sec, but that this is still only one ten-thousandth of the velocity of light. Thus the relativity correction for the observation of positions from the earth compared with observations from the sun is only about $5 \times 10^{-7}\%$. Relativity makes no significant difference for "ordinary" engineering applications.

The relativistic transformation equations, however, point the way to important philosophical advances. The portion of special relativity we have developed applies only to observers not accelerated relative to each other. Note, however, that neither of these observers has a *preferred* viewpoint. If the transformation equations for primed quantities in terms of unprimed quantities are solved for the unprimed in terms of the primed ones, the resulting forms are *identical*. Only the *sign* of their relative velocity, v, changes. [Thus $x = k(x' + vt')$.] This one difference is expected, since if O' moves north relative to O, then O must move south relative to O'. A step has been taken toward the goal of general relativity, namely, that the laws of physics shall take on the same form for *all* observers.

We can now also "explain" the Michelson-Morley experiment. The *ad hoc* factor of Fitzgerald and Lorentz is the factor k which has been derived from the basic relativistic assumption that all observers must get the same result if they measure the velocity of light. The price we have paid for these seemingly minor advances is great. Under relativity, space is not a rigid fixed thing but changes in "size" depending on the motion of the observer. If we recomputed the distance between the two points in Fig. 39–3, the relativistic transformation would disclose that their separation appears different to the observers at O and O'.

Even more striking is the fact that if we are to accept relativity, we must use a transformation equation to compare the same time interval measured by two different observers. In classical physics, time marches on at the same pace for all observers, whereas in relativity each observer has his own "local" time, which may be quite different from the times of other observers.

39–10 The relativistic velocity transformation. To illustrate how the transformation equations of space and time are used, let us repeat a calculation we made classically. We found the classical velocity transformation for observers with relative velocity v to be $u' = u - v$. To get the corresponding relativistic expression, we use the definitions employed before:

$$u' = \frac{x'_2 - x'_1}{t'_2 - t'_1} \quad \text{and} \quad u = \frac{x_2 - x_1}{t_2 - t_1}.$$

We now express u' in terms of unprimed quantities by using the relativistic transformation equations. The result is

$$u' = \frac{k(x_2 - vt_2) - k(x_1 - vt_1)}{k[t_2 - (vx_2/c^2)] - k[t_1 - (vx_1/c^2)]}$$

$$= \frac{(x_2 - x_1) - (t_2 - t_1)v}{(t_2 - t_1) - (x_2 - x_1)(v/c^2)} - \frac{[(x_2 - x_1)/(t_2 - t_1)] - v}{1 - [(x_2 - x_1)/(t_2 - t_1)](v/c^2)}$$

or

$$u' = \frac{u - v}{1 - (uv/c^2)} \, .$$ (39–26)

This is the relativistic rule for transforming velocities when the observed velocity is *parallel* to the relative velocity of the observers. We see that, as in the classical case, the velocity transformation is not invariant. Consider, however, what happens when the velocity under observation is the velocity of light, c. If one observer measures the velocity of light and gets $u = c$, what will another observer moving relative to the first obtain?

The equation yields

$$u' = \frac{u - v}{1 - (uv/c^2)} = \frac{c - v}{1 - (cv/c^2)} = \frac{c - v}{(c - v)/c} = c.$$ (39–27)

Thus, regardless of their own relative velocity v, any two observers will agree that the velocity of light is c. In relativity, the velocity of light is *invariant*. This result should not surprise us, since it was used as a basic assumption for the derivation of the transformation equations.

Although the result just derived follows logically from the assumptions of relativity and therefore should not surprise us, a further comment may be helpful. Suppose observer O measures the distance light travels during an interval of time and computes the velocity of light, obtaining c. Let another observer O' moving relative to O perform the same experiment. Intuitively we feel he cannot get the same result, c. But if O and O' both have "rubber" rulers and "defective" clocks, we see that their results may have any values—including c. The transformation equations of the special theory of relativity are a description of how "rubber" rulers and "defective" clocks vary so that the velocity of light can be unique, so that velocities small compared with c behave classically, and so that intermediate cases lead to no contradictions.

If this were the end of the matter, there is no doubt relativity would have been forgotten or remembered only as a fantastic speculation of a fertile mind. No one would make such a tremendous break with traditional thought merely to "explain" the Michelson-Morley experiment. Before it can be taken seriously, the inductive structure of relativity or any other theory must be subjected to deductive verification. If relativity is to be "true" or useful, it must correctly foretell some unforeseen events that can be subjected to experimental tests.

There are several such verifications of relativity. Some come from general relativity, which we are not treating here, but the most striking and important deductive consequence of relativity comes from the special relativity which we are treating. This is the mass transformation equation. To introduce mass into the picture, we next consider an impact situation.

39–11 Relativistic mass transformation.   Consider two basketballs which are spherical, perfectly elastic, and have identical masses when compared by an observer at rest relative to them. We give one ball to an observer O' on a railroad train, moving relative to the ground with a constant translational velocity v. We give the other ball to an observer O on the ground at a distance d from the railroad track. The observers have not yet passed each other and we tell each that he is to throw his ball with the same velocity in a direction perpendicular to the track in such a way that the basketballs bounce perfectly off each other just at the moment when the two observers pass each other. (Deflections due to gravity are irrelevant to this discussion.)

Assuming sufficient skill, this experiment could be carried out and fully understood on the basis of classical mechanics. Each observer sees his ball hit and return to him just as though it had bounced from a perfectly elastic wall with kinetic energy conserved. Each observer must anticipate the moment of passing, and the movements of the balls are as shown in Fig. 39–4.

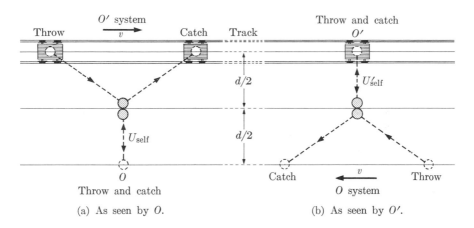

(a) As seen by O. (b) As seen by O'.

FIG. 39–4. Perfectly elastic collision of two identical basketballs as viewed from systems in relative motion.

In the analysis that follows we will consider four velocities. U'_{self} is the velocity O' observes he has given to his ball, and U_{self} is the velocity O observes he has given to his ball. By a condition of the experiment, $U'_{\text{self}} = U_{\text{self}}$. The velocity that observer O assigns to the ball thrown by O' will be called U'_{other}, and the velocity O' assigns to the ball thrown by O will be U_{other}.

If we now treat the situation just described from the standpoint of Einsteinian relativity, a new idea emerges. Distances perpendicular to the relative velocity of the balls are unaffected by relativity considerations, since we found that $y = y'$ and $z = z'$. Thus both observers agree that their basketballs move to and from the impact point a total distance d. But the two observers have different kinds of time. Observer O' was told how fast he should throw his ball. He throws at time t'_1 and catches at time t'_2, so that in his opinion

$$U'_{\text{self}} = \frac{d}{t'_2 - t'_1}. \tag{39-28}$$

Observer O disagrees with observer O' as to when and where O' threw and caught his ball. Observer O says O' threw the ball from x_1 at the time $t_1 = k[t'_1 + (vx'_1/c^2)]$ and caught it at x_2 at the time $t_2 = k[t'_2 + (vx'_2/c^2)]$. Observer O computes the velocity with which O' threw his ball to be U'_{other}, where

$$U'_{\text{other}} = \frac{d}{t_2 - t_1} = \frac{d}{k[(t'_2 - t'_1) + (v/c^2)(x'_2 - x'_1)]}. \tag{39-29}$$

In this expression, the quantity $(x'_2 - x'_1)$ is the amount observer O' must displace himself in order to catch the ball. Since we stated that the ball comes directly back to each observer, this quantity is zero, and Eq. (39–29) becomes

$$U'_{\text{other}} = \frac{d}{k(t'_2 - t'_1)} = \frac{U'_{\text{self}}}{k}. \tag{39-30}$$

Since k is always greater than unity, it appears to observer O that observer O' has thrown his ball more slowly than he was told to. A similar calculation would show that observer O' would think observer O had thrown *his* ball more slowly than he was told to, or

$$U_{\text{other}} = \frac{U_{\text{self}}}{k}. \tag{39-31}$$

We are now faced with a dilemma. If we assume that the masses remain the same as when they were compared without relative velocity, then conservation of momentum is violated. If we keep conservation of momentum, then the relative motion which made a difference in the observed velocities of the basketballs also resulted in an observed difference in their masses. In relativity it is assumed that momentum is conserved. Therefore observer O, who sees his ball change in momentum an amount $2m_{\text{self}}U_{\text{self}}$, equates this change to the change he observes for the other ball. He writes

$$2m_{\text{self}}U_{\text{self}} = 2m_{\text{other}}U'_{\text{other}}. \tag{39-32}$$

When the value of U'_{other} from Eq. (39–30) is substituted in Eq. (39–32) it becomes

$$2m_{\text{self}} U_{\text{self}} = 2m_{\text{other}} \frac{U'_{\text{self}}}{k}, \qquad (39\text{–}33)$$

which, since the throws were equal such that $U_{\text{self}} = U'_{\text{self}}$, reduces to

$$m_{\text{other}} = k m_{\text{self}}. \qquad (39\text{–}34)$$

Thus observer O concludes that the masses of the balls are not equal, and that there must be a transformation equation for mass in addition to those for the other quantities we have discussed.

In this derivation we have considered an especially simple situation in order to get our result as quickly as possible. We have computed the observed change in mass by considering the effect of a relative x-velocity on observed y-velocities. We could neglect the changes in mass each observer produced in his own ball when he threw it because both observers threw in the same way ($U'_{\text{self}} = U_{\text{self}}$). A general derivation would have led to a result of the same form, namely

$$\boxed{m = k m_0 = \frac{m_0}{\sqrt{1 - (v^2/c^2)}},} \qquad (39\text{–}35)$$

where m_0 is the mass of a body at rest (called the rest mass) relative to the measurer, and m (called the moving mass) is the observed mass of the body when it has a velocity v relative to the measurer. The system in which the observer is at rest is often called the laboratory system.

This result, which has been deduced from the space transformation equations, can be tested experimentally. What is required is the measurement of the mass of a body moving at great speed relative to an observer. J. J. Thomson was startled when he computed the speed of electrons in his cathode-ray tubes. These speeds were greater than any previously measured by man and, by modern methods, can be made significant compared with the free-space velocity of light, c. Furthermore, an e/m experiment is a measure of m if we assume that the charge e of the particle is constant. In principle, then, J. J. Thomson provided a technique for the testing of the mass-transformation equation. The first test of this equation was made in 1908 by Bucherer, using electrons from a radioactive source, and since then the mass-transformation equation has been confirmed innumerable times. It is now a cornerstone of atomic physics.

39–12 Relativistic mass-energy equivalence. The derived and experimentally verified mass-transformation equation has important consequences. Whereas in classical physics we considered that the kinetic energy of a body could be increased only by increasing its velocity, we now must take mass variation into account. Suppose we increase the kinetic energy of a body an amount dE_k by exerting a force through a distance. The change of kinetic energy equals the work done, or

$$dE_k = F\,ds. \tag{39–36}$$

Since we cannot regard mass as constant in relativity, we write Newton's second law in its more general form, force equals the time rate of change of momentum:

$$F = \frac{d(mv)}{dt}. \tag{39–37}$$

The change of kinetic energy then is

$$dE_k = \frac{d(mv)}{dt}\,ds. \tag{39–38}$$

But since $ds/dt = v$, we can write the preceding equation as

$$dE_k = v\,d(mv) = v^2\,dm + mv\,dv. \tag{39–39}$$

This expression can be simplified by using the mass-transformation equation, Eq. (39–35), which after squaring and rearranging becomes

$$m^2c^2 = m^2v^2 + m_0^2c^2. \tag{39–40}$$

We now differentiate, noting that both m_0 and c are constant, and obtain

$$2mc^2\,dm = 2mv^2\,dm + 2m^2v\,dv. \tag{39–41}$$

When $2m$ is divided out of this equation, the right side becomes identical with our expression for dE_k in Eq. (39–39), so we have, finally,

$$\boxed{dE_k = c^2\,dm.} \tag{39–42}$$

This famous equation shows that in relativity a change in kinetic energy can be expressed in terms of mass as the variable. This equation is valid for a change of energy in any form whatever, although it was derived here for a change of kinetic energy.

Since the kinetic energy is zero when $v = 0$, then it is also zero when $m = m_0$. Therefore we integrate, and obtain

$$E_k = \int_0^{E_k} dE_k = c^2 \int_{m_0}^{m} dm = c^2(m - m_0)$$

or

$$E_k = mc^2 - m_0c^2. \tag{39-43}$$

This is the relativistic expression for kinetic energy. The classical relation $E_k = \frac{1}{2}mv^2$ does *not* give the correct value of the kinetic energy even when the relativistic values of the mass and the velocity are used.

Like the other transformation equations, this expression for E_k should, for $v \ll c$, reduce to the classical expression. If we transform m in Eq. (39–43), we obtain

$$E_k = \frac{m_0c^2}{\sqrt{1 - (v^2/c^2)}} - m_0c^2. \tag{39-44}$$

Now, since $v \ll c$, we can say

$$\frac{1}{\sqrt{1 - (v^2/c^2)}} = \left(1 - \frac{v^2}{c^2}\right)^{-1/2} = \left(1 + \frac{v^2}{2c^2} + \frac{3}{8}\frac{v^4}{c^4} + \cdots\right), \tag{39-45}$$

where we have carried three terms of the binomial expansion. We then have, from Eq. (39–44),

$$E_k = m_0c^2\left(1 + \frac{v^2}{2c^2} + \frac{3}{8}\frac{v^4}{c^4} + \cdots - 1\right)$$

$$= \frac{1}{2}m_0v^2 + \frac{3}{8}m_0\frac{v^4}{c^2} + \cdots \tag{39-46}$$

The first term of this is the classical expression for the kinetic energy. Obviously it is the only significant term for low velocities.

Equation (39–42) suggests a broader interpretation of Eq. (39–43). Equation (39–42) implies that, in addition to the familiar forms of energy, such as kinetic, potential, and internal, there is yet another kind, *mass-energy*. Just as Joule's constant relates heat to energy by telling us the number of joules per calorie, so Eq. (39–42) relates mass to energy by telling us the number of joules per kilogram. Just as heat is energy and energy can be observed as heat, so mass is energy and energy can be observed as mass. According to this view, Eq. (39–43) can be written as

$$E = mc^2 = m_0c^2 + E_k, \tag{39-47}$$

where E and mc^2 are the total energy, m_0c^2 is the *rest mass-energy*, and E_k is the kinetic energy of a body. The equivalence of mass and energy brings a satisfying consequence. The broad principle of conservation of energy now takes unto itself another broad conservation principle, the conservation of mass. The identity of mass and energy resulting in a unified concept of mass-energy is certainly the most "practical" consequence of relativity. We shall see in Chapter 43 how nuclear reactions illustrate the fact that neither mass nor energy as conceived classically are conserved separately. In relativity we see that it is mass-energy that is concerved. In any interaction the *total mass*, m (which includes any kinetic energy in mass units), is *the same before and after* the interaction. Similarly, in any interaction, the *total energy E* (which includes any rest mass in energy units), is *the same before and after* the interaction. We are now witnessing the growth of the whole new field of nuclear engineering, which is based on E equals mc^2.

Most of the mass-energy we use comes from the sun, where rest mass-energy is converted into thermal mass-energy. Today mankind is converting rest mass-energy into thermal mass-energy here on the earth. We shall see that nuclear fission and fusion are the techniques for this conversion.

39–13 The upper limit of velocity. An examination of Eq. (39–35), the mass transformation equation, shows that for $v = c$, $m = \infty$. Thus, as the velocity of a body increases toward the free-space velocity of light, the mass of the body increases toward infinity. An infinite mass moving at a snail's pace would have infinite energy. Since it is absurd for any body with finite rest mass m_0 to have infinite energy, we must conclude that it is impossible for such a body to move with the free-space velocity of light. Thus in relativistic mechanics the free-space velocity of light is the greatest velocity that can be given to any material particle. If a tiny particle is given equal increments of energy, the first increments increase the velocity significantly and the mass insignificantly. But as the particle gains more and more energy, the velocity changes become less as the velocity approaches the velocity of light. As the velocity changes become insignificant, the mass changes become significant.

Putting the same argument another way, we have two equations for the kinetic energy of a body, both of which are correct relativistic expressions. Equation (39–44) expresses E_k in terms of m_0 and v. For v small compared with c, this is the convenient formula, especially since it reduces to the first term of Eq. (39–46), the classical expression. The other equation is $E_k = c^2(m - m_0)$, Eq. (39–43). This equation expresses E_k in terms of m_0 and the variable moving mass, m. When the velocity is near c, the mass is the more convenient variable. E_k can be expressed in terms of either m or v, since we have the mass-variation equation, Eq. (39–35), relating m and v.

Since we argued that the free-space velocity of light is an upper limit for material particles, it is fair to ask whether any velocities equal or exceed this velocity. We have been careful in this discussion to emphasize that the limit is the *free-space* velocity of light. Light itself often travels more slowly than its free-space velocity. The index of refraction of a medium is the ratio of the free-space velocity of light to the actual velocity in the medium. In water, for example, a particle may travel faster than light *in that medium*. An example of this will be discussed when we consider Cherenkov radiation in Chapter 44.

Photons in free space obviously travel with the free-space velocity of light. We have found that photons have energy hf, and since we have shown that mass and energy are equivalent we can conclude that each photon has a mass hf/c^2. Here, then, is a mass particle actually traveling with the free-space velocity of light. But there is no contradiction here. A photon has no rest mass m_0. If we stop a photon to measure its mass, all its mass-energy is transferred to something else and the photon no longer exists. Perhaps the main difference between a "material" particle and a photon particle is that one has rest mass while the other does not.

There are times when one may encounter velocities greater than the free-space velocity of light, but on these occasions the thing moving is a mathematical function rather than a physical reality. The transmission of a "dot" in radio telegraphy may be regarded as the resultant of the transmission of several frequencies having different velocities. These velocities, called phase velocities, may exceed the free-space velocity of light. The motion of the resultant "dot" is called a group velocity, and it can never exceed the free-space velocity of light. (These two types of velocities associated with waves will be discussed in Chapter 41.) We may state with complete generality that no observer can find the *velocity of mass-energy in any form to exceed the free-space velocity of light.*

39–14 Examples of relativistic calculations. (1) The basic mass unit of nuclear physics is the atomic mass unit, amu, which is 1/12 of the rest mass of carbon-12. One amu $= 1.66 \times 10^{-27}$ kgm, and this is nearly the proton's mass. In relativity, this mass-energy may be expressed in energy units as

$$E = m_0 c^2 = 1.66 \times 10^{-27} \text{ kgm} \times (3.00 \times 10^8)^2 \frac{\text{m}^2}{\text{sec}^2}$$

$$= 1.49 \times 10^{-10} \text{ joule.}$$

Or 1 amu may be expressed in ev and Mev:

$$1 \text{ amu} = \frac{E}{e_c} = 1.49 \times 10^{-10} \text{ joule} \times \frac{1 \text{ ev}}{1.60 \times 10^{-19} \text{ joule}}$$

$$= 9.31 \times 10^8 \text{ ev} = 931 \text{ Mev.}$$

We have now expressed the relativistic rest mass-energy of one amu in five ways:

$$1 \text{ amu} = \tfrac{1}{12} C^{12} = 1.66 \times 10^{-27} \text{ kgm} = 1.49 \times 10^{-10} \text{ joule}$$

$$= 9.31 \times 10^8 \text{ ev} = 931 \text{ Mev.}$$

This same quantity could also be expressed in any other units of mass or energy—slugs, calories, grams, kwh, ft·lb, etc. We could have made similar calculations with any quantity of mass or energy. We chose the amu as an important example. It is very useful to *remember* that 1 amu = 931 Mev.

(2) Consider next the velocity that one amu would have if it had a kinetic energy equal to twice its rest mass-energy. It would be very difficult to give a particle with a mass of one amu so much energy, since it would be about equivalent to accelerating a proton through 2 × 931 million volts, but the situation provides a good example of calculating velocity relativistically.

This kinetic energy can be expressed as 2 amu, 3.32×10^{-27} kgm 2.98×10^{-10} joule, 1.86×10^9 ev, or 1.86 Bev.

The total or moving mass of the particle is the sum of its rest mass and its kinetic energy. Thus its moving mass, m, is $1 + 2 = 3$ amu, 4.47×10^{-10} joule, etc.

We now have everything necessary to calculate the relativistic velocity. The mass-velocity equation, Eq. (39–35), solved for the velocity is

$$v = c\sqrt{1 - (m_0/m)^2}.$$

We may substitute for the rest and moving masses in any consistent units. The velocity will have the same units as those used for c. Using the masses in amu, we have

$$v = c\sqrt{1 - (1/3)^2} = 0.942c = 2.83 \times 10^8 \frac{m}{sec}.$$

This is a very large velocity, and we may expect that a classical calculation will be seriously in error. To show this, we next calculate v on the basis of classical physics. We know that the kinetic energy is $E_k = 2.98 \times 10^{-10}$ joule, and that the mass is $m = 1.66 \times 10^{-27}$ kgm. Solving $E_k = \frac{1}{2}mv^2$ for v, we have

$$v = \sqrt{\frac{2E_k}{m}} = \sqrt{2 \times 2.98 \times 10^{-10} \text{ joule} \times \frac{1}{1.66 \times 10^{-27} \text{ kgm}}}$$

$$= 6.0 \times 10^8 \frac{m}{sec} = 2.0c.$$

Not only is this result very different from the relativistic one, but it is also greater than the velocity of light. Whenever the two methods differ significantly, the relativistic method must be used.

(3) We next seek the kinetic energy of a 1-slug earth satellite traveling with a velocity of 18,600 mi/hr. Since the velocity of light in English

units is 186,000 mi/sec, the ratio of the satellite's velocity to the velocity of light, v/c, is

$$\frac{v}{c} = 18,600 \frac{\text{mi}}{\text{hr}} \times \frac{1 \text{ hr}}{3600 \text{ sec}} \times \frac{1 \text{ sec}}{186,000 \text{ mi}} = \frac{1}{36,000}.$$

Strictly speaking, we should compute the satellite's moving mass from Eq. (39–35), $m = m_0/\sqrt{1 - (v/c)^2}$, and then the kinetic energy from Eq. (39–43), $E_k = (m - m_0)c^2$. But the satellite's velocity is so small compared with c that slide rule calculations would make the use of Eq. (39–46), $E_k = \frac{1}{2}m_0v^2 + \frac{3}{8}m_0(v^4/c^2) \ldots$, much more convenient. In this example the second term on the right is negligible. This shows that a classical calculation is sufficient for a body moving so slowly.

(4) The labor of calculating the numerical results in problems in special relativity may often be reduced by a trigonometric substitution. To illustrate this, let us find the relativistic velocity of an electron that has been accelerated from rest through a potential difference of 120,000 volts.

If we find the final moving mass of the electron, the velocity can be obtained from the equation

$$m = \frac{m_0}{\sqrt{1 - (v^2/c^2)}}.$$

The moving mass is

$$m = m_0 + dm = m_0 + \frac{dE_k}{c^2} = m_0 + \frac{qV}{c^2}$$

$$= 9.11 \times 10^{-31} \text{ kgm} + 1.60 \times 10^{-19} \text{ coul}$$

$$\times 120,000 \frac{\text{joules}}{\text{coul}} \times \frac{\text{sec}^2}{(3 \times 10^8)^2 \text{ m}^2}$$

$$= (9.11 + 2.13) \times 10^{-31} \text{ kgm} = 11.24 \times 10^{-31} \text{ kgm}.$$

Rather than substitute the values of m and m_0 in the mass-variation equation and perform the long operations of squaring, taking a difference, and obtaining a square root, let us substitute $\sin \theta = v/c$. Then we have

$$\sqrt{1 - (v^2/c^2)} = \sqrt{1 - \sin^2 \theta} = \cos \theta,$$

and the mass-variation equation becomes

$$\cos \theta = \frac{m_0}{m}.$$

Upon substituting the values of the mass, we get

$$\cos \theta = \frac{m_0}{m} = \frac{9.11 \times 10^{-31} \text{ kgm}}{11.24 \times 10^{-31} \text{ kgm}} = 0.810.$$

From trigonometric tables we then find that

$$\theta = 35°53' \quad \text{and} \quad \sin\theta = 0.586.$$

Therefore, the result sought is

$$\sin\theta = \frac{v}{c} = 0.586$$

or

$$v = 0.586c = 0.586 \times 3 \times 10^8 \frac{m}{sec} = 1.76 \times 10^8 \frac{m}{sec}.$$

39–15 Pair production. Certainly one of the most dramatic instances of the relativistic change of energy from one form to another is in the phenomenon known as pair production. *Pair production* is the process in which a photon becomes an electron and a new positive particle. This new particle was anticipated by Dirac in 1928 from his relativistic wave-mechanics theory of the energy of an electron, and was experimentally observed by Anderson in 1932.

The discovery was made in the course of cosmic-ray research with a cloud chamber. We shall discuss cloud chambers in Chapter 42. All we need say now is that a cloud chamber is a device which makes the paths of charged particles visible and subject to photographic recording. Figure 39–5 is Anderson's most famous cloud-chamber photograph. It shows a charged particle moving with high speed and with its path curved by a magnetic field directed into the paper. The particle is seen to traverse a sheet of lead 6 mm thick in the middle of the chamber. From the beady nature of the track it was established that the particle was electronlike. Since the lead sheet could have only slowed the particle, its direction of motion must have been from the region of low curvature to the region of high curvature. From the observed direction of curvature and the known direction of the motion and of the magnetic field, it was concluded that the charge of the particle was positive. On the basis of this picture and others similar to it, Anderson announced the discovery of a new particle which he called the *positron* or positive electron.[*] The positron is just like the electron except for the sign of its electric charge.

The source of the positron is not visible in Fig. 39–5 but several sources are apparent in Fig. 39–6. Notice the three sets of diverging tracks from the lower side of the lead plate. These are tracks originating at the lead but with no corresponding tracks coming into the lead on the upper side. Evidently these pairs of particles are not produced by other charged particles but by something else that cannot produce tracks, namely, photons. The curvature of the paths is due to a magnetic field normal to

---

[*] At this same time it was proposed that the electron be called the *negatron* or negative electron. These names have never come into general use.

FIG. 39–5. Cloud-chamber track of a positive electron (positron) in a magnetic field. (Courtesy of C. D. Anderson, California Institute of Technology)

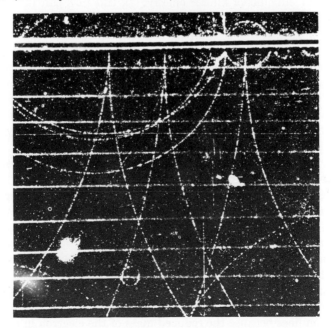

FIG. 39–6. Cloud-chamber tracks of three electron-positron pairs in a magnetic field. Three gamma-ray photons entering at the top materialize into pairs within a lead sheet. The coiled tracks are due to low-energy photoelectrons ejected from the lead. (Courtesy of Radiation Laboratory, University of California)

the plane of the paper. Since the tracks of the particles of the pair are oppositely curved, the individuals must have opposite charges. In each case one particle is a positron and the other an ordinary electron. A quantum of radiant energy coming from above the lead sheet has changed into matter forming a *pair* consisting of a positron and an electron. In the process of *pair production* we have the *materialization* of energy.

It is easy to show that the rest mass of an electron is equivalent to 0.51 Mev. Thus, to create a pair, a photon must have at least enough energy to convert into two electron masses or 1.02 Mev. A photon could never convert into just one electron or positron, since this would violate the law of conservation of electric charge. The photons which produced the pairs shown in Fig. 39-6 must each have had more than 1.02 Mev of energy, since these pairs were not only created but also were given considerable kinetic energy.

A photon cannot produce a pair just anywhere. The process must take place in an intense field such as that close to the nucleus of an atom. Since a nucleus must be involved in pair production, conservation of energy and of momentum become a bit complex. If the nucleus involved is massive, it can carry away its share of momentum without taking away an appreciable amount of kinetic energy. In this case pair production can occur if the energy of the photon is just a little above the mass-required minimum of 1.02 Mev. If the pair is produced near a light nucleus, on the other hand, the light nucleus carries away appreciable kinetic energy at the expense of the originating photon and thus this photon must have considerably more than 1.02 Mev of energy. For 20-Mev photons, the nuclei of the air are about as effective as of lead in "catalyzing" pair production. Since pair production occurs near the nucleus of an atom, the repelled positron emerges with a somewhat higher velocity than the attracted electron.

Because electrons are common in all matter, the lives of positrons are very short. Once a positron has lost most of its kinetic energy in passing near charged particles, it will move quickly toward an attracting electron. Before union occurs, however, these particles sometimes revolve momentarily about their center of mass in a semi-stable configuration called *positronium*.

Positronium is a non-nuclear "element" with an average existence of less than 10^{-7} sec. Despite its short life, its spectrum has been measured. These measurements show that positronium is hydrogenlike, as expected. The frequencies of its spectral lines are about half those of the corresponding hydrogen lines because the reduced mass of the electron in positronium is about half its value in hydrogen.

When the electron and positron finally join, they annihilate each other and become electromagnetic radiation. The production of *annihilation radiation* is the converse of the materialization of energy. Just as pair production requires a photon of at least 1.02 Mev of energy, so annihilation produces photons whose energies add up to at least 1.02 Mev. Annihilation resulting in two photons is by far the most common, but the three-photon case has been observed. This rare event is discussed in advanced books. The laws of conservation of mass-energy, of momentum, and of charge hold in all these processes.

Pair production is not limited to the positron and electron. In 1955 the *antiproton* was produced in experiments with high-energy particles from accelerators. The antiproton and the proton have equal charges of opposite sign and equal masses. It requires a minimum of 1.88 Bev of energy to produce a proton-antiproton pair. The antiproton is usually quickly captured by an atomic nucleus, but it occasionally disappears with the proton in annihilation radiation. The positronium analogue of this pair has not been observed.

The positron and the antiproton are often called *antiparticles*. They may be thought of as plane mirror images of the electron and proton respectively. Since the discovery of these pairs, there has been speculation about the possibility of the existence of *antihydrogen*. This would have an antiproton nucleus and an orbital positron. One can indeed imagine the existence of the *antimatter* form of each of the elements. No such mirror-image forms have been found, but perhaps other galaxies are composed of them. Note that the term "antimatter" does not mean negative mass.

The processes of pair production and annihilation are both inconceivable without relativity. These are cases where an appreciable amount of radiant energy without rest mass and particles with appreciable rest mass are alternately materialized and destroyed.

39–16 Summary. We have seen how Einstein's attention to a flaw in logic in Newtonian mechanics led him to consider the importance of an observer's viewpoint. We have seen how the "failure" of the Michelson-Morley experiment led Einstein to assign special significance to the velocity of light in free space. We have seen how these considerations led to new concepts of space, time, mass, energy, and matter. When we realize that this was but one of Einstein's achievements, we begin to sense the magnitude of his contribution to human thought.

Problems

39–1. A person who knows Galilean-Newtonian mechanics leaves his earth-bound laboratory and establishes an isolated one in a closed, over-the-road trailer which a truck can pull along a level highway without noise or vibration. Is it possible for him to perform at least one experiment in his new laboratory system to determine whether the trailer has (a) a linear acceleration, (b) a radial acceleration, (c) a constant linear velocity, or no velocity? Describe an experiment he might perform in each case.

39–2. An experimenter who is skilled in Newtonian mechanics moves from a laboratory in an astronomical observatory to one in a cave which is shut off from all contact with the outside world. Could he perform any experiment in his new laboratory system which would determine (a) whether the earth is rotating and (b) whether it is moving with constant linear velocity? Describe an experiment he might perform in each case.

39–3. (a) The ends of a rectangular loop of wire are connected to a sensitive galvanometer. If the whole system (loop and galvanometer) is then moved with constant velocity in a uniform magnetic field where the lines of induction are normal to the plane of the loop, will the galvanometer deflect? Explain. (b) It is proposed to make a ground-speed indicator for an airplane in the following way: A galvanometer on the instrument panel is to be connected to the ends of a wire stretched between the wing tips (or simply to the tips themselves for a metal airplane). It is believed that there will be an induced emf in the wire that is directly proportional to the speed of "cutting" the vertical component of the magnetic field of the earth when in level flight. Will the proposed indicator work? Explain. (Assume that the magnetic field is constant.) (c) Is it possible to measure the speed of an automobile relative to the earth from the fact that it is moving in the earth's magnetic field? Explain.

39–4. A person who is unaware of Newtonian mechanics and who has always lived in a closed trailer is told that a plumb line points in the direction of the force of gravity. (a) In what direction will he think this force acts if, as viewed by an observer on the earth, the trailer has always been moving at a constant speed around a horizontal circular track? (b) Does a plumb line on your trailer system, the earth, point in the direction of the gravitational pull of the earth? (c) Does it point in the direction of the acceleration due to gravity?

39–5. A super-searchlight which is rotating at 120 rev/min throws its beam on a screen 50,000 mi away. What is (a) the sweep speed of the beam across the screen, (b) the speed of a photon from the searchlight to the screen, and (c) the speed with which any particular photon sweeps across the screen? (d) Do any of these results violate the second postulate of the special theory of relativity? (The value of c is 186,000 mi/sec.)

39–6. Cathode-ray tubes have been made in which the sweep speed or trace speed of the electron beam across the fluorescent screen exceeds the free-space velocity of light. Does this require that the velocity of any one of the electrons exceed the limiting relativistic velocity? Explain.

39-7. (a) With respect to the laboratory, ball A rolls eastward with a constant speed of 2 m/sec and ball B rolls westward with a constant speed of 2 m/sec. What is the relative velocity of A with respect to B, calculated relativistically? (b) With respect to the laboratory, the electrons in accelerator A are projected toward the east with a speed of 2×10^8 m/sec and electrons in accelerator B are projected toward the west with a speed of 2×10^8 m/sec. What is the relative velocity of the A electrons with respect to the B electrons, calculated relativistically?

39-8. Show from Eq. (39-25) that the relativistic equations to transform space and time to system S from observations on S' are $x = k(x' + vt')$ and $t = k[t' + (vx'/c^2)]$ respectively.

39-9. Show that if the time interval between two events occurring at the same place on the S' system is $\Delta t'$, then the time interval observed in the S system is $\Delta t = k \Delta t'$. Is the time interval measured in S dilated or contracted with respect to that in S'?

39-10. In elementary optics, some derivations of the equation for the Doppler effect for light contain a step in which the velocity of the light source is added vectorially to the velocity of the light emitted. Relativistically, the velocity of light is independent of that of the source. How would you explain the possibility of the Doppler effect on the basis of the special theory of relativity? [Consider time intervals (frequency), etc.]

39-11. An electron in a certain x-ray tube is accelerated from rest through a potential difference of 180,000 volts in going from the cathode to the anode. When it arrives at the anode what is its (a) kinetic energy in ev, (b) its relativistic mass, (c) its relativistic velocity, and (d) the value of e/m? (e) What is the velocity of the electron calculated classically?

39-12. A kilogram of water is heated from 0°C to 100°C. (a) What is its increase in mass due to its increase in thermal energy? (b) What is the ratio of this increase to the initial mass? (c) Could this mass increase be measured?

39-13. A doubly ionized helium atom is accelerated from rest through a potential difference of 6×10^8 volts in a linear accelerator. Find (a) its kinetic energy in Mev, (b) its relativistic mass in kgm, and (c) its relativistic velocity. (Assume that the rest mass of a helium atom is equal to four times that of a hydrogen atom.)

39-14. Show that the expression $E_k = \frac{1}{2}mv^2$ does *not* give the relativistic value of the kinetic energy of a body even if the relativistic mass is used. [*Hint:* Substitute m from Eq. (39-35) into the given relation for kinetic energy, expand by the binomial theorem, and compare the result with Eq. (39-46).]

39-15. Calculate, relativistically, the amount of work in Mev that must be done (a) to bring an electron from rest to a velocity of $0.4c$, and (b) to increase its velocity from $0.4c$ to $0.8c$. (c) What is the ratio of the kinetic energy of the electron at the velocity of $0.8c$ to that of $0.4c$ when computed from (1) relativistic values and (2) from classical values?

39-16. Plot the ratio of m/m_0 of a particle as a function of v/c for the following values of the independent variable: 0.0, 0.2, 0.4, 0.6, 0.8, 0.9, and 0.99.

39-17. Through what potential difference must a charged particle be accelerated from rest in a vacuum so that its moving or relativistic mass exceeds its rest mass by 1% of the rest mass if the particle is (a) an electron, (b) a proton?

39–18. Through what potential difference must a charged particle be accelerated from rest in a vacuum so that its classical velocity is 1% more than its relativistic velocity if the particle is (a) an electron, (b) a proton?

39–19. When the radioactive isotope cobalt-60 disintegrates, it emits two gamma-ray photons and one 0.31-Mev beta particle (electron). (a) What is the relativistic velocity of the ejected beta particle? (b) If the cobalt-60 is immersed in water, is the velocity of ejection calculated in part (a) less than the velocity of light in water, which has an average index of refraction of 1.33?

39–20. What is the energy equivalent in joules and in kilowatt·hours of 1 kgm of uranium, or of wood, or of sand?

39–21. Show that the rest mass of an electron is equivalent to 0.511 Mev.

39–22. The fissioning of an atom of uranium-235 releases 200 Mev of energy. What percent is this fission energy of the total which would have been available if all the mass of the uranium atom had appeared as energy?

39–23. In a famous experiment on nuclear reactions performed by Cockcroft and Walton a stationary target composed of the isotope lithium-7 was bombarded with 0.70-Mev hydrogen ions. It was found that these elements then combine and change to two alpha particles, each having a kinetic energy of 9.0 Mev. (An alpha particle is doubly ionized helium-4.) (a) Calculate and compare the total mass, in amu, of the initial particles with the total mass of the final particles. (The rest masses of the neutral atoms are given in Appendix 4. Use the conversion factor 1 amu/931 Mev. Assume that all data are precise enough to warrant answers to three significant figures.) (b) Calculate and compare the total energy (includes rest mass energy) in Mev of the initial particles with the total energy of the final particles. (c) Show that the difference between the sum of the kinetic energies of the final particles and the sum of the kinetic energies of the initial particles is equal to the energy equivalent of the difference between the sum of the rest masses of the initial particles and the sum of the rest masses of the final particles. (d) Using the results of the preceding parts, discuss the law of conservation of mass and the law of conservation of energy in relativity. In which part might one say that mass has been "transformed" or "changed" into energy? Why might this be said?

39–24. How much work must be done in terms of the rest-mass energy, m_0c^2, to increase the velocity of a particle (a) from rest to 0.90c, and (b) from 0.90c to 0.99c? (c) What is the increase in mass in terms of m_0 for each case?

39–25. A gamma-ray photon having a wavelength of 0.0045 A materializes into an electron-positron pair in the neighborhood of a heavy nucleus. (a) What is the total kinetic energy of the pair in Mev immediately after being produced? (b) Is it possible for two 0.75-Mev quanta which are passing through lead to materialize into an electron-positron pair? Explain.

39–26. An electron and a positron which have negligible velocities combine to produce two-photon annihilation radiation. (a) What is the energy of each photon? (b) What will be the relative direction of motion of these photons? Explain.

39–27. A 2.90-Mev quantum of radiation, passing through lead, materializes into an electron-positron pair. If these particles have equal kinetic energies, find (a) the relativistic mass, and (b) the relativistic velocity of each. Neglect the recoil energy of the lead atom. (c) What is the direction of and the smallest value of the magnetic induction which will cause each of these particles to have a trajectory with a radius of curvature of 12 cm?

CHAPTER 40

X-RAYS

40–1 Discovery. In Chapter 24 we reported how the study of electric discharges through gases at low pressure led Thomson to the discovery of the electron and the proton. We now consider an earlier discovery made in 1895 in connection with electric discharges: Roentgen's discovery of x-rays. We quote a translation of Roentgen's words*:

"If the discharge of a fairly large induction-coil be made to pass through a Hittorf vacuum-tube, or through a Lenard tube, a Crookes tube, or other similar apparatus, which has been sufficiently exhausted, the tube being covered with thin, black card-board which fits it with tolerable closeness, and if the whole apparatus be placed in a completely darkened room there is observed at each discharge a bright illumination of a paper screen covered with barium platino-cyanide, placed in the vicinity of the induction-coil, the fluorescence thus produced being entirely independent of the fact whether the coated or the plain surface is turned towards the discharge-tube . . .

"The most striking feature of this phenomenon is the fact that an active agent here passes through a black card-board envelope which is opaque to the visible and the ultra-violet rays of the sun or of the electric arc; an agent, too, which has the power of producing active fluorescence . . .

"We soon discover that all bodies are transparent to this agent, though in very different degrees. I proceed to give a few examples: Paper is very transparent; behind a bound book of about one thousand pages I saw the fluorescent screen light up brightly, the printers' ink offering scarcely a noticeable hindrance. In the same way the fluorescence appeared behind a double pack of cards; a single card held between the apparatus and the screen being almost unnoticeable to the eye. A single sheet of tin-foil is also scarcely perceptible; it is only after several layers have been placed over one another that their shadow is distinctly seen on the screen. Thick blocks of wood are also transparent, pine boards two or three centimeters thick absorbing only slightly. A plate of aluminum about fifteen millimetres thick, though it enfeebled the action seriously, did not cause the fluorescence to disappear entirely."

The history of science has many instances of "accidental" discovery and of these the discovery of x-rays is a prime example. Columbus' dis-

---

* Reprinted by permission of the publishers from William Francis Magie, *Source Book in Physics*. Cambridge, Mass.: Harvard University Press, 1935.

covery of America was another instance where a man looking for one thing found another. Although accidents can happen to anyone, "accidental" discovery of truth seems to be reserved to those observers who have earned the right to be lucky. Such luck falls on the deserving few whose courage, patience, insight, and objectivity enable them to take advantage of the "breaks of the game." There is a word for this process that is better than the word "accident." It is "serendipity"—the process or art of taking advantage of the unexpected.

Of all the discoveries made by man, there is probably none that attracted public attention more quickly than the discovery of x-rays. The fact that the rays permitted one to "see" through opaque objects was sensational "tabloid material" and there was great consternation lest, by their use, fully-dressed people might be made to appear unclothed. When such speculation died down, however, there was wide appreciation of the value of x-rays in setting broken bones, and the rays were quickly put to this use.

40–2 Production of x-rays. As Roentgen said in his paper, the observed x-rays came from low-pressure gas discharge tubes like those already described in our discussion of cathode rays. We quote further from Roentgen's original paper published in 1895:* "According to experiments especially designed to test the question, it is certain that the spot on the wall of the discharge-tube which fluoresces the strongest is to be considered as the main centre from which the x-rays radiate in all directions. The x-rays proceed from that spot where, according to the data obtained by different investigators, the cathode rays strike the glass wall. If the cathode rays within the discharge-apparatus are deflected by means of a magnet, it is observed that the x-rays proceed from another spot—namely, from that which is the new terminus of the cathode rays."

Modern x-ray tubes still produce x-rays by causing cathode rays to strike a solid target, but the techniques have been greatly refined. In a modern Coolidge tube, the source of the cathode-ray electrons is a heated filament. There is no need for a residual gas to be ionized, and so modern tubes are evacuated to a high degree. The target material can be made of any element for research purposes, but the target of modern tubes is a metal having a high melting point and a high atomic number. In the production of x-rays, a large amount of heat is generated in the target and so it is usually made hollow to permit cooling water or oil to be circulated through it. In addition to the tube itself, the other major part of the apparatus is a source of high potential to accelerate the cathode-ray electrons. Originally, this was provided by an induction coil (spark coil), but the common technique today is to use step-up transformers which

---

* loc. cit.

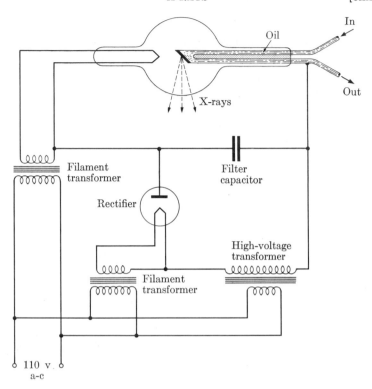

FIG. 40-1. X-ray apparatus: Coolidge tube.

operate from power-line frequency alternating current. If a-c is applied to the tube, cathode rays and consequently x-rays are produced during only one-half of the cycle and the potential across the tube is constantly changing. Most x-ray machines rectify and filter the high alternating potential so that there is a steady high voltage across the tube. The potential used depends on the ultimate use of the x-rays, but it usually ranges between ten thousand and a million volts. A schematic diagram of the essential features of an x-ray machine is shown in Fig. 40-1.

40-3 The nature of x-rays. X-ray diffraction. Roentgen failed to determine the nature of x-rays. He eliminated some possibilities and he suggested what they might be, but his own uncertainty is shown by the fact that he chose the name x-rays.

Upon finding that x-rays are not deflected by electric or magnetic fields on the one hand or perceptibly refracted or diffracted on the other, Roentgen concluded that the rays were neither charged particles nor light of any ordinary sort. Tongue-in-cheek, he proposed that x-rays might be the "longitudinal component" of light, in analogy with the fact that acoustic vibrations in solids have both a longitudinal and a transverse part. There is some appeal in the idea that light might have a component which, being longitudinal, might be "slimmer" than the transverse part and therefore penetrate solids more easily than the "fatter" transverse waves. But Maxwell's wave theory of light, which was then at its height, accounted for light being a transverse wave motion, and an effort was made to identify x-rays with this more familiar phenomenon.

In 1912, Max von Laue conceived of a way of testing the idea that x-rays might be light of very short wavelength. Recall the diffraction grating formula,

$$n\lambda = d \sin \theta, \tag{40–1}$$

where n is the spectrum order $(1, 2, 3, \ldots)$, λ is the wavelength, d is the grating space, and θ is the angle of diffraction. We can see that if λ is very small compared with d, the diffraction angle must be very small unless the order n is large. Since the intensity in high orders is very weak, we can see that assuming λ to be very small can account for the observed failure of gratings to produce measurable diffraction for x-rays.

The obvious remedy is to make gratings with much finer rulings, although we shall see in Section 40–12 that there is another remedy. But the art of making gratings was already in a high state of mechanical perfection. To improve gratings by reducing their grating space by a few orders of magnitude would have required better materials for both the ruling machine and the grating material itself. However, the basic granularity of matter imposes limitations. This dilemma led Laue to the idea of taking advantage of the very granularity that stood in his way. It was felt that the regular shapes of crystals, with their plane cleavage surfaces and well-defined edges, must mean that the atoms are regularly arranged throughout their structure. Laue thought that the atoms of a single crystal might provide the grating needed for the diffraction of x-rays. At Laue's suggestion, Friedrich and Knipping directed a narrow beam (pencil) of x-rays at a crystal and set a photographic plate beyond it. The result was a picture like that shown in Fig. 40–2. (Most of the x-rays go directly through the crystal and strike the plate at its center. To prevent gross overexposure at this point it is usual to fasten a disk of lead over the center of the plate. When the photograph shown in Fig. 40–2 was taken, a lead disk masked the center for all but the last second of a 40-min exposure.) Laue knew he had met with success when he observed the complicated but symmetrical pattern on the plate. These spots could only be due to diffraction from the atoms of the crystal. [Strictly, the structural units of such crystals as NaCl and KCl are ions, not neutral atoms. These are called *ionic crystals* because they are held together by strong electrostatic forces acting between charged particles, e.g. (Na^+) (Cl^-) and (K^+) (Cl^-).]

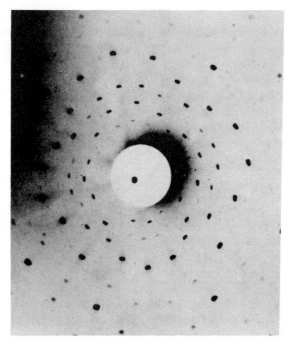

Fig. 40–2. Laue diffraction of NaCl taken with radiation from a tungsten-target tube operated at 60 kv. The faint radial streaks are due to continuous radiation and most of the spots are due to the characteristic L wavelengths of tungsten. The dark patch at the right of the center disk was caused by scattered x-rays.

This diffraction pattern is hardly like that produced by a man-made grating. In optical spectroscopy, the grating consists of parallel lines in a plane. You can appreciate that its diffraction would become more complex if a grating were turned ninety degrees and then ruled again with a second set of lines perpendicular to the first. (Ordinary window screening is like a coarse, cross-ruled grating. When a distant street light is viewed through it, one sees an intricate but symmetrical pattern.) If many such gratings made of glass were stacked behind one another, the diffraction pattern would be further complicated. Since a crystal consists of a regular array of atoms in three-dimensional space, it produces an intricate pattern.

Later we shall discuss qualitatively why a Laue pattern looks as it does. Our immediate point, however, is that by diffracting x-rays Laue demonstrated that x-rays can be combined destructively—the sole, unique experimental criterion for wave motion. At the same time, Laue patterns established that x-rays have very short wavelengths, and confirmed the supposition that crystals have their atoms arranged in a regular structure.

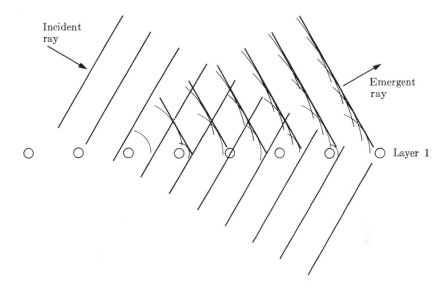

Incident
ray

Emergent
ray

Layer 1

FIG. 40–3. Bragg "reflection" of x-rays from a row of atoms.

Late in 1912, shortly after the Laue experiment, Sir William Bragg
devised another technique for diffracting x-rays. Instead of observing the
effect of passing the rays through a crystal, Bragg considered how x-rays
are scattered by the atoms in the crystal lattice. Consider an x-ray wavefront falling on the surface of a crystal, as shown in Fig. 40–3. Each atom
becomes a source of scattered x-rays and, according to Huygens' principle,
becomes the center of expanding wavelets. In general, these wavelets
combine destructively as they fall on top of one another in a random
manner. If two conditions are met, however, the wavelets combine constructively. The *first condition* is that all the wavelets combine destructively
except in the direction which lies in the plane that contains the incident
x-rays and that is perpendicular to the crystal surface, and the emergent
rays must make the same angle with the crystal surface as the incident
rays. This is precisely the condition of regular optical reflection: the angle
of incidence equals the angle of reflection. Because of this property of
Bragg scattering, it is often called Bragg "reflection." This is actually a
misnomer but we shall follow common usage. The *second condition* that
must be fulfilled is that reflections from the several layers in the crystal
must combine constructively. This second condition imposes restrictions
on the wavelengths that can be reflected by a crystal of given layer spacing d. Figure 40–4 is a representation of three layers of a crystal. An x-ray
wavefront enters from the upper left, making an angle θ with the crystal
surface. According to the first condition, if the x-ray beam is to be reflected

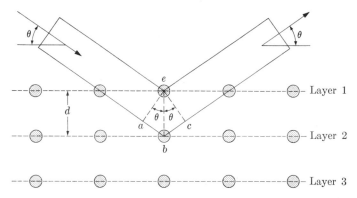

F<small>IG</small>. 40–4. Construction for deriving the Bragg diffraction relation.

at all, it must be reflected toward the upper right, again making the angle θ with the surface. We note that rays reflected from the second layer travel a greater distance than those from the first layer. In order that reflections from the second and successive layers shall reinforce, it is necessary that these additional distances shall be some integral multiple of the x-ray wavelength, or $n\lambda$. If we construct the lines $\overline{ea}$ and $\overline{ec}$ perpendicular to the directions of the incident and reflected rays respectively, we see that each of these lines makes an angle θ with the line $\overline{eb}$ whose length is the separation d of the layers. The additional length of the path of the ray reflected from the second layer is $\overline{ab}$ plus $\overline{bc}$, each of which is equal to $d \sin \theta$.* Thus the second Bragg condition can be stated as

$$n\lambda = 2d \sin \theta, \qquad (40\text{--}2)$$

where n is the order of the spectrum.

The Bragg technique of using crystals as diffraction gratings for an x-ray spectrometer is shown in Fig. 40–5. X-rays from the tube at the left are restricted to a narrow beam or collimated by a lead sheet which absorbs all rays except those which pass through a small slit. These rays fall on a crystal which can be rotated about an axis parallel to the slit and perpendicular to the plane of the figure. The angle θ between the crystal planes and the original x-ray direction can be measured. Since Bragg reflection can take place only in the direction 2θ from the original x-ray

---

* Note that whereas in optics it is usual to measure angles of incidence and reflection between the rays and the normal to the surface, the Bragg angle is measured between the ray and the crystal surface.

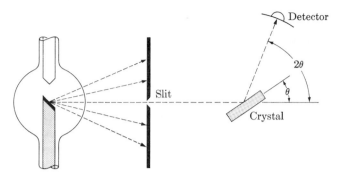

FIG. 40–5. Crystal spectrometer.

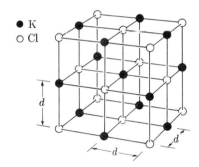

FIG. 40–6. Cubic lattice of sylvite, KCl.

direction, a fluorescent screen or photographic film can detect only the rays in this one direction. Whether or not the rays actually reinforce one another in this direction depends on whether the second Bragg condition is fulfilled. Since d is a fixed crystal property, the measurements of those angles for which reflections do occur provide a measure of the x-ray wavelengths that are present. In order that spectra measured in this way may be quantitative, the crystal spacing d must be known.

The regular arrangement of the space positions of the atoms in a crystal is called a *lattice array*. The basic interplanar distance or *principal grating space, d,* is shown for the cubic crystal KCl in Fig. 40–6. Notice that d is the distance between *adjacent* atoms. The *unit cell* of a lattice is the smallest block or geometric figure of a crystal which is repeated again and again to form the lattice structure. The length of the side of a unit cell is the distance between atoms of the *same* kind. This is equal to $2d$ for the cubic crystal in Fig. 40–6. The length of the side of the unit cell is equal to the basic distance d only in the case of a simple cubic structure in which all of the atoms are of the same kind. Some pure metals form crystals of this

type. These basic interatomic distances can be computed from knowledge
of the molecular weight of the crystalline compound, Avogadro's number,
the density of the material, and its crystalline form. For the cubic type
the general procedure is to calculate the number of atoms per unit volume,
multiply this by the volume associated with each atom, and equate the
product to unity. This procedure is illustrated in the example that follows.

EXAMPLE. KCl (sylvite) is a cubic crystal having a density of 1.98 gm/cm³.
(a) Find the distance between adjacent atoms in this crystal, and (b) find the
distance from one atom to the next one of the same kind.
  (a) Molecular weight of KCl = 39.10 + 35.45 = 74.55.

$$\text{Mass of KCl molecule} = 74.6 \, \frac{\text{gm}}{\text{mole}} \times \frac{1 \text{ mole}}{6.03 \times 10^{23} \text{ molecules}}$$

$$= 12.4 \times 10^{-23} \text{ gm.}$$

$$\frac{\text{No. KCl molecules}}{\text{unit volume}} = 1.98 \, \frac{\text{gm}}{\text{cm}^3} \times \frac{\text{molecule}}{12.4 \times 10^{-23} \text{ gm}}$$

$$= 1.60 \times 10^{22} \, \frac{\text{molecules}}{\text{cm}^3}.$$

Since KCl is diatomic,

$$\frac{\text{No. of atoms}}{\text{unit volume}} = \frac{2 \text{ atoms}}{\text{molecule}} \times 1.60 \times 10^{22} \, \frac{\text{molecules}}{\text{cm}^3}$$

$$= 3.20 \times 10^{22} \, \frac{\text{atoms}}{\text{cm}^3}.$$

Let d be the distance, measured along the edge of the cube, between adjacent
atoms in the crystal and let n be the number of atoms along the edge of a 1-cm
cube. Then the length of an edge is nd, and the volume of this unit cube is $n^3 d^3$.
However, n^3 is the number of atoms in 1 cm³, therefore

$$3.20 \times 10^{22} \, \frac{\text{atoms}}{\text{cm}^3} \times d^3 = 1$$

or

$$d = (3.20 \times 10^{22})^{-1/3} \text{ cm} = 3.14 \times 10^{-8} \text{ cm}$$

$$= 3.14 \text{ A} = 3140 \text{ XU.*}$$

---

  * X-ray wavelengths and crystal lattice constants are commonly less than an
angstrom, 10^{-10} m, and are often expressed in X-units, abbreviated XU. The
XU is about 10^{-13} m. Its true definition is not based on the meter but on the
interatomic distance or lattice constant of rock salt, NaCl. When the XU was
first used the lattice constant of rock salt was taken to be 2.8140 A or 2814.0 XU.
High-precision measurements have revised the rock-salt lattice constant so that
we now have 1000.00 XU = 1.00202 A.

This is the principal grating space, or basic interplanar distance, of KCl.

(b) The distance between two atoms of the same kind is twice the above value, or 6.28 A. This is the length of the side of a unit cell of KCl.

The calculation of the grating space is simple only for a cubic crystal, and the distance thus computed is only the *basic* or *principal* interplanar distance. Within a crystal there are many crystal planes from which Bragg reflection can result. Consider the many possibilities presented by the two-dimensional situation of a marching band on a football field, Fig. 40–7. The basic distance between any adjacent members of the band might be 5 ft. But as the band marches past, it is evident that there are many lines through the band which resemble a three-dimensional array of parallel planes. These sets of parallel lines or planes are separated from one another by different amounts which can be computed from the basic interatomic distance. The population densities of these sets of lines or planes are different, so that reflections from some sets of planes are more intense than those from some other sets. Additional intensity variations are introduced by the differences in the nature of the population of the planes in crystals composed of more than one type of atom. Elements of high atomic number scatter radiation more effectively than those of low atomic number. If the x-marked band members in Fig. 40–7 represent one kind of atom and dot-marked ones another kind, we note that some planes contain only x-marked scatterers, some only the dot-marked type, and some have a mixed population. (It should be kept in mind that the lines in Fig. 40–7 are actually analogous only to the traces of the crystal planes in the plane of the paper. These planes of the crystal are not neces-

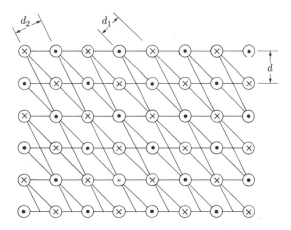

FIG. 40–7. Marching band analogy to a crystal lattice.

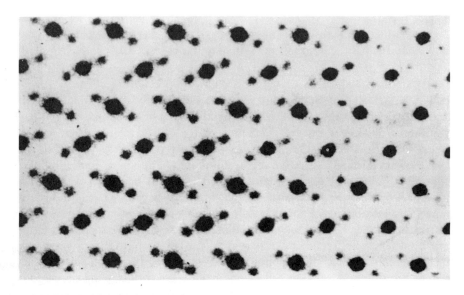

Fig. 40–8. Atoms in marcasite, FeS_2, looking along the crystallographic c-axis, magnified 4.5 million times. The larger spots are iron atoms with 26 electrons each; the smaller dots are sulfur atoms with 16 electrons each. The regular array of the atoms in the crystal is quite evident. This remarkable photograph was taken with a two-wavelength microscope. (Courtesy of M. J. Buerger, Massachusetts Institute of Technology)

sarily normal to the paper. It is evident from a study of Fig. 40–6, for example, that a plane containing only potassium atoms is not perpendicular to any of the faces of the cube.)

We are now in a position to appreciate both why the Bragg method of x-ray spectroscopy is simple and why Laue pictures are complex. In the Bragg method, the crystal can be set so that one densely populated set of planes is reflecting a beam of x-rays, and the three-dimensional crystal is used in a two-dimensional manner. In the Laue method, a pencil of x-rays is made to pierce the crystal perpendicular to a densely populated set of planes of the crystal. Most of the spots are due to diffraction from sparsely populated planes that happen to be situated so that both of the Bragg conditions for reflection are satisfied. The Bragg method is better for the study of the wavelengths of x-rays, but the Laue technique is very useful for the study of crystals. It is a tedious but rewarding task to start with a Laue pattern and work back to the geometry of the array of atoms that must have produced it. An ingenious type of microscope employing both x-rays and visible light has been devised for crystal study. With its aid an enormous, useful magnification can be obtained, so that one can "look" into the lattice structure, as shown in Fig. 40–8.

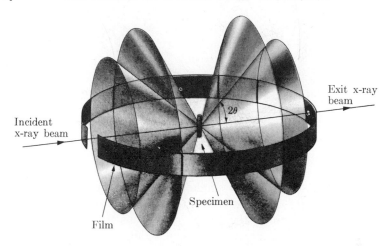

FIG. 40–9. Relation of film to specimen and incident beam in the Debye-Scherrer powder diffraction method. X-rays forming the cone having a half-angle of 2θ were reflected from the same kinds of planes, all oriented at an angle θ to the incident beam. Other cones are formed in a similar way.

We shall not dwell on the subject of crystallography, but there is another x-ray crystallographic technique we must mention in passing. The Bragg and Laue methods require single crystals large enough for study. Many materials that are basically crystalline cannot be obtained as large single crystals, but these materials may be studied by means of the powder technique. One form of this technique, the Debye-Scherrer method, requires that the substance be ground and powdered, so that it can be assumed that all the tiny crystals have random orientation. When a pencil of x-rays is passed through this powder, a series of rings is formed on a photographic film. Each ring is the intersection of the film plane and a cone of rays. Each cone is the locus of rays for which some set of crystal planes is so oriented that both Bragg conditions of reflection are fulfilled. The formation of a powder diffraction pattern is shown schematically in Fig. 40–9, and Fig. 40–10 is the pattern for NaCl made with the x-radiation from copper.

Another form of powder technique is used to study the orientation of crystals in an extruded or drawn material like wire. If the crystallites in the wire actually are random in their orientation, a true powder pattern of circles results. But if the crystallites are somewhat oriented, then each circle has nonuniform intensity and the pattern on the film tends toward a Laue pattern. The degree of orientation can be determined from such pictures.

Laue patterns of metals or other materials rather opaque to x-rays are sometimes obtained by studying the x-rays scattered back from the side

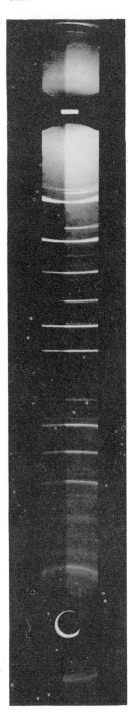

of the material nearer the x-ray source. This technique is used, for example, to study the crystalline structure of steel.

In crystallographic work, it is helpful if the x-rays have a single wavelength. One way of obtaining such monochromatic rays is to use x-rays that have undergone a single-crystal Bragg reflection before they are used for powder studies. Later, we shall discuss filters which strongly absorb all but one of the wavelengths in certain x-ray spectra.

Since a single crystal is used for Laue patterns, there are only a very small number of planes which fulfill the Bragg conditions for constructive interference for any one x-ray wavelength. Therefore, to obtain many Laue spots requires the use of an incident beam containing many wavelengths. On the other hand, the minute crystals in a powder have random orientations, so that many planes are available for the production of interference maxima even when monochromatic x-rays are used.

40–4 Mechanism of x-ray production. Roentgen reported in his original paper that x-rays are produced where cathode rays strike some material object. Since we now know that cathode rays are high-velocity electrons, we can restate Roentgen's observation by saying that x-rays are produced when high-velocity electrons hit something. To explore the mechanism of x-ray production, let us ask what happens when electrons strike solid matter.

About 99% of the electrons that strike matter do nothing spectacular at all. Most of them undergo glancing collisions with the particles of the matter, and in the course of these collisions, the electrons lose their energy a little at a time and thus merely increase the average kinetic energy of the particles in the material. The result is that the temperature of the target material is increased. It is found that

---

Fig. 40–10. Powder diffraction pattern of NaCl made with the K_α and K_β wavelengths of copper. During exposure, the *left* portion of the film was covered with nickel foil. This filtered out the K_β line.

about 99% of the energy of the electron beam goes into heating the target.

Some of the bombarding electrons make solid hits and lose most or all of their energy in just one collision. These electrons are rapidly decelerated. We have pointed out that radiation results when a charged body is accelerated. Therefore when an electron loses a large amount of energy by being decelerated, an energetic pulse of electromagnetic radiation is produced. This is an *inverse photoelectric effect* in which an electron produces a photon. In Chapter 37 we found that photons of a given energy produce photoelectrons with a certain maximum energy. Here we find that electrons of a given energy produce x-ray photons with a certain maximum energy. Both effects confirm the quantum view of radiation. According to classical electromagnetic theory, there is no lower limit to the wavelength of the radiation that a moving electron can produce when it is stopped suddenly. But there is a quantum limit. If an electron has been accelerated through a difference of potential of V volts, we can use Eq. (37–23), which Duane and Hunt showed was valid for x-rays, to compute the wavelength of the resulting radiation in angstroms if the electron loses all its energy in a single encounter. In this case the energy loss of the electron in ev is numerically equal to the accelerating potential in volts. Therefore we have

$$\lambda_{\min} \text{ (A)} = \frac{12396}{V}. \tag{40–3}$$

This expression gives the minimum wavelength, since no electron can lose more energy than it has, and there will be a continuous distribution of radiation toward longer wavelengths because there are all sorts of collisions, from direct hits to glancing ones. Thus glancing collisions account for the *continuous spectrum* of x-rays from any target material and also for the inefficiency of the conversion of electron energy into x-ray energy. The Germans named this continuous radiation *bremsstrahlung*, meaning literally "braking radiation." This is a highly descriptive term, since it refers to the radiation that results from the braking or stopping of charged particles. Some continuous spectra are shown in Fig. 40–11.

Looking at the collision process more closely, however, we find there is another very important kind of collision energy exchange. The bombarding electron may also give energy to electrons bound to the target atoms. If these atomic electrons are freed from their home atoms, ions are produced. Since x-ray producing electrons have energies of the order of many thousands of electron volts, it is very easy for them to produce ions by removing outer electrons. X-ray producing electrons may also have enough energy to produce ions by removing inner electrons from the atom, even down to the innermost or K-shell. Such an ion has a low-energy hole in its electronic structure, and this vacancy is promptly filled when one of its

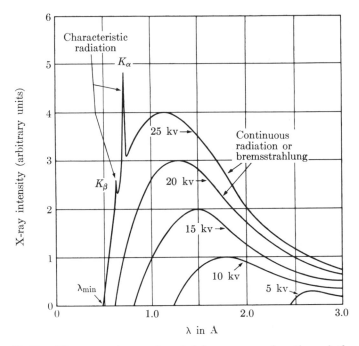

FIG. 40–11. X-ray spectrum of molybdenum as a function of the applied voltage. Line widths not to scale. The K-series excitation potential of this element is 20.1 kv. The shortest L-series wavelength is 4.9 A.

electrons in a higher energy state falls to this low-energy level. When an electron falls into a low-energy level, it releases its energy as radiation, just as in the Bohr theory. Although the energy required to ionize an atom by removing an outer electron is much less than 100 ev, the energy required to ionize by removing an inner electron may be as high as 70,000 ev. When an outer electron falls into such a vacancy, it will radiate a photon of this energy. Such photons are in the x-ray region and have wavelengths which are fractions of angstroms. This mechanism, which accounts for a significant part of x-ray production, produces x-rays having particular wavelengths which are *characteristic* of the target material.

40–5 X-ray energy levels. In our discussion of the periodic table we noted that a heavy element has two electrons with $n = 1$, eight with $n = 2$, etc. The two electrons with $n = 1$ have energies which differ only slightly. The electrons for which $n = 2$ have much more energy than those for which $n = 1$, but they differ among themselves very little. In discussing x-rays, it is often convenient to ignore the minor energy differences of those electrons having the same n and concentrate on the

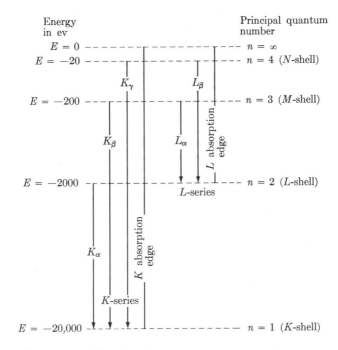

Fɪɢ. 40–12. Hypothetical x-ray energy-level diagram.

large differences associated with different values of n. In the discussion of shell structure in Section 38–11 we said that those electrons having $n = 1$ constitute the K-shell electrons. Those electrons with $n = 2$ form the L-shell. The heaviest elements have seven populated shells, K, L, M, N, O, P, and Q. However, the N, O, P, and Q shells have energies which give rise to the optical spectrum and their energies are *negligible* so far as x-rays are concerned.

With these simplifications we can at once make an energy-level diagram which is typical of all the heavy elements, Fig. 40–12. It is important now to point out the similarities and differences between this energy-level diagram and that of hydrogen.

The one electron in hydrogen is normally in the level for which $n = 1$, and the higher levels in hydrogen are vacant unless the atom is excited. The x-ray diagram represents a typical heavy element having an atomic number of about 40. This element has many electrons. In general, the levels of the heavy elements are occupied by 2, 8, 8, 18, etc., electrons. A hydrogen atom may be excited from the state $n = 1$ to the state $n = 3$. But in a heavy element, a K-shell electron, $n = 1$, cannot be excited to the states $n = 2$ or $n = 3$, since these L- and M-shells are normally filled.

The electron in hydrogen is bound to its nucleus by only one proton with a charge of plus e. The inner electrons of a heavy element are bound by electrostatic forces due to a nucleus with a large charge Ze. This difference in nuclear charges leads to vast differences in the energies of the various levels. Whereas the level having $n = 1$ in hydrogen has an energy of only -13.6 ev, in a heavy element the level for which $n = 1$ has an energy of the order of minus thousands of electron volts. It is $-20,000$ ev in our hypothetical example.

For both light and heavy elements, each level except K is actually a narrow group of levels within which we are ignoring the energy range. Indeed, in x-ray studies, we frequently ignore the energy difference between the energy of the N-shell ($n = 4$) and the energy of a free electron ($n = \infty$). This leads to an interesting result: all heavy elements have x-ray spectra which are similar in character.

Suppose the hypothetical substance whose energy-level diagram is shown in Fig. 40–12 were the target of an x-ray tube across which there is a potential difference of 50,000 volts; then all the cathode-ray electrons strike this target with 50,000 electron volts of energy. Most of these electrons fritter their energy into heat. Some cathode-ray electrons undergo collisions which produce radiation quanta having energy equal to the energy loss in each collision. These cause x-rays with a *continuous* spread of wavelengths down to 0.248 A, as determined by the exciting voltage. Some cathode-ray electrons undergo collisions which cause the removal of target electrons from the various target shells. If an outer, N-shell electron is knocked out, the optical spectrum of the target material will be excited. Light will be emitted as electrons fall into the N-shell vacancy. This is a negligible effect so far as x-rays are concerned, and the light cannot be seen, since it is usually produced at a slight depth within the target which is opaque to visible light. If an M-shell electron is removed, the same remarks apply except that the radiation is in the far ultraviolet region. If an L-shell electron is knocked out, we have a more interesting situation. An L vacancy can be filled in two important ways: an electron can fall into the L-shell from outside the atom (or from the N-shell—we ignore the difference), producing an x-ray of wavelength 6.20 A, or the vacancy in the L-shell can be filled from the M-shell. This energy difference is 1800 ev, and causes an x-ray of wavelength 6.89 A. (In the latter case, the vacancy in the M-shell will also be filled, by the production of a far ultraviolet photon.) These x-radiations of the target are called the L_β and L_α radiations respectively. Since it is more probable that the L-shell will be filled from the nearer M-shell, the less energetic or longer wavelength L_α radiation is more intense than the L_β. If the bombarding electrons had less than 2000 ev of energy, they would not be able to remove electrons from the L-shell and *neither* the L_α nor L_β radiation could result.

We have assumed, however, that the bombarding electrons have 50,000 ev of energy, so that they can not only remove electrons from the L-shell but also from the K-shell. If a K vacancy is filled from the L-shell, the radiation would have wavelength 0.689 A and would be called K_α radiation. (The consequent L vacancy would then result in L_α or L_β radiation.) If the K vacancy is filled from the M-shell, there will be more energetic radiation, K_β, of wavelength 0.626 A. Or if the K vacancy is filled from the N-shell (or from infinity), there will be slightly more energetic radiation, K_γ, of wavelength 0.620 A. These K-series radiations are listed in the order of their relative probability. The K radiations of this example are quite energetic or "hard," whereas the L-series radiations are in the "soft" x-ray region.

In this example we have used a hypothetical substance in order to have simple numbers to work with, but what we have done is typical of all x-ray spectra. If we ignore the small energy differences of the electrons within a given shell, all elements produce x-ray spectra of similar character and with an upper limit of five lines. The short-wavelength limit of the x-ray series terminating at any shell is called the *absorption edge wavelength* of that shell, for reasons given later in this chapter. The corresponding energy is equal to that needed to remove an electron from the shell to infinity.

40–6 X-ray spectra of the elements. Atomic number. In 1913, Moseley used a large number of elements as x-ray tube targets and found that the K_α radiation of each element was distinct from that of any other element. This result not only provides a unique way of identifying the various elements, but also is of theoretical significance. Specifically, Moseley's law states that the frequencies of corresponding x-ray spectral lines, such as K_α's, as we go from element to element, may be represented by an equation of the form

$$\sqrt{f} = a(Z - b) , \qquad\qquad (40\text{–}4)$$

where a and b depend on the particular line and Z is the atomic number of the element.

The original ordering of the elements in the periodic table was on the basis of their atomic weights. Initially, atomic numbers were mere ordinal numbers specifying where the element lay in a list based on these weights. These atomic numbers had no more physical significance than the house numbers that identify the houses on a given street. Moseley found that if he arranged the wavelengths of the K_α lines in the order of atomic weights, these wavelengths formed a remarkably regular progression. The sequence was not perfect, however, since he found both gaps and wavelengths out

of order. Moseley judged that the wavelengths formed a more consistent
set of data than did the atomic weights. He attributed the gaps in the series
to undiscovered elements and proposed that there should be a unique
correlation between the wavelength series and atomic number. His words
were, "We have here a proof that there is in the atom a fundamental
quantity, which increases by regular steps as we pass from one element to
the next. This quantity can only be the charge on the central positive
nucleus." In Moseley's day, nickel with an atomic weight of 58.69 was
listed ahead of cobalt with an atomic weight of 58.94. There was some
chemical evidence that the order of these two elements in the periodic
table should be reversed, and Moseley demonstrated this by showing that
the atomic number of cobalt is 27 and that of nickel is 28.

Moseley's work was announced in 1913, the same year that Bohr accounted for the hydrogen spectrum. In the case of hydrogen, Bohr came
to the same conclusion that Rutherford had reached from alpha-particle
scattering and that Moseley verified for all elements. Recall that in the
Bohr model the charge of the nucleus was basic to his analysis and the
mass of the nucleus played a minor role. Note how nicely Bohr's idea of
electrical forces accounts for the Moseley observation of the regular progression of the K radiations. The electron in hydrogen is a K-shell electron
held to the nucleus by the attraction of one proton. The two K electrons
of helium are held by two protons and thus their binding energies are
greater (more negative) than that of the electron in hydrogen. The two
K electrons of a heavy element are bound by the attraction of many
protons. As we move from one element to the next, the energy to remove
a K electron, the K binding energy, increases in a regular way.

We can now combine the work of Bohr and Moseley in an interesting
and quantitative way that strengthens both their views. From Eq. (38–21)
for the frequency of the spectral lines of hydrogen, we have

$$f = \left(\frac{me^4}{8\epsilon_0^2 h^3}\right) Z^2 \left(\frac{1}{n_1^2} - \frac{1}{n_2^2}\right), \tag{40–5}$$

or

$$\sqrt{f} = \left[\left(\frac{me^4}{8\epsilon_0^2 h^3}\right)\left(\frac{1}{n_1^2} - \frac{1}{n_2^2}\right)\right]^{1/2} Z. \tag{40–6}$$

This bears some resemblance to Moseley's law, so we are encouraged to go
further. Suppose we remove one of the two K-shell electrons of an element
to infinity. The remaining outer electrons will be attracted to the nucleus
not by the nuclear charge Ze as Bohr assumed, but by a charge $(Ze - e)$.
One may think of the remaining K electron as "screening" the outer
electrons from the full nuclear attraction. Thus the b term of Moseley's

law is a nuclear screening constant and it equals one for the K-series lines. Since the K_α line is a transition from $n_2 = 2$ to $n_1 = 1$, we have every-thing we need to attempt a Bohr theory calculation of an x-ray K_α line. Choosing molybdenum ($Z = 42$), we have

$$f = \frac{me^4}{8\epsilon_0^2 h^3} \left(\frac{1}{1^2} - \frac{1}{2^2} \right) (42 - 1)^2. \tag{40-7}$$

Expressed in energy units, we obtain 17.2 kev for this line, which is in remarkable agreement with the experimental value of 17.4 kev.

40–7 X-ray absorption. The most spectacular property of x-rays is their ability to penetrate materials that are opaque to less energetic radiation. The basic mechanism of absorption of ultraviolet, visible, and infrared radiation is the transfer of photon energy to the electronic, vibrational, and rotational energy states of the material doing the absorbing. For x-ray photons, whose energy is orders of magnitude greater, these mech-anisms are trivial in that each such transfer removes from the x-ray only a small percentage of the energy the photon has. To absorb the energy of an x-ray photon by these means requires a large number of such energy transfers. To lose a large fraction of its energy in one encounter, the x-ray photon must interact with a deep electron in the K- or L-shells. Further-more, high-energy x-ray photons are less likely to interact with electrons in the matter they traverse than low-energy ones. Thus high-energy (short-wavelength or hard) x-rays have remarkable penetrating ability.

40–8 Intensity measurements. To discuss the penetrating ability of x-rays further, we must first consider the techniques for measuring x-ray intensities.

Roentgen first detected x-rays by the fluorescence they produce in certain materials. This effect can be used for quantitative intensity measurements if it is coupled with an objective measurement of the fluorescent light produced. Roentgen also observed that x-rays blacken

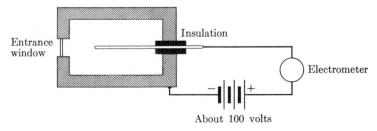

FIG. 40–13. Ionization chamber.

a photographic plate, and this may be used to measure the intensity if a densitometer is used to measure the blackening. A third method was suggested by Roentgen's experiments on the conductivity of air due to x-rays. The x-rays ionize the air, and this effect can be measured quantitatively with an ionization chamber. There are many forms of ionization chambers. One of these is shown schematically in Fig. 40–13. The chamber itself is a metallic box into which an electrode is inserted through an insulating plug. This electrode is maintained at a positive potential, so that any free electrons within the chamber will be attracted to it. The potential difference is chosen low enough so that the dielectric strength of the air prevents a discharge, and high enough so that the charges are collected before the electrons recombine with positive ions. When x-rays enter the chamber and produce ions, the collected charges constitute a small current which is very nearly proportional to the intensity of the x-rays. This current is amplified and measured by an electrometer, an instrument which is very convenient because it is sensitive and responds quickly to changes in x-ray intensity.

40–9 Absorption coefficients. An ionization chamber can be used to study the penetrating ability of x-rays with apparatus like that shown in Fig. 40–14. X-rays are collimated by slits, rendered monochromatic by a Bragg reflection, and passed through a material under study; then their intensity is measured by the ionization chamber. If we vary the thickness of the absorbing material, a plot of transmitted intensity against thickness

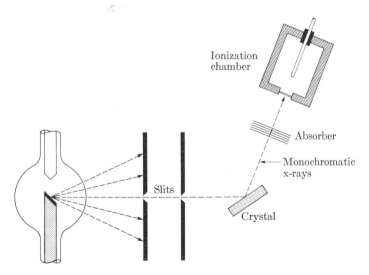

Fig. 40–14. Schematic diagram of the apparatus for x-ray absorption experiments.

looks like that in Fig. 40–15. This is an exponential decay curve which can be derived by assuming that a small thickness of absorber, dx, reduces the intensity of the beam by an amount $-dI$ proportional to both the intensity I and the thickness dx. This assumption leads to the differential equation

$$dI = -\mu I\, dx, \quad (40\text{–}8)$$

where μ is a constant of proportionality. Dividing by I separates the variables so that we can integrate, and we obtain

$$\ln I = -\mu x + C. \quad (40\text{–}9)$$

The constant of integration can be evaluated because I is the incident intensity I_0 when $x = 0$. In exponential form, the result is

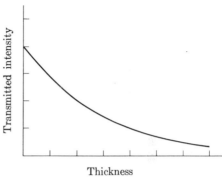

Fig. 40–15. Graph of x-ray transmission through a material.

$$\boxed{I = I_0 e^{-\mu x},} \qquad (40\text{–}10)$$

where I is the intensity of the *transmitted* beam. This is the equation of the curve in Fig. 40–15.

The quantity μ is usually called the *linear absorption coefficient,* although *macroscopic absorption coefficient* and *linear attenuation coefficient* are also used. When Eq. (40–8) is solved for μ, we see that the linear absorption coefficient is equal to the fractional decrease in intensity of the radiation per unit thickness of the absorber. Thus it has the dimensions of reciprocal length. The value of this coefficient depends on the x-ray wavelength and the material used.

It is interesting to express the absorption properties of a material in another way. If we let $I = I_0/2$, we can solve for the corresponding value of x. Since this gives the thickness of absorber that reduces the intensity of the transmitted beam to one-half that of the incident beam, it is called the *half-value layer,* T, or hvl. Thus, from Eq. (40–10), we have

$$\mu T = \ln 2 = 0.693, \qquad (40\text{–}11)$$

or

$$\boxed{T\,(\text{hvl}) = \frac{0.693}{\mu}.} \qquad (40\text{–}12)$$

Although the equations we have derived are correct for a narrow beam of
x-rays, they must be modified before applying them to the general case of
shielding against dangerous radiation. The absorber in the apparatus shown
in Fig. 40–14 reduces the intensity of the beam both by "soaking up" x-rays
and by scattering them in a new direction. Thus when a broad beam of
x-rays passes through an extended absorber, x-ray photons removed from
the beam at one point may be scattered into it again at another point.
When these photons have less than 200 kev of energy, a rule-of-thumb
method for correcting the calculations for the scattered rays is to assume
that the source is one and one-half times as intense as it is measured to be.
This requires increasing the absorber thickness originally calculated by
about 0.6 of a half-value layer. For energies above 1 Mev, two other
effects, which will be discussed later in this chapter, also become significant
in preventing a rapid exponential decrease in the intensity of the transmitted beam. The *"buildup factor"* due to all the processes may then be
such that the transmitted intensity I is four times the value calculated
from Eq. (40–10).

The value of μ depends on the x-ray wavelength and on the absorbing
material. The basic variation of μ with λ is that μ is proportional to λ^3.
But this basic variation is profoundly influenced by the nature of the
absorbing material. If the x-ray wavelengths are so long that they can
excite only outer electrons of the absorbing material, then interaction

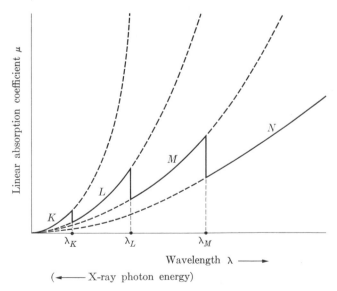

Fig. 40–16. Simplified graph of the linear absorption coefficient of a material
as a function of x-ray wavelength. Fine structure of the absorption edges is not
shown.

between x-rays and the K, L, or M electrons of the absorber must be elastic. But if the x-rays have shorter wavelengths, they may be able to eject M, L, or even K electrons. The various absorption mechanisms are additive, and each varies as λ^3. The variation of μ with the wavelength of a particular material is shown in Fig. 40–16. In this figure λ_K, λ_L, and λ_M are absorption edge wavelengths.

X-rays of short wavelength are very penetrating despite the fact that they can be absorbed by ejecting electrons from any shell of the absorber, that is, by the photoelectric effect. If the wavelength is longer than the K_γ emission wavelength of the absorber, the x-rays are unable to ionize the absorber from the K level and one mechanism of absorption is eliminated. At this wavelength, there is an abrupt change in the absorption coefficient, called an absorption edge. The absorption coefficient again rises with increasing wavelength until suddenly the x-rays are unable to ionize from the L-shell and there is another absorption edge. The value of μ for each mechanism varies as λ^3 and the discontinuities occur when the number of absorption mechanisms changes.

Figure 40–16 is a simplified diagram, since it shows but one absorption edge for each shell. The fact is that there is one K edge, there are three L edges, and five M edges. This fine structure of the variation of absorption coefficient with wavelength comes about because the two K electrons have practically the same energy, but the L and M electrons fall into three and five energy subgroups respectively. These energy levels of a substance are more easily observed in absorption than in emission and were ignored when we discussed x-ray emission spectra. One might be tempted to assign absorption edges to electron transitions within the atom, such as from K to L. These transitions cannot occur in absorption, however, since there is normally no vacancy in the L-shell to which a K electron can go. For this reason, an atom which absorbs energy from an x-ray beam must absorb enough energy to lift some electron *entirely free* of the atom. If an absorbing atom is ionized by having one of its K electrons removed, that atom then has a K-shell vacancy and so it will emit one or more of its characteristic wavelengths as it returns to the ground state. Since this secondary emission can be radiated in any direction, the effect of the process is the removal of an x-ray photon from the direction of the original beam. The characteristic radiations emitted as a result of absorbing photons of high energy are often called *fluorescent* x-rays.

Just as there is a regular progression of x-ray emission wavelengths as we vary the atomic number of the target material, there is also a regular progression in the absorption edges of different elements. The shifting of x-ray spectra with atomic number provides an important technique for obtaining essentially monochromatic x-rays. Suppose we have an x-ray tube with a copper target. The K-series of the copper consists of an intense

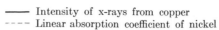

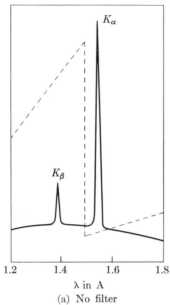
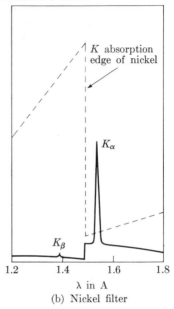

Fɪɢ. 40–17. Comparison of the spectrum of x-radiation from copper (a) before and (b) after passing through a nickel filter.

K_α line, and weak K_β and K_γ radiations, listed in the order of decreasing wavelength and of increasing energy. Nickel is a metal whose atomic number is one less than that of copper. Its energy levels are less negative than those of copper, and its emission lines and absorption edges are at slightly longer wavelengths than those of copper. It happens that the K_γ wavelength of nickel is almost identical with its λ_K absorption edge, and it falls between the strong K_α and the weaker K_β and K_γ emission lines of copper. Figure 40–17 shows the K-series emission spectrum of copper and the linear absorption coefficient of nickel as a function of wavelength. Since the minimum of the absorption curve is at a slightly shorter wavelength than one of the K lines but at a longer wavelength than the others, nickel filters out most of the radiation from the copper except its strong K_α line. There are several sets of elements such that by using one as a filter for the emission of the other, nearly monochromatic x-rays are obtained. The filtering effect of nickel for copper radiation was also shown in Fig. 40–10.

We have described how the linear absorption coefficient depends on the wavelength of the x-rays. We now consider how it depends on the absorbing material.

The absorption coefficient depends strongly on the density of the absorbing material which, of course, changes greatly if the material goes from gaseous to solid states.

We can write

$$\mu x = \frac{\mu}{\rho}\, x\rho, \tag{40–13}$$

where ρ is the mass density of the material. The quantity μ/ρ is called the *mass absorption coefficient*, μ_m. Its units are of the form of area divided by mass. Dimensional analysis shows that $(x\rho)$ is a mass per unit area, m_a. It is the mass of a sheet or slab of the absorber which has the thickness x and a unit of surface area normal to the incident x-ray beam. In these terms, the exponent of Eq. (40–10) becomes $-\mu_m m_a$ and we have

$$\boxed{I = I_0 e^{-\mu_m m_a}.} \tag{40–14}$$

Although the mass absorption coefficient varies from material to material far less than the linear coefficient does, it is not completely invariant. Materials with large atomic numbers absorb x-rays more readily than the lighter elements, so that a certain mass per unit area of lead is more effective than the same mass per unit area of, say, carbon. In general, μ_m varies as the atomic number cubed. Combining this empirical fact with the dependence on λ stated earlier, we can say that

$$\mu_m = k\lambda^3 Z^3, \tag{40–15}$$

where k is approximately constant so long as λ does not vary through absorption edges of the materials being compared.

Concrete is a shielding material which is widely used at the present time. It has about the same mass absorption coefficient as aluminum, but this is often increased by adding barytes to the mix or by using ground limonite instead of sand and steel punchings instead of gravel. Looking ahead to the problem of shielding against gamma rays, we note that we then have radiations which are much more energetic than the x-rays usually used and which have much shorter wavelengths than the K absorption edge of any element. In the 1-Mev range, the absorbing properties of the heavy elements depend more on the number of electrons per unit mass than upon the electronic structure. For a given attenuation at a given photon energy, the mass per unit area required does not vary widely from one material to another. For 1-Mev radiation, the weight per square foot of five half-value layers of water is 112 lb, of concrete is 138 lb, of steel is 134 lb, and of lead is 110 lb. These change to other sets of values at other energies.

40–10 Compton scattering. The mechanism of absorption that we have
considered is the photoelectric effect, in which the x-rays lose energy by
ejecting electrons from the absorbing material. There is another effect
which is weaker than the photoelectric effect in the usual range of x-ray
energies but which becomes more important than the photoelectric effect
at high x-ray energies (about 0.1 Mev and above). This is Compton
scattering. A scattered x-ray is not really absorbed, since it does not lose
a very large fraction of its energy. But, as mentioned earlier, the apparatus
of Fig. 40–14 is sensitive to scattering, since an x-ray photon deflected out
of the beam will fail to reach the detector, just as if it had been absorbed
completely.

Planck introduced the idea that radiation must be emitted in bundles
of energy, although he believed that once emitted, the energy spread in
waves. Einstein extended the Planck idea to the absorption of radiation
in his explanation of the photoelectric effect. He added the assumption
that once a quantum of energy was radiated, it preserved its identity as a
photon until it was finally absorbed. In the chapter on relativity we
showed that mass and energy are identical. Since photons have energy,
they must have mass. This developing concept that photons are true
particles throughout their life comes to its climax in the Compton effect.

Compton endowed photons with the very "mechanical" property of
momentum and solved the problem of impact of a photon and a material
particle by means of relativistic mechanics.

Let us consider a material particle which is initially at the origin and at
rest relative to the coordinate frame shown in Fig. 40–18. (The thermal
motion of the particle is negligible compared with the other velocities in
the following analysis.) Initially, it has no momentum M_1 and its energy
E_1 is only its rest-mass energy, m_0c^2. This particle is then hit by a photon
moving along the x-axis. This photon brings to the impact an energy

$$E = hf = \frac{hc}{\lambda}. \qquad (40\text{--}16)$$

The photon has no rest mass, but its moving mass is equivalent to its
energy, or

$$m_p = \frac{E}{c^2} = \frac{h}{c\lambda}. \qquad (40\text{--}17)$$

The momentum of the photon is its mass times its velocity, which is c.
Thus its momentum M, which is all in the x-direction, is

$$M = \frac{h}{c\lambda} c = \frac{h}{\lambda}. \qquad (40\text{--}18)$$

We assume that the impact is slightly glancing, so that the motion of

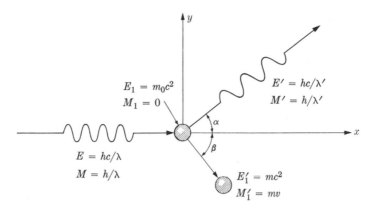

$E_1 = m_0c^2$
$M_1 = 0$

$E' = hc/\lambda'$
$M' = h/\lambda'$

$E = hc/\lambda$
$M = h/\lambda$

$E_1' = mc^2$
$M_1' = mv$

FIG. 40–18. Compton scattering.

the material particle is directed below the x-axis, while the photon is deflected above the x-axis. The impact gives the material particle kinetic energy, so that its total energy becomes mc^2. The material particle also acquires momentum, mv, which is directed at an angle β to the x-axis. The mass of the particle in these statements is the relativistic moving mass.

The photon leaves the impact with its energy changed to hc/λ' and its momentum changed in magnitude and direction to h/λ' at an angle α to the x-axis. The above statements are summarized in Fig. 40–18.

We may now use the laws of conservation of mass-energy and of momentum to describe the impact situation. If we neglect any binding energy that the particle may have and apply the law of conservation of mass-energy, we obtain

$$\frac{hc}{\lambda} - \frac{hc}{\lambda'} = mc^2 - m_0c^2. \tag{40–19}$$

For the conservation of the x-component of momentum, we may write

$$\frac{h}{\lambda} = \frac{h}{\lambda'} \cos \alpha + mv \cos \beta, \tag{40–20}$$

and for the y-component,

$$0 = \frac{h}{\lambda'} \sin \alpha - mv \sin \beta. \tag{40–21}$$

The experimental test of the theory we are developing consists in measuring the wavelength λ' of the deflected photons as a function of their angle of deflection α. The initial photon wavelength λ is known. Since the material particles are usually electrons, m_0 is also known. We find, then, that the three equations (40–19) through (40–21) involve five variables, m, v, λ', α, and β, of which three, m, v, and β, must be eliminated. This requires an additional equation which is the relativistic interdependence of m and v. From Eq. (39–35), we have

$$m = \frac{m_0}{\sqrt{1 - (v^2/c^2)}},$$

or

$$m^2v^2 = c^2(m^2 - m_0^2). \tag{40–22}$$

We first eliminate β between Eqs. (40–20) and (40–21) by isolating the terms containing β and squaring both equations. We thus obtain

$$m^2v^2 \cos^2 \beta = h^2 \left(\frac{1}{\lambda^2} - \frac{2 \cos \alpha}{\lambda\lambda'} + \frac{\cos^2 \alpha}{\lambda'^2} \right) \tag{40–23}$$

and

$$m^2v^2 \sin^2 \beta = h^2 \left(\frac{\sin^2 \alpha}{\lambda'^2} \right). \tag{40–24}$$

Upon adding these equations and using $\sin^2 x + \cos^2 x = 1$, we find

$$m^2v^2 = h^2 \left(\frac{1}{\lambda^2} - \frac{2 \cos \alpha}{\lambda\lambda'} + \frac{1}{\lambda'^2} \right). \tag{40–25}$$

We next eliminate v between Eqs. (40–25) and (40–22), obtaining

$$c^2(m^2 - m_0^2) = h^2 \left(\frac{1}{\lambda^2} - \frac{2 \cos \alpha}{\lambda\lambda'} + \frac{1}{\lambda'^2} \right). \tag{40–26}$$

Solving Eq. (40–19) for m and squaring yields

$$m^2 = m_0^2 + \frac{2m_0h}{c} \left(\frac{1}{\lambda} - \frac{1}{\lambda'} \right) + \frac{h^2}{c^2} \left(\frac{1}{\lambda} - \frac{1}{\lambda'} \right)^2. \tag{40–27}$$

We eliminate m by substituting from Eq. (40–27) into Eq. (40–26). This gives

$$2m_0hc \left(\frac{1}{\lambda} - \frac{1}{\lambda'} \right) + h^2 \left(\frac{1}{\lambda^2} - \frac{2}{\lambda\lambda'} + \frac{1}{\lambda'^2} \right) = h^2 \left(\frac{1}{\lambda^2} - \frac{2 \cos \alpha}{\lambda\lambda'} + \frac{1}{\lambda'^2} \right).$$
$$\tag{40–28}$$

By canceling terms and multiplying both sides of the equation by $\lambda\lambda'/h$, we find that Eq. (40–28) simplifies to

$$m_0c(\lambda' - \lambda) - h = -h \cos \alpha. \tag{40–29}$$

We have finally

$$\boxed{\Delta\lambda = \lambda' - \lambda = \frac{h}{m_0c} (1 - \cos \alpha).} \tag{40–30}$$

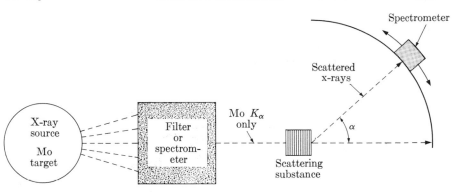

FIG. 40–19. Schematic diagram of the apparatus for measuring Compton scattering.

The experimental test of Eq. (40–30) can be made with apparatus which is schematically represented in Fig. 40–19. Monochromatic x-rays are scattered through an angle α and the spectrum of the scattered radiation is measured. The measuring spectrometer must be free to swing in an arc about the scatterer, so that the scattered wavelength can be measured as a function of the scattering angle α. Compton's results for the molybdenum K_α line scattered by carbon for four values of α are shown in Fig. 40–20. The solid vertical lines correspond to the primary wavelength, λ, and the dashed ones to the calculated modified wavelength λ'. The electrons which, when hit, modify the photon wavelength must suffer a change of energy, as required by our derivation. Such electrons must be either free or loosely bound. If the photon encounters a tightly bound electron, the whole atom is involved in the collision, and the value of m_0 in Eq. (40–30) then becomes the mass of the atom rather than the mass of an

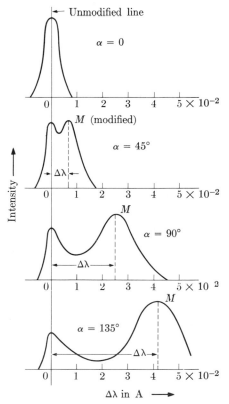

FIG. 40–20. Wavelength displacement of the modified line, M, of the K_α radiation of molybdenum scattered from carbon, as a function of scattering angle.

electron. Since the mass of the atom is several thousand times the electronic mass, the Compton wavelength shift for it is too small to detect. Such photons comprise the unmodified peaks shown in Fig. 40–20.

For very high-energy photons most of the atomic electrons appear free and a large fraction suffer a wavelength shift. For low-energy x-rays most electrons appear bound unless the scattering atom has a low atomic number. For visible photons, all the electrons appear bound and there is no observed Compton shift.

Although we have just seen that the likelihood of a Compton wavelength shift depends on the photon energy and the scattering material, the amount of the wavelength shift depends only on the scattering angle. This aspect of Compton scattering has been tested, and the same change in wavelength was found for x-rays scattered from fifteen different elements.

The breadth of the peaks of both the primary and the modified photons in Fig. 40–20 is attributed to the Doppler effect. In our derivation we assumed that the electron doing the scattering was initially at rest. Motion of the target electron fully accounts for the fact that, for a given angle, some photons had their energy changed a little more or less than what would be expected for stationary electrons.

Not only does the Compton effect contribute to our understanding of absorption coefficients, its theory also provides a good check of relativity and extends the particle concept of photons. With photons behaving like billiard balls, we are nearly back to Newton's particle theory of light. In the next chapter we shall synthesize the divergent wave and particle theories of radiation.

40–11 Absorption by pair production. The third mechanism of x-ray absorption is pair production, which was discussed in Section 39–15. Although it cannot occur if the photon has less than about 1 Mev of energy, above 5 Mev pair production in lead is a more important process than either photoelectric absorption or Compton scattering. The radiation arising from the annihilation of the pair contributes to the buildup factor in the absorber.

The three mechanisms of x-ray absorption are summarized in Fig. 40–21. The contribution of each of these to the linear absorption coefficient in lead for photons of different energies is shown in Fig. 40–22. The slope of the photoelectric variation in Fig. 40–16 is positive because the abscissa is the wavelength. In Fig. 40–22 this slope is negative because the abscissa is energy. The discontinuities of Fig. 40–16 do not show on Fig. 40–22 because the scales are very different.

40–12 Diffraction with ruled gratings. X-rays were first diffracted with crystals but eventually a method was also devised for diffracting them with man-made gratings. This method leads to nothing new or startling,

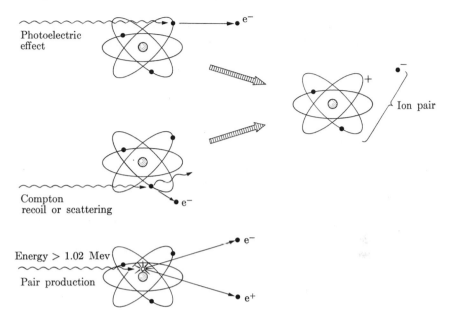

Photoelectric effect

Ion pair

Compton recoil or scattering

e⁻

Energy > 1.02 Mev

Pair production

e⁻

e⁺

Fig. 40–21. Summary of x-ray and gamma-ray interactions with matter.

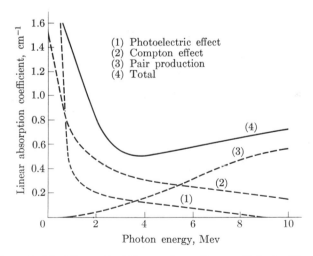

(1) Photoelectric effect
(2) Compton effect
(3) Pair production
(4) Total

Linear absorption coefficient, cm⁻¹

Photon energy, Mev

Fig. 40–22. Theoretical linear absorption coefficient of lead.

but it is an interesting and important example of how physical research often builds crosslinks that reenforce the entire structure of our ideas.

We stated earlier that x-rays were not diffracted by man-made gratings because the wavelength of x-rays is much less than the separation of the closest lines man can rule with the granular materials at his disposal.

Compton found a way around this difficulty which was certainly ingenious. In the first place he used soft, relatively long-wavelength x-rays. These rays, though still classed as x-rays, were so soft that they were easily absorbed by air. He therefore placed all his apparatus in a vacuum (inside a large x-ray tube). In the second place, he used the grating in an unusual way. The index of refraction of glass for x-rays is slightly *less* than one. Thus when x-rays go from vacuum into glass, they are passing from a medium of higher index into one of lower index, and the rays are refracted away from the normal. Recall that whenever light goes from a medium of higher index to a medium of lower index, there is a critical angle, and that if the rays approaching the interface make an angle greater than the critical angle, total reflection results. X-rays striking glass at "grazing incidence" will not enter the glass at all, but will be totally reflected. If, now, the glass surface is a ruled grating, these rulings will appear closer together from a grazing angle than when viewed from a point normal to the grating surface. Thus the very geometrical situation which makes the bands between the rulings of the grating capable of reflecting also makes the apparent grating space much less. Compton found that with his ingenious arrangement he could diffract x-rays by measurable amounts.

The important result of this work was that Compton could measure x-ray wavelengths absolutely. The grating space was determined by a screw whose pitch could be measured by counting the threads in a length measured with an ordinary length standard. Compton knew the grating space from very direct elementary measurement. All prior x-ray wavelength measurements had been made in terms of a calculated crystal spacing which depended on Avogadro's number, and Avogadro's number depended in turn upon the charge of the electron. Compton found the wavelengths he measured differed from those measured with crystal diffraction by about 1%. Since his was the absolute measurement, he concluded that the crystal spacings that had been used formerly were in error. He traced this back through Avogadro's number to the charge of the electron and concluded that Millikan's value was in error. Millikan contested this conclusion until it was found that he had used a faulty value for the viscosity of air in his application of Stokes' law. Once Compton's value was accepted, the accepted value of the charge of the electron and all physical constants based on that charge were revised. It is interesting that an experiment in x-ray spectroscopy should provide a technique for measuring the basic unit of electrical charge.

40–13 Radiation units. Some of the energy absorbed from ionizing radiation which passes through matter damages the medium by causing molecular changes or by altering the crystalline form. The amount of damage produced depends upon the nature of the absorbing material, the energy of the photon, and the intensity of the radiation. The effects are large in complex organic molecules and so x-rays are injurious to living tissue. To study this quantitatively, it is necessary to define a unit for amount of radiation absorbed.

The internationally accepted unit of x-ray quantity is determined by the ionization produced in air. It was defined by the Fifth International Congress of Radiology in 1937 as follows: "The *roentgen*, r, is that quantity of x- or gamma radiation such that the associated corpuscular emission per 0.001293 grams of dry air produces, in air, ions carrying 1 esu of quantity of electricity of either sign." This mass of air has a volume of 1 cm^3 at 0°C and a pressure of 760 mm of mercury, and 1 esu of charge is equal to $1/(3 \times 10^9)$ coul. Air was chosen for the ionized medium because its mass absorption coefficient is nearly the same as that of water and of body tissue over a considerable range of wavelengths, and because it is easily obtained and reproduced.

The absorbed radiation frees photoelectrons and Compton recoil electrons. The secondary particles or corpuscles will also ionize the air as they move toward the collecting electrodes in the ionization chamber. The charges carried by these ion pairs produced by the secondaries must be counted as a part of the quantity of charge to be measured. [An ion pair, ip, is composed of the positive ion and the negative ion (usually an electron) produced when a neutral particle is ionized. The magnitude of the charge on each member of the pair is necessarily the same. Each ion of an ion pair produced in air is singly charged.] Although all the secondary particles originate in 1 cm^3 of air where the absorption occurred, the measured charge comes from the whole volume through which these secondaries range.

Since the production of ions requires the absorption of energy, the roentgen is actually a unit of energy absorbed and not a measure of the total energy flux in a beam of radiation. We can now restate our definition of this absorption unit. The *roentgen* is the amount of radiant energy which must be *absorbed* by 1 cm^3 of *air* under standard conditions to produce ions carrying $1/(3 \times 10^9)$ coul of charge of either sign. The *milliroentgen*, mr, is a thousandth of a roentgen. In radiobiology these units are usually called the *exposure* or *dose* or *dosage* units for radiation delivered to a specified area or volume of the body. Note that the units of amount of radiation absorbed do not depend upon the time.

The *exposure rate* or *dose rate* or *dosage rate* is measured by the radiation absorbed per unit time. Some of the units are the *roentgen per hour*, r/hr, the *milliroentgen per hour*, mr/hr, and so on.

When a large number of ions are formed in air, it is found that the *average* energy required to produce an ion pair is 34 ev. This is much greater than the minimum energy needed to ionize either oxygen or nitrogen. The value is larger because some photons eject inner electrons whose binding energies are much greater than the minimum ionization energy, and others excite an atom without ionizing it by a Compton scattering involving the whole atom. If we take the product of the number of ion pairs in air corresponding to a roentgen and the average energy required to produce such a pair, we find that the roentgen is equivalent to 1.13×10^{-8} joule of energy absorbed per cubic centimeter of standard air. When a beam which produces a roentgen in air enters another medium where the atoms have different atomic numbers, the absorption of energy changes. Thus x-rays producing a roentgen in air will result in the absorption of *about* 9.3×10^{-6} joule per gram of soft body tissue. The *rep* (roentgen equivalent physical) is that dose of ionizing radiation which results in the absorption of 9.3×10^{-6} joule per gram of body tissue. This unit is *not* very *definite* because of the variations in the composition of the body. However, a definite unit is the *rad* (radiation absorbed dose), which is 100 ergs (10^{-5} joule) of absorbed energy per gram of *any* absorbing material. The *millirad*, mrad, is a thousandth of a rad. Additional units will be discussed in the chapter on natural radioactivity.

Radiation damage to the human body depends upon the dose, the dose rate, and the part of the body exposed. The safe limit for those exposed to radiation over the *whole* body during their working day is now set at 250 mr/week. This is a dose rate of 6.25 mr/hr based on a 40-hour week. Up to a few years ago, the safe tolerance level was thought to be twice this amount. It is likely that it will be lowered again soon. Although the dose due to long exposure to low-level radiation is large, the resulting direct damage is negligible because the body has time to repair the injury. The effects of acute radiation exposure over the *whole* body are about as follows: 20–50 r, some blood changes; 100–250 r, severe illness but recovery within 6 months; 400 r, fatal to 50% of the persons affected (this is called the median lethal dose, MLD or LD-50); and 600 r, fatal to all.

The mechanism of tissue destruction is not completely understood. When radiation is absorbed by the various complex organic molecules in the body, an electron is either raised to a higher energy level within the molecule or removed altogether. One might expect that after the electron returns, all would be normal again, as in the case of hydrogen and other single atoms. However, during the time the molecule is in the excited state, its constituent atoms sometimes rearrange themselves. Then, although the system is again neutral after the electron's return, it is no longer the same molecule. A reaction which occurs in some cases is that two hydroxyl radicals, OH, combine to form hydrogen peroxide, H_2O_2. The molecular situation is somewhat analogous to a high tower which a child builds with small wooden blocks. If we "ionize" the tower by pulling out a block near the base, it is evident that the tower will not rebuild itself when we return the "electron" to the heap. It is unlikely that any substantial change would have occurred if only the topmost block had been removed and then returned. Destruction of a body cell depends upon which electron in the molecular structure absorbs the radiation energy.

In the human body, the hands and feet can receive a much larger dose of radiation without permanent injury than any other part. However, the genes in the cells of the body are readily damaged. Injury to those in the reproductive cells is particularly serious because it gives rise to muta-tions in the generations which follow. These mutations are almost always adverse and the process is irreversible. There is no safe lower limit of radiation when considering the inheritance of genetic damage. It has been said that "a little radiation is a little bad, and a lot is a lot bad." This means that the probability of absorption by any one gene or group of genes is less for a small dose than for a large one. However, the damage per quantum of radiation absorbed is the same in both cases. It is estimated that the rate of mutation will show significant increase if persons receive a dose of more than 10 r during their reproductive lifetime—a period of about 30 years. During that length of time, one will receive about 4 r from cosmic rays and from the radioactive materials which are found in low concentrations everywhere. Any exposure to x-rays adds to the accumulated dose. Remember that the damage discussed here is trans-mitted to the generations to come. A dose of 10 r would not harm the parent.

The things considered in this section lie in the field of radiological physics. As we advance into the nuclear age, the solution of an increasing number of problems of public health will become the responsibility of persons trained in this area of science.

PROBLEMS

40–1. Potassium iodide, KI, is a cubic crystal which has a density of 3.13 gm/cm^3. Find (a) the basic interplanar distance, and (b) the length of a side of the unit cell.

40–2. The spacing between the principal planes in a crystal of NaCl is 2.820 A. It is found that a first-order Bragg reflection of a monochromatic beam of x-rays occurs at an angle of 10°. (a) What is the wavelength of the x-rays in A and in XU, and (b) at what angle would a second-order reflection occur?

40–3. What is the shortest wavelength that can be emitted by the sudden stopping of an electron when it strikes (a) the screen of a TV tube operating at 10,000 volts and (b) the plate of a high-power radio transmitter tube operating at 30,000 volts? (c) Determine the spectral region in which these wavelengths lie by referring to Fig. 30–5.

40–4. An x-ray tube is operating at 150,000 volts and 10 ma. (a) If only 1% of the electric power supplied is converted into x-rays, at what rate is the target being heated, in calories per second? (b) If the target weighs 300 gm and has a specific heat of 0.035 cal/gm·°C, at what average rate would its temperature rise if there were no thermal losses? (c) What must be the physical properties of a practical target material? What would be some suitable target elements?

40–5. Since the index of refraction of all materials for x-rays is very close to unity, they cannot be converged by lenses. Therefore all radiographs (x-ray photographs) are necessarily shadowgraphs. (a) What requirement is imposed on the target area from which the radiation originates so that the

pictures will be sharply defined? (b) What is the smallest size film with respect to the size of the object that can be used in radiographing it?

40–6. X-rays from a certain cobalt target tube are composed of the strong K series of cobalt and weak K lines due to impurities. The wavelengths of the K_α lines are 1.785 A for cobalt, and 2.285 A and 1.537 A for the impurities. (a) Using Moseley's law, calculate the atomic number of each of the two impurities. (b) What elements are they?

40–7. The K absorption edge of tungsten is 0.178 A and the average wavelengths of the K-series lines are $K_\alpha = 0.210$ A, $K_\beta = 0.184$ A, and $K_\gamma = 0.179$ A. (a) Construct the x-ray energy-level diagram of tungsten. (b) What is the least energy required to excite the L-series? (c) What is the wavelength of the L_α line? (d) If a 100-kev electron struck the tungsten target in a tube, what is the shortest x-ray wavelength it could produce, and (e) what is the shortest wavelength characteristic of tungsten that could be emitted?

40–8. A thin sheet of nickel is placed successively in a beam of x-rays from cobalt, then in one from copper, and finally in one from zinc. Discuss the effect of each of these beams on the nickel atoms and show that the filtered radiation from copper is essentially

Element	Emission wavelengths, A		
	K_α	K_β	$K_{absorp.}$
Co	1.79	1.62	1.61
Ni	1.66	1.49	1.48
Cu	1.54	1.39	1.38
Zn	1.43	1.29	1.28

monochromatic. X-ray data for these elements are given in the accompanying table. Consider only K-shell absorption.

40-9. A tungsten target is bombarded with 80-kev electrons. (a) Using the wavelengths characteristic of tungsten given in Problem 40-7, find the maximum energies of the photoelectrons ejected from the K-, L-, and M-shells, in ev. (b) What is the range of energies of the photoelectrons ejected from the shells between M and infinity?

40-10. (a) How does the linear absorption coefficient vary with the atomic number of an absorber? (b) Before an examination of the gastrointestinal tract of a patient is made with x-rays, the patient drinks a suspension of barium sulfate, $BaSO_4$. Why must this be done? (c) Some fluids in the human body can be followed by the use of x-rays if a solution of potassium iodide, KI, is introduced into the region to be studied. Why must this be done?

40-11. How many half-value layers of a material are necessary to reduce the intensity of an x-ray beam to (a) 1/16, (b) 1/80, and (c) 1/200 of its incident value?

40-12. The half-value layer of steel for 1.5-Mev radiation is 0.5 in. (a) Plot the curve of transmitted intensity against thickness in half-value layers for a sheet of steel 3 in. thick when the intensity of the incident beam is 200 units. (b) Using the same coordinate scales as in part (a), plot the radiation that has been absorbed against the thickness. (c) Most of the radiation absorbed appears as heat. Assuming low thermal conductivity so that the temperature gradient in the steel is approximately the slope of the absorption curve, discuss the variation of this gradient within the sheet. (d) Will the sheet have thermal stresses?

40-13. For 0.2-A x-rays, the mass absorption coefficients in cm^2/gm for several metals are: aluminum, 0.270; copper, 1.55; and lead, 4.90. (a) What is the half-value thickness of each for a narrow beam of x-rays? (b) What thickness of each is required to reduce the intensity of the transmitted beam to 1/32 of its incident value? (c) If the "buildup" due to scattering and other processes for a broad beam of radiation is equivalent to making the incident beam 1.5 times its actual intensity, what thickness of each material is then needed to obtain an intensity reduction to 1/32?

40-14. Show that the tenth-value layer of an absorber equals $2.30/\mu$.

40-15. The linear absorption coefficient of a certain material for x-rays having a wavelength of 1 A is $\mu_1 = 3.0$ cm^{-1}, and for those having a wavelength of 2 A is $\mu_2 = 15$ cm^{-1}. If a narrow beam of x-rays containing equal intensities of 1-A and 2-A radiation is incident on the absorber, for what thickness of the material will the ratio of the intensities of the transmitted rays be 4 to 3?

40-16. Show that when the exponent μx in $I = I_0 e^{-\mu x}$ is equal to or less than 0.1, then, with an error of less than 1%, (a) the transmitted radiation equals $I_0(1 - \mu x)$, and (b) the absorbed radiation equals $I_0 \mu x$. [Hint: Expand the exponential term into a series.]

40-17. For 2-Mev x- or gamma rays, the half-value layers of some commonly used shielding materials are: water, 5.9 in.; ordinary concrete (relative density, 2.6), 2.3 in.; iron, 0.80 in.; and lead, 0.53 in. Find (a) the mass absorption coefficient of each in ft^2/lb, and (b) the weight per unit area in lb/ft^2 of each material for shielding walls which are 5 half-value layers thick.

40–18. Three quanta, each having 2 Mev of energy, are absorbed in a material. One of the quanta is absorbed by the photoelectric process, another is involved in a Compton scattering, and the third is involved in pair production. (a) Discuss the possible methods by which the scattered photon and each of the charged particles produced can be involved in energy interchanges until all the original photon energy is reduced to thermal energy. (b) Will all this final thermal energy be freed at the point where absorption occurred originally?

40–19. The K_α line of molybdenum (wavelength, 0.712 A) undergoes a Compton collision in carbon. What is the wavelength change of the line scattered at 90° if the scattering particle is (a) an electron, and (b) the whole carbon atom? (c) What is the scattered wavelength in each case?

40–20. Using the data and results of Problem 40–19 for Compton scattering of the K_α line of molybdenum by carbon, find the energy of the recoil particle if it is (a) an electron and (b) the whole carbon atom. (c) What is the direction of motion of the recoil particle in each case, with respect to the direction of incidence of the photon?

40–21. Show that the roentgen is equivalent to (a) 2.083×10^9 ion pairs per cm^3 of standard air, and (b) 1.611×10^{12} ion pairs per gm of air. The density of air is 1.293 gm/liter at standard conditions.

40–22. Given that it requires 34 ev of energy to produce an ion pair in air,

show that the roentgen is equivalent to an energy absorption of (a) 7.09×10^4 Mev per cm^3 of standard air, (b) 5.48×10^7 Mev per gm of air, (c) 87.8×10^{-7} joule or watt·sec per gm of air, and (d) 2.09×10^{-6} cal per gm of air.

40–23. An x-ray beam having a dose rate or exposure rate of 480 mr/hr produces ions in 6 cm^3 of standard air in an ionization chamber. What is the saturated ionization current, in amperes?

40–24. A common form of dose meter or dosimeter is a cylindrical capacitor filled with a gas. One model worn by personnel working in the vicinity of x-ray equipment has an absorption equivalent to 6 cm^3 of standard air. (a) If the electrodes are charged to a difference of potential of 400 volts, what must be the resistance of the electrode insulation so that the charge leakage in 8 hr shall not exceed 10% of an assumed safe tolerance level of 50 mr/8-hr day? (Assume that the voltage remains constant.) (b) What would be the effect on the accuracy of the dosimeter if (1) there are finger streaks on the insulator, and (2) the relative humidity is high?

40–25. When a beam of hard x-rays travels through the length of a column of standard air 2 cm^2 in cross section and 4 cm long in an ionization chamber, the saturated ion current is 5×10^{-12} amp. (a) What is the dose rate in mr/hr and in Mev/cm^3·sec? (b) What is the intensity of the beam incident on the air column in Mev/cm^2·sec? The linear absorption coefficient of air for hard x-rays is 2.5×10^{-4} cm^{-1}.

CHAPTER 41

WAVES AND CORPUSCLES

41–1 The de Broglie hypothesis. In our discussion of the Compton effect we treated photons as though they were billiard balls. We calculated the moving mass of a photon, $h/c\lambda$, by combining Planck's expression for the energy of a photon, $E = hf = hc/\lambda$, with Einstein's mass-energy relation, $E = mc^2$. Since this photon mass moves with the velocity of light, we found the photon momentum to be $M = h/\lambda$. Thus we can express the wavelength of a photon in terms of its momentum as

$$\lambda = \frac{h}{M}. \tag{41-1}$$

In contemplating the dual character of light, which seems to possess both wave and particle properties, de Broglie had the novel idea that matter particles should have wave properties. He felt that nature was symmetrical and that the dual nature of light should be matched with a dual nature of matter. He assumed that Eq. (41–1) is a general equation applying to photons and material particles alike. Since the momentum of a material particle is its mass times its velocity, he assumed that the *de Broglie wavelength* of a material particle is

$$\boxed{\lambda = \frac{h}{mv}.} \tag{41-2}$$

When de Broglie published his hypothesis in 1924, there was no experimental evidence to justify it. His only real argument was his intuitive feeling that nature must be symmetrical.

41–2 Bohr's first postulate. The theoretical consequences of the de Broglie wavelength of matter are interesting. We next describe how the de Broglie wavelength fits into the Bohr model of the atom.

If a stretched string is caused to vibrate, the disturbances move down the string in both directions, are reflected at the ends with a 180° change in phase, and come back on one another. In general, this disturbance of the string causes a complex motion that makes the string appear blurred everywhere. If the exciting frequency, the length of the string, or the string tension is varied, the adjustments can be made so that stationary waves result. Displacement loops and nodes appear. Instead of running up and down the string, the waves appear to stand still, with transverse activity at the loops and only rocking activity at the nodes. The condition for stationary waves is that the length of the string be a *whole* number of *half* wavelengths of the disturbance. The reason for the *half* in the stable stationary wave condition is the existence of the 180° phase shift due to reflections at the ends.

If we could induce a skilled cowboy to twirl his lariat so the loop at the end formed a horizontal circle (nearly), we can imagine ourselves vibrating the cowboy and causing stationary waves in the loop. (Admittedly this would be pretty difficult to do. In order to observe the stationary waves, we would have to rotate our bodies with the loop and observe the motion from its center.) In this case the disturbances would run around the loop in both directions, forming stationary waves without the need for reflections. Here the condition for stationary waves would be that the length of the loop be a whole number of wavelengths of the disturbance.

We can now draw an analogy with the hydrogen atom by likening the cowboy to the proton and the lariat to the electron orbit. The disturbance is the de Broglie wave of the electron. We next assume that the electron forms a stable standing wave, so that the length of its orbit divided by its wavelength is a whole number n. We have

$$\frac{2\pi r}{\lambda} = \frac{2\pi r}{h/mv} = n$$

or

$$2\pi r = n \frac{h}{mv}. \tag{41-3}$$

Recalling that the angular momentum of a particle moving in a circular orbit is $I\omega$ or mvr, we find that the angular momentum of the Bohr electron is

$$mvr = \frac{nh}{2\pi}, \tag{41-4}$$

which is precisely Bohr's first postulate. If Bohr had known about the wave nature of matter, his first postulate would not have been an assumption but a derived equation.

41–3 Matter waves. Einstein pointed out that if the de Broglie hypothesis is valid, then it should be possible to diffract electrons. Schroedinger felt that if de Broglie were right, then the waves associated with matter should suffer refraction.

Light usually travels in straight lines, but when it goes from one medium to another it is refracted. Refractive bending is due to changes in the velocity of propagation of light, which is low in a medium of high refractive index. We are aware of abrupt refractions such as occur at the surfaces of a lens. However, the refractions at layers of air of differing temperatures are quite gradual. When the summer sun beats on a blacktop highway, the layers of air next to the road are expanded. Although the refractive index of air is very close to unity, the hot air over the highway has an index even nearer unity. Light coming down to the highway enters a region of lower index and is refracted away from the normal because of the refractive index gradient. If the light approaches this region of index gradient at a grazing angle, total reflection causes the familiar mirage effect. In this case, the bending of the path of light by refraction is not abrupt. The light rays form a continuous curve.

Schroedinger felt that the continuous curved paths of material objects might be such a continuous refraction of the associated matter waves. To see how this works out, we consider the following example. The parabolic flight of a baseball is a simple case of a material body moving in a curved path. At the top of the flight the path is concave downward, the instantaneous velocity v is horizontal, and the path may be regarded momentarily as the arc of a circle of radius of curvature R. The acceleration of the ball is the centripetal acceleration, v^2/R, which is the acceleration due to gravity, g. Equating these two expressions for the acceleration, we can solve for the radius of curvature of the path:

$$R = \frac{v^2}{g}.$$
(41–5)

To express this result in terms of energy, we note that the total energy E of the baseball is constant and that the gravitational potential energy is $E_p = m_0 g y$, where y is the height of the ball above the ground. The velocity of the ball is so small that we may use classical physics. Since the kinetic energy must be $(E - E_p)$, we have

$$E_k = \tfrac{1}{2} m_0 v^2 = E - E_p$$
or
$$v^2 = \frac{2(E - E_p)}{m_0},$$
(41–6)

so that R, in terms of energy, becomes

$$R = \frac{2(E - E_p)}{m_0 g}.$$
(41–7)

Having found R by classical, nonrelativistic means, we next attempt to solve the same problem by considering the refraction of matter waves.

The de Broglie wavelength of a particle is $\lambda = h/mv$, where λ is the wavelength of an "associated wave." The frequency of this associated wave may be determined from relativity and quantum relations. Assuming that the total energy of a particle, mc^2, is given by hf (as for photons), we find that the frequency of the associated wave is $f = mc^2/h$. Since the phase velocity of any wave motion is $v_p = \lambda f$, we find the velocity of the associated waves to be

$$v_p = \frac{h}{mv}\frac{mc^2}{h} = \frac{c^2}{v}.$$

(41–8)

In this equation, v is the *velocity* of the *material particle*, which we have seen must be *less* than the velocity of light, c. Thus v_p is much *greater* than the velocity of light. The quantity v_p is a *phase velocity* which applies to the associated waves. The velocity of the mass-energy of the particle does not exceed the speed of light in free space, but the velocity of propagation of the phase of its associated waves does. In the chapter on relativity we warned that we would encounter situations where we would compute velocities greater than c.

We next apply Eqs. (41–8) and (41–6) to determine the phase velocity of the associated waves of the baseball, and obtain

$$v_p = c^2\sqrt{m_0/2(E - E_p)} = c^2\sqrt{m_0/2(E - m_0gy)}, \qquad (41–9)$$

where $E_p = m_0gy$. It is evident that v_p is a function of the height y, and that v_p increases when y increases. This means that the higher the ball, the less is the "refractive index" of the space in which the associated waves move. Let us again compute the radius of curvature that this "refraction" imparts to the trajectory of the ball.

We assume, as before, that for an instant dt the ball moves on the arc of a circle of radius R. As in the study of optical refraction, we shall talk in terms of an infinitesimal wavefront of width dy perpendicular to the "ray." In Fig. 41–1 the phase waves move at a height y above the earth, and they curve concave downward because the top of the wavefront moves faster than the bottom. From the figure we find that

$$\theta = \frac{v_p\,dt}{R} = \frac{(v_p + dv_p)\,dt}{R + dy}. \qquad (41–10)$$

To find dv_p, we first put Eq. (41–9) in the form

$$v_p(E - m_0gy)^{1/2} = c^2\left(\frac{m_0}{2}\right)^{1/2}$$

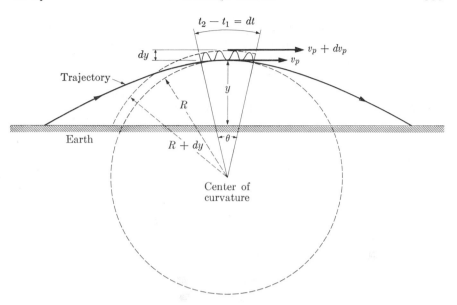

FIG. 41–1. Wave-mechanical representation of projectile motion.

and then differentiate v_p with respect to y. The result reduces to

$$dv_p = \frac{1}{2} \frac{m_0 g}{E - m_0 g y} \cdot v_p \cdot dy. \qquad (41\text{--}11)$$

Upon substituting this expression for dv_p in Eq. (41–10), we get a relation which simplifies to

$$m_0 g R = 2E - 2m_0 g y. \qquad (41\text{--}12)$$

Substituting from $E_p = m_0 g y$, we finally have

$$R = \frac{2(E - E_p)}{m_0 g}. \qquad (41\text{--}13)$$

Agreement between Eqs. (41–7) and (41–13) supports Schroedinger's idea that it may be possible to devise a system of mechanics in which the paths of rays of matter waves replace the classical Newtonian trajectories.

In 1926 Schroedinger announced his system of wave mechanics. In analogy to Maxwell's wave equation, which completely describes the wave properties of light, Schroedinger wrote the wave equation which completely describes the wave nature of matter. But physicists generally were not excited by the speculations of de Broglie, Schroedinger, and others. There was at first no real experimental evidence, such as the observation of interference effects that provided the most convincing proof of the wave nature of light. However, in 1925 Elsasser deduced from de Broglie's theory that a beam of electrons should be diffracted by a crystal and show interference phenomena. This prediction eventually led to the experimental verification of the wave nature of matter.

41–4 The Davisson and Germer experiment. In 1927 Davisson and Germer were studying the scattering of electrons by nickel. Their technique was reminiscent of both Rutherford alpha-particle scattering and Compton x-ray scattering. They directed a beam of electrons onto a block of nickel and measured the intensity of the electrons as they scattered from the nickel in different directions. In the course of the experiment, their vacuum system broke accidentally and had to be repaired.

When the vacuum system broke the nickel target was at a high temperature, and the air caused the nickel to acquire a heavy coat of oxide. To remove the oxide from the block of nickel, Davisson and Germer reduced the oxide slowly in a high-temperature oven. When their apparatus was reassembled, they began to get very different results. Whereas the number of scattered electrons had previously become continuously less as the scattering angle increased, they now found that the number of electrons went through maxima and minima. *The electrons were being diffracted.* Using the familiar techniques of x-ray diffraction by crystals, Davisson and Germer computed the wavelength their electrons must have, and they found that this wavelength agreed with the de Broglie formula.

The prolonged heating to clean the nickel block had caused it to become a single crystal, and the electron diffraction pattern was completely analogous to x-ray diffraction by the Laue technique. This experiment verified the de Broglie hypothesis and indicated that material particles have wave properties.

To consider the Davisson and Germer experiment in more detail, we show their apparatus schematically in Fig. 41–2. At the right is an electron gun that provides a collimated beam of electrons whose energy is known from the accelerating potential. These electrons were scattered by the nickel target, which could be rotated about an axis perpendicular to the page. The movable electron collector could be swung about the same axis as the target, so that it could receive the electrons coming from the target in any direction included in the plane of the diagram. Figure 41–3 shows the results obtained for two target orientations both before and after the target was heat-treated. The wavelength of the electrons observed experimentally agreed well with the de Broglie wavelength, which could be computed from the accelerating potential, V. Since Davisson and Germer used 75-ev electrons, they could obtain the electron velocity from the classical expression

$$E_k = Ve = \frac{mv^2}{2},$$ (41–14)

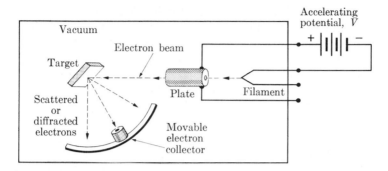

FIG. 41-2. Schematic diagram of the Davisson-Germer electron diffraction apparatus.

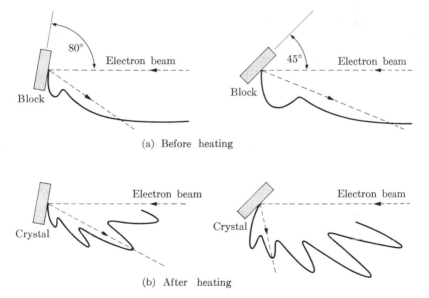

(a) Before heating

(b) After heating

FIG. 41-3. (a) Electron scattering from a block of nickel, and (b) electron diffraction from a single crystal of nickel.

and substitute into the de Broglie relation, obtaining

$$\lambda = \frac{h}{mv} = \frac{h}{\sqrt{2Vem}}. \tag{41-15}$$

The de Broglie hypothesis was further verified in Germany when Estermann and Stern diffracted helium atoms from a lithium fluoride crystal, and in the United States when Johnson diffracted hydrogen from the same kind of crystal. G. P. Thomson, son of J. J. Thomson, obtained excellent powder diffraction patterns by sending a collimated beam of electrons through very thin sheets of various metals. Davisson and Germer, using electrons instead of x-rays, repeated Compton's experiment of diffracting soft x-rays from a man-made grating at grazing incidence.

With the complete verification of the de Broglie hypothesis, we have arrived at a point where our atomic world has strange aspects. Compton scattering showed that waves have particle aspects and the de Broglie hypothesis shows that particles have wave characteristics. Another result of all these experiments is contained in Bohr's principle of *complementarity*, which states that in no single experiment does a photon show both wave and particle properties, nor does a particle simultaneously show both particle and wave properties. In Section 41–6 we will attempt to resolve this duality more seriously than Eddington did when he humorously suggested that the primordial entity is really a "wavicle."

41–5 Electron optics. The resolving power of good microscopes is ultimately limited by the light itself. No microscope can reveal details which are small compared with the wavelength of the light being used. Thus microscopes can resolve better detail with blue light than they can with red. Since radar employs radiation with a wavelength of about 0.1 meter, it would be impossible to read this book by radar.

On the other hand, electrons which have been accelerated through a potential difference of only 100 volts have a de Broglie wavelength of about one angstrom. With higher potentials, the wavelength is even less. Electric and magnetic fields can be shaped to focus electrons. These fields are called "lenses" and their "power" can be specified in terms of their focal lengths. Every aspect of visual optics has its electronic counterpart, and electron microscopes are now routine scientific tools. Just as visual optics is divided into geometrical and physical optics, electron optics involves electron ballistics and the waves associated with electrons.

Electron optics plays an important part in television, where an electronic image is made visible by fluorescent material on the face of the tube.

A simple experiment can be done with most ordinary cathode-ray oscillographs. If the sweep and vertical amplifiers are turned down so that the spot can be examined closely, the focus control permits the spot to be made very small. This spot is a reduced image of a tiny hole through which the cathode-ray electrons passed at the back of the tube in the electron gun. By manipulating the focus control and sometimes the intensity control too, it is usually possible to form a large circular image with a slightly ragged edge. This is an enlarged electron image of the same hole, and the instrument is now a crude electron microscope. (Never leave a small bright spot fixed on the screen longer than necessary lest the fluorescent screen become "burned.")

41–6 Waves and particles. We regretfully passed over the mathematical details of Maxwell's wave equation, and our treatment of the Schroedinger wave equation must also be brief. For purposes of comparison we reproduce both of their time-dependent equations in vector notation. Maxwell's electrodynamic wave equation, in terms of the electric field, is

$$\nabla^2 E - \frac{\epsilon\mu}{c^2} \frac{\partial^2 E}{\partial t^2} = 0, \tag{41–16}$$

and Schroedinger's particle wave equation is

$$\frac{h^2}{8\pi^2 m} \nabla^2 \Psi + \frac{hi}{2\pi} \frac{\partial \Psi}{\partial t} - E_p \Psi = 0. \tag{41–17}$$

It would be pointless for us to define all the terms of these equations, but the symbol ∇^2 introduces the space coordinates as second-order partial derivatives. The complexity of these equations does not hide the fact that they are similar in form. Rather than solve either equation, we shall continue to use the optical analogy on which the Schroedinger equation is based to convey something of the nature of wave-mechanical solutions of problems.

The "conflict" between Newton and Huygens over whether light consists of particles or waves was debated over the years, and as the evidence has accumulated it now appears necessary to synthesize these two views. From the wave theory, one can compute the diffraction pattern which results from passing light through a slit or a series of slits. The calculated pattern is confirmed both visually and photographically. But if the pattern is detected by scintillation or Geiger counters, which are sensitive to individual photons, it is found that the computed diffraction pattern is verified only *statistically*. In Fig. 41–4, the computed diffraction pattern of a single slit is shown as a smooth curve. The step curve represents what might be obtained by counting the number of photons as a function of position. It thus appears that in a detailed experiment where the apparatus is sensitive to individual events, wave theory tells us what should happen *on the average* but fails to tell what will happen to individual photons. We have met this situation before in the kinetic theory of gases. If we compute the number of gas particles in a leaky automobile tire as a function of time, we get a smooth curve. But if we could actually count the number of particles, we would surely find that the particles leaked out as whole particles and that the curve would be a step function of time. Thus the wave theory of light and the kinetic theory of gases do not say what individual photons or molecules will do. These theories predict in a statistical way what the individual entities will *probably* do. In this synthesis of the particle and wave theories of light suggested by Einstein (there are other

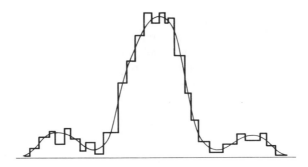

FIG. 41–4. Statistical nature of optical diffraction pattern.

syntheses), we assign the reality—the mass-energy—to particle photons. These photons do not obey classical Newtonian mechanics, but instead obey a set of statistical generalizations which can be derived from Maxwell's equation. We assume that light waves are not "real." They do not occur in nature but only in the minds of Huygens, Maxwell, and all of us who make wave calculations. Maxwell's wave theory is an elegant and beautiful invention of the human mind which enables man to describe the behavior of photons in a very satisfactory way. When the waves of Maxwell are regarded as a description of physical reality rather than reality itself, the fact that photons have properties not described by Maxwell is no longer disturbing.

The following is another very clever and useful trick of the human mind. A hollow rubber ball has its center of gravity at its center. Discussion of the motion of the ball can be greatly facilitated by regarding the ball as a point mass with all its mass at the center of gravity. The center of gravity has no objective reality, and if someone cuts the ball open, points to the center, and says, "Ha, you see there is no mass there," we calmly reply that the center of gravity makes a poor description of what is at the center of the ball, but that it continues to be useful in describing the motion of the ball. No one description of the ball can ever completely represent what the reality of the ball is.

The mistake of those who said that Maxwell showed that light *is* a wave phenomenon is a verbal mistake we make every day. We point to a map and say this *is* the United States. What we mean is that this diagram on a piece of paper is a scale representation of many of the physical and political features of the United States. We know that the real United States cannot be folded, rolled up, or burned. We know that the states are not different in color, only a few square inches in area, and completely flat. The map is a clever, useful, elegant invention of the human mind. You may learn more about some aspects of the United States in one hour of map study than you could learn in a lifetime of looking at the *real* United States. We do not scoff at maps because they are unreal, we admire them as beautiful descriptions.

The discovery that matter has dual properties—wave and particle—could have set off a century of conflict over the *true* nature of matter. Instead, the dual nature of matter reinforced the Einstein synthesis we have described. Max Born proposed that matter, like light, *is* composed of real particles having mass-energy. These particles move in a manner which is described by Schroedinger's wave equation. The waves are *not real* but they provide a better description of particle behavior than newtonian mechanics does.

41–7 Wave mechanics.

The statement that Schroedinger's equation describes particle behavior better than newtonian mechanics does requires justification. Finding analytical solutions of Schroedinger's equation is so difficult that only a few problems have been solved exactly. But these few solutions are in excellent agreement with experiment, and many other approximate solutions have indicated that the method is correct even though it is difficult. Modern digital computers are providing numerical solutions of great accuracy at an increasing rate.

One of the problems completely solved by the Schroedinger method is that of atomic hydrogen. The electronic structure of hydrogen, according to the Schroedinger method, includes everything that comes from the Bohr analysis and a lot more besides. The wave-mechanical solution of the hydrogen atom correctly answers every question about the behavior of this atom *for which there is an experimental check*. It covers the behavior in electric and magnetic fields. It describes the intensity and breadth of the spectral lines as well as their wavelengths.

The Bohr theory of energy levels is confirmed, but the concept of circular or elliptical electron orbits is gone. As in the wave theory of photons, the definite electron locations of Bohr's pseudoclassical analysis is replaced by probability distributions. These probability distributions are computed as interference patterns between matter waves. The various quantum numbers come out of the theory logically and systematically.

In principle, the Schroedinger equation should apply to such gross problems in dynamics as the motion of baseballs or the motions of the solar system—and it does. Because of their large masses, such bodies have tremendous energies compared with the energies of atomic electrons. For such gross bodies, the quantum numbers are fantastically large and the energy levels are so close together that they cannot be detected separately. By using the Bohr correspondence principle, which shows that for large quantum numbers the quantum solution of a problem tends to the classical solution, it can be shown that the wave equation is general. Where wave mechanics and classical mechanics agree, classical mechanics is *much* easier to use. Where the two disagree, wave mechanics must be used in spite of its difficulties.

How these two methods of mechanics tend toward each other is worthy of a closer look. Let us consider a simple harmonic oscillator consisting of a mass suspended by a vertical spring. If we shrink the apparatus to atomic size or increase the value of Planck's constant many orders of magnitude, then the two methods of analysis will show the comparison we are interested in discussing.

In elementary mechanics we discussed the linear oscillator and computed the period, velocity, acceleration, and the position of the moving mass as a function of time. We learned that if the oscillator is given a certain energy, the motion proceeds with a certain amplitude.

The wave-mechanical treatment does not give the path of a linear oscillator any more than it does the orbit of the electron in a hydrogen atom. What we get is a distribution of the probable locations of the mass. Since we can get this probability from the classical treatment too, it is this distribution that we will compare.

The classical expression for the frequency of oscillation, f, of a body suspended by a spring is the familiar equation $f = (1/2\pi)\sqrt{k/m}$, where k is the spring constant and m is the mass of the body. The wave-mechanical treatment yields the same frequency. But whereas the classical treatment permits the oscillator to have any energy and consequently any amplitude, the wave-mechanical treatment quantizes the energy. The oscillator may have only those energies given by

$$E_n = (n + \tfrac{1}{2})hf, \tag{41--18}$$

where n is an integer. If the oscillator were of atomic size or if h were not a tiny number, these energy steps would be observable. It would be particularly striking that the oscillator would be impossible to stop ($E = hf/2$ even for $n = 0$).

If, for the sake of comparison, we choose to give the classical solution only those energies permitted by the quantum solution, we get a set of amplitudes $a_0, a_1, a_2, \ldots, a_5$, where the subscripts are the quantum numbers. These amplitudes are shown as dashed vertical lines in Fig. 41--5. The curves which are drawn concave upward show the relative probability, on a classical basis, of finding the moving mass at any distance from its equilibrium position. These curves are concave upward because the mass moves through the equilibrium position with maximum velocity and spends most of its time near one end of the path or the other.

The shaded areas represent the wave-mechanical solution for the probable location of the mass for several energies. In the lowest energy state, with $n = 0$, the classical and quantum solutions violently disagree. In-

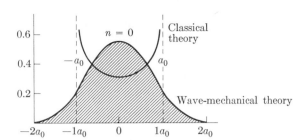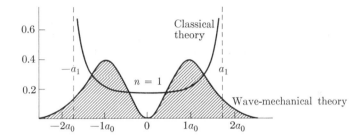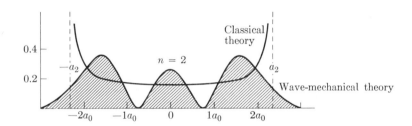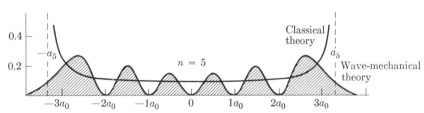

Displacement of the particle

FIG. 41-5. Each diagram shows the relative probability of finding a harmonic oscillator at various displacements both classically and wave-mechanically. Four different energies are shown, corresponding to quantum numbers $n = 0$, 1, 2, and 5. The classical amplitudes are a_2 for $n = 2$, etc. Thus $2a_0$ is twice the classical amplitude for $n = 0$. (Reprinted with permission from Blackwood, Osgood, and Ruark, *An Outline of Atomic Physics*, 3rd ed, 1955, John Wiley and Sons, Inc.)

stead of the equilibrium position being least likely, it turns out to be the most likely in the new mechanics. Another violent disagreement may be seen at the extremes of the motion. The quantum solution shows that the mass has a finite probability of *being beyond the classical amplitude.* The quantum theory says the mass may be where the classical theory says it cannot be.

As the energy becomes greater, the classical probability retains its form, but the number of peaks in the quantum solution increases. This number is always $(n + 1)$. As the number of these peaks increases, their maxima begin to resemble the classical curve. Projecting this tendency to large values of n, we see that the classical curve and the average of the quantum curve merge and finally become experimentally indistinguishable, in accord with the correspondence principle. Thus the motion of a mass at the end of a spring, as treated in most mechanics laboratories, could be analyzed on the basis of the quantum theory according to the Schroedinger equation.

41–8 The Heisenberg uncertainty principle. We have pointed out that the wave theory of light describes the motion of photons statistically but fails to specify in detail how any particular photon will move. We have seen also that the wave theory of matter describes the probable location of particles but fails to specify precise orbits like those described by Bohr. These wave theories seem to have uncertainties built into them. It is true that we used statistical methods in the kinetic theory of gases, but this was for a different reason. We assumed then that we understood the collisions between gas molecules and could discuss their individual motions if only we had infinite patience. We turned to statistical methods not because any theory forced us to, but because of the hopeless tedium of discussing individually an Avogadro's number of molecules. We may now ask, is the uncertainty or indeterminacy built into the wave theories necessary, and if it is necessary, is it a flaw of the theories or a mark of their excellence? Although the point is still not finally settled, we take the view that the uncertainty of the wave theory is an inherent property of nature.

It is a fact of great generality that the process of making a measurement alters the quantity being measured. When interviewers take a poll of public opinion, the questions they ask cannot avoid altering the opinion of the public. A perfectly accurate voltmeter, connected across a resistor, measures the potential difference across itself and the resistor. This may be significantly different from the potential difference before the meter was connected. When a thermometer is used to measure the temperature of a bath, there is exchange of heat between the thermometer and the water which alters the temperature of the bath. In each of these examples it may be possible to modify the measurement so that its disturbance is of no practical consequence. Indeed, any quantity that can be measured at all can *in principle* be measured with extreme precision, but it develops that whenever one quantity is measured with extreme precision, some other related quantity becomes less certain. A public opinion poll may be made more accurate by increasing the size of the sample. The obvious way of doing this is to have a general referendum which is sensitive to every person's opinion. But a general referendum would attract everyone's attention to the question of interest. There would be speeches and discussion. Although the results of the referendum might give perfectly the public opinion on election day, that opinion would not fairly represent what the opinion would have been had there been no referendum. Suppose, on the other hand, that instead of having a referendum which alters public opinion, the poll takers move quietly about the country. They unobtrusively get every citizen in casual conversation, they ask the question as though the answer were of no consequence, and they never announce their results. Such a poll could conceivably avoid influencing the quantity being measured. But such a poll would have to be taken over a long period of time, and no one would know when (if ever) the public actually had the opinion measured. A detailed analysis shows that every measurement, social, biological, and physical, has the characteristic that as one quantity is measured with more precision, another related quantity is known with less precision. In engineering practice this is seldom a problem since, in general, the uncertainties produced by the act of measurement are completely overshadowed by the experimental difficulties of measurement.

Let us now consider how Heisenberg developed a principle involving the uncertainties of measured quantities. He had no concern for experimental difficulties. He imagined himself equipped with perfect apparatus and infinite skill in its use, because his concern was the theoretical difficulty of making measurements.

Consider the precise measurement of frequency. In order that any wave have a unique frequency, that wave must last for an infinite time. One note from an organ or one dot of code from a radio transmitter must involve a collection of frequencies. Any variation in amplitude, as at the beginning and end of the note or dot, represents a deviation from what might otherwise be a pure sine wave. (A Fourier series analysis shows that an infinite number of different sinusoidal frequencies are required to represent accurately the initial rise and final decrease of amplitude.) In the radio example these departures from a pure sinusoidal form are called sidebands. In amplitude-modulated radio, the amplitude variations and consequent frequency variations are very complex, since they contain the speech or music being broadcast. In this case, the broadcast frequency deviates above and below the "assigned" frequency by an amount equal to the frequencies of the sounds being broadcast. This is why radio stations occupy not one frequency, but a range of frequencies in the frequency spectrum. This explains why AM radio stations are not permitted to broadcast high-fidelity material. If they broadcast audiofrequencies up to 20,000 cycles, each station would occupy a band of frequencies 40,000 cycles wide. Since the stations are assigned frequencies only 10,000 cycles apart, they would overlap and interfere with one another.

Going back to the simpler case of the organ note or the code transmission, we find that the amplitude of the waves may be regarded as constant except for the beginning and end of the wave train, but the ends constitute amplitude changes which introduce sidebands and which prevent the frequency from being unique. Only when the wave has no ends (lasts infinitely long) does it have a truly unique frequency.

If the organ note has always been sounding and always will be sounding and therefore has a unique frequency, what about the measurement of that frequency? In order to measure the frequency perfectly, we must observe the wave through all eternity. If our observation of the wave has a beginning and an end, then our observation cannot determine a unique frequency. A finite observation has sidebands even if the wave under study does not.

Frequency is measured by measuring the number of events in a known time interval. Because of the nonsinusoidal character of parts of the observed wave, there is an uncertainty of about one cycle in the number of cycles. This uncertainty is not an experimental error but is an inherent part of either the wave or our observation of it.

Suppose we measure the frequency of a wave by counting n, the number of cycles, in a time interval Δt. Since the uncertainty in our count is about ± 1, we have for the frequency

$$f = \frac{(n \pm \text{ about } 1)}{\Delta t} \tag{41–19}$$

or

$$\Delta f \approx \frac{1}{\Delta t}. \tag{41–20}$$

If the frequency is that of a radio signal, light, or other photon, then the uncertainty of its energy will be $h \, \Delta f$, so that

$$\Delta E = h \, \Delta f \approx \frac{h}{\Delta t} \tag{41–21}$$

or

$$\boxed{\Delta E \, \Delta t \approx h.} \tag{41–22}$$

This is one statement of the *Heisenberg uncertainty principle*. In words: the uncertainty of an energy times the time spent in its measurement is approximately Planck's constant.

This result is immediately applicable to matter waves and throws light on a question not considered in Bohr theory. An electron in an atom spends most of its time in its unexcited state, and since, in this state, Δt is large, ΔE is small and the energy of the electron is well determined. Although the time electrons spend in excited states is usually rather short, it is highly variable. We said in Chapter 38 that phosphorescence is due to some energy states being metastable, in which case Δt may be hours. Transitions to and from short-lived excited states and the ground state may be completed quickly and result in strong spectral lines. Transitions to and from metastable states take longer, occur less frequently, and result in weak spectral lines. This accounts for the fact that weak spectral lines are sharper than strong ones. The longer an electron remains in a particular state, the better its energy in that state is determined; and the better its energy change is determined, the more nearly unique is the frequency of the photons radiated.

A detailed analysis of any measurement has always shown inevitable indeterminacies of the form of Eq. (41–20). Another example is that which shows that the uncertainties of measurement of the momentum M_x and position x of a particle are related by the equation

$$\Delta M_x \, \Delta x \approx h. \tag{41–23}$$

Although the theoretical uncertainties we have discussed all arise from the wave aspects of photons and matter, these aspects have been thoroughly documented experimentally. Some philosophers have regarded the uncertainty principle as one of the profound truths of nature and have applied it beyond the field of physics where it originated. We hinted at this when we discussed the public-opinion poll.

We cannot here go into a philosophical discussion of causality, but we can point out that the idea that a set of physical causes uniquely determines a set of physical consequences is considerably weakened if the causes and effects cannot be precisely measured. According to classical theory, a ball thrown with a certain momentum from a certain position will, at a later time, strike the earth with a certain momentum at a certain place. Although the behavior of the ball may indeed be determined, it is hard to be sure. An insurmountable barrier prevents measurement of the initial and final conditions with certainty.

The wave mechanics of photons and material particles have the uncertainty principle built into them. Instead of saying in a determined way what particles *will* do, these theories tell only what they will *probably* do. Since experiment and the wave theories agree that photons and material particles behave statistically, the uncertainties of these theories is a mark of their excellence.

41–9 Phase and group waves. This section reviews and illustrates several of the things we have said about the wave representation of both particles and photons. There is a simple and instructive demonstration experiment on wave phenomena that can be performed with a pair of pocket combs which have slightly different tooth spacings. We have found that a set of black combs is best—one with 18 and the other with about 21 teeth to the inch. If the combs are held in front of a light surface and superimposed with their teeth parallel, light and dark regions can be observed. These bands are like acoustical "beats" and the number of bands per inch is the difference in the number of teeth in the combs, per inch. The light regions correspond to constructive interference and the dark regions to destructive interference.

As an example of wave mechanics, let the teeth of the two combs represent the *phase* waves associated with a matter particle like an electron. The light bands of constructive interference are called wave *groups* and they represent the regions in which the particle could be found. Clearly, the wave groups of these two phase waves do a poor job of specifying the position of the electron. There are several bands of constructive interference, and if the wave train were infinitely long, there would be an infinite number of places where there would be a high probability of finding the electron. By adding many more combs with different tooth spacings one behind the other, we could form an arrangement such that only one constructive region remained. This superimposing of phase waves of different frequency would finally specify the electron position with considerable precision.

Returning to the two combs, if we now slide one over the other in a direction perpendicular to the teeth, we observe that the bands move with a velocity different from that of the comb motion. Groups move faster or slower than the phase teeth and have a direction with or against the comb motion, depending on which comb is moved. It is much better to experience this than to read a description. It is possible to move both combs in such a way that the bands move slowly or not at all. This accounts for the situation in Eq. (41–8). The comb or *phase velocity can be much greater than the particle or group velocity.* Indeed, the phase velocity of a particle at rest is infinite.

If the combs are interpreted as representing the phase waves of light, then the constructive bands represent the photons where the energy is situated. Just as it takes many phase frequencies (combs) to localize a particle, so also it takes many phase frequencies to localize a group of photons. Therefore, as we stated before, the radio transmission of an isolated code "dot" requires the transmission of many frequencies.

For both photon and material particles, the theory of relativity sets a limit on the velocity of the particles, but this limit applies to the wave group that describes the particle location and not to the phase waves that mathematically characterize the group. Snell's law of refraction applies to the phase velocity and not to group velocity. The fact that the index of refraction of glass is *less* than unity for x-rays is no contradiction of relativity. The phase waves of x-rays in glass move faster than the free-space velocity of light, but the photons themselves never exceed this free-space velocity.

41–10 Matrix mechanics. Along with the development of the Schroedinger method of quantum mechanics on the basis of matter waves, Dirac also developed another formulation which uses entirely different mathematical techniques, called matrix algebra, and which is impossible to visualize. These two formulations were considered to be basically different for some years and as such they were in competition with each other. But it has since been shown that although Schroedinger and Dirac spoke in two different "languages" they were both saying the same thing. Although a motion picture and a book may seem very different, they may both tell the same story. Just as some stories lend themselves to one medium better than to another, some physical problems are better suited to one treatment than the other. The competition of these formulations has become co-operation.

41–11 Summary. In this chapter we have presented the wave properties of matter and outlined some of the characteristics of the wave mechanics based on these properties. But, equally important, we have emphasized that the dual nature of matter and the dual nature of light together lend themselves to a synthesis. Somewhat arbitrarily, we assigned physical reality to the mass-energy aspect of particles and we used the Einstein "ghost field" concept for the associated waves. We maintained that these waves are not real but are a device for determining the behavior of the real particles. These waves enable the calculation of probability functions which statistically describe particle behavior.

Having thus emphasized the similarity between material particles and photon particles, we now review their differences. Photons never carry electrical charge; material particles may or may not carry charge. (We have discussed electrons, protons, and positrons. The uncharged neutrinos and neutrons will be presented later.) Photons always move with the velocity of light, c, in free space. In other media, the velocity of photons is less than c, depending on the medium and the photon energy. The velocity of photons is always very great. Material particles never achieve the free-space velocity of light. Except for stellar bodies on the one hand and atomic particles on the other, all velocities of gross material particles are very much less than c. If a photon is stopped, its mass-energy is transferred to another body and the photon ceases to exist. It has no rest mass. If a material particle is stopped, it transfers its kinetic mass-energy to another body, but it continues to exist and retains its rest-mass energy.

PROBLEMS

41-1. What is the de Broglie wavelength of the waves associated with an electron which has been accelerated from rest through a potential difference of 100 volts?

41-2. Show that relativistically the wavelength associated with a particle having a rest mass m_0 and a velocity v is

$$\lambda = \frac{h(1 - v^2/c^2)^{1/2}}{m_0 v}.$$

41-3. Show that the de Broglie wavelength in angstroms for an electron accelerated from rest through a potential difference V in volts is (a) classically, $\lambda = 12.27/V^{1/2}$, and (b) relativistically,

$$\lambda = \frac{12.27}{V^{1/2}} \left(\frac{Ve}{2m_0 c^2} + 1 \right)^{-1/2}.$$

41-4. Show that the de Broglie wavelength for a particle of mass m moving with the most probable speed of a maxwellian distribution at temperature T is $\lambda = h/(2mkT)^{1/2}$, where k is Boltzmann's constant.

41-5. Calculate the de Broglie wavelength for a particle moving with the most probable speed of a maxwellian distribution at 20°C if the particle is (a) a hydrogen molecule, (b) a neutron.

41-6. Derive Eq. (41-13) from Eqs. (41-9) and (41-10).

41-7. At what glancing angle will a thermal neutron (refer to Problem 41-5) undergo a first-order Bragg reflection from the principal planes of KCl, which is a cubic crystal with a principal grating space of 3.14 A?

41-8. What is the de Broglie wavelength (a) for a 22-caliber rifle bullet having a mass of 1.1 gm and a speed of 3×10^4 cm/sec, and (b) for a 75-kgm (165-lbm) student ambling along at 0.5 m/sec? (c) What would have to be the grating space of a plane grating which would diffract the "particles" in parts (a) and (b) through an angle of 30° in the first order, assuming normal incidence? (d) Discuss the feasibility of such diffraction.

41-9. An alpha particle (doubly ionized helium) is ejected from the nucleus of a radium atom with 5.78 Mev of kinetic energy. (a) What is the relativistic de Broglie wavelength of this particle? (b) How does this wavelength compare with the nuclear diameter, which is about 2×10^{-14} m?

41-10. A 40-gm mass suspended from a helical spring is oscillating vertically with an amplitude of 3 cm and a period of $\pi/5$ sec. (a) Find the energy of the oscillating mass. (b) Assuming that mechanical energy can be quantized according to $E = hf$, how many quanta of energy does this mass have? (c) What is the distance between the peaks of the probability curve for locating the oscillating mass along its path? (d) Could this distance be observed?

41-11. (a) Find by actual experiment with two combs whether the group velocity of the waves is greater or less than their phase velocity when the "long-wavelength" comb is moved faster than the "short-wavelength" one. (b) Which is the greater, the group velocity or the phase velocity, (1) in a beam of white light in glass, and (2) in a beam of sound waves having different frequencies in air? (c) Except in free space, the group and the phase velocity of light are identical only for ideally monochromatic light. Is it possible to obtain such light? (Consider Doppler effect in the source of light, filters, finite slit widths of monochromators, etc.)

41-12. (a) Show from Eqs. (41-2) and (41-8) that the phase velocity of the de Broglie waves associated with a moving particle having a rest mass m_0 is given by

$$v_p = c\sqrt{1 + \left(\frac{m_0 c}{h}\lambda\right)^2}.$$

(b) According to this equation, which wavelengths will have the greater phase velocity, the long ones or the short ones? Will each exceed c? (c) Does the equation indicate that there is dispersion of de Broglie waves in free space? (d) Having the answer to part (b), go to the experiment in part (a) of Problem 41-11 and show that there is no contradiction in saying that the velocity of a particle is less than c and that the phase velocity of its associated waves is greater than c.

CHAPTER 42

NATURAL RADIOACTIVITY

42–1 Discovery of radioactivity. We now go back to the year after Roentgen discovered x-rays when, in March 1896, Becquerel announced the discovery of radioactivity. Although Roentgen rays had been discovered less than four months earlier, it was already known that x-rays came from the fluorescent walls of the discharge tube, and thus it was thought that fluorescence and phosphorescence might be responsible for them. Becquerel knew that uranium salts became luminescent when exposed to bright sunlight, and he had heard that the phosphorescent radiations from these activated salts could penetrate opaque bodies. Upon studying these effects, he found that the radiations from light-activated uranium did cast shadows of metallic objects on photographic plates which were wrapped in black paper. But the particularly *new* thing Becquerel found was that the radiations came from uranium salts whether those salts were excited by light or not. He found that uranium salts which had been protected from all known exciting radiations for months still emitted penetrating radiations without any noticeable weakening. He recognized the parallel between his discovery and the discovery of x-rays, and he found that the new radiations could discharge electrified bodies as x-rays do. He realized that these radiations were not due to fluorescence, but that the uranium metal was their source. This property of uranium, that it spontaneously emits radiation, is called *radioactivity*.

42–2 The seat of radioactivity. In showing that radioactive radiations came from uranium metal, Becquerel worked with many uranium salts and the metal itself. He used these materials crystallized, cast, and in solution. In every case it appeared that the radiations were proportional to the concentration of the uranium. It has been found that this proportionality between radiation intensity and uranium concentration continues unchanged through variations of temperature, electric and magnetic fields, pressure, and chemical composition. Since the radioactive behavior of uranium is independent of the environment of the uranium atom or its electronic structure, which changes from compound to compound, the radioactive properties of uranium were attributed to its nucleus.

42–3 Radium. Becquerel's discovery of the radioactivity of uranium immediately raised the question whether other elements are radioactive. Pierre and Marie Curie investigated a uranium ore called pitchblende which contains uranium, bismuth, barium, and lead. Upon chemical separation, the uranium showed the expected activity, and the bismuth and barium fractions also showed activity. Since neither bismuth nor barium shows activity when pure, the Curies assumed that each fraction contained a new element, one chemically like bismuth and the other chemically like barium. They called these new elements polonium and radium and set out to isolate each. The skill, enthusiasm, and patience that went into this task has been beautifully told by her daughter in Madame Curie's biography.

Radium had to be separated from barium on the basis of its slightly different physical properties by the technique of fractional crystallization. The magnitude of the task may be seen from the fact that the Curies separated about one-fifth of a gram of a radium salt from a ton of pitchblende. They could trace their progress by noting the increased activity of the samples as they became more and more concentrated. Weight for weight, polonium is about 10 billion times more active than uranium, and radium is 20 million times more active than uranium.

42–4 The radiations. Although the penetrating radiations from radioactive substances were immediately likened to x-rays, Rutherford found, in 1897, that the radiations were of more than one kind, some rays being more penetrating than others. He called the less penetrating rays alpha (α) rays and the more penetrating ones beta (β) rays. In 1899, several investigators found that the beta component of the radiation could be deflected by a magnetic field, and that it had about the same charge-to-mass ratio (e/m) as the cathode corpuscles which had been discovered by Thomson just two years earlier, in 1897. We now know that beta rays* are electrons.

Madame Curie deduced from their absorption properties that alpha rays were material particles and, in 1903, Rutherford succeeded in deflecting alpha particles with a magnetic field, where the deflection direction showed them to be positive. By causing alpha particles to discharge an electrometer and by simultaneously counting their scintillations, Rutherford determined that the alpha-particle charge was about twice the electronic charge. Since the charge was larger than that of electrons and the magnetic deflection much less, it was obvious that alpha particles are much more massive than electrons.

---

* During the 1930's it was discovered that positrons are emitted by some radioactive isotopes, and the term "beta ray" or "beta particle" has now come to mean an electron or a positron of nuclear origin. Their symbols, β^- and β^+, respectively, are used only in connection with nuclear reactions. Because of earlier custom, "beta ray" still usually means an electron when the sign of the charge is not stated.

Conclusive proof that the alpha particles are helium nuclei was given by Rutherford and Royds in 1909. Their apparatus is shown in Fig. 42–1. The radioactive sample was placed inside a glass tube G which was so thin that alpha particles could pass through it. The tube G was inside an evacuated tube T which had a narrow end E with electrodes sealed into it. By raising the level of the mercury, any gas in T could be compressed into E. An electric discharge through this gas produced its spectrum and permitted the positive identification of the gas. With the tube G empty no helium was found, but with radioactive material in G, helium was found in the apparatus after two days. The alpha particles were trapped in the tube T, where they picked up electrons and became helium atoms.

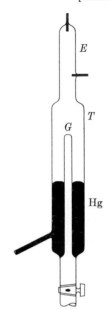

FIG. 42–1. Apparatus of Rutherford and Royds for identifying alpha particles.

The identification of alpha particles as helium nuclei makes it clear that radioactivity is a drastic process in which elements change in kind. If radium emits helium, it can no longer be radium. The *parent* or original substance becomes a new element called the *daughter* or product substance. Although the element lead cannot be changed into gold (the alchemists' dream of centuries before), the experiment by Rutherford and Royds leaves no doubt that one element may be transmuted into another element.

In 1900, Villard found a third kind of radiation from radioactive materials which is even more penetrating than either alpha or beta rays. These rays, called gamma (γ) rays, are not influenced by magnetic fields and therefore carry no charge. Their energy can be measured by measuring the energy of the photoelectrons they produce. They can be diffracted by crystals. Their wavelengths are found to range from about 0.5 to 0.005 A. Crystal diffraction of these very short wavelengths is difficult and special techniques must be used, but we know that these rays are photons whose energy range overlaps that of x-rays and extends to several Mev. The term "gamma ray" is restricted to short-wavelength radiation from the nucleus, and "x-ray" is used only for similar radiation from the extranuclear part of the atom.

Most pure radioactive substances emit gamma rays accompanied by either alpha or beta rays, but since samples are seldom pure, one usually finds all three types of rays present. The three types of radiation can be

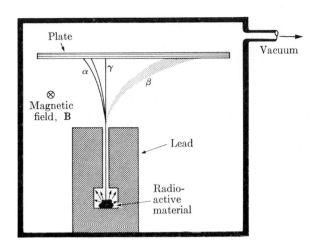

FIG. 42–2. Magnetic separation of the radiations from radioactive materials.

characterized by the famous diagram of Fig. 42–2, which shows how the rays are deflected by a magnetic field.

These radiations from the nucleus are absorbed as they pass through matter. Gamma rays are absorbed exponentially. Both the linear and mass absorption equations for x-radiation, Eqs. (40–10) and (40–14) respectively, are valid for gamma rays, although the absorption coefficients for gamma rays are usually much less than they are for x-rays. The absorption of beta rays is more complex. It is approximately exponential up to a certain thickness of the absorber and then absorption becomes complete. The exponential relation is entirely fortuitous in this case. As beta particles are stopped in an absorber some of their energy is converted into bremsstrahlung. The absorption coefficients for beta rays are less well defined than for x- and gamma rays, but in one respect the absorption of beta rays is simpler than photon absorption. Because the mass absorption coefficient is nearly the same for all absorbing materials, the mass per unit area, m_a, required to produce a given beta absorption is independent of the material. The value of m_a for an absorber of either alpha or beta rays is often called the "thickness" of the material. The absorption of alpha particles will be discussed in Chapter 43.

42–5 Radiation detectors. Before considering the laws of radioactive disintegration, we digress to summarize and extend our descriptions of the techniques used to observe the radiations from radioactive elements.

We have discussed fluorescence, which is sensitive to radiations with energies equal to or greater than those of visible photons. Fluorescence

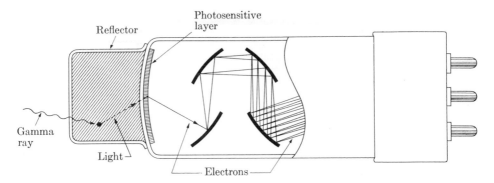

FIG. 42–3. Photomultiplier tube.

gives visible evidence of the radiation, but the radiation must be very intense.

We have discussed ionization chambers, which are used to measure the ionization currents radiation produces. This technique is quite sensitive in the same energy range as fluorescence, and it is quantitative.

We have discussed the use of photographic materials, which are sensitive to visible radiations and to those of higher energies. Since the effect is cumulative, the method is very sensitive if long exposures can be employed. The method is quantitative if the density of the image is carefully measured.

We now turn to *scintillation*, which is really fluorescence examined closely. Because it can detect individual particles, this technique is extremely sensitive. If the scintillations are to be visually observed the particles of radiation must have high energy; that is, they must be capable of producing a large number of visible photons when they strike the fluorescent material. However, very sensitive scintillation techniques developed during the past few years have eliminated the necessity for visual observation. Instead, the light is allowed to fall on a very sensitive photoelectric cell called a *photomultiplier tube* (Fig. 42–3), in which a single photoelectron is accelerated until it can knock "secondary" electrons from an anode. This anode is the cathode relative to another anode, where more secondary electrons are liberated. This process continues through several stages until the burst of electrons becomes great enough to constitute a disturbance that can be amplified by an electronic amplifier. Pulses from this amplifier are then electronically counted. By this technique, individual radiation particles of rather low energy can be counted.

This scintillation technique is a two-step affair. The original radiation produces photons by fluorescence and these photons are then counted by photomultiplier tubes. The technique is particularly convenient when the radiation source is in solution with the fluorescent material. The fluorescent material is near the source, and if the solution is transparent to the photons, the photomultiplier tubes can be outside the solution. The extremely sensitive photomultiplier tube must, of course, be protected from visible light. This protection will also exclude ultraviolet light, which might produce spurious scintillations if allowed to reach the scintillation material.

42-6 Geiger-Mueller counters. The Geiger-Mueller or G-M counter tube, Fig. 42-4, evolved from the ionization chamber. The tube, usually made of glass, is filled with a gas and contains two electrodes. One of these is a metal cylinder and the other a thin wire mounted coaxially with the cylinder. In a counter circuit, the d-c potential applied between the wire and cylinder is often 1000 volts or more.

In the Geiger tube, a measurable current is initiated by the ions formed by the radiation under study. The ions are swept out of the region between the cylinder and the wire by an electric field strong enough to prevent the recombination of the ions and weak enough so that the dielectric strength of the gas is not exceeded. If this electric field is made very intense, the tube can be brought to a critical condition, where the introduction of a single charge will initiate a discharge. Electrons from the original (primary) ion pair produce more ions by collision. In the intense electric field near the central electrode, the secondary ions produce still more ions, in a geometric progression. Thus a single electron may initiate a cascade of a million or more electrons. When this avalanche strikes the central electrode, the drop in potential is easily detected electronically. Meanwhile, the relatively massive positive ions migrate toward the outer cylinder, where they pick up electrons and become excited atoms or molecules. If these atoms emit photons which can liberate photoelectrons from the outer cylinder, these photoelectrons may initiate other avalanches which tend to keep the tube in continuous discharge. But if the gas of the tube is an organic gas which dissociates easily, the excitation energy may cause the molecule to come apart rather than to emit a photon. In the first case, the electric discharge must be stopped by reducing the potential across the tube to nearly zero. This available electrode potential difference does become very small each time a pulse of current resulting from ionization

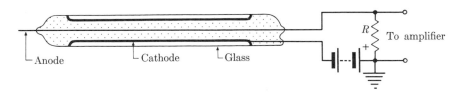

FIG. 42-4. Geiger-Mueller counter tube.

flows around the circuit containing the high resistance R shown in the figure. In the second case, the life of the tube is reduced as the chemical composition of the organic gas is changed. Thus in either type of Geiger counter the discharge must be "quenched" between counts. Since a finite time is required for quenching and for starting the voltage rise across the electrodes, there is always a dead time between possible counts. This is of the order of 10^{-4} sec. Geiger counters readily respond to low-intensity radiations which have enough energy to enter their sensitive region. If, however, the intensity of the radiation is too high, a Geiger counter "freezes" or "jams" because the interval between successive primary ionizing events is less than the dead time.

Modern G-M counters can have no open window, since the gas is not air and the pressure is below atmospheric. High-energy particles can penetrate into the sensitive region within the metal cylinder from any direction, but lower energy particles enter more readily through the ends. Since particles of very low energy are stopped by the glass, the absorption of the glass is sometimes reduced by making an extremely thin window at one end. These windows are almost invisible and are very fragile. Their "thickness" is usually given in terms of their mass per unit area. Values of the order of 3 mgm/cm^2 are common. Such windows are so thin that they easily transmit short-wavelength ultraviolet light. These photons have enough energy to "trigger" the tube by causing photoemission from the electrodes, or they even ionize the gas in a few cases. The flame of an ordinary match furnishes ample ultraviolet light to operate a thin-window, clear-glass tube.

42–7 Cloud and bubble chambers. Certainly the most dramatic radiation detectors are cloud and bubble chambers. The principle of their operation is basically the same, although cloud chambers contain a supercooled vapor, while a bubble chamber contains a superheated liquid.

A supercooled vapor is most likely to condense on some discontinuity, and once precipitation begins it continues readily by condensing onto droplets already formed. Supercooled water vapor may remain in the vapor phase and not condense, but in dusty and smoky regions there are discontinuities on which condensation can begin and fog or smog form readily.

The cloud chamber illustrates the fact that charged particles are discontinuities on which precipitation can be initiated. The schematic diagram of a Wilson cloud chamber is shown in Fig. 42–5. It consists of a gastight chamber having a large glass window, so that its volume can be illuminated and the events within seen or photographed. One wall of the chamber is a movable piston. The chamber contains a saturated vapor from an excess amount of some liquid, usually a mixture of alcohol and

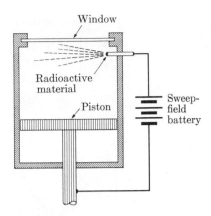

Fɪɢ. 42–5. A simple expansion cloud chamber.

water. If the volume of the chamber is suddenly increased by moving the piston, the adiabatic expansion causes cooling which renders the vapor supersaturated, unstable, and likely to condense. If there are ions within the chamber, precipitation occurs preferentially on them.

Since we have no interest in stray ions that may happen to be about, the cloud chamber is provided with electrodes which permit maintaining a weak electric "sweep field."

If a high-energy particle enters the chamber just before the piston expansion makes the chamber sensitive, the ions will not have had time to be swept away (the sweep field is sometimes cut off just before the expansion), and the droplets that form make the location of the ions visible. The droplets tend to move because of gravity and gas turbulence, and since they also tend to evaporate as a new equilibrium condition is established, the "picture" soon spoils. If the piston is then returned to its original position for about a minute the chamber can again be expanded.

If a high-energy electron passes through this chamber the picture formed (Fig. 42–6) is a thin, beady line or "track" which shows very beautifully where the electron went. The droplet on each ion in its wake becomes visible. If a magnetic field is established in the space of the cloud chamber, the velocities of the electrons can be measured. Cloud-chamber photographs, such as Figs. 39–5 and 39–6 which accompanied the discussion of pair production, permit the measurement of the radius of curvature of the path of a charged particle, and since m, e, and B are known, the velocity can be computed from Eq. (24–4).

We first considered alpha particles in the Rutherford scattering experiment. Figure 42–7 shows that these doubly ionized helium nuclei produce very dense cloud-chamber tracks that resemble the vapor trails of high-flying airplanes. Alpha trails are easily distinguished from those made by

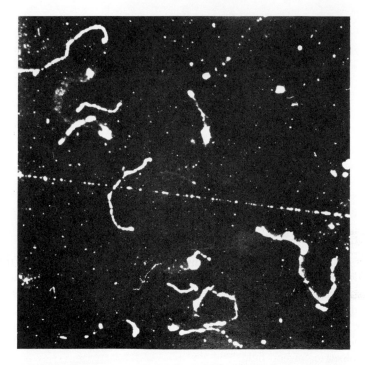

FIG. 42–6. Beady track produced by a high-energy electron. Broader tracks are due to low-energy photoelectrons. (Courtesy of C. T. R. Wilson, and the Royal Society, London)

FIG. 42–7. Alpha-particle tracks. Note that there are two groups, which differ in range. (Courtesy P. M. S. Blackett and D. S. Lees, Imperial College of Science and Technology, London)

electrons. The former are more dense, primarily because alpha particles carry twice as much charge as do electrons. But since alpha particles are much more massive than electrons, they are very difficult to deviate in a magnetic field. It turns out, however, that alpha-particle energies are a function of the lengths of their tracks, or ranges. This energy-measuring stick has been calibrated in the following ingenious way. If the relative proportions of vapor and gas in the chamber are known, the average ionization energy of the chamber atoms can be computed. If there is a momentary lapse between the chamber expansion and the photographic exposure, the track becomes diffuse and it is then possible to count the individual drops. Determining the number of ions produced by the alpha particle permits calculating the energy loss along its path.

Alpha particles produce an average of about 50,000 ion pairs per centimeter in air at atmospheric pressure, while beta particles produce only about 50 ion pairs per centimeter. Since both kinds of particles lose energy by giving up about 34 ev per ion pair produced, alpha tracks are short and thick, and beta tracks are long and thin. If the two kinds of particles have the same initial energies, each produces about the same total number of ions. The slower the particle moves, the more ions it produces per unit length of path. (This will be discussed in Section 43–1.) Thus tracks are more dense near their ends, and the range-energy relationship is not linear. Only charged particles produce cloud-chamber tracks, although photoelectrons ejected by photons do leave short, feathery trails which give some idea of the photon path. To the practiced eye, cloud-chamber tracks due to different particles are as dissimilar as the tracks different animals leave in the snow.

Cloud-chamber studies have been exceedingly revealing. These chambers are much more than radiation detectors. They almost enable us to see atomic processes, and sometimes the analysis of a single picture has led to a basic discovery.

Extremely high-energy particles, such as are found in cosmic rays or are produced by the most modern nuclear accelerators, produce cloud-chamber tracks that are so long the chamber shows only a small fraction of the event. Such events can be studied better with bubble chambers, where the instrument is filled with a dense liquid instead of a gas.

Consider for a moment a bottle of "pop." Before it is opened, the carbon dioxide over the drink and that dissolved in it are in equilibrium. When the bottle is opened, the pressure is reduced and the solution of gas in the drink is supersaturated. Bubbling results from the unstable condition and we have effervescence. That the bubbles form most readily on discontinuities is best demonstrated by pouring the drink into a glass and noting that often there are streams of bubbles rising from some speck inside the glass. These bubbles are formed because the same discontinuity

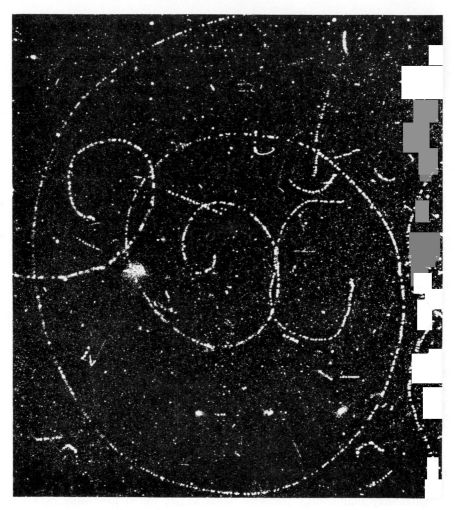

FIG. 42–8. A 4-Mev electron slowing down in a liquid hydrogen bubble cham
ber traversed by a magnetic field. (Courtesy of Radiation Laboratory, University of California)

is a bubble nucleus over and over again. Adding sugar, salt, cracked ice,
or ice cream provides many discontinuities, so that most of the carbon
dioxide effervesces almost at once. Similarly, when ions are produced in a
bubble chamber they act as nuclei for the formation of small bubbles.

In actual bubble chambers, a liquid such as isopentane or liquid hydrogen
is maintained at a temperature above its normal boiling point but is pre-
vented from boiling by the application of pressure. The chamber is made
sensitive by suddenly reducing the pressure. Since boiling starts preferen-

tially on the ions in the liquid, the bubbles formed along the path of an ionizing particle are visible, much as are the droplets in a cloud chamber. Such a trail of bubbles is shown in Fig. 42–8. A bubble track can be observed only during the brief period (a few milliseconds) before general boiling begins throughout the liquid.

42–8 Energies of the radiations. Nuclear spectra. One gram of radium gives off nearly two gram-calories of heat per second. This may not seem like much energy, since the oxidation of a gram of carbon to carbon dioxide liberates about 8000 gram-calories. But whereas the carbon might be oxidized in one second and be consumed, the gram of radium will continue to liberate two calories per second for years and the rate will only be reduced to one calorie per second in 1600 years. If we allow infinite time for the gram of radium to disintegrate, more than 10^{17} calories would be liberated, and this calculation does not take into account the energy liberated by the daughter products of the radium. If radium were cheap and plentiful, it would be a useful source of energy.

Since the energies of alpha, beta, and gamma rays from radioactive substances can be measured, we speak of the "spectra" of various radioactive substances. The nucleus is not nearly so well understood as the atom's electronic structure. There is no nice theory of the nucleus to compare with the Bohr analysis of the hydrogen atom. But the evidence from nuclear spectroscopy indicates that nuclei do have energy levels. Thus Pa^{231} (protactinium) emits alpha particles with nine distinct energies and also thirteen different gamma-ray wavelengths.

The existence of energy levels makes it clear that nuclear phenomena are quantum-mechanical. The spectra of beta particles, however, presented an interesting problem. Although a given substance emits beta particles with a definite upper limit of energy, a continuous range of energies below that limit is found. The reason for an upper limit is evident from Fig. 42–9(a), which shows the energy-level diagram for a typical beta-ray emitter. In this case, a nucleus having an atomic number Z ejects an electron and thus changes to an excited state of a new nucleus, $Z + 1$. This then goes to the stable state by emitting two gamma-ray photons in cascade. The single energy transition of the electron accounts for the maximum beta-particle energy, but fails to account for the continuous range of smaller beta energies found when a large number of atoms of a substance is observed. It appeared, at first, that the law of conservation of energy was violated. Of all the generalizations of physics, conservation of energy is the most basic. We would like to think that this principle holds exactly and without exception.

The difficulty was resolved by supposing that there is a new particle, called a *neutrino* (ν), which carries away the energy difference (refer to

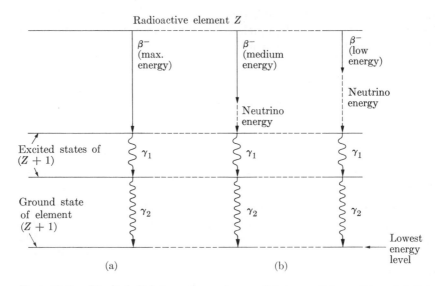

Radioactive element Z

β^-
(max.
energy)

β^-
(medium
energy)

β^-
(low
energy)

Neutrino
energy

Neutrino
energy

Excited states of
$(Z + 1)$

γ_1 γ_1 γ_1

Ground state
of element
$(Z + 1)$

γ_2 γ_2 γ_2

Lowest
energy
level

(a)   (b)

Fig. 42–9. Typical disintegration scheme of beta-particle emitter: (a) beta particle with maximum energy, and (b) two cases of beta-neutrino emission.

Fig. 42–9b). Conservation of energy and of momentum required that this new particle have much less mass than the electron and that it be uncharged. This particle, proposed by Pauli in 1931, could carry away the energy difference undetected because of its small mass and zero charge. In addition to preserving the exactness of conservation of energy, the neutrino fitted into other theoretical considerations in the theory of beta decay developed by Fermi in 1934. The existence of this new particle was generally accepted long before it was experimentally observed in 1956 by Reines and Cowan.

Although nuclear energy states, unlike electronic energy states, cannot be computed theoretically, we apply the electronic language to the nucleus and speak of excited states, ground states, etc.

42–9 Law of radioactive disintegration. Every radioactive disintegration involves the emission of either an electron or a helium nucleus from the nucleus of the disintegrating atom. This leaves the original nucleus changed, so that the number of atoms of the original kind is reduced. Furthermore, scintillation observations show that these disintegrations occur in a random manner which can only be discussed statistically. The idea of treating the disintegrations statistically may have been originally a matter of convenience, but we have seen that wave mechanics makes the statistical analysis of such quantum phenomena a necessity.

The discovery of radioactivity antedated Planck's quantum idea, Einstein's quantum interpretation of the photoelectric effect, Bohr theory, and wave mechanics. In Chapter 41 we saw that whereas the kinetic theory of gases is statistical as a matter of convenience, wave mechanics is statistical from theoretical necessity. The unpredictability of individual radioactive disintegrations was really the *first* experimental indication that the mechanistic determinism in the physical sciences of the 19th century was due for revision. Thus radioactivity had two shocking aspects: it showed that the elements were not inviolate but could change from one kind to another, and that radioactivity was not subject to causal analysis. This latter aspect was assimilated as an integral and useful part of physics, particularly after the advent of wave mechanics in 1925.

To present the statistical description of radioactivity, let us begin at time $t = 0$ with N_0 radioactive atoms. We let λ represent the probability that one of these atoms will disintegrate in unit time. If there are N atoms at any time t later, then the probable number that will disintegrate in unit time is λN. Since each disintegration reduces the number N, we can also represent the probable number of disintegrations per unit time or activity as $-dN/dt$. Therefore we have

$$\boxed{\frac{-dN}{dt} = \lambda N.}$$

(42–1)

The quantity dN must be an integer, but if it is a relatively small integer compared with N, then N will vary in an approximately continuous way and we may treat dN as a mathematical differential. Upon integrating and using the initial condition, we have for the *number of atoms of the original kind still present* at time t

$$\boxed{N = N_0 e^{-\lambda t}.}$$

(42–2)

Each nuclear disintegration makes an equal contribution to the beam of radiation from a radioactive material. Thus the intensity I of the beam is directly proportional to $-dN/dt$. If we call I_0 the intensity when $t = 0$, then Eqs. (42–1) and (42–2) lead to

$$I = I_0 e^{-\lambda t}.$$

(42–3)

If we plot $\ln N$ or $\ln I$ against t, both Eqs. (42–2) and (42–3) become straight lines whose slopes are $-\lambda$. This sometimes is a convenient way of obtaining λ from experimental data. These equations are identical in form to that which describes the intensity of monochromatic x-rays as a function of absorber thickness. They show that the number of atoms and the intensity of radiation require infinite time to disappear completely. (It must be remembered that differential calculus breaks down and dN becomes a step function when N is small.)

Although we cannot get a meaningful answer to the question "How long will a given radioactive sample last?," we can compute how long it will be before the sample is reduced to some fraction of its initial amount. Just as we computed the thickness of absorber that will reduce the intensity of an x-ray beam to one-half its initial value, we can compute the *half-life* $t_{1/2}$ or T, of a radioactive sample. If we let $N = N_0/2$ in Eq. (42–2), then $t = T$ and we have

$$T = \frac{1}{\lambda}\ln 2 = \frac{0.693}{\lambda}.$$

(42–4)

Before we can use any of these equations, the *disintegration (decay) constant* λ must be known. It depends on the radioactive material and varies widely from material to material, but this constant is completely independent of the environment, whether it is chemical combination, or pressure, or temperature, or whatever.

If λ is very small, the half-life is very large (1620 years for radium) and the reduction in N during an experiment may be neglected. By measuring the disintegration rate dN/dt (with scintillation, for example) from a sample of N atoms, λ can be computed from Eq. (42–1).

If λ is large enough so that the decay of the sample during an experiment cannot be neglected, then the reduction in intensity may be observed as a function of time and fitted to Eq. (42–3). A simple way to do this is to measure the time it takes for the intensity to be reduced to one-half (T) and solve for λ by means of Eq. (42–4).

If λ cannot be measured by either of the two methods described then the decay constant must be determined from radioactive equilibrium, which will be discussed in Section 42–13.

We can make another calculation which is conceptually important to the statistical view we are taking. Let us find the *mean* or *average life, $\bar{t}$,* of a radioactive atom. Some atoms survive much longer than others, so what we seek is the numerical average of the ages of the atoms as the number of atoms decreases from N_0 to 0. The expression for determining this can be found by considering the radioactive decay curve of Fig. 42–10. Let N be the number of atoms that have survived for a time t, and $N - dN$ those still existing at the time $t + dt$; then dN is the number of atoms that disintegrated during the time dt. Therefore the combined ages of the atoms in this group at the time of disintegration is $t\,dN$. The average life of an atom will be the sum of the combined ages of all the age groups of atoms

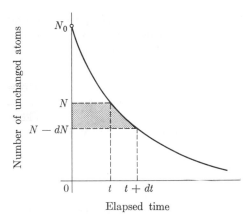

FIG. 42–10. Typical radioactive decay curve.

from N_0 to 0 divided by the total number of atoms. Stated in mathematical terms, this is

$$\bar{t} = \frac{\displaystyle\int_{N_0}^{0} t \, dN}{\displaystyle\int_{N_0}^{0} dN}. \tag{42-5}$$

For integrating, we need t as a function of N. Substituting for t from Eq. (42–2) and noting that the denominator in Eq. (42–5) equals $-N_0$, we have

$$\bar{t} = \frac{1}{\lambda} \frac{\displaystyle\int_{N_0}^{0} [-\ln (N/N_0)] \, dN}{-N_0} = \frac{1}{\lambda} \int_{N_0}^{0} \left(\ln \frac{N}{N_0}\right) d\left(\frac{N}{N_0}\right). \tag{42-6}$$

We integrate by parts, obtaining

$$\bar{t} = \frac{1}{\lambda} \left[\frac{N}{N_0} \left(\ln \frac{N}{N_0}\right) - \frac{N}{N_0} \right]_{N_0}^{0}. \tag{42-7}$$

This is indeterminate at the upper limit but, by using l'Hospital's rule,* we find

$$\boxed{\bar{t} = \frac{1}{\lambda}.} \tag{42-8}$$

Thus $\bar{t} = 1/\lambda$ is the mean life or life expectancy of an individual radioactive atom. Since λ is the probability that an atom will decay in unit

---

* The expression within brackets must be rearranged before applying this rule. Note that the quantity $[(x \ln x) - x]$ can be written $[(\ln x - 1)/x^{-1}]$.

time, it follows at once that $1/\lambda = \bar{l}$ is the probable time of disintegration per atom. This simpler argument is the one we used to get the mean free path of a molecule in the kinetic theory of gases (Eq. 18–26).

———————

EXAMPLE. (a) If a radioactive material initially contains 3.00 mgm of U^{234}, how much will it contain after 150,000 yr? (b) What will be its U^{234} activity at the end of that time? ($T = 2.50 \times 10^5$ y, $\lambda = 8.80 \times 10^{-14}$ sec^{-1}.)

(a) From Eq. (42–2), we have

$$N = N_0 e^{-\lambda t}.$$

We obtain the N's from Avogadro's number and the mass number (strictly isotopic mass). It will be convenient to express λ in terms of T. Let m be the mass of uranium remaining; then, substituting in the equation, we obtain

$$m \times \frac{6.03 \times 10^{23} \text{ atoms}}{234 \text{ gm}} = 3.00 \times 10^{-3} \text{ gm} \times \frac{6.03 \times 10^{23} \text{ atoms}}{234 \text{ gm}}$$

$$\times \exp\left[-\frac{0.693}{2.5 \times 10^5 \text{ y}} \times 1.5 \times 10^5 \text{ y}\right]$$

or

$$m = 3 \times 10^{-3} \times e^{-0.416} \text{ gm.}$$

Therefore

$$\ln \frac{3 \times 10^{-3}}{m} = 0.416$$

or, if we choose to use logarithms to the base 10,

$$\log \frac{3 \times 10^{-3}}{m} = \frac{0.416}{2.30} = 0.181;$$

then

$$m = \frac{3 \times 10^{-3}}{1.52} = 1.98 \times 10^{-3} \text{ gm.}$$

(b) From Eq. (42–1), we have

$$\frac{dN}{dt} = \lambda N$$

$$= \frac{8.80 \times 10^{-14}}{1 \text{ sec}} \times 1.98 \times 10^{-3} \text{ gm} \times \frac{6.03 \times 10^{23} \text{ atoms}}{234 \text{ gm}}$$

$$= 4.50 \times 10^5 \text{ dis/sec.}$$

42–10 Radioactive series. We have stated that when a radioactive disintegration occurs with the emission of an alpha or beta particle, the original atom, called the parent, changes into something else, called the daughter. In 1903 Rutherford and Soddy proposed that the nature of the daughter could be inferred from the nature of the parent and the particle emitted. Since we have already established the concepts of the atomic nucleus, atomic number, and atomic mass numbers, we can state the Rutherford-Soddy rules for balancing nuclear reaction equations in modern terms. They are: (1) *the total electric charge (atomic number) or algebraic sum of the charges before the disintegration must equal the total electric charge after the disintegration,* and (2) *the sum of the mass numbers of the initial particles must equal the sum of the mass numbers of the final particles.* Thus if uranium with atomic number 92 emits an alpha particle with atomic number 2, the daughter must have an atomic number 90. This element is thorium. Similarly, since uranium has a mass number of 238 and the alpha particle a mass number of 4, the thorium must have a mass number of 234. Both rules are summarized in the equation

$$_{92}U^{238} \rightarrow {}_{90}Th^{234} + {}_{2}He^{4}.$$

If the parent is a beta emitter, the atomic number of the daughter must be one higher than that of the parent, since the beta particle is a negative electron. Furthermore, the electron is so light that the atomic mass numbers of the parent and daughter are the same. For example, Th^{234}, daughter of U^{238}, is radioactive and is a beta emitter. The daughter of Th^{234} must have the atomic number 91 (protactinium, Pa) and the mass number 234, as shown in the equation

$$_{90}Th^{234} \rightarrow {}_{91}Pa^{234} + {}_{-1}e^{0}.$$

The Rutherford-Soddy rules came before the establishment of the physical atomic weights or the discovery of isotopes by Thomson and Aston described in Chapter 24. These rules predicted daughter atoms with atomic weights quite different from the then-accepted chemical atomic weights. Rutherford and Soddy had more faith in their rules (based on conservation of mass and charge) than they had in the chemical atomic weights. Their rules implied that the same chemical element could exist in forms having different masses and they predicted the discovery of isotopes, which we have already discussed.

In Tables 42–1, 42–2, and 42–3 space limitations preclude listing more than the principal energy of the type of particle ejected and the energy range of the gamma-ray spectrum. A branch-point element is marked with an asterisk. The percentage proportion of each of the two daughter products of branch-point atoms is given in parentheses. Nuclear isomers are connected by a dotted line. The abbreviations under half-life are: s, second; m, minute; d, day; and y, year.

TABLE 42–1

THE URANIUM SERIES

Radioactive species	Nuclide	Type of disintegration	Half-life T	Disintegration constant λ, sec^{-1}	Principal particle energy, Mev
Uranium I (U I)	$_{92}U^{238}$	α	4.50×10^9 y	4.88×10^{-18}	α, 4.18; γ, 0.05
Uranium X$_1$ (UX$_1$)	$_{90}Th^{234}$	β	24.1 d	3.33×10^{-7}	β, 0.19; γ, 0.03–0.09
Uranium X$_2$ (UX$_2$)	$_{91}Pa^{234}$	β	1.18 m	9.77×10^{-3}	β, 2.31; γ, 1.0
Uranium Z (UZ)	$_{91}Pa^{234}$	β	6.7 h	2.88×10^{-5}	β, 0.5; γ, 0.10–0.57
Uranium II (U II)	$_{92}U^{234}$	α	2.50×10^5 y	8.80×10^{-14}	α, 4.76; γ, 0.02–0.12
Ionium (Io)	$_{90}Th^{230}$	α	8.0×10^4 y	2.75×10^{-13}	α, 4.69; γ, 0.07–0.18
Radium (Ra)	$_{88}Ra^{226}$	α	1620 y	1.36×10^{-11}	α, 4.78; γ, 0.19–0.66
Ra emanation (Rn)	$_{86}Em^{222}$	α	3.82 d	2.10×10^{-6}	α, 5.47; γ, 0.51
*Radium A (RaA)	$_{84}Po^{218}$	α, β	3.05 m	3.78×10^{-3}	α, 6.00
Radium B (RaB) (99+)	$_{82}Pb^{214}$	β	26.8 m	4.31×10^{-4}	β, 0.65; γ, 0.05–0.35
Astatine-218 (0.02)	$_{85}At^{218}$	α	1.5–2.0 s	0.4	α, 6.63
*Radium C (RaC)	$_{83}Bi^{214}$	α, β	19.7 m	5.86×10^{-4}	α, 5.44; β, 1.65; γ, 0.61–2.43
Radium C' (RaC') (99+)	$_{84}Po^{214}$	α	1.64×10^{-4} s	4.23×10^3	α, 7.68
Radium C'' (RaC'') (0.04)	$_{81}Tl^{210}$	β	1.32 m	8.75×10^{-4}	β, 1.8
Radium D (RaD)	$_{82}Pb^{210}$	β	22 y	1.00×10^{-9}	β, 0.02; γ, 0.05
*Radium E (RaE)	$_{83}Bi^{210}$	α, β	5.0 d	1.60×10^{-6}	α, 4.8; β, 1.17
Radium F (RaF) (99+)	$_{84}Po^{210}$	α	138.3 d	5.80×10^{-8}	α, 5.30; γ, 0.80
Thallium-206 (2×10^{-4})	$_{81}Tl^{206}$	β	4.2 m	2.75×10^{-3}	β, 1.51
Radium G (RaG)	$_{82}Pb^{206}$	Stable			

TABLE 42-2

THE ACTINIUM SERIES

Radioactive species	Nuclide	Type of disintegration	Half-life T	Disintegration constant λ, sec^{-1}	Principal particle energy, Mev
Actinouranium (AcU)	$_{92}U^{235}$	α	7.10×10^8 y	3.09×10^{-17}	α, 4.39; γ, 0.18–0.37
Uranium Y (UY)	$_{90}Th^{231}$	β	24.6 h	7.82×10^{-6}	β, 0.30; γ, 0.02–0.06
Protoactinium (Pa)	$_{91}Pa^{231}$	α	3.43×10^4 y	6.40×10^{-13}	α, 5.01; γ, 0.03–0.33
*Actinium (Ac)	$_{89}Ac^{227}$	α, β	22.0 y	1.00×10^{-9}	α, 4.94; γ, 0.05
Radioactinium (RdAc) (1.2)	$_{90}Th^{227}$	α	18.6 d	4.31×10^{-7}	α, 5.97; γ, 0.05–0.34
Actinium K (AcK) (98.8)	$_{87}Fr^{223}$	β	21 m	5.50×10^{-4}	β, 1.15; γ, 0.05–0.31
Actinium X (AcX)	$_{88}Ra^{223}$	α	11.2 d	7.16×10^{-7}	α, 5.72; γ, 0.14–0.34
Ac emanation (An)	$_{86}Em^{219}$	α	3.92 s	0.177	α, 6.82; γ, 0.20–0.59
*Actinium A (AcA)	$_{84}Po^{215}$	α, β	1.83×10^{-3} s	3.79×10^2	α, 7.37
Actinium B (AcB) (99+)	$_{82}Pb^{211}$	β	36.1 m	3.20×10^{-4}	β, 1.4; γ, 0.07–0.83
Astatine-215 (5 × 10⁻⁴)	$_{85}At^{215}$	α	10^{-4} s	7×10^3	α, 8.00
*Actinium C (AcC)	$_{83}Bi^{211}$	α, β	2.16 m	5.25×10^{-3}	α, 6.62; γ, 0.35
Actinium C′ (AcC′) (0.3)	$_{84}Po^{211}$	α	0.52 s	1.33	α, 7.43; γ, 0.56–0.88
Actinium C″ (AcC″) (99+)	$_{81}Tl^{207}$	β	4.79 m	2.41×10^{-3}	β, 1.47; γ, 0.87
Actinium D (AcD)	$_{82}Pb^{207}$	Stable			

TABLE 42-3

THE THORIUM SERIES

Radioactive species	Nuclide	Type of disintegration	Half-life T	Disintegration constant λ, sec^{-1}	Principal particle energy, Mev
Thorium (Th)	$_{90}$Th^{232}	α	1.39×10^{10} y	1.58×10^{-18}	α, 3.98; γ, 0.06
Mesothorium 1 (MsTh 1)	$_{88}$Ra^{228}	β	6.7 y	3.28×10^{-9}	β, 0.01
Mesothorium 2 (MsTh 2)	$_{89}$Ac^{228}	β	6.13 h	3.14×10^{-5}	β, 1.11; γ, 0.06–1.59
Radiothorium (RdTh)	$_{90}$Th^{228}	α	1.90 y	1.16×10^{-8}	α, 5.42; γ, 0.08–0.21
Thorium X (ThX)	$_{88}$Ra^{224}	α	3.64 d	2.20×10^{-6}	α, 5.68; γ, 0.24
Th emanation (Tn)	$_{86}$Em^{220}	α	54.5 s	1.27×10^{-2}	α, 6.28; γ, 0.54
Thorium A (ThA)	$_{84}$Po^{216}	α	0.16 s	4.33	α, 6.77
Thorium B (ThB)	$_{82}$Pb^{212}	β	10.6 h	1.82×10^{-5}	β, 0.35; γ, 0.14–0.25
*Thorium C (ThC)	$_{83}$Bi^{212}	α, β	47 m	2.46×10^{-4}	α, 6.09; β, 2.25 γ, 0.72–2.2
Thorium C′ (ThC′) (66.3)	$_{84}$Po^{212}	α	3.0×10^{-7} s	2.31×10^{6}	α, 8.78
Thorium C″ (ThC″) (33.7)	$_{81}$Tl^{208}	β	2.1 m	3.73×10^{-3}	β, 1.80; γ, 0.86–2.62
Thorium D (ThD)	$_{82}$Pb^{208}	Stable			

We now know that there are three series of naturally radioactive elements which form a sequence of parent-daughter relationships: the uranium, actinium, and thorium series.* They are shown graphically in Figs. 42–11, 42–12, and 42–13 respectively, and also are tabulated in Tables 42–1, 42–2, and 42–3. Each series ends with a stable isotope of lead. Note that some elements can emit either an alpha or a beta particle. Although no one atom can go both ways, some atoms can go either of two ways and cause *branches* in the series. No matter which way the parent goes, the daughter goes the other way, so that even though the series branches they always come together again. The two types of disintegration of a given branch-point element always occur in the same proportion. This proportion is independent of the amount of the element.

The time required for the nuclear transitions which produce gamma rays is usually of the order of 10^{-12} sec. However, some delayed transitions with half-lives as long as several years have been observed. Because of such delayed transitions, some nuclear species have the same mass number, the same atomic number, and the same decay scheme, but have different half-lives. Such species are called *nuclear isomers* and they are said to undergo *isomeric transitions*, IT. The nuclei of UX_2 or $_{91}Pa^{234}$ and UZ or $_{91}Pa^{234}$ are isomers.

The tables of the radioactive series are redundant in the naming of the various isotopes. The names at the left antedate our full understanding of isotopes; they are names used in early discussion of the series. Even the more compact modern notation, like $_{92}U^{238}$, is redundant, since element 92 must be uranium.

The distribution of the natural radioactive materials is nonuniform over the surface of the earth. It has been estimated that, on the average over the earth's crust, each square mile has, within one foot of the surface, 8 tons of uranium and 12 tons of thorium.

To complete the account of radioactive series, we now consider one that has been obtained only from an artificially produced radioactive material. The first element in this series is Pu^{241} and the stable end product is Tl^{205}. This series is called the neptunium or $4n + 1$ series because the longest-lived element in it is Np^{237}, which has a half-life of 2.2×10^6 years. If this element existed when the earth was formed about 4.4×10^9 years ago, the amount now remaining must be infinitesimal, because 2000 half-lives of Np^{237} have elapsed since that time.

----

* The uranium series is also called the $4n + 2$ series because the mass numbers of the atoms in it are given by this expression. The quantity n is an integer which decreases by unity in going from any radioelement to the next one below it. The actinium series can be represented by $4n + 3$, and that of thorium by $4n$. The value of n is not the same for the first element in each series

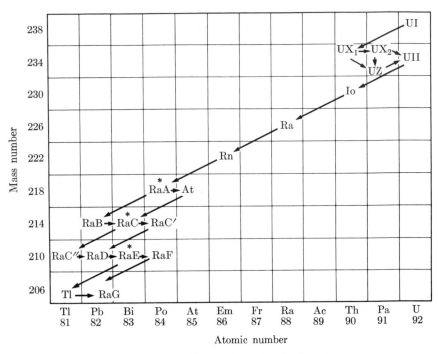

FIG. 42–11. The uranium $(4n + 2)$ series.

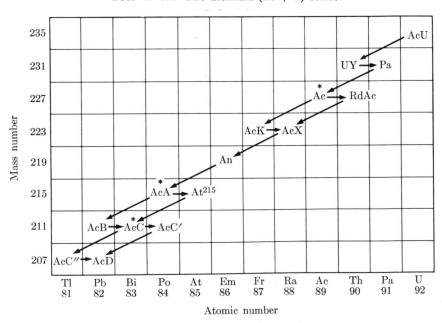

FIG. 42–12. The actinium $(4n + 3)$ series.

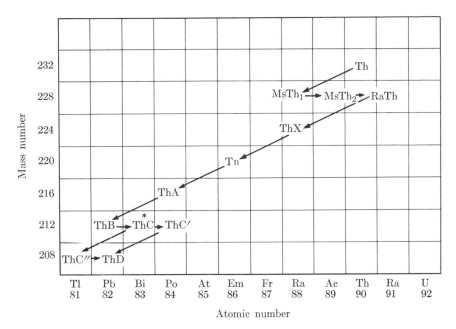

FIG. 42–13. The thorium $(4n)$ series.

42–11 Radioactive growth and decay. These series of radioisotopes present interesting problems in relative abundances. Instead of considering a whole series, let us consider what happens to the abundance of substance B if A decays to B and B decays to C.

Let us call the number of A atoms at any instant N_1 and the initial number N_0. We can call the number of B atoms N_2 and assume that the initial number of B atoms is zero.

Every time an A atom disintegrates, it increases the number of B atoms. But every B disintegration reduces the number of B atoms. From Eq. (42–1) we have

$$\text{Number entering the } B \text{ category} = \frac{-dN}{dt} = \lambda_1 N_1, \qquad (42\text{--}9)$$

and

$$\text{Number leaving the } B \text{ category} = \lambda_2 N_2, \qquad (42\text{--}10)$$

where λ_1 is the decay constant for element A and λ_2 that for element B.

The net change in N_2 is the difference between Eqs. (42–9) and (42–10), or

$$\frac{dN_2}{dt} \text{ (net)} = \lambda_1 N_1 - \lambda_2 N_2. \qquad (42\text{--}11)$$

From Eq. (42–2) we can write $N_1 = N_0 e^{-\lambda_1 t}$ and use this to eliminate N_1 from Eq. (42–11). This gives

$$\frac{dN_2}{dt} = \lambda_1 N_0 e^{-\lambda_1 t} - \lambda_2 N_2. \tag{42–12}$$

If we transpose $\lambda_2 N_2$ and multiply by the integrating factor $e^{\lambda_2 t} \, dt$, we have

$$e^{\lambda_2 t} \, dN_2 + \lambda_2 N_2 e^{\lambda_2 t} \, dt = \lambda_1 N_0 e^{(\lambda_2 - \lambda_1) t} \, dt. \tag{42–13}$$

This may be integrated at once, to yield

$$N_2 e^{\lambda_2 t} = \frac{\lambda_1}{\lambda_2 - \lambda_1} N_0 e^{(\lambda_2 - \lambda_1) t} + C. \tag{42–14}$$

Since we are assuming that $N_2 = 0$ when $t = 0$, we have

$$0 = \frac{\lambda_1 N_0}{\lambda_2 - \lambda_1} + C. \tag{42–15}$$

Eliminating C from Eq. (42–14), we obtain

$$N_2 e^{\lambda_2 t} = \frac{N_0 \lambda_1}{\lambda_2 - \lambda_1} (e^{(\lambda_2 - \lambda_1) t} - 1), \tag{42–16}$$

and finally

$$N_2 = \frac{N_0 \lambda_1}{\lambda_2 - \lambda_1} (e^{-\lambda_1 t} - e^{-\lambda_2 t}). \tag{42–17}$$

The decay of A and the growth and decay of B are shown in Fig. 42–14.

We have considered the mathematics of but one link in the chain of events that constitute a radioactive series. The complete solution requires the simultaneous solution of as many differential equations as there are elements in the series. The general solution gives the number of daughter atoms as a function of time under the assumptions that at time zero there were no daughter atoms, and that there were a known number of atoms of the parent. These equations are called the Bateman equations, after the man who derived them.

In our minds, at least, we can build an analog computer to solve the problem. Suppose we have a series of tanks which can drain water from one to another in succession (Fig. 42–15). Assume that the nozzles have openings proportional to λ and the tanks are so shaped that the velocity of flow is proportional to the amount of water in the tank. If the first tank

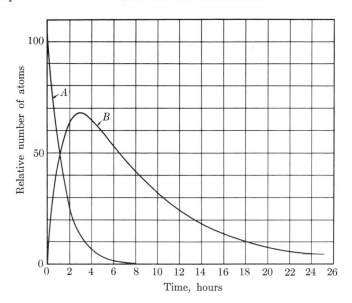

FIG. 42–14.   Decay of element A ($T = 1$ hr) and growth and decay of element B ($T = 5$ hr).

is filled and the water is released at time zero, then the water in each tank is the same function of time as the concentration of radioactive atoms in a radioactive series. Since each radioactive series ends on a stable isotope of lead, the bottom tank should have no outlet.

42–12 The age of the earth. Another way of avoiding a detailed treatment of the involved Bateman equations is to take advantage of the fact that in any radioactive series the decay constants vary widely. This permits many reasonable approximations. The U^{238} series, for example, begins with uranium whose half-life is 4.5 billion years and whose decay constant is less than 1/1000 that of any other element in the series until we come to Pb^{206}. This lead is stable, has an infinite half-life, and has a decay constant of zero. This means that after a billion years or so the only elements present in any appreciable concentration will be uranium and lead. In terms of the water analogy, the intervening tanks are practically empty and serve only as a pipe through which the water in the first tank drains into the last. Thus it becomes reasonable to apply our Eq. (42–17) not only to the first and second elements of the series but also to the first and last. Since λ_2 becomes the decay constant of lead, which is zero, we have

$$N_{\mathrm{Pb}} = N_{0\mathrm{U}}(1 - e^{-\lambda_{\mathrm{U}}t}). \qquad (42\text{--}18)$$

U^{238} ore always contains Pb^{206} because this lead is the end element of the

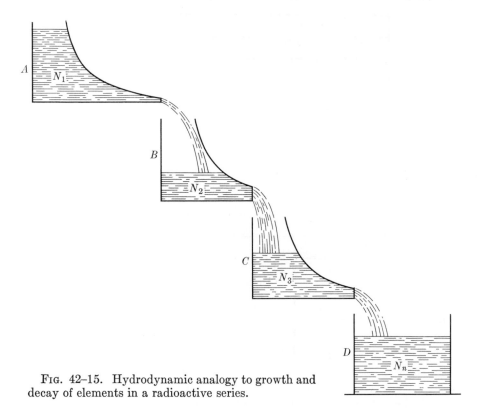

FIG. 42–15. Hydrodynamic analogy to growth and decay of elements in a radioactive series.

uranium radioactive series. It is reasonable to assume that this is the only reason lead is present, since there is no other compelling reason why uranium and lead should be found together. It then follows that the present number of lead atoms plus the present number of uranium atoms must equal the number of uranium atoms originally present, or

$$N_{Pb} + N_U = N_{0U}. \tag{42–19}$$

The present concentrations of Pb^{206} and U^{238} can be measured experimentally and Eqs. (42–18) and (42–19) can be solved simultaneously. Eliminating the unknown original uranium concentration, we can solve for t:

$$t = \frac{1}{\lambda_U} \ln \left(\frac{N_{Pb} + N_U}{N_U} \right). \tag{42–20}$$

This t is the time that has passed since the earth solidified and the original pocket of uranium was sealed in the rock. There have been many assumptions in our argument, but they are justified by the fact that Eq. (42–20) has been applied to many ore samples from different parts of the earth and the results have consistently shown its age to be about four billion years. Since radioactive processes are independent of conditions of temperature and pressure, pockets of radioactive material constitute reliable clocks that have been running throughout geological history.

42–13 Radioactive equilibrium. Another useful approximation in discussing the radioactive series is the concept of *radioactive* or *secular equilibrium*. We have seen that decay constants vary widely, and it frequently happens that our observations of a particular parent-daughter relationship occupy a period of time very small compared with the half-life of the parent substance. In this case we can neglect the fact that the number of parent atoms is decreasing exponentially, and we can assume that parents decay to daughters at a constant rate. Under this assumption, the number of daughter atoms begins to grow linearly. But if the daughter is unstable, with a short half-life, the daughter disintegrates at a significant rate. The more daughter atoms there are, the more daughters disintegrate, until the production and disintegration of daughter atoms becomes equal.

If the parent is nearly stable compared with the daughter, then $\lambda_2 \gg \lambda_1$ and Eq. (42–17) becomes approximately

$$N_2 = \frac{N_0 \lambda_1}{\lambda_2} (1 - e^{-\lambda_2 t}). \qquad (42\text{–}21)$$

After an appreciable time, this further reduces to

$$N_2 \lambda_2 = N_0 \lambda_1. \qquad (42\text{–}22)$$

If, instead of considering just one parent-daughter relationship, we treat a whole radioactive series, then there will be a whole series of differential equations like Eq. (42–11). If we wait until equilibrium is established in any such series which begins with an element with a long half-life, the time dependency disappears. All the (dN/dt)'s approach zero and we can write

$$\boxed{N_1 \lambda_1 = N_2 \lambda_2 = N \lambda = \text{etc.*}} \qquad (42\text{–}23)$$

Even if the parent substance cannot be regarded as strictly constant,

---

* Note that the N's in Eq. (42–23) refer to different kinds of atoms and so their isotopic masses will *not* divide out of the equation as they did in the example at the end of Section 42–9.

Eq. (42–23) may hold very closely once equilibrium is established. In this case each N in Eq. (42–23) decreases slowly and exponentially according to the small decay constant of the long-lived parent substance.

In terms of our water analog, if some tank leaks so slowly that the water level will not change noticeably while we watch it, then we can regard its leakage rate as constant. That tank will begin to fill the one below it. Presently the second tank will leak to a third, etc. Once equilibrium is established, the level in each tank will become constant at a level determined by its nozzle size. Tanks with large nozzles (λ's) will contain few water molecules (N's). The tank levels will not now be time-dependent.

Furthermore, if we leave the system running for a long time, so that the level in the original tank is noticeably decreased, then we will find the level in all the succeeding tanks decreased in the same proportion.

It must be appreciated, however, that the extent to which equilibrium is achieved depends on the relations among the half-lives and on the time since all the atoms were of the original kind. The age of the earth is about one U^{238} half-life, which is much greater than any half-lives of uranium daughters except Pb^{206}. Thus for the past three billion years there has been very precise equilibrium between U^{238} and most of its daughters. The age of the earth can be computed only because Pb^{206} has an infinite half-life ($\lambda_{Pb} = 0$) and is *never* in equilibrium with uranium.

At the other extreme, equilibrium is very nearly established in a few seconds between such pairs as $_{83}Bi^{214}$ and $_{84}Po^{214}$. The bismuth half-life is 19.7 min., while that of the polonium is 1.64×10^{-4} sec. Equilibrium between these two permits the evaluation of the very short polonium half-life. The bismuth decay constant can be found by methods already described in Section 42–9. If the relative concentrations of bismuth and polonium can be measured after equilibrium has been established, then the very large polonium decay constant can be found from the equilibrium equation, Eq. (42–23).

42–14 Secondary radiations. Extensive study of the radiations from disintegrating nuclei have revealed two additional processes which result in the emission of electromagnetic radiation.

In some cases the nucleus will absorb one of the orbital electrons of the atom. Since this probability is greatest for the adjacent K-shell electron, the process is often called *K-electron capture*. When such electron capture occurs, the product atom will have an atomic number which is one less than that of the original nucleus. The remaining orbital electrons rearrange themselves to correspond to the structure of this new atom. X-rays characteristic of the product atom are emitted during the formation of the stable state of the new atomic system. Orbital electron capture is shown schematically in one part of Fig. 42–16.

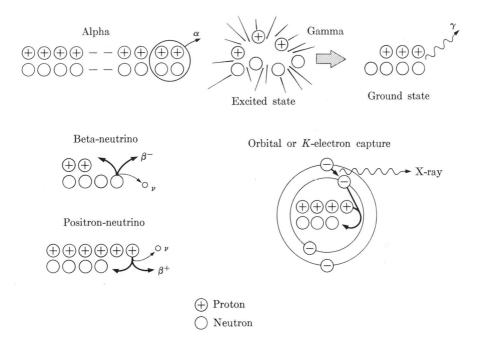

Alpha

Gamma

Excited state

Ground state

Beta-neutrino

Orbital or K-electron capture

X-ray

Positron-neutrino

⊕ Proton
◯ Neutron

FIG. 42–16. Mechanisms of radiation in radioactivity.

The emission of a charged particle from a parent nucleus often leaves the daughter or product nucleus in an excited state. The latter usually goes to the ground state by emitting one or more gamma photons. In some elements, however, the transition energy is given to an orbital electron by direct interaction with the nucleus. This process is called *internal conversion*, IC. It causes a photoelectron to be ejected from a shell with a kinetic energy equal to the difference between the nuclear transition energy and the binding energy of the emitted electron. Thus internal conversion electrons give a line spectrum of beta particles. Note that these beta particles come from the extranuclear structure. Those from the nucleus always have a continuous energy distribution up to some maximum value. X-rays characteristic of the daughter element from which an electron was ejected are emitted when this element returns to the normal state. These x-rays sometimes also eject electrons from the outer levels in their own atoms. This particular type of self-ionization is called the *Auger effect*, and the associated low-energy photoelectrons are referred to as Auger electrons.

The data obtained from the study of internal conversion show that the gamma rays in radioactive decay are often emitted *after* particle disintegration. Therefore they come from the product nucleus instead of the parent nucleus. This was represented in Fig. 42–9. Since the half-life of the parent element determines the rate of formation of the daughter element, and since gamma rays are emitted as the product "settles down," the gamma decay rate in this case follows the decay of the parent. This is the reason for a confusion in terminology. For example, when RaB, which has a half-life of 26.8 min, disintegrates to RaC, the associated gamma activity also decays with a half-life of 26.8 min. Thus it has become customary to call the radiation gamma rays from RaB even though they actually come from RaC.

42–15 Radiation hazards. All high-energy rays are hazardous to living tissue. They have enough energy to dissociate the complicated molecules of living tissue and to kill cells. We saw in Section 42–6 how the instability of organic molecules is utilized to quench Geiger counters. Thus high-energy radiation is able to convert the molecules of living structures into alien forms, or produce "burns."

Beta particles are not particularly hazardous because they are charged and therefore are not very penetrating. Clothing and skin provide adequate shielding for our vital organs.

Alpha particles are still less penetrating and on this basis are less dangerous than beta particles, although the specific ionization of the former greatly exceeds that of other radiations. There is a gaseous alpha-particle emitter in each one of the three natural radioactive series. Each of these gases is an isotope of the element having the atomic number 86. This element is usually called emanation (sometimes radon), and the gases are Em^{219} (actinon), Em^{220} (thoron), and Em^{222} (radon). Emanation is chemically inert. These gases are liberated whenever radioactive ore is dug or crushed. Since they are inert, no gas mask can separate them from the air chemically. Those who work with radioactive ores must necessarily breathe these gases unless they are flushed away by very active ventilation.

In the lungs, these gases are very destructive, since there they are literally within a vital organ. The maximum permissible safe concentration of radon in the atmosphere is about $10^{-15}\%$ by volume. It is said that every miner who has worked in the Joachimstal uranium mines in Czechoslovakia for more than ten years has died of lung cancer. It may be that Pierre and Marie Curie were very fortunate that they had to perform their separation of radium from uranium ore in a dilapidated shed. The then-unwanted ventilation blew the radon away.

Because beams of different radiations cause very different biological damage even when the body absorbs the same amount of energy from each type, it is necessary to define certain units in addition to the roentgen and the rad which were discussed in Section 40–13. The absorbed dose of any ionizing radiation is the amount of energy imparted to matter by ionizing particles per unit mass of irradiated material at the place of interest. This leads to defining the *relative biological effectiveness*, RBE, of an ionizing radiation as the ratio of the absorbed dose in rads of x-rays of about 200 kev of energy which produces a specific biologic effect, to the absorbed dose in rads of the ionizing radiation which produces the same effect. A few RBE factors are listed in Table 42–4.

TABLE 42–4

Radiation	RBE
X-ray, gamma ray, beta ray	1
Thermal neutrons	2–5
Fast neutrons	10
Alpha particles and high-energy ions of O, N, etc.	10–20

From the values listed we see that if the absorption in body tissue of 1 rad from a 200-kev x-ray beam produces a particular injury, then the absorption of only 0.1 rad from a beam of fast neutrons will produce the same injury. The unit of biological dose is the *roentgen equivalent man*, rem. The biological dose in rems is equal to the absorbed dose in rads times the RBE factor. The *millirem*, mrem, is a thousandth of a rem. The variations in body sensitivity to radiation are evident from the recommended maximum permissible doses. Some of these are: appendages of the body, 1500 mrem per week; and the lens of the eye, the gonads, and the blood-forming organs, each 100 mrem per week.

In general, the most hazardous radiations are the penetrating radiations. These include x-rays and gamma rays, together with neutral particles and the extremely high-energy particles produced by cosmic rays, which are penetrating despite their charge.

Not only are these penetrating radiations the ones that are destructively hazardous to vital organs, they are also the kind used purposefully when cancerous tissues are to be killed.

42–16 The "radium radiations" in medicine. The first radioactive material used in medical treatments was radium. But radium itself is primarily an alpha emitter. It was neither radium nor its daughter radon that was effective in destroying cancerous tissue. Indeed, one must go to the fourth radioactive generation below radium before coming to a strong gamma emitter. Even when radium was administered to a patient, it was the Bi^{214} or RaC in equilibrium with the radium that was the important gamma-ray emitter.

Radium treatment required careful attention in the hospital. Radium has a half-life of 1620 years, which is certainly long compared with the duration of the treatment. In order to specify a given dose, the radiologist had to specify both the activity of the radium sample and the length of time it should be administered.

The radium daughter (radon or Em^{222}) has a much shorter half-life, 3.82 days. In administering radon to a patient, the length of time of the application is far less critical or even inconsequential. A given amount of radon will give half its dose in 3.82 days and practically all its dose in 10 days or so. Thus the amount of radon to be administered can be specified with less concern for the removal of the radioactive material.

Hospitals usually keep radium as a solution of radium chloride. Periodically, the radon accumulated over the solution is chemically separated from the other gases over the solution and sealed into small glass or gold tubes called "radon seeds." These seeds grow in gamma activity as the radon descendants Po^{218}, Pb^{214}, and Bi^{214} come to equilibrium with the radon. Maximum gamma activity is reached in about 4 hr, since these products have half-lives of 3.05, 25.8, and 19.7 min, respectively. Once equilibrium is established, the number of Bi^{214} or RaC atoms is proportional to the number of the longer-lived radon atoms that are present. When the gamma activity begins to decline, the seed can be calibrated and its future activity can be calculated from the decay constant of radon.

42–17 Units of radioactivity and dose. The procedure we have just described led to the historical unit of radioactivity, the curie. Originally, it was the activity of 1 gm of radium or the activity of the amount of radon in equilibrium with 1 gm of radium. The original definition of the curie was replaced, in 1950, by a more general one which is closely equivalent to the old definition. By international agreement, *the curie*, c, is 3.7000×10^{10} disintegrations per second.* The *millicurie*, mc, and *microcurie*, μc, are also frequently encountered. Since the definition of the curie was peculiarly associated with radium, another unit of activity was proposed for all decaying elements. It is the *rutherford*, rd, which is 10^6 dis/sec.

Medical doses are expressed in millicurie-hours. If a radon seed has reached its maximum activity and is found to have an activity of I_0 mc

---

* The value given for the number of disintegrations per second of one gram of radium had to be changed several times because of the increasing precision in the determinations of its half-life. To avoid further changes, the international curie was arbitrarily assigned a fixed value. According to current data, 1 gm of Ra^{226} undergoes 3.61×10^{10} dis/sec. This is about 2.5% less than the adopted curie.

at a time which we call zero, and if the seed is administered to a patient during the period from t_1 to t_2 (hours) later, the dose is

$$\text{dose in mc-hr} = I_0 \int_{t_1}^{t_2} e^{-\lambda t} \, dt, \qquad (42\text{--}24)$$

where λ is the radon decay constant in reciprocal hours.

There is no one conversion factor between the activity of a radioactive material and the dose rate in the surrounding medium. This is obvious from the fact that the ionization produced depends on the activity of the material and on the *kind* and the *energy* of the emitted radiation. It can be shown (Problem 42–26) that at a point P in air the *gamma-ray* dose rate due to a *point* source of radioactive material is given, approximately, by

$$I = \frac{5.3 \times 10^3 CE}{d^2}. \qquad (42\text{--}25)$$

In this expression, I is the dose rate in roentgens per hour, C is the activity of the source in curies, E is the energy of the gamma photon in Mev, and d is the distance from the source to the point P, in centimeters. If more than one photon is emitted per disintegration, the total dose rate will be the sum of the individual dose rates. Since Eq. (42–25) is a point source law, it is essentially a differential expression which must be integrated subject to boundary conditions for an actual distribution of radioactive material.

42–18 Conclusion. In this chapter we have described some of the most important properties of natural radioactivity, together with some of the uses that have been found for it. Most of what was said also applies to artificial radioactivity, which is discussed in Chapter 43. In Chapter 43 we shall also discuss the reasons why some nuclei are radioactive and others are not.

PROBLEMS

(The constants of various radioactive elements needed for solving problems can be found in Tables 42–1, 42–2, and 42–3, and in Appendix 5.)

42–1. A certain radioactive element has a half-life of 20 days. (a) How long will it take for $\frac{3}{4}$ of the atoms originally present to disintegrate? (b) How long will it take until only $\frac{1}{8}$ of the atoms originally present remain unchanged? (c) What are the disintegration constant and average life of this element?

42–2. The original activity of a certain radioactive element is I_0. (a) Plot the subsequent activity, I, as ordinate against half-life as abscissa for a period of 6 half-lives. (b) Mark the average life, $\bar{t}$, on the abscissa and estimate the activity then in terms of I_0. (c) Assuming that the daughter product of the element is stable, plot the growth of this product on the graph for part (a).

42–3. (a) How many alpha particles are emitted per second by 1 microgram of radium? (b) How many alpha particles will be emitted per second after the original microgram has disintegrated for 500 years? (Neglect the contribution of daughter products.)

42–4. What fraction of a given sample of radium emanation, radon, will disintegrate in two days?

42–5. What is the lowest value and the highest value of the integer n for (a) the uranium $4n + 2$, (b) the actinium $4n + 3$, and (c) the thorium $4n$ series?

42–6. RaC, $_{83}Bi^{214}$, is a branch point in the uranium series. Some of its atoms disintegrate by alpha emission and some by beta emission. Write the nuclear reaction equation (a) for each case, and (b) for the disintegration of each daughter product.

(c) Identify the elements resulting from the decays in part (b).

42–7. Discuss the changes in the amount of water in tank B after opening A in the hydrodynamic analog shown in Fig. 42–15. Correlate the growth and decay of a radioactive element with your discussion for the following sets of relative sizes of the nozzles: (a) A small, B large; (b) both equal; (c) A large, B small; (d) A any size, B zero (closed); and (e) both zero (closed).

42–8. How much radium-B, Pb^{214}, will be present after 1 mgm of radium-A, Po^{218}, has been disintegrating for 20 min? Assume that all of RaA decays into RaB.

42–9. How much radium emanation will be present after 1 gm of radium has disintegrated for one day?

42–10. Show from Eq. (42–17) that if there are initially N_0 radioactive atoms of the parent present, the time at which the number of radioactive daughter atoms is maximum is

$$t_{max} = \frac{\ln (\lambda_2/\lambda_1)}{\lambda_2 - \lambda_1}.$$

42–11. (a) How long after obtaining a pure sample of radium-A will the amount of radium-B be maximum? (b) How long after obtaining a pure sample of radium will the amount of radium emanation be maximum?

42–12. If a radioactive element disintegrates for a period of time equal to its average life, (a) what fraction of the original amount remains, and (b) what fraction will have disintegrated?

42–13. (a) If a piece of uranium ore contains 2 gm of U^{238} after disintegrating for a period equal to its average life, how much U^{238} did it contain originally? (b) If all the helium released during the disintegration of the original amount of uranium for one average life were collected, what would be its mass and its volume under standard conditions? (Note that substantially all the disintegrated uranium will have become stable lead in this period of time.)

42–14. Show that the slope of the curve of the logarithm to the base 10 of the activity of a radioactive substance plotted against time is equal to $-\lambda/2.30$. Start with Eq. (42–3).

42–15. A certain radioactive element is a beta-particle emitter. When the beta activity of a freshly prepared sample of this element is measured as a function of time, the following data are obtained:

Time, min	Activity, units
0	1080
20	730
40	504
70	303
100	173
130	106
160	63
190	35

(a) Plot the logarithm of the activity against time. (b) Determine the disintegration constant from the slope of the curve. (c) Find the half-life of the element.

42–16. When the activity of a mixture of radioactive elements is measured as a function of time, the following data are obtained:

Time, min	Activity, units
10	252
30	105
50	46.8
70	25.0
90	15.5
110	11.5
130	9.1
160	6.8
190	5.2
220	4.0
280	2.4

(a) Plot the logarithm of the activity against time. (b) How many radioactive elements are in the mixture? (c) Find the disintegration constant of each from the slopes of the corrected curve, and (d) the half-life of each. [*Hint:* To obtain the activity of each element from the combined curve, project the curve for the longest-lived element back to $t = 0$. The actual activity ordinates (not log activity) of this projected curve must be subtracted from those of the total activity curve to obtain the activity due solely to the other element present. The use of semilog paper will simplify plotting and solving.]

42–17. Lead-206 is found in a certain uranium ore. This indicates that the lead is of radioactive origin. What is the age of the uranium ore if it now contains 0.80 gm of Pb^{206} for each gm of U^{238}?

42–18. What is the mass of one curie of (a) U^{238}, (b) Pb^{210} (RaD), and (c) Po^{214} (RaC′)?

42–19. What is the mass and the volume under standard conditions of one curie of radium emanation (radon)?

42–20. (a) Assuming that radioactive equilibrium has been established, how many grams of radium and of radium emanation are contained in a 2-lb piece of U^{238} ore which is 40% uranium oxide, U_3O_8? (b) What are the activities of these amounts of uranium, radium, and radium emanation in millicuries and in rutherfords?

42–21. For health protection, the maximum permissible concentration of radium emanation in air for continuous exposure is 10^{-8} microcuries per milliliter of air. For this concentration, what is the radon content of 1 ml of standard air (a) in percent by mass and (b) in percent by volume?

42–22. If the piece of uranium ore in Problem 42–20 is ground to a fine powder so that the entrapped radium emanation is released, with how many cubic feet of air must this radon be mixed to reduce the concentration to the safe tolerance level of 10^{-8} microcuries per milliliter?

42–23. (a) Assuming that there are 8 tons of U^{238} and 12 tons of Th^{232} uniformly distributed in the first foot of depth under each square mile of the surface of the earth, find the combined activity of these two radioelements in microcuries in the cubic foot of soil under each square foot of surface. (b) Assuming radioactive equilibrium, find the mass of Ra^{226} in one cubic foot of soil. (c) What would be the kinds and energies of the radiations from this soil?

42–24. If either radium or radioactive strontium were swallowed, where would these elements concentrate in the body? To answer this, consider the chemical properties of the elements in

the groups or columns in the periodic table.

42–25. (a) In the medical use of radium, it is actually the combined gamma radiation from RaB and especially from RaC which irradiates the part of the body treated. However, the half-life of radium emanation is used to calculate the dose. Why? (b) After reaching its maximum gamma activity, calibration shows that a tube containing radium emanation has an activity of 2 mc. If it is placed in a tumor 24 hr later, what is the dose in millicurie-hours if it remains there (1) 2 days, (2) 4 days, and (3) forever?

42–26. A point-source radioactive element has an activity of C curies and emits one gamma-ray photon having E Mev of energy per disintegration. (a) Neglecting the rather small absorption of the air, show that the gamma-ray energy flux at d cm from the source is $3.7 \times 10^{10} CE/4\pi d^2$ Mev/(cm²/sec). (b) The linear absorption coefficient of air for gamma rays in the 0.5- to 2-Mev range is about 3.4×10^{-5}/cm. Show, to two significant figures, that the energy absorbed per cm³ of air in the region between d and $(d + 1)$ cm is $13 \times 10^5 CE/4\pi d^2$ Mev/sec, and (c) that the dose rate in r/hr at the distance d is $5.3 \times 10^3 CE/d^2$ when d is in centimeters and $5.7 CE/d^2$ when d is in feet.

42–27. What is the dose rate in mr/hr in air at a distance of 10 ft from an unshielded 50-curie point source of Co^{60}? Each cobalt atom emits a 1.1- and a 1.3-Mev gamma-ray photon per disintegration.

CHAPTER 43

NUCLEAR REACTIONS AND ARTIFICIAL RADIOACTIVITY

43–1 Protons from nitrogen. We have seen how Rutherford and his associates discovered the atomic nucleus in 1911 by analyzing the way in which alpha particles are scattered by thin metal foils. Their continued study of the interaction between alpha particles and matter led to another striking discovery in 1919. As before, Rutherford used alpha particles from a radioactive source and scintillation as the detection technique, but in this work attention was directed to the absorption of the alpha particles.

In the case of x-ray absorption, we found that the intensity of the rays penetrating an absorber depends exponentially on the thickness of the absorber, as in Eq. (40–10). This type of absorption equation applies whenever the absorption is due to a process or processes in which the incident rays are removed from a beam in one catastrophic event. We saw that for x-rays these processes could be the production of photo-electrons, Compton scattering, or pair production. As we mentioned in our discussion of the Wilson cloud chamber, the process of absorption of alpha particles is quite different. The energy of the alpha particle is usually lost by producing a very large number of low-energy ion pairs. Thus the alpha particle loses energy more or less continuously rather than in one catastrophic event. Instead of being absorbed according to an exponential law, the absorption is slight until the particles are stopped, as shown in Fig. 43–1. Alpha particles of a given energy are completely stopped by traversing a certain thickness of absorber and, for a particular kind of absorber, they have a rather definite range which is a function of their energy. Alpha particles lose more energy per unit length of path

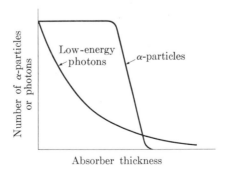

FIG. 43–1. Absorption of alpha particles and photons by matter.

near the end of their range, since they are moving more slowly and have more time to interact with atoms near which they pass. This leads us to assume that the energy loss per unit length of path is inversely proportional to the velocity, and therefore we have

$$-\frac{dE_k}{dx} = \frac{k}{v},$$

(43-1)

where k is a constant that depends on the absorbing material. Since the velocity of alpha particles is considerably less than the velocity of light, we can eliminate dE_k by substituting the derivative of the classical expression for kinetic energy, $E_k = \frac{1}{2}mv^2$. We obtain

$$-mv\frac{dv}{dx} = \frac{k}{v}.$$

(43-2)

Since the particle is stopped in a distance R, its range, we have $v = V_0$ for $x = 0$ and $v = 0$ for $x = R$, and we can separate the variables in Eq. (43-2) and write

$$\int_{V_0}^{0} -mv^2\,dv = \int_{0}^{R} k\,dx$$

(43-3)

Upon integrating, this becomes

$$\frac{mV_0^3}{3} = kR$$

or

$$\boxed{V_0^3 = k'R,}$$

(43-4)

where k' is another constant depending on the absorbing material. This is *Geiger's rule*, which is approximately correct for any charged particles in any medium if the velocities of the particles are small compared with the velocity of light.

If we use alpha particles from the same source, V_0 is then a constant, and variations in k' can be studied by observing the range in different materials. The interaction between alpha particles and the absorbing medium is electrical, and it is not surprising that k' depends both on the atomic number of the absorber and its concentration. Indeed, if the absorber is a gas, it is convenient to study alpha-particle velocities by having a chamber in which the source and detector are separated a fixed distance and the "stopping power" of the absorber is varied by changing the pressure. Since k' is proportional to the pressure P and since R here is constant, Eq. (43-4) may be written

$$V_0^3 = k''P,$$

(43-5)

where k'' depends on the kind of gas and the fixed distance, and where P is the gas pressure.

Rutherford found that his variable-pressure gas chamber worked very nicely with dried oxygen or carbon dioxide as the gas. But with dried air in the chamber, he found *more scintillations than when the chamber was evacuated.* He was using alpha particles from radium-C′, whose range in air at atmospheric pressure is about 7 cm. When Rutherford increased the pressure in the chamber until the absorption of the gas was equivalent to 19 cm of atmospheric air, the number of scintillations was about twice that observed when the chamber was evacuated. The brightness of the scintillations suggested that the long-range scintillations might be due to hydrogen nuclei (protons) rather than to alpha particles.

Here was an effect obviously related to the particular gas in the chamber. Since the scintillations appeared to be hydrogen nuclei, Rutherford first suspected that the alpha particles were knocking protons off water-vapor molecules in the air. But since the effect was greatest in nitrogen even when the nitrogen was prepared so as to be scrupulously free of any hydrogen, Rutherford decided the new particles came from the nitrogen itself.

It remained to be shown whether the scintillations that appeared to be due to protons were actually protons or were nitrogen atoms. Rutherford attempted to make this distinction by deflecting the particles in a magnetic field. The geometry of his beam was poorly defined because narrowing the beam further reduced the already small number of scintillations. He felt reasonably sure, however, that the mass of the particles was two or less—certainly not 14.

Thus Rutherford became sure that either the alpha particle was breaking a proton fragment off the nitrogen nucleus or the nitrogen was breaking a fragment off the alpha particle. He sensed that the alpha particle is particularly stable, since he regarded the nitrogen nucleus as consisting of three alpha particles and two hydrogen nuclei. He felt that the alpha particles preserved their identity and that the fragment he was observing was one or both of the hydrogens which he called "outriders of the main system of mass 12."

Although Rutherford was uncertain about the details of what he observed, he was aware that he had produced the first man-controlled nuclear rearrangement and that by similar techniques "we might expect to break down the nuclear structure of many of the lighter elements."

Rutherford could speculate about the kind of nucleus remaining after the alpha particle knocked a proton from nitrogen. The alpha particle might simply knock the proton off and continue with reduced energy according to the equation

$$_2\mathrm{He}^4 + {}_7\mathrm{N}^{14} \rightarrow {}_1\mathrm{H}^1 + {}_2\mathrm{He}^4 + {}_6\mathrm{C}^{13}, \qquad (43\text{–}6)$$

or the alpha particle could penetrate the nucleus and remain with it, as in equation

$$_2\text{He}^4 + {}_7\text{N}^{14} \rightarrow {}_9\text{F}^{18} \rightarrow {}_1\text{H}^1 + {}_8\text{O}^{17}. \tag{43–7}$$

A choice between these possibilities could have been made if carbon, fluorine, or oxygen could be found in the gas by chemical or spectrographic means. But the amount of any of these elements formed was far too small to identify.

In 1925 Blackett reported that out of more than 20,000 cloud chamber photographs, including 400,000 alpha-particle tracks in nitrogen, eight were like Fig. 43–2, which shows the nuclear disintegration taking place. The two parts of the figure are two pictures of the same event taken from different angles—a stereograph. As in all Blackett's pictures, most of the tracks are straight alpha-particle tracks. But in Fig. 43–2 one alpha track ends abruptly. At the end of the alpha track may be seen two tracks, a thin one caused by a proton and a thick one due to a heavy nucleus. There appear to be two rather than three products of the nuclear reaction.

Furthermore, the stereographic picture permits a complete analysis of the three-dimensional situation. The fact that the two product-particle tracks determine a plane which includes the original alpha-particle track makes it highly unlikely that a third particle escaped undetected. Thus we can be sure that Eq. (43–7) is the correct one.

Blackett's photographs also show that the probability of having an alpha particle collide with another atom while traveling several centimeters in a gas is only about 1 in 50,000. This verifies the concept that most of the volume occupied by a gas is free space and that the atomic nucleus is actually a very minute target.

Fig. 43–2. Cloud-chamber stereograph of the ejection of a proton from a nitrogen nucleus. The slight curvature of the tracks is due to mass motion of the gas caused by a small leak in the expansion chamber. (Courtesy of P. M. S. Blackett)

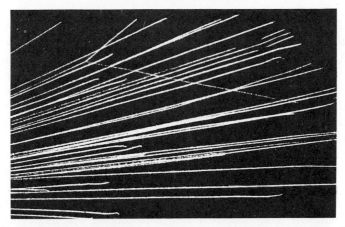

FIG. 43–3. Elastic collision of an alpha particle with hydrogen—the long, thin track. (Courtesy of P. M. S. Blackett and D. S. Lees, Imperial College of Science and Technology, and the Royal Society, London)

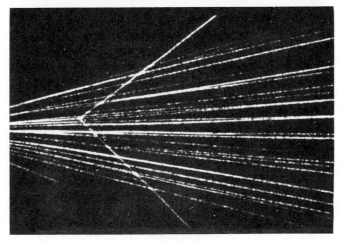

FIG. 43–4. Elastic collision of an alpha particle with helium. (Courtesy of P. M. S. Blackett)

Rutherford and Chadwick bombarded all the light elements with alpha particles. They found about ten cases where protons were produced. By studying the range of these protons, they determined that in some cases the proton has more energy than the original alpha particle. This further refutes the idea that the proton is knocked off the bombarded nucleus and supports the idea that the alpha particle is first absorbed by the nucleus, which then ejects a proton whose energy is largely determined by the instability of the intermediate nucleus. These experiments also indicated that the proton is a fundamental nuclear particle.

43–2 Penetrating radiation puzzle. One of the light elements which failed to give protons under alpha-particle bombardment was beryllium. In 1930, Bothe and Becker in Germany reported that beryllium bombarded with alpha particles from polonium produced a very penetrating radiation which they assumed to be gamma rays. Others showed that boron also had this property, and the energy of the photons was estimated to be about 10 Mev—greater than that of any gamma rays from radioactive sources.

In 1932, the daughter and son-in-law of Madame Curie, Mme. Curie-Joliot and M. Joliot, announced that these radiations could eject rather high-energy protons from matter containing hydrogen. When paraffin wax was placed in front of their ionization chamber, the ionization was nearly doubled. They assumed that this process was analogous to the Compton effect. Instead of an x-ray knocking out an electron, they thought a gamma ray was striking a proton. They could compute the energy the gamma-ray photon must have in order to give the proton its observed energy. Assuming a direct hit in which the gamma ray scatters back on itself, they computed the gamma-ray energy to be about 50 Mev, a tremendous amount.

It is interesting to see how this calculation is made. Repeating the Compton equation, Eq. (40–30), which gives the change in wavelength of a photon upon being deflected through an angle α by a particle of mass m_0, we have

$$\Delta\lambda = \frac{h}{m_0 c}(1 - \cos\alpha). \qquad (43\text{–}8)$$

The photon suffers the largest change of wavelength and transfers the greatest amount of energy when the angle of scattering is 180°, in which case Eq. (43–8) becomes

$$\Delta\lambda = \frac{2h}{m_0 c}. \qquad (43\text{–}9)$$

Since we shall show that only a small fraction of the photon energy E_f is transferred to the proton, the changes in the wavelength, frequency, and energy of the photon are slight, and these quantities may be treated as differentials. Thus the maximum change in the energy of the photon is

$$dE_f = h\,df = h\,d\left(\frac{c}{\lambda}\right) = -\frac{hc\,d\lambda}{\lambda^2}. \qquad (43\text{–}10)$$

Using $\lambda = c/f$ and Eq. (43–9) to eliminate λ and $d\lambda$, we have

$$dE_f = -\frac{2(hf)^2}{m_0 c^2} = -\frac{2E_f^2}{m_0 c^2}. \qquad (43\text{–}11)$$

Now, the energy lost by the photon is just that gained by the proton, dE_p. Furthermore, m_0c^2 is the rest mass-energy of the proton being hit, which is about 1 amu. Thus we have

$$dE_p = 2E_f^2 \text{ in amu.} \tag{43–12}$$

The observed proton ranges were up to about 26 cm in air, which corresponds to an initial proton velocity of about 3×10^7 m/sec. This velocity permits a nonrelativistic calculation of the kinetic energy, which is 7.5×10^{-13} joule or 4.7 Mev. Since Eq. (43–12) is in amu, we must convert the observed proton energy of 4.7 Mev to 0.005 amu. This is the change in the proton energy, dE_p; therefore we can compute the photon energy, E_f:

$$E_f = \sqrt{dE_p/2} = \sqrt{0.005/2} = 0.05 \text{ amu} = 47 \text{ Mev.} \tag{43–13}$$

Thus it would take about a 50-Mev gamma-ray quantum to give a proton having about 5 Mev of kinetic energy in an ideal Compton-type collision.

It was found that the penetrating radiations could also expel nitrogen nuclei from nitrogenous compounds. The kinetic energy of the nitrogen was 1.2 Mev, and a calculation such as we have just made indicated that the necessary photon energy was about 95 Mev. It appears that these gamma-ray energies are not only very great, but are not unique.

By 1932 the isotopic masses of the elements had been measured fairly accurately. All these masses were very nearly integers, and the minor differences were attributed to the relativistic equivalence of mass and energy, $E = mc^2$. Thus if the mass of an atom was found to be less than the sum of the masses of its parts (then assumed to be alpha particles, protons, and electrons), the difference was assigned to the mass-energy that would be released if the nucleus were assembled from those parts.

We have seen that the equivalence of mass and energy permits the use of mass units for the measurement of energy and that one atomic mass unit is equivalent to 931 Mev. Using the available data for the energies of the particles, one might, in the early thirties, have made the following calculation. The alpha particle from polonium has a kinetic energy of 5.26 Mev, which may be expressed as 0.00565 amu. The rest energy or isotopic mass of an alpha particle was then thought to be 4.00106 amu. Let this alpha particle strike a boron atom assumed to be at rest and to have a mass-energy of 11.00825 amu.* There would then be a total mass-energy of 15.01496 amu going into the reaction. If the products

---

* Since it was known that alpha particles produced protons from $_5\text{B}^{10}$, it was logical to assume that the penetrating radiation came from $_5\text{B}^{11}$.

of the reaction are assumed to be a gamma ray and a new nucleus, the new nucleus would have to be $_7N^{15}$, whose rest mass-energy was thought to exceed 14.999. Assuming that the nitrogen nucleus is left with no kinetic energy and that the gamma ray carries away all the energy difference, the gamma ray would have an energy of $15.015 - 14.999 = 0.016$ amu. Thus the maximum energy the gamma ray could have would be $0.016 \times 932 = 14.9$ Mev, far less than 50 or 90 Mev.

Similar results were obtained from the alpha-particle bombardment of beryllium.

43–3 Discovery of the neutron. Ever since 1924, Rutherford and Chadwick had believed that there was an electrically neutral particle and Chadwick had been looking for experimental proof of its existence. He found that proof in the data we are discussing. Chadwick assumed that when boron is bombarded with alpha particles, the products are not $_7N^{15}$ and a gamma ray, but $_7N^{14}$ and $_0n^1$, a *neutron*. Such a particle would have tremendous penetrating ability, since it has no charge. Whereas charged particles interact with the electric fields of the nuclei in the matter they penetrate, an uncharged particle would interact with nuclei only when within the influence of the very short-range nuclear forces. Most important, however, Chadwick assumed that the mass of the neutron was nearly equal to the mass of the proton, so that if it hit a proton, the transfer of its energy to the proton could be complete. To find this energy transfer let us consider in detail an elastic collision between two bodies. We assume a direct (head-on) hit so that both bodies move on along the extension of the line of incidence. Let the first body have a mass m_1 and a velocity v_1. Then its kinetic energy, E_{k1}, is $\frac{1}{2}m_1v_1^2$. Its momentum M_1 is m_1v_1, which may be conveniently expressed as $\sqrt{2m_1E_{k1}}$. After the collision, v_1, E_{k1}, and M_1 change to v_1', E_{k1}', and M_1'. Let the target particle have a mass m_2 which is initially at rest, so that $v_2 = E_{k2} = M_2 = 0$. After the collision, these become v_2', E_{k2}', and M_2' respectively.

Since the collision is elastic, kinetic energy is conserved, and

$$E_{k1} = E_{k1}' + E_{k2}' \quad \text{or} \quad E_{k1}' = E_{k1} - E_{k2}'. \quad (43\text{–}14)$$

Because the collision is linear, the momenta add algebraically and we have

$$M_1 = M_1' + M_2'$$

or

$$\sqrt{2m_1E_{k1}} = \sqrt{2m_1E_{k1}'} + \sqrt{2m_2E_{k2}'}. \quad (43\text{–}15)$$

We can eliminate one quantity between these two equations, and we choose to eliminate E'_{k1} since it is difficult to measure. Then, substituting E'_{k1} from Eq. (43–14) into Eq. (43–15), we have

$$\sqrt{2m_1 E_{k1}} = \sqrt{2m_1(E_{k1} - E'_{k2})} + \sqrt{2m_2 E'_{k2}}. \qquad (43\text{–}16)$$

Upon squaring and dividing by 2, we obtain

$$m_1 E_{k1} = m_1 E_{k1} - m_1 E'_{k2} + m_2 E'_{k2} + 2\sqrt{m_1 m_2 (E_{k1} - E'_{k2}) E'_{k2}}.$$

$$(43\text{–}17)$$

Canceling, transposing, squaring again, and dividing by E'_{k2}, we get

$$(m_1^2 - 2m_1 m_2 + m_2^2) E'_{k2} = 4m_1 m_2 E_{k1} - 4m_1 m_2 E'_{k2}. \qquad (43\text{–}18)$$

Upon rearranging, we obtain

$$(m_1 + m_2)^2 E'_{k2} = 4m_1 m_2 E_{k1},$$

or

$$E'_{k2} = \frac{4m_1 m_2 E_{k1}}{(m_1 + m_2)^2}. \qquad (43\text{–}19)$$

By putting E'_{k2} from Eq. (43–19) into Eq. (43–14), we can get E'_{k1} in terms of E_{k1} and thus

$$E'_{k1} = E_{k1} - \frac{4m_1 m_2 E_{k1}}{(m_1 + m_2)^2} = \left(\frac{m_1 - m_2}{m_1 + m_2}\right)^2 E_{k1}, \qquad (43\text{–}20)$$

which shows that E'_{k1} is zero for $m_1 = m_2$ so that in this circumstance $E_{k1} = E'_{k2}$, and all the incident energy is transferred.

We now follow Chadwick's procedure and apply these equations to collisions between particles of unknown mass and energy and particles of known mass and energy, namely hydrogen and nitrogen nuclei. (These may be considered at rest because the thermal kinetic energies are relatively insignificant.) If m_2 is a proton, $m_2 = 1$ amu, $E'_{k2} = 4.7$ Mev and Eq. (43–19) becomes

$$4.7 = \frac{4m_1 E_{k1}}{(m_1 + 1)^2}, \qquad (43\text{–}21)$$

whereas if m_2 is a nitrogen nucleus, $m_2 = 14$ amu, $E'_{k2} = 1.2$ Mev, and we have

$$1.2 = \frac{4m_1 \times 14 E_{k1}}{(m_1 + 14)^2}. \qquad (43\text{–}22)$$

Solving Eqs. (43–21) and (43–22) simultaneously, we find that $m_1 = 1.03$ amu and $E_{k1} = 4.7$ Mev.

Thus Chadwick proposed that the penetrating radiation was not gamma radiation but neutral particles, each having a mass of about 1 amu. Such a particle would transfer energy to other nuclei more efficiently than photons, and both recoil protons and nitrogen nuclei can be attributed to a particle having a single reasonable energy, instead of the two large contradictory values required by the puzzling gamma-photon proposal.

Our equations have been applied to the collision between neutrons and other observable nuclei. Chadwick went back and analyzed the nuclear reaction itself to obtain a further check of his hypothesis and a better estimate of the neutron's mass.

For the case of boron, the reaction equation assumed was

$$_{2}He^{4} + {}_{5}B^{11} \rightarrow {}_{7}N^{15} \rightarrow {}_{7}N^{14} + {}_{0}n^{1}. \qquad (43\text{--}23)$$

To apply the law of conservation of mass-energy, he had to know the various particle energies. The alpha particle was known to have a kinetic energy equivalent to 0.00565 amu. The boron was assumed to be at rest. The neutrons were detected by letting them collide with protons. The proton range indicated their energy to be 0.0035 amu, and since neutrons and protons have nearly the same mass, Chadwick could take the measured proton energy to be the neutron energy. The nucleus of $_{7}N^{15}$ recoils as it emits the neutron and becomes $_{7}N^{14}$. From the law of conservation of momentum we have

$$\sqrt{2m_{a}E_{ka}} = \sqrt{2m_{N}E_{kN}} + \sqrt{2m_{n}E_{kn}}. \qquad (43\text{--}24)$$

Here everything is known except E_{kN}, which turns out to be 0.00061 amu. Aston had measured the isotopic masses of $_{2}He^{4}$, $_{5}B^{11}$, and $_{7}N^{14}$ to be 4.00106, 11.00825, and 14.0042 respectively. Chadwick wrote the complete mass-energy equation:

$$_{2}He^{4} + E_{k_{a}} + {}_{5}B^{11} = {}_{7}N^{14} + E_{kN} + {}_{0}n^{1} + E_{kn}, \qquad (43\text{--}25)$$

where every quantity was known except the mass of $_{0}n^{1}$. Upon substituting, we have

$$4.00106 + 0.00565 + 11.00825 = 14.0042 + 0.00061 + {}_{0}n^{1} + 0.0035.$$

Soliving for the mass of the neutron, Chadwick obtained 1.0067 amu. This is surprisingly near the best modern value.

We have treated the discovery of the neutron in great detail for several reasons. The neutron is a new fundamental particle so important that we shall devote Chapter 44 to its effects. The discovery is an excellent example of discovery by inference. [Neutrons do not cause fluorescence, do not cause photographic images, do not make cloud-chamber tracks, and do not trip Geiger counters. Neutrons cause weak ionization by colliding with electrons (about one ion per meter of path) and neutrons interact with nuclei.] Furthermore, the methods used in this discovery, the mechanics of impact and conservation of mass-energy, will clarify material that still lies before us.

In 1950, it was found that a free neutron, one outside the nucleus, is radioactive. It has a half-life of 13 min and disintegrates into a proton, an electron, and a neutrino.

43–4 Accelerators. Although important discoveries came from nuclear reactions produced by alpha-particle bombardment, the only elements disintegrated by alpha particles were the light elements. In our discussion of the Rutherford alpha-particle scattering, we obtained an equation for the distance of closest approach when an alpha particle is directly aimed at a nucleus, Eq. (38–3). In words, the equation states that the minimum distance is proportional to the charge of the alpha particle times the charge of the target nucleus divided by twice the kinetic energy of the alpha particle. The reason it is easy to disintegrate light elements is that these elements have small nuclear charges. If the heavier elements repel alpha particles and therefore resist disintegration, the remedy is to use bullets with more energy, less charge, or both.

Protons are not ejected by radioactive atoms, but they are easily formed by ionizing hydrogen. They have half the charge of alpha particles and should be good bullet particles if given enough energy. Because of their charge, they can be accelerated by causing them to fall through a potential difference.

The first particle accelerators or "atom smashers" consisted of an ion source such as Thomson used to produce canal rays, an evacuated region in which the ions could be accelerated, and a source of high potential to do the accelerating. With such machines the main problem is to develop the necessary high voltage. One scheme of historic interest involved charging capacitors in parallel and then connecting them to the accelerator in series. Another scheme was to use transformers such as had been developed for producing x-rays, either singly or in cascade. The only high-voltage system in wide use today is the Van de Graaff electrostatic generator (Section 21–8), in which charges are transported to bodies by means of moving belts, to supply the required large potentials. Of these schemes, the Van de Graaff generator is unique in that it provides a constant potential which accelerates the ions to a well-defined and measurable energy. Accelerators of this type can supply ions with energies of a few million electron volts at most.

Another type of machine is the cyclotron (Section 24–13), invented by Lawrence and Livingston in 1932. Rather than obtain higher energies by going to higher potentials, these investigators devised an ingenious method for using a comparatively low voltage over and over.

The cyclotron operates successfully only with relatively massive particles such as protons or deuterons. It cannot be used to accelerate electrons for the following reason. In order that a particle shall remain in phase with the alternating electric field, its angular velocity, Bq/m, must remain constant. Now although q and B are constants, the same is not true of the mass m. The latter increases with increasing velocity because of relativistic effects. For a given energy, the velocity of an electron is much greater than that of a more massive proton or deuteron and the relativistic increase of mass is correspondingly more pronounced. For example, the mass of a 2-million volt electron is about five times its rest mass, while the mass of a 2-million volt deuteron differs from its rest mass by only about 0.01 percent. Hence electrons very quickly get out of phase with the electric field and do not arrive at the gap between the dees at the proper times to be accelerated. This difficulty does not arise in a generator of the Van de Graaff type, and it can also be surmounted by a device called a *betatron*, described in Section 27–4. In the betatron, electrons gain their final energy in less than one cycle of the varying field and do not have to remain in phase with the field for a large number of cycles.

Even with protons or deuterons, the relativistic increase of mass sets an upper limit of about 30 million volts to the equivalent voltage through which these particles can be accelerated in a cyclotron. This limit can be increased to several hundred million volts in the *frequency modulated cyclotron*, where the frequency of alternation of the electric field is decreased as a particle spirals out from the center, at the same rate that the angular velocity decreases because of increasing mass. Of course the frequency cannot be decreased indefinitely. It is alternately decreased and increased and a burst of particles is accelerated during each interval of decreasing frequency.

43–5 The Cockcroft-Walton experiment. The first nuclear disintegrations induced without the help of alpha particles from radioactive substances were made by Cockcroft and Walton in the same year that Chadwick discovered the neutron, 1932. They used protons as bombarding particles. The protons were accelerated by a high voltage which was achieved by charging capacitors in parallel and discharging them in series, a technique in use at that time in x-ray technology. Proton energies up to 700,000 ev were obtained in this way.

Cockcroft and Walton found reactions which were often the converse

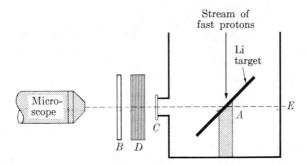

FIG. 43–5. Schematic diagram of the Cockcroft-Walton apparatus.

of reactions already known. It was known that alpha bombardment often produced protons, but they also found that proton bombardment often produced alpha particles. Although they bombarded 16 different elements, the quantitative data they reported for lithium and fluorine are of particular interest.

The target region of their apparatus is shown in Fig. 43–5. The fast protons struck the target material at A. A zinc-sulphide fluorescent screen was placed at B, and any scintillations produced could be observed with the microscope at the left. The mica sheet at C held the vacuum in the accelerating tube and it had sufficient stopping power to prevent scintillations due to scattered protons. With lithium as the target, scintillations were observed which appeared to be alpha particles. When additional mica sheets, D, of known stopping power were introduced, the rays were found to have a range equivalent to about 8 cm of air. An ionization chamber and a cloud chamber were also used to positively identify the alpha particles and to determine that their range was 8.4 cm. This range indicated an energy of 8.5 Mev for each particle. Evidently the reaction taking place was

$$_1H^1 + {_3}Li^7 \rightarrow {_4}Be^8 \rightarrow {_2}He^4 + {_2}He^4. \tag{43–26}$$

Since the lithium atom had only thermal motion, it could be regarded as being at rest, and since the proton velocity was small compared with that of the observed alpha particle, Cockcroft and Walton assumed that the two product alpha particles must acquire equal and opposite velocities (conservation of energy and of momentum require this if the initial energy and momentum may be neglected). Cockcroft and Walton tested this assumption in the following way. They made the target very thin and added another scintillation detector at E, opposite the original one, as shown in Fig. 43–5. They could then observe *simultaneous* scintillations, which indicated that both alpha particles came from a single disintegration.

F IG . 43–6.   Cloud-chamber photograph of pairs of alpha particles from proton disintegration of lithium. The lithium target is close to a thin mica window at the center of the chamber. (Courtesy of P. I. Dee, University of Glasgow)

They also checked their assumption by setting up the mass-energy equation of the reaction, as Chadwick did:

Proton mass + lithium mass + input energy in mass units

= 2(alpha-particle mass + alpha-particle energy in mass units).

When they substituted numerical values in this equation they disregarded the kinetic mass-energy of the proton because this was less than the uncertainty in the isotopic mass of lithium known at that time. Using values from their data, we have, in amu,

$$1.0072 + 7.0134 = 2(4.0011 + E_{k\alpha})$$

or

$$E_{k\alpha} = 0.0092 \text{ amu} = 8.6 \text{ Mev.} \qquad (43\text{--}27)$$

This is in good agreement with the energy determined from the range, 8.5 Mev.

In the case of fluorine, the reaction was

$$_1\text{H}^1 + {}_9\text{F}^{19} \rightarrow {}_{10}\text{Ne}^{20} \rightarrow {}_8\text{O}^{16} + {}_2\text{He}^4. \qquad (43\text{--}28)$$

They again set up the mass-energy equation to find the energy liberated. By dividing the energy between the oxygen and the alpha particle according to the laws of conservation of energy and of momentum, they again obtained good agreement between the measured and computed alpha-particle energies.

The significance of the Cockcroft-Walton experiments can hardly be over-emphasized. They were the first to use an ion accelerator to produce nuclear disintegrations, and they proved, beyond any doubt, the equivalence of mass and energy. Together with Chadwick, their effective use of the mass-energy equation to account for the mass-energy balance of nuclear reactions provided a powerful tool for nuclear physics.

It is appropriate that we pause here and reflect on the power of abstract reasoning. When the search for the ether drift failed, Einstein decided to make physics valid without an ether medium. His theory of relativity gave a unique significance to the velocity of light. He proposed that mass and energy are different manifestations of the same thing, with the velocity of light squared as the constant of proportionality. This consequence of relativity was in violent disagreement with the highly successful Newtonian mechanics, and Einstein had not a shred of experimental evidence to support him. In the Cockcroft-Walton experiment we find that Einstein is not only justified, but also that his concept of mass-energy equivalence provides the basic key to the application of conservation of energy to nuclear processes. Einstein, who helped Perrin establish the atomic view of matter, had never heard of the nucleus when he proposed the theory of relativity.

43–6 Nuclear mass-energy equations. Q-value. We have already given examples of the mass-energy equation; we now consider its use in detail. This equation is the relativistic combination of the two classical principles of conservation of mass and of energy. The combination is effected through the use of the relation $E = mc^2$, which expresses the equivalence of mass and energy. Mass-energy may be measured in either mass or energy units. The conversion factor is c^2. Using units convenient to nuclear physics, we may say that 1 amu has an energy of 931 Mev or that an energy of 931 Mev has a mass of 1 amu. Nuclear mass-energy equations are usually written in atomic mass units, although any consistent units of mass or energy can be used. The fundamental equation is simply that the total mass-energy before a reaction equals the total mass-energy after the reaction.

Let us consider the most general kind of reaction involving moving particles and photons. Let m_1 and m_2 be the rest masses of the initial particles and E_{k1} and E_{k2} their respective kinetic energies; let m_3 and m_4 be the rest masses of the final particles and E_{k3} and E_{k4} their respective kinetic energies; finally, let f_0 be the frequency of an initial photon and f be the frequency of a final photon. Upon equating the total mass-energy before the reaction to that afterwards, we obtain

$$m_1c^2 + E_{k1} + m_2c^2 + E_{k2} + hf_0 = m_3c^2 + E_{k3} + m_4c^2 + E_{k4} + hf$$
$$(43\text{--}29)$$

or, transposing and collecting similar terms,

$$[(m_1 + m_2) - (m_3 + m_4)]c^2$$
$$= [(E_{k3} + E_{k4}) - (E_{k1} + E_{k2})] + h(f - f_0). \quad (43\text{--}30)$$

The right side of this equation is the change in energy resulting from the reaction. The energy that is released or absorbed in a nuclear reaction is called the *Q-value* or *disintegration energy* of the reaction. Thus from Eq. (43–30) we have

$$Q = [(m_1 + m_2) - (m_3 + m_4)]c^2$$
$$= [(E_{k3} + E_{k4}) - (E_{k1} + E_{k2})] + h(f - f_0). \quad (43\text{--}31)$$

If the rest masses are in amu, then the Q-value in amu is

$$\boxed{Q = (m_1 + m_2) - (m_3 + m_4).} \quad (43\text{--}32)$$

The Q-value may be either positive or negative. If it is positive, then rest mass-energy is converted to kinetic mass-energy or radiation mass-energy or both and the reaction is said to be exoergic or exothermic. If it is negative, the reaction is endoergic or endothermic and then either kinetic mass-energy or radiation mass-energy must be supplied if the reaction is to take place.

We are particularly interested in applying the equations we have just obtained to nuclear reactions. When we calculate the Q-value of a nuclear reaction, the masses used in either Eq. (43–31) or Eq. (43–32) must be the rest masses of the nuclei. However, the isotopic masses given in tables such as that in Appendix 4 are the rest masses of the neutral atoms. To obtain the rest mass of the nucleus of an atom, we must subtract the rest masses of all the orbital electrons from the isotopic mass. Are there any circumstances in which the rest masses of the neutral atoms may be used instead of those of the bare nuclei to calculate the disintegration energy?

Consider the reaction

$$_5\text{B}^{11} + {_1}\text{H}^1 \rightarrow {_4}\text{Be}^8 + {_2}\text{He}^4. \quad (43\text{--}33)$$

To obtain the Q-value of this reaction, we will substitute the nuclear masses into Eq. (43–32). Let the chemical symbols represent the isotopic masses of the atoms in amu and let e represent the rest mass of an electron in the same units; then we have

$$Q = [(B - 5e) + (H - e)] - [(Be - 4e) + (He - 2e)]$$
$$= (B + H - 6e) - (Be + He - 6e)$$
$$= (B + H) - (Be + He).$$

This result shows that the *isotopic masses of the atoms can be used* to compute the Q-value in this case.

Next we consider a radioactive substance undergoing beta decay, that is, emitting an electron. An example is

$$_{47}Ag^{106} \rightarrow {}_{48}Cd^{106} + {}_{-1}e^0 \text{ (or } \beta^-). \tag{43-34}$$

Following the same procedure as before, we find

$$Q = [(Ag - 47e)] - [(Cd - 48e) + e]$$
$$= (Ag - 47e) \quad (Cd - 47e)$$
$$= Ag - Cd.$$

Therefore, *to find the disintegration energy in reactions involving electron emission, the isotopic masses may be used if the mass of the emitted electron is disregarded.* It should be remembered that the kinetic energy of the beta particle calculated from this and similar reactions is the maximum value it can have under the circumstances. In general, this amount of energy is actually shared between the emitted electron and the neutrino. Since the latter has negligible rest mass, it does not enter into the calculation of the Q-value.

In some cases positrons are emitted from nuclei. A reaction of this type is

$$_7N^{13} \rightarrow {}_6C^{13} + {}_{+1}e^0 \text{ (or } \beta^+). \tag{43-35}$$

In this case, we have

$$Q = [(N - 7e)] - [(C - 6e) + e]$$
$$= (N - 7e) - (C - 7e + 2e)$$
$$= N - (C + 2e).$$

Therefore, to compute the energy change *in reactions involving positron emission, the isotopic masses may be used if two electron masses are added to the masses of the products.* In this case too, in general, the positron shares kinetic energy with the neutrino.

In following these rules for reactions involving alpha particles, α, or protons, p, we use the isotopic masses of $_2He^4$ and $_1H^1$. The isotopic masses of α and p, which are the masses of the completely ionized atoms, are given in some tables.

In obtaining data to determine isotopic masses, the results of mass spectroscopy provide only a starting point. We saw how Chadwick used the mass-energy equation to compute the mass of the neutron. In Eq. (43–25) the rest-mass terms are much larger than the kinetic energy-mass terms; therefore Chadwick could obtain the mass of the neutron to five significant figures. The repeated application of the mass-energy equation to a large number of nuclear reactions has enabled the computation of isotopic masses with great precision. Many are now known to either seven or eight significant figures.

In collisions involving nuclear reactions having a Q-value, the treatment is like that given in Eqs. (43–14) through (43–20) except that the sum of the kinetic energies of the final particles is equal to $E_{k1} + Q$ instead of E_{k1}. Also, if the collision is not head-on, the law of conservation of momentum must be written in component form.

43–7 Artificial (induced) radioactivity. Although the work of Cockcroft and Walton stimulated the investigation of many nuclear reactions with better and better ion accelerators, we have not come to the end of important discoveries made with alpha particles from radioactive sources. In 1934, while I. Curie-Joliot and F. Joliot were bombarding aluminum with alpha particles from polonium, they observed neutrons, protons, and positrons coming off the aluminum. We have seen that alpha bombardment of light elements often produces protons and sometimes neutrons. Even the presence of positrons was not too surprising, since protons could be thought of as a neutron and positron combined. Their new discovery was made when they noted that the emission of positrons continued *after* the alpha bombardment was stopped. The positron activity decreased with time according to an exponential law and the phenomenon was clearly just like natural radioactivity. They assumed that the artificially radioactive element was $_{15}P^{30}$, formed according to the reaction

$$_{13}Al^{27} + {}_2He^4 \rightarrow {}_{15}P^{30} + {}_0n^1. \tag{43–36}$$

The phosphorus decays with a half-life of 2.55 min into silicon and a positron:

$$_{15}P^{30} \rightarrow {}_{14}Si^{30} + {}_{+1}e^0. \tag{43–37}$$

To justify their assumption, the Joliots irradiated aluminum for a long period and then separated the phosphorus chemically. Since the radioactivity went with the phosphorus fraction, their assumption was verified.

In their original paper, the Joliots also reported the formation of radioactive nitrogen and silicon isotopes by bombardment of boron and magnesium respectively. These new isotopes have half-lives of 10.1 min and

4.9 sec. We can call these isotopes "new" since, if they ever were abundant in nature, they are now present in negligible amounts.

In the years since the original discovery of artificial radioactivity, it has been found possible to form radioactive isotopes of all the elements, and for most elements there are many radioactive isotopes. Thus many more than half the known isotopes are radioactive.

When Madame Curie separated radium, she could follow the progress of the separation by observing the increased activity of the radium fraction. The radium was radioactively "tagged." In the discovery of artificial radioactivity, a crucial point was that in the separation of the aluminum and phosphorus the radioactivity went with the phosphorus. The actual amount of phosphorus was exceedingly small, but radioactivity is easy to detect and small amounts can be traced through successive chemical processes. This property of radioisotopes has been developed into a fine art called "tracer technique." We give a few examples of its applicability.

When iodine is taken into the body, it tends to collect in the thyroid gland. If a patient has cancer of the thyroid, he may be given radioactive iodine. The radioactivity goes just where it should to fight the malignancy.

One pipeline may be used to transport, successively, several kinds of petroleum products with surprisingly little mixing at the boundaries. At the source end of the line, a radioactive material is introduced between products. At the receiving end of the line, Geiger counters outside the pipe announce the arrival of the new product.

If a small amount of a radioelement is mixed with a large amount of the same stable element, the relative proportions of these remain fixed except for the predictable decay of the radioelement. Thus the concentration of that element can be followed through all kinds of chemical and physical processing by measuring the intensity of the activity. It may well be that the new knowledge of phenomena in the basic sciences, obtained by the use of radioactive tracers, will be more important than power from nuclear reactors.

43–8 Carbon dating. One of the radioactive isotopes that is midway between natural radioactivity and artificial radioactivity is C^{14}. It is natural radioactivity in the sense that it occurs in nature, and it is artificial in the sense that it would not occur in nature if it were not constantly being re-formed. Carbon-14 is formed in the atmosphere by high-energy particles from outer space called cosmic rays. It has a half-life of 5600 years. In the atmosphere there is a kind of "radioactive equilibrium" between the production of C^{14} by cosmic rays and its diminution by radioactive disintegration. Fortunately for us, the concentration of C^{14} in the air we breathe and the food we eat is very small. In the body the concentration is only about $10^{-6}\%$ of the C^{12} in living tissue.

But we, the plants, and every living thing contain carbon, and all living things have an amount of C^{14} which is in equilibrium with the C^{14} in the atmosphere. When death comes, living things stop breathing and stop eating food. The intake of C^{14} stops. From the time of death, the C^{14} disintegrates without further replacement. Thus, at death, equilibrium is ended and exponential radioactive decay is the only process remaining.

Old wood contains less C^{14} than new wood. Old bones have less C^{14} than new bones. By measuring the concentration of C^{14}, the time since death occurred can be computed. Thus C^{14} provides a radioactive clock for anthropologists just as uranium provides a radioactive clock for geologists. The C^{14} half-life is suitable for the dating of cultural history, just as the half-life of uranium is suitable for the dating of the history of the earth.

43–9 Nuclear binding energy. In Chapter 42 on radioactivity we said nothing about the *cause* of radioactivity. Why are some isotopes stable while others are not? Why do those that are unstable postpone their disintegration and have probable lives ranging from microseconds to billions of years? We can say something definite about the first question and something plausible about the second.

We shall limit our discussion to radioactive alpha emitters, although a similar argument can be made for the other cases. Let us inquire whether ordinary aluminum, $_{13}Al^{27}$, is alpha radioactive on the basis of mass-energy. The assumed reaction would be

$$_{13}Al^{27} \rightarrow {}_{11}Na^{23} + {}_{2}He^{4} + Q. \qquad (43\text{–}38)$$

From our table of isotopic masses, we find for this case that

$$26.99008 = 22.99705 + 4.00387 + Q$$

or

$$Q = -0.01084 \text{ amu} = -10.1 \text{ Mev}. \qquad (43\text{–}39)$$

The negative Q-value indicates that instead of taking place spontaneously, this reaction cannot proceed unless we supply 10.1 Mev of energy per disintegration. This isotope of aluminum is very stable against alpha decay. Now consider radium,

$$_{88}Ra^{226} \rightarrow {}_{86}Rn^{222} + {}_{2}He^{4} + Q. \qquad (43\text{–}40)$$

This gives

$$226.09600 = 222.08690 + 4.00387 + Q$$

or

$$Q = +0.00523 \text{ amu} \qquad \text{or} \qquad +4.87 \text{ Mev}. \qquad (43\text{–}41)$$

The positive Q-value indicates that radium is unstable and can emit an alpha particle, giving off 4.87 Mev of energy in the process. This result is the combined kinetic energy of the alpha particle and the radon nucleus.

Rather than carry out in detail energy calculations like those of Eqs. (43–39) and (43–41) for every reaction in which we might be interested, it is very helpful to view the matter graphically. Every energy calculation involves an energy difference and requires that the energy reference level be specified. The total *binding energy* of a nucleus is defined as the energy that would be required to separate the nucleus into isolated particles. Before the discovery of the neutron, nuclei were thought to be composed of protons and electrons. This view presented certain theoretical difficulties which were resolved by regarding the nucleus as composed of protons and neutrons—collectively called *nucleons*. When an atom is discussed with particular emphasis on its nuclear composition, it is called a *nuclide*.

The total binding energy is equal to the difference between the isotopic mass of the atom and the sum of the masses of its neutrons, protons, and extranuclear electrons. (The mass of a proton and an extranuclear electron is equal to that of hydrogen.) It is obvious that the total binding energy of heavy nuclei is greater than that of light nuclei because they have more nucleons to separate. But one might expect the binding energy per nucleon to be about constant, and indeed it is about constant for heavy elements. However, the variations are significant, as is shown in Fig. 43–7, which is based on data for stable and nearly stable nuclides. This figure is usually presented with the curve concave downward, and is called the binding-energy curve. Our figure is consistent with the scheme we used in discussing the Bohr energy levels in hydrogen. The distance from the curve up to the abscissa is proportional to the energy per nucleon that would be required to take the nucleus apart, just as the distance from a Bohr energy level to the top is proportional to the energy required to free an electron from an atom. The important characteristic of this curve is that it is concave upward with a minimum around mass number 56. From this curve we can see, qualitatively, the results we obtained for the alpha emission of aluminum and radium.

Alpha-particle emission always produces a new nucleus with a mass number that is four less than that of the original nucleus. If we find aluminum with mass number 27 on the curve and move to the left to sodium with mass number 23, the ordinate becomes less negative. Therefore, in going from aluminum to sodium, we must have done some of the work necessary to take aluminum apart. Since we must do work to make the reaction proceed, the reaction is endothermic and cannot take place spontaneously. In going from radium to radon, however, we go to a new element that is harder to take apart than the element with which we

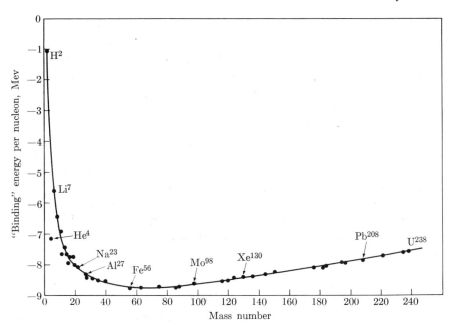

Fig. 43–7. Potential energy per nucleon of stable or near-stable nuclides relative to the state of complete separation.

started. Since the new element is more stable than the original element, the reaction is exothermic and can take place spontaneously. This graph makes it evident that those reactions which produce new nuclei with mass numbers nearer the minimum of the curve are the ones that are likely to be exothermic. In general, to release energy a nuclide having a mass number greater than about 56 has to disintegrate, whereas one below about 56 will have to combine with a particle. The fission of uranium is an outstanding example of the release of energy by disintegration; the fusion of hydrogen is a case of releasing energy by nuclear combination. From this curve we can understand too why there is a limit to the number of naturally occurring elements. Since the naturally radioactive series of elements are all at the right where the curve bends upward, it is logical to assume that if there were any heavier elements at the time of creation they were very unstable and have long since ceased to exist. We shall see in Chapter 44 that several of these elements have been man-made and have been found to be unstable, with short half-lives compared with the age of the earth.

In addition to the mass-energy equation, there are subtler factors that influence the stability of a nuclide. For example, a nuclide of atomic number Z and mass number A has A nucleons, of which Z are protons and

$A - Z$ are neutrons. Nuclides having the same value of Z are *isotopes*; those having the same value of A are called *isobars*; those having the same number of neutrons are called *isotones*; and those having the same excess of neutrons over protons, $A - 2Z$, are *isodiapheres*. Thus $_{17}Cl^{37}$ is an isotope of $_{17}Cl^{35}$, an isobar of $_{16}S^{37}$, an isotone of $_{19}K^{39}$, and an isodiaphere of $_{19}Ar^{41}$.

A survey of 281 stable nuclides shows that 165 of them have an even number of protons and an even number of neutrons; 53 have an odd number of protons and an even number of neutrons; 57 have the number of neutrons odd and the number of protons even; and only 6 have odd numbers of both kinds of nucleon. All of these odd-odd nuclides except $_7N^{14}$ are rare. The even-even type are more stable and are, therefore, the least likely to be radioactive. Six nuclides of this type together comprise about 80% of the earth's crust: $_8O^{16}$, $_{12}Mg^{24}$, $_{14}Si^{28}$, $_{20}Ca^{40}$, $_{22}Ti^{48}$, and $_{26}Fe^{56}$. Further light on the question of nuclear stability comes from wave mechanics.

43–10 Radioactivity and wave mechanics. No elements except hydrogen could be stable were it not for very strong, short-range attractive forces between nucleons. Without such forces, the protons would fly apart by coulomb repulsion. Figure 43–8 is an approximate potential energy diagram for an alpha particle in or near a nucleus having an effective radius b. When the alpha particle is far from the nucleus, $r > b$, it is repelled according to Coulomb's law, and its electric potential energy is

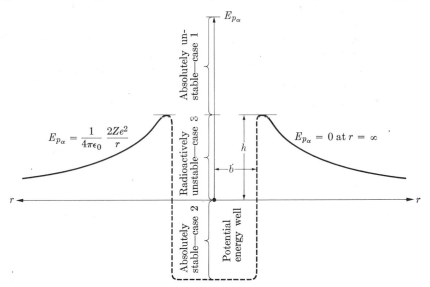

FIG. 43–8. Potential energy of an alpha particle in and near a nucleus.

then given by $E_{p\alpha} = (1/4\pi\epsilon_0)(2Ze^2/r)$. In the figure, the solid curve sloping away from the nucleus represents $E_{p\alpha}$ as a function of r. The coulomb force on the alpha particle can be found from the relation $F = -dE_{p\alpha}/dr$. The central part of the curve is shown dotted because we do not know its shape, but we do know that the curve must dip as the strong attractive forces overcome the coulomb repulsion. The distance b is equal to the nuclear radius introduced in our discussion of Rutherford's alpha-particle scattering. This potential energy wall around the nucleus tends to prevent the entrance or exit of alpha particles whose energies are less than the height h of the potential barrier. The barrier is higher for nuclei of larger atomic number, and would be half as high for protons as it is for alpha particles. Thus this barrier illustrates the difficulty of disintegrating heavy elements with alpha particles, and shows why protons with a given energy can disintegrate more nuclides than can alpha particles. The situation is much like the problem of rolling a ball up a volcanic cone into the crater.

Although the alpha particle emitted by a radioactive substance like radium probably forms from two protons and two neutrons at the moment of ejection, we can think of the alpha particle as an entity within the radium nucleus. There are three cases we must consider. If this alpha particle had more energy than the height of the potential barrier, it could easily overcome the attractive force and thus nuclear disintegration would occur at once. If the alpha particle in the nucleus has a negative energy, the barrier is insurmountable and the particle can never get out. If the alpha particle has positive energy but it is less than h, the nucleus is radioactive.

An example of the first case is the intermediate nuclide, Ne^{20}, Eq. (43–28). The neon nucleus immediately emits an alpha particle. An example of the second case is the fluorine, F^{19}, of this same reaction, which is completely stable. Samples of the third case include all the radioactive nuclides, both natural and artificial. Radium C', Po^{214}, is very unstable, with a half-life of 1.64×10^{-4} sec, and U^{238} is nearly completely stable, with a half-life of 4.5×10^9 years.

Cases one and two are perfectly understandable from the classical energy viewpoint. Particles with more energy than the barrier are not hindered by it. Particles with energy far below the barrier are completely stopped by it. But, according to the classical energy viewpoint, the nuclides of case three should also be stable. If the nuclear alpha particle has less energy than the height of the barrier, it should be confined just as certainly as if its energy were negative. If this classical view were correct, there would be no radioactivity.

In our discussion of wave mechanics, we compared the classical and wave-mechanical treatments of a mass oscillating on a spring. Since we neglected friction, the mass had a fixed energy which was alternately potential and kinetic. The mass moved subject to an attractive force determined by the spring. This force may be described as producing a potential barrier which prevents the mass from getting away. According to the classical solution of the problem, the mass never gets farther from its central position than its amplitude, which is the distance to the potential barrier. But in the wave-mechanical solution, we found that there is a finite probability that the mass can have a displacement from the center greater than the amplitude. Some authors attempt to salvage some of the classical view by saying that there are a few holes in the potential barrier around the nucleus and that a nuclear particle can "tunnel through" it. We prefer to dispense with classical models and simply say that classical physics does not apply. Because of the wave nature of matter, there is a finite probability that the particle will escape. Every radioactive disintegration demonstrates this.

The energy of the emitted alpha particle (and the recoil nucleus) does not depend on the height of the potential barrier. The kinetic energy after the disintegration is the same as the energy of the nucleus and its alpha particle before the disintegration. But this energy does have a bearing on the decay process. If the energy is nearly equal to the energy height of the potential barrier, then disintegration is likely, the decay constant is large, and the half-life is small. If the energy is small compared with the barrier height, then the radioactive nucleus is relatively stable and has a long half-life. This point is not covered by our analogy between an alpha particle in a nucleus and a mass on a spring. The reason is that whereas the spring exerts an attractive force on the mass everywhere the mass moves, the alpha particle experiences a repulsive force after r exceeds b. If the potential energy well for the oscillating mass had had a shape like that in which the alpha particle moves, the probability of finding the mass beyond its amplitude would increase as its energy increased.

One might try to explain radioactivity classically by imagining that the nucleons in a nuclide are like gas molecules having a maxwellian energy distribution. Every once in a while some nucleons "gang up" on one or more of their fellows and give them enough energy to eject them from the nuclide. If this were so, the ejected particle would have energy at least as great as the potential barrier. This is not observed experimentally.

We may use wave-mechanical ideas to resolve another dilemma. If radium disintegrates into radon and an alpha particle with the release of 4.87 Mev of energy, why should not radium be formed when radon is bombarded with alpha particles of about this energy? No doubt this reverse reaction can and does occur, but consider how unlikely it is. If you could place a radium atom on the table and watch it disintegrate, you might be rewarded in a few seconds. On the other hand, you might have to watch for millions of years. If you want a 50-50 chance of seeing the disintegration, you must be prepared to sit with wrapt attention for about 2340 years, the average life. The probability of finding the radium alpha particle outside the nucleus in a short time is exceedingly small. Conversely, suppose you were to try to introduce a 4.87-Mev alpha particle into radon to form radium. To have a 50-50 chance of succeeding, you would have to keep the alpha particle near the radon nucleus for about 2340 years. This would be even more difficult than waiting for radium to disintegrate. It would be necessary to bombard the radon nucleus untold numbers of times. If one must penetrate the radon nucleus with an alpha particle, it is far more promising to bombard it with particles whose energy exceeds the radon potential barrier. Recall that alpha particles from radioactive materials were used successfully in disintegrating light nuclei whose potential barriers are relatively low.

43–11 The bombarding particles. Thus far we have discussed the use of alpha particles and protons to bombard nuclei. With the advent of particle accelerators the study of nuclear physics became very popular and a great number of reactions were studied. Many of these transitions were excited by high-energy electrons and high-energy photons or gamma rays. Many new isotopes were discovered. One of these, which deserves special mention, is deuterium.

As early as 1920, Harkins and Rutherford predicted that there should be a heavy isotope of hydrogen having mass number 2. It was not found in mass spectroscopy because it was masked by the hydrogen molecule H_2. In 1931 Urey, Brickwedde, and Murphy separated heavy hydrogen from ordinary hydrogen by evaporating liquid hydrogen. Since light hydrogen is more volatile, it evaporated a little more readily than the heavy hydrogen. This isotope was positively identified spectroscopically. The atomic spectrum of heavy hydrogen is shifted from that of ordinary hydrogen because its greater mass causes a small but measurable difference in the Rydberg constant. Soon after its discovery, heavy hydrogen was separated in considerable quantities by the electrolysis of water, where again the molecules formed with light hydrogen were more mobile and electrolyzed more readily. Since heavy hydrogen has twice the mass of its common isotope, it has many striking properties. Water formed from heavy hydrogen, called "heavy water," has a specific gravity of 1.108, which is quite different from that of ordinary water. Because of its special importance, heavy hydrogen has been given a special name, *deuterium*, and the symbol D. Thus $_1H^2$ and $_1D^2$ have identical meaning. (Ordinary hydrogen, $_1H^1$, also has a special name, *protium*, but it is seldom used.) Just as ionized hydrogen is called a proton, p, ionized deuterium is called a *deuteron*, d. A third hydrogen isotope, $_1H^3$, is called *tritium* and is sometimes represented by the symbol T. The tritium nucleus is called *triton* and is indicated by t. Tritium is radioactive, with a half-life of 12.26 years.

One of the important uses of deuterium was as a bombarding particle. It has unit charge like the proton, but it has twice the mass of a proton. Deuterium bombardment led to still more nuclear reactions, such as

$$_1D^2 + {}_1D^2 \rightarrow {}_2He^3 + {}_0n^1 + Q. \tag{43–42}$$

We choose this particular reaction as an example because it is one of many reactions which produce neutrons.

It is easy to see why neutrons were also used as bombarding particles. Because they have no charge, they are not subject to coulomb repulsion. With no potential barrier to penetrate, neutrons can enter almost any nucleus with ease. The number of nuclear transitions that can be produced with neutrons is greater than the number induced by all other particles combined.

43–12 Neutron reactions. Modes of nuclide decay. Nuclear reactions are often represented in a shorthand notation in which the participating particles are identified in this order: target particle, bombarding particle, ejected particle, and product particle. The symbols for the bombarding and ejected particles are enclosed in parentheses. Thus Eq. (43–42) may be written $D^2(d, n)He^3$. Equation (43–36) becomes $Al^{27}(\alpha, n)P^{30}$. Any reaction in which a deuteron produces a neutron is called a (d, n) reaction, and the second example is called an (α, n) reaction.

The first type of neutron reaction observed was of the (n, α) type, where the target was, successively, nitrogen, oxygen, fluorine, and neon. A second type is called simple *radiative capture*, (n, γ). The first observed reaction of this type was the formation of deuterium from hydrogen and a neutron with the emission of a gamma photon. Nearly all elements undergo radiative capture of neutrons and it is probably the most common nuclear process. It is particularly important that the probability of this type of reaction taking place is greater for slow neutrons than for fast ones.

A third type of neutron reaction is the (n, p) type. Except for the lighter elements, the potential barrier inhibiting the escape of the proton causes these reactions to have negative Q-values. Therefore the incident neutron must be fast, with an energy of 1 Mev or more. Although they are less probable than (n, p) reactions, (n, d) and (n, t) reactions are also found.

The second type of reaction, (n, γ), is especially interesting. It adds a neutron to the bombarded nucleus and frequently makes it radioactive. An examination of the periodic table shows that atomic weight is not proportional to atomic number. The higher the atomic number of a nuclide,

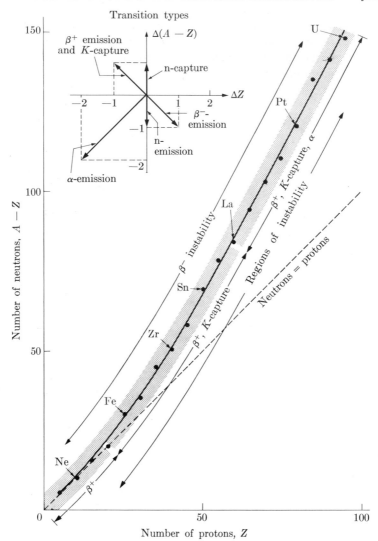

FIG. 43–9. Modes of decay of nuclides.

the more the number of neutrons exceeds the number of protons. If we plot the number of neutrons, $A - Z$, against the number of protons, Z, for the stable nuclides, we obtain the result shown in Fig. 43–9.

In the inset on this figure, the abscissa is the change ΔZ in atomic number due to a nuclear reaction, and the ordinate is the corresponding change $\Delta(A - Z)$ in the neutron content of the nucleus. Five arrows are shown in this inset. One, directed upward, represents the change in a nuclide for simple neutron radiative capture, (n, γ). Another, downward and to the right, represents beta decay in which the emission of a negative electron is accompanied by the conversion of a neutron into a proton. The one pointing directly downward represents neutron emission. The fourth arrow represents the emission of an alpha particle in which two neutrons and two protons are removed. The remaining arrow, upward and to the left, represents both positron emission and orbital electron or K electron capture, where a proton is converted to a neutron. Nuclides off the full-line curve tend to be unstable, and the particle each emits is likely to be one which brings the new nuclide nearer the curve. Thus the region above the curve is the region of likely beta decay. A nuclide in the region below the curve disintegrates in such a way that its atomic number decreases. In general, elements of low mass number disintegrate by positron emission; those in the middle range, either by positron emission or by orbital electron capture; and the heavy elements, by positron emission or by orbital electron capture or by ejecting an alpha particle. The natural radioactive series involve alpha and beta decay in such a way that the series of nuclides tend to follow the curve of stability. Since neutron capture makes a new nuclide above the original one on the chart of Fig. 43–9, the new nuclide tends to be beta-unstable. As a typical example, we have

$$_{45}\text{Rh}^{103} + {}_0\text{n}^1 \rightarrow {}_{45}\text{Rh}^{104} + \gamma. \tag{43–43}$$

The Rh^{104} is beta-unstable, with a half-life of 42 sec, and disintegrates according to the equation

$$_{45}\text{Rh}^{104} \rightarrow {}_{46}\text{Pd}^{104} + {}_{-1}\text{e}^0. \tag{43–44}$$

43–13 The discovery of fission. Since neutron capture followed by beta decay produces a new nuclide of higher atomic number, the process suggested to Fermi an intriguing possibility. Why not cause neutron capture in uranium, the last (then known) element of the periodic system? If uranium formed a beta-unstable isotope, the disintegration product would be element number 93, a "transuranic" element. In 1934, Fermi and his associates attempted the experiment. Apparently the uranium did undergo neutron capture. Apparently the product was beta-unstable. But the beta activity included no less than four different half-lives. As in the discoveries of natural and artificial radioactivity, an attempt was made to identify the product nuclide by chemical separation. Early in 1938, Hahn and Strassmann showed that the beta-active product was chemically like radium and concluded that the new nuclides were new isotopes of radium. In order to get from uranium to radium, whose atomic number is four less, the uranium would have to emit two alpha particles. These alpha particles were not found.

The chemical analysis of such tiny amounts of material is very difficult, but in September 1938 Mme. Joliot-Curie and P. Savitch published a report of their work that identified one activity as due, apparently, to a rare-earth element *lanthanum* which has a much smaller mass number than uranium. This led Hahn and Strassmann to repeat their own earlier work very carefully. In December 1938 they concluded, "As chemists we should replace the symbols Ra, Ac, and Th . . . in [our] scheme . . . by Ba, La, and Ce . . . As nuclear chemists, closely associated with physics, we cannot decide to take this step in contradiction to all previous experience in nuclear physics."

The correct interpretation of the puzzling data came in January 1939 when Meitner and Frisch wrote, "It seems possible that the uranium nucleus has only small stability of form, and may, after neutron capture, divide itself into two nuclei of roughly equal size." Because of its resemblance to the splitting of one living cell into two of equal size, this nuclear process was named after the biological process, *fission*.

All previous nuclear reactions had had as their products particles no more massive than alpha particles and nuclei no farther removed from the original nucleus than two atomic numbers. Even in this decade of rapid advance, it took five years to break away from the limitation of the old conceptions and break through to the conception of this strikingly new process.

Once the fission process was regarded as plausible, the chemical evidence for its correctness was almost immediately reenforced by physical evidence. There were literally scores of laboratories around the world that were already equipped to verify fission. If one uranium atom splits into two atoms near the middle of the periodic series, a glance at Fig. 43–7 or a few moments of calculation will show that the Q-value of the reaction is tremendous. It is 200 Mev, which is about ten times that of the most energetic reaction previously known. Within a short time after hearing the news, many laboratories confirmed this energetic reaction.

PROBLEMS

43-1. Show that the range of a charged particle in a material is proportional to the 3/2 power of its kinetic energy at the beginning of its range.

43-2. Radium-C' emits some of the most energetic alpha particles observed from naturally radioactive elements. The energy of these particles is 7.68 Mev and their range is 6.90 cm in air at 15°C and 1 atm pressure. (a) Show that the moving mass and the relativistic velocity of an alpha particle just ejected from RaC' do not differ from the rest mass and the classical velocity, respectively, by more than 1%. (b) Repeat part (a) for a 7.68-Mev proton. (c) Do you think that the differences between the classical and relativistic results are so significant that relativistic mechanics must be used in calculations involving high-energy particles such as those in this problem?

43-3. Using the data of Problem 43-2, calculate (a) the classical velocity of an alpha particle from RaC' and (b) the total number of ion pairs it produces over its range in air. (It requires 34 ev to produce an ion pair in air.) (c) If all the ion pairs produced by the alpha particles from a microcurie of RaC' constitute the current in an ionization chamber, what would be the current in amperes?

43-4. An alpha particle just ejected from RaC' undergoes an elastic collision with one of the nuclei of molecular hydrogen in a region filled with this gas. If both particles continue in the original direction of motion of the alpha particle, find, classically, (a) the ratio of the velocity of the proton after collision to that of the incident particle, and (b) the kinetic energy of the

proton. (It requires about 2 ev of energy to dissociate the hydrogen molecule. The data for RaC' are given in Problem 43-2.)

43-5. An alpha particle going through a cloud chamber undergoes an elastic collision with a nucleus of unknown mass number initially at rest. A photograph of the event shows a forked track. It is seen from measurements of the track that the collision deviated the alpha particle 60°, and the struck nucleus went off at an angle of 30° with the direction of motion of the incident particle. What is the mass number of the unknown nucleus? (Since this is not a head-on collision and since momentum is a vector quantity, the law of conservation of momentum must be applied in component form.)

43-6. A 7.68-Mev alpha particle has an elastic collision with a hydrogen nucleus. If the path of the alpha particle is deflected upward 10° from its original direction and this particle then has 2.57 Mev of energy, what is the velocity and direction of motion of the proton?

43-7. (a) Show from Eq. (43-20) that when a particle of mass m_1 has a head-on elastic collision with a particle of mass m_2 which is initially at rest, then the fraction of the energy lost by m_1 is $4m_1m_2/(m_1 + m_2)^2$. (b) Considering m_1 constant and m_2 variable, show that this loss is maximum for $m_1 = m_2$. (c) How much is this maximum loss in percent?

43-8. How many head-on, elastic collisions must a neutron have with other particles to reduce its energy from 1 Mev to 0.025 ev if the particles are atoms of (a) deuterium, (b) carbon, and (c) lead?

43–9. Complete each of the following by writing the nuclear reaction equation:

$$Al^{27}(n, \alpha)?,$$

$$Cu^{58} \rightarrow Ni^{58} + ?,$$

$$B^{11}(\gamma, ?)Be^{8},$$

$$N^{14}(\alpha, n)?,$$

$$In^{115}(n, \gamma)?,$$

$$Na^{24} \rightarrow Mg^{24} + ?,$$

$$P^{31}(\gamma, n)?,$$

$$P^{31}(d, p)?,$$

$$P^{30} \rightarrow ? + {}_{+1}e^{0} \text{ (or } \beta^{+}),$$

$$Ni^{58}(p, n)?,$$

$$C^{12}(\gamma, \alpha)?,$$

$$Co^{59}(n, ?)Co^{60}.$$

43–10. A certain photonuclear reaction is $Mg^{24}(\gamma, n)Mg^{23}$. What is the least energy the photon must have to produce this reaction, *assuming that the products have negligible kinetic energy?* The isotopic mass of the product nuclide is 23.001453. (To conserve momentum, the product particles must have velocities and therefore some kinetic energy.)

43–11. The Q-value of the disintegration of Ra^{226} by alpha-particle emission to form Rn^{222} was found, from Eq. (43–41), to be 4.87 Mev. Using this result and the laws of conservation of energy and of momentum, find (a) the recoil energy of the radon nucleus, and (b) the kinetic energy of the alpha particle. (c) Does your answer to part (b) agree with the value of the energy of the alpha particle ejected by radium given in Table 42–1?

43–12. (a) Calculate the Q-value of the reaction in the Cockcroft-Walton experiment in which Li^{7}, when bombarded with 0.7-Mev protons,

produced two alpha particles having equal kinetic energies. (b) What is the kinetic energy of each alpha particle? (c) What is the range of each of these alpha particles in air at 15°C and 1 atm pressure? [Use Eq. (43–4) and the result of Problem 43–1. Comparative data for alpha particles from RaC' are given in Problem 43–2.]

43–13. A bombarding particle of mass m_1 and kinetic energy E_{k1} strikes a nucleus at rest having a mass m_2. The resulting nuclear reaction produces two particles having masses m_3 and m_4 and kinetic energies E_{k3} and E_{k4} respectively.

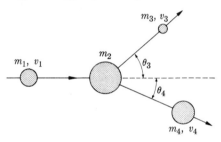

FIGURE 43–10

The directions of their motions are shown in the accompanying figure. Using classical mechanics, show that

$$Q = \left(1 + \frac{m_3}{m_4}\right) E_{k3}$$

$$- \left(1 - \frac{m_1}{m_4}\right) E_{k1}$$

$$- \frac{2\sqrt{m_1 m_3 E_{k1} E_{k3}}}{m_4} \cos \theta_3.$$

43–14. (a) Compute the Q-value of the reaction $N^{14}(\alpha, p)O^{17}$, which occurred in Rutherford's alpha-range-in-nitrogen experiment. (b) If a 7.68-Mev alpha particle causes the reaction in part (a) in a nitrogen atom which is initially at rest, what is the kinetic energy of the proton produced, assuming that it and the product nucleus continue in the direction of the motion of the incident alpha particle?

43–15. Two reactions which occur in the upper atmosphere due to the effects of cosmic "rays" are $N^{14}(n, p)$?; and $N^{14}(n, ?)C^{12}$. (a) Complete the nuclear reaction equation for each and calculate the Q-value of each. (b) Is the nuclide formed in each case stable or radioactive? (See Appendixes 4 and 5.)

43–16. Due to C^{14}, the charcoal from the fire pit in an ancient Indian camp site has an average beta activity of 12.9 disintegrations per minute per gram of carbon in the sample (dpm/gm). The absolute specific activity of the C^{14} in the wood from living trees is independent of the species of the tree and it averages 15.3 dpm/gm. What is the age of the charcoal sample?

43–17. If each of the average counts in Problem 43–16 has a numerical uncertainty of ±0.1 dpm/gm and if the half-life of C^{14} is 5568 ± 30 years, what is the probable error in the determination of the age of the charcoal sample?

43–18. The tritium content of the water from certain deep wells is only 33% of that in the water from recent rains. (a) How long has it been since the water in the well came down as rain? (b) What assumption did you make about tritium in solving this problem?

43–19. What must be the activity of a radiosodium (Na^{24}) compound when it is shipped from Oak Ridge National Laboratory so that upon arrival at a hospital 24 hr later its activity will be 100 millicuries?

43–20. The steel compression ring for the piston of an automobile engine has a mass of 30 gm. The ring is irradiated with neutrons until it has an activity of 10 microcuries due to the formation of Fe^{59} ($T = 45.1$ days). Nine days later the ring is installed in an engine. After being used for 30 days, the crankcase oil has an average activity due to Fe^{59} of 12.6 disintegrations per minute per 100 cm^3. What was the mass of iron worn off this piston ring if the total volume of the crankcase oil is 6 qt?

43–21. Determine, by referring to Fig. 43–7, whether energy must be supplied or will be released if we assume that the following transmutations can be accomplished: Fe → Xe, Li → Na, and Pb → Al.

43–22. (a) Find the total binding energy and the binding energy per nucleon of H^2, He^4, and Fe^{56}. (b) How much energy would be involved in removing the nucleons in He to infinity? Would energy be released or have to be supplied for this dispersion?

CHAPTER 44

NUCLEAR ENERGY

44–1 Nuclear energy. Although one wink of your eye requires the expenditure of many billions of electron volts of chemical energy, nuclear processes are potentially far more energetic than chemical processes. The Q-values we have been discussing are energies per single disintegration, whereas the energy to wink an eye comes from the chemical conversion of many billions of molecules. The liberation of chemical energy is usually expressed on a per-gram, per-pound, or per-mole basis, and the conversion factor between per kilogram-mole and per molecule basis is Avogadro's number, about 6×10^{26}. In Section 42–8 we compared the energy from oxidizing carbon and from radioactive disintegration on a per-gram basis. Table 44–1 lists some energies on a per-particle basis.

TABLE 44–1

ENERGIES PER PARTICLE

Kinetic energy of one water molecule, 450-ft waterfall	0.00025	ev
Average kinetic energy of a gas molecule at room temperature	0.025	ev
Carbon atom oxidized to CO_2	4.0	ev
Visible photon	2.0	ev
Ultraviolet photon	3.0 to 100.0	ev
Hard x-ray photon	0.1 to 1.0	Mev
Gamma-ray photon	1.0 to 3.0	Mev
Radium disintegration	4.8	Mev
Fission disintegration, uranium	200.0	Mev
Cosmic-ray particle	1.0 to 10.0	Bev

The first and third processes of Table 44–1 account for most of the energy utilized in industrial and life processes.

We have seen that radioactive disintegrations are nuclear processes in which an appreciable amount of rest mass-energy is converted to kinetic mass-energy. The mass-energy equation which we have repeatedly applied to nuclear reactions is perfectly general and can be applied to chemical reactions as well. We can write

$$C + 2(O) = CO_2 + Q, \qquad (44\text{–}1)$$

but nothing useful can be learned from applying the equivalence of mass-energy to a chemical equation. The Q-value in amu is $4.0/(931 \times 10^6)$ or 4.3×10^{-9} amu. In the chemical reaction, the carbon and oxygen would be mixtures of isotopes, but even if pure isotopes were used the uncertainty of the isotopic masses far exceeds the Q-value. Thus in chemical reactions it is proper to assume that mass and energy are conserved separately. We write Eq. (44–1) in order to emphasize the contrast between chemical and nuclear reactions.

44–2 Chain reaction. Highly energetic radioactive disintegrations are not very promising as practical sources of energy. Although man-made radioactive nuclides are available in far greater quantities than the naturally radioactive nuclides, there is none whose abundance would justify fleeting consideration as a prime source of energy in a class with coal or oil. Nevertheless, the United States Atomic Energy Commission has announced that radioactivity may be utilized to make electric batteries of exceptionally long life. Thus energy from radioactivity will find limited use in special applications.

Some nuclear transmutations provide more energy per event than the natural radioactive disintegrations. The $Li^6(d, \alpha)He^4$ process has a Q-value of 22.4 Mev. But this reaction requires accelerated deuterons, and the energy required to operate the apparatus is millions of times greater than the energy derived from the process.

Although fission reactions release more energy per event than any type of reaction known earlier, it is another property of fission that makes it a practical source of energy.

The principal isotope of uranium that undergoes fission is U^{235}. This nuclide, which has about a 0.7% concentration in natural uranium, fissions in many ways. The *fission yield* of a fission product is the percentage of the fissions that lead to the formation of a particular nuclide or a group of isobars. Since there are two nuclides produced per fission, the total of all the fission yields for a given process is 200%. The fission yield from U^{235} of nuclides of different mass numbers is shown in Fig. 44–1 (note that the ordinate scale is logarithmic). Obviously, we can write no unique reaction, but a typical one is

$$_{92}U^{235} + {_0}n^1 \rightarrow {_{92}}U^{236} \rightarrow {_{54}}Xe^{140} + {_{38}}Sr^{94} + 2\ {_0}n^1 + \gamma + 200 \text{ Mev.}$$
$$(44\text{–}2)$$

The fission energies and the fission-yield curves for U^{238} and Pu^{239} do not differ appreciably from U^{235}. Some heavy nuclei undergo *spontaneous fission* in which the nucleus divides in the ground state without being bombarded by neutrons or other particles. The half-life of U^{238} and certain other heavy nuclei for this process is of the order of 10^{16} years.

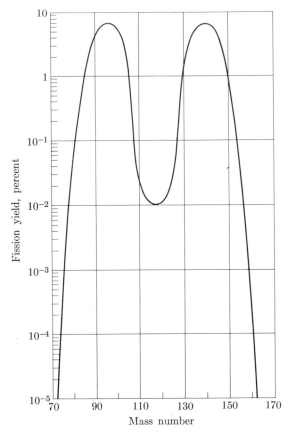

FIG. 44–1. Fission yield from U^{235}.

Therefore, only about 20 nuclei per gram of these elements undergo fission every hour. Their contribution to the operation of a reactor is insignificant and will be neglected in further discussion.

Figure 43–9 is a graph of the number of nuclide neutrons as a function of nuclide protons for the stable elements. This figure shows that the heavier the element, the greater its neutron excess. When a fission occurs, the product nuclides are lighter than the parent element and, to be stable, they must have a smaller excess of neutrons. The nuclides first formed have neutron excesses which make them either absolutely or radioactively unstable against neutron emission (see the first and third cases of Section 43–10). Both Xe^{140} and Sr^{94} are radioactive beta emitters; therefore Eq. (44–2) does not take us to the end of the disintegration. Before these two nuclides were formed, they had a parent nuclide which was a neutron emitter. Its two neutrons appear on the right side of the equation along with the large Q-value.

The *average* number of neutrons from U^{235} is 2.5 per fission. They provided the real potentiality of fission as a power source because they made a chain reaction appear feasible. Here was a reaction that had among its products the same kind of particle that initiated it. If, on the average, at least one neutron from the first fission could produce another fission, and at least one neutron from the second could produce a third, etc., then a self-sustaining chain of events would take place with no necessity for accelerators or other devices to keep the process going. The first fission reactions were obviously not self-sustaining chain reactions since the fission activity stopped when the neutron source was removed. Although some of the neutrons from the first fission reactions undoubtedly caused other fission reactions, it was evident that too many of the neutrons produced were being absorbed in some nonfission-producing manner. The problem that faced nuclear physicists can be stated simply: Under what experimental conditions—if any—could the fission reaction be made self-sustaining?

Soon after the fission of U^{235} was accomplished, two more reactions were found. These produced the transuranic nuclides Fermi set out to produce in his original experiments in 1934. Just as he expected, simple neutron capture is followed by beta activity and the formation of the transuranic element neptunium, Np.

$$_{92}U^{238} + {_0}n^1 \rightarrow {_{92}}U^{239} \rightarrow {_{93}}Np^{239} + {_{-1}}e^0. \qquad (44\text{--}3)$$

The neptunium, which is radioactive with a half-life of 2.33 days, becomes plutonium, Pu:

$$_{93}Np^{239} \rightarrow {_{94}}Pu^{239} + {_{-1}}e^0. \qquad (44\text{--}4)$$

The plutonium is also radioactive, but its half-life is 24,400 years. It, like U^{235}, is fissionable, and we shall see that it is a very important nuclide.

Enough has now been said to account for the fact that a chain reaction did not occur when the first uranium sample was bombarded with neutrons. In the first place, we know that neutrons are very penetrating. Thus the most likely fate of neutrons from the first fission was escape from the uranium sample. The original uranium samples were mixtures of U^{235} and U^{238}. Since U^{238} is much more abundant than U^{235}, the neutrons that did not escape from the first fission reactions had an excellent chance of nonfission capture by U^{238}. It was anticipated that if U^{235} could be separated from U^{238} and other neutron-capturing nuclides, and if enough of this pure U^{235} could be prepared so that neutrons had a good chance of causing fission before they could escape, then a chain reaction would probably occur. If the chain reaction grew within a large body of U^{235}, energy should be liberated in explosive amounts.

44–3 Neutron cross sections. In our previous discussion of nuclear reactions we have been concerned with "what happens" rather than with "how much happens." Although the reaction products have been so minute that identification was difficult, the minuteness did not detract from interest in "what happened." In discussing a chain reaction where one event must successfully cause another, "how much" is just as important as "what."

In Chapter 18 we introduced the concept of mutual collision cross section as a way of describing the probability of one particle hitting another. We showed that this cross section was a property of both the bullet and the target particles, since it is defined as

$$\sigma = \pi(r_{\text{bullet}} + r_{\text{target}})^2. \qquad (44\text{–}5)$$

By assigning this area to the target particle, we could regard the bullet particle as a point and still have a measure of the likelihood of a collision. When we introduced this concept we were discussing the kinetic theory of gases. The particles were whole, uncharged atoms, and we were thinking of the collisions as being pure mechanical hits, like those between billiard balls. If we considered collisions between positive ions, the cross section for deflection would be bigger. The coulomb force of repulsion would extend beyond the physical limits of the particles, so that the bullet particle would be deflected without coming so near the target particle. Although the ion-deflection cross section would be bigger than if the same atoms were not ionized, the cross section for chemical interaction would be less. The mutual repulsion that increases the probability of deflection diminishes the probability of near approach. Thus the concept of cross section becomes a general and useful measure of the probability of many classes of "collisions." If two particles can interact in more than one way, the probabilities of the various interactions can be measured in terms of the cross section of each.

If, instead of thinking of a gas molecule moving through a gas, we think of a neutron moving through matter, we find that a variety of kinds of collision interactions are possible. Each has its own probability, which is directly proportional to its cross section. Some of the possibilities are listed in Table 44–2.

In Chapter 18 we showed that the probability of a particle making a simple collision in going through a gas for a distance dx was $n\sigma\,dx$, where σ is the mutual collision cross section, and n is the number of particles per unit volume (Eq. 18–24). In complete analogy, we may now say that the probability of a neutron causing fission in moving a distance dx through matter composed of an element whose atoms are at rest is

$$P_f = \sigma_f N\,dx, \qquad (44\text{–}6)$$

TABLE 44–2

Process name	Reaction type	Cross-section symbol
Radiative capture	(n, γ)	σ_r
Fission	(n, f)	σ_f
Elastic scattering	(n, n)	σ_s
Proton capture, etc. (absorption)	(n, p), (n, d), etc.	σ_a
Total	$\sum \sigma$'s	σ_t

where the nuclear concentration, N, is the number of nuclei per unit volume. The *microscopic cross sections*, σ's, become the *macroscopic cross sections*, $N\sigma$'s, when multiplied by N. The total probability that some type of interaction will occur is

$$P_t = (\sigma_f + \sigma_s + \sigma_a + \text{etc.})N \, dx. \qquad (44\text{–}7)$$

If the material is composed of more than one element then the neutron may collide with any nuclide present, depending on the concentration of the nuclide and its cross sections. Thus if there are two nuclides present in concentration N and N', the *total probability* that the neutron will undergo some interaction in going a distance dx is

$$P_t = (N\sigma_t + N'\sigma_t') \, dx. \qquad (44\text{–}8)$$

Before these equations can be used quantitatively, the values of the σ's must be known. Although many σ's were known before the period of secrecy about the fission process, one of the first tasks in calculating the feasibility of a chain reaction was the determination of many more cross sections. Mathematically, this process is very much like the determination of the probabilities of radioactive decay, the decay constants.

If I_0 incident neutrons per second produce I_f fissions per second, then the probability of fission is

$$P_f = \frac{I_f}{I_0}. \qquad (44\text{–}9)$$

But P_f is also given by Eq. (44–6), so we may write

$$\frac{I_f}{I_0} = N\sigma_f \, dx$$

or

$$\sigma_f = \frac{I_f}{I_0 N \, dx}. \qquad (44\text{–}10)$$

Thus if we know the number of fissions produced per second by a known number of neutrons per second in a material of known concentration and thickness, the fission cross section can be determined. By measuring the number of absorptions per second or the number of scatters per second, etc., these cross sections can be determined.

In this differential method it is assumed that dx is so small that the intensity of the neutron beam can be considered constant throughout the thickness of material, and that the nuclei in the material cannot hide behind one another.

If the slab of material has finite thickness, then the neutron intensity is a variable, I, and we must integrate to determine its value. In penetrating a slab of the material of thickness dx, the intensity of the neutron beam is changed an amount $(-dI)$ by any interactions that remove neutrons from the beam. The total probability of interaction is then

$$P_t = -\frac{dI}{I} = N\sigma_t\,dx. \qquad (44\text{--}11)$$

Upon integrating, and noting that for $x = 0$ we have $I = I_0$, we obtain

$$\boxed{I = I_0 e^{-N\sigma_t x},} \qquad (44\text{--}12)$$

where I is the intensity of the *transmitted* beam. This equation permits the evaluation of the total cross section from data such as those given in Fig. 44–2 and provides a check on the more difficult differential method through the equation

$$\boxed{\sigma_t = \sigma_f + \sigma_s + \sigma_a + \text{etc.}} \qquad (44\text{--}13)$$

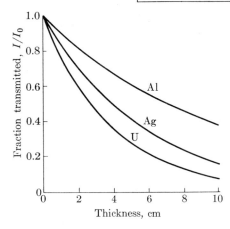

FIG. 44–2. Neutron absorption curves.

As in Eq. (18–26), we can now speak of the neutron mean free path:

$$\boxed{L_t = \frac{1}{N\sigma_t}\cdot} \qquad (44\text{--}14)$$

Or for the mean neutron path per fission we may write

$$L_f = \frac{1}{N\sigma_f}\cdot \qquad (44\text{--}15)$$

If the material is a mixture of two

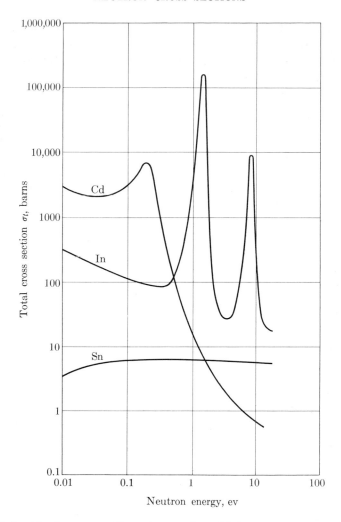

1,000,000

100,000

10,000

1000

Total cross section σ_t, barns

100

10

1

0.1

0.01   0.1   1   10   100

Neutron energy, ev

Cd

In

Sn

FIG. 44–3. Total cross section of several nuclei for neutrons as a function of energy.

fissionable materials having different fission cross sections and different nuclear concentrations, the mean neutron path per fission becomes

$$L_f = \frac{1}{N\sigma_f + N'\sigma_f'}. \qquad (44\text{--}16)$$

The measurement of cross sections is complicated by the fact that not only does each nuclide have several cross sections but also cross sections are often complicated functions of the neutron energy. The total cross sections of three nuclides are shown in Fig. 44–3. Since the microscopic cross sections are usually very small quantities, it is convenient to have a special unit for them, the *barn*. One barn is an area equal to 10^{-24} cm^2. Cross sections are proportional to the probabilities of neutron reactions. Although cross sections have area units, they are not the physical cross sections of the nuclei. Nevertheless, it is interesting to note that most nuclides have "diameters" of about 10^{-12} cm and consequently their physical cross sections are about 1 barn.

Although every cross section should be expressed as a function of energy, as in Fig. 44–3, many elements have cross sections which can be represented by a simple equation. These nuclides have cross sections which vary inversely as the velocity of the neutron. Such materials are called *1/v-absorbers*. The most important neutron energy distinction is that between fast neutrons and thermal neutrons. Neutrons from a fission reaction are fast and have an average energy of about 2 Mev. Neutrons which have traversed enough matter to be in thermal equilibrium with the molecular motions of the material are called *slow* or *thermal* neutrons, and these have energies distributed about the value of 0.025 ev. Table

TABLE 44–3

NEUTRON CROSS SECTIONS IN BARNS

Values in parentheses are less certain than the others. Data taken or deduced from *Neutron Cross Sections*, Brookhaven National Laboratory (325).

	σ_t (slow)	σ_t (fast)	σ_s (slow)	σ_a (slow)	σ_f (slow)	σ_f (fast)
H^1	(38)	(4.3)	38	0.33	0	0
H$_2$O	(110)					
D^2	(7)	(3.4)	7	0.0005	0	0
D$_2$O	(14.5)				0	0
T^3	5400	(1.9)	1	5400	0	0
Li	(72)	(1.7)	1.4	71	0	0
Li^6	(951)	(0.26)	(6)	945	0	0
Li^7	(1.4)		(1.4)	(0)	0	0
B	(760)		4	755	0	0
C	(4.8)		4.8	0.0032	0	0
O	(4.2)		4.2	0.0002	0	0
Zr	(8)		8	0.18	0	0
Cd	(2560)		7	2550	0	0
Hf	(113)		8	105	0	0
U (natural)		(7)	4.7 (fast)	(2) (fast)		0.5
U^{235}	697	6.5	10	107	580	1.3
U^{238}	2.8		0	2.8	0.0005	0.5
Pu^{239}	1075		9.6	315	750	

44–3 gives values of the cross sections of several important nuclides for these two energies.

Obtaining neutron cross sections as a function of velocity requires methods for measuring neutron velocities. We cannot discuss these methods in detail, but it is easy to see that for uncharged particles many familiar methods must be excluded. We can diffract neutrons by crystals and thus obtain the de Broglie wavelength, from which the velocity can be computed. Also there are mechanical devices which can "chop" a slow neutron beam so as to eliminate all neutrons outside a narrow energy range.

44–4 Reactor criticality. We are now in a position to make simple calculations that give some idea of what we may expect in various circumstances. Consider first that we have a very large body of pure U^{238}. It is known that each fission produces about 2.5 neutrons having energies of about 2 Mev. Since the body of metal is very large, we can neglect the loss of neutrons by escape and consider the probable fate of neutrons within the metal. We consider three possibilities.

(1) Neutrons may scatter elastically within the metal. These collisions have a cross section of 4.7 barns for fast neutrons, so that scattering collisions are rather common. That scattering collisions deflect the neutrons is of no consequence. So long as the neutrons remain within the metal, their direction of motion makes no difference. Scattering collisions slow the neutrons but, since the uranium nuclei are 238 times as massive as the neutrons, it takes many collisions to slow the neutrons appreciably. We therefore ignore the influence of scattering.

(2) The neutrons may be absorbed in some nonfissioning manner, such as that described in Eq. (44–3). These absorptions have a cross section of 2 barns for high-energy (fast) neutrons and represent neutron loss so far as the possibility of a chain reaction is concerned.

(3) The neutrons may produce fission reactions for which the cross section is 0.5 barn. These neutrons are productively absorbed and tend to maintain the chain reaction. Under our assumptions, the probability that one neutron will produce another fission is the microscopic fission cross section divided by the total cross section, or

$$P_f = \frac{\sigma_f}{\sigma_a + \sigma_f} = \frac{0.5}{2 + 0.5} = 0.2.$$

Thus about one out of five neutrons produces a fission. Since each fission produces 2.5 neutrons on the average, each neutron probably produces $0.2 \times 2.5 = 0.5$ neutron. We can summarize this result in the following way. If there were ten neutrons in one neutron generation, eight of these would be unproductively absorbed and two would produce fission. Each fission would produce 2.5 neutrons, so that in the next generation there would be five neutrons. Thus each generation has half as many neutrons as the preceding one and no chain reaction can occur. The ratio of the number of neutrons in one generation to the number in the preceding generation is called the production factor or *multiplication constant, k*. When the body of material is so large that leakage may be neglected, the multiplication constant is represented by the symbol k_∞, called *k-infinity* or *infinite (k)*. Since we have found $k_\infty = 0.5$ for a body of U^{238}, we know that any amount of U^{238} will be *subcritical*. This means that k is less than unity and that any fission process that may be initiated will quickly die out.

If we repeat these calculations for U^{235} under the same assumptions, we find a very different result. Every U^{235} nucleus that absorbs a high-energy neutron produces a fission. Since every absorbed neutron produces another fission, the multiplication constant is simply the number of neutrons per fission, or $k_\infty = 2.5$, and it is evident that each neutron generation is much larger than the preceding one. A large mass of U^{235} would explode. The only way to prevent a body of pure U^{235} from exploding would be to break it into pieces so small that 60% of the neutrons would escape without producing fission. These pieces would each be under the critical size for U^{235}.

The concept of critical size results from the fact that fissions occur throughout the volume of a reacting body and neutrons escape through the surface of that body. As the size of a body is changed, the volume changes according to the cube of its dimensions, while its area changes as the square of its dimensions. Thus the ratio of neutron production to neutron leakage varies as the first power of the dimensions. If the configuration of the reactor is such that k_∞ is greater than unity, there is always a smaller size for which the material will be just critical, with k equal to unity. Below this size k is less than unity. In summary: above the critical size, k is greater than unity and the neutron population increases exponentially with time; *at the critical size, k is equal to one* and the neutron population is constant; below the critical size, k is less than unity and the neutron population falls off exponentially with time.

The calculations we have made are sufficient to show that natural uranium, which is about 99.3% U^{238} and 0.7% U^{235}, cannot chain react and that the concentration of the U^{235} must be increased. In order to estimate the degree of enrichment required, we make a third calculation under the same assumptions as before, except that we now have a metal composed of a mixture of U^{235} and U^{238} in which the number of nuclei per unit volume is designated by N_5 and N_8, respectively. The calculation is made just as before, but now we must use the fast-neutron cross sections of both nuclides weighted according to their concentrations.

Since $\sigma_a = 0$ for fast neutrons in U^{235}, we have

$$k_\infty = 2.5 \frac{N_5\sigma_{f5} + N_8\sigma_{f8}}{N_5(\sigma_{a5} + \sigma_{f5}) + N_8(\sigma_{a8} + \sigma_{f8})} \qquad (44\text{–}17)$$

$$= 2.5 \frac{1.3N_5 + 0.5N_8}{(0 + 1.3)N_5 + (2 + 0.5)N_8}. \qquad (44\text{–}18)$$

Letting $N_5 = 0$ gives the result of our first calculation and letting $N_8 = 0$ gives our second result. Letting $k_\infty = 1$, we can find the concentration ratio that will make a large mass of uranium critical. Solving for N_8/N_5, we obtain 1.5, which tells us that for a large body of uranium metal to be critical it must be about 40% U^{235}. For a body of finite size, the enrichment of U^{235} would have to be greater than 40%. Calculations such as these led to the decision to attempt the enrichment of U^{235} in uranium metal.

The separation of isotopes is always difficult, but since uranium is the heaviest natural element, the fractional mass difference between U^{235} and U^{238} is especially small.

The most effective method of separation found was the gaseous diffusion of uranium hexafluoride, UF_6. Although the enrichment of U^{235} to about 99% purity requires about 4000 diffusion stages, a tremendous plant based on this principle was built at Oak Ridge, Tennessee, which has been in production since 1945. A measure of the difficulty of this process is contained in the fact that in 1955 the AEC evaluated natural uranium at $40 per kgm and 95% U^{235} at $16,258 per kgm. With fuel enriched with U^{235}, the construction of a fast-neutron bomb reactor is, in principle, simple. The uranium parts must each be less than critical size lest they explode spontaneously from stray neutrons or an occasional spontaneous fission. Detonation is accomplished by bringing the subcritical parts together into a *supercritical* whole. The critical size of the U^{235} enriched uranium is about the size of a grapefruit.

44–5 Moderators. A glance at Table 44–3 shows that the uranium cross sections for slow neutrons are very different from those for fast neutrons. Whereas most nuclear reactions are best induced with high-energy particles, neutron-induced reactions usually have cross sections which increase as the neutron energy is decreased. This may be phrased in a somewhat naive way by saying that since there is no coulomb repulsion, slow neutrons spend more time near the nuclei they pass and therefore the short-range nuclear attractive forces have a better chance to take effect. This is why many cross sections vary as $1/v$.

The nonfission capture cross section of U^{238} increases as the neutron energy is reduced, but the fission cross section of U^{235} increases even more.

Thus the relative probability of fission in natural uranium is much greater for low-energy neutrons than for high-energy neutrons. To show how marked this difference is, we next compute the production factor that a large body of natural uranium *would* have *if* each fission produced 2.5 *thermal* neutrons. We again use Eq. (44–17), except that we substitute the thermal cross sections and take $N_8/N_5 = 1/0.007 = 143$, which yields

$$k_\infty = 2.5 \frac{1 \times 580 + 143 \times 0.0005}{1 \times (107 + 580) + 143(2.8 + 0.0005)} = 1.33. \quad (44\text{–}19)$$

Since k_∞ is considerably greater than unity, it appears that even a finite size of natural uranium would chain react if the fission neutrons were slow. Since fission neutrons are fast rather than slow, the calculation we have just made is purely academic unless neutrons can be slowed. Even before the period of secrecy, it was proposed that if the fast-fission neutrons could be slowed (*moderated*) critical conditions might be achieved in natural uranium.

Another important consideration is brought out qualitatively in Fig. 44–4(a). For neutrons with an energy of about 7 ev, U^{238} has a neutron resonance capture in which the U^{238} nucleus has a very large probability of going into an excited state. Thus, in a natural mixture of U^{235} and U^{238}, there is very little chance that a neutron will be slowed below 7 ev, to the energy for which the probability of U^{235} fission capture is very great.

The idea of using a moderator to increase the probability of a chain reaction was based on these variations of cross section with neutron velocity. If the fast-fission neutrons could escape from a lump of uranium and be slowed to very low energies, and were then allowed to fall on natural

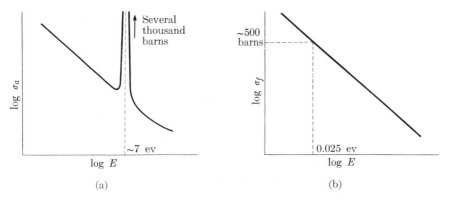

FIG. 44–4. (a) Capture cross section of U^{238} for slow neutrons, and (b) fission cross section of U^{235} for slow neutrons, assuming a $1/v$ relationship.

uranium, the relative probability of fission might be increased enough so that a chain reaction would result.

There are reactions in which a neutron is absorbed and then one, two, or even three neutrons of lower energy are emitted. Such reactions have the effect of slowing neutrons and even increasing their number, but these reactions are most easily produced in heavy nuclei with high-energy neutrons. For the slowing of neutrons with the average energy of fission neutrons, about 2 Mev, elastic scattering is much more suitable.

In our discussion of the discovery of the neutron, we worked out the mechanics of head-on collisions between moving particles and particles at rest (Section 43–3). We found that the energy transfer depends on the relative masses of the bodies involved in the collision and, in particular, that if a body strikes another body having the same mass, all the energy of the first body is transferred to the second one. If the collision is not head-on, the fraction of the energy transferred is certainly less. It is not too difficult to compute the *average fractional energy loss* between two bodies whose relative masses are known when the effect of *glancing collisions* is taken into account. This fraction is greatest when the two bodies have the same mass.

If a neutron enters a material, it loses a certain average fraction of its energy with each collision so long as the material nuclei can be considered at rest. If the neutron survives capture until its energy is reduced nearly to that due to thermal motion of the material molecules, then its energy loss per collision is much less than before. Indeed, at these energies there is a chance that the neutron may acquire energy from the molecules. Thus thermal agitation sets a lower limit to the energy a neutron acquires by the collision process. In Chapter 18 we showed that the average kinetic energy of a gas molecule depends only on its temperature, and we can consider neutrons in equilibrium with a moderator to be a gas at the same temperature as the moderator. Thus no moderator can reduce the energies of neutrons below the energies of the moderator molecules. The energies of the molecules of a gas at room temperature, 20°C, are distributed about a value of 0.025 ev. Neutrons in thermal equilibrium with matter at 20°C will have the same energy distribution as such gas molecules. These neutrons are called thermal neutrons.

Assuming that fission neutrons are emitted with an average energy of 2 Mev and have an energy of 0.025 ev when they have been "thermalized," we find the total fractional energy reduction to be $0.025/(2 \times 10^6) = 1.3 \times 10^{-8}$. This fractional energy loss must equal the average fractional energy loss per collision to the nth power, where n is the average number of collisions required to produce thermalization. Since the absorption cross sections are functions of the neutron energy, it is awkward to compute the chance a neutron has to survive the thermalization process, but if

TABLE 44–4

Element	σ (absorption), barns	σ (scatter), barns	Average fractional energy loss per collision	Average number of collisions to thermalize, n
H	0.33	38	0.63	18
D	0.0005	7	0.52	25
He	0.000	1	0.35	42
Li	71	1.4	0.27	62
Be	0.01	7	0.18 ·	90
B	755	4	0.17	98
C	0.0032	4.8	0.14	114
N	1.7	10	0.12	132
O	0.0002	4.2	0.11	150

criticality is to be achieved this chance times the number of neutrons per fission must be at least one.

Table 44–4 shows some of the characteristics of light elements as neutron moderators. Mechanically, hydrogen is the best moderating nuclide, since it requires, on the average, only 18 collisions to achieve thermalization. But since hydrogen can absorb neutrons to form deuterium, the chance of a neutron surviving the 18 collisions is not too good. We shall see, however, that hydrogen in ordinary water can be used as a moderator.

Deuterium requires 25 collisions on the average, but it has more promise as a moderator because its capture cross section is small. Oxygen also has a small capture cross section. Since a gas moderator has a very small number of nuclei per unit volume, both hydrogen and deuterium are used as moderators in the form of water.

Helium would be a superior moderator except that its inertness prevents its concentration in a chemical compound.

Both lithium and boron have absorption cross sections that are too high. Thus beryllium and carbon are the lowest atomic weight elements that are solid at room temperature and whose neutron absorption cross sections are low enough for consideration as moderators. Of these, carbon is by far the more abundant and thus it is used more frequently.

After neutrons have undergone a number of random glancing collisions in a material, the motions of some of them will have been deviated so much that they return to the region from which they came. This "back scattering" is equivalent to diffuse reflection. Any material that has a low neutron absorption cross section can be used as a *neutron reflector*. If the "reflected" beam is to be thermalized, then the scatter cross section of the atoms of the reflector must be large.

44–6 The first reactor. In 1942 many physicists believed that chain reaction would occur in pure U^{235} and possibly in ordinary unenriched uranium in a properly moderated reactor. The first alternative required the very difficult separation of a considerable amount of U^{235} from its isotope, U^{238}. The second alternative appeared to be the faster way of testing the theoretical calculations.

Graphite for the moderator had to be prepared in an especially pure form, since any impurities such as boron and cadmium (neutron absorbers) would reduce the number of neutrons that survived the slowing-down process.

Uranium had never been used commercially, and in 1941 there were only a few grams of the pure metal in the United States. By the fall of 1942 about six tons of uranium metal had been prepared. It, too, had to be free of neutron-absorbing impurities.

Before the reactor (pile) could be built, there had to be instrumentation for its control. In the first pile and in all controlled reactors that have followed it, the basis for control is the presence of materials which are good neutron absorbers. We have seen that boron has a large absorption cross section and cadmium is another good neutron absorber. These elements, alloyed with steel in the form of rods, can be pushed into the pile to make it subcritical and to adjust the multiplication constant k.

Before the pile could be built, it was important to know how rapidly it would respond to control-rod manipulation. Fortunately, not all the neutrons emitted by fission appear at once. Although most neutrons are produced without delay, i.e., *prompt neutrons*, some of the fission products are radioactive neutron emitters that produce *delayed neutrons*. Measurements showed that 0.4% of the neutrons are delayed at least 0.1 sec and that 0.01% are delayed about a minute. Thus a reaction which is subcritical for prompt neutrons can be critical for prompt and delayed neutrons together. (This latter state is sometimes called *delayed critical*.) The idea was that by putting the reactor together with the control rods in place, the rods could be carefully withdrawn at frequent intervals during construction. By seeing to it that the reactor never went critical for prompt neutrons, that is, *prompt critical*, it was assumed that the reactor would be sufficiently sluggish so that human responses could prevent the reactor from "running away" destructively.

This first pile was assembled by Fermi and his associates in a squash court under the stadium of Stagg Field at the University of Chicago. It was a cubic lattice of lumps of uranium in a *pile* of graphite blocks. The lump size was a compromise. They were made large, so as to include as many U^{235} nuclei as possible, and yet small enough so that most of the fast-fission neutrons escaped without capture by U^{238}. They were about 10 cm in diameter. The graphite space between the lumps was chosen so that most of the neutrons from one lump would be thermalized by the time

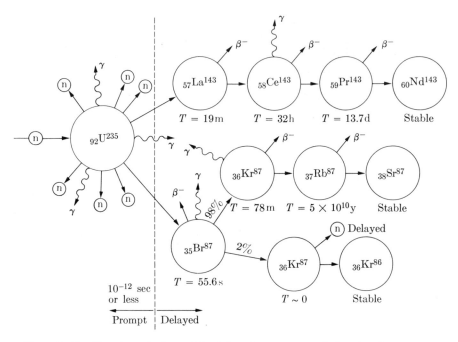

FIG. 44–5. Uranium fission with delayed neutron emission in the bromine fission fragment decay chain. The six fission neutrons shown in this example are many more than the 2.5 average.

they reached the next lump about 30 cm away. On the average, then, fission neutrons left the lumps at high energy, were in the graphite when their energy was 7 ev, and re-entered the uranium at 0.025 ev. Since the neutrons were not in the uranium when their energy was at the resonance absorption of U^{238}, the loss of neutrons to U^{238} was small.

The reactor was built around a neutron source using alpha particles from a radioactive source to excite an (α, n) reaction, as in beryllium. As the blocks of graphite and the lumps of uranium were assembled, some fissions occurred and the number of neutrons increased. The neutrons that were not absorbed in the pile material escaped. As the size of the structure grew, the chance that a neutron from one lump would find another lump became greater and the neutron intensity increased. By observing the neutron intensity as the pile grew, Fermi and his associates could anticipate at what stage of the construction the pile would become self-sustaining. The pile first became critical on the afternoon of December 2, 1942, and operated at a power level of $\frac{1}{2}$ watt. It was later increased to 200 watts—the maximum considered safe in that location.

Fermi was concerned that nitrogen of the air in the gaps of the pile would absorb enough neutrons to prevent criticality. He was prepared to encase the entire pile in balloon cloth and flush out the nitrogen with

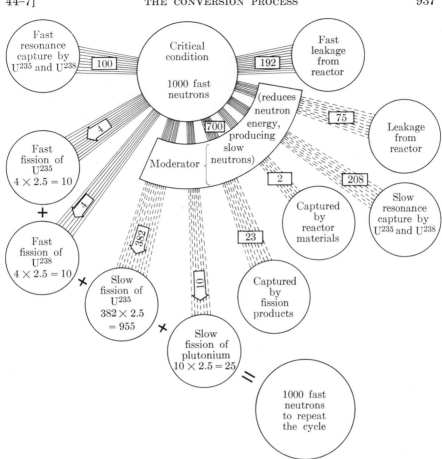

FIG. 44–6. The neutron balance in a natural uranium reactor that is just critical. This sketch shows what might happen to 1000 representative neutrons out of the many millions present within a reactor. (Courtesy of Westinghouse Electric Corporation)

helium or some other gas that has a low absorption cross section. This cloth can be seen in the sketch reproduced in Fig. 44–7.

This first reactor was of tremendous significance. It proved that a chain reaction could be produced and controlled. It is the prototype of all the controlled power-production reactors that have followed it. But in 1942 the motivation was to produce a destructive reactor, and the Chicago pile facilitated this end by making the conversion process practical.

44–7 The conversion process. We have noted that the U^{238}, which absorbs neutrons and hinders the operation of a thermal pile, is ultimately converted to plutonium according to Eqs. (44–3) and (44–4). Plutonium

FIG. 44–7. Sketch of the first nuclear reactor. (Courtesy of the General Electric Company) The inscription on a plaque on the outside wall of the building is: "On December 2, 1942 man achieved here the first self-sustaining chain reaction and thereby initiated the controlled release of nuclear energy."

is fissionable and, since it is a different chemical element, it can be separated from the uranium by chemical methods. Once the Chicago reactor proved that a chain reaction could be maintained, reactors specifically designed for the manufacture of plutonium were built at Oak Ridge, Tennessee and at Hanford, Washington. In these cases, the reactors served only as prolific neutron sources for the bombardment of U^{238}. Although these reactors were designed to permit easy insertion and removal of fuel elements and the removal of heat energy, they used natural uranium and a graphite moderator, just as in the first reactor. A fuel element is left in the reactor until a point of diminishing returns is reached in the conversion of U^{238}. This point comes well before all the U^{235} is used up because the fission products have large neutron capture cross sections and begin *poisoning* the reactor. The impurities absorb an appreciable fraction of the neutrons that are needed to maintain the reaction and to convert U^{238} into plutonium. Once a fuel rod is spent, it is dissolved and the plutonium is separated by chemical processes. This seemingly straightforward operation is complicated by the fact that tremendous quantities of radioactively dangerous material must be handled. This radioactivity is due principally to the fission products which poisoned the fuel element. The mere disposal of these radioactive fission products is a problem of mammoth proportions.

A large amount of this transuranic, man-made element was prepared by this method during World War II. The first atomic bomb was of uranium, but the second contained plutonium.

44–8 Converter reactors. Although there is enough fissionable material in the earth's crust to operate reactors for a long time to come, there is an exciting possibility which may extend that source many fold. Experiments indicate that it is possible to operate a reactor on U^{235} or on Pu^{239} which will not only produce power, but will also convert U^{238} into Pu^{239}. An element like U^{238} which can be transformed into a fissionable substance is called a *fertile material*. The new fuel that is formed in a layer or *blanket* of fertile material placed within a *converter reactor* can supply a significant portion of the total energy output of the system. Eventually, however, the new fissionable material can no longer be utilized effectively because of poisoning in the blanket. This must then be removed and reprocessed. Nevertheless, since U^{238} is otherwise useless, this conversion operation may greatly reduce the net cost of fissionable material.

Thorium is another important fertile material. Nonfissioning thorium is more plentiful than uranium, and it can be converted to a fissionable nuclide by neutron bombardment. The reaction steps are

$$_{90}Th^{232} + {}_0n^1 \rightarrow {}_{91}Pa^{233} + {}_{-1}e^0, \tag{44–20}$$

$$_{91}Pa^{233} \xrightarrow{27.4\ d} {}_{92}U^{233} + {}_{-1}e^0. \tag{44–21}$$

Uranium-233 is fissionable and radioactive. It has a half-life of 1.62×10^5 years.

At present, the word "converter," as applied to reactors, has two meanings that are somewhat different. The broad, general meaning is any reactor that converts fertile atoms into fuel by neutron capture. We have used converter in that sense. But *converter* can also refer to a reactor that uses one kind of fuel and produces another (for example, U^{235} produces Pu^{239} from U^{238}), and then *breeder* is used to designate a reactor in which the primary and the produced fuels are the same (for example, Pu^{239} produces more Pu^{239} from U^{238}). Finally, a *breeder* can also mean a converter that produces more fissionable atoms than it consumes. It usually requires careful reading to determine which of these meanings is being used in articles on reactors.

44–9 Research reactors. Chain reactors may be used for explosions, research, and for power. The primary value of reactors for research is that they are prolific sources of neutrons. Neutrons are produced from reactions excited by particles from radioactive elements and by those produced with accelerators, but the neutrons from chain reactions are many orders of magnitude more numerous than from these other sources. Of all the bombarding particles, neutrons are the best able to produce nuclear rearrangements, and an intense source of neutrons is a powerful tool for the study of nuclear reactions.

In some reactors a window in the protective shielding permits the escape of an intense beam of neutrons that can be used in many ways to learn more about nuclear physics. Another technique is to insert a slug of material into the reactor, where it is subjected to intense neutron irradiation. Practically every element thus irradiated forms radioactive isotopes in significant amounts. Such man-made radioisotopes are used in medical and tracer applications, where they have virtually replaced the naturally radioactive elements. These artificial radionuclides are available to qualified users at very reasonable prices.

The availability of intense radioactive sources permits the study of the effects of their radiations. Cobalt-60 is an example of a man-made isotope which is an intense gamma-ray source. One effect of gamma-ray irradiation under active study is the sterilization of food. Beta or electron irradiation produces promising structural changes in molecules, particularly in high polymers. By this means rubber can be vulcanized, and the melting temperature of polyethylene can be raised.

Since Co^{60} is an intense source of gamma radiation, it is dangerous to be near this material. In laboratories equipped with "gamma facilities" the Co^{60} is immersed to a depth of about ten feet in a deep tank filled with water, to shield the personnel from its radiation. Materials to be irradiated are either lowered into the water near the gamma source or, more commonly, placed near the top of the tank, and the Co^{60} raised out of the water by remote control. Upon disintegrating, Co^{60} nuclei emit beta particles whose maximum energy is 0.31 Mev and gamma rays having energies of 1.17 and 1.33 Mev.

In this section we have seen that a research reactor provides a series of research possibilities. One may study the characteristics of the reactor itself, the nuclear effects produced by excess neutrons, and the properties and behavior of materials made by the reactor.

44–10 Cherenkov radiation. When an intense radioactive source ejects high-energy charged particles into a transparent material such as water, plastic, or glass, a ghostly bluish glow extending some distance into the medium can be seen. This phenomenon is easily observed when a room containing a swimming pool reactor or a gamma facility is darkened. This *Cherenkov radiation* has an interesting explanation and use. Let us consider a particular case, Co^{60} immersed in water. The most energetic beta particles emitted by this radioelement have a relativistic velocity of about $0.8c$. But these electrons move through water, where the velocity of light is about $0.75c$ (computed from c/n, where n is the index of refraction of water). Thus the electrons in the water travel faster than the phase velocity of light *in that medium*. The situation is much like that of a boat going through water faster than the velocity of water waves, or of

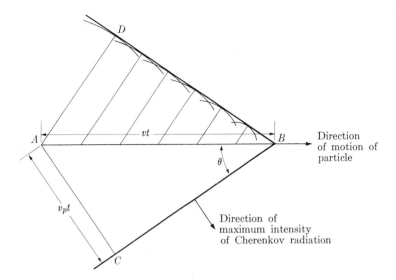

Fɪɢ. 44–8. Bow wave in Cherenkov radiation.

a jet plane going through air faster than the speed of sound in air. The electron produces a "bow-wave" of light. Let a projectile (boat, plane, or electron) move with a velocity v from A to B in time t, as shown in Fig. 44–8. This projectile causes a sequence of disturbances in the medium which combine constructively to form the wavefronts represented by the lines from B to C and from B to D. These wavefronts move with a phase velocity v_p, and while the projectile goes from A to B the Huygens' wavelet (disturbance) from A goes from A to C, a distance $v_p t$. Thus the angle θ between the direction of motion of the projectile and the wavefront is given by

$$\sin \theta = \frac{v_p t}{vt} = \frac{c}{nv}. \qquad (44\text{–}22)$$

It can be shown that the number of quanta emitted as Cherenkov radiation in a wavelength interval $d\lambda$ is proportional to $[1 - (c^2/n^2 v^2)]/\lambda^2$. It is evident from this expression that the short wavelengths will be predominant, and therefore that the color will be bluish white.

Cherenkov radiation can be used to measure electron velocities. The radiation is most intense in the direction of advance of the wavefront, as shown in Fig. 44–8. If the electron beam is collimated so that its direction is known and if the direction of maximum radiation intensity is measured, then θ is determined. Since c and n are known, v can be calculated. The value of n depends on the wavelength of the light. For precision measurements, the direction of Cherenkov radiation should be measured for a particular color.

44–11 Power reactors. Any chain reactor can be adjusted to produce tremendous amounts of energy. It is only necessary to let the chain reaction become supercritical and wait for it to grow. The Chicago reactor was operated first at one-half watt and then at 200 watts, but the power level could have been run much higher. The main reason that the first reactor was operated at so low a level was that it was inadequately shielded and the neutron leakage might have endangered the personnel. The second reason was that there was no provision for cooling the reactor, and if it became too hot it would destroy itself. (There was little chance that the reactor would explode violently. The entrapped gases could have become hot enough to push the pile apart, but this would have made the reactor subcritical and stopped the reaction.) Thus the main physical limitation on the power a reactor can develop is the provision for the removal of heat.

Research reactors can be aircooled because no attempt is made to utilize the heat energy developed, but for power reactors a more dense material is indicated. We naturally think of water as a cooling material, especially since we shall see that water can also serve as a moderator. Boiling-water reactors will be discussed in Section 44–12. An efficient coolant should have a large specific heat capacity (specific heat times density). Since it must flow through the reactor, the use of dense liquid is indicated; and since it should have good thermal conductivity, metals appear attractive. Mercury, a dense liquid metal, has been used for the transfer of thermal energy and has replaced water in some boiler-turbine power systems. But mercury has a slow-neutron absorption cross section of 380 barns for the natural mixture of its isotopes, and this is too great. Not only would mercury absorb neutrons from the chain reactor, but it would also form radioactive isotopes which would render all the apparatus near which it passed radioactive. It turns out that despite its chemical activity, especially when molten, liquid sodium is a good reactor coolant. It is a rather dense material with good thermal conductivity and with a thermal neutron absorption cross section of only 0.5 barn. The sodium is usually alloyed with potassium to lower the melting temperature. The essentials of a sodium-cooled reactor power system are sketched in Fig. 44–9. The reactor itself is cooled by the molten metal and the energy of the molten metal is transferred to water in a heat exchanger. The steam that is generated operates a conventional turbine and electric generator.

The way in which the molten metal is pumped is an ingenious application of basic electrical theory. It is a well-known fact that good thermal conductors are good electrical conductors, and molten sodium is a good electrical conductor. Electric charges moving perpendicular to a magnetic field experience a force perpendicular to both the current and the field, as expressed in Eq. (24–1). Figure 44–10 is a sketch of a liquid-metal pump

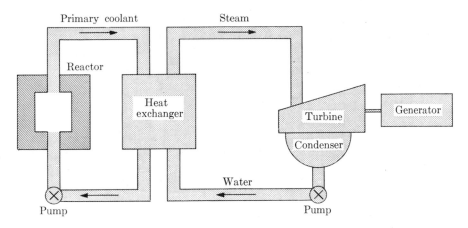

FIG. 44–9. Schematic representation of a liquid-metal coolant reactor.

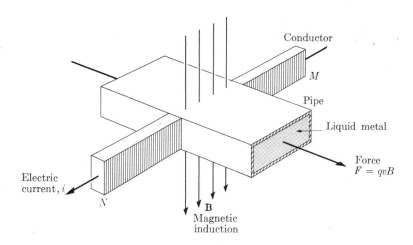

FIG. 44–10.   Schematic diagram of an electromagnetic pump for liquid metals.

based on this law. The electric current from M to N flows partly through the pipe but largely through the conducting liquid metal. Since there is a magnetic field directed toward the bottom of the page, the moving charges experience a force parallel to the pipe. By varying the current or the field or both, the force and pumping action can be controlled. There is obviously no need for sealed bearings, since there are no moving parts.

A heat-transfer "fluid" consisting of a high concentration of finely divided graphite in a stream of compressed air has been developed recently. Because it is inert and has good thermal properties, it may replace corrosive liquid metals as well as coolants that are made radioactive by neutrons.

On the average, the fission energy of either uranium or plutonium is 200 Mev. This is distributed approximately as follows: kinetic energy of the fission fragments, 167 Mev; kinetic energy of the fission neutrons, 5 Mev; prompt gamma rays and delayed gamma rays from the fission fragments, each 6 Mev; and the beta particles and neutrinos from the fission products, 5 Mev and 11 Mev respectively. All of the neutrino energy and some of the gamma-ray and neutron energy escape through the walls of the reactor. This loss is just about compensated by the heat produced in moderating the neutrons plus the energy released in various parts of the reactor by the radioactive decay of atoms that were activated by gamma rays and neutrons. Because the fission fragments and the beta particles are easily absorbed, their energies are converted into heat close to their points of origin. Therefore, about 75% of the heat appears in the fuel rods and their cladding.

44–12 The boiling-water reactor. We have reserved the boiling-water reactor for more detailed discussion because one of the largest all-nuclear-powered generating stations in the United States is of this type.

Although it is impossible to achieve a chain reaction with unenriched uranium and ordinary water as the moderator, ordinary water can moderate a reactor with enriched fissionable fuel. The boiling-water reactor is particularly attractive for two reasons. The moderating water can be converted to steam within the reactor and fed to a turbine without an intermediate heat exchanger, and a boiling-water reactor has an inherent stability which contributes to safety.

If the control rods in a reactor having a solid moderator are set so that the multiplication factor is greater than one, the chain reaction grows without practical limit until the reactor destroys itself. It is not too difficult to prevent this from happening by having safety control rods which can be thrust into the reactor quickly in the event anything goes amiss. (Such a shutdown is called a *scram*.) But a reactor having a solid moderator is basically unstable and always presents the possibility of a minor explosion that might break the shielding walls and spread dangerous radioactive materials in its vicinity.

In a water-moderated reactor even this unlikely hazard is eliminated. If the reactor gets out of hand, the water moderator will boil, and since the bubbles of vapor are not dense enough to moderate the neutrons effectively, the reactor automatically goes *subcritical*. To test this point, the USAEC built a boiling-water reactor and tried to blow it up. They were able to produce a moderate explosion only when all the control rods were jerked out of the reactor simultaneously.

44–13 Natural fusion. In 1928, Professor A. A. Knowlton wrote a physics text in which a unifying theme was the question: Where does the sun's energy come from? He considers the possibility that the sun is leaking energy stored within it during some stage of astronomical evolution. He treats the sun as a coal pile deriving its energy from chemical reaction. He estimates the energy brought to the sun by falling meteors. He assumes that possibly the sun is contracting, with the potential energy of its parts becoming kinetic and thermal. He concludes as follows:*

"The English astronomer Eddington has calculated that if $\frac{1}{10}$ of the hydrogen now present in the sun were to be converted into helium, the reaction would liberate a supply of heat great enough to keep the sun radiating at its present rate for a billion years. If such a process is going on anywhere, it must be at some place where atomic nuclei are forced to approach one another either as in the impact of swiftly moving atoms or by enormous external pressure. A few years ago, we had not the slightest ground for believing that either atomic disintegration or atom building was possible. Perhaps there are other things happening in the great solar crucible of which we have as yet no suspicion. At any rate we have here a plausible and fascinating hypothesis as to the source of solar energy which, unlike any of those previously considered, is quantitatively adequate."

By 1939, enough was known about nuclear reactions for Bethe to propose a set of reactions by which hydrogen might be converted to helium in the sun. It is called the carbon cycle, since carbon serves as a sort of nuclear catalyst. The steps are:

Reaction	Product half-life
$_6\mathrm{C}^{12} + {_1\mathrm{H}^1} \rightarrow {_7\mathrm{N}^{13}} + Q$	10.1 min
$_7\mathrm{N}^{13} \rightarrow {_6\mathrm{C}^{13}} + {_{+1}\mathrm{e}^0}$	
$_6\mathrm{C}^{13} + {_1\mathrm{H}^1} \rightarrow {_7\mathrm{N}^{14}} + Q$	
$_7\mathrm{N}^{14} + {_1\mathrm{H}^1} \rightarrow {_8\mathrm{O}^{15}} + Q$	125 sec
$_8\mathrm{O}^{15} \rightarrow {_7\mathrm{N}^{15}} + {_{+1}\mathrm{e}^0}$	
$_7\mathrm{N}^{15} + {_1\mathrm{H}^1} \rightarrow {_6\mathrm{C}^{12}} + {_2\mathrm{He}^4}$	

$$(44\text{–}23)$$

---

* Quoted by permission from *Physics for College Students*, 1st ed, by A. A. Knowlton, McGraw-Hill Book Co., Inc., 1928.

If we add these equations, cancel out nuclides that appear on both sides, and calculate the total Q-value, we have

$$4(_1H^1) \rightarrow \ _2He^4 + 2(_{+1}e^0) + 24.7 \text{ Mev.} \qquad (44\text{--}24)$$

The annihilation of the positrons supplies an additional 2 Mev of energy, so that the total released is actually 26.7 Mev.

To produce these reactions on earth, the carbon and nitrogen nuclides must be bombarded with accelerated protons. But the temperature at the center of the sun is so great that some thermal protons at the high-energy end of their maxwellian velocity distribution are able to react. The fraction of high-energy thermal protons is so small that it may take a million years to go through this cycle once with particular atoms, but the total number of protons able to produce the reactions is so great that it accounts for the enormous solar energy. Measurements indicate that there is enough hydrogen in the sun to keep this carbon cycle going for about 30 billion years.

The sun is in equilibrium because of two opposing effects. If the temperature of the sun were to rise, the fraction of the protons able to cause the cycle would increase. This would increase the rate of energy production and further increase the solar temperature. On the other hand, if the temperature increases the sun tends to expand and the concentration of the nuclides tends to decrease, making reactions less likely. These two effects balance each other.

There is every reason to believe that the sun is not unique in this respect, and that all stars are nuclear furnaces of one sort or another. Sometimes weak or unknown stars grow to great brilliance quite suddenly. These *new stars (nova)* are unquestionably unstable stars whose nuclear reactions have gone wild.

Since all animals derive their energy ultimately from plants, which get their energy from photosynthesis of the sun's light, since coal and oil were formed from plant life, and since water power is derived from solar heat, we can trace almost all the energy we use to the sun. Thus we live and breathe and have our being because solar hydrogen is converted to helium.

Radioactivity, atom smashers, and nuclear fission cause processes in which matter is taken apart. The solar carbon cycle is a "putting-together process" in which matter is fused, and the process is called *fusion*.

44–14 Man-made fusion. If fusion can take place in the stars, is it possible to cause fusion here on earth? Before Bethe proposed the carbon cycle for the sun, each of the reactions of that cycle had been produced on the earth. Thus by 1939 there had been man-made fusion in a limited sense. But like many other exothermic nuclear reactions, there was no possibility of making practical use of the energy liberated so long as it took extensive apparatus using much *more* energy to make the reaction proceed. The key to practical nuclear power is a chain reaction which runs itself. The links of the fission chain are neutrons, while the links of a fusion chain are protons.* Fission proceeds best with thermal *neutrons*, where thermal means at or near room temperature. Fusion proceeds best with thermal *particles*, where thermal means temperatures measured in millions of degrees. If the solar fusion of hydrogen into helium is a slow process in the sun, where Eddington estimated the temperature to be 15,000,000°K, the prospect of fusion on earth looks dim.

Our best hopes lie in some of the possible fusion reactions listed below, together with their Q-values in Mev:

$$\begin{array}{llll}
\text{D(d, p)T} & 4.0 & \text{Li}^6\text{(d, } \alpha\text{)He}^4 & 22.4 \\
\text{T(p, } \gamma\text{)He}^4 & 19.8 & \text{Li}^7\text{(p, } \alpha\text{)He}^4 & 17.3 \\
\text{T(d, n)He}^4 & 18.6 & \text{Li}^7\text{(d, n)Be}^8 & 14.9 \\
\text{Li}^6\text{(n, } \alpha\text{)T} & 4.8 & &
\end{array} \tag{44-25}$$

A fusion reactor might utilize several of the reactions in this list. For example the fourth reaction could be initiated with a neutron. If the tritium product struck deuterium, the third reaction would provide a neutron. This neutron might excite the fourth reaction again, etc. Hydrogen isotopes have been ignited to fusion in a fission bomb. This so-called hydrogen bomb (fusion bomb) is a hideous thing because its energy release is "open-ended." Once the fusion is started, the fusion itself maintains the temperature to keep the process going. The energy liberated is a function of how much fusible material is present, and there is no theoretical limit. Recall that in a fission bomb the parts, before detonation, must each be smaller than the critical size lest the parts explode spontaneously. A fusion bomb cannot explode until it is "ignited" and any amount of fusible material is safe until ignited. Thus the amount of fusible material in a fusion bomb is not limited.

The constructive utilization of the energy released from fusion is now a major field of research endeavor, and there is still some doubt that a way can be found. Fusion on the sun is "contained" by the tremendous gravitational field of the sun, and therefore a continuous reaction takes place. Fusion in an H-bomb is a destructive explosion, since it is not contained. At first glance it appears entirely hopeless, not only to achieve the temperatures necessary for fusion, but at the same time to contain the reac-

---

* There are other stellar cycles besides the Bethe carbon cycle we have described and there are fusion reactions in which deuterons, alpha particles, etc. provide the "links" of the chain.

tion at a temperature many orders of magnitude above that at which earth materials vaporize.

One answer to the achievement of suitable temperature is already implied by our discussion. We do not need temperature as such. What we need is high-velocity particles. Although both the sun and the H-bomb produce these velocities with thermal energy, all the fusion reactions have been produced on a small scale by using particle accelerators. We have seen that the kinetic energy of a particle moving with the most probable speed in a maxwellian distribution for a group of particles at room temperature, 293°K, is 0.025 ev. *By stretching the concept of temperature from a statistical property associated with the random motion of all the atoms or molecules in a piece of gross matter to a description of individual particle energy* we get a new concept, called *kinetic temperature*. Thus any particle with 0.025 ev of energy has a kinetic temperature of 293°K. Multiplying each of these quantities by 4×10^4, we find that any particle having 1 kev of energy has a kinetic temperature of 11.6 million °K. A well-thrown baseball may have a kinetic temperature of one hundred billion billion electron volts or about a million billion billion degrees kelvin. Calculations show that it may be possible to maintain fusion continuously at a temperature as low as 45 million degrees. Charged particles may be given this kinetic temperature by accelerating them through a mere 4000-volt potential difference.

If an electric arc is maintained by a potential of this order of magnitude, any gas of low atomic number in the arc becomes completely ionized. The space between the electrodes is then filled with a mixture of two gases, one consisting of negative electrons and the other consisting of positive nuclei. This mixture of charged-particle gases is called a *plasma*.

Even though the number of particles per unit volume in a plasma may be much smaller than in the atmosphere, a kinetic temperature of 100 kev may produce a pressure as high as 1000 atm.

Assuming that a plasma can be produced in which fusion can take place, how might a body of gas with a pressure of 1000 atm and a kinetic temperature of about a billion degrees be contained? Obviously, contact with any material container will result in the absorption of energy from the plasma, thereby reducing its kinetic temperature. One important mechanism that causes the plasma to lose energy rapidly is radiative, not thermal, in character. When a high-energy particle from the plasma strikes the wall of the container, some of the material (usually stainless steel) is vaporized. The atoms of high atomic number that are released diffuse into the plasma stream and cause a marked increase in the rate at which the moving, colliding, charged particles lose energy by bremsstrahlung. Even minute amounts of impurities cause a large increase because the power radiated by bremsstrahlung varies as the square of the atomic num-

ber of the atom causing deceleration. Since the presence of elements of
high atomic number lowers the kinetic temperature of the plasma, a container must be fantastically clean before deuterium or some other gas is
introduced. The best hope of preventing contact between a stream of
charged particles and the walls of the container lies in the restraining
effect that can be produced by a magnetic field. If the plasma arc is
along the axis of a solenoid, any charges moving parallel to this axis
experience no magnetic force. If charges are knocked out of their parallel
paths, however, their paths become helices, since their velocities now have
components perpendicular to the field. Thus a strong enough magnetic
field turns escaping charged particles back into the body of the plasma
and constitutes a "bottle."

The high kinetic temperature necessary to establish fusion conditions is
reached by shrinking the plasma with what is known as the *pinch effect*.
We know that two parallel wires carrying currents in the same direction
attract each other. In a plasma carrying a current we may think of the
current as taking place in a bundle of wires each attracting all the others.
If a large bank of highly charged capacitors is discharged through the
plasma, there may be a transient current of many million amperes. Such
a current, properly directed through the plasma parallel to the axis of the
existing magnetic field produces an intense pinch effect. Charges at the
outside edges of the plasma are thrown toward its axis, where they collide,
with high kinetic temperature. Fusion conditions have been produced
momentarily in this way for deuterium nuclei. The energy released, however, has been small compared with the energy required to operate the
apparatus.

If a pinch-initiated fusion reaction were to sustain itself continuously,
or long enough for the energy liberated to exceed the energy input to the
apparatus, then electromagnetic radiation and uncharged particles (principally neutrons) could carry away energy to heat a boiler. There is also
hope that because of the electrical nature of the fusion plasma it may
be possible to generate electricity by pulsing the plasma and thereby
inducing currents in a secondary coil.

It is easy to see why research on fusion continues in spite of its many
discouraging aspects. Although fission presents a far greater energy source
than our remaining fossil fuels, this source could be used up in a few
centuries of modern civilization. Furthermore, fission produces radioactive wastes which are certain to be an increasingly serious problem,
possibly requiring that these "poisons" be projected into space. On the
other hand, the product materials of fusion are almost harmless, and the
known fuel supply is sufficient for man's extravagant use for billions of
years. If hydrogen nuclides are what we need, every water molecule in
the oceans has two of them.

PROBLEMS

44–1. (a) If Sr^{90} constitutes 5% of the fission-fragment yield of uranium (see Fig. 44–1), how many grams of this strontium are formed when a uranium bomb having the explosive equivalent of one megaton of TNT is exploded? (All the atoms in 50 kgm of uranium must fission to produce the equivalent blast effect.) (b) If all this strontium is distributed uniformly throughout the atmosphere over the whole earth within a few months, what is the approximate radioactivity in microcuries above each square mile of the surface of the earth due to this one kind of fission fragment? (c) Comment on the likelihood of the uniform distribution assumed. (d) What happens to this strontium?

44–2. Show that the graph of the logarithm of the microscopic cross section of a "$1/v$ absorber" against the logarithm of the kinetic energy of the bombarding neutron is a straight line with a negative slope.

44–3. A piece of Co^{59} whose dimensions are 3 cm $\times$ 4 cm $\times$ 0.5 mm is to be irradiated by neutrons in a graphite pile until its total activity is 2 curies, due to the formation of Co^{60} by the reaction Co^{59} $(n, \gamma)Co^{60}$. (a) How many atoms of Co^{60} does the activated piece of metal contain? (b) How many neutrons must interact with the Co^{59}, according to the reaction given, to produce the number of atoms in part (a)? (c) The microscopic activation cross section of Co^{59} for the given reaction is 34 barns. If the irradiating beam is 2×10^{12} neutrons/cm^2/sec normal to the 3 $\times$ 4 cm face, how long will it take to achieve the total activity of 2 curies? Assume that the radioactive disintegration of the Co^{60} being formed during the time of bom-

bardment is negligible. (d) Under what conditions is the assumption in part (c) reasonable?

44–4. (a) What fraction of the total number of atoms in the sheet of activated cobalt in Problem 44–3 changes into the daughter product in a day? (b) The population of the United States is 167 million and the annual birthrate is 4 million. What fraction of the total population becomes "daughter products" each day? (c) How much greater is this fractional birthrate than the fractional rate of radioactive disintegration in the cobalt sheet in part (a)? (d) Is radioactive "blowing up" a commonplace event from the viewpoint of the atoms in this piece of cobalt? (The cobalt sheet in this problem actually has a high activity for a radioactive material.)

44–5. A borated-steel sheet (relative density 7.81) which is used as a control "rod" in a reactor is 1/16 inch thick and contains 2% boron by weight. The microscopic absorption cross section of iron for neutrons is 2.5 barns and for boron, 755 barns. (a) Find the macroscopic absorption cross sections of each of these elements in the borated-steel sheet. (b) What fraction of a neutron beam is absorbed in passing through this sheet?

44–6. 100 ml of a solution contains 2 gm of boric acid, H_3BO_3, dissolved in 100 gm of water. (a) What is the macroscopic neutron absorption coefficient of each element in the solution, and (b) what is the total absorption cross section of the solution? (The microscopic absorption cross sections for these elements are given in Table 44–3.)

44–7. Using the same method as that to obtain the average life of a radioactive atom, Eq. (42–8), show (a) from Eq. (44–12) that the neutron mean free path in a material is $1/N\sigma$; and (b) from Eq. (40–10) that the mean free path of an x-ray or gamma-ray photon is $1/\mu$.

44–8. (a) What fraction of a beam of radiation is transmitted by a sheet of material having a thickness equal to the mean free path? (b) When a part of the human body, say the arm, is overexposed to a beam of soft x-rays, a "burn" appears on the skin on the side of incidence, but for rather hard x-rays, the "burn" usually occurs only on the skin farthest from the incident side. Explain.

44–9. What is the absorption mean free path of (a) neutrons in iron ($\sigma_a = 2.5$ barns), (b) neutrons in borated-steel (Problem 44–5), and (c) 1-Mev gamma radiation in steel for which the hvl is 0.5 in?

44–10. (a) It is said that the effective neutron shielding property of concrete depends primarily on its hydrogen content but that its gamma-ray absorbing property depends mostly on its aluminum and silicon content. Do Eq. (40–15) and the data in Table 44–4 confirm this? (b) What would be the effect on the scattering property for neutrons and the absorption for gamma radiations if the concrete were made denser by using steel punchings in the mix instead of gravel?

44–11. The index of refraction of water at 20°C for red light is 1.33 and for blue light is 1.34. (a) What is the half-angle, θ, of the bow wave for red light and for blue light in the Cherenkov radiation produced by a beta particle emitted from a sheet of Co^{60} with a speed of $0.8c$? (b) At what particle speed will (1) the red light and

(2) the blue light in Cherenkov radiation in water disappear?

44–12. The energy received from the sun by the earth and its surrounding atmosphere is 2.00 gm-cal/(cm²·min) on a surface normal to the rays of the sun. (a) What is the total energy received in joules per minute by the earth and its atmosphere? (Diameter of earth-atmosphere system is 1.27×10^4 km.) (b) What is the total energy radiated in joules per minute by the sun to the universe? (Distance from sun to earth is 1.49×10^8 km.) (c) At what rate, in tons/min, must hydrogen be consumed in the fusion reaction, Eq. (44–24), to provide the sun with the energy it radiates?

44–13. A deuterium reaction that occurs in experimental fusion reactors is D(d, p)T followed by a reaction of the tritium product with another deuterium atom. This second reaction is T(d, n)He⁴. (a) Compute the combined Q-value of these successive reactions. (b) What is the energy released in the combined reactions per unit mass of the deuterium particles? (c) What percent of the total rest mass-energy of the initial particles is released in the combined reactions? (d) Compare the answers for parts (b) and (c) with the corresponding calculations for uranium fission in Problem 39–22. (e) Compare U^{235} fission with deuterium fusion as a source of energy on the basis of the availability of the isotopes and of the energy released per unit mass.

44–14. It is believed that the microscopic absorption cross section of iron for neutrinos is of the order of 10^{-20} barn. In kilometers, what is the half-value layer of iron for neutrinos?

CHAPTER 45

COSMIC RAYS AND THE FUNDAMENTAL PARTICLES

45–1 Introduction. In this concluding chapter we return again to the early part of this century to describe the discovery and some of the properties of cosmic rays. We shall see how studies of these natural phenomena, together with studies of events produced by the modern superaccelerators, serve to clarify some matters already discussed. But this chapter will not tie up a neat package. Our hope is that the reader will gain some comprehension of the problems that are most challenging to the physicists of today.

45–2 Cosmic rays. Cosmic rays were discovered during the search for a cause of ionization chamber leakage. Of course no insulator is perfect, and some ionization chamber leakage was expected. When it was found that the leakage rate was greater than could be accounted for by imperfect insulation, it was assumed that the difference was due to ionization from traces of radioactivity in the earth. To test this point, ionization chambers were carried above the earth in balloons. During the first part of the ascent, the ionization did indeed decrease slightly. But in 1909, Gockel found that at greater heights the ionization began to increase, and at 2.5 miles the ionization was greater than at the surface of the earth. In 1910, Hess and Kohlhoerster carried a chamber even higher and, after extensive study, they proposed that there must be a very penetrating radiation coming from outside the earth—*cosmic rays*. It was estimated that these rays were at least ten times as penetrating as the most energetic gamma rays known.

Just as cosmic-ray research was begun by moving ionization chambers up into the air, so it was continued by moving them into the earth and over its surface. The presence of cosmic rays was traced deep inside mines, where the effect of any radioactive material was excluded with lead shields. They were found deep in lakes. Glacier-fed lakes were chosen because their water is "distilled" and free of radioactive materials. Recording ionization chambers were sent all over the world on ships.

As a result of these geographic explorations, it was concluded that cosmic rays are extremely penetrating, and that although they come to the earth from all directions, a few more reach the earth in the latitudes of the magnetic poles than at the equator.

The fact that the intensity is greater toward the polar regions is called the *latitude effect* and it suggests that at least some of the cosmic rays are charged. Charged particles approaching the earth at the equator must move perpendicular to the magnetic field of the earth. Depending on the sign of the charge, these particles experience a force either toward the east or toward the west which may cause some rays to miss the earth that would otherwise have hit it. Charged particles approaching the high-latitude portions of the earth move nearly parallel to the magnetic field and experience a negligible deflecting force.

Although this analysis indicated that at least some of the rays were charged, it did not indicate the sign of the charge. It also follows from the analysis that at the magnetic equator charged particles should strike the earth from a preferred direction, either east or west of the vertical, depending on the sign of the charge. Ionization chambers have no directional sensitivity, therefore clever arrangements of Geiger-Mueller tubes were used to investigate the east-west effect. A single G-M tube has no directional sensitivity, but several of them, connected electronically so that no count is recorded unless they all count in coincidence, may be physically arranged like the rungs of a ladder. With such an apparatus, called a *cosmic-ray telescope*, the direction of a ray capable of firing all the tubes could be determined.

The east-west experiment was performed by observing the counting rate of a cosmic-ray telescope set at a variety of angles east and west of the vertical. A symmetrical distribution was found at 35° south latitude (Buenos Aires). At the magnetic equator, however, although the distribution had the same general shape, it skewed a little to the west. The slightly greater intensity from the west indicated a preponderance of positive charges, but it was impossible to conclude from this that there were no negative particles or uncharged particles present.

45–3 Cosmic-ray showers. In 1928 Skobeltsyn photographed cosmic-ray tracks in a Wilson cloud chamber. He found that the tracks appeared in groups and that all the particles in a group seemed to originate from some point near and above the apparatus, such as the ceiling. It was later found that G-M tubes that were widely separated horizontally had more coincidence counts than could be accounted for by chance. These observations led to the discovery of what are called *cosmic-ray showers*. The mechanism of these bursts of rays is well understood. Somewhere in the atmosphere a cosmic ray may produce a photon with several Bev of energy. This photon may produce an electron-positron pair. (Recall that positrons were discovered by Anderson while using a cloud chamber in cosmic-ray research.) These very high-energy electrons can next produce high-energy photons by the mechanisms of x-ray production and also by the eventual production of annihilation radiation. Consequently, one initiating particle (either photon or electron) may be multiplied into thousands of shower particles.

The discovery of showers points up the difficulty of establishing the nature of the real primary cosmic radiation that comes to the earth from outer space. The nature of the rays changes as they come down through the atmosphere, and sea-level cosmic rays may bear little resemblance to their initial state.

Furthermore, the known absorption characteristics of photons and electrons precluded the possibility that they were the only components of cosmic rays. These particles simply do not possess the observed penetrating ability. The heavier particles like protons and neutrons were considered, until help came from another direction—theoretical physicists.

45–4 Discovery of mu-mesons. In trying to explain the binding force between neutrons and protons in the nucleus, Fermi had attributed it to the "exchange" of electrons between the two types of particle. It developed that the magnitude of a force from this cause was too small to fit the experimental evidence. In 1935, Yukawa followed the same general idea but postulated that the exchange particle was not an electron but a new particle having a mass intermediate between those of an electron and a proton. Since this postulated particle, if it existed, would have the penetrating properties consistent with cosmic-ray data, cosmic-ray researchers set out to find it. In 1936, Anderson and Neddermeyer observed a cloud-chamber track of such a particle, now called a *mu-meson*, but it was shown some years later that it was not identical with the one assumed by Yukawa. In 1940, Leprince-Ringuet obtained the first good cloud-chamber picture that showed a collision between a mu-meson and an electron. Since both tracks were curved by a magnetic field, the particle energies could be calculated. The mass of the mu-meson was calculated from the mechanics of the collision; the modern accepted value is 207 electron rest masses.

The discovery of the mu-meson, also called a *muon*, accounted for the penetrating ability of cosmic rays, but it was soon evident that the mu-meson could not be the primary radiation from outer space. It developed that the mu-meson is itself radioactive, with a very short half-life. Measurement of this half-life is complicated by the fact that mu-mesons formed in the upper atmosphere by cosmic-ray bombardment are projected toward the earth with a speed close to that of light. In our discussion of relativity we saw that there is a time transformation equation which takes into account the relative velocity of two observers. An observer moving with a mu-meson would conclude that its half-life was a few microseconds. To an observer on earth, the half-life appears considerably longer—long enough, in fact, to let a mu-meson traverse the atmosphere but not long enough for it to have come from outer space. Thus mu-mesons cannot be primary radiation but must be created by something else at the top of the atmosphere. Present data indicate that most of the primary cosmic rays are protons, but there are also some positive nuclei or stripped atoms of elements up to $Z = 26$. These very high-energy primary particles produce a large variety of other particles by *spallation* (nuclear smashing) of the atoms in the outer atmosphere.

Although much more is known about the primary radiation than we have discussed here, there is still speculation going on. Earth satellites are now sending us information from beyond the atmosphere. We will soon know more of the nature of primary cosmic rays and the hazards they may present to space travel.

45–5 Nuclear emulsion technique. It is difficult to study penetrating radiations with Wilson cloud chambers because the absorption of the gas within the chamber is so small. We have already pointed out that bubble chambers containing dense material are better in this respect, but both these devices are sensitive only intermittently and neither is portable. These considerations led to the development of special photographic emulsions. Ordinary photographic materials are unsuitable because they contain too small a fraction of sensitive silver halides and because they are too thin. C. F. Powell and others developed satisfactory emulsions that contain about 80% silver bromide by dry weight and are about 1 mm thick. These can be stacked to make a sensitive region of practically any size. Such blocks of emulsion are continuously sensitive and are portable enough to be carried by balloons and other high-altitude craft. It requires elaborate techniques to develop, piece together, and read nuclear emulsions, but the resultant "tracks" closely resemble those formed in cloud and in bubble chambers. The important characteristics of a track are its density, range, direction, and deviation in direction, and these characteristics often permit the positive identification of the particle causing the track. The emulsion record of a nuclear disintegration is shown in Fig. 45–1.

45–6 Discovery of pi-mesons. One of the first discoveries made with nuclear emulsions was that of the pi-meson. A block of emulsions was exposed for several weeks on a mountain. One mosaic of track pieces showed a meson slowing down and then emitting a new high-speed meson in a new direction. The second meson could be identified as the familiar mu-meson. Since the first could create a mu-meson and give it kinetic energy as well, this first meson had to be more massive. It is called the *pi-meson* (primary meson) and its mass is now known to be 270 electron masses. Three types of pi-mesons, or *pions*, have been discovered. One has a positive charge, another is negative, and the third is neutral. All are radioactive. The charged ones have mean lives* of the order of 10^{-8} sec, but the life of a neutral pion is only about 10^{-15} sec.

---

* In describing the fundamental particles mean lives rather than half-lives are usually stated. The definition of mean life is given in Section 42–9.

Fig. 45–1. Photomicrograph, enlarged 100 times, of photographic emulsion film exposed to 2-Bev nuclear particles in the Cosmotron. The incoming particle, presumably a neutron, which is invisible, hit the nucleus of an atom of the emulsion and exploded it into 17 visible particles which formed tracks in a star-shaped pattern. In general, the broad tracks are made by slow particles (protons) and the narrow tracks by fast particles. The spots in the background are grains in the emulsion. (Courtesy of Brookhaven National Laboratory)

In flight, the positive and negative pi-mesons decay into the positive and negative mu-mesons respectively, and also into neutrinos. When negative pions are slowed down in matter, they are captured by atoms, make x-ray transitions down to the K level, and then are absorbed by the nucleus, causing violent explosions called "stars." Positive pi-mesons stopped by matter decay into mu-mesons, all of which have about the same energy. Experiments show that neither the positive nor the negative mu-meson has an affinity for atomic nuclei. Because of this, it is difficult to assign to muons the role of providing the nuclear exchange forces of the Yukawa theory. According to present nuclear theory, all three types of pi-mesons are found in the nucleus, and it is believed that both protons and neutrons are continuously emitting or absorbing positive, negative, and neutral pi-mesons. The particular process depends upon which nucleons are paired in experiencing exchange forces at the moment, that is, proton-neutron, proton-proton, or neutron-neutron. Thus the general view is that each

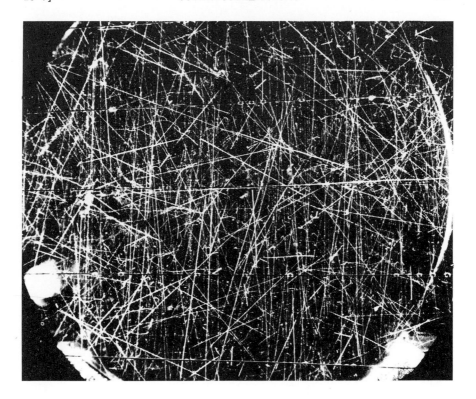

FIG. 45–2. Cloud-chamber picture showing the high-energy particles result-ing from a single pulse of 1.2-Bev protons striking a one-eighth inch brass target inside the Cosmotron. Particles reaching the chamber, located 195 ft from the Cosmotron, traversed an inch of stainless steel in the outside wall of the vacuum chamber of this superaccelerator, two heavy doors, and the quarter-inch stain-less steel wall of the cloud chamber. (Courtesy of Brookhaven National Laboratory)

nucleon has an associated meson field through which it interacts with other nucleons. This is analogous to the action through an electromag-netic field of one electrically charged body on another. The pions play the same role in the meson field as photons do in an electromagnetic field.

45–7 Superaccelerators. Both pi- and mu-mesons were discovered in cosmic-rays, but some of their properties that we have already discussed were discovered with the aid of superaccelerators. The chief limitation of the cyclotron already described is the relativistic mass variation of the accelerated particle. Superaccelerators like the Berkeley synchrocyclotron or Bevatron and the Brookhaven Cosmotron take the relativistic mass variation into account and take advantage of another basic relativistic fact—the simplification that results from all high-energy particles having

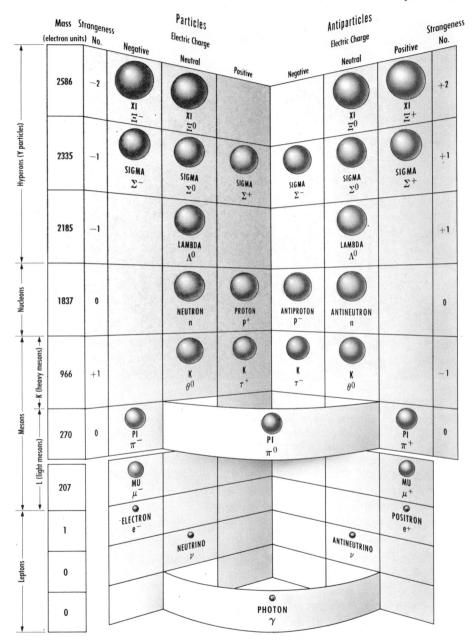

FIG. 45–3. The mirror symmetry of elementary particles. Of the thirty particles shown, a full sixteen—the four K's and the twelve hyperons—were unsuspected a dozen years ago. Only seven of the thirty are intrinsically stable: photons, protons, electrons, neutrinos, *and* antineutrinos, antiprotons, and positrons. The last two, however, share the usual fate of antiparticles that wander into this world: they are annihilated when they meet their counter-

approximately the same velocity, which is very close to the free space velocity of light. These machines can accelerate particles into the cosmic-ray range of billions of electron volts.

When protons or alpha particles are given such extreme energies they can do remarkable things to nuclei. Instead of "nudging" nuclei into new and possibly unstable forms, these particles can knock nuclear particles out of a nucleus as easily as though the nuclear particles were "free." Often, unexpected particles are knocked out or formed during the collision process. It is evident from the nuclear "wreckage" shown in Fig. 45-2 that high-energy particles are destructive even though they have traveled far from their source.

45-8 The strange particles.   Electrons, protons, and neutrons are familiar in our scheme of things. In earlier chapters we introduced positrons and neutrinos. The mu- and pi-mesons facilitate our understanding of the penetrating ability of cosmic rays, and pi-mesons fit into the theory of nuclear binding forces. But at least sixteen additional particles have been discovered. These particles, quite literally, are called the *strange* particles. They have no place in the scheme of things presented in this text. No one knows what they mean, why they exist, or to what extent they constitute a threat to our present modes of thinking about the structure of matter. Some, called *hyperons*, are more massive than neutrons and therefore cannot be fragments of the familiar nuclear particles.

45-9 The symmetry of matter.   We shall not attempt to enumerate the known properties of these strange particles, but they and the familiar elementary particles are presented schematically and summarized in Fig. 45-3. Notice the symmetry. There are particles on the left and anti-particles on the right. The most familiar pair are the electron and the positron. From bottom to top the particles are arranged in the order of increasing rest mass. The *leptons* have electronic mass or less. Then come mesons, nucleons, and hyperons. The "strangeness numbers" introduced by Murray Gell-Mann successfully predict which particles should arise and which should not when two particles interact. Strangeness is con-

---

parts. Antineutrinos may possibly be an exception to this rule. Photons and neutral pi-mesons commute freely between both worlds, since each is its own antiparticle—although the neutral pi-meson has little time for traveling because it is the second shortest-lived of all the known particles. A neutron is stable if bound in an atomic nucleus; otherwise it has a half-life of 13 minutes, decaying into a proton, an electron, and a neutrino. Similarly, all unstable particles decay, directly or indirectly, into two or more of the seven stable ones. Their mean lifetimes range from a few millionths to less than a quadrillionth of a second. (Adapted by permission from Fortune Magazine; copyright 1957 by Time Inc.)

served in strong interactions, i.e., those in which new particles are formed, but it is not conserved in weak interactions, where particles simply decay into other particles.

45–10 Conclusion. The ideas presented in this book have fallen into two major categories. The first category was an introduction to the ideas of classical physics: mechanics, sound, heat, electricity, and light. These traditional subdivisions of physics were all well developed by 1900, when the view was expressed that except for "two small clouds on the horizon" all problems had been solved. No new basic discoveries were expected, and the future work in physics was believed to lie in improved methods of measurement "to the sixth decimal place." In terms of the mystery story analogy at the beginning of the book, the detectives had done their work. All the clues were in and except for a few minor details the mystery was solved.

These minor details—the two small clouds—each grew into a major hurricane. One cloud was the negative result of the Michelson-Morley experiment, and the other was the unexplained photoelectric effect. The first led to the theory of relativity and the second showed the importance and generality of the quantum theory. (Recall that Einstein successfully met the challenge each cloud presented.)

The second category of this book was an introduction to the ideas of "modern" physics. Modern physics (which one day may give way to "ultramodern" physics) is essentially the study of these two new theories, the relativity and the quantum theory. New clues appeared, and the detectives had to reopen the case. Classical physics had to be reinterpreted, and we now know that classical physics is a special case of something more general.

The story we have told has, in general, followed a familiar pattern: a large body of information had been gathered before some genius saw that the data led to new concepts and new generalizations. These interpretations of data have lifted the human intellect so that the past could be seen in perspective and the future could present exciting challenge. Avogadro, Newton, Planck, Einstein, Rutherford, Bohr—all built on the strong basis of experiment and breathed the heady air of speculation. De Broglie, on the other hand, exemplifies the genius who speculated before the fact.

Just as Rutherford discovered the nucleus of the atom by probing with high-energy alpha particles, today the interior of the nucleus is being probed with particles of still higher energy. A great deal of information has been gathered, and much of it is reasonably well understood. But there are far more questions than answers and the time is ripe for some genius to put the house in order.

Except for mention of the mesons and the neutrino, we have discussed the nucleus as though it involved only protons and neutrons, whereas there have now been identified no less than thirty nuclear particles. We spoke of short-range attractive nuclear forces, potential barriers, and binding energies, but we said almost nothing about the nature of the forces within the nucleus. There are partial theories about these nuclear forces and the thirty or so particles certainly have a lot to do with the ways in which these forces act. But the impressive thing about nuclear forces (if indeed the term force is to be retained) is not what we know about them but what we do not know about them.

With the exception of continued work on the process of fusion, physicists have turned away from devising nuclear reactors, and are back at the task of unraveling the basic problems of the structure of matter. The newest particles found in high-energy processes are completely foreign to our present scheme of things. Let us hope that out of this chaotic riddle will come a profound and simplifying answer. We may be likened to those who knew only Ptolemy's complex description of the solar system. What we need is a Copernicus to assimilate and interpret the data with a generalization which will not only solve the riddle, but lift our sights to levels we cannot now foresee.

APPENDIX 1

COMMON LOGARITHMS

N	0	1	2	3	4	5	6	7	8	9
0	....	0000	3010	4771	6021	6990	7782	8451	9031	9542
1	0000	0414	0792	1139	1461	1761	2041	2304	2553	2788
2	3010	3222	3424	3617	3802	3979	4150	4314	4472	4624
3	4771	4914	5051	5185	5315	5441	5563	5682	5798	5911
4	6021	6128	6232	6335	6435	6532	6628	6721	6812	6902
5	6990	7076	7160	7243	7324	7404	7482	7559	7634	7709
6	7782	7853	7924	7993	8062	8129	8195	8261	8325	8388
7	8451	8513	8573	8633	8692	8751	8808	8865	8921	8976
8	9031	9085	9138	9191	9243	9294	9345	9395	9445	9494
9	9542	9590	9638	9685	9731	9777	9823	9868	9912	9956
10	0000	0043	0086	0128	0170	0212	0253	0294	0334	0374
11	0414	0453	0492	0531	0569	0607	0645	0682	0719	0755
12	0792	0828	0864	0899	0934	0969	1004	1038	1072	1106
13	1139	1173	1206	1239	1271	1303	1335	1367	1399	1430
14	1461	1492	1523	1553	1584	1614	1644	1673	1703	1732
15	1761	1790	1818	1847	1875	1903	1931	1959	1987	2014
16	2041	2068	2095	2122	2148	2175	2201	2227	2253	2279
17	2304	2330	2355	2380	2405	2430	2455	2480	2504	2529
18	2553	2577	2601	2625	2648	2672	2695	2718	2742	2765
19	2788	2810	2833	2856	2878	2900	2923	2945	2967	2989
20	3010	3032	3054	3075	3096	3118	3139	3160	3181	3201
21	3222	3243	3263	3284	3304	3324	3345	3365	3385	3404
22	3424	3444	3464	3483	3502	3522	3541	3560	3579	3598
23	3617	3636	3655	3674	3692	3711	3729	3747	3766	3784
24	3802	3820	3838	3856	3874	3892	3909	3927	3945	3962
25	3979	3997	4014	4031	4048	4065	4082	4099	4116	4133
26	4150	4166	4183	4200	4216	4232	4249	4265	4281	4298
27	4314	4330	4346	4362	4378	4393	4409	4425	4440	4456
28	4472	4487	4502	4518	4533	4548	4564	4579	4594	4609
29	4624	4639	4654	4669	4683	4698	4713	4728	4742	4757
30	4771	4786	4800	4814	4829	4843	4857	4871	4886	4900
31	4914	4928	4942	4955	4969	4983	4997	5011	5024	5038
32	5051	5065	5079	5092	5105	5119	5132	5145	5159	5172
33	5185	5198	5211	5224	5237	5250	5263	5276	5289	5302
34	5315	5328	5340	5353	5366	5378	5391	5403	5416	5428
35	5441	5453	5465	5478	5490	5502	5514	5527	5539	5551
36	5563	5575	5587	5599	5611	5623	5635	5647	5658	5670
37	5682	5694	5705	5717	5729	5740	5752	5763	5775	5786
38	5798	5809	5821	5832	5843	5855	5866	5877	5888	5899
39	5911	5922	5933	5944	5955	5966	5977	5988	5999	6010
40	6021	6031	6042	6053	6064	6075	6085	6096	6107	6117
41	6128	6138	6149	6160	6170	6180	6191	6201	6212	6222
42	6232	6243	6253	6263	6274	6284	6294	6304	6314	6325
43	6335	6345	6355	6365	6375	6385	6395	6405	6415	6425
44	6435	6444	6454	6464	6474	6484	6493	6503	6513	6522
45	6532	6542	6551	6561	6571	6580	6590	6599	6609	6618
46	6628	6637	6646	6656	6665	6675	6684	6693	6702	6712
47	6721	6730	6739	6749	6758	6767	6776	6785	6794	6803
48	6812	6821	6830	6839	6848	6857	6866	6875	6884	6893
49	6902	6911	6920	6928	6937	6946	6955	6964	6972	6981
50	6990	6998	7007	7016	7024	7033	7042	7050	7059	7067
N	0	1	2	3	4	5	6	7	8	9

COMMON LOGARITHMS

N	0	1	2	3	4	5	6	7	8	9
50	6990	6998	7007	7016	7024	7033	7042	7050	7059	7067
51	7076	7084	7093	7101	7110	7118	7126	7135	7143	7152
52	7160	7168	7177	7185	7193	7202	7210	7218	7226	7235
53	7243	7251	7259	7267	7275	7284	7292	7300	7308	7316
54	7324	7332	7340	7348	7356	7364	7372	7380	7388	7396
55	7404	7412	7419	7427	7435	7443	7451	7459	7466	7474
56	7482	7490	7497	7505	7513	7520	7528	7536	7543	7551
57	7559	7566	7574	7582	7589	7597	7604	7612	7619	7627
58	7634	7642	7649	7657	7664	7672	7679	7686	7694	7701
59	7709	7716	7723	7731	7738	7745	7752	7760	7767	7774
60	7782	7789	7796	7803	7810	7818	7825	7832	7839	7846
61	7853	7860	7868	7875	7882	7889	7896	7903	7910	7917
62	7924	7931	7938	7945	7952	7959	7966	7973	7980	7987
63	7993	8000	8007	8014	8021	8028	8035	8041	8048	8055
64	8062	8069	8075	8082	8089	8096	8102	8109	8116	8122
65	8129	8136	8142	8149	8156	8162	8169	8176	8182	8189
66	8195	8202	8209	8215	8222	8228	8235	8241	8248	8254
67	8261	8267	8274	8280	8287	8293	8299	8306	8312	8319
68	8325	8331	8338	8344	8351	8357	8363	8370	8376	8382
69	8388	8395	8401	8407	8414	8420	8426	8432	8439	8445
70	8451	8457	8463	8470	8476	8482	8488	8494	8500	8506
71	8513	8519	8525	8531	8537	8543	8549	8555	8561	8567
72	8573	8579	8585	8591	8597	8603	8609	8615	8621	8627
73	8633	8639	8645	8651	8657	8663	8669	8675	8681	8686
74	8692	8698	8704	8710	8716	8722	8727	8733	8739	8745
75	8751	8756	8762	8768	8774	8779	8785	8791	8797	8802
76	8808	8814	8820	8825	8831	8837	8842	8848	8854	8859
77	8865	8871	8876	8882	8887	8893	8899	8904	8910	8915
78	8921	8927	8932	8938	8943	8949	8954	8960	8965	8971
79	8976	8982	8987	8993	8998	9004	9009	9015	9020	9025
80	9031	9036	9042	9047	9053	9058	9063	9069	9074	9079
81	9085	9090	9096	9101	9106	9112	9117	9122	9128	9133
82	9138	9143	9149	9154	9159	9165	9170	9175	9180	9186
83	9191	9196	9201	9206	9212	9217	9222	9227	9232	9238
84	9243	9248	9253	9258	9263	9269	9274	9279	9284	9289
85	9294	9299	9304	9309	9315	9320	9325	9330	9335	9340
86	9345	9350	9355	9360	9365	9370	9375	9380	9385	9390
87	9395	9400	9405	9410	9415	9420	9425	9430	9435	9440
88	9445	9450	9455	9460	9465	9469	9474	9479	9484	9489
89	9494	9499	9504	9509	9513	9518	9523	9528	9533	9538
90	9542	9547	9552	9557	9562	9566	9571	9576	9581	9586
91	9590	9595	9600	9605	9609	9614	9619	9624	9628	9633
92	9638	9643	9647	9652	9657	9661	9666	9671	9675	9680
93	9685	8689	9694	9699	9703	9708	9713	9717	9722	9727
94	9731	9736	9741	9745	9750	9754	9759	9763	9768	9773
95	9777	9782	9786	9791	9795	9800	9805	9809	9814	9818
96	9823	9827	9832	9836	9841	9845	9850	9854	9859	9863
97	9868	9872	9877	9881	9886	9890	9894	9899	9903	9908
98	9912	9917	9921	9926	9930	9934	9939	9943	9948	9952
99	9956	9961	9965	9969	9974	9978	9983	9987	9991	9996
100	0000	0004	0009	0013	0017	0022	0026	0030	0035	0039
N	0	1	2	3	4	5	6	7	8	9

APPENDIX 2
NATURAL TRIGONOMETRIC FUNCTIONS

Angle					Angle				
De-gree	Ra-dian	Sine	Co-sine	Tan-gent	De-gree	Ra-dian	Sine	Co-sine	Tan-gent
0°	.000	0.000	1.000	0.000					
1°	.017	.018	1.000	.018	46°	0.803	0.719	0.695	1.036
2°	.035	.035	0.999	.035	47°	.820	.731	.682	1.072
3°	.052	.052	.999	.052	48°	.838	.743	.669	1.111
4°	.070	.070	.998	.070	49°	.855	.755	.656	1.150
5°	.087	.087	.996	.088	50°	.873	.766	.643	1.192
6°	.105	.105	.995	.105	51°	.890	.777	.629	1.235
7°	.122	.122	.993	.123	52°	.908	.788	.616	1.280
8°	.140	.139	.990	.141	53°	.925	.799	.602	1.327
9°	.157	.156	.988	.158	54°	.942	.809	.588	1.376
10°	.175	.174	.985	.176	55°	.960	.819	.574	1.428
11°	.192	.191	.982	.194	56°	.977	.829	.559	1.483
12°	.209	.208	.978	.213	57°	.995	.839	.545	1.540
13°	.227	.225	.974	.231	58°	1.012	.848	.530	1.600
14°	.244	.242	.970	.249	59°	1.030	.857	.515	1.664
15°	.262	.259	.966	.268	60°	1.047	.866	.500	1.732
16°	.279	.276	.961	.287	61°	1.065	.875	.485	1.804
17°	.297	.292	.956	.306	62°	1.082	.883	.470	1.881
18°	.314	.309	.951	.325	63°	1.100	.891	.454	1.963
19°	.332	.326	.946	.344	64°	1.117	.899	.438	2.050
20°	.349	.342	.940	.364	65°	1.134	.906	.423	2.145
21°	.367	.358	.934	.384	66°	1.152	.914	.407	2.246
22°	.384	.375	.927	.404	67°	1.169	.921	.391	2.356
23°	.401	.391	.921	.425	68°	1.187	.927	.375	2.475
24°	.419	.407	.914	.445	69°	1.204	.934	.358	2.605
25°	.436	.423	.906	.466	70°	1.222	.940	.342	2.747
26°	.454	.438	.899	.488	71°	1.239	.946	.326	2.904
27°	.471	.454	.891	.510	72°	1.257	.951	.309	3.078
28°	.489	.470	.883	.532	73°	1.274	.956	.292	3.271
29°	.506	.485	.875	.554	74°	1.292	.961	.276	3.487
30°	.524	.500	.866	.577	75°	1.309	.966	.259	3.732
31°	.541	.515	.857	.601	76°	1.326	.970	.242	4.011
32°	.559	.530	.848	.625	77°	1.344	.974	.225	4.331
33°	.576	.545	.839	.649	78°	1.361	.978	.208	4.705
34°	.593	.559	.829	.675	79°	1.379	.982	.191	5.145
35°	.611	.574	.819	.700	80°	1.396	.985	.174	5.671
36°	.628	.588	.809	.727	81°	1.414	.988	.156	6.314
37°	.646	.602	.799	.754	82°	1.431	.990	.139	7.115
38°	.663	.616	.788	.781	83°	1.449	.993	.122	8.144
39°	.681	.629	.777	.810	84°	1.466	.995	.105	9.514
40°	.698	.643	.766	.839	85°	1.484	.996	.087	11.43
41°	.716	.658	.755	.869	86°	1.501	.998	.070	14.30
42°	.733	.669	.743	.900	87°	1.518	.999	.052	19.08
43°	.751	.682	.731	.933	88°	1.536	.999	.035	28.64
44°	.768	.695	.719	.966	89°	1.553	1.000	.018	57.29
45°	.785	.707	.707	1.000	90°	1.571	1.000	.000	∞

APPENDIX 3

PERIODIC TABLE OF THE ELEMENTS

(Numbers in parentheses indicate mass number of most stable known isotope.)

Outer electrons are in the	I	II	III	IV	V	VI	VII	VIII			O	Electrons per shell
First or K-shell											2 He 4.003	2
Second or L-shell	3 Li 6.940	4 Be 9.013	5 B 10.82	6 C 12.011	7 N 14.008	8 O 16.000	9 F 19.00				10 Ne 20.183	2, 8
Third or M-shell	11 Na 22.991	12 Mg 24.32	13 Al 26.98	14 Si 28.09	15 P 30.975	16 S 32.066	17 Cl 35.457				18 Ar 39.944	2, 8, 8
Fourth or N-shell	19 K 39.100	20 Ca 40.08	21 Sc 44.96	22 Ti 47.90	23 V 50.95	24 Cr 52.01	25 Mn 54.94	26 Fe 55.85	27 Co 58.94	28 Ni 58.71		
	29 Cu 63.54	30 Zn 65.38	31 Ga 69.72	32 Ge 72.60	33 As 74.91	34 Se 78.96	35 Br 79.916				36 Kr 83.80	2, 8, 18, 8
Fifth or O-shell	37 Rb 85.48	38 Sr 87.63	39 Y 88.92	40 Zr 91.22	41 Nb 92.91	42 Mo 95.95	43 Tc (99)	44 Ru 101.10	45 Rh 102.91	46 Pd 106.4		
	47 Ag 107.880	48 Cd 112.41	49 In 114.82	50 Sn 118.70	51 Sb 121.76	52 Te 127.61	53 I 126.91				54 Xe 131.30	2, 8, 18, 18, 8
Sixth or P-shell	55 Cs 132.91	56 Ba 137.36	57–71 La series*	72 Hf 178.50	73 Ta 180.95	74 W 183.86	75 Re 186.22	76 Os 190.2	77 Ir 192.2	78 Pt 195.09		
	79 Au 197.0	80 Hg 200.61	81 Tl 204.39	82 Pb 207.21	83 Bi 209.00	84 Po (210)	85 At (210)				86 Rn (222)	2, 8, 18, 32, 18, 8
Seventh or Q-shell	87 Fr (223)	88 Ra 226.05	89 — Ac series**									

																Electrons per shell
*Lanthanide series:	57 La 138.92	58 Ce 140.13	59 Pr 140.92	60 Nd 144.27	61 Pm (145)	62 Sm 150.35	63 Eu 152.0	64 Gd 157.26	65 Tb 158.93	66 Dy 162.51	67 Ho 164.94	68 Er 167.27	69 Tm 168.94	70 Yb 173.04	71 Lu 174.99	2, 8, 18, 32, 9, 2
**Actinide series:	89 Ac (227)	90 Th 232.05	91 Pa (231)	92 U 238.07	93 Np (237)	94 Pu (244)	95 Am (243)	96 Cm (247)	97 Bk (247)	98 Cf (251)	99 Es (254)	100 Fm (253)	101 Md (256)	102 No (253)	103	2, 8, 18, 32, 32, 9, 2

APPENDIX 4

PARTIAL LIST OF ISOTOPES

Isotopes which are naturally radioactive are indicated by (NR). Only those most commonly found are listed. The values of the isotopic masses are based on O^{16}.

The data for this table were obtained from the *Trilinear Chart of Nuclides* by William H. Sullivan. (Courtesy of Oak Ridge National Laboratory.)

At. no. Z	Element	Symbol	Mass no., A	Isotopic mass, amu (phys. scale)	Relative abundance, %	No. of isotopes Stable	No. of isotopes Radio-active
0	Neutron	n	1	1.008986			1
1	Hydrogen					2	1
		H	1	1.008145	99.985		
		D	2	2.014740	0.015		
		T	3 (NR)	3.017005	...		
2	Helium	He				2	2
			3	3.016986	1.3×10^{-4}		
			4	4.003874	99.9999		
3	Lithium	Li				2	4
			6	6.017034	7.5		
			7	7.018232	92.5		
4	Beryllium	Be				1	5
			9	9.015046	100		
5	Boron	B				2	4
			10	10.016119	18.7		
			11	11.012795	81.3		
6	Carbon	C				2	4
			12	12.003803	98.89		
			13	13.007478	1.11		
7	Nitrogen	N				2	4
			14	14.007520	99.635		
			15	15.004862	0.365		
8	Oxygen	O				3	3
			16	16.000000	99.759		
			17	17.004534	0.037		
			18	18.004855	0.204		
9	Fluorine	F				1	4
			19	19.004448	100		

At. no. Z	Element	Symbol	Mass no., A	Isotopic mass, amu (phys. scale)	Relative abundance, %	No. of isotopes	
						Stable	Radio-active
10	Neon	Ne				3	4
			20	19.998769	90.92		
			21	21.000499	0.257		
			22	21.998354	8.82		
11	Sodium	Na				1	6
			23	22.997053	100		
12	Magnesium	Mg				3	3
			24	23.992640	78.60		
			25	24.993752	10.11		
			26	25.990854	11.29		
13	Aluminum	Al				1	6
			27	26.990081	100		
14	Silicon	Si				3	4
			28	27.985775	92.18		
15	Phosphorus	P				1	6
			31	30.98356	100		
16	Sulfur	S				4	4
			32	31.98220	95.018		
17	Chlorine	Cl				2	7
			35	34.97990	75.53		
			37	36.97754	24.47		
18	Argon	Ar				3	5
			40	39.97505	99.60		
19	Potassium	K				2	7
			39	38.97604	93.08		
			40 (NR)	39.97665	0.0119		
			41	40.97476	6.91		
20	Calcium	Ca				5	7
			40	39.97523	96.96		
			48 (NR)	47.9677	0.185		
21	Scandium	Sc				1	10
			45	44.97007	100		
22	Titanium	Ti				5	4
			48	47.96312	73.99		
23	Vanadium	V				1	8
			50 (NR)	49.96312	0.24		
			51	50.96004	99.76		

(Continued)

At. no. Z	Element	Symbol	Mass no., A	Isotopic mass, amu (phys. scale)	Relative abundance, %	No. of isotopes	
						Stable	Radio-active
24	Chromium	Cr				4	6
			52	51.95699	83.76		
25	Manganese	Mn				1	7
			55	54.95540	100		
26	Iron	Fe				4	7
			56	55.95264	91.68		
27	Cobalt	Co				1	10
			59	58.9519	100		
28	Nickel	Ni				5	6
			58	57.9538	67.8		
			60	59.9499	26.2		
29	Copper	Cu				2	9
			63	62.9494	69.1		
			65	64.9484	30.9		
30	Zinc	Zn				5	9
			64	63.9493	48.89		
			66	65.9469	27.81		
			68	67.9465	18.56		
31	Gallium	Ga				2	9
			69	68.9476	60.2		
			71	70.9474	39.8		
32	Germanium	Ge				5	10
			70	69.9464	20.55		
			72	71.9446	27.37		
			73	72.94645	7.67		
			74	73.94459	36.74		
			76	75.94533	7.67		
33	Arsenic	As				1	14
			75	74.94540	100		
34	Selenium	Se				6	11
			78	77.94209	23.52		
			80	79.9420	49.82		
35	Bromine	Br				2	14
			79	78.94341	50.54		
			81	80.9421	49.46		
36	Krypton	Kr				6	15
			82	81.9394	11.56		
			83	82.9403	11.55		
			84	83.9381	56.90		
			86	85.9382	17.37		

At. no. Z	Element	Symbol	Mass no., A	Isotopic mass, amu (phys. scale)	Relative abundance, %	No. of isotopes	
						Stable	Radio-active
37	Rubidium	Rb				1	16
			85	84.9389	72.15		
			87 (NR)	86.93687	27.85		
38	Strontium	Sr				4	12
			88	87.9338	82.56		
39	Yttrium	Y				1	14
			89	88.9341	100		
40	Zirconium	Zr				4	9
			90	89.9328	51.46		
			96 (NR)	95.9385	2.80		
41	Niobium (Columbium)	Nb (Cb)				1	10
			93	92.9353	100		
42	Molybdenum	Mo				7	7
			98	97.9366	23.75		
43	Technetium	Tc				0	15
			98 (NR)	97.9391	...		
44	Ruthenium	Ru				7	9
			102	101.9364	31.5		
45	Rhodium	Rh				1	13
			103	102.9379	100		
46	Palladium	Pd				6	12
			106	105.9364	27.33		
47	Silver	Ag				2	14
			107	106.0389	51.35		
			109	108.9393	48.65		
48	Cadmium	Cd				8	9
			106	105.9395	1.21		
			108	107.9382	0.88		
			110	109.9383	12.39		
			111	110.9394	12.75		
			112	111.9382	24.07		
			113	112.9403	12.26		
			114	113.9396	28.86		
			116	115.9418	7.58		
49	Indium	In				1	14
			113	112.9401	4.23		
			115 (NR)	114.9405	95.77		

(Continued)

At. no. Z	Element	Symbol	Mass no., A	Isotopic mass, amu (phys. scale)	Relative abundance, %	No. of isotopes Stable	No. of isotopes Radio-active
50	Tin	Sn	120	119.9401	32.97	10	15
51	Antimony	Sb	121 123	120.9420 122.9431	57.25 42.75	2	18
52	Tellurium	Te	128 130 (NR)	127.9461 129.9478	31.79 34.49	6	15
53	Iodine	I	127	126.9448	100	1	21
54	Xenon	Xe	132	131.9460	26.89	9	14
55	Cesium	Cs	133	132.9472	100	1	20
56	Barium	Ba	138	137.9487	71.66	7	12
57	Lanthanum	La	138 (NR) 139	137.9501 138.9495	0.089 99.911	1	13
58	Cerium	Ce	140	139.9489	88.48	4	10
59	Praseodymium	Pr	141	140.9511	100	1	11
60	Neodymium	Nd	142 144 (NR)	141.9515 143.954	27.09 23.83	5	8
61	Promethium	Pm	145 (NR)	. . .		0	16
62	Samarium	Sm	147 (NR) 152	146.9603 151.9673	15.07 26.63	6	9
63	Europium	Eu	151 153	. . . . . .	47.77 52.23	2	15
64	Gadolinium	Gd	158	157.9734	24.87	7	9

At. no. Z	Element	Symbol	Mass no., A	Isotopic mass, amu (phys. scale)	Relative abundance, %	No. of isotopes	
						Stable	Radio-active
65	Terbium	Tb	159	...	100	1	12
66	Dysprosium	Dy	164	163.980	28.18	7	11
67	Holmium	Ho	165	164.981	100	1	11
68	Erbium	Er	166 168	... 167.9839	33.4 27.1	6	7
69	Thulium	Tm	169	...	100	1	9
70	Ytterbium	Yb	174	173.981	31.84	7	9
71	Lutetium	Lu	175 176 (NR)	... 175.997	97.4 2.6	1	11
72	Hafnium	Hf	180	...	35.25	6	6
73	Tantalum	Ta	181	...	100	1	10
74	Tungsten (Wolfram)	W	180 (NR) 184	180.001 184.006	0.135 30.6	4	9
75	Rhenium	Re	187 (NR)	187.011	62.93	1	13
76	Osmium	Os	192	192.022	41.0	7	8
77	Iridium	Ir	191 193	191.021 193.025	38.5 61.5	2	12
78	Platinum	Pt	190 (NR) 195	... 195.0264	0.012 33.7	5	10
79	Gold	Au	197	197.028	100	1	17

(*Continued*)

At. no. Z	Element	Symbol	Mass no., A	Isotopic mass, amu (phys. scale)	Relative abundance, %	No. of isotopes Stable	No. of isotopes Radio-active
80	Mercury	Hg				7	10
			202	202.0354	29.80		
81	Thallium	Tl				2	14
			205	205.03848	70.50		
82	Lead	Pb				4	15
			204	204.03686	1.5		
			206	206.03883	23.6		
			207	207.04058	22.6		
			208	208.041640 (Standard)	52.3		
83	Bismuth	Bi				0	19
			209 (NR)	209.04579	100		
84	Polonium	Po				0	23
			210 (NR)	210.04850	...		
85	Astatine	At				0	19
			210 (NR)	210.0526	...		
			211 (NR)	211.05345	...		
86	Emanation	Em				0	16
			222 (NR)	222.08690	...		
87	Francium	Fr				0	9
			223 (NR)	223.08960	...		
88	Radium	Ra				0	13
			226 (NR)	226.09600	...		
89	Actinium	Ac				0	10
			227 (NR)	227.09888	...		
90	Thorium	Th				0	12
			232 (NR)	232.11080	100		
91	Protactinium	Pa				0	12
			231 (NR)	231.10827	...		
92	Uranium	U				0	14
			234 (NR)	234.11408	5.8×10^{-3}		
			235 (NR)	235.11750	0.72		
			238 (NR)	238.12522	99.27		
93	Neptunium	Np				0	11
			237	237.12220	...		
94	Plutonium	Pu				0	15
			239	239.12700	...		
			242	242.13445	...		

At. no. Z	Element	Symbol	Mass no., A	Isotopic mass, amu (phys. scale)	Relative abundance, %	No. of isotopes Stable	No. of isotopes Radio-active
95	Americium	Am				0	10
			241	241.13213	. . .		
			243	243.13748	. . .		
96	Curium	Cm				0	13
			243	243.13748	. . .		
97	Berkelium	Bk				0	8
			245	245.14292	. . .		
98	Californium	Cf				0	11
			246	246.14575	. . .		
99	Einsteinium	Es				0	11
			253	253.1637	. . .		
100	Fermium	Fm				0	7
			255	255.1696	. . .		
101	Mendelevium	Md				0	2
			256	256.1738	. . .		
102	Nobelium	No				0	2
			253	. . .	. . .		

APPENDIX 5

PARTIAL LIST OF RADIOISOTOPES

Element	Nuclide	Isotopic mass (based on O^{16})	Half-life, T	Decay constant λ, $\sec^{-1}$	Principal particle energy, Mev
Antimony	$_{51}Sb^{122}$	121.9437	2.80 d	2.87×10^{-6}	β, 1.41; γ, 0.10–1.9
Argon	$_{18}Ar^{37}$	36.97842	34.1 d	2.35×10^{-7}	K-capture
Arsenic	$_{33}As^{76}$	75.94653	26.6 h	7.24×10^{-6}	β, 3.04; γ, 0.55–2.05
Barium	$_{56}Ba^{140}$	139.9544	12.8 d	6.27×10^{-7}	β, 1.02; γ, 0.03–0.54
Bismuth	$_{83}Bi^{210}$ (NR)	210.04976	5.00 d	1.60×10^{-6}	β, 1.17
	$_{83}Bi^{209}$ (NR)	209.04579	2×10^{18} y	1.10×10^{-26}	α, 2.87
Cadmium	$_{48}Cd^{115}$	114.9421	53 h	3.63×10^{-6}	β, 1.11; γ, 0.34–0.53
Calcium	$_{20}Ca^{45}$	44.97035	164 d	4.89×10^{-8}	β. 0.254
Carbon	$_{6}C^{14}$	14.007687	5600 y	3.92×10^{-12}	β, 0.155
Cerium	$_{58}Ce^{141}$	140.95290	32.5 d	2.47×10^{-7}	β, 0.44; γ, 0.15
Cesium	$_{55}Cs^{134}$	133.9490	2.3 y	9.54×10^{-9}	β, 0.65; γ, 0.56–0.79
	$_{55}Cs^{137}$	136.950	30 y	7.32×10^{-10}	β, 0.52
Chlorine	$_{17}Cl^{36}$	35.97969	3.2×10^5 y	6.86×10^{-14}	β, 0.71
Chromium	$_{24}Cr^{51}$	50.96084	27.8 d	2.89×10^{-7}	γ, 0.32
Cobalt	$_{27}Co^{58}$	57.95394	72 d	1.11×10^{-7}	β, 0.47; γ, 0.81
	$_{27}Co^{60}$	59.9529	5.3 y	4.14×10^{-9}	β, 0.31; γ, 1.17–1.33
Copper	$_{29}Cu^{64}$	63.9499	12.82 h	1.50×10^{-5}	β, 0.57; γ, 1.34

Element	Isotope	Atomic mass	Half-life	Cross section	Radiation
Hafnium	$_{72}\text{Hf}^{181}$	181.004	46 d	1.74×10^{-7}	β, 0.41; γ, 0.13–0.61
Hydrogen	$_{1}\text{H}^{3}$	3.017005	12.26 y	1.79×10^{-9}	β, 0.018
Indium	$_{49}\text{In}^{114}$	113.9416	72 s	9.62×10^{-3}	β, 1.98; γ, 0.55–1.30
	$_{49}\text{In}^{114}$	113.9418	49 d	1.64×10^{-7}	γ, 0.19
Iodine	$_{53}\text{I}^{131}$	130.9477	8.05 d	9.96×10^{-7}	β, 0.61; γ, 0.28–0.72
Iron	$_{26}\text{Fe}^{59}$	58.9536	45.1 d	1.78×10^{-7}	β, 0.46; γ, 0.19–1.29
Krypton	$_{36}\text{Kr}^{85}$	84.9396	10.60 y	2.07×10^{-9}	β, 0.70; γ, 0.54
Lanthanum	$_{57}\text{La}^{140}$	139.9530	40.2 h	4.78×10^{-6}	β, 1.32; γ, 0.09–2.50
Mercury	$_{80}\text{Hg}^{203}$	203.0365	45.8 d	1.75×10^{-7}	β, 0.21; γ, 0.28
Molybdenum	$_{42}\text{Mo}^{99}$	98.9400	67.0 h	1.20×10^{-7}	β, 1.23; γ, 0.04–0.78
Neptunium	$_{93}\text{Np}^{237}$	237.12220	2.20×10^{6} y	9.98×10^{-15}	α, 4.79; γ, 0.09
	$_{93}\text{Np}^{239}$	239.12777	2.33 d	3.44×10^{-6}	β, 0.33; γ, 0.27
Nickel	$_{28}\text{Ni}^{63}$	62.9495	80 y	2.74×10^{-10}	β, 0.07
Phosphorus	$_{15}\text{P}^{32}$	31.98403	14.3 d	5.61×10^{-7}	β, 1.70
Plutonium	$_{94}\text{Pu}^{239}$	239.12700	2.44×10^{4} y	9.01×10^{-13}	α, 5.15; γ, 0.04–0.053
Potassium	$_{19}\text{K}^{40}$ (NR)	39.97665	1.3×10^{9} y	1.69×10^{-17}	β, 1.35; γ, 1.46
	$_{19}\text{K}^{42}$	41.97583	12.47 h	1.54×10^{-5}	β, 3.58; γ, 1.51
Rubidium	$_{37}\text{Rb}^{86}$	85.9385	18.6 d	4.31×10^{-7}	β, 1.82; γ, 1.08
Rhodium	$_{45}\text{Rh}^{106}$	105.9402	30 s	2.31×10^{-2}	β, 3.53; γ, 0.51–2.41

(Continued)

Element	Nuclide	Isotopic mass	Half-life, T	Decay constant λ, sec^{-1}	Principal particle energy, Mev
Selenium	$_{34}\text{Se}^{75}$	74.94633	127 d	6.31×10^{-8}	γ, 0.07–0.41
Silver	$_{47}\text{Ag}^{111}$	110.9406	7.5 d	1.07×10^{-6}	β, 1.04; γ, 0.24–0.34
Sodium	$_{11}\text{Na}^{24}$	23.998565	15.0 h	1.28×10^{-5}	β, 1.39; γ, 1.37–2.75
Strontium	$_{38}\text{Sr}^{89}$	88.9357	51 d	1.57×10^{-7}	β, 1.46
	$_{38}\text{Sr}^{90}$	89.9358	28 y	7.83×10^{-10}	β, 0.61
Sulfur	$_{16}\text{S}^{35}$	34.97844	87.1 d	9.21×10^{-8}	β, 0.17
Tantalum	$_{73}\text{Ta}^{182}$	182.005	112 d	7.16×10^{-8}	β, 0.53; γ, 0.07–1.22
Xenon	$_{54}\text{Xe}^{135}$	...	9.20 h	2.09×10^{-5}	β, 0.91; γ, 0.36–0.60
Zinc	$_{30}\text{Zn}^{65}$	64.9498	245 d	3.27×10^{-8}	β, 0.33; γ, 1.12

APPENDIX 6

THE MKS SYSTEM

Conversion Factors

A conversion factor is a dimensionless ratio used to make a change in units. Thus the conversion factor

$$\frac{12 \text{ in}}{1 \text{ ft}}$$

(read, "There are 12 inches in 1 foot") may be used to convert 10 feet to inches by direct multiplication and cancellation of the units, feet. To convert 15 inches to feet we evidently must invert the conversion factor to produce the desired result and multiply by

$$\frac{1 \text{ ft}}{12 \text{ in}}$$

(read, "In 1 foot there are 12 inches"). When the conversion factor is used incorrectly we notice immediately that the desired cancellation of units is not obtained and this is the signal to invert the factor.

To convert speed in mi·hr^{-1} to m·sec^{-1} we proceed as follows:

$$1 \frac{\text{mi}}{\text{hr}} \times \frac{1 \text{ hr}}{3600 \text{ sec}} \times \frac{5280 \text{ ft}}{1 \text{ mi}} \times \frac{12 \text{ in.}}{1 \text{ ft}} \times \frac{2.540 \text{ cm}}{1 \text{ in.}} \times \frac{1 \text{ m}}{100 \text{ cm}}$$
$$= 0.4470 \text{ m·sec}^{-1}$$

The conversion factor then is

$$\frac{0.4470 \text{ m·sec}^{-1}}{1 \text{ mi·hr}^{-1}}.$$

The conversion factors in the following table can be considered exact except where they are given to five significant figures.

		in 1	there are	
Distance	s	cm	10^{-2}	meter, m
		in.	2.5400×10^{-2}	
		ft	0.30480	
		mi	1609.4	
		μ (micron)	10^{-6}	
		$m\mu$ (millimicron)	10^{-9}	
		A (angstrom)	10^{-10}	
Velocity	u, v	ft·sec^{-1}	0.30480	m·sec^{-1}
		mi·hr^{-1}	0.44704	

(Continued)

		in 1	there are	
Mass	m	gm	10^{-3}	kilogram, kgm
		slug	14.594	
Force F		dyne	10^{-5}	newton, n
and weight	w, W, F	poundal	0.13826	
		lb	4.4482	
Energy	E	erg	10^{-7}	joule, j
		ev	1.6019×10^{-19}	
		kwh	3.6×10^6	
		cal (15°C)	4.1861	
		kcal	4.1861×10^3	
		ft·lb	1.3558	
		Btu (60°F)	1054.6	
Power	P	erg·sec^{-1}	10^{-7}	watt, w
		cal·sec^{-1}	4.1861	
		Btu·hr^{-1}	0.29294	
		ft·lb·sec^{-1}	1.3558	
		hp	746.00	
Pressure	p	dyne·cm^{-2}	10^{-1}	n·m^{-2}
		lb·in^{-2}	6.8947×10^3	
		atm (standard)	1.0133×10^5	
		cm-mercury	1.3332×10^3	
Density	ρ, D	gm·cm^{-3}	10^3	kgm·m^{-3}
		lb·ft^{-3}	16.018	
Specific heat	c	cal·gm^{-1}·(C°)$^{-1}$	4.1861×10^3	j·kgm^{-1}·(C°)$^{-1}$
		Btu·lb^{-1}·(F°)$^{-1}$	4.1861×10^3	
Charge	q, Q	statcoul (esu)	$1/(3 \times 10^9)$	coulomb, coul
		abcoul (emu)	10	
Potential		statvolt (esu)	300	volt, v
difference	V	abvolt (emu)	10^{-8}	
Capacitance	C	statfarad (esu)	$1/(9 \times 10^{11})$	farad, f
		abfarad (emu)	10^9	
Permittivity	ϵ	esu	$1/(36\pi \times 10^9)$	f·m^{-1}
Electric field		v·cm^{-1}	10^2	v·m^{-1}
intensity	E	dyne·statcoul^{-1} (esu)	3×10^4	
Electric flux		esu	$1/(12\pi \times 10^5)$	coul·m^{-2}
density or				
electric		emu	$10^5/4\pi$	
displacement D				
Current	i, I	statamp (esu)	$1/(3 \times 10^9)$	ampere, amp
		abamp (emu)	10	

		in 1	there are	
Resistance	r, R	statohm (esu) abohm (emu)	9×10^{11} 10^{-9}	ohm
Resistivity	ρ	ohm·cm ohm·(mil-ft)$^{-1}$	10^{-2} 1.6624×10^{-9}	ohm·m
Magnetic flux density or magnetic induction	B	gauss (emu) line·in^{-2} esu	10^{-4} 1.5500×10^{-5} 3×10^{6}	weber·m^{-2}
Magnetic flux	ϕ	maxwell (emu) esu	10^{-8} 3×10^{2}	weber
Inductance	L	abhenry (emu) stathenry (esu)	10^{-9} 9×10^{11}	henry, h
Permeability	μ	emu	$4\pi \times 10^{-7}$	h·m^{-1}
Magnetic field intensity	H	amp-turn·cm^{-1} oersted (emu)	10^{2} $10^{3}/4\pi$	amp-turn·m^{-1}

APPENDIX 7

ATOMIC CONSTANTS

(The values given are within ± 0.1 percent of the most precise values known at present.)

		cgs	mks
F	Faraday	9.65×10^3 emu$\cdot$(gm-equiv)$^{-1}$ (phys.)	9.65×10^7 coul$\cdot$(kgm-equiv)$^{-1}$ (phys.)
N_0	Avogadro's number	6.025×10^{23} (gm-mole)$^{-1}$ (phys.)	6.025×10^{26} (kgm-mole)$^{-1}$ (phys.)
h	Planck's constant	6.625×10^{-27} erg$\cdot$sec	6.625×10^{-34} j$\cdot$sec
c	Velocity of light in vacuum	3.00×10^{10} cm$\cdot$sec^{-1}	3.00×10^8 m$\cdot$sec^{-1}
e	Electronic charge	$\begin{cases} 1.602 \times 10^{-20} \text{ emu} \\ 4.80 \times 10^{-10} \text{ esu} \end{cases}$	1.602×10^{-19} coul
m	Electron rest mass	$\begin{cases} 9.11 \times 10^{-28} \text{ gm} \\ 5.49 \times 10^{-4} \text{ amu} \end{cases}$	9.11×10^{-31} kgm 5.49×10^{-4} amu
e/m	Specific electronic charge	1.760×10^7 emu$\cdot$gm^{-1}	1.760×10^{11} coul$\cdot$kgm^{-1}
h/mc	Compton wavelength, electron	2.426×10^{-10} cm	2.426×10^{-12} m
M_0	1 amu $= \frac{1}{12}$ mass $C^{12} = 1/N_0$	1.6603×10^{-24} gm	1.6603×10^{-27} kgm
M	Proton rest mass	1.6724×10^{-24} gm	1.6724×10^{-27} kgm
H	H-atom rest mass	1.6733×10^{-24} gm	1.6733×10^{-27} kgm
n	Neutron rest mass	1.6747×10^{-24} gm	1.6747×10^{-27} kgm
M/m	Ratio, proton to electron mass	1.836×10^3	1.836×10^3
mc^2	Energy equiv. of electron rest mass	0.511 Mev	0.511 Mev
$M_0 c^2$	Energy equiv. of 1 amu	931 Mev	931 Mev
σ	Stefan-Boltzmann constant	5.67×10^{-5} erg$\cdot$cm$^{-2}\cdot$($^\circ$K)$^{-4}\cdot$sec^{-1}	5.67×10^{-8} j$\cdot$m$^{-2}\cdot$($^\circ$K)$^{-4}\cdot$sec^{-1}
k	Boltzmann constant	1.380×10^{-16} erg$\cdot$($^\circ$K)$^{-1}$	1.380×10^{-23} j$\cdot$($^\circ$K)$^{-1}$
$c_1 = 8\pi hc$	First radiation constant	4.992×10^{-15} erg$\cdot$cm	4.992×10^{-24} j$\cdot$m
$c_2 = hc/k$	Second radiation constant	1.439 cm$\cdot^\circ$K	1.439×10^{-2} m$\cdot^\circ$K
$\lambda_{max}T$	Wien displacement law constant	0.290 cm$\cdot^\circ$K	0.290×10^{-2} m$\cdot^\circ$K
R_∞	Rydberg const. for infinite mass	1.097×10^5 cm^{-1}	1.097×10^7 m^{-1}
R	Gas constant	8.31×10^7 erg$\cdot$(gm-mole$\cdot^\circ$K)$^{-1}$	8.31×10^3 j$\cdot$(kgm-mole$\cdot^\circ$K)$^{-1}$
V_0	Standard volume of ideal gas	2.242×10^4 cm^3(gm-mole)$^{-1}$	22.42 m^3(kgm-mole)$^{-1}$

ANSWERS TO ODD-NUMBERED PROBLEMS

CHAPTER 1

1-1. 25.7 lb, 30.6 lb

1-3. (a) 18.5 lb (b) 9.2 lb

1-7. (a) 19.3 lb in a direction midway between the 10-lb
forces
(b) 8.46 lb in a direction midway between the 10-lb
forces

1-9. 308 lb, 25° above the x-axis

1-11. (a) 2 in. (b) 3.46 in.

1-13. (a) 7 lb, 2.9 lb (b) 7.6 lb
(c) 11 lb

1-15. $F_x = 430$ lb, W; $F_y = 973$ lb, N

CHAPTER 2

2-3. (a) 10 lb (b) 20 lb

2-5. (a) 150 lb in A, 180 lb in B,
200 lb in C
(b) 200 lb in A, 280 lb in B,
200 lb in C
(c) 550 lb in A, 670 lb in B,
200 lb in C
(d) 167 lb in A, 58 lb in B,
125 lb in C

2-7. (a) Parts (b) and (c) can be
solved

(b) In part (a) another side or
angle is needed

2-9. 630 lb

2-11. (a) 20 lb (b) 30 lb

2-13. Sliding down, 53°; sliding up, 37°

2-15. $\mu w/(\cos \phi + \mu \sin \phi)$

2-17. (a) 3 lb (b) 4 lb (c) 5 lb

2-19. (a) 4 lb (b) 0.398

2-21. (a) $F = w/(2 \sin \theta)$
(b) $T = w/(2 \tan \theta)$

CHAPTER 3

3-3. (a) 133 lb
(b) 107 lb to the right, 20 lb upward

3-5. 12 lb horizontal, 16 lb vertical

3-7. (a) 54 lb (b) 24 lb

3-9. 722 lb, 722 lb, 1500 lb

3-11. 15 lb each

3-13. (a) $V_A = 20$ lb, $V_B = 140$ lb
(b) 4 ft

3-15. (a) 15 lb (b) 5 lb on each front
leg, 20 lb on each rear leg

(c) 8.75 lb on each front leg,
16.25 lb on each rear leg
(d) 3.33 ft above floor

3-17. 81.5 lb, 78° above the horizontal

3-19. 32.5 lb and 13 lb on each front
leg, 17.5 lb and 7 lb on each rear
leg

3-21. 70 lb down and 1.4 ft to the left
of left end

3-23. On centerline, 5.29 in. from the
bottom

CHAPTER 4

4–1. (a) 15 mi/hr
      (b) 22 ft/sec
      (c) 672 cm/sec

4–3. 61 cm/sec, 60.1 cm/sec,
      60.01 cm/sec, 60 cm/sec

4–5. (a) 0 (b) 6.3 ft/sec^2
      (c) -11 ft/sec^2 (d) 100 ft
      (e) 230 ft (f) 320 ft

4–7. 4 ft/sec^2, 620 ft

4–9. (a) 2.67 mi/hr·sec, 3.92 ft/sec^2
      (b) 7.5 sec (c) 441 ft, 550 ft
      between 15 sec and 22.5 sec

4–11. (a) 12.5 cm/sec^2 (b) 7840 cm

4–13. (a) 300 ft (b) 60 ft/sec

4–15. (a) 24 ft/sec, 29 ft/sec,
      34 ft/sec
      (b) 2.5 ft/sec^2
      (c) 21.5 ft/sec (d) 8.6 sec
      (e) 23 ft (f) 1 sec
      (g) 24 ft/sec

4–17. (a) 32 ft/sec (b) 2.83 sec
      (c) 16 ft (d) 22.6 ft/sec
      (e) 16 ft/sec

4–19. (a) 8.7 sec (b) 75 ft
      (c) $v_A = 52$ ft/sec,
      $v_T = 35$ ft/sec

4–21. (a) 94 ft/sec (b) 124 ft
      (c) 53 ft/sec (d) 150 ft/sec^2
      (e) 1.96 sec (f) 93 ft/sec

4–23. 39.4 ft

4–25. (a) 48 ft/sec (b) 36 ft (c) Zero
      (d) 32 ft/sec^2, downward
      (e) 80 ft/sec

4–27. (a) 32 ft (b) 13 ft/sec, -32
      ft/sec^2
      (c) -51 ft/sec, -32 ft/sec^2
      (d) 37 ft/sec

4–29. (a) 36 ft (b) 0.5 sec
      (c) 32 ft/sec, -32 ft/sec^2,
      -16 ft/sec, -32 ft/sec^2

4–31. (a) 4 m/sec^2 (b) 6 m/sec
      (c) 4.5 m

4–33. 6.55 knots

4–35. (a) 50 mi/hr, 53° S of W
      (b) 60° S of W

4–37. (a) 5 mi/hr, 53° E of N
      (b) 0.75 mi (c) 15 min

4–39. 11.6 mi/hr, 59° N of E

4–41. (a) $v = -2\pi f A \sin 2\pi ft$
      (b) $a = -4\pi^2 f^2 A \cos 2\pi ft$
      (c) $a = -4\pi^2 f^2 y$

CHAPTER 5

5–1. (a) 400 lb (b) 12,800 dynes
      (c) 12,800 n

5–3. (a) 2 m/sec^2 (b) 100 m
      (c) 20 m/sec

5–7. (a) 0.5 slug (b) 500 ft

5–9. (a) 1.62×10^{-10} dyne
      (b) 3.33×10^{-9} sec
      (c) 1.8×10^{17} cm/sec^2

5–11. (a) 19.6 n (b) 2.55 sec

5–13. (a) 4 lb (b) 128 ft

5–15. 48 ft/sec^2

5–17. (a) 40 lb (b) 4 ft/sec^2 down-
      ward (c) zero

5–19. 240 ft

5–21. (a) 12 sec after force is applied
      (b) 8 ft/sec^2

5–23. $W = 2wa/(g + a)$

5–25. (a) 37° (b) 6.4 ft/sec^2
      (c) 2.5 sec

5–27. (a) 6 lb, (b) 8 ft/sec^2

5–29. (a) 2 lb (b) 1.9 lb

5–31. (a) 196 cm/sec^2
      (b) 314,000 dynes

5–33. (a) to left (b) 2.13 ft/sec^2
      (c) 43.3 lb

5–35. 1.33 lb

5–37. (a) 4 lb (b) 4 lb (c) no

5–39.

	a_1	a_2
(a)	0	0
(b)	0	0
(c)	0	16 ft/sec^2
(d)	4 ft/sec^2	28 ft/sec^2
(e)	16 ft/sec^2	48 ft/sec^2

5–41. (a) 4.4 ft/sec^2
     (b) 1.2 lb
5–43. (a) $dv/dt = -Kv^2/m$
     (b) No
     (c) $-Kv_0^2/m$
     (d) $1/v = (1/v_0) + (Kt/m)$
     (e) 150 lb

5–45. 5 ft
5–47. g/μ
5–49. 6.2×10^{27} gm
5–51. 6.32 ft/sec^2
5–53. (a) $v = \sqrt{2g_0 R}$

CHAPTER 6

6–1. 10 ft/sec
6–3. (a) 20 sec (b) 6000 ft
    (c) $v_x = 300$ ft/sec,
      $v_y = 640$ ft/sec
6–5. (a) 100 ft (b) 200 ft
    (c) $v_x = 80$ ft/sec,
      $v_y = 80$ ft/sec
      $v = 113$ ft/sec at 45° below
      horizontal
6–7. (a) 0.56 mi (b) 296 mi/hr at 47°
    below horizontal
    (c) 10 sec
6–9. (a) 40 sec (b) 55°
6–11. (a) 121 ft/sec (b) 57.2 ft
     (c) 3.8 sec
6–13. 100 ft
6–15. Yes. Ball clears fence by 10 ft
6–17. (a) 67 ft/sec (b) 39 ft/sec at 31°
     below horizontal

6–19. 1.98 sec, 157 sec
6–21. 1300 ft
6–23. 22°
6–27. (a) Above
     (b) 169 ft/sec at 57° 40′ below
      the horizontal
6–29. (a) 6.5 cm/sec, 25° E of N
     (b) 3.25 cm/sec^2, 25° E of N
6–31. 22 m/sec
6–33. (a) 1.02 rev/sec
     (b) 2.77×10^5 dynes
6–35. 0.302
6–37. (a) 33° (b) 1.43 mi
6–39. $\cos^2 \theta$
6–41. 9.8 oz
6–43. 1.97 hr
6–45. 1.69×10^4 mi/hr

CHAPTER 7

7–1. 63.4×10^6 ft·lb
7–3. 9850 ft·lb
7–5. (a) 55,000 ft·lb (b) 4 times
7–7. 4.5×10^{-10} erg
7–9. 9.8 joules
7–11. (a) 5 lb, 10 lb, 20 lb
     (b) 1.3 ft·lb, 5 ft·lb, 20 ft·lb
7–13. (a) 33 ft·lb
     (b) about 15 ft·lb
7–15. (a) 160 ft·lb (b) 160 ft·lb
7–17. (a) 3300 ft·lb (b) 1300 ft·lb
     (c) 1500 ft·lb (d) 500 ft·lb
     Goes into heat.
     (e) $b + c + d = a$
7–19. (a) 42 lb (b) 105 ft·lb
7–21. (a) 40 ft/sec (b) 20 ft/sec
7–23. 10 cm

7–25. (a) 0.25 (b) 3.5 ft·lb
7–29. 1.81 m/sec
7–31. 0.655 hp, 489 watts, 0.489 kw
7–33. 154 hp
7–35. $1.29
7–37. (a) 250 lb (b) 5 hp (c) 80 hp
7–39. (a) 8200 joules (b) 8200 joules
     (c) 0.55 hp
7–41. (a) 6300 lb (b) 30 ft/sec
     (c) 68,000 ft·lb (d) 220,000 ft·lb
     (e) 250 hp
7–43. (a) 250 lb (b) 39 hp (c) 16 hp
     (d) 10.5% grade
7–45. (a) 24.6 ft/sec (b) 27.2 ft/sec
     (c) 22.5 lb (d) 10 ft/sec
7–47. (a) 6 lb (b) 48 lb
     (c) 22.5 ft·lb

CHAPTER 8

8–1. (a) 28,000 slug·ft/sec
(b) 60 mi/hr (c) 43 mi/hr
8–3. (a) 8×10^5 m/sec^2
(b) 4×10^4 n (c) 5×10^{-4} sec
(d) 20 n·sec
8–5. 1.5 ft/sec
8–7. 0.65 mi/hr
8–9. 17 mi/hr 53° E of S
8–13. (a) 10 cm/sec (b) 0.14 joule
(c) —70 cm/sec, 80 cm/sec
8–15. (a) 100 gm (b) 16 cm/sec
8–17. 58,700 ft

8–19. 1.82 ft/sec
8–21. (a) 149° from direction of electron
(b) 10.6×10^{-16} gm·cm/sec
(c) 14.5×10^{-10} erg
8–23. 780 ft/sec
8–25. (a) 0.39 ft (b) 1950 ft·lb
(c) 3.9 ft·lb
8–27. 3.3 cm
8–29. 4.22 lb
8–31. (a) 25×10^6 dynes, 250 n

CHAPTER 9

9–1. (a) 1.5 rad (b) 1.6 rad, 90°
(c) 120 cm, 120 ft
9–3. (a) 20 ft/sec (b) 230 rev/min
9–5. 5 rad/sec^2, 1000 rad
9–7. 20 rad/sec^2
9–11. (a) At the bottom of the wheel
(b) 360 ft/sec at 3° from the vertical
9–13. (a) 135°
(b) 2.36 ft/sec^2, 11.03 ft/sec^2
9–15. 164,000 rev/min
9–17. (a) 2.67 kgm·m^2
(b) 10.7 kgm·m^2
(c) 1.6×10^{-3} kgm·m^2
9–19. (a) A smallest (b) D largest
9–21. (a) 2.56×10^{28} slug·mi^2
(b) 2530 mi
9–23. (a) 278 ft·lb (b) 70 ft
9–25. 1.1 slug·ft^2
9–27. (a) 2×10^7 joules (b) 18 min
9–29. (a) 4 rad/sec^2 (b) 14 rad/sec^2
(c) 32,000 ft·lb

9–31. 0.47
9–33. (a) 17.4 kgm·m^2 (b) 1.82 n·m
(c) 91.6 rev
9–35. (a) 63 m (b) 38 newtons
(c) 185 newtons
9–37. (a) 0.0625 slug·ft^2
(b) 12 lb, 4 lb
9–39. (a) 2 rad/sec^2 (b) 8 rad/sec
(c) 240 ft·lb (d) 7.5 slug·ft^2
9–41. (a) 4400 lb·ft
(b) 5900 lb (c) 190 ft/sec
9–43. (a) 24 slug·ft^2/sec
(b) 6 rad/sec
(c) 24 ft·lb, 72 ft·lb
9–45. 1 ft
9–47. (a) 6 rev/min (b) 6 rev/min
9–49. 4500 ft·lb
9–51. 0.15 rad/sec in same direction
9–53. (a) 1.8 hr (b) 130,000 lb·ft
9–55. 2.5 rad/sec

CHAPTER 10

10–1. 25×10^6 lb/in^2
10–3. (b) 14×10^6 lb/in^2
(c) 0.016×10^6 lb/in^2
10–5. (a) 27.5 lb (b) 0.028 ft
10–7. 0.0253 in.

10–9. (a) 1.8 ft (b) 30,000 lb/in^2 in steel, 12,000 lb/in^2 in copper (c) 0.001 in steel, 0.0006 in copper
10–13. 2000 lb

10–15. Steel, 0.64×10^{-6} atm^{-1}
        Water, 50×10^{-6} atm^{-1}
        Water is 78 times more compressible

10–17. 5.1 in.

CHAPTER 11

11–1.   (a) 9470 cm/sec^2, 377 cm/sec
        (b) 5680 cm/sec^2, 301 cm/sec
        (c) 0.0368 sec
11–3.   (a) $2400\pi^2$ ft/sec^2
        (b) 740 lb   (c) 43 mi/hr
11–5.   23 lb
11–7.   6.20 cm
11–9.   (a) $L_1 = 35$ cm, $L_2 = 25$ cm
        (c) 1 sec
11–11. (a) 1.4 sec, 3.5 cm
11–13. (a) 9 vib/sec
        (b) 20×10^6 lb/in^2

11–15. (a) $\pi/4$ sec
        (b) 10.7 ft/sec^2 downward
        (c) 5.3 lb
        (d) $\pi/48$ sec
        (e) Remain
        (f) 6 in. above equilibrium
11–17. (a) 4 lb
        (b) 2.59 in. below equilibrium,
            moving upward
        (c) 5.2 lb
11–19. 0.817 ft
11–21. (a) 97 cm   (b) -2×10^{-4}

CHAPTER 12

12–1.   316 m/sec
12–3.   0.164 sec
12–5.   (a) 17 m, 0.017 m
        (b) 73 m, 0.073 m

12–9.   (a) 2 cm, 4 cm, 100 sec^{-1},
            0.01 sec, 400 cm/sec
        (c) 8×10^5 dynes

CHAPTER 13

13–3.   (a) 200 cycles/sec
        (b) 49th overtone
13–5.   (a) 3600 cm/sec
        (b) 6.5×10^6 dynes
13–7.   (a) 4960 m/sec
        (b) 342 m/sec
13–9.   (a) 1140, 2280, 3420, 4560,
            5700 cycles/sec
        (b) 570, 1710, 2850, 3990,
            5130 cycles/sec (c) 16, 17
13–11. (a) 428 cycles/sec
        (b) 423 cycles/sec
13–13. 2%

13–15. (a) 2.08 ft
        (b) 2.48 ft
        (c) 548 cycles/sec
        (d) 459 cycles/sec
        (e) 572 cycles/sec
        (f) 439 cycles/sec
        (g) 2.14, 2.42 ft; 547, 458, 570,
            438 cycles/sec
13–17. 2.8 beats/sec
13–19. (b) 256 cycles/sec
        (c) No
        (d) Yes

CHAPTER 14

14–1.   21 lb/in^2
14–3.   120 lb/in^2, 18,000 lb/ft^2
14–5.   34.8 ft^2

14–7.   270,000 ft^3, 9.3 tons lift, using
        helium
14–9.   (a) 5 cm   (b) 4900 dynes/cm^2

14–11. (a) 100 lb/ft^3 (b) E will read
5 lb, D will read 15 lb
14–15. (a) 4500 lb (b) 10,000 lb
(c) 230 lb

14–17. 100.87 gm
14–19. (b) 4 lb (c) 1 ft^3
14–21. 0.781 gm/cm^3

CHAPTER 15

15–1. (a) 1800°F
(b) 7.8 × 10^{-6} (F°)$^{-1}$
(c) 42 × 10^{-6} (C°)$^{-1}$
(d) −40°F = −40°C
15–3. 1.6 ft
15–5. 0.03 cm

15–7. 1.0 × 10^{-5} (C°)$^{-1}$
15–9. (a) 13 × 10^{-6} (C°)$^{-1}$
(b) 19 × 10^4 lb/in^2
15–11. (a) 76°C (b) −63.3°C
15–13. (a) 1.2 × 10^{-4}
(b) 5.18 sec/day

CHAPTER 16

16–1. 91 ft^3
16–3. 4.0 Btu
16–5. (a) 18.7 × 10^7 Btu
(b) 42.2 ft
16–7. (a) 80.5% (b) 330 Btu
16–9. 370 years
16–11. 0.1 Btu/lb·F°
16–13. 1.00, 0.827, 0.35
16–15. (a) 0.092 cal/gm·C°
(b) 27.6 gm
16–17. 725 cal
16–19. It melts the ice
16–21. 0°C with 0.2 gm of ice left
16–23. 539 cal/gm

16–25. 24°C
16–27. 40°C
16–29. 1.84 kgm
16–31. 17,100 cm
16–33. 445 cal/gm
16–35. 103°F
16–37. (a) 2500k (b) 250k
(c) 1000k
16–39. (a) 20.5 cal/sec (b) 22.2°C
16–41. (a) 1.13 cal/sec
(b) 4% through steel
96% through copper
16–43. 20°C
16–45. 0.23 cent

CHAPTER 17

17–1. 6.6 × 10^4 ft·lb
17–3. (a) Yes (b) No
(c) Negative
17–5. (a) No (b) Yes (c) Yes
(d) Work done on the resistor
= heat transferred to the
water
17–7. 10.8 ft^3
17–11. $U_1 = U_2$
17–13. (a) 60 Btu (b) liberate 70 Btu
(c) 50 Btu; −10 Btu

17–15. 4
17–17. 93 C°
17–19. 15%
17–21. (a) 2 atm, 5 liters;
1 atm, 5 liters;
1 atm, 3 liters;
2 atm, 3 liters;
(b) 2 liter·atm
17–23. (a) 6.6 (b) 0.64 kwh
(c) 3 cents

CHAPTER 18

18–1. 3.6 lb/in^2
18–3. (a) 0.75 atm (b) 2 gm
18–5. 3.25
18–7. (a) 927°C (b) 0.325 gm
18–9. (a) 7.06 ft (b) 106 lb/in^2
18–11. 24 cm
18–13. (a) 71.53 cm (b) 70 cm
18–19. 4.00
18–21. (a) 1.91×10^3 m/sec,
            1.76×10^3 m/sec,
            1.56×10^3 m/sec

(b) 2.21×10^3 m/sec,
     2.04×10^3 m/sec,
     1.80×10^3 m/sec
18–23. (a) 327°C (b) 0.76 mm
18–27. (a) 4.74×10^{-17} kgm
         (b) 6.73×10^{26} molecules
              per kgm-mole
         (c) 3.19×10^{10}

CHAPTER 19

19–1. (b) $(1/4\pi\epsilon_0)q^2[x/(a^2 + x^2)^{3/2}]$;
        (d) $x = \pm a/\sqrt{2}$
19–3. (b) $0.41a$ to the right of q_2,
            $0.77a$ above q_2

19–5. (a) 4×10^6 electrons
19–7. (a) About 110,000 lb
        (b) About 1,200,000 lb

CHAPTER 20

20–1. (a) 4 n/coul upward
        (b) 6.4×10^{-19} n/coul down-
             ward
20–3. (a) 50 n/coul in pos. x-direc-
             tion
        (b) 10.8 n/coul in pos. x-direc-
             tion
20–5. (a) Zero
        (b) 10×10^3 n/coul to the
             right
        (c) 5×10^3 n/coul, 77°, first
             quad.
        (d) 6.3×10^3 n/coul vert. up
20–7. 9.04×10^3 electrons
20–9. 41°
20–13. Two electrons
20–15. (a) 2.50×10^{-4} m/sec

(b) 1.11×10^{-4} m/sec,
     3.58×10^{-4} m/sec,
     2.26×10^{-4} m/sec,
     5.21×10^{-4} m/sec,
     1.74×10^{-4} m/sec
(c) 3.61×10^{-4} m/sec,
     6.08×10^{-4} m/sec,
     4.76×10^{-4} m/sec,
     7.71×10^{-4} m/sec,
     4.21×10^{-4} m/sec
(d) 6, 10, 8, 13, 7
(e) 1.63×10^{-19} coul
20–17. (a) 4.8×10^{-15} n
         (b) 5.3×10^{15} m/sec^2
20–19. (a) 0.704 cm (b) arctan 0.352
         (c) 4.92 cm

CHAPTER 21

21–1. (a) -1.5×10^{-5} joule
        (b) 10^5 n/coul
21–3. (b) 0.667 mm
21–11. (a) 2.17×10^{-3} cm
         (b) $v_e/v_p = 42.8$
         (c) Energies are equal

21–13. (a) 3 m (b) 2×10^{-7} coul
21–15. 10.3×10^6 m/sec
21–17. 2.24×10^7 m/sec

CHAPTER 22

22–1.   (a) 20 ma
     (b) 2.75×10^{-6} m/sec
22–3. 1.3×10^5 electrons/mm^3
22–5.   0.96 ma
22–7.   (a) Yes; 4.36 ohms
     (b) No; R varies with i

22–9.   53.5 volts
22–13. 90 ohms
22–15. 0.188 watt/meter
22–19. (a) 0.106 coul
     (b) Zero
     (c) 12.7 amp

CHAPTER 23

23–1.   (a) 0.05 ohm (b) 0.15 ohm
     (c) 0.006 ohm
23–3.   Switch open: (a) 12 volts
     (b) Zero (c) 12 volts
     Switch closed: (a) 11.1 volts
     (b) 11.1 volts (c) Zero
23–7.   7.98 cm
23–9.   (a) 25 volts (b) 2 ohms
23–11. (a) 0.5 ohm (b) 10 volts
23–13. (a) $+$ (b) 1000 amp
     (c) 9.9 ohms (d) 13 volts
     (e) 1120 watts (f) 990 watts
     (g) 120 watts (h) 6.7 cents
23–15. (a) 99.1 volts (b) 0.0527

23–17. (a) 2.83 volts (b) 1.33 volts
23–19. (a) 32 ohms (b) 20 volts
23–21. 9.6 watts in 60-watt lamp,
     14.4 watts in 40-watt lamp
23–23. (a) 141 volts (b) 4.5 watts
     (c) 2 groups of resistors in
     parallel, each consisting of
     2 resistors in series
23–25. (a) 15 ohms
     (b) 3.3×10^{-3} amp,
     6.7×10^{-3} amp
23–27. (a) 8 ohms (b) 72 volts
23–29. In parallel
23–31. $V_{ab} = 0.22$ volt

CHAPTER 24

24–1.   (a) 0.24 weber, 24×10^6 max-
     wells (b) Zero
     (c) 0.24 weber
24–3.   3.27 w/m^2 perpendicular to di-
     rection of v
24–5.   (a) 1.14×10^{-3} w/m^2
     toward the reader
     (b) 1.57×10^{-8} sec
24–7. 2.14×10^{-7} w
24–9.   (a) 4.58×10^7 reversals/sec
     (b) 5.03×10^7 m/sec
     (c) 1.32×10^7 volts

24–11. 21
24–13. 0.1248 cm
24–15. (a) **E** and **B** downward
     (b) **E** upward, **B** downward
     (c) **E** and **B** upward
24–17. Higher velocity. Collisions of
     gas molecules

CHAPTER 25

25–1. $F_{ab} = 1.20$ n in neg. z-direction
     $F_{bc} = 1.20$ n in neg. y-direction
     $F_{cd} = 1.70$ n, 45° up, 11 to
     y-z plane
     $F_{de} = 1.20$ n, in neg. y-direction

25–3.   (a) 16,000 dynes,
     83,000 dyne·cm
     (b) 16,000 dynes,
     48,000 dyne·cm
     (c) Same torque

25–5. 3.6×10^{-6} n·m

25–7. (a) 0.0331 ohm for 1-amp range, 0.00331 ohm for 10-amp range

(b) 0.033 watt for 1-amp shunt, 0.33 watt for 10-amp shunt

25–9. 30°

25–11. $R_1 = 0.00802$ ohm, $R_2 = 0.0324$ ohm, $R_3 = 0.404$ ohm

25–13. 2985 ohms, 12,000 ohms, 135,000 ohms; 3000 ohms, 15,000 ohms, 150,000 ohms

25–15. (a) 23.3 ohms (b) 116.5 volts

25–17. 4.97 ohms

25–19. 20 volts

25–21. (a) 1200 ohms (b) 30 volts

25–23. (a) 150 ohms, 300 ohms (b) 1.55 volts, 13.2 ohms

25–25. (a) 1000 ohms (b) 13.6 watts

25–27. 90%

25–29. (a) 213 volts (b) 11.7 cal/sec

CHAPTER 26

26–1. (a) 20×10^{-6} w/m² (b) 7.1×10^{-6} w/m² (c) 20×10^{-6} w/m² (d) Zero (e) 5.4×10^{-6} w/m²

26–3. (a) Zero (b) 1.41×10^{-6} w/m² (c) 3×10^{-6} w/m² in pos. x-direction

26–5. (a) 2 amp out of diagram (b) 2.13×10^{-5} w/m² (c) 1.64×10^{-5} w/m²

26–7. 238 amp

26–9. 72×10^{-5} n

26–11. 2.51×10^{-3} w/m²

26–13. 6.29×10^{-3} w/m²

26–15. (a) $(\mu_0/4\pi)(2i/x)$ (b) $(\mu_0/4\pi)(2i/x)l\,dx$ (c) $(\mu_0 i l/2\pi) \ln (b/a)$

26–17. $\mu_0 Qn/R$

26–19. (b) 0.0108 w/amp·m (c) 0.005 w/amp·m (d) 3.7×10^{-6} w/amp·m

26–21. Upward

CHAPTER 27

27–1. $\mathcal{E}_A = 0$, $\mathcal{E}_C = 0.0707$ volt, $\mathcal{E}_D = 0.10$ volt

27–3. (a) 1 volt from B to A (b) 1.25 n (c) 5 watts

27–5. 12 volts

27–7. (a) 0.885 rev/sec (b) Zero

27–9. 9×10^{-6} volt

27–11. (a) $B = mv/qR$ (b) $\mathcal{E} = A(\Delta B/\Delta t)$

27–13. (a) 2080 rev/min (b) 157 volts

27–15. (a) 1.19 volts (b) 0.59 volt

27–17. 0.05 w/m²

27–19. 2.7×10^{-4} coul

CHAPTER 28

28–1. 4.25×10^{-4} coul

28–3. (a) 5 μf (b) 64 volts

28–5. (a) 0.02 coul (b) 800 volts (c) 8 joules (d) 2 joules

28–7. (a) 1.2×10^{-3} coul, 2.4×10^{-3} coul, 1200 volts (b) 4×10^{-4} coul, 8×10^{-4} coul, 400 volts

28–9. (a) 3.8×10^{-7} coul
       (b) 7600 volts
       (c) 1.43×10^{-3} joule
       (d) 1.35×10^{-3} joule
28–11. (a) 16.5 (b) Infinity
28–13. 7.08×10^{-7} coul/m^2
28–15. 1.7 m^2

28–17. (a) 2.66×10^{-5} coul/m^2
       (b) 1.77×10^{-5} coul/m^2
28–19. (a) $V_{ab} = (Q/4\pi\epsilon_0)[(1/r_a) - (1/r_b)]$
28–21. (a) $dC = -(\epsilon_0 A/x^2)\, dx$
       (b) $dW = -\frac{1}{2}(Q^2/C^2)\, dC$
       (c) $F = \frac{1}{2}QE$

CHAPTER 29

29–3. 1.87 h
29–5. (a) $\dfrac{V_{ab}R}{R_0 + R}\left(1 + e^{-\frac{R_0+R}{L}t}\right)$

29–7. (a) 6 watts (b) 1.5 watts
       (c) 4.5 watts (d) 6 joules
29–9. (a) $\mathcal{E}Q$ (b) $\frac{1}{2}$

CHAPTER 30

30–1. (a) 127 cycles/sec
       (b) 7.97 cycles/sec
30–3. (a) 377 ohms (b) 2.65 mh
       (c) 2650 ohms
       (d) 2650 μf
30–5. (a) 103.5 ohms, 613 ohms
       (b) 63.9 ohms, 628 ohms

30–7. 6.85 μf
30–9. (a) 6 ohms, 6×10^{-5} h
       (b) 0.12 amp
30–11. 47.2 ohms
30–13. 104 stations

CHAPTER 31

31–1. (a) 1.5×10^{-9} m,
           1.5×10^{-3} μ,
           1.5 mμ, 15 A
       (b) 5.37×10^{-7} m, 0.537 μ,
           537 mμ, 5370 A

31–3. (a) 16 cm^2 (b) 48 cm^2
31–5. (a) 2×10^8 m/sec
       (b) 333 mμ
31–7. 1.87
31–9. 16.6 min

CHAPTER 32

32–3. (a) 54° 46′
       (b) 82° 50′
32–5. 34° 50′
32–7. (a) 26° 14′
       (b) Does not depend on it
32–9. 18.2 in.

32–11. 1.30
32–13. (a) 14.5° (b) Air
32–15. 1.02 cm
32–17. 30°
32–19. 12.2°

CHAPTER 33

33–1. Half the observer's height
33–5. 9.88 cm, 5 cm
33–7. 3
33–9. 0.643 in., 0.143
33–11. (a) 45° (b) 0.53 in.

33–13. 3.0 cm
33–15. 1.35
33–17. $s' = 30$ cm, $m = -1$
33–19. 0.667 cm
33–21. At vertex of silvered surface

CHAPTER 34

34–1. $4R$ from center of sphere

34–3. (a) The first image
(b) 30 cm (c) Real (d) At ∞
(e) Infinite

34–5. 50 cm

34–7. 1.5 cm

34–11.

R_1	R_2	f
10 cm	20 cm	40 cm
10 cm	−20 cm	13.3 cm
−10 cm	20 cm	−13.3 cm
−10 cm	−20 cm	−40 cm

34–13. (a) 6 cm and 12 cm from the object
(b) −2, −0.5

34–15. 60 cm to right of third lens

34–17. (a) $4f$ (b) Zero

34–19. (a) 20.0 cm (b) 18.7 cm

34–21. (b) 12 cm

34–23. $t = 0.375$ in.

34–25. 0.67 in. to left of first lens, 0.67 in. to right of second lens

CHAPTER 35

35–1. 1 mm

35–3. 480 mμ

35–5. 0.71×10^{-5} cm

35–7. 106 mμ

35–9. 0.014 cm

35–11. 12.5°

35–13. 500 mμ

CHAPTER 36

36–1. 35° 32′

36–3. (a) 37°

36–5. 67° 22′

CHAPTER 37

37–3. 1.41×10^{19}/sec

37–9. (a) 0.025 ev (b) 0.00025 ev

37–11. Coal:
(a) 4.03 ev
(b) 49.5×10^6
(c) 2.53×10^6
Ethyl alcohol:
(a) 14.2 ev
(b) 14.1×10^6
(c) 2.74×10^6
Starch:
(a) 29.4 ev
(b) 6.80×10^6
(c) 4.69×10^6

TNT:
(a) 35.6 ev
(b) 5.62×10^6
(c) 5.42×10^6
Gasoline:
(a) 50.0 ev
(b) 4.00×10^6
(c) 1.71×10^6

37–13. (a) 1.04 ev
(b) 11,900 A
(c) 2.52×10^{14}/sec

37–15. (a) 1.44 volts
(b) 1.44 ev
(c) 7.10×10^5 m/sec

CHAPTER 38

38–3. (a) 0.532 A, 2.13 A, 4.79 A
(b) 1.06 A

38–5. 21.8×10^{-19} joule, 13.6 ev;
5.44×10^{-19} joule, 3.40 ev;
2.12×10^{-19} joule, 1.51 ev; 0, 0

38–7. 1.079×10^7 m

38–9. (a) 6.16×10^{14}/sec
(b) 4861 A
(c) 2.06×10^6/m

38–11. 1836

38–13. (a) 15.6 volts
      (b) 2340 A
      (c) 12.5 volts
      (d) $1.013 \times 10^7/\text{m}$
      (e) 6 ev, 0.7 ev

38–17. (a) 5.28×10^{45}
      (c) 3.03×10^{-39} m

CHAPTER 39

39–5. (a) 6.28×10^5 mi/sec
     (b) 1.86×10^5 mi/sec
     (c) Zero
     (d) No

39–7. (a) 4.00 m/sec
     (b) 2.77×10^8 m/sec

39–11. (a) 1.80×10^5 ev
      (b) 12.3×10^{-31} kgm
      (c) 2.02×10^8 m/sec
      (d) 1.30×10^{11} coul/kgm
      (e) 2.52×10^8 m/sec

39–13. (a) 1200 Mev
      (b) 8.82×10^{-27} kgm
      (c) 1.96×10^8 m/sec

39–15. (a) 0.047 Mev
      (b) 0.294 Mev
      (c) 7.2, 4.0

39–17. (a) 5.11×10^3 volts
      (b) 9.38×10^6 volts

39–19. (a) 2.35×10^8 m/sec
      (b) No

39–23. (a) 8.03 amu
      (b) 7.47×10^3 Mev
      (c) 17.3 Mev,
          1.86×10^{-2} amu

39–25. (a) 1.73 Mev (b) No

39–27. (a) 25.8×10^{-31} kgm
      (b) 2.81×10^8 m/sec
      (c) 0.038 w/m^2 normal to the
          trajectories

CHAPTER 40

40–1. (a) 3.53 A
     (b) 7.06 A

40–3. (a) 1.24 A
     (b) 0.413 A
     (c) X-ray

40–5. (a) Point source
     (b) Size of object

40–7. (b) 10,600 volts
     (c) 1.48 A
     (d) 0.124 A
     (e) 0.178 A

40–9. (a) 10.4 kev, 69.4 kev, 77.8 kev
     (b) 77.8 to 80.0 kev

40–11. (a) 4.00
      (b) 6.35
      (c) 7.65

40–13. (a) 0.95 cm, 0.050 cm,
         0.0125 cm

     (b) 4.75 cm, 0.250 cm,
        0.063 cm
     (c) 5.31 cm, 0.280 cm,
        0.070 cm

40–15. 0.024 cm

40–17. (a) 0.023 ft^2/lb, 0.022 ft^2/lb,
        0.021 ft^2/lb, 0.022 ft^2/lb
      (b) 154 lb, 156 lb, 163 lb,
        157 lb

40–19. (a) 0.0243 A, 0.111×10^{-5} A
      (b) 0.736 A, 0.712 A

40–23. 2.66×10^{-13} amp

40–25. (a) 6750 mr/hr,
        133 Mev/(cm^3·sec)
      (b) 5.32×10^5 Mev/(cm^2·sec)

CHAPTER 41

41–1. 1.23 A

41–5. (a) 1.28 A

(b) 1.80 A

41–7. 16°42′

41–9. (a) 5.93×10^{-5} A

(b) Smaller

41–11. (a) Less

(b) Phase; equal

(c) No

CHAPTER 42

42–1. (a) 40 days

(b) 60 days

(c) 0.0346/day, 28.9 days

42–3. (a) 3.62×10^4/sec

(b) 2.92×10^4/sec

42–5. (a) 51, 59

(b) 51, 58

(c) 52, 58

42–9. 4.42×10^{-6} gm

42–11. (a) 10.8 min

(b) 6.58 days

42–13. (a) 5.44 gm

(b) 0.462 gm

(c) 2.59 liters

42–15. (b) 2.95×10^{-4}/sec

(c) 39.2 min

42–17. 4.25×10^9 years

42–19. 6.47×10^{-6} gm, 0.654 mm^3

42–21. (a) 5.0×10^{-15}%

(b) 6.5×10^{-16}%

42–23. (a) 0.13 μc

(b) 8.9×10^{-8} gm

(c) All in U^{238} and Th^{232} series

42–25. (b) 67.4 mc-hr, 114 mc-hr,

220 mc-hr

42–27. 6840 mr/hr

CHAPTER 43

43–3. (a) 1.92×10^7 m/sec

(b) 2.26×10^5 ion pairs

(c) 1.34×10^{-11} amp

43–5. 4

43–7. (c) 100%

43–9. Na^{24}, F^{17}, P^{30}, Cu^{58}; β^+, In^{116}, P^{32}, Be^8; H^3, β^-, Si^{30}, γ

43–11. (a) 0.086 Mev

(b) 4.78 Mev

(c) Yes

43–15. (a) 0.63 Mev, −3.72 Mev

(b) Radioactive

43–17. ±81 yr

43–19. 303 mc

43–21. Supply, release, release

CHAPTER 44

44–1. (a) 945 gm

(b) 663 μc/mi^2

44–3. (a) 1.79×10^{19}

(b) 1.79×10^{19}

(c) 60 days

44–5. (a) B, 6.56/cm; Fe, 0.21/cm

(b) 0.66

44–9. (a) 4.70 cm

(b) 0.15 cm

(c) 0.72 in.

44–11. (a) Red, 69°43′; blue, 68°54′

(b) Red, 0.750c; blue, 0.746c

44–13. (a) 22.6 Mev

(b) 3.74 Mev/amu

(c) 0.40%

(d) Per atom: U, 200 Mev; D,

7.53 Mev

Per amu: U, 0.85 Mev; D,

3.74 Mev

INDEX

INDEX